Engaging Students and Helping Them to Succeed

Chapter Highlights

A brief outline at the beginning of each chapter provides a preview of topics to help students prepare for reading and studying.

Key Terms

Each Key Term is defined and placed in a coloured box on the same page where the term is introduced. In addition, all Key Terms are included in the Glossary at the back of the text.

In Focus Boxes

In Focus boxes in each chapter offer more in-depth information about a particular topic or research study mentioned in the chapter. Many of the boxes deal with multicultural and multiethnic perspectives, and explore cultures around the world, as well as in Canada.

End-of-Chapter Study and Review Tools

Chapter Summaries; Questions for Thought, Discussion and Debate; and *Suggestions for Further Reading* are found at the end of each chapter.

Author Biographies

Janet Shibley Hyde, the Helen Thompson Woolley Professor of Psychology and Women's Studies at the University of Wisconsin–Madison, received her education at Oberlin College and the University of California, Berkeley. She has taught a course in Human Sexuality since 1974, first at Bowling Green State University, then at Denison University, and now at the University of Wisconsin. Her research interests are in gender differences and gender development in childhood and adolescence. Author of the textbook *Half the Human Experience: The Psychology of Women*, she is a past president of the Society for the Scientific Study of Sexuality and is a Fellow of the American Psychological Association. She has received many other honours, including an award for excellence in teaching at Bowling Green State University, the Chancellor's Award for teaching at the University of Wisconsin, and the Kinsey Award from the Society for the Scientific Study of Sexuality for her contributions to sex research. In 2000–01 she served as one of the three scientific editors for U.S. Surgeon General David Satcher's report, *Promoting Sexual Health and Responsible Sexual Behavior*. She is married to John DeLamater.

John D. DeLamater, Professor of Sociology at the University of Wisconsin–Madison, received his education at the University of California, Santa Barbara and the University of Michigan. He created the Human Sexuality course at the University of Wisconsin in 1975 and has taught it regularly since then. His current research and writing are focused on the effects of life-course transitions on sexuality. He has published papers on the effects of having a child, of dual-career couples, and of divorce, and is studying the effects of menopause and later-life transitions on sexual attitudes and behaviour. He is the co-author of the textbook *Social Psychology*. He is a Fellow of the Society for the Scientific Study of Sexuality, and is the 2002 recipient of the Kinsey Award from the Society for Career Contributions to Sex Research. He has received awards for excellence in teaching from the Department of Sociology and Interfraternity Council-Panhellenic Association, and is a Fellow and past Chair of the Teaching Academy at the University of Wisconsin. He regularly teaches a seminar for graduate students on teaching undergraduate courses. He is married to Janet Hyde.

E. Sandra Byers is a Professor of Psychology at the University of New Brunswick. She grew up in Montreal and received her university education at the University of Rochester and West Virginia University. She created the human sexuality course at the University of New Brunswick in 1979 and has taught it annually since then, as enrollment had grown from 9 students to more than 200 students. She is the author or co-author of more than 70 journal articles and book chapters, and has supervised the research of 32 students. Much of her research has been in the areas of sexual satisfaction, sexual communication, sexual violence, and sexual dysfunction. She also has a private practice in clinical psychology specializing in sex therapy and regularly teaches a graduate seminar on sex therapy. She is president of the Canadian Sex Research Forum, on the Board of Directors of the Society for the Scientific Study of Sexuality, a fellow of the Canadian Psychological Association and the Society for the Scientific Study of Sexuality, a member of the Advisory Board of the Sex Information and Education Council of Canada, and the Founding Director of the Muriel McQueen Fergusson Centre for Family Violence Research. She has given more than 100 invited addresses and workshops, and has been interviewed about sexual issues by numerous radio and television stations, magazines, and newspapers. As a sexuality educator, researcher, and therapist in Canada, Dr. Byers is uniquely placed to provide a Canadian perspective on human sexuality. She is married to Larry Heinlein and has two daughters.

THIRD CANADIAN EDITION

UNDERSTANDING
HUMAN SEXUALITY

Janet Shibley Hyde
University of Wisconsin–Madison

John D. DeLamater
University of Wisconsin–Madison

E. Sandra Byers
University of New Brunswick

McGraw-Hill Ryerson

Toronto   Montréal   Boston   Burr Ridge, IL   Dubuque, IA   Madison, WI   New York
San Francisco   St. Louis   Bangkok   Bogotá   Caracas   Kuala Lumpur   Lisbon   London
Madrid   Mexico City   Milan   New Delhi   Santiago   Seoul   Singapore   Sydney   Taipei

The McGraw-Hill Companies

McGraw-Hill
Ryerson

UNDERSTANDING HUMAN SEXUALITY
THIRD CANADIAN EDITION

ISBN: 0-07-095201-9

1 2 3 4 5 6 7 8 9 10 SOL 0 9 8 7 6

Printed and bound in Canada

Statistics Canada information is used with the permission of Statistics Canada. Users are forbidden to copy the data and redisseminate them, in an original or modified form, for commercial purposes, without the expressed permission of Statistics Canada. Information on the availability of the wide range of data from Statistics Canada can be obtained from Statistics Canada's Regional Offices, its World Wide Web site at http://www.statscan.ca, and its toll-free access number 1-800-263-1136.

Care has been taken to trace ownership of copyright material contained in this text; however, the publisher will welcome any information that enables them to rectify any reference or credit for subsequent editions.

Executive Sponsoring Editor: James Buchanan
Developmental Editor: Jodi Lewchuk
Marketing Manager: Marc Trudel
Supervising Editor: Jaime Smith
Copy Editor: Kelli Howey and Erin Moore
Senior Production Coordinator: Jennifer Wilkie
Photo Research: Christina Beamish
Page Layout: Tom Dart and Kim Hutchinson/First Folio Resource Group, Inc.
Interior Design: Dianna Little
Cover Design: Sharon Lucas
Cover Image: © Barnaby Hall/Photonica.
Printer: Solisco Printers

Library and Archives Canada Cataloguing in Publication

Hyde, Janet Shibley
    Understanding human sexuality / Janet Shibley Hyde, John D. DeLamater, E. Sandra Byers. — 3rd Canadian ed.

Includes bibliographical references and index.
ISBN 0-07-095201-9

    1. Sex. I. DeLamater, John D. II. Byers, E. Sandra, 1951-   III. Title.

HQ12.H92 2006   306.7   C2005-907730-1

Contents

Cʜᴀᴘᴛᴇʀ 8 **Sexually Transmitted Infections 216**

Chapter 17   Sexual Coercion   478

Our goal in creating the Third Canadian Edition of *Understanding Human Sexuality* was to maintain the best features of the highly regarded American textbook while providing a truly Canadian focus. Over the past two decades, *Understanding Human Sexuality* has been widely recognized for its comprehensive and multidisciplinary coverage of a broad range of topics, its commitment to excellent scholarship, and its appeal and accessibility to students. The Third Canadian Edition retains these strengths while incorporating the latest information about a range of sexual topics including Internet issues related to sexuality, adolescent sexual behaviour, transgender individuals, the causes and treatment of sexual disorders, and legal decisions related to the rights of gays and lesbians.

■ What Is Unique about the Third Canadian Edition of *Understanding Human Sexuality*?

A Commitment to Canadian Content
First and foremost is the Canadian content. There are many ways in which sexuality in Canada is different than sexuality in the United States—whether it's rates of breast-feeding, teenage pregnancy, and STIs; attitude towards same-sex relationships; or laws regulating sexuality. These differences are reflected throughout the text—every chapter has significant Canadian content. Thus, students are provided with information that is relevant to their own lives, their own experiences, and their own communities. In keeping with the substantial amount of excellent sexuality research being conducted in Canada, the textbook also highlights Canadian sexuality research and researchers. Professors who reviewed the Third Canadian Edition were extremely positive about the inclusion of Canadian content, enthusiastically praising both the *extent* and *relevance* of Canadian information compared to other texts on the market.

A Focus on Diversity and an Inclusive Approach
Second, in the Third Canadian Edition we have paid special attention to making the text more inclusive. In keeping with the diversity within Canadian society, we use inclusive language that respects diversity and does not assume any particular lifestyle or life choices. Thus, for example, we have substituted "partner" for "spouse," and we have used language that applies equally to gay, lesbian, bisexual, and heterosexual students. We have also highlighted sexuality in Canadian ethnocultural communities, including the Chinese, South Asian, Caribbean, and First Nations communities, as well as regional differences, such as between Canadians living in Quebec and those living in other provinces.

Canadian Legal Information in Every Chapter
Third, students will find discussion of Canadian laws and Canadian legal issues in each chapter. This includes laws related to homosexuality, sexual assault, child sexual abuse, contraception and abortion, pornography, and prostitution, among others. We have provided a complete list of the sexually related statutes in the Criminal Code of Canada, as well as a history of the evolution of some of these statutes.

Relevant, Engaging In Focus Boxes
Fourth, we highlight research and issues of particular interest to Canadian students in each chapter's In Focus boxes. For example, the Third Canadian Edition features In Focus boxes on regional attitudes toward sex and sexuality; a comprehensive listing of Canadian sex researchers and their fields of interest; and unique profiles of Canadians living with HIV. Approximately 16 In Focus boxes have been extensively updated or are new to this edition.

■ Plan of the Book

First and foremost, we have kept in mind that students *want* to learn about sexuality and that our job as writers is to help them learn. We have covered topics completely, with as clear a presentation as possible, and have made a special effort to use language that will enlighten rather than intimidate. In the selection and preparation of illustrations for the book, our goal has always been to convey as much information as possible, simply and clearly.

The book assumes no prior university or college courses in biology, psychology, or sociology. It is designed as an introduction following the four major objectives of our own courses in human sexuality:

1. To provide practical information needed for everyday living and to deal with problems in sexual functioning.
2. To help students appreciate the fabulous diversity of human sexuality along many dimensions, including age, sexual orientation and identity, ethnicity within Canada, and culture around the world.
3. To help students feel more comfortable with thinking and talking about sex, both to minimize their own personal anxiety about a tension-causing topic and to help them become responsible decision-makers in an important aspect of their lives.
4. To familiarize students with methods used in research on sexuality, and particularly with problems inherent in some of these methods, so that they can read research reports critically and intelligently.

Our own courses are surveys, designed to provide students with a broad range of information about sexuality. Reflecting that approach, this book is intended to be complete and balanced in its coverage. For instructors who lack the time or resources to cover the entire book, or for those who prefer to rearrange the order of topics, we have written all the chapters to be fairly independent of one another.

The background of the Hyde, DeLamater, and Byers team is quite compatible with this interdisciplinary approach. Janet Hyde's original graduate training was in psychology, with specialties in behaviour genetics and statistics; later her interests expanded to include psychology of women and gender roles. As a result, her expertise is in the biological and psychological viewpoints. John DeLamater's graduate training was in psychology and sociology, so his expertise includes sociological and cultural viewpoints. Sandra Byers's graduate training was in clinical psychology. She adds the clinical and Canadian perspectives. The team's goal has been to cover all aspects of sexuality with integrity.

Certainly some aspects of sexuality are very serious. Nonetheless, it is our belief that, in modern North American culture, we are in danger of taking some aspects of sexuality far too seriously. We may not be serious about it in the same way as were our Victorian ancestors, but we are serious nonetheless—serious about whether we are using the best and most up-to-date sexual techniques, serious about whether our partners are having as many orgasms as possible, and so on. To counteract this tendency, we have tried to use a light touch, with occasional bits of humour, in this book. We hope this will help us all keep things in perspective.

One thing we are serious about is the quality of research. The quality of sex research is highly variable, to put it mildly. Journalists think they are sex researchers if they have interviewed 10 people and written a book about it! We see other sexuality textbooks that cite an article from the local newspaper with equal authority as a refereed journal article from *The New England Journal of Medicine* or *The Journal of Sex Research*—and readers have to do a lot of detective work to find out what the real source is for a statement. We believe that it is our responsibility as textbook authors to sift through available studies and *not* cite all of them, but rather present those that are of the best quality. We are pleased to observe that the quality of sex research improves every decade. In this edition we were able to prune out many studies of lesser quality and rely much more on recent studies that are of excellent quality, in terms of sampling, research design, and measurements.

■ What's New in the Third Canadian Edition?

Building on the First and Second Canadian Editions, this new edition provides Canadian data wherever reliable figures are available, features Canadian research and researchers, describes sexuality in the major Canadian ethnocultural communities, highlights issues important to Canadian students, and ensures inclusive language and visuals appear throughout. Some of the major content changes and additions to the Third Canadian Edition are as follows:

Chapter 1: Sexuality in Perspective

- Includes summary of Internet issues in section on media.
- Makes the definition of "culture" explicit.
- Adds an In Focus box comparing sexuality in Quebec with other Canadian provinces.

Chapter 2: Theoretical Perspectives on Sexuality

- (Re)introduces the concept of *parental investment* and related research.
- Discusses critiques of evolutionary psychology.
- Reduces coverage of psychoanalytic theory and includes discussion of *neuropsychoanalysis,* the use of contemporary imaging techniques to study Freudian ideas.
- Introduces social exchange theory of relationships and symbolic interaction theory of social behaviour.
- Introduces concept of *medicalization of sexuality* (Tiefer).
- Provides discussion and definition of *sexual health.*
- Updates table of sexual offences to include recent changes to the Criminal Code of Canada.

Chapter 3: Sex Research

- Features new introduction describing reasons for and goals of sex research.
- Adds detailed section on Internet methods of research.
- Updates In Focus box on sex researchers in Canada, with several researchers added.
- Updates Canada Youth and AIDS Study with Canada Youth Sexual Health and HIV/AIDS Study (2003).
- Examines rape in popular films in section on Media Content Analysis.
- Updates Kinsey In Focus box with new biography by Gathorne-Hardy.
- Describes the principle of justice in section on research ethics and provides a Web-based ethics tutorial.

Chapter 4: Sexual Anatomy

- Includes new material on the Skene's glands, or female prostate (G-spot).
- Explains vulvar vestibule and vulvar vestibulitis.
- Provides updated information on cancer of the sexual/reproductive organs.

Chapter 5: Sex Hormones, Sexual Differentiation, and Menstruation

- Provides rewritten and updated section on sexual differentiation of the brain to reflect latest research, including MRI studies.
- Integrates information on menstruation.
- Includes latest findings on the biology of the menstrual cycle, including the role of inhibin.
- Updates section on treatment of intersex individuals with new studies that address and assess long-term outcome.
- Examines the life of David Reimer in depth.
- Adds latest research on leptin and the onset of puberty.

Chapter 6: Conception, Pregnancy, and Childbirth

- Updates recommendations for weight gain during pregnancy.
- Includes discussion of father's role in preparing for the baby.
- Streamlines section on effects of substances taken pregnancy.
- Updates statistics on Caesarean section rates and VBAC attempts.
- Discusses doulas.
- Revises substantially discussion of postpartum psychological changes.
- Offers new coverage of breast-feeding.
- Mentions abruption placentae.
- Provides completely rewritten coverage of infertility issues, including theories and treatments of infertility.
- Expands coverage of online sperm banks and ICSI.

Chapter 7: Contraception and Abortion

- Updates coverage of contraceptive methods approved by Health Canada and new advances in contraception.
- Expands coverage of the advantages and effectiveness of condoms.
- Incorporates data from the CYSHHAS.

Chapter 8: Sexually Transmitted Infections

- Updates information on risk of HIV infection to highlight risk behaviours rather than risk groups.
- Includes discussion of living with HIV and updates stories of individuals living with HIV.
- Adds sections on microbicides and behavioural prevention to discussion of AIDS research.
- Provides new lines for negotiating safer sex.

Chapter 9: The Physiology of Sexual Response

- Updates Masters and Johnson's findings on physiology of sexual response with recent cutting-edge research; includes the latest neuroscience and genome research.
- Discusses new findings on the G-spot.
- Provides a new In Focus box reporting on the latest neuroimaging studies of the brain during sexual arousal.
- Describes Rosemary Basson's Intimacy Model of Sexual Response.
- Reports exciting new findings on pheromones in humans and the vomeronasal organ.

Chapter 10: Techniques of Arousal and Communication

- Includes new subsection on media and masturbation.
- Discusses "intrusive sexual thoughts" and their frequency among college students.
- Reexamines role of visual stimuli in sexual arousal.
- Integrates discussion of sexual techniques used in same-sex and opposite-sex relationships.
- Shortens section on aphrodisiacs and adds discussion of "natural" aphrodisiacs.
- Explains role of Viagra and Cialis in sexual arousal.
- Includes new In Focus box on tantric sex.

Chapter 11: Sexuality and the Life Cycle: Childhood and Adolescence

- Provides information from CYSHHAS throughout.
- Includes new data on masturbation and sexual experience with another child in childhood.
- Updates discussion of the mass media's impact on adolescent sexuality with data from three recent empirical studies.
- Offers information on adolescent definitions of permissiveness with affection.

- Provides new subsection on abstinence during adolescence with data on characteristics of abstainers.
- Includes discussion of *friends with benefits* and *hooking up*.
- Explores the role of adolescent sexuality in the development of the person and capacities for adult relationships.

Chapter 12: Sexuality and the Life Cycle: Adulthood

- Includes new information on types of and influences on celibacy; speed dating; common-law relationships; legality of same-sex marriage; polyamory; online relationships (cybersex and cyberaffairs); and breakdown of marital and cohabiting relationships.
- Reports frequency with which adults engage in various activities to enhance their sexual interactions and factors related to frequent sexual behaviour among older men and women.
- Updates In Focus box on changes in adults' sexual behaviour in response to AIDS.
- Revises discussion of swingers and motivations for swinging.
- Integrates material on menopause and includes discussion of andropause.
- Explains latest developments on HRT for women.

Chapter 13: Attraction, Intimacy, and Love

- Includes discussion of physical attractiveness as an aspect of sex appeal.
- Explores the relationship between sex and love in relationships and in theories of love.
- Revises In Focus box on jealousy.
- Expands section on biology and passionate love and updates discussions of hormones and use of MRI to measure brain activity associated with love.

Chapter 14: Gender and Sexuality

- Incorporates data from CYSHHAS and research on gender differences in sexuality.
- Describes bogus pipeline study of the truthfulness of reports of gender differences in sexuality.
- Revises section on transgender to include more inclusive terminology, define changing terminology, and discuss findings from brain research.
- Mentions Devor's stages of transsexual identity formation.
- Profiles a trans man.

- Updates debate on gender identity disorder in children.

Chapter 15: Sexual Orientation: Gay, Lesbian, Bi, or Straight?

- Expands discussion of terminology, including social/political implications of various terms and uses inclusive and appropriate terminology throughout.
- Revamps coverage of bisexuality and incorporates discussion throughout.
- Updates data on Canadian attitudes toward gays and lesbians and same-sex marriage; includes Census data on same-sex partnerships.
- Covers recent legal decisions regarding same-sex marriage in Canada and their adoption by same-sex couples.
- Includes new In Focus box profiling a lesbian couple living in Ottawa.
- Completely updates coverage of biological influences on sexual orientation.
- Adds section on differences between gay men and lesbians.

Chapter 16: Variations in Sexual Behaviour

- Expands coverage on compulsive sexual behaviour.
- Differentiates transvestism and transvestic fetishism from cross-dressing for gender-related issues.
- Updates coverage of S-M.
- Mentions treatment of exhibitionists' cognitive distortions.
- Discusses highly sexual women.
- Expands coverage of cybersex use and abuse.
- Adds research on people with sexual interest in animals.

Chapter 17: Sexual Coercion

- Increases coverage of "date-rape" drugs.
- Introduces concept of posttraumatic growth following trauma such as sexual assault.
- Updates In Focus box "What Should I Do after a Sexual Assault?" with advice for person who has experienced sexual assault as well as those who know someone has experienced sexual assault.
- Increases coverage of pedophilia.
- Includes new research on recovered memories.
- Describes research on sexual harassment by youth.

Chapter 18: Sex for Sale

- Changes language from "prostitutes" to "sex workers" and revises discussion of sex work and sex workers.
- Increases coverage of sex trafficking.
- Includes discussions of risks to sex workers, the role of early abuse, and leaving the life.
- Adds sections on transgender sex workers and sex tourism.
- Includes new In Focus box on the making of X-rated videos.
- Expands discussion of sexually suggestive advertising.

Chapter 19: Sexual Disorders and Sex Therapy

- Includes discussion of crystal methamphetamine.
- Adds research on pathways between sexual communication and sexual satisfaction.
- Increases coverage of Viagra, as well as Levitra and Cialis, including impact on partner.
- Critiques diagnostic categories for persons with disabilities.

Chapter 20: Ethics, Religion, and Sexuality

- Adds table on the religious affiliation of Canadians.
- Mentions issue of honour killings.
- Includes discussion of religious objections to proposed same-sex marriage legislation in Canada.
- Discusses therapeutic cloning and stem cell research.
- Presents World Health Organization list of sexual rights.

Chapter 21: Sexuality Education

- Gives examples of questions children ask about sex at various ages.
- Revises description of different types of sex education programs.
- Includes In Focus box and discussion of sex education for persons with disabilities.

■ Superior Service

Service takes on a whole new meaning with McGraw-Hill Ryerson and *Understanding Human Sexuality*. More than just bringing you the textbook, we have consistently raised the bar in terms of innovation and educational research. These investments in learning and the educational community have helped us to understand the needs of students and educators across the country and allowed us to foster the growth of truly innovative, integrated learning.

Integrated Learning

Your Integrated Learning Sales Specialist is a McGraw-Hill Ryerson representative who has the experience, product knowledge, training, and support to help you assess and integrate any of our products, technology, and services into your course for optimum teaching and learning performance. Whether it's using our test bank software, helping your students improve their grades, or putting your entire course online, your *i*Learning Sales Specialist is there to help you do it. Contact your local *i*Learning Sales Specialist today to learn how to maximize all of McGraw-Hill Ryerson's resources!

*i*Learning Services Program

McGraw-Hill Ryerson offers a unique *i*Services package designed for Canadian faculty. Our mission is to equip providers of higher education with superior tools and resources required for excellence in teaching. For additional information visit **http://www.mcgrawhill.ca/highereducation/iservices**.

Teaching, Learning, & Technology Conference Series

The educational environment has changed tremendously in recent years, and McGraw-Hill Ryerson continues to be committed to helping you acquire the skills you need to succeed in this new milieu. Our innovative Teach, Learning, & Technology Conference Series brings faculty together from across Canada with 3M Teaching Excellence award winners to share teaching and learning best practices in a collaborative and stimulating environment. Pre-conference workshops on general topics such as teaching large classes and technology integration are also offered. We will also work with you at your own institution to customize workshops that best suit the needs of your faculty.

■ Supplements

A complete, integrated supplements package supports students and instructors to help them meet their learning and teaching challenges.

For Instructors

Instructor Online Learning Centre with PowerWeb

The Online Learning Centre (**www.mcgrawhill.ca/college/hyde**) includes a password-protected Web site for instructors. The site offers downloadable supplements and links to PageOut, the McGraw-Hill Ryerson Web site development centre, as well as animations that demonstrate biological processes and polls to measure students' behaviour and attitudes toward sexuality. The Online Learning Centre also provides a gateway to PowerWeb content, putting 6,000 academic articles and a powerful search engine at your fingertips. Contact your *i*Learning Sales Specialist to learn more about making this valuable resource available to your students

Instructor's CD-ROM

This CD-ROM contains all the necessary instructor supplements, fully adapted to accord with the Third Canadian Edition:

- An **Instructor's Manual** that provides ideas for lectures, class discussions, and class activities.
- A **Computerized Test Bank** that contains more than 1,500 questions that vary in type and level of difficulty and are keyed to the appropriate page number in the textbook.
- **Microsoft® PowerPoint® slides** to accompany each chapter.

eInstruction's Classroom Performance System (CPS)

CPS is a student response system using wireless connectivity. It gives instructors and students immediate feedback from the entire class. The response pads are remotes that are easy to use and engage students. **CPS** helps to increase student preparation, interactivity, and active learning; allows you to administer quizzes, tests, and immediate grading; and facilitates evaluation of classroom attendance and activity.

CPS-ready content is available for use with Hyde/DeLamater/Byers, *Understanding Human Sexuality*. Please contact your *i*Learning Sales Specialist for more information on how you can integrate CPS into your psychology classroom.

Course Management

Visit **www.mhhe.com/pageout** to explore PageOut, the McGraw-Hill Ryerson Web site development centre. This Web page–generation software is free to adopters and is designed to help faculty create an online course, complete with assignments, quizzes, links to relevant Web sites, and more.

In addition, content cartridges are available for the course management systems **WebCT** and **Blackboard**. These platforms provide instructors with user-friendly, flexible teaching tools. Please contact your local McGraw-Hill Ryerson *i*Learning Sales Specialist for details.

The McGraw-Hill Human Sexuality Psychology Image Database

Over 160 images were developed using the best selection of human sexuality art and tables. Instructors can add their own lecture notes to the CD-ROM as well as organize the images to correspond to their particular classroom needs.

Videocases in Human Sexuality

Four 35-minute videotapes contain spontaneous, unrehearsed interviews. A video guide with case vignettes and classroom discussion questions is also included. Please see your McGraw-Hill Ryerson *i*Learning Sales Specialist for further information on policy, price, and availability.

Annual Editions—Human Sexuality

This McGraw-Hill publication offers articles on topics related to the latest research and thinking in human sexuality from more than 300 public press sources. These editions are updated annually and contain helpful features such as a topic guide, an annotated table of contents, unit overviews, and a topical index. An Instructor's Guide containing testing materials is also available.

Sources: Notable Selections in Human Sexuality

This is a collection of articles, book excerpts, and research studies that have shaped the study of human sexuality and our understanding of it. The selections are organized topically around major areas of study within human sexuality.

Taking Sides: Clashing Views on Controversial Issues in Human Sexuality

This debate-style reader carefully examines issues with pro and con essays representing the arguments of leading scholars and commentators. An instructor's guide with testing materials is also available.

For Students

Student SexSource CD-ROM

This CD-ROM comes free with all new copies of the textbook and offers video segments fully integrated with the text. A still from the video segment and an informative caption will motivate students to view the videos.

To learn more about social influences on sexual identity, watch the video "Learning to be Straight" in Chapter 11 of your CD.

Online Learning Centre with PowerWeb

The Online Learning Centre (**www.mcgrawhill.ca/college/hyde**) provides chapter quizzes and review questions, interactive exercises, Web links, a searchable Glossary, a Directory of Resources in Human Sexuality, and other study tools. The password-protected portion of the site provides students with additional articles and helps them with online research by directing them to more than 6,000 high-quality academic sources.

■ Acknowledgements

I am extremely fortunate to have been able to call on a wide network of Canadian scholars in preparing the Canadian editions of *Understanding Human Sexuality*. Many of my colleagues and friends have been as generous with their time and expertise as I prepared this Third Edition as they were for the previous editions. I appreciate their contributions enormously. I am also appreciative that so many people were willing to provide me with copies of their scholarly work—their work is cited throughout this book. I have also benefited from the students in my classes. They keep me up to date on what university students are thinking and wondering about sexuality; a number of them also provided specific suggestions for improvements to the textbook.

I am extremely indebted to the current and former member of my sexuality research group at the University of New Brunswick who provided input for all three editions. Thank you especially to Shannon Archibald, Cindy Letts, Angela Weaver, and Sarah McAulay for their substantial contributions to the whole text, but also to Marvin Claybourn, Jacqueline Cohen, Christie Little, Sheila MacNeil, Jennifer Thurlow, and Lorna Scott. In preparing the Third Edition, Jacqueline Cohen's contributions regarding transgender issues and discussion of sexual orientation were fabulous. I am also indebted to her for the interviews she conducted for two new In Focus boxes. Guy Grenier provided dozens and dozens of suggestions for improving the textbook; I particularly appreciate the In Focus box he prepared on tantric sex.

I am also enormously grateful to Susan Voyer, who has served as my research assistant for both the Second and Third Canadian Editions. She was not only relentless in tracking down information, regardless of how obscure, but also proactive in bringing new developments and new sources to my attention. Her organizational skills are without equal. This book would be noticeably poorer without her contributions.

The Third Canadian Edition of *Understanding Human Sexuality* has benefited from the careful reviews and valuable feedback of the following instructors:

Nancy Barlett, *Mount Saint Vincent University*
Tony F. Bogaert, *Brock University*
Deborah Boutilier, *Niagara College*
Guy Grenier, *University of Western Ontario*
Maria Gurevich, *Ryerson University*
Lindsay Harris, *Algonquin College*
Darryl Hill, *College of Staten Island, City University of New York*
Carla LaBella, *Mohawk College*
Duane Lesperance, *University of Manitoba*
Scott Mattson, *University of Windsor*
James Ponzetti, *University of British Columbia*
Sandra Preston, *McMaster University*
E. Lisa Price, *Acadia University*
Caroline F. Pukall, *Queen's University*
Christine Purdon, *University of Waterloo*
Elke Reissing, *University of Ottawa*
BJ Rye, *St. Jerome's University at the University of Waterloo*
Christine Storm, *Mount Allison University*
Karen Tee, *Vanier College*

I also owe many thanks to the editors and staff at McGraw-Hill Ryerson whose friendly and encouraging support through every step of the process made my job so much easier: James Buchanan, Executive Sponsoring Editor; Jodi Lewchuk, Development Editor; Jaime Smith, Supervising Editor; Jennifer Wilkie, Production Coordinator; Kelli Howey, Copy Editor; and Christina Beamish, Photo Researcher.

Finally, I could not have written this book without the enthusiastic support of my family. The love and gratitude I feel toward my husband Larry and our daughters Krista and Alyssa are immeasurable.

E. Sandra Byers

Sexuality in Perspective

CHAPTER HIGHLIGHTS

You're so beautiful," he whispered. "I want a picture of you just like this with your face flushed and your lips wet and shiny."… He tore open a foil packet he'd retrieved from his pocket. Mesmerized, she watched him sheath himself, amazed at how hard he was. She reached out to touch him, but he moved back, made sure she was ready, and then slid neatly inside her, so deeply she gasped. She contracted her muscles around him, and he closed his eyes and groaned, the sound so primal, it made her skin tingle.*

Human sexual behavior is a diverse phenomenon. It occurs in different physical locations and social contexts, consists of a wide range of specific activities, and is perceived differently by different people. An individual engages in sexual activity on the basis of a complex set of motivations and organizes that activity on the basis of numerous external factors and influences. Thus, it is unlikely that the tools and concepts from any single scientific discipline will suffice to answer all or even most of the questions one might ask about sexual behavior.†

Having children and healthy families are important goals to most Canadians, but some people cannot reach those goals without help. If there are technologies that can be used to help, a caring society should provide these. But there are misuses and harms, as well as benefits, that may come from use of the technologies—harms to both individuals and society.‡

Strikingly different though they may seem, all of the above quotations are talking about the same thing—sex. The first quotation is from a romance novel. It is intended to stimulate the reader's fantasies and arousal. The second is from a scholarly book about sex. It aims to stimulate the brain but not the genitals. The third is from a Royal Commission on treatment of infertility. It points out the complexity of many sexual issues. From reading these brief excerpts, we can quickly see that the topic of sexuality is diverse, complex, and fascinating.

Introductory textbooks on most subjects generally begin with a section designed to motivate students to study whatever topic the text is about. No such section appears in this book; the reason people want to study sex is obvious, and your motivation for studying it is probably already quite high. Most people are curious about sex, particularly because exchanging sexual information is somewhat taboo in our culture, so curiosity motivates us to study sex. Sex is an important force in many people's lives, so there are practical reasons for wanting to learn about it. Finally, most of us at various times experience problems with our sexual functioning or wish that we could function better, and we hope that learning more about sex will help us. This book is designed to address all of these needs. So let us consider various perspectives on sexuality—the effects of religion, science, and culture on our understanding of sexuality. These perspectives will give you a glimpse of the forest before you study the trees: sexual anatomy and physiology (the "plumbing" part), and sexual behaviour (the "people" part), which are discussed in later chapters. First we must draw an important distinction between sex and gender.

*Debbi Rawlins. (2003). *Anything goes*. New York: Harlequin Blaze.

†Laumann et al. (1994).

‡Royal Commission on New Reproductive Technologies. (1993). *Proceed with care: Final report of the Royal Commission on New Reproductive Technologies*. Ottawa: Minister of Government Services Canada.

■ Sex and Gender

Sometimes the word "sex" is used ambiguously. In some cases it refers to being male or female, and sometimes it refers to sexual behaviour or reproduction. In most cases, of course, the meaning is clear from the context. If you are filling out a job application form and one item says "Sex," you do not write, "I like it" or "As often as possible." It is clear that your prospective employer wants to know whether you are a male or a female. In other cases, though, the meaning may be ambiguous. For example, when a book has the title *Sex and Temperament in Three Primitive Societies*, what is it about? Is it about the sexual practices of primitive people and whether having sex frequently gives them pleasant temperaments? Or is it about the kinds of personalities that males and females are expected to have in those societies? Not only does this use of "sex" create ambiguities, but it also clouds our thinking about some important issues.

To remove—or at least reduce—this ambiguity, the term "sex" will be used in this book in contexts referring to sexual anatomy and sexual behaviour, and the term **gender** will be used to refer to the state of being male or female.

This is a book about sex, not gender; it is about sexual behaviour and the biological, psychological, and social forces that influence it. Of course, although we are arguing that sex and gender are conceptually different, we would not try to argue that they are totally independent of each other. Certainly gender roles—the ways in which males and females are expected to behave—exert a powerful influence on the way people behave sexually, and so one chapter will be devoted to gender roles and their effects on sexuality.

How should we define "sex," aside from saying that it is different from "gender"? A biologist might define sexual behaviour as "any behavior that increases the likelihood of gametic union [union of sperm and egg]" (Bermant & Davidson, 1974). This definition emphasizes the reproductive function of sex. However, particularly in the last few decades, medical advances such as the birth control pill have been developed that allow us to separate reproduction from sex. Most Canadians now use sex not only for procreation but also for pleasure and intimacy. Actually, even in former times sex was not always associated with reproduction. For example, a man

in 1850 might have fathered 10 children; using a very conservative estimate that he engaged in sexual intercourse 1,500 times during his adult life (once a week for the 30 years from age 20 to age 50), one concludes that only 10 in 1,500 of those acts, or fewer than 1 percent, resulted in reproduction.

The noted sex researcher Alfred Kinsey defined "sex" as behaviour that leads to orgasm. Although this definition has some merits (it does not imply that sex must be associated with reproduction), it also presents some problems. If one person has intercourse with another person but does not have an orgasm, was that not sexual behaviour for her or him?

To try to avoid some of these problems, **sexual behaviour** will be defined in this book as *behaviour that produces arousal and increases the chance of orgasm.*[1]

■ The History of Understanding Sexuality: Religion and Science

Religion

Religion is a source of values and ethics regarding sexuality and, as such, is a powerful influence on the sexual attitudes and behaviour of many individuals. The moral code for each religion is unique—each religion has different views on what is right and what is wrong with respect to sexuality. Throughout most of recorded history, at least until about 100 years ago, religion (and rumour) provided most of the information that people had about sexuality, and in some cultures it still does. Here are a few historical examples of how different religions understood sexuality.

The ancient Greeks openly acknowledged both heterosexuality and homosexuality in their society and explained the existence of the two in a myth in

[1]This definition, though an improvement over some, still has its problems. For example, consider a woman who feels no arousal at all during intercourse. According to the definition, intercourse would not be sexual behaviour for her. However, intercourse would generally be something we would want to classify as sexual behaviour. It should be clear that defining "sexual behaviour" is very difficult.

Gender: The state of being male or female.
Sexual behaviour: Behaviour that produces arousal and increases the chance of orgasm.

which the original humans were double creatures with twice the normal number of limbs and organs; some were double males, some were double females, and some were half male and half female (LeVay, 1996). The gods, fearing the power of these creatures, split them in half, and forever after each one continued to search for its missing half. Heterosexuals were thought to have resulted from the splitting of the half male, half female; male homosexuals, from the splitting of the double male; and female homosexuals, from the splitting of the double female. It was through this mythology that the ancient Greeks understood sexual orientation and sexual desire.

Fifteenth-century Christians believed that "wet dreams" (nocturnal emissions) resulted from intercourse with tiny spiritual creatures called *incubi* and *succubi,* a notion put forth in a papal bull (an official document) of 1484 and a companion book, the *Malleus Maleficarum* ("witch's hammer"). The *Malleus* became the official manual of the Inquisition, in which people, particularly women, were tried as witches. Wet dreams, sexual dysfunction, and sexual lust were seen to be caused by witchcraft (Hergenhahn, 2001).

Muslims believed that sexual intercourse was one of the finest pleasures of life, reflecting the teachings of the great prophet Muhammad. Muhammad himself had several wives.

People of different religions hold different understandings of human sexuality, and these religious views often have a profound impact. The influence of religion on Canadians is particularly apparent in the discussion of homosexuality and abortion. For example, conservative Christians often use their interpretation of the Bible, an interpretation that is not shared by other Christian denominations, to justify their opposition to homosexuals, same-sex sexual behaviour, and same-sex marriage. Other Canadians feel that these arguments have more to do with anti-gay prejudice and homophobia than religion. A detailed discussion of religion and sexuality is provided in Chapter 20.

Science

It was against this background of religious understandings of sexuality that the scientific study of sex began in the nineteenth century, although, of course, religious notions continue to influence our ideas about sexuality. In addition, the groundwork for an understanding of the biological aspects of sexuality had already been laid by the research of physicians and biologists. The Dutch microscopist Anton van Leeuwenhoek (1632–1723) and his student John Ham had discovered sperm swimming in human semen. In 1875 Oskar Hertwig (1849–1922) first observed the actual fertilization of the egg by the sperm in sea urchins, although the ovum in humans was not directly observed until the twentieth century.

A major advance in the scientific understanding of the psychological aspects of human sexuality came with the work of the Viennese physician Sigmund Freud (1856–1939), founder of psychiatry and psychoanalysis. His ideas will be discussed in detail in Chapter 2.

It is important to recognize the cultural context in which Freud and the other early sex researchers crafted their research and writing. They began their work in the Victorian era, the late 1800s, both in North America and Europe. Norms about sexuality were extraordinarily rigid and oppressive (see Figure 1.2). Historian Peter Gay characterized this repressive aspect of Victorian cultural norms as

> . . . a devious and insincere world in which middle-class husbands slaked their lust by keeping mistresses, frequenting prostitutes, or molesting children, while their wives, timid, dutiful, obedient, were sexually anesthetic and poured all their capacity for love into their housekeeping and their child-rearing. (Gay, 1984, p. 6)

Yet at the same time the actual sexual behaviour of Victorians was sometimes in violation of societal norms and expectations. Dr. Clelia Mosher was a physician who conducted a sex survey of Victorian women in the U.S. over a period of 30 years. Although the sample was small (47 women) and nonrandom, her results provide an alternative description of female sexuality during this period. For example, despite the Victorian stereotype that women felt no sexual desire, 80 percent of women who answered the question said that they felt a desire for sexual intercourse. Similarly, 72 percent of women indicated that they experienced orgasm. One woman commented that sex had been unpleasant for her for years because of her "slow reaction" but "orgasm [occurs] if time is taken." In his history of sexuality in the Victorian era, Gay documented the story of Mabel Loomis Todd, who, though married, carried on a lengthy sensual affair with Austin Dickinson, a community leader in Amherst, Massachusetts. Many people actually knew about the "secret" affair, yet Mrs. Loomis did not become an outcast (Gay, 1984). Another demonstration of a discrepancy between social norms and behaviour occurred in a somewhat earlier era. Many fur traders married Aboriginal women—at least until white women began to arrive—knowing that this would not be acceptable in Europe (Kinsman, 1996).

An equally great—though not so well known—early contributor to the scientific study of sex was Henry Havelock Ellis (1859–1939). A physician in Victorian England, he compiled a vast collection of information on sexuality—including medical and anthropological findings, as well as case histories—which was published in a series of volumes entitled *Studies in the Psychology of Sex* beginning in 1896. Havelock Ellis was a remarkably objective and tolerant scholar, particularly for his era. He believed that women, like men, are sexual creatures. A sexual reformer, he believed that sexual deviations from the norm are often harmless, and he urged society to accept them. In his desire to collect information about human sexuality rather than to make judgments about it, he can be considered the forerunner of modern sex research (for his autobiography, see Ellis, 1939; numerous biographies exist).

Another important figure in nineteenth-century sex research was the psychiatrist Richard von Krafft-Ebing (1840–1902)(Oosterheis, 2000). His special interest was "pathological" sexuality. He managed to collect more than 200 case histories of pathological individuals, which appeared in his book entitled *Psychopathia Sexualis*. His work tended to be neither objective nor tolerant. Nonetheless, it has had a lasting impact. He coined the concepts of sadism, masochism, and pedophilia. The terms "heterosexuality" and "homosexuality" entered the English language in the 1892 translation of his book (Oosterhuis, 2000). One of his case histories is presented in Chapter 16.

One other early contributor to the scientific understanding of sexuality deserves mention, the German Magnus Hirschfeld (1868–1935). He founded the first sex research institute and administered the first large-scale sex survey, obtaining data from 10,000 people on a 130-item questionnaire. Unfortunately, most of the information he amassed was destroyed by Nazi hoodlums. Hirschfeld also established the first journal devoted to the study of sex, established a marriage coun-

(a)

(b)

Figure 1.1   Two important early sex researchers. *(a)* Sigmund Freud. *(b)* Henry Havelock Ellis.

selling service, worked for legal reforms, and gave advice on contraception and sex problems. His special interest, however, was homosexuality. He made important contributions as a pioneer sex researcher (Bullough, 1994).

In the twentieth century, major breakthroughs in the scientific understanding of sex came with the massive surveys of human sexual behaviour in the United States conducted by Alfred Kinsey and his colleagues in the 1940s and with Masters and Johnson's investigations of sexual disorders and the physiology of sexual response. At about the same time that the Kinsey research was being conducted, some anthropologists—most notably Margaret Mead and Bronislaw Malinowski—were beginning to collect data on sexual behaviour in other cultures. The 1990s saw a significant increase in research on sexuality in close relationships (Christopher & Sprecher, 2000).

There has never been a major national survey of the sexual behaviour of Canadians. However, Statistics Canada has included some questions about sexuality in a number of national surveys, such as the Canada Community Health Survey (formerly called the National Population Health Survey), the General Social Survey, and the National Longitudinal Survey of Children and Youth. Canadian researchers have also conducted a large number of smaller investigations that have provided important information on a rich array of sexual topics (see In Focus 3.2 for a description of the work of some of these researchers).

The scientific study of sexuality has not emerged as a separate, unified academic discipline like biology or psychology or sociology, although some researchers do call themselves sexologists. Rather, it tends to be interdisciplinary—a joint effort by biologists, psychologists, sociologists, anthropologists, and physicians (see Figure 1.3). This approach to understanding sexuality gives us a better view of humans in all their sexual complexity.

■ The Media

In terms of potency of influence, the mass media in North America today may play the same role that religion did in previous centuries. Canadians are influenced both by Canadian programs and, perhaps more so, by American prime-time television. Prime-time television programs feature an average of 10 instances of sexual behaviour per hour. In a study of sex on the soaps, the most frequent sexual activity was heterosexual intercourse between unmarried persons (Greenberg & Busselle,

(a)

(b)

Figure 1.2   *(a)* The Victorian era, from which Freud and Ellis emerged, was characterized by extreme sexual repression. Here are some apparatuses that were sold to prevent onanism (masturbation). *(b)* Are things so different today? Here are current devices for sale on the Web, for the same purpose.

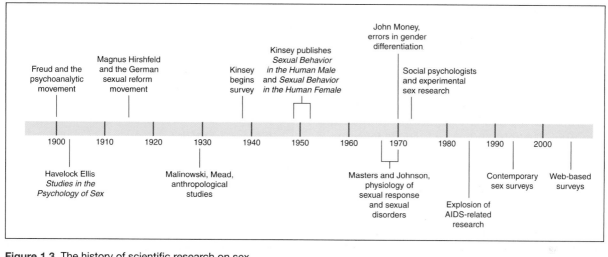

Figure 1.3 The history of scientific research on sex.

Figure 1.4 The explicit sexual content of the cable TV series *Sex and the City* didn't prevent its star Sarah Jessica Parker from winning a Golden Globe award for her performance in the show.

1996)—although this pattern is far from what occurs in the real world, where marital sex is most frequent. References to safer sex—for prevention of both sexually transmitted infections and pregnancy—are rare. Only 2 percent of sexual scenes portray any sexual precautions (Kunkel et al., 2003). Nonetheless, references to safer sex are increasing (Kaiser Family Foundation, 2003). Many Canadians (47 percent) think there is too much sexually explicit programming on prime-time TV (*Maclean's/Global Poll*, 2000).

In short, the average Canadian's views about sexuality are likely to be much more influenced by the mass media than by scientific findings. Communications theorists believe that the media can have three types of influence (Brown, 2002). The first, called **cultivation,** refers to the notion that people begin to think that what they see on television and in other media really represents the mainstream of what happens in our culture (Gerbner et al., 2002). For example, university students who watch the soaps are more likely than non-viewing students to overestimate the incidence of divorce. The second influence is **agenda-setting.** News reporters select what to report and what to ignore

Cultivation: In communications theory, the view that exposure to the mass media makes people think that what they see there represents the mainstream of what really occurs.

and, within the stories they report, what to emphasize. For example, in 1998 the U.S. media chose to highlight the sexual dalliances of President Bill Clinton, suggesting to the public that these matters were important. In contrast, the Canadian media have rarely focused on the sexual activities of Canadian politicians. The media in many ways tell us what the agenda is to which we should pay attention. The third influence is **social learning,** a theory we will take up in detail in Chapter 2. The contention here is that characters on television, in the movies, or in romance novels may serve as models whom we imitate, perhaps without even realizing it. Research has found, for example, that teens who watch more sexy television engage in first intercourse earlier than do other teens (Brown, 2002).

The Internet is the newest, and perhaps most powerful, mass media influence. Computer and Internet use is spreading more rapidly than any previous technology, and it is estimated that by 2010 most North American homes with children will have Internet access (Brown, 2002). In 2004, 66 percent of Canadian adults were online, spending an average of 7.1 hours per week (Leger Marketing, 2004). The most frequent search term on Google for 2003 was Britney Spears (Cyberatlas, 2004), the sex kitten with growing pains. As we will discuss in later chapters, the Internet has the potential for both positive and negative effects on sexual health. A number of sites, such as that for the Society of Obstetricians and Gynaecologists of Canada, sexualityandu.ca, provide excellent information about sexuality and promote sexual health. At the same time, a well-sampled study of youth between the ages of 10 and 17 who use the Internet regularly indicated that approximately 20 percent had received at least one sexual solicitation or approach over the Internet in the last year, and 3 percent had received an aggressive sexual solicitation, in which the initiator asked to meet the recipient somewhere or sent him or her money or gifts (Finkelhor et al., 2000).

In the chapters that follow, we will examine the content of the media on numerous sexual issues and we will consider what the effects of exposure to this media content might have on viewers.

Let us now consider the perspectives on sexuality that are provided by scientific observations of humans in a wide variety of societies.

■ Cross-Cultural Perspectives on Sexuality

Ethnocentrism tends to influence people's understanding of human sexual behaviour. Most of us have had experience with sexuality in only one culture—Canada, for example—and we tend to view our sexual behaviour as the only pattern in existence, and certainly as the only "natural" pattern. But anthropologists have discovered that there are wide variations in sexual behaviour and attitudes from one culture to the next. Considering these variations should help us to put our own sexual behaviour in perspective.

One source of data on the enormous cross-cultural variations in sexual behaviour is the classic study by anthropologist Clellan Ford and psychologist Frank Beach (1951), who surveyed sexual behaviour in 190 societies around the world and also across various animal species. Other major sources are massive cross-cultural surveys of sexual practices done by anthropologists Edgar Gregersen (1996) and Suzanne Frayser (1985).

Ford and Beach concluded, in 1951, that the American culture was a relatively sexually restricted one compared to the majority of those studied. On the other hand (see Chapters 11 and 12), sexual behaviour and attitudes among Canadians and Americans have changed substantially in the 50 years since Ford and Beach wrote their book. Canadians tend to have more permissive attitudes toward sexuality than do Americans. For example, 29 percent of Americans (compared to 12 percent of Canadians) feel that sex before marriage is always wrong. Canadians are also more accepting of same-sex relationships and extramarital sex than Americans (Widmer et al., 1998).

Agenda-setting: In communications theory, the idea that the media define what is important and what is not by which stories they cover.

Social learning: In communications theory, the idea that the media provide role models whom we imitate.

Ethnocentrism: The tendency to regard one's own ethnic group and culture as superior to others and to believe that its customs and way of life are the standards by which other cultures should be judged.

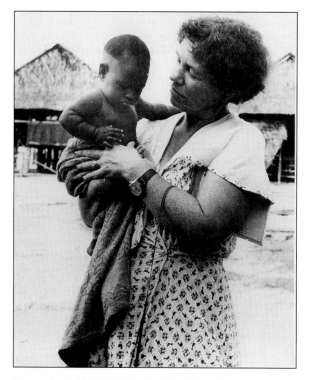

Figure 1.5   Margaret Mead, an anthropologist who contributed much to the early cross-cultural study of sexuality.

What do anthropologists mean by the term "culture"? Generally, **culture** refers to traditional (that is, passed down from generation to generation) ideas and values transmitted to members of the group by symbols (such as language). These ideas and values then serve as the basis for patterns of behaviour observed in the group (Frayser, 2004; Kroeber & Kluckhohn, 1963). Although various other primates do display some elements of culture, humans are unique in the complexity of their cultures and in their reliance on culture to adapt successfully.

The major generalization that emerges from cross-cultural studies is that all societies regulate sexual behaviour in some way, though the exact regulations vary greatly from one culture to the next (DeLamater, 1987). Apparently no society has seen fit to leave sexuality totally unregulated, perhaps fearful that social disruption would result. As an example, **incest taboos** are nearly universal: Sex is regulated in that intercourse between blood relatives is prohibited (Gregersen, 1996). Most societies also condemn forced sexual relations such as rape.

Beyond this generalization, though, regulations vary greatly from one society to the next, and sexual behaviour and attitudes vary correspondingly (see In Focus 1.1). Let's look at the ways in which various societies treat some key areas of human sexual behaviour.

Variations in Sexual Techniques

Kissing is one of the most common sexual techniques in our culture. It is also very common in most other societies (Gregersen, 1996). There are a few societies, though, in which kissing is unknown. For example, when the Thonga of Africa first saw Europeans kissing, they laughed and said, "Look at them; they eat each other's saliva and dirt." There is also some variation in techniques of kissing. For example, among the Kwakiutl of British Columbia and the Trobriand Islanders, kissing consisted of sucking the lips and tongue of the partner, permitting saliva to flow from one mouth to the other. Many Canadians might find such a practice somewhat repulsive, but other peoples find it sexually arousing.

Cunnilingus (mouth stimulation of the female genitals) is fairly common in our society, and it occurs in a few other societies as well, especially in the South Pacific. A particularly interesting variation is reported on the island of Ponape; the man places a fish in the woman's vulva and then gradually licks it out prior to coitus.

Inflicting pain on the partner is also a part of the sexual technique in some societies. The Apinaye woman of the Brazilian highlands may bite off bits of her partner's eyebrows, noisily spitting them aside. Ponapean men usually tug at the woman's eyebrows, occasionally yanking out tufts of hair. The Trukese women of the South Pacific poke a finger into the man's ear when they are highly aroused. People of various societies bite their partners to the point of drawing blood and leaving scars; most commonly men and women mutually inflict pain on each other (Frayser, 1985).

The frequency of intercourse for married couples varies considerably from one culture to the

---

Culture: Traditional ideas and values passed down from generation to generation within a group and transmitted to members of the group by symbols (such as language).

Incest taboo: A regulation prohibiting sexual interaction between close blood relatives, such as brother and sister or father and daughter.

In Focus 1.1

How Much Can Behaviours Vary? Sexuality in Three Societies

Inis Beag

Inis Beag is a small island off the coast of Ireland. It is probably one of the most naive and sexually repressive societies in the world.

The people of Inis Beag seem to have no knowledge of a number of sexual activities, such as French kissing, mouth stimulation of the breast, or hand stimulation of the partner's penis, much less oral sex or homosexuality. Sex education is virtually nonexistent; parents do not seem to be able to bring themselves to discuss such embarrassing matters with their children, and they simply trust that, after marriage, nature will take its course.

Menstruation and menopause are sources of fear for the island women because they have no idea of their physiological significance. It is commonly believed that menopause can produce insanity; in order to ward off this condition, some women have retired from life in their mid-forties, and a few have confined themselves to bed until death years later.

The men believe that intercourse is hard on one's health. They will desist from sex the night before they are to do a job that takes great energy. They do not approach women sexually during menstruation or for months after childbirth; a woman is considered dangerous to the male at these times.

The islanders abhor nudity. Only babies are allowed to bathe while nude. Adults wash only the parts of their bodies that extend beyond their clothing—face, neck, lower arms, hands, lower legs, and feet. The fear of nudity has even cost lives. Sailors who never learned to swim because it involved wearing scanty clothing have drowned when their ships have sunk.

Premarital sex is essentially unknown. In marital sex, foreplay is generally limited to kissing and rough fondling of the buttocks. The husband invariably initiates the activity. The male-on-top is the only position used, and both partners keep their underwear on during the activity. The man has an orgasm quickly and falls asleep immediately. Female orgasm either is believed not to exist or is considered deviant.

Mangaia

In distinct contrast to Inis Beag is Mangaia, an island in the South Pacific. For the Mangaians, sex—for pleasure and for procreation—is a principal interest.

The Mangaian boy first hears of masturbation when he is about 7, and he may begin to masturbate at age 8 or 9. At around age 13 he undergoes the superincision ritual (in which a slit is made on the top of the penis, along its entire length). This ritual initiates him into manhood; more important, however, the expert who performs the superincision gives him sexual instruction. He shows the boy how to perform oral sex, how to kiss and suck

next. The lowest frequency seems to be among the Irish natives of Inis Beag, discussed in In Focus 1.1, who engage in intercourse perhaps only once or twice a month; however, the anthropologists who studied them were unable to determine exactly how often couples did have sex because so much secrecy surrounds the act. At the opposite extreme, the Mangaians, also described in In Focus 1.1, have intercourse several times a night, at least among the young. The Santals of southern Asia engage in sexual intercourse as often as five times per day

every day early in marriage (Gregersen, 1996). Surveys of Canadian sexuality in the 1990s indicated that our frequency of intercourse was then about in the middle compared with other societies (e.g., *Maclean's*/CBC Poll, 1999).

Very few societies encourage people to engage in sexual intercourse at particular times (Frayser, 1985). Instead, most groups have restrictions that forbid intercourse at certain times or in certain situations. For example, almost every society has a postpartum sex taboo; that is, a prohibition on sex-breasts, and how to bring his partner to orgasm several times before he has his own. About two weeks after the operation, the boy has intercourse with an experienced woman, which removes the scab from the superincision. She provides him with practice in various acts and positions and trains him to hold back until he can have simultaneous orgasms with his partner.

After this, the Mangaian boy actively seeks out girls, or they seek him out; soon he has coitus every night. The girl, who has received sexual instruction from an older woman, expects demonstration of the boy's virility as proof of his desire for her. What is valued is the ability of the male to continue vigorously the in-and-out action of coitus over long periods of time while the female moves her hips "like a washing machine." Nothing is despised more than a "dead" partner who does not move. A good man is expected to continue his actions for 15 to 30 minutes or more.

The average "nice" girl will have three or four successive boyfriends between the ages of 13 and 20; the average boy may have 10 or more girlfriends. Mangaian parents encourage their daughters to have sexual experiences with several men. They want them to find marriage partners who are congenial.

At around age 18, the Mangaians typically have sex most nights of the week, with about three orgasms per night. By about age 48, they have sex two or three times per week, with one orgasm each time.

All women in Mangaia apparently learn to have orgasms. Bringing his partner to orgasm is one of the man's chief sources of sexual pleasure.

Mehinaku

Between Inis Beag, where there is little sex and plenty of anxiety, and Mangaia, where there is plenty of sex and little anxiety, is Mehinaku, where there is plenty of sex and plenty of anxiety.

In the central Brazilian village of Mehinaku, sex is believed to be very fascinating and the culture is highly eroticized. There is an openness with children about sex, and children can easily list the names of their parents' extramarital lovers, who are typically many. The men have a very high libido, leading them to compete with each other for women's sexual favours by bringing small gifts such as fish.

On the other hand, the culture is very gender-segregated. There is a men's house and if a woman enters it and sees what she is forbidden to see, she is taken to the woods and gang raped, in a culture that is otherwise very non-violent. Mehinaku women are believed to have a much weaker sex drive than men, and there seems to be no recognition of female orgasm. Women's menstruation is believed to be dangerous.

The dreams and mythic stories told by the people testify to their sexual anxieties—for example, those in myths who engage in extramarital sex typically die in fantastic ways. In reality the people continue with a great deal of sexual activity while feeling intense ambivalence and anxiety about it.

Sources: Messenger, 1993, in Suggs & Miracle, 1971; Marshall & Suggs, 1985; Gregor, 1985.

---

ual intercourse for a period of time after a woman has given birth, with the taboo lasting from a few days to more than a year (Gregersen, 1996).

Masturbation

Attitudes toward **masturbation,** or sexual self-stimulation of the genitals, vary widely across cultures. Some societies tolerate or even encourage masturbation during childhood and adolescence, whereas others condemn the practice at any age. Almost all human societies express some disap-

proval of adult masturbation, ranging from mild ridicule to severe punishment (Gregersen, 1996). On the other hand, at least some adults in all societies appear to practise it.

Female masturbation certainly occurs in other societies. The African Azande woman uses a phallus made of a wooden root; however, if her husband catches her masturbating, he may beat her severely.

Masturbation: Self-stimulation of the genitals to produce sexual arousal.

The following is a description of the Lesu of the South Pacific, one of the few societies that express no disapproval of adult female masturbation:

> A woman will masturbate if she is sexually excited and there is no man to satisfy her. A couple may be having intercourse in the same house, or near enough for her to see them, and she may thus become aroused. She then sits down and bends her right leg so that her heel presses against her genitalia. Even young girls of about six years may do this quite casually as they sit on the ground. The women and men talk about it freely, and there is no shame attached to it. It is a customary position for women to take, and they learn it in childhood. They never use their hands for manipulation. (Powdermaker, 1933, pp. 276–277)

Premarital and Extramarital Sex[2]

Societies differ considerably in their rules regarding premarital sex (Frayser, 1985). At one extreme are the Marquesans of eastern Polynesia. Both boys and girls in that culture have participated in a wide range of sexual experiences before puberty. Their first experience with intercourse occurs with a heterosexual partner who is 30 to 40 years old. Mothers are proud if their daughters have many lovers. Only later does marriage occur. In contrast are the Egyptians of Siwa. In this culture a girl's clitoris is removed at age 7 or 8 in order to decrease her potential for sexual excitement and intercourse. Premarital intercourse is believed to bring shame on the family. Marriage usually occurs around the age of 12 or 13, shortening the premarital period and any temptations it might contain.

These two cultures are fairly typical of their regions. According to one study, 90 percent of Pacific Island societies permit premarital sex, as do

---

[2]Although marriage as an institution is found in most, if not all, cultures, some people never marry or marry late in life. Some people choose not to marry; others are in same-sex relationships and cannot marry legally, as many countries do not permit same-sex marriages. For these individuals the terms "premarital sex" and "extramarital sex" do not have much meaning. For example, is a 50-year-old person who has never been married engaging in premarital sex? Is a person who is having sex outside a common-law relationship engaging in extramarital sex? Nonetheless, the pervasiveness of marriage as an institution (for example, 90 to 95 percent of Canadians marry) makes it meaningful to discuss cultural rules regarding premarital and extramarital sex.

88 percent of African and 82 percent of Eurasian societies; however, 73 percent of Mediterranean societies prohibit premarital sex (Frayser, 1985).

Extramarital sex is more complex and conflicted for most cultures. Extramarital sex ranks second only to incest as the most strictly prohibited type of sexual contact. One study found that it was forbidden for one or both partners in 74 percent of the cultures surveyed (Frayser, 1985). Even when extramarital sex is permitted, it is subjected to regulations; the most common pattern of restriction is to allow extramarital sex for husbands but not wives.

Sex with Same-Sex Partners

A wide range of attitudes toward same-sex sexual expression—what we in Canada call "homosexuality"—exists in various cultures (Murray, 2000). At one extreme are societies that strongly disapprove of same-sex sexual behaviour for people of any age. In contrast, some societies tolerate the behaviour for children but disapprove of it in adults. Still other societies actively encourage all their male members to engage in some same-sex sexual behaviour, usually in conjunction with puberty rites (Herdt, 1984). A few societies have a formalized role for the adult gay man that gives him status and dignity.

While there is wide variation in attitudes toward homosexuality and in same-sex sexual behaviour, three general rules do seem to emerge (Ford & Beach, 1951; Murray, 2000; Whitam, 1983): (1) No matter how a particular society treats homosexuality, the behaviour always occurs in at least some individuals—that is, same-sex sexuality is found universally in all societies; (2) males are more likely to engage in same-sex sexual behaviour than females; and (3) same-sex sexual behaviour is never the predominant form of sexual behaviour for adults in any of the societies studied. (See Chapter 15 for a discussion of theories about the causes of sexual identity.)

In Canada and other Western nations, we hold an unquestioned assumption that people have a sexual identity, whether gay, lesbian, bisexual, or heterosexual. Yet sexual identity as an unvarying, lifelong characteristic of the self is unknown or rare in some cultures, such as Indonesia (Stevenson, 1995). In those cultures, the self and individualism, so prominent in Canadian culture, are downplayed.

Instead, a person is defined in relation to others and behaviour is seen as much more the product of the situation than of lifelong personality traits. In such a culture, having a "gay identity" just doesn't make sense. Sex with same-sex partners is discussed in detail in Chapter 15.

Standards of Attractiveness

In all human societies physical characteristics are important in determining whom one chooses as a sex partner. What is considered attractive varies considerably, though. For example, the region of the body that is judged for attractiveness varies from one culture to the next. For some peoples, the shape and colour of the eyes are especially significant. For others, the shape of the ears is most important. Some societies go directly to the heart of the matter and judge attractiveness by the appearance of the external genitals. In a few societies, elongated labia majora (the pads of fat on either side of the vaginal opening in women) are considered sexually attractive, and it is common practice for a woman to pull on hers in order to make them longer. Among the Nawa women of Africa elongated labia majora are considered a mark of beauty and are quite prominent.

Our society's standards are in the minority in one way: In most cultures, a plump woman is considered more attractive than a thin one.

One standard does seem to be a general rule: A poor complexion is considered unattractive in the majority of human societies Research on sexual attraction is discussed in detail in Chapter 13.

Social-Class and Ethnic-Group Variations in Canada

The discussion so far may have seemed to imply that there is one uniform standard of sexual behaviour in Canada and that all Canadians behave alike sexually. In fact, though, there are large variations in sexual behaviour within our culture. Some of these subcultural variations can be classified as social-class differences and some as ethnic differences.

How do you define beauty? Think about it as you watch the "Beautiful" video in Chapter 1 of your CD.

Social Class and Sex

Table 1.1 shows data on some social-class variations in sexuality. Education is used as an indicator of social class. The more educated the respondents, the older they were likely to be at first intercourse. In particular, respondents with university degrees are more than a year older than other Canadians at first intercourse. This is true for both men and women. Similarly, men and women from

Table 1.1 Social-Class Variations in Sexual Behaviour in Canada (education is used as an indicator of social class)					
	Less Than High School	High School Graduates	Some College or University	University Graduates	Graduate Degree
Percentage who have ever had intercourse					
Men	Data unavailable	94%	96%	97%	96%
Women	93%	96%	96%	95%	96%
Percentage who had intercourse in the last 12 months					
Men	88%	93%	91%	92%	93%
Women	84%	90%	88%	88%	83%
Percentage who have had two or more partners in the last 12 months					
Men	12%	11%	11%	10%	7%
Women	8%	6%	6%	4%	4%
Percentage of respondents in short-term relationships (less than 12 months) who always used a condom					
Men	57%	56%	53%	62%	52%
Women	55%	40%	48%	51%	63%

Source: Statistics Canada (1998), *National Population Health Survey, 1996–97* [Computer file], Ottawa: Statistics Canada. Percentages are based only on members of the sample who responded to the question.

lower social classes are more likely to have had two or more partners in the previous 12 months, and in some cases the differences are large. Those who did not finish high school are almost twice as likely as those with advanced degrees to have had two or more sexual partners.

The pattern for intercourse within the last 12 months is a bit more complex. For men, there are few important social-class differences. Women who had not completed high school and those with graduate degrees were somewhat less likely to have engaged in intercourse during this period. In addition, there are some differences in sexual behaviour across social classes. A study conducted in Montreal using a francophone sample found that manual workers engaged in both sexual intercourse and oral–genital sex more frequently than respondents with office and professional jobs (Sampson et al., 1991, 1993).

Although there are some social-class variations in sexuality, there are also some similarities. The data in Table 1.1 show that there are no clear social-class variations in experience with intercourse—most respondents in all social classes had engaged in intercourse; there was also little variation in condom use.

Ethnicity and Sexuality in Canada

The Canadian population is composed of many cultural and ethnic groups, and there are both variations and similarities among these groups in sexual behaviour. Here we discuss variations in sexual behaviour and attitudes in different provinces, as well as differences between French-speaking and English-speaking Canadians of European descent. We also examine sexual behaviour and attitudes in six of the largest ethnocultural communities in Canada.

Regional Differences in Sexuality in Canada

A number of surveys have found differences in sex-

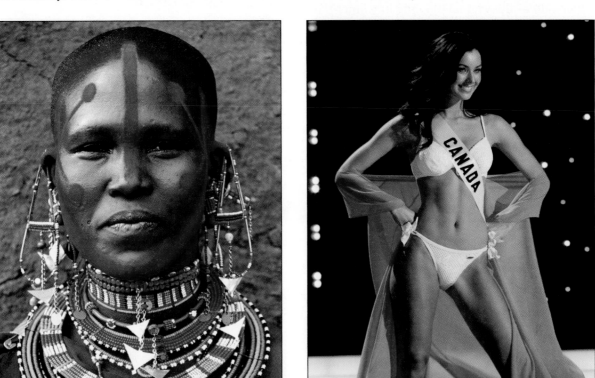

(a)   *(b)*

Figure 1.6   Cross-cultural differences, cross-cultural similarities. *(a)* Woman of West Africa. *(b)* Miss Canada, Natalie Glebova, winner of the Miss Universe 2005 beauty pageant. The custom of female adornment is found in most cultures, although the exact definition of beauty varies from culture to culture.

ual behaviour and attitudes across Canada. Table 1.2 shows data from three of the national polls that are conducted for *Maclean's* magazine every year. The highest reported frequencies of sexual activity were in Newfoundland and Labrador, whereas the lowest were in Saskatchewan and New Brunswick. Frequency of sexual activity is not always the best predictor of high sexual satisfaction, as the highest percentages of respondents who were "very satisfied" with their sex lives were in Newfoundland and Labrador (a province with a high sexual frequency) and New Brunswick (a province with a low sexual frequency). The lowest percentages of very sexually satisfied Canadians were in Quebec and British Columbia. Residents of the Maritime provinces are the least likely to use erotic materials and sexual aids.

These polls did not report the findings by ethnic group, linguistic group, age, or gender. Therefore, it is difficult to determine the reasons for these regional differences. For example, why do Newfoundlanders in this and in previous *Maclean's* polls report more frequent sexual activity and greater sexual satisfaction than most other Canadians? Differences in culture and in ethnic makeup may account for some of these regional differences.

Canadians are becoming increasingly accepting and tolerant of a diversity of forms of sexual expression (Barrett et al., 2003). Table 1.2 also shows the attitudes of Canadians on several of these issues. Francophones in Quebec tend to be the most tolerant in terms of their attitudes toward masturbation, homosexuality, prostitution, and use of erotic materials, and are the most likely to have engaged in extramarital sex. For example, 78 percent of Quebec residents agreed that "Masturbation is a healthy part of one's sex life"; only between 41 and 64 percent of Canadians in other provinces agreed with this statement. Table 1.2 shows that there also are other differences in sexual attitudes and behaviour from province to province and region to region; however, these trends are not always consistent within a region or from issue to issue. In Focus 1.2 discusses the differences between Quebec and the rest of Canada in more depth.

Aboriginal Peoples and Sexuality

Before contact with Europeans, most First Nations populations were considered sexually permissive by European standards. For example, among First Nations peoples, women were encouraged to take the initiative, and premarital and extramarital sex were acceptable. In many cultures, gay men, lesbians, and people who assumed cross-gender roles were respected and admired (McCormick, 1993). Sex was considered a magical spiritual gift to humans designed to bring pleasure—a gift that

Table 1.2 Regional Variation in Sexual Behaviour and Attitudes in Canada

	Nfld	PEI	NS	NB	Que	Ont	Man	Sask	Alta	BC
Very satisfied with sex life[1]	53%	40%	40%	51%	33%	43%	45%	39%	44%	37%
Frequency of sex per month[2]	10.0	8.0	6.4	5.9	8.0	6.4	6.6	5.4	7.6	6.9
Average length of sexual encounter in minutes[2]	40	35	30	37	45	38	34	34	40	38
Had an affair[3]	6%	4%	7%	10%	16%	9%	5%	8%	12%	7%
Used erotic materials or sexual aids[1]	15%	8%	9%	3%	18%	14%	16%	10%	19%	21%
Agree that masturbation is healthy part of one's sex life[2]	53%	54%	43%	57%	78%	64%	48%	41%	59%	63%
Agree that prostitution should be legal[2]	25%	30%	50%	30%	59%	52%	42%	36%	52%	57%
Agree that erotic materials can make your sex life more interesting[2]	37%	28%	21%	35%	48%	49%	35%	29%	45%	36%
Agree that would be fine if one of children was gay[2]	42%	50%	45%	49%	85%	49%	40%	32%	40%	52%

[1]*Maclean's*/CBC Poll (1999). *N* = 1,200 respondents contacted by telephone.
[2]*Maclean's*/CTV Poll (1994). *N* = 1,610 respondents contacted by telephone.
[3]*Maclean's*/CTV Poll (1995). *N* = 1,200 respondents contacted by telephone.

In Focus 1.2

Is Quebec a Sexually Distinct Society?

Prior to the 1950s, the attitudes of Quebec franco-phones on sexual issues were very conservative. For example, talking about sex, except in the context of reproduction, was seen as taboo. However, starting at the end of the 1950s Quebec began a period of rapid social change sometimes called the "Quiet Revolution," which included liberalization of attitudes and behaviour. The revolution in sexual attitudes and behaviour began in the 1970s (Gemme & Badeau, 1997). Today, partly due to a decline in the influence of the Roman Catholic Church, *les Québécois(e)* tend to be tolerant of different forms of sexual expression. Just how different are Quebecers from Canadians in other parts of Canada?

Table 1.3 compares Quebecers to Canadians as a whole on a number of attitudes and behaviours related to sexuality. The data for Quebec include not only francophones, but also anglophones and allo-phones (people whose first language is neither Eng-lish nor French) living in Quebec; these groups differ in many ways from *les Québécois(e)*. These data show that Quebecers are more liberal in their atti-tudes; for example, they are more accepting of teenagers engaging in sexual activity and they are more likely to favour same-sex marriage (also see the differences in attitudes toward masturbation, prostitution, and having a child who is gay that are reported in Table 1.2). The 2002 *Maclean's* Poll showed that the highest percentage of Canadians who report having an active sex life are in Quebec; in past polls, Newfoundlanders were the most likely to report having an active sex life. A higher percentage of Quebecers live in common-law relationships; a smaller percentage live in marital relationships. Que-becers are also more likely to report having engaged in extradyadic sexual activity (see Table 1.2). How-ever, there are no differences between Quebecers and other Canadians in attitudes toward equal rights for gays and lesbians or in their likelihood to fantasize about a person of their same sex. In terms of sexual health indicators, Quebec women are less likely to breast-feed compared to the national aver-age but so are women in the Atlantic provinces; the teenage pregnancy rate in Quebec is below the national average but so are the rates in the Atlantic provinces; and Quebec has a lower rate of chlamy-dia, a common sexually transmitted infection, than the national average but so do Ontario and the

should be used only with respect for others and for ourselves (Newhouse, 1998).

Depictions of Aboriginal peoples in the popular media over the last century have portrayed them as noble savages who are both exotic and erotic (Bird, 1999). Aboriginal males have been shown nearly naked, emphasizing well-developed, masculine bodies. In romance novels of the 1990s, they became cultural icons for vanishing standards of masculin-ity—handsome and virile, yet tender and vulnerable and magnificent lovers for white women (Van Lent, 1996). Aboriginal women, although less visible in the popular media, are stereotyped as princesses or squaws (Bird, 1999). The princess is noble, beautiful, and erotic. The Disney animated film *Pocahontas* features such a voluptuous princess. The stereotypi-cal squaw, in contrast, is unattractive, uninteresting, and ignored.

Today, the sexual behaviour and attitudes of most Aboriginal communities have been influenced by the Judeo-Christian tradition, abusive experiences in residential schools, whether they live on or off the reserve, and the poor economic and crowded social conditions in which many live. Unfortunately, there have been few studies of sexual behaviour within Aboriginal communities or of the influence of Abo-riginal culture on sexual behaviour. This is important because a study of Aboriginal people living on-reserve in Ontario found that cultural variables, such as the traditions of learning through the telling of stories by elders, had an important influence on sex-ual behaviour. For example, in many communities

Atlantic provinces. This suggests that Quebecers are not distinct from the rest of Canada in their likelihood of engaging in safer sex.

The only academic Department of Sexology in Canada is in Quebec, at l'Université du Québec à Montréal (UQAM). In other Canadian universities, human sexuality is studied through departments such as psychology, sociology, family studies, or

education. The Sexology Department at UQAM is interdisciplinary and students can earn either a Bachelor of Sexology or a Masters of Sexology specializing in counselling or research.

So is Quebec a sexually distinct society? In terms of attitudes, the answer appears to clearly be yes. However, in terms of behaviour, the answer is less clear.

Table 1.3 Comparison of the Sexuality in Quebec to Sexuality in Canada Overall

	Quebec	Canada
Parents who agree that teens should be allowed to spend the night together in their home with their sex partner	41%	13%
Parents who agree that it's appropriate for 16-year-olds to have sex outside of marriage	35%	6%
In favour of same-sex marriage	51%	43%
Think homosexuals should have the same rights as heterosexuals	77%	74%
Fantasized about having sex with a person of the same sex	5%	7%
Active sex life	76%	62%
Couples living in common-law relationships	30%	14%

Sources: NLSCY, Statistics Canada; *Maclean's,* 2000, 2002; Leger Marketing, 2004.

AIDS was seen as a gay white man's disease. As a result, safer sex behaviours such as consistent condom use are rare (Myers et al., 1994, 1999).

Ethnocultural Communities in Canada and Sexuality

Changing patterns of immigration to Canada in recent years have resulted in a Canadian population that is becoming more and more ethnically diverse. There have been few studies of sexual behaviour in Canadian ethnocultural communities. However, a federally funded study, *Ethnocultural Communities Facing AIDS,* which focused on preventing HIV and AIDS in the communities with large recent immigration, examined selected aspects of sexual behaviour and attitudes in six ethnic com-

munities. Participants were from the Chinese, South Asian, Horn of Africa, English-speaking Caribbean, North African Muslim, and Latin American communities.[3] The researchers made sure that the sam-

[3]Communities in Vancouver (Chinese and South Asian), Toronto (English-speaking Caribbean and Horn of Africa), and Montreal (North African Muslim and Latin American) were studied. The Chinese participants came from Hong Kong, Taiwan, and the People's Republic of China. Most of the participants from the South Asian communities were from India and Pakistan. The English-speaking Caribbean participants were from all of the English-speaking Caribbean islands and Guyana. Participants from the Horn of Africa came largely from Ethiopia, Eritrea, and Somalia. The North African Muslim participants came mostly from North Africa and the Middle East. The Latin American participants came primarily from Peru, Chile, Guatemala, and El Salvador.

(a)   (b)

Figure 1.7   The sexuality of members of different ethnic groups is profoundly shaped by their cultures. *(a)* This advertisement for a Montreal conference on childhood sexuality included a drawing of two children that showed their genitals. Consistent with cultural attitudes, the French-language newspaper in Montreal published the drawing at the left. The children's genitals are not shown in the advertisements run by the English-language newspaper in Toronto (right). *(b)* There is strong emphasis on the traditional family among Asian Canadians.

ple was representative of the community in terms of age and how long respondents had lived in Canada. The study used both focus groups (a research procedure in which participants discuss their answers to the research questions in small groups) and questionnaires (Singer et al., 1996).

The sexual behaviour of individuals from ethnic minorities is influenced both by the culture of their country of origin as well as by the process of adapting to Canada's majority culture. The study found that in many ways sexual attitudes and behaviour in these Canadian communities resemble attitudes and behaviour in the countries of origin. Generally men and women are seen as having distinct roles, with men expected to be the head of the family and women expected to be the caregivers. Sex is not talked about in the family, even between husbands and wives. Women are expected to be passive, inexperienced, and to fulfil men's sexual needs, whereas men are expected to be sexually active and experienced. Women have little power in sexual relationships to refuse sex or to insist on condom use. In many of these communities it is expected that men, but not women, will have extramarital affairs or use prostitutes. Homosexuality is often considered abnormal and shameful. Thus most gay men and lesbians keep their same-sex relationships or feelings secret.

Expectations regarding adolescent dating and sexual behaviour in these ethnocultural communi-

ties are different than in the dominant Canadian culture. In general, virginity at marriage is highly valued in women but is not expected of men. In the South Asian communities, girls may not be allowed to date. On the other hand, young people do not always conform to these expectations and are adopting some aspects of the dominant culture after learning about them from friends and the media. This often creates conflict between youth and their more traditional parents. For example, Chinese youth, including girls, are becoming increasingly likely to engage in sexual activity. However, a Vancouver study found that both male and female Asian university students are more conservative and less experienced than are non-Asians in their sexual behaviour. For example, half as many Asian students (36 percent) as non-Asian students (66 percent) had engaged in sexual intercourse (Meston et al., 1996). However, research has also shown that the attitudes of Asian-Canadians become increasingly less sexually permissive the longer they have lived in Canada and the more acculturated they have become (Brotto et al., in press; Meston et al., 1998).

Of course, there are also many ways in which the behaviour and attitudes of members of one ethnocultural community are different from those of other communities. For example, single South Asian men are more likely than single men from Latin America or the English-speaking Caribbean to report having had more than one sexual partner in the previous year. In contrast, married South Asian men were the least likely to report having had more than one partner in the previous year (Maticka-Tyndale et al., 1996).

The Significance of Cross-Cultural Studies

What relevance do cross-cultural data have to an understanding of human sexuality? They are important for two basic reasons. First, they give us a notion of the enormous variation that exists in human sexual behaviour, and they help us put our own standards and behaviour in perspective. Second, these studies provide impressive evidence concerning the importance of culture and learning in the shaping of our sexual behaviour; they show us that human sexual behaviour is not completely determined by biology or drives or instincts. For example, a woman of Inis Beag and a woman of Mangaia presumably have vaginas that are similarly constructed and clitorises that are approximately the same size and have the same nerve supply. But the woman of Inis Beag never has an orgasm, and all Mangaian women orgasm.[4] Why? Their cultures are different, and they and their partners learned different things about sex as they were growing up. Culture is a major determinant of human sexual behaviour.

The point of studying sexuality in different cultures is *not* to teach ourselves that there are a lot of exotic people out there doing exotic things. Rather, the point is to remind ourselves that each group has its own culture, and this culture has a profound influence on the sexual expression of the women and men who grow up in it. We will return with more examples in many of the chapters that follow.

■ Cross-Species Perspectives on Sexuality

Humans are just one of many animal species, and all of them display sexual behaviour. To put our own sexual behaviour in evolutionary perspective, it is helpful to explore the similarities and differ-

---

[4]We like to use the word "orgasm" not only as a noun but also as a verb. The reason is that alternative expressions, such as "to *achieve* orgasm" and "to *reach* orgasm," reflect the tendency of Canadians to make sex an achievement situation (an idea to be discussed further in Chapter 10). To avoid this, we use "to have an orgasm" or "to orgasm."

ences between our own sexuality and that of other species. There is one other reason for this particular discussion. Some people classify sexual behaviours as "natural" or "unnatural," depending on whether other species do or do not exhibit those behaviours. Sometimes, though, the data are twisted to suit the purposes of the person making the argument, and so there is a need for a less biased view. Let's see exactly what some other species do!

Masturbation

Humans are definitely not the only species that masturbates. Masturbation is found among many species of mammals, particularly among the primates (monkeys and apes). Male monkeys and apes in zoos can be observed masturbating, often to the horror of the proper folk who have come to see them. At one time it was thought that this behaviour might be the result of the unnatural living conditions of zoos. However, observations of free-living primates indicate that they, too, masturbate. Techniques include hand stimulation of the genitals or rubbing the genitals against an object. In terms of technique, monkeys and non-human apes have one advantage over humans: their bodies are so flexible that they can perform mouth–genital sex on themselves. A unique form of male masturbation is found among red deer; during the rutting season they move the tips of their antlers through low-growing vegetation, producing erection and ejaculation (Beach, 1976).

Female masturbation is also found among many species besides our own. The prize for the most inventive technique probably should go to the female porcupine. She holds one end of a stick in her paws and walks around while straddling the stick; as the stick bumps against the ground, it vibrates against her genitals (Ford & Beach, 1951). Human females are apparently not the only ones to enjoy vibrators.

Same-Sex Sexual Behaviour

Same-sex behaviour is found in many species besides our own (Bagemihl, 1999; Vasey, 2002; Wallen & Parsons, 1997). Indeed, observations of other species indicate that our basic mammalian heritage is bisexual, composed of both heterosexual and homosexual elements (Bagemihl, 1999).

Males of many species will mount other males,

(a)   *(b)*

Figure 1.8   The sexual behaviour of animals. *(a)* Females have various ways of expressing choice. Here a female Barbary macaque presents her sexual swelling to a male. He seems to be interested. (Photograph by Frans deWaal.) *(b)* Same-gender sexuality in animals: Two male giraffes "necking." They rub necks and become aroused. (Photograph by Stephen G. Maka.)

and anal intercourse has been observed in some male primates (Wallen & Parsons, 1997). Among domestic sheep, 9 percent of adult males strongly prefer other males as sex partners (Ellis, 1996; Roselli et al., 2002). In a number of primate species, including bonobos and Japanese macaques, females mount other females and sometimes exhibit a preference for same-sex partners (Small, 1993; Vasey, 2002).

In What Ways Are Humans Unique?

Are humans in any way unique in their sexual behaviour? The general trend, as we move from lower species such as fish or rodents to higher species like primates, is for sexual behaviour to be more hormonally (instinctively) controlled among the lower species and to be controlled more by the brain (and therefore by learning and social content) in the higher species (Beach, 1947; Wallen, 2001). However, environmental influences are much more important in shaping primate— especially human—sexual behaviour than they are in shaping the sexual behaviour of other species.

Nonetheless, research has shown that in addition to instinctual or hard-wired preferences (such as the preference of males for sexually receptive females), learning affects the sexual preferences of a number of different species. For example, Quebec psychologist James Pfaus and his colleagues have shown in laboratory experiments that male rats can be conditioned (see Chapter 3 for an explanation of classical conditioning) to prefer female rats with a particular neutral odour, such as almond or lemon extract, to unscented females by first pairing the neutral odour with ejaculation (Kippin et al., 1998; Pfaus et al., 2003). They have found similar results in female rats.

An illustration of this fact is provided by studies of the adult sexual behaviour of animals raised in deprived environments. If mice are reared in isolation, their adult sexual behaviour will nonetheless be normal (Scott, 1964). But if rhesus monkeys are reared in isolation, their adult sexual behaviour is severely disturbed, to the point that they may be incapable of reproducing (Harlow et al., 1963). Thus, environmental experiences are crucial in shaping the sexual behaviour of higher species, particularly humans; for us, sexual behaviour is a lot more than just "doin' what comes naturally."

Female sexuality provides a particularly good illustration of the shift in hormonal control from lower to higher species. Throughout most of the animal kingdom, female sexual behaviour is strongly controlled by hormones. In virtually all mammals, females do not engage in sexual behaviour at all except when they are in "heat" (estrus), which is a particular hormonal state. In contrast, human females are capable of engaging in sexual behaviour—and actually do engage in it—during any phase of their hormonal (menstrual) cycle. Thus the sexual behaviour of the human female is not nearly as much under hormonal control as that of females of other species.

Traditionally it was thought that female orgasm is unique to humans and does not exist in other species. Then some studies found evidence of orgasm in macaques (monkeys), as indicated by the same physiological responses indicative of orgasm in human females—specifically, increased heart rate and uterine contractions—in stump-tailed macaques as a result of female same-sex sexual activity, and perhaps for heterosexual activity as well (Burton, 1970; Goldfoot et al., 1980; Zumpe & Michael, 1968). Thus humans can no longer claim to have a corner on the female orgasm market. This fact has interesting implications for understanding the evolution of sexuality. Perhaps the higher species, in which the females are not driven to sexual activity by their hormones, have the pleasure of orgasm as an incentive.

In summary, then, there is little in human sexuality that is completely unique to humans, except for eloborate, complex cultural influences. In other respects, we are on a continuum with other species.

The Non-sexual Uses of Sexual Behaviour

Two male baboons are locked in combat. One begins to emerge as the victor. The other "presents" (the "female" sexual posture, in which the rump is directed toward the other and is elevated somewhat).

Two male monkeys are members of the same troop. Long ago they established which one is dominant and which is subordinate. The dominant one mounts (the "male" sexual behaviour) the subordinate one.

These are examples of animals sometimes using sexual behaviour for non-sexual purposes (Small, 1993; Wallen & Zehr, 2004). Commonly such behaviour signals the end of a fight, as in the first example. The loser indicates his surrender by presenting, and the winner signals victory by mounting. Sexual behaviours can also symbolize an animal's rank in a dominance hierarchy. Dominant animals mount subordinate ones. As another example, male squirrel monkeys sometimes use an exhibitionist display of their erect penis as part of an aggressive display against another male in a phenomenon called *phallic aggression* (Wickler, 1973).

The bonobo, an ape that is perhaps our closest genetic relative, is a particularly interesting example of the use of sexual behaviour for non-sexual purposes (de Waal, 1995). Bonobos live in female-centred, egalitarian groups and use sex for peace-making in situations that might lead to aggression among other animals, such as situations involving food or jealousy. Since sex is a key part of their social life, bonobos engage in a wide range of sexual behaviours (including oral sex, massage of another's genitals, and intense tongue-kissing) with a wide range of partners, both homosexual and heterosexual. The female is sexually attractive and sexually active during most of her cycle, rather than for just a few days around estrus.

All this is perfectly obvious when we observe it in monkeys. But do humans ever use sexual behaviour for non-sexual purposes? Consider the rapist, who uses sex as an expression of aggression against and power over a woman or another man (Holmstrom & Burgess, 1980). Another example is the exhibitionist, who uses such a display of his erect penis to shock and frighten women, much as the male squirrel monkey uses such a display to shock and frighten his opponent. Humans also use sex for economic purposes; the best examples are male and female prostitutes.

There are also less extreme examples. Consider the couple who have a fight and then make love to signal an end to the hostilities.[5] Or consider the person who goes to bed with an influential—though unattractive—politician because this gives him or her a vicarious sense of power.

You can probably think of other examples of the non-sexual use of sexual behaviour. Humans, just like members of other species, can use sex for a variety of non-sexual purposes.

---

[5]It has been our observation, particularly for couples in therapy, that this practice may not mean the same thing to men and women. To men it can mean that everything is fine again, but women can be left feeling dissatisfied and not at all convinced that the issues are resolved. Thus this situation can be a source of miscommunication in heterosexual couples.

■ ■ ■ SUMMARY

"Sexual activity" is activity that produces arousal and increases the chance of orgasm. "Sex" (sexual behaviour and anatomy) is distinct from "gender" (being male or female).

Throughout most of human history, religion was the main source of information concerning sexuality. In the late 1800s and early 1900s, important contributions to the scientific understanding of sex were made by Sigmund Freud, Havelock Ellis, Richard von Krafft-Ebing, and Magnus Hirschfeld. These early researchers emerged from the Victorian era, in which sexual norms were highly rigid—although many people's actual behaviour violated these norms. By the 1990s, major, well-conducted sex surveys were available. Today, the mass media are a powerful influence on most North American and European people's understanding of sexuality.

Studies of various human cultures around the world provide evidence of the enormous variations in human sexual behaviour. For example, the frequency of intercourse may vary from once a week in some cultures to three or four times a night in others. All societies regulate sexual behaviour in some way. Attitudes regarding premarital and extramarital sex, masturbation, same-sex sexual behaviour, and gender roles vary considerably from one culture to the next. The great variations provide evidence of the importance of learning in shaping sexual behaviour.

Within Canada, sexual behaviour varies with one's social class and ethnic group. For example, French-speaking Canadians in Quebec are more permissive in their sexual attitudes and behaviour than are English-speaking Canadians. Canada's ethnocultural communities with large recent immigration are characterized by traditional gender roles and restrictions on female sexuality, but not on male sexuality. Asian cultures tend to be conservative about sexuality for both males and females.

Studies of sexual behaviour in various animal species show that masturbation, mouth–genital stimulation, and same-gender sexual behaviour are by no means limited to humans. They also illustrate how sexual behaviour may be used for a variety of non-sexual purposes, such as expressing dominance.

■ ■ ■ QUESTIONS FOR THOUGHT, DISCUSSION, AND DEBATE

1. In the wide spectrum of sexual practices in different cultures, from the conservatism of Inis Beag to the permissiveness of Mangaia, where would you place Canada today? Are we permissive, restrictive, or somewhere in between? Why?

2. Research indicates that masturbation, mouth–genital stimulation, and same-gender sexual behaviours are present in other species besides humans. What is the significance of that finding?

3. Sally is a newspaper reporter in Captown, the provincial capital. She learns, through a trusted friend, that the highly popular premier, George Smith, has been having a long-term affair with a local woman lawyer, despite the fact that each of them is apparently happily married. Should Sally break the news in an article? In terms of communications theories, what effects might she expect her article to have on the public's attitudes about sexuality?

4. How does premarital sexual behaviour in Canada compare with premarital sex in Mangaia and Inis Beag (see In Focus 1.1)? Which of these three cultures do you think is best for adolescents to grow up in? Why? In which of those three cultures do you think adults are likely to have the most positive feelings about their sexuality? Why?

■ ■ ■ SUGGESTIONS FOR FURTHER READING

Bagemihl, Bruce. (1999). *Biological exuberance: Animal homosexuality and natural diversity.* New York: St. Martin's. The author documents the blindness of scientists to the homosexual behaviour they observed and at the same time catalogues the extensiveness of homosexual behaviours in hundreds of species.

Bullough, Vern L. (1994). *Science in the bedroom: A history of sex research.* New York: Basic Books. Bullough is one of the most knowledgeable historians of sexuality, and this book provides fascinating details about sex research from the ancient Greeks to Hirschfeld, Ellis, and Freud and brings us up to the 1990s.

Greenberg, Bradley S., Brown, Jane D., & Buerkel-Rothfuss (Eds.). (1993). *Media, sex, and the adolescent.* This is a marvellous collection of articles on the sexual content of the media to which adolescents are exposed and tells how they respond.

Gregersen, Edgar. (1996). *The world of human sexuality.* New York: Irvington. Gregersen, an anthropologist, has compiled a vast amount of information about sexuality in cultures around the world. The book also is a treasure trove of fascinating illustrations.

Zuk, Marlene. (2002). *Sexual selections: What we can and can't learn about sex from animals.* Berkeley: University of California Press. Zuk, a biologist, carefully analyzes what can be inferred from studies of the sexual behaviour of animals.

Online **Learning Centre**

For Review Questions, Web Resources, and other learning and study tools, visit the *Understanding Human Sexuality* Online Learning Centre at www.mcgrawhill.ca/college/hyde.

CHAPTER 2

Theoretical Perspectives on Sexuality

CHAPTER HIGHLIGHTS

One of the discoveries of psychoanalysis consists in the assertion that impulses, which can only be described as sexual in both the narrower and the wider sense, play a peculiarly large part, never before sufficiently appreciated, in the causation of nervous and mental disorders. Nay, more, that these sexual impulses have contributed invaluably to the highest cultural, artistic, and social achievements of the human mind.*

From an evolutionary perspective, no single decision is more important than the choice of a mate. That single fork in the road determines one's ultimate reproductive fate.†

Imagine, for a moment, that you are sitting in a bedroom watching two people making love. Imagine, too, that sitting with you in the room, thinking your same thoughts, are Sigmund Freud (creator of psychoanalytic theory), E. O. Wilson (a leading sociobiologist), Albert Bandura (a prominent social learning theorist), and John Gagnon (a proponent of script theory). The scene you are imagining may evoke arousal and nothing more in you, but your imaginary companions would have a rich set of additional thoughts as they viewed the scene through the specially coloured lenses of their own theoretical perspectives. Freud might be marvelling at how the biological sex drive, the *libido,* expresses itself so strongly and directly in this couple. Wilson, the sociobiologist, would be thinking how mating behaviour in humans is similar to such behaviour in other species of animals, and how it is clearly the product of evolutionary selection for behaviours that lead to successful reproduction. Bandura might be thinking how sexual arousal and orgasm act as powerful positive reinforcers that will lead the couple to repeat the act frequently, and how they are imitating a technique of neck nibbling that they saw in an X-rated film last week. Finally, Gagnon's thoughts might be about the social scripting of sexuality; this couple begins with kissing, moves on to stroking and fondling, and finishes up with intercourse, following a script written by society.

Some of the major theories in the social sciences have had many—and different—things to say about sexuality, and it is these theories that we consider in this chapter. Theories provide us with answers to the question "why?" We often wonder why others do or do not engage in particular sexual behaviours and relationships. We sometimes ask the "why" question about our own sexuality. Creative minds have developed theories to answer such questions. Given the diversity of human sexuality, we need a range of theories to understand it.

■ Evolutionary Perspectives

Sociobiology

Sociobiology is a controversial theory. It was heralded by Harvard biologist E. O. Wilson's book *Sociobiology: The New Synthesis* (1975). **Sociobiology** is defined as the application of evolutionary biology to understanding the social behaviour of animals, including humans (Barash, 1982). Sexual behaviour, of course, is a form of social behaviour, and so the sociobiologists, often through observations of other species, try to understand why certain patterns of sexual behaviour have evolved in humans. Donald Symons has applied sociobiological thinking to human sexuality in his book *The Evolution of Human Sexuality* (1979; Symons, 1987).

Before we proceed, we should note that in terms of

*Sigmund Freud. (1924). *A general introduction to psychoanalysis.* New York: Permabooks, 1953 (Boni & Liveright edition, 1924), pp. 26–27.

†David Buss. (2000). *The dangerous passion: Why jealousy is as necessary as love and sex.* New York: Free Press, p.10.

Sociobiology: The application of evolutionary biology to understanding the social behaviour of animals, including humans.

evolution, what counts is producing lots of healthy, viable offspring who will carry on one's genes. Evolution occurs via **natural selection,** the process by which the individuals that are best adapted to their environment are more likely to survive, reproduce, and pass on their genes to the next generation.

How do humans choose mates? One major criterion is the physical attractiveness of the person (see Chapter 13). The sociobiologist argues that many of the characteristics we evaluate in judging attractiveness—for example, physique and complexion—are indicative of the health and vigour of the individual. These in turn are probably related to the person's reproductive potential; the unhealthy are less likely to produce many vigorous offspring. Natural selection would favour individuals preferring mates who would have maximum reproductive success. Thus, perhaps our concern with physical attractiveness is a product of evolution and natural selection. (See Barash, 1982, for an extended discussion of this point and the ones that follow.) We choose an attractive, healthy mate who will help us produce many offspring. Can you guess why it is that the sociobiologist thinks most men are attracted to women with large breasts?

From this viewpoint, dating, going steady, getting engaged, and similar customs are much like the courtship rituals of other species (see Figure 2.1). For example, many falcons and eagles have a flying courtship in which objects are exchanged between the pair in midair. The sociobiologist views this courtship as an opportunity for each member of the prospective couple to assess the other's fitness. For example, any lack of speed or coordination would be apparent during the airborne acrobatics. Perhaps that is exactly what we are doing in our human courtship rituals. The expenditure of money by men on dates indicates their ability to support a family. Dancing permits the assessment of physical prowess, and so on.

Sociobiologists can also explain why the nuclear family structure of a man, a woman, and their offspring is found in every society. Once a man and a woman mate, there are several obstacles to reproductive success; two being infant vulnerability and maternal death. Infant vulnerability is greatly reduced if the mother provides continuing physical care, including breast-feeding. It is further reduced if the father provides resources and security from attack for mother and infant. Two mechanisms that facilitate these conditions are a *pair-bond* between mother and father, and *attachment* between infant and parent (Miller & Fishkin, 1997). Thus, an offspring's chances of survival are greatly increased if the parents bond emotionally, that is, love each other, and if the parents have a propensity for attachment. Further, an emotional bond might lead to more frequent sexual interaction; the pleasurable consequences of sex in turn will strengthen the bond. Research with small mammals, including mice and voles, demonstrates the advantages of biparental care of offspring and the critical role of bonding (Morell, 1998).

According to this theory, parents are most interested in the survival and reproductive success of their genetic offspring. *Parental investment* refers to the behaviour and resources invested in offspring to achieve this end. Due to the high rates of divorce and remarriage in Canada, many men have both biological children and stepchildren. This situation leads to the prediction that men will tend to invest more in their genetic children than in their stepchildren. Do research results support this prediction? Fathers have been found to invest the most money in the genetic children of their current union and the least money in stepchildren from a past relationship, as would be predicted from parental investment theory. However, they spend an equal amount on their genetic children and the stepchildren of their current relationship, perhaps to cement the pair-bond with their current partner (Anderson et al., 2001).

In addition to natural selection, Darwin also proposed a mechanism that is not as much a household word, **sexual selection** (Gangestad & Thornhill, 1997). Sexual selection is selection that results from differences in traits affecting access to mates. It consists of two processes: (1) competition among members of one gender (usually males) for mating access

---

Evolution: A theory that all living things have acquired their present forms through gradual changes in their genetic endowment over successive generations.
Natural selection: A process in nature resulting in greater rates of survival of those plants and animals that are adapted to their environment.

Sexual selection: Selection that results from differences in traits affecting access to mates.

to members of the other gender *(intrasexual selection)*; and (2) preferential choice by members of one gender (usually females) for certain members of the other gender *(intersexual selection)*. In other words, in many, though not all, species, males compete among themselves for the right to mate with females; and females, for their part, prefer certain males and mate with them while refusing to mate with other males.[1] Researchers are currently testing with humans some of the predictions that come from the theory of sexual selection. For example, the theory predicts that men should compete with each other in ways that involve displaying material resources that should be attractive to women, and men should engage in these displays more than women do (Buss, 1988). Examples might be giving impressive gifts to potential mates, flashy showing off of possessions (e.g., cars, stereos), or displaying personality characteristics that are likely to lead to the acquisition of resources (e.g., ambition). Research shows that men engage in these behaviours significantly more than

[1] Sociobiologists use this mechanism to explain gender differences.

women do, and that both men and women believe these tactics are effective (Buss, 1988).

One of the most controversial ideas is the argument by some sociobiologists that rape is the product of evolutionary selection because it is adaptive for the male (Thornhill & Palmer, 2000). Over the millennia, selection favoured males who mated frequently. There are three sexual strategies available to the male. One is to be successful in intrasexual selection, to defeat other males and thereby gain access to females. The second is to be successful in intersexual selection, to possess and display the physical and material resources that females are seeking. What about the males who fail in these two arenas? A third strategy is available: the use of force to accomplish intercourse. Thornhill and Palmer (2000) suggest that this strategy might be used by physically or socially unattractive males, or in situations where the costs seem low. One problem with this argument is that if rape is punished, this may lead to less reproduction, not more. For example, if rapists are killed by the victim's relatives or executed by the state, it is a poor reproductive strategy; the single act of rape produces a

(a)

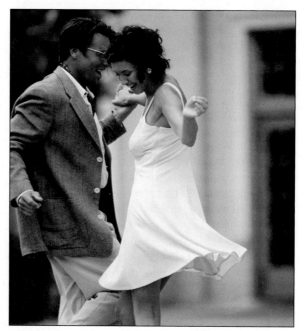

(b)

Figure 2.1 *(a)* The courtship rituals of great egrets. *(b)* Dancing is a human dating custom. According to sociobiologists, human customs of dating and becoming engaged are biologically produced and serve the same functions as courtship rituals in other species: they allow potential mates to assess each other's fitness.

certain probability (but certainly not 100 percent) of impregnating the female, but if it leads to the man's death he cannot reproduce any more. Another problem is that it ignores mechanisms that females use to control mating (i.e., avoid rape) (Drea & Wallen, 2003). The most serious problem with the argument that rape is a product of evolutionary selection is that the data provide little support for predictions based on it (Coyne & Berry, 2000). For example, Paul Bernardo sexually assaulted (and murdered) women even though he was attractive, had an attractive mate, and had lots of material possessions. Similarly, contrary to predictions that victims of sexual assault would mostly be women in their reproductive years, girls under 11 are overrepresented among victims of sexual assault compared to their percentage of the population.

Many criticisms of sociobiology have been made. Some critics object to the biological determinism that it implies. Sociobiology also has been criticized for resting on an outmoded version of evolutionary theory that modern biologists consider naïve (Gould, 1987). For example, sociobiology has focused mainly on the individual's struggle for survival and efforts to reproduce; modern biologists focus on more complex issues such as the survival of the group and the species. Further, sociobiologists assume that the central function of sex is reproduction; this may have been true historically, but probably is not true today. Given the emphasis in the theory on reproduction, its proponents have a difficult time explaining homosexuality. Finally, recent research does not support some of the evidence that is widely cited in support of the theory. Singh (1993) reported that both the winners of the Miss America contest and *Playboy*'s centerfold models have consistently had a waist-to-hip ratio of 0.7, arguing that this reflects a universal standard related to reproductive fitness. A closer look at the data (Freese & Meland, 2002) shows that the average is not 0.7 but 0.66. The average for Miss America winners steadily declined from 0.78 in 1921 to 0.64 in 1986.

Evolutionary Psychology

A somewhat different approach is taken by **evolutionary psychology,** which focuses on psychological mechanisms and processes that have been shaped by natural selection rather than on sexual behaviour (Buss, 1991). If behaviours evolved in response to

VIDEO

Is it true that men want women, but women want relationships? Consider this as you watch the "Evolutionary Psychology" video in Chapter 2 of your CD.

selective pressures, it is plausible to argue that cognitive or emotional structures evolved in the same way. Thus, a man who accurately judged whether a woman was healthy and fertile would be more successful in reproducing. If his offspring exhibited the same ability to judge accurately, they in turn would have a competitive advantage.

One line of research has concentrated on *sexual strategies* (Buss & Schmitt, 1993). According to this theory, females and males face different adaptive problems in short-term, or casual, mating and in long-term mating and reproduction. These differences lead to different strategies, or behaviours designed to solve these problems. In short-term mating, a female may choose a partner who offers her immediate resources, such as food or money. In long-term mating, a female may choose a partner who appears able and willing to provide resources for the indefinite future. A male may choose a sexually available female for a short-term liaison, but avoid such females when looking for a long-term mate.

Based on research with college students, Buss (1994) argued that men generally relax their standards when seeking a short-term partner, for example requiring of them less education, honesty, and emotional stability; relaxing one's standards is assumed to make it more likely that one will find a mate. Women's preferences change less than men's do when looking for a short-term mate, and they are more likely to seek someone who has resources and is generous with them.

Buss (1994) and others have reported research data that support a number of specific predictions based on this theory. However, research using the

Evolutionary psychology: The study of psychological mechanisms that have been shaped by natural selection.

same measures with both men and women, and controlling for confounding effects, has found that men and women are very similar in their mating preferences. Both prefer long-term mating strategies and few or no short-term partners (Pederson, Miller, Putcha-Bhagavatula, & Young, 2002). Another criticism of evolutionary psychology is that it assumes that every characteristic we observe must have some adaptive significance—in fact, some human traits may be simply "design flaws" (de Waal, 2002).

■ Psychological Theories

Four of the major theories in psychology are relevant to sexuality: psychoanalytic theory, learning theory, social exchange theory, and cognitive theory.

Psychoanalytic Theory

Sigmund Freud's **psychoanalytic theory** has been one of the most influential of all psychological theories. Because Freud saw sex as one of the key forces in human life, his theory gives full treatment to human sexuality.

Freud termed the sex drive or sex energy **libido,** which he saw as one of the two major forces motivating human behaviour (the other being *thanatos,* or the death instinct).

Id, Ego, and Superego

Freud described the human personality as being divided into three major parts: the id, the ego, and the superego. The **id** is the basic part of personality and is present at birth. It is the reservoir of psychic energy (including libido). Basically it operates on the *pleasure principle.*

While the id operates only on the pleasure principle and can thus be pretty irrational, the **ego** operates on the *reality principle* and tries to keep the id in line. The ego functions to make the person have realistic, rational interactions with others.

> **Psychoanalytic theory:** A psychological theory originated by Sigmund Freud; it contains a basic assumption that part of human personality is unconscious.
> **Libido (lih-BEE-doh):** In psychoanalytic theory, the term for the sex energy or sex drive.
> **Id:** According to Freud, the part of the personality containing the libido.
> **Ego:** According to Freud, the part of the personality that helps the person have realistic, rational interactions.

Finally, the **superego** is the conscience. It contains the values and ideals of society that we learn, and it operates on *idealism.* Thus its aim is to inhibit the impulses of the id and to persuade the ego to strive for moral goals rather than realistic ones.[2]

To illustrate the operation of these three components of the personality in a sexual situation, consider the case of the CEO of a corporation who is at a meeting of the board of directors; the meeting is also attended by her gorgeous, muscular, hot colleague. She looks at him, and her id says, "He's a real hottie. I want to throw him on the table and make love to him immediately. Let's do it!" The ego intervenes and says, "We can't do it now because the other members of the board are also here. Let's wait until 5 P.M., when they're all gone, and then do it." The superego says, "I shouldn't make love to this hot guy at all because I'm a married woman." What actually happens? It depends on the relative strengths of this woman's id, ego, and superego.

The id, ego, and superego develop sequentially. The id contains the set of instincts present at birth. The ego develops a few years later, as the child learns how to interact realistically with his or her environment and the people in it. The superego develops last, as the child learns moral values.

Erogenous Zones

Freud saw the libido as being focused in various regions of the body known as **erogenous zones.** An erogenous zone is a part of the skin or mucous membrane that is extremely sensitive to stimulation; touching it in certain ways produces feelings of pleasure. The lips and mouth are one such erogenous zone, the genitals a second, and the rectum and anus a third.

Stages of Psychosexual Development

Freud believed that the child passes through a series of stages of development. In each of these stages a different erogenous zone is the focus of pleasure.

[2]Fans of the television show *The Simpsons* might have noticed that Homer seems to be ruled primarily by his id and the pleasure principle, Lisa by her superego, and Marge by her ego and the reality principle.

> **Superego:** According to Freud, the part of the personality containing the conscience.
> **Erogenous (eh-RAH-jen-us) zones:** Areas of the body that are particularly sensitive to sexual stimulation.

According to Freud, the first stage, lasting from birth to about 1 year of age, is the *oral stage*. The child's chief pleasure is derived from sucking and otherwise stimulating the lips and mouth. Anyone who has observed children of this age knows how they delight in putting anything they can into their mouths. The second stage, which occurs during approximately the second year of life, is the *anal stage*. During this stage, the child's interest is focused on elimination.

The third stage of development, lasting from age 3 to perhaps age 5 or 6, is the *phallic stage*. Boys' and girls' interest is focused on the genital area—the boy on his phallus (penis) and the girl on her clitoris—and they derive great pleasure from masturbating.[3] Perhaps the most important occurrence in this stage according to Freud is the development of the **Oedipus complex,** which derives its name from the Greek story of Oedipus, who killed his father and married his mother. In the male Oedipus complex, the boy loves his mother and desires her sexually. He hates his father, whom he sees as a rival for the mother's affection. The boy's hostility toward his father grows, but eventually he comes to fear that his father will retaliate by castrating him—cutting off his prized penis. Thus the boy feels *castration anxiety*. Eventually the castration anxiety becomes so great that he stops desiring his mother and shifts to identifying with his father, taking on the father's gender role and acquiring the characteristics expected of males by society. Freud considered the Oedipus complex and its resolution to be one of the key factors in human personality development.

The **female Oedipus complex** (sometimes called the Electra complex, although not by Freud) is similar to the male Oedipus complex, beginning with the girl's love for her mother and her focus on her clitoris. The little girl realizes, perhaps after observing her father or her brother, that she has no penis. She feels envious and cheated, and she suffers from *penis envy*, wishing that she too had a won-

---

[3]Masturbation to orgasm is physiologically possible at this age, although males are not capable of ejaculation until they reach puberty (see Chapter 5).

> **Oedipus (EH-di-pus) complex:** According to Freud, the sexual attraction of a little boy for his mother.
> **Female Oedipus complex:** According to Freud, the sexual attraction of a little girl for her father. Sometimes called the Electra complex.

derful wand as well as the privileges that go along with being male. Thus she shifts her desire for her mother onto her father, forming the female Oedipus complex. The girl resolves penis envy by identifying with her mother and switching her erogenous zone from her clitoris to her vagina in order to have a baby, a son, as a substitute for a penis. Unlike the boy, the girl is not driven by castration anxiety to resolve her Oedipus complex. Thus the girl's resolution of the Oedipus complex is not so complete as the boy's, and Freud wrote that for the rest of her life her superego is not as developed as men's.

Freud said that following the resolution of the Oedipus complex, children pass into a prolonged stage known as *latency*, which lasts until adolescence. During this stage, the sexual impulses are repressed or are in a quiescent state, and so nothing much happens sexually. The postulation of this stage is one of the weaker parts of Freudian theory, because it is clear from the data of modern sex researchers that children do continue to engage in behaviour with sexual components during this period (see Chapter 11).

With puberty, sexual urges reawaken, and the child moves into the *genital stage*. During this stage, sexual urges become more specifically genital, and the oral, anal, and genital urges all fuse together to promote the biological function of reproduction.

According to Freud, people do not always mature from one stage to the next as they should. A person might remain permanently fixated, for example, at the oral stage; symptoms of such a situation would include incessant cigarette smoking or fingernail biting, which gratify oral urges. Most adults have at least traces of earlier stages remaining in their personalities.

Evaluation of Psychoanalytic Theory

From a scientific point of view, one of the major problems with psychoanalytic theory is that most of its concepts cannot be evaluated scientifically to see whether they are accurate. Freud postulated that many of the most important forces in personality are unconscious, and thus cannot be studied using the scientific techniques common to the twentieth century. Recent advances in our ability to image brain activity—for example, with high-powered magnetic resonance imagery—have opened the possibility of testing Freud's ideas. He believed that dreams provide a window into the

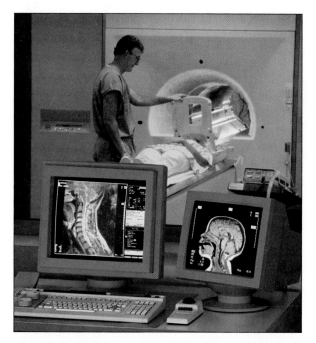

Figure 2.2 What does a magnetic resonance imaging machine have to do with psychoanalytic theory? The answer is that by studying patterns in brain waves, we can test some of Freud's ideas about the relationship between the id and the ego.

person's id, and that during sleep the activity of the ego and superego are reduced. Research in the developing area of *neuropsychoanalysis* suggests that it is activity in the prefrontal area of the brain that constrains the sometimes bizarre imagery that is generated by the limbic and postcortical regions. During rapid eye movement (REM) sleep, there is a reduction of activity in the former (the ego?) and vivid and bizarre dreams are at times associated with activity in the latter (the id?) (Solms, 1997).

Another criticism is that Freud derived his data almost exclusively from his work with patients who sought therapy from him. Thus, his theory may provide a view not so much of the human personality as of *disturbances* in the human personality.

Feminists also have been critical of Freudian theory as a male-centred theory that may cause harm to women (Lerman, 1986; Millett, 1969). They object to Freud's assumption that, because they do not have a penis, women are biologically inferior to men. One could just as easily argue that men have a powerful envy of women's reproductive capacity, which is just what psychoanalyst Karen Horney

(1926/1973) did when she coined the concept of *womb envy*, although this notion is equally open to criticism. They also criticize the distinction Freud made between *vaginal orgasm* (obtained through heterosexual intercourse with the penis stimulating the vagina) and clitoral orgasm (obtained through *clitoral stimulation*) in women. Research by Masters and Johnson (reviewed in Chapter 9) has shown that there is little or no physiological difference between orgasms resulting from clitoral stimulation and those resulting from heterosexual intercourse. Further, Freud's assertion that vaginal orgasm is more mature is not supported by findings that most adult women orgasm as a result of clitoral stimulation.

Nonetheless, Freud did make some important contributions to our understanding of human behaviour. He managed to rise above the sexually repressive Victorian era of which he was a member and teach that the libido is an important part of personality (although he may have overestimated its importance). His recognition that humans pass through stages in their psychological development was a great contribution. Perhaps most important from the perspective of this text, Freud took sex out of the closet, brought it to the attention of the general public, and suggested that we could talk about it and that it was an appropriate topic for scientific research.

Of course, psychoanalytic theory has evolved since Freud did his writing. Most contemporary psychoanalysts feel that Freud overemphasized the biological determinants of behaviour and instincts and that he gave insufficient recognition to the importance of environment and learning. For example, Erikson (1950), an influential theorist in developmental psychology, described how development continues throughout life rather than ending around age 5. Most recent psychoanalytic theories, some of which are called object-relations theories, also describe relationships with other people, particularly the child's relationship with his or her primary caretaker (usually his or her mother or father), as crucial to development, although they have not totally abandoned Freud's view that sexuality is important to development. In particular, the type of attachment relationship children have to their mothers and fathers in infancy and childhood may have a profound effect on their romantic relationships in adulthood (see Chapter 13 for more about the attachment theory of love).

Learning Theory

Although psychoanalytic and sociobiological theories are based on the notion that much of human sexual behaviour is biologically controlled, it is also quite apparent that much of it is learned. Some of the best evidence for this point comes from studies of sexual behaviour across different human societies, which were considered in Chapter 1. Here the various principles of modern learning theory will be reviewed, because they can help us understand our own sexuality (for a more detailed discussion, see Hogben & Byrne, 1998).

Classical Conditioning

Classical conditioning is a concept usually associated with the work of the Russian scientist Ivan Pavlov (1849–1936). Think of the following situations: You salivate in response to the sight or smell of food, you blink in response to someone poking a finger in your eye, or you experience sexual arousal in response to stroking the inner part of your thigh. In all these cases, an unconditioned stimulus (US; for example, appealing food) automatically, reflexively elicits an unconditioned response (UR; for example, salivation). The process of learning that occurs in classical conditioning takes place when a new stimulus, the conditioned stimulus (CS; for example, the sound of a bell) repeatedly is paired with the original unconditioned stimulus (food). After this happens many times, the conditioned stimulus (ringing bell) can eventually be presented without the unconditioned stimulus (food) and will evoke the original response, now called the conditioned response (CR; salivation).

As an example, suppose that Nadia's first serious boyfriend in high school always wears Erotik cologne when they go out. As they advance in their sexual intimacy, they have many pleasant times in the back seat of the car, where he strokes her thighs and other sexually responsive parts of her body and she feels highly aroused, always with the aroma of Erotik in her nostrils. One day she enters an elevator full of strangers in a department store, and someone is wearing Erotik. Nadia instantly feels sexually aroused, although she is not engaged in any sexual activity. From the point of view of classical conditioning, this makes perfect sense, although Nadia may wonder why she is feeling so aroused in the elevator. The thigh-stroking and sexy touching were the US. Her arousal was the UR.

The aroma of the cologne, the CS, was repeatedly paired with the US. Eventually, the aroma by itself evoked arousal, the CR.

Classical conditioning of sexual arousal has been demonstrated in an experiment using male students at Queen's University as participants (Lalumière & Quinsey, 1998). Participants were first shown 20 slides of partially clothed women; a slide rated as 5 on a scale of sexual attractiveness ranging from 1 to 10 was selected as the target slide. Ten participants were shown the target slide, followed by a 40-second segment of a sexually explicit videotape, for 11 trials; men in the control group saw only the target slide for 11 trials. Arousal was measured by a penile strain gauge, which measures the extent of engorgement or erection of the penis (see Chapter 14). Each man then rated the 20 original slides again. In the experimental group, the target slide was associated with an increase in arousal as measured by the strain gauge; in the control group, men were less aroused by the target slide following the repeated exposure. Subsequent research has also demonstrated classical conditioning of sexual arousal in women (Hoffman, Janssen, & Turner, 2004).

Classical conditioning is useful in explaining a number of phenomena in sexuality. One example is fetishes, explained in Chapter 16.

Operant Conditioning

Operant conditioning, a concept that is often associated with the psychologist B. F. Skinner, refers to the following process. A person performs a particular behaviour (the operant). That behaviour may be followed by either a reward (positive reinforcement) or a punishment. If a reward follows, the person will be likely to repeat the behaviour again in the future; if a punishment follows, the person will be less likely to repeat the behaviour. Thus if a

---

Classical conditioning: The learning process in which a previously neutral stimulus (conditioned stimulus) is repeatedly paired with an unconditioned stimulus that reflexively elicits an unconditioned response. Eventually the conditioned stimulus itself will evoke the response.
Operant (OP-ur-unt) conditioning: The process of changing the frequency of a behaviour (the operant) by following it with positive reinforcement (which will make the behaviour more frequent in the future) or punishment (which should make the behaviour less frequent in the future).

behaviour is repeatedly rewarded, it may become very frequent, and if it is repeatedly punished, it may become very infrequent or even be eliminated.

Some rewards are considered to be primary reinforcers; that is, there is something intrinsically rewarding about them. Food is one such primary reinforcer; sex another. Male rats, for example, can be trained to learn a maze if they find a willing sex partner at the end of it. Thus sexual behaviour plays dual roles in learning theory: It can itself be a positive reinforcer, but it can also be the behaviour that is rewarded or punished.

Simple principles of operant conditioning can help explain some aspects of sex (McGuire et al., 1965). For example, if a woman repeatedly experiences pain when she has intercourse (perhaps because she has a vaginal infection), she will probably want to have sex infrequently or not at all. In operant conditioning terms, sexual intercourse has repeatedly been associated with a punishment (pain), and so the behaviour becomes less frequent.

Another principle of operant conditioning that is useful in understanding sexual behaviour holds that consequences, whether reinforcement or punishment, are most effective in shaping behaviour when they occur immediately after the behaviour. The longer they are delayed after the behaviour has occurred, the less effective they become. As an example, consider a young man who has had gonorrhea three times yet continues to have unprotected sexual intercourse. The pain associated with gonorrhea is certainly punishing, so why does he persist in having sex without a condom? The delay principle suggests the following explanation. Each time he engages in unprotected intercourse, he finds it highly rewarding; this immediate reward maintains the behaviour; the punishment, gonorrhea, does not occur until several days later and so is not effective in eliminating that behaviour.

A third principle that has emerged in operant conditioning studies is that, compared with rewards, punishments are not very effective in shaping behaviour. Often, as in the case of the child who is punished for taking an illicit cookie, punishments do not eliminate a behaviour but rather teach the person to be sneaky and engage in it without being caught. As an example, some parents, as many commonly did in earlier times in our culture, punish children for masturbating; yet most of those children continue to masturbate, perhaps learning instead to do it under circumstances (such as in a bathroom with the door locked) in which they are not likely to be caught.

One important difference between psychoanalytic theory and learning theory should be noticed. Psychoanalytic theorists believe that the determinants of human sexual behaviour occur in early childhood, particularly during the Oedipal complex period. Learning theorists, in contrast, believe that sexual behaviour can be learned and changed at any time in one's lifespan—in childhood, in adolescence, in young adulthood, or later. When we try to understand what causes certain sexual behaviours and how to treat people with sex problems, this distinction between the theories will have important implications.

Behaviour Modification

Behaviour modification involves a set of techniques, based on principles of classical or operant conditioning, that are used to change (or modify) human behaviour. In particular, these methods can be used to modify problematic sexual behaviours—that is, sexual disorders such as orgasm problems (see Chapter 19) or compulsive sexual behaviour (see Chapter 16). Behaviour modification methods differ from more traditional methods of psychotherapy such as psychoanalysis in that the behavioural therapist considers only the problem behaviour and how to modify it using learning-theory principles; the therapist does not worry about an in-depth analysis of the person's personality to see, for example, what unconscious forces might be motivating the behaviour. Most often treatment programs combine behaviour modification techniques with cognitive therapy approaches—called cognitive behaviour therapy.

Social Learning

Social learning theory (Bandura, 1977; Bandura & Walters, 1963) is a somewhat more complex form of learning theory. It is based on principles of operant conditioning, but it also recognizes two other processes at work: *imitation* and *identification*. These two processes are useful in explaining the development of gender identity, or one's sense of maleness

Behaviour modification: A set of operant conditioning techniques used to modify human behaviour.

In Focus 2.1

Can Learning Theory Explain Sexual Orientation Shifts in a Non-Western Society?

The Sambia are a tribe living in Papua, New Guinea in the South Pacific, which has been extensively studied by anthropologists (see In Focus 15.3 in Chapter 15). The Sambia are interesting for a number of reasons, the chief one being that young males are expected to spend 10 or more years of their lives in exclusively homosexual relations. During this time they are taught to fear women and believe that women have polluting effects on them. After that stage of their lives, they are expected to marry women. They do, and their sexual behaviour becomes exclusively heterosexual. These observations defy our Western notions that one's sexual orientation is a permanent characteristic throughout life. Indeed, the very concepts of having a "het-erosexual identity" or "homosexual identity" are not present in Sambia culture.

Can social learning theory explain these patterns of sexual behaviour? It can, according to the analysis of John and Janice Baldwin. The thing that is puzzling is how the Sambia male, who has had years of erotic conditioning to homosexual behaviour just at puberty when he is most easily aroused and sensitive to conditioning, would then switch to heterosexual behaviour and do so happily.

According to the Baldwins' analysis, several factors in social learning theory explain this switch. First, positive conditioning in the direction of heterosexuality occurs early in life. The boy spends the first 7 to 10 years of his life with his family. He has a close,

or femaleness. For example, it seems that a little girl acquires many characteristics of the female role by identifying with her mother and imitating her, as when she plays at dressing up after observing her

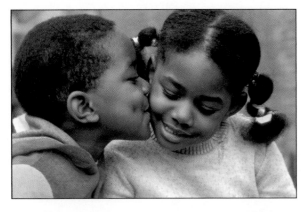

Figure 2.3   According to social learning theory, children learn about sex and gender in part by imitation. These children may be imitating their parents or a scene they have watched on TV.

mother getting ready to go to a party. Also, various forms of sexuality may be learned through imitation. In high school, for example, the sexiest girl in the senior class may find that other girls are imitating her behaviours and the way she dresses. Or a boy might see a movie in which the hero's technique seems to "turn women on"; then he tries to use this technique with his own dates. The latter example points to the importance of mass media as a source of images of sexuality that young people imitate and personalities that they identify with.

Once a behaviour is learned, the likelihood of its being performed depends on its consequences. The young man who imitates actor Brad Pitt's romantic technique may not succeed in arousing his companion. If the behaviour is not reinforced, he will stop performing it. If it is reinforced, he will repeat it. Successful experiences with an activity over time create a sense of competence or **self-efficacy** at performing

Self-efficacy: A sense of competence at performing an activity.

warm relationship with his mother. In essence, he has been conditioned to positive feelings about women.

Second, observational learning occurs. In those same first 7 to 10 years, the boy observes closely the heterosexual relationship between two adults, his mother and father. This observational learning can be used a decade later when it is time for him to marry and form a heterosexual relationship.

Third, the boy is provided with much cognitive structuring, a notion present in social learning theory as well as cognitive psychology. He is instructed that a boy must pass through a series of stages to become a strong, masculine man. This includes first becoming the receptive partner to fellatio, then being the inserting partner to fellatio, marrying, defending himself from his wife's first menstruation (girls are usually married before puberty and undergo no homosexual stage of development), and then fathering a child by her. Essentially he is given all the cog-

nitive structures necessary to convince him that it is perfectly natural, indeed desirable, to engage in sex with men for 10 years and then switch to women. Finally, there is some aversive conditioning to the homosexual behaviour that leads it to be not particularly erotic. The boy performs fellatio for the first time after several days of initiation, when he is exhausted. The activities are staged so that the boy feels fearful about it. He must do it in darkness with an older boy who may be an enemy, and he is required to do it with many males in succession. In essence, unpleasantness or punishment is associated with homosexual behaviour.

In summary, then, social learning theory provides a sensible explanation of the seemingly puzzling shift that Sambia males make from exclusively homosexual expression to exclusively heterosexual expression.

Sources: Baldwin & Baldwin, 1989; Herdt, 1982.

---

the activity (Bandura, 1982). If a woman feels efficacious at using the female condom, she will expend more effort (going to the drugstore to buy one) and will show greater persistence in the face of difficulty (continuing to adjust it until it fits properly) than she did before. The concept of self-efficacy has been widely used in designing health intervention programs such as those that encourage individuals to use condoms to prevent transmission of sexually transmitted infections and HIV (e.g., DeLamater, Wagstaff, & Havens, 2000). These programs provide opportunities for participants to practise the behaviours that are being promoted and be successful.

Social Exchange Theory

An important process based on the principle of reinforcement is social exchange. **Social exchange theory** (Cook, 1987) has emerged out of social learning theory and uses the concept of reinforcement to explain satisfaction, stability, and change in relationships among people. It is also useful in explaining *sexuality* in close relationships (Byers & Wang, 2004).

The theory assumes that we have freedom of choice and often face choices among alternative actions. Every action provides some rewards and entails certain costs. There are many kinds of rewards (money, goods, services, sexual gratification, approval by others) and costs (time, effort, money, embarrassment, emotional distance). The theory states that we are *hedonistic;* that we try to maximize rewards and minimize costs when we act. Thus, we choose actions that produce a favourable balance of rewards to costs or profits (profits equalling rewards minus costs), and avoid actions that produce poor profits.

As its name indicates, social exchange theory views social relationships primarily as exchanges of goods and services among persons. People participate in relationships only if they find that the relationships provide profitable outcomes. An

Social exchange theory: A theory that assumes people will choose actions that maximize rewards and minimize costs.

individual judges the attractiveness of a relationship by comparing the profits it provides against both the profits he or she thinks should be received in the relationship as well as to the profits available in alternative relationships. The level of expected outcomes is called the *comparison level*; the level of outcomes in the best alternative relationship is called the *comparison level for alternatives* (Byers & Wang, 2004). These ideas have been applied to personal relationships. Studies of heterosexual couples in long-term relationships have found that the concepts of rewards and costs can explain whether people stay in or exit from such relationships (Rusbult, 1983; Rusbult, Johnson, & Morrow, 1986). Individuals are more likely to stay in when the partner is physically and personally attractive, when the relationship does not entail undue costs (such as high monetary commitments, broken promises, or arguments), and when romantic relationships with attractive others are not available. In other words, they are more likely to stay in a relationship when its rewards are high, its costs are low, and the comparison level for alternatives is low.

Social exchange theory also predicts the conditions under which people try to change their relationships. A central concept is *equity* or *equality* (Walster [Hatfield], Walster, & Berscheid, 1978). A state of equity exists when participants in a relationship believe that the rewards they receive from it are proportional to the costs they bear. Equality exists when both partners experience the same balance of rewards to costs (profit). If a person feels that the allocation of rewards and costs is inequitable or unequal, then the relationship is unstable. People find inequity unpleasant and may feel cheated or angry. As we will see in Chapter 12, a married person experiencing inequity may engage in extradyadic sex as a result.

Social exchange theory has also been used to explain various other aspects of sexuality in close relationships such as partner selection, sexual frequency, and sexual satisfaction (for a review, see Byers & Wang, 2004). For example, one of your authors, New Brunswick psychologist Sandra Byers, and her colleagues have shown that, in both dating and long-term relationships, sexual satisfaction is highest the more sexual rewards exceed sexual costs (i.e., profit is high), sexual rewards and costs compare favourably to expectations, and sexual rewards and costs between partners are equal (Byers et al., 1998; Lawrance & Byers, 1995).

Social exchange theories have been criticized for applying the ideas of rewards and costs to romantic relationships. Some people believe that love is not and should not be about what one can get out of a relationship (i.e., its rewards). A related criticism is that social exchange theories downplay other motivations. Because of the emphasis on rewards and costs, such theories cannot explain, for example, selfless behaviours such as altruism and martyrdom.

Cognitive Theory

In the 1980s and 1990s, a "cognitive revolution" has swept through psychology. In contrast to the older behaviourist tradition (which insisted that psychologists should study only behaviours that could be directly observed), cognitive psychologists believe that it is very important to study people's thoughts— that is, the way people perceive and think.

Cognition and Sexuality

Cognitive psychology can readily explain some aspects of human sexuality (Walen & Roth, 1987). A basic assumption is that what we think influences what we feel. If we think happy, positive thoughts, we will tend to feel better than if we think negative ones. Therapists using a cognitive approach believe that psychological distress is often a result of unpleasant thoughts that do not reflect reality and include misconceptions, distortions, exaggerations of problems, and unreasonably negative evaluations of events.

To the cognitive psychologist, how we perceive and evaluate a sexual event makes all the difference in the world (Walen & Roth, 1987). For example, suppose that a man engaged in sexual activity with his partner does not get an erection. Starting from that basic event, his thoughts might take one of two directions. In the first, he thinks that it is quite common for a man in his age group (fifties) not to get an erection every time he has sex; this has happened to him a few times before, once every two or three months, and it's nothing to worry about. At any rate, the oral sex was fun, and his partner had an orgasm from that, so all in all it was a nice enough encounter. In the second possibility, he began the sexual activity thinking that he had to have an erection, had to have intercourse, and had to have an orgasm. When he didn't get an erection, he mentally labelled it *impotence* and worried that he would never again have an erection. He thought of the whole episode as a frustrating disaster because he never had an orgasm.

As cognitive psychologists point out, our perception, labelling, and evaluation of events are crucial. In one case, the man perceived a slight problem, labelled it a temporary erection problem, and evaluated his sexual experience as pretty good. In the other case, the man perceived a serious problem, labelled it impotence, and evaluated the experience as horrible.

We shall see cognitive psychology several times again in this book, as theorists use it to understand the cycle of sexual arousal (see Chapter 9), the causes of some sexual variations such as fetishes (see Chapter 16), and the causes and treatment of sexual disorders (see Chapter 19). Before we leave cognitive psychology, however, we will look at one cognitive theory, schema theory, that has been used especially to understand issues of sex and gender.

Gender Schema Theory

Psychologist Sandra Bem (1981, 1993) has proposed a schema theory to explain gender-role development and the impact of gender on people's daily lives and thinking. "Schema" is a term taken from cognitive psychology. A **schema** is a general knowledge framework that a person has about a particular topic. A schema organizes and guides perception; it helps us remember, but it sometimes also distorts our memory, especially if the information is inconsistent with our schema. Thus, for example, you might have a "hockey game schema," the set of ideas you have about what elements should be present at the game (two teams, spectators, stands, etc.) and what kinds of activities should occur (opening face-off, occasional goal, penalties, power plays, and so on).

It is Bem's contention that all of us possess a *gender schema*—a cognitive structure comprised of the set of attributes (behaviours, personality, appearance) that we associate with males and females. Children not only learn about appropriate roles for men and women, they also learn that the distinctions between men and women and between masculine and feminine are extremely important ways to understand reality. Thus our gender schema, accord-

---

Schema (SKEE-muh): A general knowledge framework that a person has about a particular topic.

---

ing to Bem, predisposes us to process information on the basis of gender. That is, we tend to think of things as gender-related and to want to dichotomize them on the basis of gender. A good example is the case of the infant whose gender isn't clear when we meet him or her. We eagerly seek out the information or feel awkward if we don't, because we seem to need to know the baby's gender in order to continue to process information about it.

Bem (1981) has done a number of experiments that provide evidence for her theory, and there are confirming experiments by other researchers as well, although the evidence is not always completely consistent (Ruble & Stangor, 1986). In one of the most interesting of these experiments, 5- and 6-year-old children were shown pictures of males or females performing activities that were either stereotype-consistent activities (such as a girl baking cookies) or stereotype-inconsistent (such as girls boxing) at that time (Martin & Halverson, 1983). One week later the children were tested for their recall of the pictures. The results indicated that the children distorted information by changing the gender of people in the stereotype-inconsistent pictures, while not making such changes for the stereotype-consistent pictures. That is, children tended to remember a picture of girls boxing as having been a picture of boys boxing. These results are just what would be predicted by gender schema theory. The schema helps us remember schema-consistent (stereotype-consistent) information well, but it distorts our memory of information that is inconsistent with the schema (stereotype-inconsistent).

One of the interesting implications of gender schema theory is that stereotypes—whether they are about males and females, or heterosexuals and homosexuals, or other groups—may be very slow to change. The reason is that our schemas tend to filter out stereotype-inconsistent (that is, schema-inconsistent) information so that we don't even remember it.

■ Sociological Perspectives

Sociologists are most interested in the ways in which society or culture shapes human sexuality. (For a detailed articulation of the sociological perspective, see DeLamater, 1987; the arguments that follow are taken from that source.)

Figure 2.4   Families today are no longer defined by traditional stereotypes. Here, a lesbian couple enjoy the playground with their son.

Sociologists approach the study of sexuality with three basic assumptions: (1) Every society regulates the sexuality of its members. (For a discussion of the reasons why, see Horrocks, 1997.) (2) Basic institutions of society (such as religion and the family) affect the rules governing sexuality in that society. (3) The appropriateness or inappropriateness of a particular sexual behaviour depends on the culture in which it occurs.

The Influence of Society
Sociologists view societal influences on human sexuality as occurring on several levels, including the macro-level or society as a whole and the sub-cultural level, at which one's social class or ethnic group may have an impact on one's sexuality. Our discussion here emphasizes the macro-level of influence.

Social Institutions
According to the sociological perspective, at the macro-level our sexuality is influenced by powerful social institutions, including religion, the family,

the economy, medicine, and the law. Each major institution supports a sexual ideology, or discourse, about sexual activity. This ideology influences the beliefs and behaviours of those affiliated with the institution.

Religion
Historically the Judeo-Christian religious tradition has been a powerful shaper of sexual norms in Western culture. A detailed discussion of that religious tradition and its teachings on sexuality is provided in Chapter 20. Suffice it to say here that the Christian religion has contained within it a tradition of asceticism, in which abstinence from sexual pleasures—especially by certain persons such as monks and priests—is seen as virtuous. The tradition, at least until recently, has also been oriented toward procreation—that is, a belief that sexuality is legitimate only within traditional heterosexual marriage and only with the goal of having children, a *procreational ideology*. This view has created within our culture a set of norms, or standards for behaviour, that say, for example, that premarital sex, extramar-

ital sex, and homosexual sex are wrong. The procreational ideology is one basis for asserting that marriage is exclusively for a man and a woman, since only a heterosexual couple can procreate without intervention. Many of these norms are changing, so that today many Canadians do not subscribe to some of these views.

The Economy

The nature and structure of the economy is another macro-level influence on sexuality. Before the industrial revolution, most work was done in the family unit in the home or farm. This kind of togetherness permitted rather strict surveillance of family members' sexuality and thus strict norms could be enforced. However, with the industrial revolution, people—most frequently men—spent many hours per day at work away from the home. Thus they were under less surveillance, and scripts such as extramarital affairs and same-sex sex could be acted out more often.

Today we see evidence of the extent to which economic conditions can affect sexuality. For example, the average monthly wage is very low in Russia. As a result, few people can afford to use condoms and the rate of sexually transmitted infections is very high. Economic conditions have also led to a major increase in the number of prostitutes. It is difficult to support a family on the salary earned in most jobs, including professional jobs. In contrast, a Russian prostitute may earn the equivalent of the average monthly salary in just a few hours. As a result, many Russian prostitutes are highly educated and choose prostitution for financial reasons. Many Russians see prostitution as a viable way of earning a living (Byers & Slattery, 1997).

In a capitalist economy such as Canada, goods and services become commodities that can be sold for a price (an exchange). Not surprisingly, this includes sexual images and sexual gratification, giving rise to the sale of sexually explicit materials in stores and on the Internet, and commercial sex work. The increasing globalization of the economy has led to the development of sex tourism, in which affluent men and women travel to other cultures, such as Thailand, to purchase sexual gratification from "exotic" (e.g., Asian) sex workers (see Chapter 18).

The Family

The family is a third institution influencing sexuality. As we noted earlier, before the industrial revolu-

tion the family was an important economic unit, producing the goods necessary for survival. As that function waned after the industrial revolution, there was increased emphasis on the quality of interpersonal relationships in the family. At the same time, love was increasingly seen as an important reason for marriage. Thus a triple linkage between love, marriage, and sex was formed. Ironically, the linkage eventually became a direct one between love and sex so that, by the 1970s, some people were arguing that sex outside of marriage, if in the context of a loving relationship, was permissible, as was same-sex sexual activity, again if the relationship was a loving one. This is the *relational ideology*.

The family exerts a particularly important force on sexuality through its *socialization* of children. That is, parents socialize their children—teach them appropriate norms for behaviour—in many areas, including sexuality. Others, of course, such as the peer group, also have important socializing influences.

Medicine

The institution of medicine has become a major influence on our sexuality over the last 100 years. Physicians tell us what is healthy and what is unhealthy. In the late 1800s, physicians warned that masturbation could cause various pathologies. Today sex therapists tell us that sexual expression is natural and healthy and sometimes even "prescribe" masturbation as a treatment. Another example is provided by childbirth; until the end of the nineteenth century most babies were born at home, with an experienced woman (a midwife) providing assistance to the labouring woman. Today the vast majority of births occur in hospitals and birthing facilities, with medical personnel in charge. We tend to have great confidence in medical advice, so the pronouncements of the medical establishment, based on a *therapeutic ideology*, have an enormous impact on sexuality.

The increasing influence of medicine on sexuality has not been taken lying down. The domination of contemporary theory and research by the biomedical model is referred to as the

To learn more about the relationship *between medicine and sex research, watch the video "The Medicalization of Sex" in Chapter 2 of your CD.*

medicalization of sexuality (Tiefer, 2004). Medical-ization has two components: certain behaviours or conditions are defined in terms of health and illness, and problematic experiences or practices are given medical treatment. The medicalization of male sexu-ality is being hastened by the development of drugs to treat erectile dysfunction, and many physicians and pharmaceutical companies are seeking to med-icalize female sexual dysfunction by finding a pill that will "cure" them.

Traditionally, medicine has been primarily con-cerned with diagnosing and treating disease. In con-trast, health promotion is geared toward enhancing health and preventing illness. **Sexual health** is not just the absence of disease. According to the World Health Organization (2004) definition:

> Sexual health is a state of physical, emotional, mental and social well-being related to sexuality; it is not merely the absence of disease, dysfunction or infirmity. Sexual health requires a positive and respectful approach to sexuality and sexual rela-tionships, as well as the possibility of having plea-surable and safe sexual experiences, free of coercion, discrimination and violence. For sexual health to be attained and maintained, the sexual rights of all persons must be respected, protected and fulfilled.

Using a similar framework, Health Canada (1999) proposed several principles to guide protection and promotion of the sexual health of Canadians, including:

1. All individuals are sexual beings throughout their lives.
2. Individual autonomy and responsibility should guide all aspects of decision-making.
3. The greatest benefits will be achieved by empha-sizing promotion of sexual and reproductive health and prevention of problems.
4. Access to sexual and reproductive health pro-grams and services should be equitable, respon-sive to diversity, and not limited because of

---

Medicalization of sexuality: The process by which cer-tain sexual behaviours or conditions are defined in terms of health and illness, and problematic experiences or practices are given medical treatment.
Sexual health: A state of physical, emotional, mental, and social well-being related to sexuality.

---

discrimination based on gender, race, ethnicity, marital status, sexual orientation, religion, cul-ture, language, socio-economic status, disabil-ity, or geographic location.

The Law

The legal system is another institution influencing sexuality at the macro-level. From a sociological per-spective, the law influences people's sexual behaviour in a number of ways. First, laws help to determine norms. Generally we think that what is legal is right and what is illegal is wrong. In Canada, only the fed-eral government has the right to pass criminal laws, and all sexual offences are contained in the Criminal Code of Canada and apply to all Canadians regardless of the province or territory in which they live (Roach, 2000). Provincial and municipal governments have the right to enact regulatory offences, such as zoning bylaws and licensing requirements, to help them gov-ern matters within their jurisdiction, as long as these regulations do not stray into the criminal area. In contrast, in the United States and Australia, states have the right to enact criminal laws, resulting in sig-nificant differences in sexual offences from one state to another.

A major change to Canadian criminal law occurred in 1969 when, under Prime Minister Pierre Elliott Trudeau, the House of Commons passed an omnibus bill that introduced sweeping changes to the Criminal Code of Canada. This bill removed provisions that had made consensual sexual behaviours done in private between adults illegal, such as use of contraception, oral sex, and anal sex. These changes may have reflected the fact that laws that go against prevailing social or sub-cultural norms are often ignored, and most Cana-dians agreed with Trudeau when he said, "The state has no business in the bedrooms of the nation." In contrast, although arrests for criminal sexual conduct are rare in the United States, in many states oral intercourse, anal intercourse ("sodomy"), sex with someone who is legally mar-ried to someone else (adultery), cohabitation, sex between two unmarried persons ("fornication"), and sexual contact between two persons of the same gender are crimes (Posner, 1992). Thus, every day millions of Americans engage in sexual behav-iours that are illegal.

Second, laws are the basis for the mechanisms of social control. They may specify punishments for certain acts and thus discourage people from engaging in them. It seems obvious that people ought to be free from sexual assault and coercion, and that children should not be exploited and, indeed, the Criminal Code of Canada has a number of laws prohibiting sexual assault of adults and children (see In Focus 2.2). However, sex laws also have been designed to control other behaviours that are more open to debate. For example, historically one rationale for laws against adultery or desertion of a spouse was that these laws would

Figure 2.5 In 1969, under Prime Minister Pierre Elliott Trudeau, Parliament decriminalized consensual sexual behaviour between two adults in private, including providing birth control information and engaging in anal or oral sex.

preserve the family as the principal unit of the social order. A current example is the law prohibiting nudity in a public place. One wonders how many people would prefer to be nude at the beach if they did not fear arrest and the possible embarrassing publicity such as having their names in the paper as the result of an arrest.

Third, the law reflects the interests of the powerful, dominant groups within a society. In part, the law functions to confirm the superiority of the ideologies of these dominant groups although the arguments in favour of these laws often centre on the protection of society's morals. The concern for public morality results in laws against non-procreative sex, for reasons outlined in Chapter 20. Thus there have been laws against same-sex sexual activity, bestiality, and contraception. In fact, same-sex couples have had to challenge the law that restricted marriage to the union of one man and one woman province by province to establish their legal right to marry (see Chapter 15). Consider also the Mormons in Canada and the United States. In the past, their religion approved of polygyny (a man having several wives). Mormons did not become the dominant group in North America. Rather, the Judeo-Christian tradition was the ideology of the dominant group and that tradition takes a dim view of polygyny. Accordingly, polygyny is illegal in both Canada and the United States. However, there is a breakaway sect of the Mormon Church, called the Fundamentalist Church of Jesus Christ of Latter Day Saints, located in Bountiful, British Columbia. This sect of about 1,000 people practises polygyny. However, they have not been prosecuted, in part because the B.C. government has received legal opinions that the group could likely successfully argue the law making polygyny illegal violates their Constitutional right to freedom of religion. Similarly, Canadian immigrants from some African cultures that practise polygyny cannot do so in Canada because it is illegal. Nonetheless, in keeping with ethnocultural norms, many of these men have multiple relationships although they are married to only one woman. Further, this is accepted in their community (Health Canada, 1994).

It can also be argued that another principal source of sex laws is sexism, which is deeply rooted in Western culture. Men have historically held the

In Focus 2.2

What Are Considered Sexual Offences in the Criminal Code of Canada in 2005?

Offence	Description	Maximum Sentence
Sexual assault	Sexual assault involving minor or no physical injuries to the victim	10 years
Sexual assault with a weapon or threats	Sexual assault with a weapon, threats, or causing bodily harm	14 years
Aggravated sexual assault	Sexual assault resulting in wounding, maiming, or disfiguring or endangering the life of the victim	Life
Sexual interference	Direct or indirect touching (for a sexual purpose) of a person under the age of 14 using a part of the body or an object	10 years
Invitation to sexual touching	Inviting, counselling, or inciting a person under the age of 14 to touch (for a sexual purpose) the body of any person directly or indirectly with a part of the body or with an object	10 years
Sexual exploitation	Sexual interference or invitation to sexual touching by a person in a position of trust or authority toward a young person aged 14 to 18 with whom the young person is in a position of dependency or toward a person with a disability.	5 years
Parent or guardian procuring, permitting sexual activity, or corrupting children	A parent or guardian or other person enticing or forcing a person under 18 to engage in an act prohibited under the Code or permitting them to engage in such an act on their premises	5 years
Corrupting children	Engaging in adultery or sexual immorality in the home of a child rendering the home unfit for the child	2 years
Luring a child	Using a computer to facilitate the commission of a sexual offence against a child	5 years
Incest	When an individual has sexual intercourse with a person that has a known defined blood relationship with them	14 years

power and made the laws. One scholar has suggested that the history of the regulation of sexual activity could as well be called the history of the double standard (Parker, 1983). In fact women were considered "not persons in matters of rights and privileges" under Canadian law prior to 1929. The Supreme Court of Canada had ruled that the word "persons" in the British North America Act of 1867 referred only to men. On October 18, 1929, this decision was overturned by the Judicial Committee of the Privy Council of Britain, the highest court of appeal, which ruled that the word "persons" included both men and women. It is probably not coincidental that the movement for sex-law

Offence	Description	Maximum Sentence
Anal intercourse	Anal intercourse between two people if either is under 18 or if more than two people take part or are present or if engaged in in a public place	10 years
Bestiality	Having sex with an animal	10 years
Communicating for the purpose of engaging in prostitution	Communicating with another person in public to buy or sell sexual services	6 months and/or $2,000
Bawdy-house offences	Keeping, transporting a person to, or occupying a place used for prostitution or indecent acts	2 years
Procuring	Procuring or enticing or forcing another person to engage in prostitution or living on the income of another person's prostitution activities. Also purchasing the sexual services of someone under 18	14 years
Obscenity	Making, publishing, or distributing any obscene written matter, photograph, videotape, etc.	2 years
Child pornography	Possessing, making, or distributing any material that shows a person under 18 or who is depicted as being under 18 engaging in sexual activity or shows their genitals for a sexual purpose unless the material has artistic merit or an educational, scientific, or medical purpose	5–10 years
Immoral theatrical performance	Taking part in or presenting an immoral, indecent, or obscene performance or entertainment	2 years
Mailing obscene matter	Mailing anything that is obscene, indecent, immoral, or scurrilous	2 years
Indecent acts/ exposure	Committing an indecent act in a public place or exposing genitals to a person under the age of 14	6 months and/or $2,000
Nudity	Being nude in a public place or in public view on private property	6 months and/or $2,000

Source: Canada, 2005.

reform has gone hand in hand with the movement for the equality of women.

The Canadian Charter of Rights and Freedoms guarantees freedom of conscience and religion as well as equality. Therefore, criminal law cannot be based on the religious views and practices of one specific religion or be used to enforce morality per se (Roach, 2000). To the extent that today's laws are derived from the Judeo-Christian (or any other) religious tradition, they violate this principle. Increasingly, statutes in the Criminal Code that reflected specific moral values have been eliminated or rewritten, in part as the result of Supreme Court of Canada decisions based on Charter rights. For example, the Supreme Court found that statutes on abortion and those that did not extend the same benefits to same-sex couples as to heterosexual couples violated the equality guarantees in the Charter. Nonetheless, some experts argue that certain laws, such as those pertaining to prostitution and obscenity, stem from a particular moral view or ideology.

In summary, then, the sociological perspective focuses on how society or culture shapes and controls our sexual expression, at levels from institutions such as religion and the law to the interpersonal level of socialization by family and peers.

Symbolic Interaction Theory

An important sociological theory is **symbolic interaction theory** (Charon, 1995; Stryker, 1987). Its premise is that human nature and the social order are products of symbolic communication among people. A person's behaviour is constructed through his or her interactions with others. People can communicate successfully with one another only to the extent that they ascribe similar meanings to objects and people. An object's meaning for a person depends not on the properties of the object but on what the person might do with it; an object takes on meaning only in relation to a person's plans. Thus, the theory views people as proactive and goal-seeking. Achieving most goals requires the cooperation of others. This is especially true of many forms of sexual expression. For example, suppose a woman invites a person she is dating to her apartment; what meaning does this invitation have? Does she want to prolong the conversation or engage in intimate sexual activity? The woman and her partner will have to achieve an agreement about the purpose of the visit before joint activity is possible. In terms of the theory, they have to develop a *definition of the situation.* Thus, to fit their actions together and achieve agreement, people interacting with each other must continually reaffirm old meanings or negotiate new ones.

Central to social interaction is the process of *role-taking*, in which an individual imagines how he or she looks from the other person's viewpoint. By view-

Symbolic interaction theory: A theory that proposes human nature and the social order are products of communication among people.

ing the self and potential actions from the perspective of the other person, we are often able to anticipate what behaviour will enable us to achieve our goal. One consequence of role-taking is self-control; we see ourselves from the viewpoint of others and so strive to meet their standards. In the process, we exercise control over our behaviour.

This perspective emphasizes the importance of symbolic communication (see Chapter 10). It alerts us to the mutual effort required to arrive at a definition of the situation. Criticisms of this theory include the fact that it emphasizes rational, conscious thought, whereas in the realm of sexuality, emotions are very important in many interactions. Also, this perspective portrays humans as *other-directed individuals,* concerned primarily with meeting other people's standards. A third criticism is that we don't always consciously role-take and communicate in an effort to achieve agreement. Sometimes we rely on past experience and habit. Situations such as these are the province of script theory.

Sexual Scripts

The outcome of these social influences, according to symbolic interaction theories, is that each of us learns the meanings of various behaviours through our interactions with others (Plummer, 1975). We also learn a set of *sexual scripts* (Gagnon, 1990; Gagnon & Simon, 1973). The idea is that sexual behaviour is a result of extensive prior learning that teaches us sexual etiquette and how to interpret specific situations. According to this concept, we have all learned an elaborate script that tells us the who, what, when, where, and why of sexual behaviour. For example, the "who" part of the dominant Canadian script tells us that sex should occur with someone of the other gender, of approximately our own age, of our own race, and so on. Even the sequence of sexual activity is scripted. *Scripts,* then, are plans that people carry around in their heads for what they are doing and what they are going to do; they are also devices for helping people remember what they have done in the past (Gagnon, 1977, p. 6).

How can we study these scripts? How can we find out if there are widely shared beliefs about how one should behave in a specific situation? One way is to ask people to describe what one should do in such a situation. Researchers asked male and female college students to make a list of the things that a man or woman would typically do on a first date (Rose & Frieze, 1993). The hypothetical script written by many of the participants included a core sequence of acts: dress, pick up, get to know, evaluate, eat, make out, and go home. This is the first-date script. This script is also influenced by contemporary views of gender roles. Males were portrayed as proactive, taking the initiative: pick up the female, pay for the date, attempt to make out, and ask for another date. Females were portrayed as reactive: be picked up, be treated, accept or reject the male's attempt to make out, and accept or reject the invitation to another date. The widely shared nature of this script enables relative strangers to interact smoothly on their first date.

One study attempted to identify the sequence of sexual behaviours that is scripted for male–female relationships in our culture (Jemail & Geer, 1977). People were given 25 sentences, each describing an event in a heterosexual interaction. They were asked to rearrange the sentences in a sequence that was "most sexually arousing" and then to do it again to indicate what was "the most likely to occur." There was a high degree of agreement among the participants about what the sequence should be. There was also high agreement between males and females. The standard sequence was kissing, hand stimulation of the breasts, hand stimulation of the genitals, mouth–genital stimulation, intercourse, and orgasm. Does this sound familiar?

Figure 2.6 According to some people's sexual scripts, a man taking a woman to dinner is one scene of the first act in a sexual script that features intercourse as the finale.

Interestingly, not only is this the sequence in a sexual encounter, it is also the sequence that occurs as a couple progresses in a relationship. These results suggest that there are culturally defined sequences of behaviours that we all have learned, much as the notion of a "script" suggests.

Can you imagine a young man, on the first date, attempting oral stimulation of the young lady's genitals before he has kissed her? The idea seems amazing, and perhaps humorous or shocking. Why? Because the young man has performed Act IV before Act I.

Scripts also tell us the meaning we should attach to a particular sexual event (Gagnon, 1990). Television programs and films frequently suggest but do not show sexual activity between people. How do we make sense out of these implicit portrayals? A study of how women interpret such scenes in films found that they utilize scripts. If the film showed a couple engaging in two actions that are part of the accepted script for sexual intercourse (e.g., kissing and undressing each other) and then faded out, viewers inferred that intercourse had occurred (Meischke, 1995).

The Social Importance of Sexuality

Ira Reiss (1986) has proposed a sociological theory of human sexuality. Borrowing from script theory, he defines sexuality as "erotic and genital responses produced by the cultural scripts of a society" (p. 37). As he points out, a sociological theory, because it focuses on societal influences on sexuality, must be able to account for both cross-cultural variations in sexuality as well as cross-cultural universals in sexuality.

One cross-cultural universal is that all societies believe that sexuality is important. Even in cultures that are sexually repressive, sexuality is still accorded great importance as something that is dangerous and must be controlled. Why is sexuality considered so important? Many theorists have claimed that it is the link of sexuality to making babies, which is undeniably important for any society. Reiss argues against this notion, however. Her explanation for the universal importance of sexuality has two components: (1) sexuality is associated with great physical pleasure, and 2) sexual interactions are associated with great personal self-disclosure, involving not only disclosure of one's body, but in an intimate interaction, of one's thoughts and feelings as well. Humans seem to find intrinsic value in the physical pleasures of sex and in the psychic satisfaction of the self-disclosures associated with sex—therefore its importance.

According to Reiss, sexuality is linked to the structures of any society in three areas: the kinship system, the power structure, and the ideology of the society.

First, because sexuality is the source of reproduction, it is always linked to *kinship*, and all societies seek to maintain social order through stable kinship systems. This linkage is the explanation for sexual jealousy, which is universal cross-culturally although it exists in varied forms. Jealousy is a way of setting boundaries on a relationship that is considered very important, essential enough so that it should not be breached. Marriage is typically such

Figure 2.7 According to Reiss's sociological theory, sex is important to us because it is associated with great physical pleasure and self-disclosure.

a relationship, and jealousy in marriage about extramarital affairs exists in all human societies. Kin define what relationships are and are not acceptable and enforce the resulting rules. Furthermore, all societies have structured ways of dealing with such jealousy. Even in societies that practise polygyny, rituals develop to minimize jealousy among the wives—for example, the husband must sleep one night with one wife, the next with another, and so on, and has violated norms if he spends two nights with the same wife. Reiss argues, therefore, that no society will be able to eliminate sexual jealousy because jealousy is a statement of the value or importance that kinship groups and individuals attach to a particular relationship such as marriage.

Second, sexuality is always linked to the *power structure* of a society. Reiss defines power as the ability to influence others and achieve one's objectives even if there is opposition from the other person. Powerful groups in any society generally seek to control the sexuality of the less powerful. Males are more powerful than females in most societies, so sexuality becomes linked to gender roles and males exercise control over female sexuality. Cross-cultural research shows, interestingly, that the closer females are in power to males in a society, the more sexual freedom women have; in societies in which women have little power, their sexuality is greatly restricted.

Third, sexuality is closely linked to the *ideologies* of a culture. Reiss defines "ideology" as fundamental assumptions about human nature. Societies define carefully what sexual practices are normal and abnormal, and which are right and wrong. Some cultures define homosexuality as abnormal, whereas others define it as normal—but the point is that all cultures define it one way or the other. Similarly, some cultures take a permissive attitude toward premarital sex both for males and females, some are permissive for males but not for females, and some are permissive for neither. A culture's ideologies define what is right and wrong sexually.

In summary, Reiss's sociological theory of sexuality argues that societies regard sexuality as important because it is associated with physical pleasure and with self-disclosure. Sexuality is tightly woven into the fabric of any society because of its links to the kinship system, to power structures, and to the ideologies of the society.

■ ■ ■ SUMMARY

Theories provide explanations for sexual phenomena. Sociobiologists view human sexual behaviours as the product of natural selection in evolution, and thus view these behavioural patterns as being genetically controlled. Contemporary evolutionary theorists view behaviour as the result of an interaction between evolved mechanisms and environmental influence.

Among the psychological theories, Freud's psychoanalytic theory views the sex energy, or libido, as a major influence on personality and behaviour. Freud introduced the concepts of erogenous zones and psychosexual stages of development. Learning theory emphasizes how sexual behaviour is learned and modified through reinforcements and punishments according to principles of operant conditioning. Behaviour modification techniques—therapies based on learning theory—are used in treating sexual variations and sexual disorders. Social learning theory adds the concepts of imitation, identification, and self-efficacy to learning theory. Social exchange theory highlights the role of rewards and costs in relationships. Cognitive psychologists focus on people's thoughts and perceptions—whether positive or negative—and how these influence sexuality.

Sociologists study the ways in which society influences our sexual expression. At the macro-level of analysis, sociologists investigate the ways in which institutions such as religion, the economy, the family, medicine, and the law influence sexuality. Symbolic interaction theory draws attention to processes of communication and interaction. Sexual scripts provide us with guidelines for behaviour in many situations. Reiss's sociological theory argues that all societies regard sexuality as important because it is associated with great physical pleasure and self-disclosure.

■ ■ ■ QUESTIONS FOR THOUGHT, DISCUSSION, AND DEBATE

1. Compare and contrast how a sociobiologist, a psychoanalyst, and a sociologist would explain why people engage in premarital intercourse.

2. Of the theories described in this chapter, which do you think provides the most insight into human sexuality? Why?

3. You are visiting your married sister and her family for the holidays. Her 6-year-old asks you a question: "Why do mommies stay home with kids?" Drawing on the knowledge you gained from Chapter 2, how would you answer this question? Which ideas about parental investment, social learning, or social norms and scripts would you use to explain why, in most cultures, women perform the child-rearing activities?

4. From a sociologist's point of view, how have social institutions controlled female sexuality?

5. Could script theory explain the pattern of homosexual and heterosexual behaviour of Sambia males described in In Focus 2.1? Explain your answer.

6. Find out more about a recent decision by the Supreme Court of Canada with respect to a sex law. Do you agree or disagree with the decision? To what extent does the decision reflect current Canadian social norms?

7. In Chapter 1, we identified a number of differences in the sexual behaviour of various ethnocultural communities in Canada. Which of the theories discussed in Chapter 2 can most easily explain these differences? Pick one specific difference and construct an explanation for it using that theory. How well does the theory help you to understand cultural differences in sexuality?

■ ■ ■ SUGGESTIONS FOR FURTHER READING

Baker, Robin. (1996). *Sperm wars: The science of sex.* Toronto: HarperCollins. Baker uses a series of vignettes describing sexual interactions to illustrate the many ways evolutionary mechanisms may influence our selection of mates, frequency of intercourse, success and failure to conceive, and infidelity.

Buss, David M. (1994). *The evolution of desire: Strategies of human mating.* New York: Basic Books. A detailed presentation of sexual strategy theory and data that are consistent with the theory.

Freud, Sigmund. (1943). *A general introduction to psychoanalysis.* Garden City, NY: Garden City Publishing. (Original in German, 1917.) Good for the reader who wants a basic introduction to Freud. For a good one-chapter summary, see Hall, C. S., and Lindzey, G. (1970). *Theories of personality* (2nd ed.). New York: Wiley.

Gagnon, John H., & Simon, William. (1987). The sexual scripting of oral–genital contacts. *Archives of Sexual Behavior, 16,* 1–26. An interesting discussion and application of script theory.

Online **Learning Centre**

For Review Questions, Web Resources, and other learning and study tools, visit the *Understanding Human Sexuality* Online Learning Centre at www.mcgrawhill.ca/college/hyde.

Sex Research

CHAPTER HIGHLIGHTS

> What is research, but a blind date with knowledge.
>
> —**William Henry**

This chapter is about sex research: how it is done, and how to evaluate it. It also describes some of the major sexuality studies. Why do we need sex research? What are its goals? Don't we already know everything we need to know about human sexuality? Isn't common sense sufficient?

The reality is there are still many things we do not know about human sexuality. People often have opinions and views about these issues and believe that their opinions are based on fact. Yet, too often they are based on misinformation, and sometimes even stereotypes or prejudice. Research is important because it creates accurate knowledge. Research puts beliefs, opinions, and theories to the systematic test.

There are a number of goals of sex research. First, it can be geared toward creating basic knowledge and understanding. For example, we might want to know what percentage of 15-year-olds have engaged in sexual activity, how often long-term couples have sex, or how effective the male condom is in preventing sexually transmitted infections. Second, research can be directed toward enhancing our understanding in order to influence sexual behaviour. For example, we might want to identify risk factors for individuals who might commit a sexual offence in order to prevent child sexual abuse; we might want to determine factors that affect sexual satisfaction in long-term relationships in order to help couples maintain satisfying sexual relationships; or, we might want to find out whether prepared childbirth techniques are effective in reducing anxiety and discomfort during labour and delivery. How can we provide effective prevention or intervention programs without this kind of knowledge on which to base these programs? Third, research can be geared toward public policy. For example, sexual health education is often a very controversial topic. An important question is whether individuals opposed to comprehensive sexual health education represent a majority of parents or a vocal minority of parents. Research can answer this question, thus allowing governments and school boards to take the wishes of the majority of parents into account when designing their sexual health education curriculum. Similarly, research can inform laws and regulations on a variety of issues including access to emergency contraception, new reproductive technologies, pornography, and sex work.

Throughout this book, we describe the results of research that has attempted to answer these types of questions. In this chapter, we examine some questions related to sex research in general. How do sex researchers do it? How valid are their conclusions?

There are many different types of sex research, but basically the techniques vary in terms of the following: (1) whether they rely on people's self-reports of their sexual behaviour or whether the scientist observes the sexual behaviour directly; (2) whether large numbers of people are studied (surveys) or whether a small number or just a single individual is studied (in laboratory studies, qualitative research, or case studies); (3) whether the studies are conducted in the laboratory or in the field; and (4) whether sexual behaviour is studied simply as it occurs naturally or whether some attempt is made to manipulate it experimentally.

Examples of studies using all these techniques will be considered and evaluated later in this chapter. First some issues in sex research will be discussed.

It is important to understand the techniques of sex research and their strengths as well as their limitations. This knowledge will help you evaluate the studies that are cited as evidence for various conclusions in later chapters and will also help you decide how willing you are to accept these conclusions. Perhaps more important, this knowledge will help you evaluate future sex research. Much sex research has been conducted already, but much more will be done in the future. The information in this chapter should help you understand and evaluate sex research that appears 10 or 20 years from now. Moreover, the mass media often report poor-quality research as enthusiastically as high-quality research. You should be equipped to tell the difference.

■ Issues in Sex Research

Sampling

One of the first steps in conducting sex research is to identify the appropriate **population** of people to be studied. Does the population in question consist of all adult human beings, all adults in Canada, all adolescents in Canada, all people guilty of sex crimes, or all married couples who engage in swinging? Generally, of course, the scientist is unable to get data for all the people in the population, and so a **sample** is taken.

At this point, things begin to get sticky. If the sample is a representative sample of the population in question and if it is a reasonably large sample, then results obtained from it can safely be generalized to the population that was originally identified. One way of obtaining a representative sample is by using **random sampling.** That is, if a researcher has really randomly selected 1 out of every 50 adolescents in Canada, then the results obtained from that sample are probably true of all adolescents in Canada. One technique that is sometimes used to get such a sample is **probability sampling.**[1] But if the sample consists only of adolescents with certain characteristics—for example, only those whose parents would agree to let them participate in sex research—then the results obtained from that sample may not be true of all

adolescents. Sampling has been a serious problem in sex research.

Typically, sampling proceeds in three phases: the population is identified, a method for obtaining a sample is adopted, and the people in the sample are contacted and asked to participate. The scientific techniques of the second phase—obtaining a sample—are by now fairly well developed and should not be a problem, provided investigators use them. What is perhaps the thorniest problem, though, occurs in the last phase: getting the people identified for the sample to participate. If any of the people refuse to participate, then the great probability sample is ruined. This is called the **problem of refusal (or non-response).** As a result, the researcher is essentially studying volunteers; that is, people who do agree to be in the research. The outcomes of the research may therefore contain distortions, called **volunteer bias.** In casually conducted research such as the Hite report (Hite, 1976, 1981), the response rate was only 3 percent, making it impossible to reach any conclusions about the population based on the sample. The problem of refusal in sex research is difficult, since there is no ethical way of forcing people to participate when they do not want to.

---

[1]A detailed discussion of probability sampling is beyond the scope of this book. For a good description of this method as applied to sex research, see Cochran et al. (1953). In brief, with a random sample, each individual in the population has an equal probability of being chosen. With a probability sample, the researchers can set a higher probability of inclusion for certain groups, a technique called oversampling. For example, if we had funds to interview 1,000 people in Canada, a random sample would yield only about 30 Aboriginal individuals and 30 Chinese Canadian individuals because each group constitutes about 3 percent of the Canadian population. We might not feel confident reaching conclusions about Aboriginal individuals or Chinese Canadians based on only 30 people, so we could decide to use probability sampling and give each of these groups a higher probability of inclusion compared with whites. If we tripled the probability of including these ethnocultural minority groups, the resulting sample of 1,000 would include 90 Aboriginal individuals, 90 Chinese Canadians, 82 individuals from other visible ethnocultural minorities (e.g., South Asian, black) and 738 Canadians from non–visible minority groups. Although these minority samples are still small, we would feel more confident about making conclusions about each group. We could do even more oversampling of Aboriginal individuals or of other ethnocultural groups that constitute even smaller percentages of the Canadian population to increase our confidence in our conclusions.

Population: A group of people a researcher wants to study and make inferences about.
Sample: A part of a population.
Random sampling: An excellent method of sampling in research, in which each member of the population has an equal chance of being included in the sample.
Probability sampling: An excellent method of sampling in research, in which each member of the population has a known probability of being included in the sample.
Problem of refusal or non-response: The problem that some people will refuse to participate in a sex survey, thus making it difficult to have a random sample.
Volunteer bias: A bias in the results of sex surveys that arises when some people refuse to participate, so that those who are in the sample are volunteers who may in some ways differ from those who refuse to participate.

Table 3.1 The Percentage of People Reporting Having Sex at Least Once a Week: Comparing a Convenience Sample with a Probability Sample

	Men		Women	
Age	Convenience Sample (Janus Report)	Probability Sample (General Social Survey)	Convenience Sample (Janus Report)	Probability Sample (General Social Survey)
18–26	72%	57%	68%	58%
27–38	83	69	78	61
39–50	83	56	68	49
51–64	81	43	65	25
Over 65	69	17	74	6

Source: A. M. Greeley (1994), The Janus Report, *Contemporary Sociology, 23,* 221–223. Reprinted by permission of the American Sociological Association and Andrew M. Greeley.

The problem of volunteer bias would not be so great if those who refused to participate were identical in their sexual behaviour to those who participated. But it seems likely that those who refuse to participate differ in some ways from those who agree to, and that means the sample is biased. Evidence suggests that volunteers who participate in sex research hold more permissive attitudes about sexuality and are more sexually experienced than those who don't; for example, they masturbate more frequently and have had more sexual partners (Bogaert, 1996; Morokoff, 1986; Strassberg & Lowe, 1995; Wiederman et al., 1994). In addition, women are less likely to volunteer for some but not all types of sex research than men are (Senn & Desmarais, 2001; Wiederman et al., 1994), so that female samples are even more highly selected than male samples. In sum, volunteer bias is potentially a serious problem when we try to reach conclusions based on sex research.

Table 3.1 shows how different the results of sex surveys can be, depending on how carefully the sampling is done (Greeley, 1994). The table shows results from two American surveys. The Janus report (Janus & Janus, 1993) used sampling methods so haphazard that the researchers ended up with what some call a "convenience sample." It included volunteers who came to sex therapists' offices and friends recruited by the original volunteers. In contrast, the General Social Survey conducted in 1993 by the University of Chicago obtained a probability sample. Notice that a considerably higher level of sexual activity is reported by the convenience sample in the Janus report, compared with the probability sample. This difference is especially pronounced among the elderly. Convenience samples simply do not give us a very good picture of what is going on in the general population.

Reliability of Self-Reports of Sexual Behaviour

Most sex researchers have not directly observed the sexual behaviour of their research participants. Instead, most have relied on respondents' self-reports of their sexual practices. The question is: How accurately do people report their own sexual behaviour? Inaccuracies may occur in several ways, and these inaccuracies are problems for sex surveys. These problems are discussed next.

Purposeful Distortion

If you were an interviewer in a sex research project and a 90-year-old man said that he and his wife made love twice a day, would you believe him, or would you suspect that he might be exaggerating slightly? If a 35-year-old woman told you that she had never masturbated, would you believe her, or would you suspect that she had masturbated but was unwilling to admit it?

Respondents in sex research may, for one reason or another, engage in **purposeful distortion,** intentionally giving self-reports that are distortions of reality. These distortions may be in either of two directions. People may exaggerate their sexual activity (a tendency toward "enlargement"), or

Purposeful distortion: Purposely giving false information in a survey.

they may minimize their sexual activity or hide the fact that they have done certain things ("concealment"). Unfortunately, we do not know whether most people tend toward enlargement or concealment. However, participants will often distort responses in the direction that they believe will be seen as more acceptable by the researcher, called **social desirability.** For example, an individual in a long-term relationship who believes that he or she engages in sexual activity with his or her partner much less often and masturbates much more often than other people do may exaggerate his or her sexual frequency but minimize his or her masturbation frequency. Participants are often not aware that social desirability is affecting their answers.

Distortion is a basic problem when using self-reports. To minimize distortion, participants must be impressed with the fact that because the study

---

Social desirability: The tendency to distort answers to a survey in the direction perceived to be more acceptable.

---

will be used for scientific purposes, their reports must be as accurate as possible. They must also be assured that their responses will be completely anonymous; this is necessary, for example, so that a politician would not be tempted to hide an extramarital affair or a history of sex with animals for fear that the information could be used to blackmail him or her.

But even if all respondents were very truthful and tried to give as accurate information as possible, two factors might still cause their self-reports to be inaccurate: memory and difficulties with estimates.

Memory

Some of the questions asked in sex surveys require respondents to recall what their sexual behaviour was like many years before. For example, some of the data we have on sexual behaviour in childhood come from the Kinsey study, in which adults were asked about their childhood sexual behaviour. This might involve asking a 50-year-old man to remem-

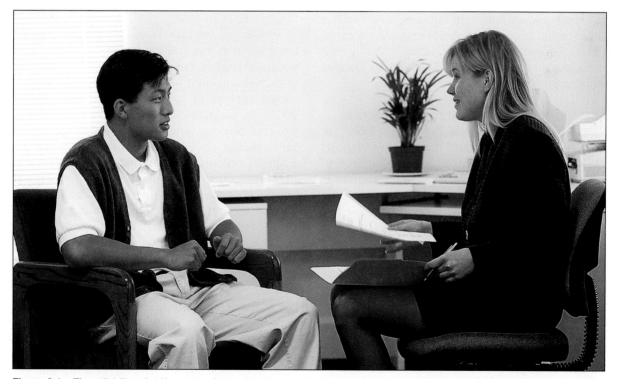

Figure 3.1 The reliability of self-reports of sexual behaviour: If you were interviewing this man in a sex survey and he said that he had never masturbated, would you believe him, or would you think that he was concealing a taboo behaviour?

ber at what age he began masturbating and how frequently he masturbated when he was 16 years old. It might be difficult to remember such facts accurately. The alternative is to ask people about their current sexual behaviour, although getting data like these from children raises serious ethical and practical problems.

Difficulties with Estimates

One of the questions sex researchers have asked is: How long, on the average, do you spend in precoital foreplay? If you were asked this question, how accurate a response do you think you could give? It is rather difficult to estimate time to begin with, and it is even more difficult to do so when engaged in an absorbing activity. For example, New Brunswick researchers found that, on average, men estimated the duration of foreplay as 13.4 minutes, which was significantly longer than the 11.3 minutes estimated by their female partners, suggesting that the men or the women or both were not accurate in the estimates of the duration of foreplay (Miller & Byers, 2004). The men and women both estimated the duration of intercourse at between seven and eight minutes, however. The point is that in some sex surveys people are asked to give estimates of things that they probably cannot estimate very accurately. This may be another source of inaccuracy in self-report data.

Evidence on the Reliability of Self-Reports

Scientists have developed several methods for assessing how reliable or accurate people's reports are (Catania et al., 1995). One is the method of **test–retest reliability**, in which the respondent is asked a series of questions and then is asked the same set of questions after a period of time has passed, for example, a week or a month. The correlation[2] between answers at the two times (test and retest) measures the reliability of responses. If people answer identically both times, the correlation

would be 1.0, meaning perfect reliability. If there were absolutely no relationship between what they said the first time and what they said the second time, the correlation would be 0, meaning that the responses are not at all reliable.

In one American study, urban African American and Latina girls between the ages of 12 and 14 were interviewed about their sexual experiences and then were interviewed again three weeks later (Hearn et al., 2003). The test–retest reliability was .84 for the age at which they had their first crush and .95 for the age at which they first touched a penis, which indicates excellent reliability. Other research generally indicates that respondents give their best estimates about short, recent time intervals (Catania et al., 1990a).

Web-based Surveys

The possibility of having surveys administered on Web-sites has opened a whole new era in sex research. Compared with other methods for administering surveys, Web-based surveys have many advantages, but also some disadvantages (Gosling et al., 2004; Kraut et al., 2004; Mustanski, 2001; Ochs et al., 2002).

Web-based sex surveys can recruit much larger samples than can traditional interview or questionnaire studies. For example, one Web survey of gays, lesbians, and bisexuals yielded 2,800 completed surveys in just two months (Mustanski, 2001). In addition, Web surveys can potentially produce broader samples than traditional survey methods can. For example, if you were conducting a survey on students' sexuality using traditional methods, you would probably sample students at your own college or university. If, instead, you administered the questionnaire on the Web, you could sample students from colleges and universities across Canada and, indeed, around the world. These new methods open up exciting possibilities for cross-cultural research.

Web-based surveys have particular advantages for studying special populations defined by their sexual behaviour, particularly if the behaviour is taboo. For example, traditional studies of gays and lesbians have used methods such as recruiting the sample through gay activist organizations and gay bars. These methods have been criticized because they omit from the sample closeted gays and those who do not actively participate in organizations or

---

[2]The statistical concept of correlation is discussed in the last section of this chapter.

Test–retest reliability: A method for testing whether self-reports are reliable or accurate; participants are interviewed (or given a questionnaire) and then interviewed a second time some time later to determine whether their answers are the same both times.

go to bars. Closeted gays have equal access to Web-based surveys and can answer them in a highly anonymous way, respecting their own decision to remain closeted. Therefore, Web methods can access this population that had previously been studied very little and can yield a much wider sample of gays and lesbians. Web methods can also locate stigmatized sexual minorities, such as those involved in sadomasochism, bondage, and discipline, by recruiting participants through virtual communities and Web-sites specialized for that particular sexual group.

Web-based surveys, then, have substantial strengths on the issue of sampling. Nonetheless, they still rely on self-reports, which as we saw earlier can be inaccurate to some degree.

Web-based surveys have the ability to eliminate extraneous influences on responding (discussed in the next section). For example, the gender or ethnicity of the interviewer may influence an individual's responses, but these factors are eliminated in a Web-administered questionnaire.

Compared with traditional survey methods, Web-based surveys have substantial advantages in terms of cost and efficiency. The cost basically involves the labour to design the questionnaire and post it effectively on the Web. There is no need to hire interviewers or to print and mail questionnaires.

Do all these substantial advantages come with any disadvantages? Some bias is introduced because not everyone has Internet access. Access grows every day, but Internet users still, on average, have incomes above the national average. Internet samples are nonetheless considerably more diverse than the university-student samples used in much research. The researcher lacks control of the environment in which the respondent completes the survey—something that can be controlled in personal interviews but cannot in mailed-out questionnaires. One can imagine, for example, a group of students living in residence filling out a Web sex survey together and having fun faking the answers. Individuals might respond multiple times or might actually try to sabotage or skew the results to show a particular outcome. Internal checks can be built into the sequence of questions that can detect faked patterns of answers, and methods have been devised to detect repeat responders. Nonetheless, these issues continue to be a concern.

On balance, Web-based surveys offer substantial advantages over traditional survey methods. Researchers will have to continue to monitor and control potential problems such as repeat responders.

Another method for assessing reliability involves obtaining independent reports from two different people who share sexual activity, such as husbands and wives. Kinsey was the first to use this method, interviewing 706 couples in the late 1930s and 1940s. Reports of objective facts—such as the number of years they had been married, how long they were engaged, and how much time elapsed between their marriage and the birth of the first child—showed perfect or near-perfect agreement. However, on items that are more difficult to estimate or remember, such as the frequency of intercourse early in marriage, the correlation was lower.

Recent research has also used this same method for checking for agreement between spouses. One study found that on a simple item such as whether a couple had engaged in intercourse in the last month, there was 93 percent agreement. Agreement on the number of times they had had intercourse in the last month, something that requires more difficult estimation, was .80, which is lower but still good (Hyde et al., 1996). Similarly, researchers in Montreal asked partners to indicate the behaviours that had occurred during lovemaking. The partners agreed 87 percent of the time on average, which is a high level of agreement (Ochs & Binik, 1999).

Interviews versus Questionnaires

In the large-scale sex surveys, three methods of collecting data have been used: the face-to-face interview, the phone interview, and the written questionnaire. Each of these methods has some advantages when compared with the others (Catania et al., 1995).

The advantage of the interview method, particularly the face-to-face interview, is that the interviewer can establish rapport with the respondent and try to convince that person of the research's worth and of the necessity for being honest. An interviewer can also vary the sequence of questions depending on the person's response. For example, if a person mentioned having had a homosexual experience, this response would be followed by a series of questions about the experience; those questions would be omitted if the person reported having had no homosexual experiences. It is hard to get this kind of flexibility in a printed questionnaire. Finally, interviews can be administered to persons who cannot read or write.

Questionnaires are much less costly, since they do not require hiring interviewers to spend the many hours necessary to interview respondents individually. It is also possible that respondents would be more honest in answering a questionnaire because they are more anonymous.

A recent innovation is the **computer-assisted self-interview method (CASI)**, which can be combined with an audio component so that the respondent not only reads but also hears the questions. This method offers the privacy of the written questionnaire while accommodating poor readers. The computer can be programmed to follow varying sequences of questions depending on respondents' answers, just as a human interviewer does.

What do the data say about which method works best for sex research? Several researchers have compared the results obtained through use of two different methods. For example, in one study, the rate of reporting rape was nearly double (11 percent) in a face-to-face interview compared with a telephone interview (6 percent) (Koss et al., 1994, p. 174). This finding seems to indicate that interviewers can establish rapport and trust better in person than over the telephone. In a study assessing risky sexual behaviour among gay men, both face-to-face interviews and written questionnaires were administered to all respondents (Siegel et al., 1994). Riskier behaviours were more likely to be reported on the questionnaire than in the interview. People evidently feel a bit freer to report particularly sensitive information on the more private written questionnaire than to an interviewer. Many experts in sex research recommend that a face-to-face interview to build rapport be combined with a written questionnaire administered during the interview to tap particularly sensitive information (Laumann et al., 1994; Siegel et al., 1994).

> **Computer-assisted self-interview method (CASI):** A method of data collection in which the respondent fills out questionnaires on a computer. Headphones and a soundtrack reading the questions can be added for young children or poor readers.

Self-Reports versus Direct Observations

As we noted earlier, one of the major ways of classifying techniques of sex research is by whether the scientist relied on people's self-reports of their behaviour or observed the sexual behaviour directly.

The problems of self-reports have just been discussed. In a word, self-reports may be inaccurate. Direct observations—such as those done by Masters and Johnson in their work on the physiology of sexual response—have a major advantage over self-reports in that they are accurate. No purposeful distortion or inaccurate memory can intervene. On the other hand, direct observations have their own set of problems. They are expensive and time-consuming, with the result that generally only a rather small sample is studied. Furthermore, obtaining a representative sample of the population is even more difficult than in survey research. While some people are reticent about completing a questionnaire concerning their sexual behaviour, even more would be unwilling to come to a laboratory where their sexual behaviour would be observed by a scientist or where they would be hooked up to recording instruments while they engaged in sex. Thus, results obtained from the unusual group of volunteers who would be willing to do this might not be generalizable to the rest of the population. One study showed that volunteers for a laboratory study of male sexual arousal felt less guilty, were less sexually fearful, and were more sexually experienced than non-volunteers (Farkas et al., 1978; for similar results with females, see Wolchik et al., 1983).

Direct observations of sexual behaviour in the laboratory, such as those made by Masters and Johnson, involve one other problem: Is sexual behaviour in the laboratory the same as sexual behaviour in the privacy of one's own bedroom? For example, might sexual response in the laboratory be somewhat inhibited?

Extraneous Factors

Various extraneous factors may also influence the outcomes of sex research. In interviews about sexual behaviour, for example, there is some indication that both male and female respondents prefer a female interviewer (DeLamater & MacCorquodale, 1979). Thus such extraneous factors as the gender, race, or age of the interviewer may influence the outcome of sex research. Questionnaires do not get around these problems, since such simple factors as the wording of a question may influence the results. In one study, respondents were given either standard or supportive wording of some items (Catania et al., 1995). For the question about extramarital sex, the standard wording was as follows:

> At any time while you were married during the past 10 years, did you have sex with someone other than your (husband/wife)?

The supportive wording was as follows:

> Many people feel that being sexually faithful to a spouse is important, and some do not. However, even those who think being faithful is important have found themselves in situations where they ended up having sex with someone other than their (husband/wife). At any time while you were married during the past 10 years, did you have sex with someone other than your (husband/wife)?

The supportive wording significantly increased reports of extramarital sex from 12 percent with the standard wording to 16 percent with the supportive wording if the interviewer was of the same gender as the respondent; the wording made no difference when the interviewer and respondent were of different genders. Sex researchers must be careful to control these extraneous factors so that they influence the results as little as possible.

Ethical Issues

There is a possibility of ethical problems involved in doing research. Ethical problems are particularly difficult in sex research, because people are more likely to feel that their privacy has been invaded when you ask them about sex than when you ask them to name their favourite political candidate or memorize a list of words. All research conducted at Canadian universities must conform to a policy established by the federal government that sets standards for conducting ethical research involving human participants (Medical Research Council of Canada, 1998). The cardinal ethical principle is respect for human dignity: above all, researchers need to keep this in mind when they are establishing the goals and the procedures of their research. The principle of respect for human dignity leads to several other ethical principles,

including respect for free and informed consent and protection from harm.

Free and Informed Consent

According to the principle of **free and informed consent,** participants have a right to be told, before they participate, what the purpose of the research is and what they will be asked to do. They can choose not to participate or not to continue. An investigator may not coerce people to be in a study, and it is the scientist's responsibility to see to it that all participants understand exactly what they are agreeing to do. In the case of children who may be too young to give truly informed consent, it is usually given by the parents.

The principle of informed consent was adopted by scientific organizations in the 1970s. It was violated in some of the earlier sex studies, as will be discussed later in this chapter.

Protection from Harm

Investigators should minimize the amount of physical and psychological stress to people in their research. Thus, for example, if an investigator must shock participants during a study, there should be a good reason for doing this. Questioning people about their sexual behaviour may be psychologically stressful to them and might conceivably harm them in some way, so sex researchers must be careful to minimize the stress involved in their procedure. The principle of respect for privacy and confidentiality of response, for example by making sure that responses are anonymous, is important to ensure that participants will not suffer afterward for their participation in research.

Justice

The principle of justice in research ethics holds that the risks of participating in research and benefits of the results of the research should be distributed fairly across groups in society. For example, early testing of the birth control pill was done on poor women in Puerto Rico, not on wealthy women in Vancouver. The risks were not distrib-

Free and informed consent: An ethical principle in research, in which people have a right to be informed, before participating, of what they will be asked to do in the research.

uted fairly, and a particular group bore a disproportionate burden. As a second example, research on the potential benefits of taking Aspirin for preventing heart attacks was conducted with an all-male sample. Whether this effect worked for women as well remained unknown. Thus, the benefits of the research did not extend fairly to everyone. Researchers have an obligation to make sure that they conduct their research in a way that benefits as wide a range of persons as possible.

Balancing Harms and Benefits

Considering the possible dangers involved in sex research, is it ethical to do such research? Officials in universities and government agencies sponsoring sex research must answer this question for every proposed sex research study. In doing so, they must do a **harms–benefits analysis**. That is, the stress to research participants should be minimized as much as possible, but some stresses will remain; they are the harms. The question then becomes: Will the benefits that result from the research be greater than the harm? That is, will the participants benefit in some way from being in the study, and will science and society in general benefit from the knowledge resulting from the study? Do these benefits outweigh the potential harms? If they do, the research is justifiable; otherwise, it is not.

As an example, Masters and Johnson considered these issues carefully and concluded that their research participants benefited from being in their research; they collected data from former participants that confirm this belief. Thus a harms–benefits analysis would suggest that their research was ethical, even though their participants might have been temporarily stressed by it. Even in a study as ethically questionable as Laud Humphreys' study of the tearoom trade (discussed later in this chapter), the potential harms to the participants should be weighed against the benefits that accrue to society from being informed about this aspect of sexual behaviour.

> **Harms–benefits analysis:** An approach to analyzing the ethics of a research study, based on weighing the harms of the research (such as stress to subjects) against the benefits of the research (gaining knowledge about human sexuality).

■ The Major Sex Surveys

In the major sex surveys, the data were collected from a large sample of people by means of questionnaires or interviews. The best known of these studies is the one done by Alfred Kinsey, so we will consider it first. His data were collected in the late 1930s and 1940s in the United States, and thus the results are now largely of historical interest. However, Kinsey documented his methods with extraordinary care, so his research is a good example to study for both the good and the bad points of surveys.

The Kinsey Report

The Sample

Kinsey (see In Focus 3.1) and his colleagues interviewed a total of 5,300 males, and their responses were reported in *Sexual Behavior in the Human Male* (1948); 5,940 females contributed to *Sexual Behavior in the Human Female* (1953). Although some African Americans were interviewed, there wasn't a big enough sample of them so only interviews with whites were included in the publications. The interviews were conducted between 1938 and 1949 in the United States.

Initially, Kinsey was not much concerned with sampling issues. His goal was simply to collect sex histories from as wide a variety of people as possible. He began conducting interviews on his university campus and then moved on to large U.S. cities, such as Chicago.

Kinsey later became more concerned with sampling issues and developed a technique called *100-percent sampling*. In this method he contacted a group, obtained its cooperation, and then got every one of its members to give a history. Once the cooperation of a group had been secured, peer pressure ensured that all members would participate. Unfortunately, although he was successful in getting a complete sample from such groups, the groups themselves were by no means chosen randomly. Thus, among the groups from which 100-percent samples were obtained were 2 sororities, 9 fraternities, and 13 professional groups.

In the 1953 volume on females, Kinsey said that he and his colleagues had deliberately chosen not to use probability sampling methods because of the problems of non-response. This is a legitimate point. But as a result, we have almost no information on how adequate the sample was. One might say that the sampling was haphazard but not random. For example, there were more respondents from Indiana than from any other state. Generally, the following kinds of people were overrepresented in the sample: university students, young people, well-educated people, Protestants, people living in cities, and people living in Indiana and the Northeast United States. Underrepresented groups included manual labourers, less well-educated people, older people, Roman Catholics, Jews, members of racial minorities, and people living in rural areas.

The Interviews

Although scientists generally regard Kinsey's sampling methods with some dismay, his face-to-face interviewing techniques are highly regarded. More than 50 percent of the interviews were done by Kinsey himself and the rest by his associates, whom he trained carefully. The interviewers made every attempt to establish rapport with the people they spoke to, and they treated all reports matter-of-factly. They were also skillful at phrasing questions in language that was easily understood. Questions were worded so as to encourage people to report anything they had done. For example, rather than asking "Have you ever masturbated?" the interviewers asked "At what age did you begin masturbating?" They also developed a number of methods for cross-checking a person's report so that false information would be detected. Wardell Pomeroy recounted an example:

Kinsey illustrated this point with the case of an older Negro male who at first was wary and evasive in his answers. From the fact that he listed a number of minor jobs when asked about his occupation and seemed reluctant to go into any of them [Kinsey] deduced that he might have been active in the underworld, so he began to follow up by asking the man whether he had ever been married. He denied it, at which Kinsey resorted to the vernacular and inquired if he had ever "lived common law." The man admitted he had, and that it had first happened when he was 14.

"How old was the woman?" [Kinsey] asked.

"Thirty-five," he admitted, smiling.

Kinsey showed no surprise. "She was a hustler, wasn't she?" he said flatly.

At this the subject's eyes opened wide. Then he smiled in a friendly way for the first time, and said, "Well, sir, since you appear to know something about these things, I'll tell you straight."

After that, [Kinsey] got an extraordinary record of this man's history as a pimp. . . . (Pomeroy, 1972, pp. 115–116)

Kinsey took strict precautions to ensure that responses were anonymous and that they remained anonymous. The data were stored on IBM cards, but using a code that had been memorized by only a few people directly involved in the project and which was never written down. The research team had even made contingency plans for destroying the data in the event that the police tried to demand access to the records for prosecuting people.

Put simply, the interviewing techniques were probably very successful in minimizing purposeful distortion. However, other problems of self-report remained: the problems of memory and of the inability to estimate some of the numbers requested.

Watch the "Alfred Kinsey" video in Chapter 3 of your CD to learn more about this controversial researcher.

How Accurate Were the Kinsey Statistics?

When all is said and done, how accurate were the statistics presented by Kinsey? The American Statistical Association appointed a blue-ribbon panel to evaluate the Kinsey reports (Cochran et al., 1953; for other evaluations see Terman, 1948; Wallin, 1949). While the panel members generally felt that the interview techniques had been excellent, they were dismayed by Kinsey's failure to use probability sampling and concluded, somewhat pessimistically:

In the absence of a probability-sample benchmark, the present results must be regarded as subject to systematic errors of unknown magnitude due to selective sampling (via volunteering and the like). (Cochran et al., 1953, p. 711)

In Focus 3.1

What Is the Legacy of Alfred C. Kinsey?

Alfred C. Kinsey was born in 1894 in New Jersey, the first child of uneducated parents. In high school he did not date, and a classmate recalled that he was "the shyest guy around girls you could think of."

His father was determined that Kinsey become a mechanical engineer. From 1912 to 1914 he tried studying mechanical engineering at Stevens Institute, but he showed little talent for it. At one point he was close to failing physics, but a compromise was reached with the professor, who agreed to pass him if he would not attempt any advanced work in the field! In 1914 Kinsey made his break and enrolled at Bowdoin College to pursue his real love: biology. Because this went against his father's wishes, Kinsey was put on his own financially.

In 1916 he began graduate work at Harvard. There he developed an interest in insects, specializing in gall wasps. While still a graduate student he wrote a definitive book on the edible plants of eastern North America.

In 1920 he went to Bloomington, Indiana, to take a job as assistant professor of zoology at Indiana University. That fall he met Clara McMillen, whom he married six months later. They soon had four children.

With his intense curiosity and driving ambition, Kinsey quickly gained academic success. He published a high school biology text in 1926, which received enthusiastic reviews. By 1936 he had published two major books on gall wasps; they established his reputation as a leading authority in the field and contributed not only to knowledge of gall wasps but also to genetic theory.

Kinsey came to the study of human sexual behaviour as a biologist. His shift to the study of sex began in 1938, when Indiana University began a "marriage" course; Kinsey chaired the faculty committee teaching it. Part of the course included individual conferences between students and faculty, which became Kinsey's first sex interviews. When confronted with teaching the course, he also became aware of the appalling lack of information on human sexual behaviour. Thus, his research resulted in part from his realization of the need of people, especially young people, for sex information. In 1939 he made his first field trip to collect sex histories in Chicago. His lifetime goal was to collect 100,000 sex histories.

His work culminated in the publication of the Kinsey reports in 1948 (*Sexual Behavior in the Human Male*) and 1953 (*Sexual Behavior in the Human Female*). While the scientific community generally received them as a landmark contribution, they also provoked hate mail.

In 1947 Kinsey founded the Institute for Sex Research (known popularly as the Kinsey Institute) at Indiana University. It was financed by a grant from the Rockefeller Foundation and, later, by book royalties. But in the 1950s United States Senator Joseph McCarthy, the communist baiter, was in power. He made a particularly vicious attack on the Institute and its research, claiming that its effect was to weaken American morality and thus make the nation more susceptible to a communist takeover. Under his pressure, the Rockefeller Foundation terminated its support.

Kinsey's health began to fail, partly as a result of the heavy workload he set for himself, partly because he was so involved with the research that

However, they also felt that this was a nearly insoluble problem for sex research; even if a probability sample were used, refusals would still create serious problems.

The statisticians who evaluated Kinsey's methods felt that one aspect of his findings might have been particularly subject to error: the generally high levels of sexual activity, and particularly the high incidence of homosexual behaviour. These conclusions might, they felt, have been seriously influenced by sampling problems, particularly Kinsey's tendency to seek out persons with unusual sexual practices.

Kinsey's associates felt that the most question-

Figure 3.2   *(a)* Alfred C. Kinsey (second from right, holding the folder), with colleagues Martin, Gebhard, and Pomeroy.

Figure 3.2   *(b)* Liam Neeson plays Kinsey in the 2004 movie *Kinsey*.

he took attacks personally, and partly because he saw financial support for the research collapsing. He died in 1956 at the age of 62 of heart failure while honouring a lecture engagement when his doctor had ordered him to convalesce.

By 1957 McCarthy had been discredited and the grant funds returned. The Institute was then headed by Paul Gebhard, an anthropologist who had been a member of the staff for many years. The Institute continues to do research today; it also houses a large library on sex and an archival collection including countless works of sexual art.

In a highly publicized, tell-all biography of Kinsey, James Jones (1997) argued that, although Kinsey's public self was a heterosexual married man, he was homosexual (more accurately, bisexual) and practised masochism. According to Jones, this discred-

its Kinsey's research. Jones's logic is poor, though, because one can evaluate the quality of the research methods independent of one's views about Kinsey's personal sex life. Moreover, Kinsey's sexual experimenting may have contributed to the innovativeness of his research.

Sources: Christensen, 1971; Gathorne-Hardy, 2000; Gebhard, 1976; Jones, 1997.

able statistic was the incidence of male homosexuality. Wardell Pomeroy commented, "The magic 37 percent of males who had one or more homosexual experiences was, no doubt, overestimated" (1972, p. 466).

In sum, it is impossible to say how accurate the Kinsey statistics are; they may be very accurate or

may contain serious errors. Probably the single most doubtful figure is the high incidence of homosexuality. Although Canadians have often used the Kinsey data to draw conclusions about the situation in Canada, Canadians differ from Americans in ways that are likely to affect sexual behaviour, such as family patterns, laws, attitudes, and health (Barrett et al.,

In Focus 3.2

Who Is Doing Sex Research in Canada?

There are many active sex researchers in Canada. Most of them are in academic departments within specific disciplines such as psychology, sociology, public health, family studies, criminology, or medicine. The only Department of Sexology located in Canada operates in French at l'Université du Québec à Montréal. Although it is impossible to name all Canadian sex researchers, here are some of the most active researchers (from east to west).

Psychologist Sandra Byers and her current and former graduate students at the University of New Brunswick are particularly well known for their research on sexual interactions in close relationships including sexual satisfaction, sexual dysfunction, and sexual coercion.

In Quebec, psychologist Francine Lavoie of Laval University studies high school students' sexually coercive experiences. Joseph Levy and Joanne Otis at the Department of Sexology at l'Université du Québec à Montréal have been active in assessing the sexual behaviour of Quebecers. In the same

department, Robert Gemme has done extensive research on prostitution, and psychologist Sophie Bergeron studies women's sexual pain disorders. At McGill University, Barbara Sherwin is well known for her work on sex hormones and sexual functioning in menopausal women, and psychologist Yitzchak Binik studies sexual pain in women. At Concordia University, sociologist Frances Shaver is a leading researcher on sex work and James Pfaus studies the neurochemical and molecular events underlying sexual behaviour.

A number of Ontario universities have active sex research programs. Researchers at the Social Program Evaluation Group at Queen's University in Kingston have published extensively on adolescent sexual behaviour. Also at Queen's, psychologists William Marshall and Vernon Quinsey have an international reputation for their work on the assessment and treatment of sex offenders. At the University of Ottawa, psychiatrist Paul Federoff studies the treatment of sex offenders; psychologist Elke Reissing

---

1997). Thus, it is impossible to be certain of the extent to which these data reflect the sexual behaviour of Canadians. Unfortunately, there have been no large-scale Canadian sexuality surveys, with the exception of a few questions contained in the National Population Health Survey and other general surveys. This makes it difficult to develop a clear picture of the sexual behaviour of adult Canadians. In contrast, the United States, England, and France have all conducted this kind of large-scale survey. Many of the statistics in the French and British surveys match quite closely those from the United States. Thus, it is likely that a Canadian survey would also have similar, but not identical, findings. There are, however, many active sex researchers in Canada (see In Focus 3.2). These researchers have conducted surveys of selected groups, such as university students, teenagers, First Nations peoples, sex trade workers, or gay and bisexual men, some of which are described in this chapter.

Sexual Behaviour in the United States

U.S. researchers identified a need to conduct a large-scale, national survey of sexuality using probability sampling methods to determine what Americans' patterns of sexual behaviour are today. Such a study appeared in 1994. The research team was headed by Edward Laumann, a distinguished sociologist at the University of Chicago, and was conducted by the National Opinion Research Center, one of the best-respected survey organizations in the United States. The survey was called the National Health and Social Life Survey; to keep things simple, we will call this study the NHSLS (Laumann et al., 1994; Michael et al., 1994).

The research method involved a probability sampling of households in the United States. This excluded less than 3 percent of Americans but did exclude people living in institutions (e.g., prisons, university dormitories) and the homeless. People investigates sexual pain disorders as well as sexual adjustment following treatment for cancer. At the Centre for Addiction and Mental Health, Clarke Division, in Toronto, psychologists Ken Zucker and Ray Blanchard are well known for their work on gender identity disorders in children and adults, and Harold Barbaree for his work with sexual offenders. Ted Myers and his colleagues at the University of Toronto have conducted a number of major surveys with respect to sexual health, particularly HIV.

Psychologist Anthony Bogaert is well-known for his work on the origins of sexual orientation. B. J. Rye at St. Jerome's University at the University of Waterloo studies HIV/AIDS and attitudes toward sexual minorities. Guelph University sociologist Edward Herold's current research focuses on youth and sexuality, most recently on sexual norms and risk behaviour in holiday environments. William Fisher of the Department of Psychology at the University of Western Ontario has an international reputation for his work on the prevention of teen pregnancy, STIs, and HIV infection. Sociologist Eleanor Maticka-Tyndale at the University of Wind-

sor is well-known for her qualitative and multi-method research on risk behaviour related to pregnancy and STI/HIV infection.

At the University of Alberta, Maryanne Doherty studies sexual health education and risky sexual health behaviours. Martin Lalumière at the University of Lethbridge does research on sexual aggression.

In British Columbia, psychiatrist Rosemary Basson of the Sexual Medicine Unit at the University of British Columbia conducts research on sexual dysfunction. At UBC psychologist Judith Daniluk is well known for her research on infertility; psychologist Boris Gorzalka conducts psychophysiological sex research. Sociologist Aaron Devor at the University of Victoria has made important contributions in his work on conceptualization of gender dysphoria.

Canadian sex researchers publish their findings in both national and international journals. There is one Canadian journal committed to the dissemination of sex research: the quarterly *Canadian Journal of Human Sexuality*. Many belong to the Canadian Sex Research Forum, the only national association for sex researchers, as well as to international sexological organizations.

were eligible if they were adults between the ages of 18 and 59.

The researchers obtained an impressive 79-percent cooperation rate. Apparently, the great majority of people are willing to respond to a carefully conducted sex survey. The response rate is particularly impressive in view of the fact that today even surveys of more neutral topics such as political opinions generally have a response rate of only about 75 percent.

The data were obtained in face-to-face interviews supplemented by brief written questionnaires, which were handed to the respondents for particularly sensitive topics (such as masturbation) and sealed in a "privacy envelope" when they had been completed. The researchers chose the face-to-face interview because they felt that it would yield a higher response rate than a written questionnaire alone, and it allowed the researchers to ask more complex, detailed sequences of ques-

tions than would have been possible with just a written questionnaire or a phone interview.

Laumann's team was careful to obtain the respondents' informed consent. About a week before an interviewer went to a household, a letter was sent explaining that the purpose of the survey was to help "doctors, teachers, and counselors better understand and prevent the spread of diseases like AIDS and better understand the nature and extent of harmful and of healthy sexual behavior in our country" (Laumann et al., 1994, p. 55). The purpose was therefore clearly and honestly described to participants before their consent was requested. In order to protect confidentiality, all identifying information about the respondent was destroyed after the interview. Each respondent was paid $35 for the interview, which lasted, on the average, 90 minutes.

The NHSLS is the best sex survey of the general population of the United States available today, and its findings will be referred to in many chapters in

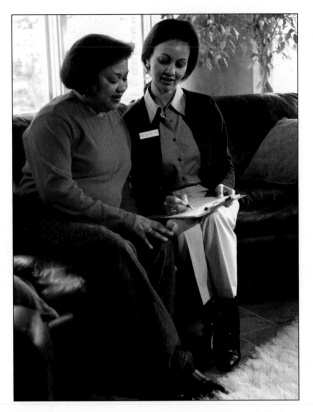

Figure 3.3   Research conducted among racial and ethnic minority groups must be culturally sensitive. Ideally, for example, interviewers should be of the same cultural background as research participants.

this book. The researchers made outstanding efforts to use the best sampling methods and interview techniques. Nonetheless, no doubt some respondents engaged in concealment and perhaps also in enlargement, because self-reports were used. The skill of the interviewers and their ability to build rapport is crucial in overcoming such problems. The researchers reported training the interviewers extensively, but nonetheless the extent of concealment, or *underreporting*, remains unknown.

One criticism of the NHSLS is that some of the interviews took place with a third person present, obviously not an ideal situation for honest reporting about sexuality. The researchers analyzed the data to see whether the presence of another person was associated with different patterns of reporting that might suggest concealment. They found some differences that might indicate concealment; for example, a lower percentage of respondents

who were interviewed with another person present reported two or more sex partners in the past year. However, in many cases a woman was being interviewed with a preschool child present. It may be that mothers with preschool children were simply less likely to have had multiple partners in the past year. When the authors reanalyzed the data controlling for simple social variables, only a few random reporting differences remained between the two groups. It seems unlikely that this methodological problem caused major difficulties with the results.

Ironically, the most controversial statistic in the study was the same as in Kinsey's research—the incidence of homosexuality. In Kinsey's case, people thought the numbers were too high. In the case of the NHSLS, some people thought they were too low. We will return to this issue in Chapter 15.

Sexual Behaviour in France and Britain

Again stimulated by a need for far better information about sexual behaviour in order to deal with the AIDS crisis, a team of French researchers, called the ACSF Investigators, conducted a major French sex survey (ACSF Investigators, 1992). The data were collected in 1991 and 1992. These researchers chose the method of telephone interviews, preceded by a letter notifying potential respondents that they had been identified for the representative sample. The response rate was 76.5 percent. The result was a sample of 20,055 adults ranging in age from 18 to 69.

The results indicate, for example, that 13 percent of French men, compared with 6 percent of French women, had multiple sex partners (two or more) in the past 12 months and therefore were at higher risk of HIV infection.

Anne Johnson and her colleagues conducted surveys in Britain in 1990–1991 and again in 1999–2001 (Johnson et al., 1992; 2001). The more recent survey used computer-assisted interviews. It yielded data for 11,161 men and women aged 16 to 44. The response rate was 63 percent. The researchers found that the average number of opposite-sex sexual partners in the previous five years was 3.8 for men and 2.4 for women; 2.6 percent of both men and women reported a same-sex partner; both rates were higher than were found in the 1990 survey. However, they also found increases in consistent condom use, particularly for men with multiple partners in the past year.

The Canada Youth, Sexual Health, and HIV/AIDS Study

Researchers from four Canadian universities—Queen's, Acadia, Laval, and the University of Alberta—conducted a study on youth sexuality and sexual health that was coordinated by the Council of Ministers of Education and funded by Health Canada (Council of Ministers of Education, Canada, 2003). The project was called the Canada Youth, Sexual Health, and HIV/AIDS Study, or CYSHHAS for short. It examined a number of factors thought to influence adolescent sexual knowledge, attitudes, and behaviour. Many of these questions were also used in the Canada Youth and AIDS Study conducted in 1987 by Alan King and his colleagues (King et al., 1988), allowing comparisons between the two studies. Because the CYSHHAS focused on sexual health, it is not a comprehensive survey of adolescent sexual behaviour and attitudes.

The researchers collected data in all 10 provinces as well as in the Yukon and Northwest Territories. They surveyed 11,074 youth in grades 7, 9, and 11. However, in order to be acceptable to school administrations, the grade 7 version included only one question about sexual experiences. The study was conducted in both French and English. The researchers used excellent sampling methods. They designed their sampling procedure so that not only would the data be representative of Canada as a whole, but also they would have enough participants from each province so that they could present the findings separately for each province. However, some selected schools refused to participate, resulting in a sample that was not equally representative of the whole country and that was too small to analyze by province or territory. As a result, the sample was only about a third the size the researchers had intended. There also were some problems related to potential volunteer bias. For example, 18 percent of students either failed to return their signed permission slip or had parents who refused to give them permission to participate, and 5 percent of the students refused to participate. The students who did participate may differ in some important ways from those who did not.

The researchers found that many youth had begun engaging in sexual intercourse by age 14. For example, 23 percent of boys and 19 percent of girls in grade 9 and 40 percent of boys and 46 per-cent of girls in grade 11 reported having engaged in sexual intercourse at least once. These percentages are similar to, and if anything somewhat lower than, those obtained in the Canada Youth and AIDS Study in 1987, indicating that the percentage of students engaging in sexual intercourse does not appear to be increasing. However, the students who are engaging in sexual intercourse reported doing so more frequently than did students in 1987. Although 78 percent of the boys and 68 percent of the girls said that they had used a condom at last intercourse, between 5 and 10 percent had not used any form of birth control. Further, students who participated in 2002 were less accurate in their sexual knowledge than were the students who participated in 1987. Although this study assessed both anglophone and francophone youth, the researchers did not assess ethnicity. Thus, we do not know how cultural background affects the sexual attitudes and behaviours of Canadian youth.

Magazine Surveys

Many large-scale sex surveys have been conducted through magazines. Often the survey is printed in one issue of the magazine and readers are asked to respond. The result can be a huge sample—perhaps 20,000 people—which sounds impressive. But are these magazine surveys really all they claim to be?

Sampling is just plain out of control with magazine surveys. The survey is distributed just to readers of the magazine, and different magazines have different clienteles. No one magazine reaches a representative sample of Canadians. If the survey appeared in *Chatelaine*, it would go to certain kinds of women; if it were in *Canadian Living*, it would go to others. It would be risky to assume that women who read *Chatelaine* have the same sexual patterns as those who read *Canadian Living*. To make matters worse, the response rate is unknown. We can't know how many people saw the survey and did not fill it out, compared with the number who did. The response rate could be something like 3 percent. One does not, therefore, even have a random sample of readers of that magazine.

As an example, let's consider a survey that was reported in the August 2000 issue of *Cosmopolitan* (Gilbert, 2000). The headline on the cover announces "Our Biggest Sex Survey Ever, Thousands of Guys Reveal What Sends Them Over the Edge (Their Answers Will Shock You)." The description of the method in the articles says that *Cosmo* polled 60,000 "loose-lipped men and women." That's a much larger sample than the NHSLS—but, in sex surveys as in some other aspects of sexuality, bigger is not always better. How did *Cosmo* distribute the surveys? If they were printed in a previous issue, which seems like a good guess, how can we know the response rate? And how did so many men receive the survey, given that *Cosmo* is a magazine carefully aimed at a female audience? Among the respondents, how many were married? Single? What about their ethnic backgrounds? How old were they? Of course, these details are probably not the sort of thing that *Cosmo* thinks will entertain its readers. Nonetheless, the editors could have printed the information in a small box at the end of the article. More importantly, these details are crucial in understanding whether one can take the survey's claims seriously.

One question asked what a guy thinks of a girl who has sex on a first date. Of the men who were polled, 44 percent said they were happy when a women went with her desires and wouldn't think negatively about her, as long as she was comfortable with her decision. From this, can we conclude that 44 percent of American men don't think ill of a woman who goes to bed with them on a first date? This conclusion would require a leap of logic that is too big for safety. *Cosmo* wasn't even close to having a random sample in this survey. For instance, perhaps the sample was 99 percent white. The results, then, might be totally different for Americans and Canadians who are black, Asian, or Aboriginal. Or maybe the respondents were in their 20s; then the results might have been totally different for men in their 30s or 40s.

For all these reasons, it would not be legitimate to infer that these statistics characterize North American women in general. We could continue with more examples of magazine surveys, but the general conclusion should be clear by now. Although they may appear impressive because of their large number of respondents, magazine sex surveys actually are poor in quality because the sample generally is seriously biased.

■ Studies of Special Populations

In addition to the large-scale surveys of Americans and of Canadian youth discussed earlier, many studies of special populations have been done. Three examples are given here: the Maticka-Tyndale study of exotic dancers, a survey of First Nations peoples in Ontario, and a survey of Canadian men who have sex with men.

Exotic Dancers

Eleanor Maticka-Tyndale and her colleagues conducted a study of exotic dancers working at strip clubs in Southern Ontario (Lewis & Maticka-Tyndale, 1998; Maticka-Tyndale et al., 1999). Their goal was to determine whether the dancers' activities, both inside and outside the club, put them at risk for STIs, including HIV infection. They interviewed 30 female exotic dancers who had been dancing from 1 to 22 years. The researchers used a qualitative methodology rather than the quantitative methodology used in the other research described in this chapter. In **qualitative research**, the researchers try to make sense of experiences in terms of the meanings that people give to them (Denzin & Lincoln, 1994). Thus, qualitative researchers emphasize the participant's point of view and represent this point of view by providing quotations from participants rather than by giving statistics.

The researchers used a procedure called *non-probability purposive sampling* to maximize the diversity in the small sample. They wanted to make sure that the conclusions drawn from the research would reflect all the situations in which dancers find themselves. Participants were identified by key informants, by research assistants who had worked as dancers themselves, and by dancers who participated in the study, a technique called *snowballing*. Thus, as with all qualitative research, this was not a random or representative sample and thus we cannot draw conclusions about frequencies and prevalences. Nonetheless, it provides an in-depth understanding of the world of exotic dancers.

> **Qualitative research:** Research, usually involving interviews, in which the researchers try to make sense of the meanings that people give to their experiences.

Participants responded to an informal set of open-ended questions that allowed them to freely express themselves. The interviews were analyzed to identify themes that emerged from the sex workers' responses. There were two different types of dancers. Women begin dancing primarily for the money, with the view that it will be temporary. Goal-oriented dancers continue to treat dancing as a temporary job and usually do not use alcohol or drugs or engage in sexual activity as part of the job. College and university students are one group of goal-oriented dancers. Dancing is attractive to them because it pays well and can fit into their class schedule. Some women shift from viewing dancing as a temporary job to viewing it as a career. These career dancers are usually part of the strip club culture, are often heavy drinkers, and may be involved in drug use. They may have sex with customers as part of the dancing or on dates with the men they meet while dancing at the clubs.

The researchers faced a number of difficulties that are common in this type of research. First, it was difficult to recruit participants. Dancers do not have much interest in participating in research and are suspicious of researchers. Second, as there is a stigma associated with exotic dancing, the researchers had to take extra steps to ensure that participants could not be identified.

Ontario First Nations AIDS and Healthy Lifestyle Survey

The Ontario First Nations AIDS and Healthy Lifestyle Survey was conducted by Ted Myers and his colleagues (1993) at the Division of Community Health at the University of Toronto in collaboration with the First Nations Steering Committee. The goal of the study was to assess knowledge, attitudes, and behaviours related to HIV infection among First Nations peoples in Ontario. All decisions were made by consensus between the academic researchers and the Steering Committee in order to take the unique concerns of communities into account. The researchers used random selection to obtain a representative sample. They selected equal numbers of men and women as well as equal numbers within each of four age groups (Myers et al., 1993).

The data were collected using face-to-face interviews as well as an answer booklet for highly personal questions. All interviewers were hired from participating communities, spoke the appropriate First Nations language, and participated in two days of training. For questions about sexual behaviour, respondents were given a choice of using technical terms or slang terms. Most communities took steps to promote the study. The researchers found that many participants had engaged in high-risk sexual behaviours. For example, 40 percent of the men and 18 percent of the women reported two or more sexual partners in the past year. Sixty percent of respondents did not consistently use a condom when engaging in vaginal or anal intercourse.

The methodology used in this study demonstrates a number of issues that need to be kept in mind in doing research with different cultural groups (Ford & Norris, 1991). First, respondents should be interviewed by an interviewer of the same gender and ethnic background as themselves. This practice is important for building rapport and establishing trust during the interview, both of which are critical in obtaining honest answers. Language is another important issue in constructing interviews. Many people, including those from the majority Canadian culture, do not know scientific terms for sexual concepts. Interviewers therefore have to be ready with a supply of slang terms so that they can switch to these if a respondent does not understand a question. This problem becomes more complex when interviewing people whose first language is not English. In keeping with these recommendations, Myers and his colleagues used interviewers from the communities involved in the study, allowed interviewers to translate the question into the appropriate First Nations language as they conducted the interview, if required, and trained them in both technical and slang terms.

This research also demonstrates another important principle—representatives of the target communities participated in the design and management of the study. This has two advantages. First, it allows the communities to have input into the research design and methodology to ensure that the research takes the unique concerns of each community into account. Second, minority-group members are more likely to agree to participate in research if they know that representatives of their communities were involved in designing the study.

In conclusion, doing sex research with people from diverse ethnocultural communities in Canada requires more than just administering the same old surveys to samples of people from these groups. It requires revisions to methodology that are culturally sensitive to issues such as the ethnicity of the interviewer, the language used in the interview, and the special sensitivity of some groups regarding some topics.

Gay and Bisexual Men

Ted Myers and a team of researchers from three Canadian universities conducted a major survey of gay and bisexual men in Canada. The study was done in collaboration with the Canadian AIDS Society and was funded by Health Canada. The goal of the study was to understand the knowledge, attitudes, and behaviours of men who have sex with men in order to make recommendations about how best to prevent the spread of HIV and AIDS among gay and bisexual men. The researchers were concerned that if they called it a study of gay and bisexual men, men who have sex with men but who identify themselves as heterosexual would not participate in the study. Therefore, they advertised the study as the *Men's Survey '91* and avoided the terms "gay" and "bisexual" (Myers et al., 1993).

The data came from questionnaires administered to 4,803 gay and bisexual men in 35 cities and metropolitan areas across Canada. One strength of the study is that participants lived in both large and small communities across Canada and not just in large cities like Toronto and Vancouver. The researchers collected data in gay bars, in bath houses, and at community dances. They were aware that not all gay men go to these types of settings, but argued that men who socialize in gay-identified venues are an important population for AIDS prevention.

In order to find prospective participants, the researchers used a promotional campaign in English and French consisting of posters and advertising in Canadian gay newspapers. They took a number of steps to make sure that the sample was representative. The number of participants from each region was proportional to the male population in that region. Data were collected in as many different venues in each region as possible. In each venue, the researchers made sure that participants could complete the questionnaire in private. The response rate was excellent: 86 percent of the men who were approached to participate completed a questionnaire. Men in the study ranged from 16 to 75 years of age. The sample came from all income levels, but the educational level tended to be high. There were four versions of the questionnaire. Some participants completed a longer version that required 20 minutes to complete. Other participants completed shorter versions of the questionnaire.

The results of the study indicated that gay and bisexual men have made significant changes in their sexual practices since the beginning of the AIDS epidemic. However, more than one-quarter of the men were still engaging in unprotected anal sex (a high-risk sexual activity) at least at times. Men who were more knowledgeable about the way HIV is transmitted were less likely to engage in high-risk sexual activities. The researchers also found regional differences and differences between English-speaking and French-speaking men. For example, men in smaller communities were more likely to engage in unprotected anal sex.

In evaluating this study, one can see that it was done more carefully and according to better scientific standards than many other surveys. The sampling was done carefully, and all regions of the country were represented. The researchers enlisted community support and cooperation and thus had a low refusal rate from potential participants. Although the results are generalizable to the population of gay and bisexual men who socialize in gay-identified establishments, the sample cannot be considered random or representative of all gay men in Canada. It omits covert gays and those gay men who do not socialize in gay-identified venues. Gay men with a low education level are not well represented. This research raises the point that studies of special populations defined by their sexual behaviour—such as homosexuals or bisexuals or fetishists—are essentially impossible to do in any kind of representative fashion. It is impossible to identify all the people in the population in the first place, and therefore it is impossible to sample them properly. In contrast, it is samples of the general population, such as the NHSLS or the national British or French studies, that are more feasible, although not easy, to obtain.

■ Media Content Analysis

To this point we have focused on methods used to analyze people's responses. Yet we also have recog-

Figure 3.4 Precise methods have been developed for analyzing the content of the media.

nized the profound impact of the mass media on Canadians' sexuality. To be able to understand this impact, we need to be able to analyze the media. As an example, let's suppose that your friend Rachel says that it is deeply disturbing that women are shown in nothing but traditional roles on prime-time TV, and this situation hasn't improved a bit over the years. Your other friend Monique disagrees, saying that there may still be some traditional images of women, but there are many examples of women in nontraditional roles such as doctors, and the media's portrayals of women have changed a lot over the years. How can you decide who is right? Arguing won't settle the debate. However, you could use a technique called **content analysis** to analyze how the media portray women today and how they have portrayed women in the past (Reinharz, 1992; Weber, 1990).

Content analysis refers to a set of procedures used to make valid inferences about text. The "text" might be romance novels, advice columns in *Chatelaine* magazine, lyrics from rap music, movies, or prime-time television programs. As it turns out, many of the same methodological issues discussed earlier also come into play with content analysis. Below, we have used a recently published study on depictions of sex and rape in popular films to exemplify these issues (Bufkin & Eschholz, 2000).

Sampling is one such issue. The first thing the researchers conducting this study needed to do was define the population. Were they interested in all films or particular types of films? Next, they needed to define the time period of interest: films

released in the current year, the past 5 years, the past 10 years, and so on. Finally, they needed to decide whether to analyze all films that met these criteria or a subsample of these films, and whether to analyze the entire film or selected parts of the film. The researchers decided to include the 50 top-grossing films in the United States in 1996 in their sample.

The next step is to create a coding scheme. First, the researchers needed to define the recording unit—was it the film, the scene, particular behaviours, or specific statements? The authors chose to use two units of analysis: the movie and the sex scene. Next, perhaps more importantly, they needed to define coding categories. Creating the coding scheme involves defining the basic content categories, the presence or absence of which will be recorded; the coding categories used depend on the research questions. In this instance, the researchers categorized sex scenes as heterosexual or homosexual and consensual or rape. They had to define what observable behaviours count as "sex"; they used a broad definition of sex including not only depictions of sexual activities but also sexual intercourse that was implied; for example, when characters were shown in bed after sexual intercourse. There were other categories used for categorizing rape scenes, including the type of rape and whether the offender was punished for the crime.

Researchers doing content analysis must demonstrate that their data are reliable and not biased. Usually a measure called **intercoder** or **interrater reliability** is used. Two or more trained individuals independently code all or some of the text in the sample. This is done to ensure that the coding is accurate and the coder is not either overreporting (e.g., recording scenes as rape when they did not actually include rape) or underreporting (e.g., failing to record scenes that include forced intercourse as rape scenes). To give a measure of the interrater reliability, the researcher computes a correlation or percentage agreement between the two coders' results. In this study, the interrater reliability for the occurrence of rape was a correla-

Content analysis: A set of procedures used to make valid inferences about text.
Intercoder or interrater reliability: In content analysis, the correlation or percentage of agreement between two coders independently rating the same texts.

tion of 0.98. This is very high, since if the coders agreed exactly the correlation would be 1.0.

Content analysis is a powerful scientific technique that allows us to know how the media portray sexuality. For example, in this study researchers found that—contrary to common perceptions that most movies contain sex—60 percent of the movies in this sample did not show a single sex scene. They found a total of 30 sex scenes, of which five were rapes.

■ Laboratory Studies Using Direct Observations of Sexual Behaviour

The numerous problems associated with using self-reports of sexual behaviour in scientific research have been discussed. The major alternative to using self-reports is to make direct observations of sexual behaviour in the laboratory. These direct observations overcome the major problems of self-reports: purposeful distortion, inaccurate memory, and inability of people to estimate correctly or describe certain aspects of their behaviour. The pioneering example of this approach is Masters and Johnson's work on the physiology of sexual response.

Masters and Johnson: The Physiology of Sexual Response

William Masters began his research on the physiology of sexual response in 1954. No one had ever studied human sexual behaviour in the laboratory before, so he had to develop all the necessary research techniques from scratch. He began by interviewing 188 female prostitutes, as well as 27 male prostitutes working for a homosexual clientele. They gave him important preliminary data in which they "described many methods for elevating and controlling sexual tensions and demonstrated innumerable variations in stimulative techniques," some of which were useful

VIDEO

Watch the "Masters and Johnson" video in Chapter 3 of your CD to learn more about this groundbreaking research team.

in the later program of therapy for sexual disorders.

Meanwhile, Masters began setting up his laboratory and equipping it with the necessary instruments: an electrocardiograph to measure changes in heart rate over the sexual cycle, an electromyograph to measure muscular contractions in the body during sexual response, and a pH meter to measure the acidity of the vagina during the various stages of sexual response.

Sampling

Masters made a major breakthrough when he decided that it should be possible to recruit normal participants from the general population and have them engage in sexual behaviour in the laboratory, where their behaviour and physiological responses could be carefully observed and measured. This approach had never been used before, as even the daring Kinsey had settled for people's verbal reports of their behaviour.

Most of the research participants were obtained from the local community simply by word of mouth. Masters let it be known in the medical school and university community that he needed volunteers for laboratory studies of human sexual response. Some people volunteered because of their belief in the importance of the research. Some, of course, came out of curiosity or because they were exhibitionists; they were weeded out in the initial interviews. Participants were paid for their hours in the laboratory, as is typical in medical research, so many medical students and graduate students participated because it was a way to earn money.

Initially, all prospective participants were given detailed interviews by Masters and his colleague Virginia Johnson. People who had histories of emotional problems or who seemed uncomfortable with the topic of sex either failed to come back after this interview or were eliminated even if they were willing to proceed. Participants were also assured that the anonymity and confidentiality of their participation would be protected carefully. In all, 694 people participated in the laboratory studies reported in *Human Sexual Response*. The men ranged in age from 21 to 89, while the women ranged from 18 to 78. A total of 276 married couples participated, as well as 106 women and 36 men who were unmarried when they entered the research program. The unmarried persons were helpful mainly in the studies that did not require sexual intercourse, as for example studies of the ejaculatory mechanism in males and of the effects of sexual arousal on the positioning of the diaphragm in the vagina.

Certainly the group of people Masters and Johnson studied were not a random sample of the population of the United States. In fact, one might imagine that people who would agree to participate in such research would be rather unusual. The data indicate that they were more educated than the general population, and the sample was mostly white, with only a few ethnic minority persons participating. Paying the participants probably helped broaden the sample since it attracted some people who simply needed the money. The sample omitted two notable types of people: those who were not sexually experienced or did not respond to sexual stimulation and those who were unwilling to have their sexual behaviour studied in the laboratory. Therefore, the results Masters and Johnson obtained might not generalize to such people.

Just exactly how critical is this sampling problem to the validity of the research? Masters and Johnson were not particularly concerned about it because they assumed that the processes they were studying are normative; that is, they work in essentially the same way in all people. This assumption is commonly made in medical research. For example, a researcher who is studying the digestive process does not worry that the sample is composed of all medical students, since the assumption is that digestion works the same way in all human beings. If this assumption is also true for the physiology of sexual response, then all people respond similarly, and it does not matter that the sample is not random. Whether this assumption is correct remains to be seen (see Chapter 9 for further critiques). The sampling problem, however, does mean that Masters and Johnson could not make statistical conclusions on the basis of their research; for example, they could not say that X percent of all women have multiple orgasms. Any percentages would be specific to their sample and could not be generalized to the rest of the population.

In defence of their sampling techniques, even if they had identified an initial probability sample they would still almost surely have had a very high refusal rate, probably higher than in survey research, and the probability sample would have been ruined. At present, this seems to be an unsolvable problem in this type of research.

Data Collection Techniques

After they were accepted for the project, participants proceeded to the laboratory phase of the study. First, they had a "practice session," in which they engaged in sexual activity in the laboratory in complete privacy, with no data being recorded and no researchers present. The purpose of this was to allow the participants to become comfortable with engaging in sexual behaviour in a laboratory setting.

The physical responses of the participants were then recorded during sexual intercourse, masturbation, and "artificial coition." Masters and Johnson made an important technical advance with the development of the artificial coition technique. In it, a female participant stimulates herself with an artificial penis constructed of clear plastic; it is powered by an electric motor, and the woman can adjust the depth and frequency of the thrust. There is a light and a recording apparatus inside the artificial penis, so the changes occurring inside the vagina can be photographed.

Measures such as these avoid the problems of distortion that are possible with self-reports. They also answer much different questions. That is, it would be impossible from such measures to tell whether the person had had any homosexual experiences or how frequently he or she masturbated. Instead, they ascertain how the body responds to sexual stimulation, with a kind of accuracy and detail that would be impossible to obtain through self-reports.

One final potential problem also deserves mention. It has to do with the problems of laboratory studies: That is, do people respond the same sexually in the laboratory as they do in the privacy of their own homes?

Ethical Considerations

Masters and Johnson were attentive to ethical principles. They were careful to use informed consent. Potential participants were given detailed explanations of the kinds of things they would be required to do in the research and were given ample opportunity at all stages to withdraw from the research if they so desired. Furthermore, Masters and Johnson eliminated people who appeared too anxious or distressed during the preliminary interviews.

It is also possible that participating in the research itself might have been harmful in some way to some people. Masters and Johnson were particularly concerned with the long-term effects of participating in the research. Accordingly, they made follow-up contacts with the participants at five-year intervals. In no case did a participant report developing a sexual disorder (for example, erectile dysfunction). In fact, many of the couples reported specific ways in which participating in the research enriched their marriages. Thus the available data seem to indicate that such research does not harm the participants and may in some ways benefit them, not to mention the benefit to society that results from gaining information in such an important area.

In sum, direct observations of sexual behaviour of the type done by Masters and Johnson have some distinct advantages but also some disadvantages compared with survey-type research. Their research avoids the problems of self-reports and is capable of answering much more detailed physiological questions than self-reports could. But the research is costly and time-consuming, making large samples impractical; furthermore, a high refusal rate is probably inevitable, so probability samples are impossible to obtain.

■ Participant-Observer Studies

A research method used by anthropologists and sociologists is the **participant-observer technique.** In this type of research, the scientist tries to become a part of the community to be studied, and she or he makes observations from inside the community. In the study of sexual behaviour, the researcher thus may be able to get direct observations of sexual behaviour combined with interview data.

Examples of this type of research are studies of sexual behaviour in other cultures, such as those done in Mangaia, Mehinaku, and Inis Beag, which were discussed in Chapter 1. Two other examples are Laud Humphreys' study of the tearoom trade and Charles Moser's study of S/M (sadomasochistic) parties.

> **Participant-observer technique:** A research method in which the scientist becomes part of the community to be studied and makes observations from inside the community.

Humphreys: The Tearoom Trade

Sociologist Laud Humphreys (1970) conducted a participant-observer study of impersonal sex between men in public places. Briefly, Humphreys acted as a lookout while men engaged in sex acts in public rest rooms ("tearooms"); his job was to sound a warning if police or other intruders approached. This permitted Humphreys to make direct observations of the sexual behaviour. He also got the licence-plate numbers of the men involved, traced them, and later interviewed them in their homes under the pretext of conducting a routine survey.

Humphreys obtained a wealth of information from the study, but in so doing he violated several ethical principles of behavioural research. He had no informed consent from his subjects; they were never even aware of the fact that they were participants in research, much less of the nature of the research. Thus this study was quite controversial.

S/M Parties

Sex researcher Charles Moser observed S/M (sadomasochistic) interactions in semi-public settings in the United States, attending more than 200 S/M parties (Moser, 1998). Parties are typically highly scripted. The person who gives the party may advertise it widely, for example on the Internet, or may issue personal invitations to only a very selected list. The parties may have a particular theme, such as female dominant/male submissive only or women only. The party might be held at a person's home or in a rented space.

Each party has a particular set of rules, which vary from one party to another, and guests may be required to sign a written agreement to follow the rules. Issues covered in these rules include who may talk to whom (can a submissive be spoken to?), who may play with whom, who may have sex with whom, prohibited S/M or sexual behaviours, what constitutes safer sex, not blocking equipment by sitting on it, and so on. Drunkenness is never acceptable; some parties allow wine or beer, but others ban all alcohol.

Some individuals plan to have a first "date" at a party. Parties clearly have the function of ensuring safety for participants, since others are always present if an interaction goes too far. Potential partners negotiate what kind of interaction they desire—for example, pain versus humiliation.

Perhaps most interesting is the fact that coitus

and genitally focused activity designed to produce orgasm are very rare at these parties. The participants describe the S/M experience as highly sexual, but orgasm typically is not the goal.

Moser did not report that he obtained informed consent from the people he observed. However, their behaviour was public, leading to a relaxation of human subjects regulations. In his report, he was careful not to divulge any identifying information about individuals.

■ Experimental Sex Research

All the studies discussed so far have had one thing in common: they were all studies of people's sexual behaviour as it occurs naturally, conducted by means of either self-reports or direct observations. Such reports are **correlational studies;** that is, at best the data they obtain can tell us that certain factors are related. They cannot tell us what *causes* various aspects of sexual behaviour.

For instance, suppose we conduct a survey and find that women who masturbated to orgasm before marriage are more likely to have a high consistency of orgasm in marriage than women who did not. From this it would be tempting to conclude that practice in masturbating to orgasm causes women to have more orgasms in heterosexual sex. Unfortunately, this is not a legitimate conclusion to draw from the data, since many other factors might also explain the results. For example, it could be that some women have a higher sex drive than others, which causes them to masturbate and also have orgasms in heterosexual sex. Therefore, the most we can conclude is that masturbation experience is related to (or correlated with) orgasm consistency in marital sex.

An alternative method that does allow researchers to determine the causes of various aspects of behaviour is the **experiment.** According to its technical definition, in an experiment one factor must be manipulated while all other factors are held constant. Thus any differences among the groups of people who received different treatments on that one factor can be said to be caused by that factor. For obvious reasons, most experimental research is conducted in the laboratory.

As an example of an experiment, let us consider a study that investigated whether being interviewed face-to-face causes children to under-report their

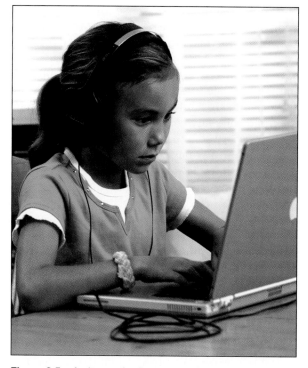

Figure 3.5 An innovation in surveys of children is the use of "talking computers" to ask questions, with the child entering her answers using the mouse or the keyboard.

sexual experiences (Romer et al., 1997). The participants were approximately 400 low-income children between the ages of 9 and 15. Some were assigned to a face-to-face interview with an experienced adult interviewer of their own gender. Others were assigned to be interviewed by a "talking computer," which had the same questions programmed into it. The questions appeared on the screen and, simultaneously, came through headphones for those who were not good readers. Presumably in the talking computer condition, the

Correlational study: A study in which the researcher does not manipulate variables but rather studies naturally occurring relationships (correlations) among variables.
Experiment: A type of research study in which one variable (the independent variable) is manipulated by the experimenter while all other factors are held constant; the researcher can then study the effects of the independent variable on some measured variable (the dependent variable); the researcher is permitted to make causal inferences about the effects of the independent variable on the dependent variable.

child feels more of a sense of privacy and anonymity and therefore responds more truthfully.

Among 13-year-old boys interviewed by the talking computer, 76 percent said they had "had sex," compared with only 50 percent of the boys in the face-to-face interview. Forty-eight percent of 13-year-old girls interviewed by computer said they had had sex, compared with 25 percent of those interviewed by a human. The children clearly reported more sexual activity to the computer than to a human interviewer.

In the language of experimental design, the *independent variable* (manipulated variable) was the type of interview (computer or human interviewer). The *dependent variable* (the measured variable) was whether they had had sex (there were a number of other dependent variables as well, but a discussion of them would take us too far afield).

The results indicated that those interviewed by humans reported significantly less sexual activity than those interviewed by computer. Because the research design was experimental, we can make causal inferences. We can say confidently that the type of interview influenced the amount of reporting. That is, we can say that the type of interview had an effect on children's answers. We might also say that a face-to-face interview causes children to underreport their activity. That statement is a bit shakier than the previous one, because it assumes that the answers given to the talking computer were "true." It is possible that children overreported or exaggerated in responding to the computer and that their answers to the human interviewer were accurate, although this interpretation seems rather far-fetched.

Experimental sex research permits us to make much more powerful statements about the causes of various kinds of sexual phenomena. As for disadvantages, much of the experimental sex research, including the study described here, still relies on self-reports. Experimental sex research is time-consuming and costly, and it can generally be done only on small samples of participants. Sometimes in their efforts to control all variables except the independent variable, researchers control too much. Finally, experiments cannot address some of the most interesting, but most complex, questions in the field of sexual behaviour, such as what factors cause people to develop heterosexual or homosexual orientations.

■ Some Statistical Concepts

Before you can understand reports of sex research, you must understand some basic statistical concepts.

Average

Suppose we get data from a sample of common-law couples on how many times per week they have sexual intercourse. How can we summarize the data? One way to do this is to compute some average value; this will tell us how often, on the average, these people have intercourse. In sex research, the number that is usually calculated is either the mean or the median although the mode is sometimes used; all of these give us an indication of approximately where the average value for that group of people is. The **mean** is calculated by adding up all the scores and dividing by the number of people. The **median** is the score that splits the sample in half, with half the respondents scoring below that number and half scoring above it. The **mode** is the score with the greatest number of responses.

Variability

In addition to having an indication of the average for the sample of respondents, it is also interesting to know how much variability there is from one respondent to the next in the numbers reported. That is, it is one thing to say that the average common-law couple in a sample had intercourse 3 times per week, with a range in the sample from 2 to 4 times per week, and it is quite another thing to say that the average was 3 times per week, with a range from 0 to 15 times per week. In both cases the mean is the same, but in the first there is little variability, and in the second there is a great deal of variability. These two alternatives are shown graphically in Figure 3.6. There is great variability in virtually all kinds of sexual behaviour.

Average versus Normal

It is interesting and informative to report the average frequency of a particular sexual behav-

---

Mean: The average of respondents' scores calculated by adding the scores and dividing by the number of people.
Median: The middle score.
Mode: The most frequent score.

Figure 3.6   Two hypothetical graphs of the frequency of intercourse for common-law couples in a sample. In both, the average frequency is about three times per week, but in *(a)* there is little variability (almost everyone has a frequency between two and four times per week), whereas in *(b)* there is great variability (the frequency ranges from zero to 15 or more times per week). The graph for most sexual behaviour looks like *(b)*, with great variability.

iour, but this also introduces the danger that people will confuse "average" with "normal." That is, there is a tendency, when reading a statistic like "The average person has intercourse twice per week," to think of one's own sexual behaviour, compare it with that average, and then conclude that one is abnormal if one differs much from the average. If you read that statistic and your frequency of intercourse is only once a week, you may begin to worry that you are undersexed or that you are not getting as much as you should. If you are having intercourse seven times per week, you might begin worrying that you are oversexed. Such conclusions are a mistake, first because they can make you miserable and second because there is so much variability in sexual behaviour that any behaviour (or frequency or length of time) within a wide

range is perfectly normal. Don't confuse average with normal.

Incidence versus Frequency

In sex statistics, the terms "incidence" and "frequency" are often used. **Incidence** refers to the percentage of people who have engaged in a certain behaviour. **Frequency** refers to how often people do something. Thus we might say that the incidence of masturbation among males is 92 percent (meaning that 92 percent of all males masturbate at least once in their lives), whereas the average frequency of masturbation among males between the ages of 16 and 20 is about once per week.

A closely related concept is that of cumulative incidence. If we consider a sexual behaviour according to the age at which each person in the sample first engaged in it, the *cumulative incidence* refers to the percentage of people who have engaged in that behaviour before a certain age. Thus the cumulative incidence of masturbation in males might be 10 percent by age 11, 25 percent by age 12, 80 percent by age 15, and 95 percent by age 20. Graphs of cumulative incidence always begin in the lower left-hand corner and move toward the upper right-hand corner. An example of a cumulative-incidence curve is shown in Figure 3.7.

Correlation

In this chapter the concept of correlation has already been mentioned several times—for example, test–retest reliability is measured by the correlation between people's answer to a question with their answer to the same question a week or two later—and the concept of correlation will reappear in later chapters.

The term "correlation" is used by laypeople in contexts such as the following: "There seems to be a correlation here between how warm the days are and how fast the corn is growing." But what do statisticians mean by the term "correlation"? A **correlation** is a number that measures the relationship between two variables. A correlation can be positive or nega-

---

Incidence: The percentage of people giving a particular response.
Frequency: How often a person does something.
Correlation: A number that measures the relationship between two variables.

tive. A positive correlation occurs when there is a positive relationship between the two variables, that is, people who have high scores on one variable tend to have high scores on the other variable—low scores go with low scores. A negative correlation occurs when there is an opposite relationship between the two variables; that is, people with high scores on one variable tend to have low scores on the other variable. We might want to know, for example, whether there is a correlation between the number of years a couple has been together and the frequency with which they have sexual intercourse. In this case we might expect that there would be a negative correlation, and that is just what researchers have found. That is, the *greater* the number of years together, the *lower* the frequency of intercourse. As another example, we might want to know whether there is a correlation between people's sexual attitudes and their sexual behaviour, specifically whether people who hold more permissive attitudes about premarital sex have more premarital partners. In this case we expect a positive correlation in the sense that the people who score high on the measure of permissive attitudes are expected to have more partners and that people who score low on the measure of permissiveness are expected to have fewer partners.

Correlations range between +1.0 and −1.0. A correlation of +1.0 indicates a perfect positive relationship between two variables, meaning that the person in the sample who scores highest on one variable also has the highest score on the other variable, the person with the second highest score on the first variable also has the second highest score on the other variable, and so on. A correlation of 0 indicates no relationship between the two variables. Knowing a person's score on one variable tells us nothing about whether the person will have a high or low score on the other variable. Positive correlations between 0 and +1.0—for example, +.62—say that the relationship is positive but not a perfect relationship. A

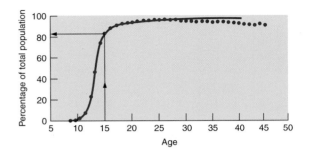

Figure 3.7   A cumulative-incidence curve for masturbation in males. From the graph, you can read off the percentage of males who report having masturbated by a given age. For example, about 82 percent have masturbated to orgasm by age 15.

correlation of −1.0 means that there is a perfect negative correlation between the two variables. That is, the person in the sample with the highest score on variable *X* has the lowest score on variable *Y*, the person with the second highest score on variable *X* has the second lowest score on variable *Y*, and so on.

Returning to the example of test–retest reliability discussed earlier in this chapter, suppose we administer a questionnaire to a sample of adults. One of the questions asks, "How many times did you masturbate to orgasm during the month of September?" We ask this question of the sample on October 1 and again on October 8. If each person in the sample gives us exactly the same answer on October 1 and on October 8, the correlation between the two variables (the number given on October 1 and the number given on October 8) would be +1.0 and the test–retest reliability would be a perfect +1.0. In fact, test–retest reliabilities for questions about sex typically range between +.60 and +.90, indicating that people's answers on the two occasions are not identical but are very similar.

■ ■ ■ SUMMARY

Knowledge of the major methods that have been used in sex research and of the problems and merits associated with each is necessary for understanding and evaluating sex research. Sex research can use quantitative or qualitative methods.

Ideally, quantitative sex research should employ probability sampling techniques.

Large-scale surveys of sexual behaviour generally rely on people's self-reports, which may be inaccurate because of purposeful distortion, problems of memory, or an inability to estimate some of the information requested. Direct observations of sexual behaviour avoid these problems, but they lead to an even more restricted sample. They also answer questions that are somewhat different from those answered by surveys. Web-based surveys offer new opportunities for sex research.

In all behavioural research, the ethical principles of informed consent, protection from harm, and justice, must be observed, although historically some sex researchers did not do this.

No major national sex surveys have been conducted in Canada. However, there are two large-scale U.S. surveys of sexual behaviour: Kinsey's interview study and the recent NHSLS, which was based on probability sampling. The Canada Youth, Sexual Health, and HIV/AIDS Study assessed adolescent sexuality across Canada. It is difficult to draw any general conclusions from large magazine surveys because the samples are so restricted.

Canadian studies of special populations include a qualitative study of exotic dancers by Maticka-Tyndale, a survey of First Nations Peoples headed by Myers, and a survey of men who have sex with men, also headed by Myers.

In media content analysis, researchers use systematic coding categories to analyze what is represented in the media, such as on television, in romance novels, or in magazine ads.

In participant-observer studies, the scientist becomes a part of the community to be studied, and uses a combination of direct observations and interviewing. Examples are studies of sexual behaviour in other cultures, Humphreys' study of the tearoom trade, and Moser's study of S/M parties.

In experimental sex research, the goal is to discover what factors cause or influence various aspects of sexual behaviour. The researcher manipulates an independent variable and measures a dependent variable.

The following statistical terms were introduced: average, mean, median, mode, variability, incidence, frequency, and correlation.

■ ■ ■ QUESTIONS FOR THOUGHT, DISCUSSION, AND DEBATE

1. Find a recent sex survey in a magazine. Evaluate the quality of the study, using concepts you have learned in this chapter.

2. Of the research techniques in this chapter—surveys, laboratory studies using direct observations, media content analysis, participant-observer studies, experiments—which do you think is best for learning about human sexuality? Why?

3. You want to conduct a survey, using face-to-face interviews, to determine whether there are differences between Asian Canadian and white Canadian teenagers ages 15 to 19 in their sexual behaviour and attitudes. In what ways would you tailor the research methods to make them culturally sensitive?

4. Imagine that you have been hired by your college or university to produce a report on the patterns of sexual behaviour of the students there, with the goal of helping the administration plan better in areas such as health services and counselling. You are given a generous budget for data collection. How would you go about collecting the data you would need in order to produce a truly excellent report?

■ ■ ■ SUGGESTIONS FOR FURTHER READING

Matsumoto, David. (1994). *Cultural influences on research methods and statistics.* Pacific Grove, CA: Brooks/Cole. This concise book, written for undergraduates, explains principles of cross-cultural research and how one should modify research methods depending on the culture being studied.

Michael, Robert T., Gagnon, John H., Laumann, Edward O., & Kolata, Gina. (1994). *Sex in America: A definitive survey.* Boston: Little, Brown. This book reports the results of the NHSLS, and is written for the general public.

Wiederman, Michael W. (2001). *Understanding sexuality research.* Belmont, CA: Wadsworth. This slim volume, written for undergraduates, takes up where the present chapter leaves off and offers an excellent analysis of method-ological issues in sex research, with interest-ing examples.

Online **LearningCentre**

For Review Questions, Web Resources, and other learning and study tools, visit the *Understanding Human Sexuality* Online Learning Centre at www.mcgrawhill.ca/college/hyde.

Sexual Anatomy

CHAPTER HIGHLIGHTS

Men and women, all in all, behave just like our basic sexual elements. If you watch single men on a weekend night they really act very much like sperm—all disorganized, bumping into their friends, swimming in the wrong direction.

"I was first."

"Let me through."

"You're on my tail."

"That's my spot."

We're like the Three Billion Stooges.

But the egg is very cool: "Well, who's it going to be? I can divide. I can wait a month. I'm not swimming anywhere."*

The women's health movement has emphasized that women need to know more about their bodies. Actually, that is a good principle for everyone to follow. The current trend is away from the elitist view that only a select group of people—physicians—should understand the functioning of the body and toward the view that everyone needs more information about his or her own body. The purpose of this chapter is to provide basic information about the structure and functions of the parts of the body that are involved in sexuality and reproduction. Some readers may anticipate that this will be a boring exercise. Everyone, after all, knows what a penis is and what a vagina is. But even today, we find some bright college and university students who think a woman's urine passes out through her vagina. And how many of you know what the epididymis and the seminiferous tubules are? Even if you know, keep reading. You may find out a few interesting things about the penis and the vagina that you were not aware of.

■ Female Sexual Organs

The female sexual organs can be classified into two categories: the *external organs* and the *internal organs*.

External Organs

The external genitals of the female consist of the clitoris, the mons pubis, the inner lips, the outer

*Jerry Seinfeld. (1993). *SeinLanguage*. New York: Bantam Books, p. 17.

lips, and the vaginal opening (see Figure 4.1). Collectively, they are known as the **vulva** ("crotch"; other terms such as "cunt" and "pussy" may refer either to the vulva or to the vagina, and some eth-

Vulva (VULL-vuh): The collective term for the external genitals of the female.

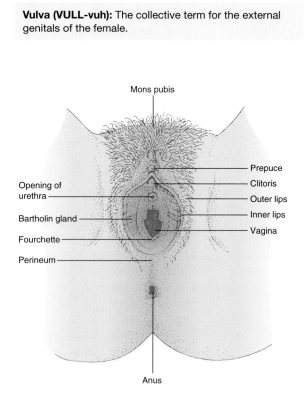

Figure 4.1   The vulva: The external genitals of the female.

Figure 4.2 The shape of the vulva varies widely from one woman to the next.

nic groups use "cock" for the vulva—slang, alas, is not so precise as scientific language).[1] "Vulva" is a wonderful term but, unfortunately, it tends to be underused—the term, that is. The appearance of the vulva varies greatly from one woman to another (see Figure 4.2).

The Clitoris

The **clitoris** is a sensitive organ that is exceptionally important in female sexual response (Figure 4.3). It consists of the tip, a knob of tissue situated externally in front of the vaginal opening and the urethral opening; a shaft consisting of two corpora cavernosa (spongy bodies similar to those in the male's penis) that extends perhaps an inch into the body; and two crura, longer spongy bodies that lie deep in the body and run from the tip of the clitoris to either side of the vagina, under the major lips (Clemente, 1987). Some refer to the entire structure as having a "wishbone" shape. Close to the crura are the vestibular bulbs, which will be discussed in the section on internal organs.

As discussed in Chapter 5, female sexual organs and male sexual organs develop from similar tissue before birth; thus we can speak of the organs of one

gender as being *homologous* (in the sense of developing from the same source) to the organs of the other gender. The female's clitoris is homologous to the male's penis; that is, both develop from the same embryonic tissue. The clitoris has a structure similar to that of the penis in that both have corpora cavernosa. The clitoris varies in size from one woman to the next, much as the penis varies in size from man to man. Also, the clitoris, like the penis, is erectile. Its erection is possible because its internal structure contains corpora cavernosa that fill with blood, as the similar structures in the penis do. The corpora cavernosa and the mechanism of erection will be considered in more detail in the discussion of the male sexual organs. Like the penis, the clitoris has a rich supply of nerve endings, making it very sensitive to stroking. Most women find it to be more sensitive to erotic stimulation than any other part of the body.

The clitoris is unique in that it is the only part of the sexual anatomy with no known reproductive function. All the other sexual organs serve sexual and reproductive functions. For example, not only is the vagina used for sexual intercourse, but it also receives the sperm and serves as

For an example of how a woman may become more familiar with her external genitals, watch the "Genital Self-Examination" video in Chapter 4 of your CD.

[1]For a discussion of slang terms for female and male genitals see Braun and Kitzinger (2001).

Clitoris (KLIT-or-is): A small, highly sensitive sexual organ in the female, found in front of the vaginal entrance.

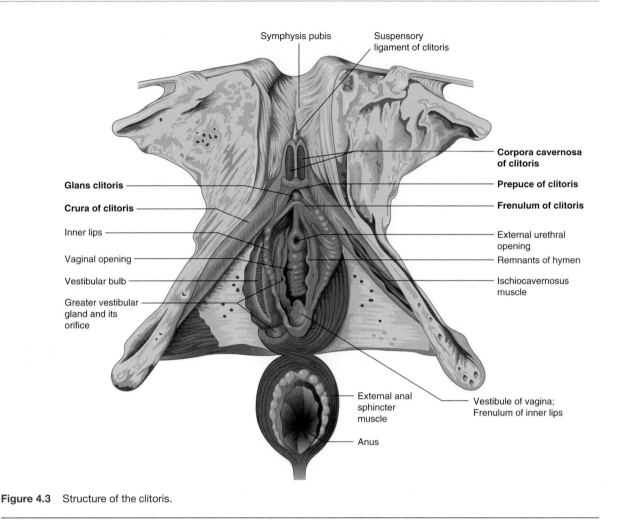

Figure 4.3 Structure of the clitoris.

the passageway through which the baby travels during childbirth. The penis not only produces sexual arousal and pleasure but also is responsible for ejaculation and impregnation. The clitoris clearly has an important function in producing sexual arousal. Unlike the other sexual organs, however, it appears to have no direct function in reproduction.

The Mons

Other parts of the vulva are the mons pubis, the inner lips, and the outer lips. The **mons pubis** (also called the *mons* or the *mons veneris,* for "mountain of Venus") is the rounded, fatty pad of tissue, cov-

ered with pubic hair, at the front of the body. It lies on top of the pubic bones (which come together in the centre at a point called the *pubic symphysis*).

The Labia

The **outer lips** (or *labia majora,* for "major lips") are rounded pads of fatty tissue lying along both sides of the vaginal opening; they are covered with pubic hair. The **inner lips** (or *labia minora,* for "minor lips") are two hairless folds of skin lying between the outer lips and running right along the edge of the vaginal opening. Sometimes they are folded

Mons pubis (PYOO-bis): The fatty pad of tissue under the pubic hair.

Outer lips: Rounded pads of fatty tissue lying on either side of the vaginal entrance.
Inner lips: Thin folds of skin lying on either side of the vaginal entrance.

Figure 4.4 Twenty-eight African nations practise some form of ritualized genital cutting of young girls as an initiation into womanhood. Clitoridectomy is also practised in Muslim countries outside Africa, and was practised in North America during the Victorian era (see In Focus 4.1).

over, concealing the vaginal opening until they are spread apart. The inner lips extend forward and come together in front, forming the clitoral hood. The inner and outer lips are well supplied with nerve endings and thus are also important in sexual stimulation and arousal.

A pair of small glands, the **Bartholin glands**, lie just inside the inner lips (refer to Figure 4.1). Their function is unknown, and they are of interest only because they sometimes become infected.[2]

A few more landmarks should be noted (Figure 4.1). The place where the inner lips come together behind the vaginal opening is called the *fourchette*. The area of skin between the vaginal opening and the anus is called the **perineum.** The vaginal opening itself is sometimes called the **introitus.** Notice also that the urinary opening lies about midway between the clitoris and the vaginal opening. Thus urine does not pass out through the clitoris (as might be expected from analogy with the male) or through the vagina, but instead through a separate pathway, the *urethra*, with a separate opening.

The Vulvar Vestibule

The area enclosed by the inner lips is called the **vestibule** ("entranceway"). It contains the openings to the vagina and the urethra. This area is highly sensitive to pleasurable stimulation because it is well-supplied with nerve endings. However, some women develop vulvar vestibulitis, in which the vestibule gets extremely sensitive and red such that any touch of the

[2]And there is a limerick about them:

There was a young man from Calcutta
Who was heard in his beard to mutter,
"If her Bartholin glands
Don't respond to my hands,
I'm afraid I shall have to use butter."

Actually, there is a biological fallacy in the limerick. Can you spot it? If not, see Chapter 9.

Bartholin glands: Two tiny glands located on either side of the vaginal entrance.
Perineum (pair-ih-NEE-um): The skin between the vaginal entrance and the anus.
Introitus: Another word for the vaginal entrance.
Vestibule: Area of the vulva enclosed by the inner lips.

In Focus 4.1

What Is Female Genital Cutting?

Today a worldwide sexual health controversy rages over female genital cutting (FGC, also known as female genital mutilation or FGM). FGC is practised in 28 African nations as well as in several countries in the Middle East and among Muslim populations in Indonesia and Malaysia. It is estimated to affect between 80 million and 110 million women worldwide. Typically girls are subjected to the procedure between the ages of 4 and 10, although sometimes it is done during infancy. Often the procedure is performed by a village woman, with no anaesthetic and under unsanitary conditions. If these practices seem remote to many North Americans, it is important to recognize that immigrant women from these countries now reside in North America. Moreover, some of these practices were performed in Britain and North America in the 1800s, during the Victorian era, to cure various "female weaknesses" such as masturbation. Currently there is a cult in the United States that practises genital surgeries such as removal of the outer lips, because they believe that the vulva is more beautiful and erotic that way.

FGC is practised in several forms, depending on the customs of the particular culture. The mildest form, called *sunna,* refers to the removal of just the clitoral hood (prepuce), not the clitoris; it is the only procedure that could legitimately be called "female circumcision," analogous to male circumcision. In its mildest form, it may involve only making a slit in the prepuce, not removing it. A second form of FGC is *excision* (sometimes known as clitoridectomy), which refers to complete removal of the clitoris and perhaps some of the inner lips. The most extreme form is *infibulation* or pharaonic circumcision (named for the pharaohs of Egypt, under whose reign the practice is said to have originated thousands of years ago). It involves the removal of the clitoris, all of the inner lips, and part of the outer lips; the raw edges of the outer lips are then stitched together to cover the urethral opening and the vaginal entrance, with only a small opening left for the passage of urine and menstrual fluid.

Infibulation poses severe health problems for women. Hemorrhaging may occur, leading to shock and even to bleeding to death. Because of the unsanitary conditions present during the procedure, tetanus and other infections are risks. Because the same instrument may be used on many girls, HIV and hepatitis B can be transmitted. A common problem is that the pain of the wound is so severe and the stitching so tight that the girl avoids urinating or cannot urinate properly, leading to urinary infections and other complications. A tightly infibulated woman can only urinate drop by drop, and her menstrual period may take 10 days and be extremely painful.

The sexual and reproductive health consequences are no less severe. Infibulation is an effective method for ensuring virginity until marriage, but on the wedding night the man must force an opening through stitching and scar tissue. This is painful and may take days; a midwife may be called to cut open the tissue. Some men report wounds to the penis as a result of attempts at intercourse with wives who have had FGC. Orgasm would be only a remote possibility for a woman whose clitoris has been removed. Infibulated women have a substantial risk of complications during childbirth. The scar must always be cut open to permit delivery and, if done too late, the baby may die. Women who have

area around the vaginal opening elicits moderate to severe pain. For women with vulvar vestibulitis, pain can result from genital touching during sexual activity and vaginal penetration, but also from biking, exercise, tight clothing, and tampon insertion.

Self-Knowledge

One important difference between the male sex organs and the female sex organs—and a difference that has some important psychological consequences—is that the female's external genitals are undergone FGC are also at higher risk of infections such as herpes and bacterial vaginosis.

In a study in the Sudan, 90 percent of the women said that they had had or would have these procedures performed on their daughters, and about half the women favoured the most severe procedures (Williams & Sobieszczyk, 1997). If these procedures are so harmful, why do they persist? Why do girls submit to them, and even ask for them, and why do their parents permit or even encourage it? The answer lies in the complex and powerful interplay of culture and gender. Being infibulated indicates not only virginity but also a woman's loyalty to and identification with her culture and its traditions, a particularly sensitive issue for people long dominated by European colonizers. A woman who is not infibulated is not marriageable in these cultures in which marriage is the only acceptable way of life for an adult woman. When those are the rules of the game, it is less surprising that girls submit or even want to be circumcised and that their parents require them to do it. Particular communities may also hold certain beliefs that make these procedures seem necessary. For example, in some areas there is a belief that the clitoris contains poison and can harm men during sexual intercourse and kill children during birth. Some Muslims mistakenly believe that it is required by their faith, although it is not mentioned in the Koran.

Infibulation raises a dilemma for Canadians. As a multicultural country, we generally encourage the approach of "cultural relativism," an openness to and appreciation of the customs of other cultures. FGC is definitely a custom of other cultures. If we apply standards of cultural relativism, we should say, "Great, if that's what people from those cultures want." However, the World Health Organization, as well as many of the organizations that regulate the practice of medicine in Canada, has condemned the practice of FGC. Both the parents who arrange FGC and the person who performs it may be charged with sexual assault and/or child abuse under Canadian law. Recent immigrants to Canada from Somalia and other areas of Africa may feel torn between loyalty to their native cultures and the realities of Canadian law in deciding about FGC for their daughters. In addition, many immigrant women from these areas who have been subjected to FGC before arriving in Canada may have physicians who are not knowledgeable about FGC. While physicians may cut open an infibulated woman to permit childbirth, they are not allowed to reconstruct the infibulation following childbirth, regardless of the wishes of the woman.

On a more hopeful note, a grass-roots movement of women has sprung up in a number of African nations, including Kenya, Gambia, Sudan, Somalia, and Nigeria, that is dedicated to eliminating these practices. Furthermore, to put matters into perspective, only about 15 percent of cultures that practise FGC do the severe form, infibulation. The remaining cultures practise the milder forms ranging from a slit in the prepuce to clitoridectomy. Although far more cultures practise male genital modification (such as circumcision, supercision, and subcision) than practise FGC, these procedures do not cause either the considerable daily discomfort or the health risks associated with FGC.

Sources: Almroth et al., 2001; Council on Scientific Affairs, 1995; Gregersen, 1996; Gruenbaum, 2000; Horowitz & Jackson, 1997; Kiragu, 1995; Lightfoot-Klein, 1993; Leonard, 2000; Morrison et al., 2001; Schroeder, 1994; Toubia, 1994, 1995; Williams & Sobieszyczyk, 1997.

much less visible than the male's. A male can view his external genitals directly either by looking down at them or by looking into a mirror while naked. Either of these two strategies for the female, however, will result at best in a view of the mons. The clitoris, the inner and outer lips, and the vaginal opening remain hidden. Indeed, many adult women have never taken a direct look at their own vulva. This obstacle can be overcome by the simple method of using a mirror. The genitals can be viewed either by putting a mirror on the floor and sitting in front of it or by standing up and putting one foot on the edge of a chair, bed, or something similar and holding the mirror up near the genitals (see Figure 4.5). We recommend that all women use a mirror to identify on their own bodies all the parts shown in Figure 4.1.

The Hymen

Before the internal structures are discussed, one other external structure deserves mention: the hymen. The **hymen** ("cherry," "maidenhead") is a thin membrane which, if present, partially covers the vaginal opening. The hymen may be one of a number of different types (see Figure 4.6), although it generally has some openings in it; otherwise the menstrual flow would not be able to pass out.[3] For many women the hymen is broken or stretched at the time of first intercourse as the penis moves into the vagina. This may cause bleeding and possibly some pain. Typically, though, it is an untraumatic occurrence and goes unnoticed in the excitement of the moment. For a woman who is very concerned about her hymen and what will happen to it at first coitus, there are two possible approaches. A physician can cut the hymen neatly so that it will not tear at the time of first intercourse, or the woman herself

[3]The rare condition in which the hymen is a tough tissue with no opening is called i*mperforate hymen* and can be corrected with fairly simple surgery.

> **Hymen (HYE-men):** A thin membrane that may partially cover the vaginal entrance.

Figure 4.5   Body education: The mirror exercise lets women see their own genitals. (Photograph by Hazel Hankin Photography.)

can stretch it by repeatedly inserting a finger into the vagina and pressing on it.

The hymen, and its destruction at first intercourse, has captured the interest of people in many cultures. In Europe during the Middle Ages, the lord might claim the right to deflower a peasant bride on her wedding night before passing her on to her husband (the practice is called *droit du*

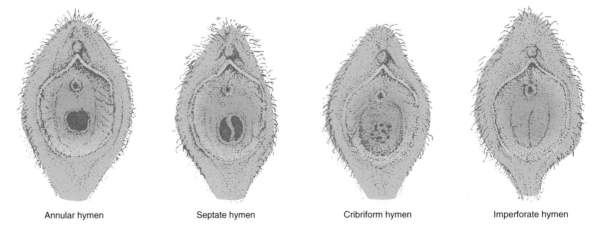

Annular hymen   Septate hymen   Cribriform hymen   Imperforate hymen

Figure 4.6   There are several types of hymens.

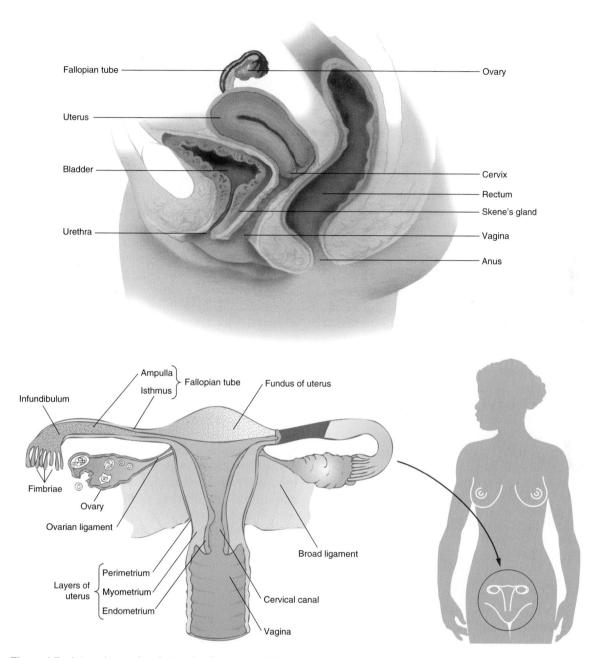

Figure 4.7 Internal sexual and reproductive organs of the female from a side view (top) and a front view.

seigneur in French for "right of the lord," and *jus primae noctis* in Latin for "law of the first night"). The hymen has been taken as evidence of virginity. Thus bleeding on the wedding night was proof that the bride had been delivered intact to the groom; the parading of the bloody bed sheets on the wedding night, a custom of the Kurds of the Middle East, is one ritual based on this belief.

Such practices rest on the assumption that a woman without a hymen is not a virgin. However, we now know that this is not true. Some girls are simply born without a hymen, and others may tear it in active sports such as horseback riding. Unfortunately, this means that in cultures that prize female virginity, some women have been humiliated unjustly for their lack of a hymen.

Internal Organs

The internal sex organs of the female consist of the vagina, the vestibular bulbs, the Skene's glands, the uterus, a pair of ovaries, and a pair of fallopian tubes (see Figure 4.7).

The Vagina

The **vagina** is the tube-shaped organ into which the penis is inserted during coitus; it also receives the ejaculate. Because it is the passageway through which a baby travels during birth, it is sometimes also called the *birth canal*. In the resting or unaroused state, the vagina is about 8 to 10 centimetres (3 to 4 inches) long and tilts slightly backward from the bottom to the top. At the bottom it ends in the vaginal opening, or *introitus*. At the top it connects with the cervix (the lower part of the uterus). It is a very flexible organ that works somewhat like a balloon. In the resting state its walls lie against each other like the sides of an uninflated balloon; during arousal it expands like an inflated balloon, allowing space to accommodate the penis.

The walls of the vagina have three layers. The inner layer, the *vaginal mucosa,* is a mucous membrane similar to the inner lining of the mouth. The middle layer is muscular, and the outer layer forms a covering. The walls of the vagina are

Vagina (vuh-JINE-uh): The tube-shaped organ in the female into which the penis is inserted during coitus and through which a baby passes during birth.

extremely elastic and are capable of expanding to the extent necessary during intercourse and childbirth, although with age they become thinner and less flexible.

The nerve supply of the vagina is mostly to the lower one-third, near the introitus. That part is sensitive to erotic stimulation. The inner two-thirds of the vagina contains almost no nerve endings and is therefore relatively insensitive except to feelings of deep pressure. Some women have a spot on the front wall of the vagina that is more sensitive than the rest of the vagina, but even it is not nearly so sensitive as the inner lips, outer lips, or clitoris (Schultz et al., 1989). This spot is referred to by some as the G-spot (see Chapter 9).

The number of slang terms for the vagina (for example, "beaver," "cunt") and the frequency of their usage testify to its power of fascination across the ages. One concern has been with size: whether some vaginas are too small or too large. As noted earlier, though, the vagina is highly elastic and expandable. Thus, at least in principle, any penis can fit into any vagina. The penis is, after all, not nearly so large as a baby's head, which manages to fit through the vagina. The part of the vagina that is most responsible for the male's sensation, that is "tight," "too tight," or "too loose," is the introitus. One of the things that can stretch the introitus is childbirth; indeed, there is a considerable difference in the appearance of the vulva of a woman who has never had a baby *(nulliparous)* and the vulva of a woman who has *(parous)* (see Figure 4.8).

Surrounding the vagina, the urethra, and the anus is a set of muscles called the *pelvic floor muscles.* One

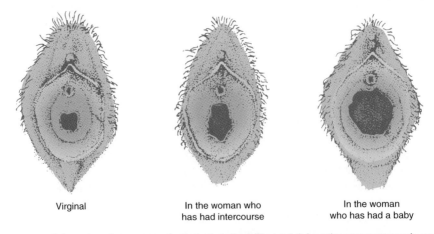

| Virginal | In the woman who has had intercourse | In the woman who has had a baby |

Figure 4.8 Appearance of the vulva of a woman who is a virgin (see Figure 4.6 for other appearances); a woman who has had intercourse but has not had a baby (nulliparous); and a woman who has had a baby (parous).

of these muscles, the **pubococcygeus muscle,** is particularly important. It may be stretched during childbirth, or it may simply be weak. However, it can be strengthened through exercises in which the woman contracts the muscle 10 times in a row six times a day, and this is recommended by sex therapists as well as by many popular sex manuals and magazines. Details of how to do these exercises are provided in Chapter 19.

The Vestibular Bulbs

The **vestibular bulbs** (or bulbs of the clitoris) are two organs about the size and shape of a pea pod (refer to Figure 4.3). They lie on either side of the vaginal wall, near the entrance, under the inner lips (O'Connell et al., 1998). They are erectile tissue and lie close to the crura of the clitoris.

The Skene's Gland, or Female Prostate

The **Skene's gland**, or female prostate (also called the *paraurethral gland)*, lies between the wall of the urethra and the wall of the vagina (Zaviačič et al., 2000). Its ducts empty into the urethra, but it can be felt on the front wall of the vagina. Although controversial in the past, the evidence indicates that it secretes fluid that is biochemically similar to male prostate fluid. Many women find it to be a region of special erotic sensitivity on the wall of the vagina. The size of the female prostate varies considerably from one woman to the next, as does the amount of its secretions. Some women experience no secretion, whereas others have an actual ejaculation when they orgasm. This is the organ dubbed the G-spot, which is responsible for female ejaculation, discussed in Chapter 9.

The Uterus

The **uterus** (womb) is about the size and shape of an upside-down pear. It is usually tilted forward and is held in place by ligaments. The narrow lower third, called the *cervix,* opens into the vagina. The top is the *fundus,* the main part the *body.* The entrance to the uterus through the cervix is very narrow, about the diameter of a drinking straw, and is called the *os* (or cervical canal). The major function of the uterus is to hold and nourish a developing fetus.

The uterus, like the vagina, consists of three layers. The inner layer, or *endometrium,* is richly supplied with glands and blood vessels. Its state varies according to the age of the woman and the phase of the menstrual cycle. It is the endometrium that is sloughed off at menstruation and creates the menstrual discharge. The middle layer, the *myometrium,* is muscular. The muscles are very strong, creating the powerful contractions of labour and orgasm, and also highly elastic, capable of stretching to accommodate a nine-month-old fetus. The outer layer—the *perimetrium* or *serosa*—forms the external cover of the uterus.

The Fallopian Tubes

Extending out from the sides of the upper end of the uterus are the **fallopian tubes,** also called the *oviducts* ("egg ducts") or *uterine tubes* (refer to Figure 4.7). The fallopian tubes are extremely narrow and are lined with hairlike projections called *cilia.* The fallopian tubes are the pathway by which the egg travels toward the uterus and the sperm reach the egg. Fertilization of the egg typically occurs in the *infundibulum,* the section of the tube closest to the ovary; the fertilized egg then travels the rest of the way through the tube to the uterus. The infundibulum curves around toward the ovary; at its end are numerous fingerlike projections called *fimbriae,* which extend toward the ovary.

The Ovaries

The **ovaries** are two organs about the size and shape of unshelled almonds; they lie on either side of the uterus. The ovaries have two important functions; they produce eggs (ova), and they manufacture the sex hormones *estrogen* and *progesterone.*

Each ovary contains numerous follicles. A *follicle* is a capsule that surrounds an egg (not to be confused with hair follicles, which are quite different). A female is born with an estimated 400,000 immature eggs. Beginning at puberty, one or several of the follicles mature during each menstrual cycle. When the egg has matured, the follicle bursts open and releases the egg. The ovaries do not actually connect

---

Pubococcygeus muscle (pyoo-bo-cox-ih-GEE-us): A muscle around the vaginal entrance.
Vestibular bulbs: Erectile tissue running under the inner lips and Skene's gland.
Skene's gland: The female prostate. Also called the *paraurethral gland.*
Uterus (YOO-tur-us): The organ in the female in which the fetus develops.
Fallopian (fuh-LOW-pee-un) tube: The tube extending from the uterus to the ovary; also called the *oviduct.*
Ovaries: Two organs in the female that produce eggs and sex hormones.

(a)

Figure 4.9   The internal structure of the breast.

(b)

(c)

Figure 4.10*a, b, c*   Breasts come in many sizes and shapes.

directly to the fallopian tubes. Rather, the egg is released into the body cavity and reaches the tube by moving toward the fimbriae. If the egg does not reach the tube, it may be fertilized outside the tube, resulting in an abdominal pregnancy (see the section on ectopic pregnancy in Chapter 7). There have also been cases recorded of women who, although they were missing one ovary and the opposite fallopian tube, nonetheless became pregnant. Apparently, in such cases the egg migrates to the tube on the opposite side.

The Breasts

Although they are secondary sex characteristics and not actually sex organs, the *breasts* deserve discussion here because of their erotic and reproductive significance. The breast consists of about 15 or 20 clusters of *mammary glands,* each with a separate opening to the nipple, and of fatty and fibrous tissue that surrounds the clusters of glands (see Figure 4.9). The nipple, into which the milk ducts open, is at the tip of the breast. It is richly supplied with nerve endings and therefore very important in erotic stimulation for many women. The nipple consists of smooth muscle fibres; when they contract, the nipple becomes erect. The area surrounding the nipple is called the *areola.*

There is wide variation among women in the size and shape of the breasts. One thing is fairly consistent, though: many women are not satisfied with the size of their breasts. Many women think they are either too small or too large. It is well to remember that there are the same number of nerve endings in small breasts as in large breasts. It follows that small breasts are actually more erotically sensitive per square inch than are large ones.

Watch the "Breasts" video in Chapter 4 of your CD to learn how some women feel about their breasts.

Breasts may take on enormous psychological meaning; they can be a symbol of femininity or a means of attracting men. Ours is a very breast-oriented culture. Many Canadian men develop a powerful interest in, and attraction to, women's breasts. The social definition of beauty is a compelling force; many women strive to meet the ideal and a few overadapt, going too far in their striving (Mazur, 1986). Breast augmentation surgery has increased steadily since the 1960s, while other women undergo breast reduction surgery, in both cases to meet a socially defined standard of beauty.[4] Breast reduction is also done for medicinal reasons, for example to reduce back pain.

■ Male Sexual Organs

Externally, the most noticeable parts of the male sexual anatomy are the penis and the scrotum, or scrotal sac, which contains the testes (see Figure 4.11).

External Organs

The Penis
The **penis** (phallus, "prick," "cock," "johnson," and many other slang terms too numerous to list) serves important functions in sexual pleasure, reproduction, and elimination of body wastes by urination. It

[4]We can see this trend on the reality makeover television shows. In the 2003–2004 season of *The Swan*, of the 16 women who received major surgery, 10 received breast augmentation (three of them also received nipple lifts), two received breast lifts, and one received a breast reduction. That is, only three of the women did not have surgery on their breasts. Similarly, on *Extreme Makeover*, half of the women received surgery to their breasts, in most cases breast augmentation.

Penis: The male external sexual organ, which functions both in sexual activity and in urination.

is a tubular organ with an end or tip called the *glans.* The opening at the end of the glans is the *meatus,* or *urethral opening,* through which urine and semen pass. The main part of the penis is called the *shaft.* The raised ridge at the edge of the glans is called the *corona* ("crown"), or *coronal ridge.* While the entire penis is sensitive to sexual stimulation, the corona and the rest of the glans are the most sexually excitable regions of the male anatomy.

Internally, the penis contains three long cylinders of spongy tissue running parallel to the *urethra,* which is the pathway through which semen and urine pass (see Figure 4.12). The two spongy bodies lying on top are called the **corpora cavernosa,** and the single one lying on the bottom of the penis is called the **corpus spongiosum** (the urethra runs through the middle of it). During erection, the corpus spongiosum can be seen as a raised column on the lower side of the penis. As the names suggest, these bodies are tissues filled with many spaces and cavities, much like a sponge. They are richly supplied with blood vessels and nerves. In the flaccid (unaroused, not erect) state, they contain little blood. *Erection,* or *tumescence,* occurs when they become filled with blood (engorged) and expand, making the penis stiff.

Contrary to popular belief, the penis does not contain a muscle, and no muscle is involved in erection. Erection is purely a vascular phenomenon; that is, it results entirely from blood flow. It is also commonly believed that the penis of the human male contains a bone. This is not true either, although in some other species—for example, dogs—the penis does contain a bone, which aids in intromission (insertion of the penis into the vagina). In human males, however, there is none.

The skin of the penis usually is hairless and is arranged in loose folds, permitting expansion during erection. The **foreskin,** or *prepuce,* is an additional layer of skin that forms a sheathlike covering over the glans; it may be present or absent in the adult male, depending on whether he has been circumcised (see Figure 4.13). Under the foreskin are small glands (Tyson's glands) that produce a substance called *smegma,* which is cheesy in texture.

Corpora cavernosa: Spongy bodies running the length of the top of the penis.
Corpus spongiosum: A spongy body running the length of the underside of the penis.
Foreskin: A layer of skin covering the glans or tip of the penis in an uncircumcised male; also called the *prepuce.*

Vas deferens

Pubic bone

Prostate gland

Corpus spongiosum

Corpus cavernosum

Urethra

Glans

Scrotum

Bladder

Seminal vesicle

Rectum

Cowper's gland

Vas deferens

Epididymis

Testis

Figure 4.11   The male sexual and reproductive organs from a side view.

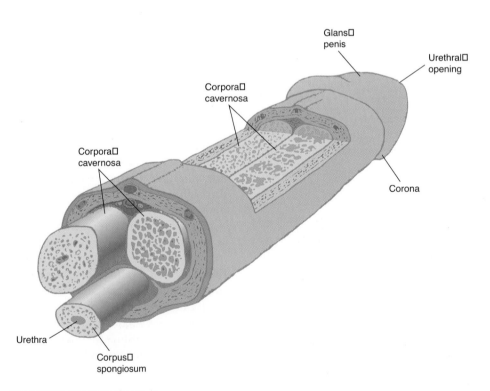

Glans penis

Urethral opening

Corpora cavernosa

Corpora cavernosa

Corona

Urethra

Corpus spongiosum

Figure 4.12   The internal structure of a penis.

(a)   (b)

Figure 4.13   *(a)* A circumcised penis and *(b)* an uncircumcised penis, showing the foreskin.

The foreskin is easily retractable,[5] and its retraction is extremely important for proper hygiene. If it is not pulled back and the glans washed thoroughly, the smegma may accumulate, producing a very unpleasant smell.

Circumcision refers to the surgical cutting away or removal of the foreskin. Circumcision is practised in many parts of the world and, when parents so choose, is done to boys in Canada within a few days after birth.

Circumcision may be done for cultural and religious reasons. Circumcision has been a part of Jewish religious practice for thousands of years. It symbolizes the covenant between God and the Jewish people and is done on the eighth day after birth, according to scriptural teaching (Genesis 17:9–27). Circumcision is also common in Muslim cultures. In most cultures circumcision may be done at puberty as an initiation ritual, or *rite de passage*. The ability of

[5]In a rare condition, the foreskin is so tight that it cannot be pulled back; this condition is called *phimosis* and requires correction by circumcision.

Circumcision: Surgical removal of the foreskin of the penis.

the young boy to stand the pain may be seen as a proof of manhood.

In the 1980s, an anticircumcision movement began gaining momentum in North America. Its proponents argue that circumcision does not have any health benefits and does entail some health risk as well as psychological trauma. According to this view, circumcision is nothing more than cruel mutilation. (For a statement of this anticircumcision position, see Wallerstein, 1980.) In fact, as early as 1975 and again in 1982 and 1996, the Canadian Pediatric Society reviewed the literature and reached the conclusion that there are no valid medical indications for circumcision of newborn boys. Reflecting this advice, the controversy about circumcision, and the fact that circumcision is not usually covered by provincial health insurance plans, currently only 20 to 25 percent of infant boys are circumcised in Canada. In the past, circumcision was widespread in Canada.

New evidence has accumulated, however, that there are potential medical benefits and advantages to circumcision, as well as potential risks. The new evidence indicates, for example, that uncircumcised male babies are 11 times more likely to get urinary tract infections than are circumcised babies, although the risk of urinary tract infections is low (Wiswell et al., 1987). There is also growing evidence that uncircumcised men have a higher risk of infection with HIV, the AIDS virus (Quinn et al., 2000; Szabo, 2000). It is thought that the inner surface of the foreskin is particularly susceptible to HIV and other viruses. In a study of different geographic and ethnic groups in Africa, some of which practise circumcision and some of which do not, it was found that HIV infection rates were very low among groups that practise circumcision and high among those that do not (Moses et al., 1990). In a five-nation study including Spain, Colombia, Brazil, Thailand, and the Philippines, circumcised men showed lower rates of HPV infection (Catellsagué et al., 2002). HPV is the virus that causes genital warts and predisposes women to cervical cancer (see Chapter 20). In this same study, the monogamous women partners of the circumcised men had lower rates of cervical cancer. Yet there are contradictory data showing no health advantages to circumcision in developed nations such as Australia and the United States (Donovan et al., 1994; Laumann et al., 1997). In our view, the scientific data on the health benefits and risks of circumcision are simply not conclusive at the present time.

Other arguments have focused on whether the circumcised or the uncircumcised male receives more pleasure from sexual intercourse. In fact, Masters and Johnson (1966) found that there is no difference in excitability between the circumcised and the uncircumcised penis.

Other forms of male genital cutting are done throughout the world. In fact, male genital cutting is done in more cultures than is female genital cutting (Gregersen, 1996). A common form across most of Polynesia is **supercision** (also known as *superincision*), which involves making a slit the length of the foreskin on the top, with the foreskin otherwise remaining intact (Gregersen, 1996). With **subincision**, which is common in some tribes in central Australia, a slit is made on the lower side of the penis along its entire length and to the depth of the urethra. Urine is then excreted at the base rather than at the tip of the penis.

> **Supercision (superincision):** A form of male genital cutting in which a slit is made the length of the foreskin on top.
> **Subincision:** A form of male genital cutting in which a slit is made on the lower side of the penis along its entire length.

To say the least, the penis has been the focus of quite a lot of attention throughout history. In some cultures, the attention has become so pronounced that the male genitals have actually become the object of religious worship (phallic worship). Not surprisingly, the male genitals were often seen as symbols of fertility and thus were worshipped for their powers of procreativity. In ancient Greece, phallic worship centred on Priapus, the son of Aphrodite (the goddess of love) and Dionysus (the god of fertility and wine). Priapus is usually represented as a grinning man with a huge penis.

In contemporary Canadian society, phallic concern often focuses on the size of the penis. Internet users are bombarded with e-mail spam that promises products to increase penis size. It is commonly believed that a man with a large penis is a better lover and can satisfy a woman more than can a man with a small penis. Masters and Johnson (1966), however, found that this is not true. While there is considerable variation in the length of the penis from one man to the next—the average penis is generally somewhere between 6.4 centimetres (2.5 inches) and 10 centimetres (4 inches) in length when flaccid (not erect)—there seems to be a tendency for the small penis to grow more in erection than one that starts out large. As a result, there is little correlation between the length of the penis when flaccid and its length when erect. As the saying has it, "Erection is the great equalizer." The average erect penis is about 15 centimetres (6 inches) long, although erect penises longer than 33 centimetres (13 inches) have been measured (Dickinson, 1949). Further, as noted earlier, the vagina has relatively few nerve endings and is relatively insensitive. Hence penetration to the far reaches of the vagina by a very long penis is not essential and may not even be noticeable. Many other factors are more important than penis size in giving a woman pleasure (see Chapters 10 and 19).

Phallic concern has also included an interest in the variations in the shape of the penis when flaccid and when erect, as reflected in this limerick:

> There was a young man of Kent
> Whose kirp in the middle was bent.
> To save himself trouble
> He put it in double,
> And instead of coming, he went.

Phallic concern has also been expressed in psychological theory, especially in psychoanalytic theory. As we saw in Chapter 2, Freud viewed concern for the penis and a related castration anxiety as the key factors in male psychological development, leading to the resolution of the Oedipus complex, increased independence from parents, and increased psychological maturity. All this from such a small part of the body! (Indeed, psychoanalytic theory even says that the key factor in female psychological development is the lack of a penis.)

The Scrotum

The other major external genital structure in the male is the **scrotum;** this is a loose pouch of skin, lightly covered with hair, which contains the testes ("balls" or "nuts" in slang).[6] The testes themselves are considered part of the internal genitals.

Internal Organs

The **testes** are the *gonads,* or reproductive glands, of the male, which thus are analogous to the female's ovaries. Like the ovaries, they serve two major functions: to manufacture germ cells (sperm) and sex hormones, in particular *testosterone*. Both testes are about the same size, although the left one usually hangs lower than the right one.

In the internal structure of the testes, two parts are important: the seminiferous tubules and the interstitial cells (see Figure 4.14). The **seminiferous tubules** carry out the important function of manufacturing and storing sperm, a process called *spermatogenesis*. They are a long series of threadlike tubes curled and packed densely into the testes. There are about 1,000 of these tubules, which, if they were stretched out end to end, would be several hundred metres in length.

The **interstitial cells** (or *Leydig's cells*) carry out the second important function of the testes, the production of testosterone. These cells are found in the connective tissue lying between the seminiferous tubules. The cells lie close to the blood vessels in the testes and pour the hormones they manufacture directly into the blood vessels. Thus the testes are endocrine (hormone-secreting) glands.

Each testis is surrounded by a rigid, whitish sheath (the *tunica albuginea*). This sheath is responsible for the problem of sterility caused by mumps in the adult male. When the mumps virus invades the testes, it causes them to swell. The tunica albuginea is tight, however, and does not permit expansion. The delicate tubules are crushed, which impairs their sperm-producing function. Mumps is not a problem in the female because the ovaries are not enclosed in a comparable tight sheath.

One of the clever tricks that the scrotum and testes can perform, as any male will testify, is to move up close to the body or down away from it. These changes are brought about mainly by changes in temperature (although emotional factors may also produce them). If a man plunges into a cold lake, the scrotum will shrivel and move close to the body.[7] If the man is working in an extremely hot place, the scrotum will hang down and away from the body. This mechanism is important because the testes should remain at a fairly constant temperature, slightly lower than normal body temperature. This constancy of temperature is necessary to protect the sperm, which may be injured by extremes of temperature. Thus if the air is cold the testes move closer to the body to maintain warmth, but if the air is too hot, they move away from the body to keep cool. The mechanics of this movement are made possible by the *cremasteric reflex*, named for the cremaster muscle connecting the scrotum to the body wall. Reflex contraction of this muscle pulls the testes up.

---

[6]This brings to mind another limerick:

There once was a pirate named Gates
Who thought he could rhumba on skates.
He slipped on his cutlass
And now he is nutless
And practically useless on dates.

> **Scrotum (SKROH-tum):** The pouch of skin that contains the testes in the male.
> **Testes:** The pair of glands in the scrotum that manufacture sperm and sex hormones.
> **Seminiferous (sem-ih-NIFF-ur-us) tubules:** Tubes in the testes that manufacture sperm.

[7]Fans of the television show *Seinfeld* may recall an episode depicting George's dismay at conclusions a woman drew about his penis size after she saw his penis while he was changing after a cold swim.

> **Interstitial (int-er-STIH-shul) cells:** Cells in the testes that manufacture testosterone.

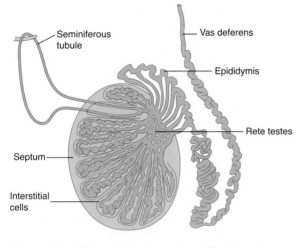

Figure 4.14 Schematic cross-section of the internal structure of the testis.

Many people believe that taking hot baths, wearing tight athletic supporters, or having a high fever can cause infertility. Indeed, in some countries the men take long, hot baths as a method of contraception. Such a practice has some basis in biological fact, because sperm can be destroyed by heat. However, as a method of contraception, this practice has not been particularly effective. In one study, it was found that the use of a special jock-strap raised the temperature of the scrotum by nearly 1°C (1.7°F) and that wearing the device daily for seven weeks caused about a 25-percent reduction in the number of sperm produced (Robinson & Rock, 1967). Thus such practices might decrease a man's fertility somewhat, but they are far from 100-percent effective as contraceptives. On the other hand, men with problems of infertility can sometimes increase the chance of conception by getting out of their tight jockstraps and jockey shorts.

Following initial cell division in the seminiferous tubules, the male germ cells go through several stages of maturation. At the earliest stage, the cell is called a *spermatogonium*. Then it becomes a *spermatocyte* (first primary and then secondary) and then a *spermatid*. Finally when fully mature, it is a *spermatozoan*, or **sperm**. *Spermatogenesis*, the manufacture of sperm, occurs continuously in adult men. An average ejaculate contains about 300 million sperm.

A mature sperm is very tiny—about 60 micrometres, or 60/10,000 millimetre (0.0024 inch), long—and consists of a head, a neck, a midpiece, and a tail. A normal human sperm carries 23 chromosomes in the head. These 23 are half the normal number in the other cells of the human body. When the sperm unites with the egg, which also carries 23 chromosomes, the full complement of 46 for the offspring is produced. (See Chapter 7 for a discussion of the sperm's role in conception.)

After the sperm are manufactured in the seminiferous tubules, they proceed into the *rete testes,* a converging network of tubes on the surface of the testis toward the top. The sperm then pass out of the testis and into a single tube, the epididymis. The **epididymis** is a long tube (about 6 metres, or 20 feet, in length) coiled into a small crescent-shaped region on the top and side of the testis. The sperm are stored in the epididymis, in which they ripen and mature, possibly for as long as six weeks.

Upon ejaculation, the sperm pass from the epididymis into the **vas deferens** (it is the vas that is cut in a vasectomy—see Chapter 8). The vas passes up and out of the scrotum and then follows a peculiar circular path as it loops over the pubic bone, crosses beside the urinary bladder, and then turns downward toward the prostate. As the tube passes through the prostate, it narrows and at this point is called the *ejaculatory duct.* The ejaculatory duct opens into the *urethra,* which has the dual function of conveying sperm and transporting urine; sperm are ejaculated out through the penis via the urethra.

Sperm have little motility of their own while in the epididymis and vas. That is, they are not capable of movement on their own until they mix with the secretions of the prostate (Breton et al., 1996). Up to this point, they are conveyed by the cilia and by contractions of the epididymis and vas.

Sperm: The mature male reproductive cell, capable of fertilizing an egg.
Epididymis (ep-ih-DIH-dih-mus): A highly coiled tube located on the edge of the testis, where sperm mature.
Vas deferens: The tube through which sperm pass on their way from the testes and epididymis, out of the scrotum, and to the urethra.

The **seminal vesicles** are two saclike structures that lie above the prostate, behind the bladder, and in front of the rectum. They produce about 70 percent of the seminal fluid, or ejaculate. The remaining 30 percent is produced by the prostate. They empty their fluid into the ejaculatory duct to combine with the sperm.

The **prostate** lies below the bladder and is about the size and shape of a chestnut. It is composed of both muscle and glandular tissue. The prostate secretes a milky alkaline fluid that is part of the ejaculate. It is thought that the alkalinity of the secretion provides a favourable environment for the sperm and helps prevent their destruction by the acidity of the vagina. The prostate is fairly small at birth, enlarges at puberty, and typically shrinks in old age. It may become enlarged enough so that it interferes with urination, in which case surgery or drug therapy is required. Its size can be determined by rectal examination.

Cowper's glands, or the *bulbourethral glands,* are located just below the prostate and empty into the urethra. During sexual arousal these glands secrete a small amount of a clear alkaline fluid, which appears as droplets at the tip of the penis before ejaculation occurs. It is thought that the function of this secretion is to neutralize the acidic urethra, allowing safe passage of the sperm. Generally it is not produced in sufficient quantity to serve as a lubricant in intercourse. The fluid often contains some stray sperm. Thus it is possible (though not likely) for a woman to become pregnant from the sperm in this fluid even though the man has not ejaculated.

◼ Cancer of the Sex Organs

Breast Cancer

Cancer of the breast is the most frequently diagnosed cancer (excluding non-melanoma skin cancer) in Canadian women. About one out of every nine Canadian women is expected to develop breast cancer at some time in her life. In 2000, 18,534 women were diagnosed and 4,857 women died of breast cancer in this country (National Cancer Institute of Canada, 2004). The risk is higher for the woman whose mother, sister, or grandmother has had breast cancer. Although it is much more common in women, men can also develop breast cancer.

Causes

Approximately 5 percent of the cases of breast cancer in women are due to genetic factors (Couzin, 2003). The remaining cases may be related to a particular virus or to diet. In countries such as Japan and Romania where the diet is low in fat, breast cancer rates are less than half that of Canada, where the diet is high in fat. The evidence also suggests that cigarette smoking increases the risk of breast cancer in women with certain genetic backgrounds (Ambrosone et al., 1996).

There have been great breakthroughs in the last few years in research into the genetics of breast cancer. Scientists have identified two breast cancer genes. These genes are also linked to ovarian cancer in women and prostate cancer in men (King et al., 2003).

Diagnosis

All women should do a breast self-exam regularly (see In Focus 4.2). The exam should be done once a month, but not during the menstrual period, when there tend to be natural lumps in the breast. It is important to do the self-exam once a month because the earlier breast cancer is detected, the better the chances of a complete recovery with proper treatment.

Unfortunately, psychological factors can interfere with this process. Many women do not do the self-exam because they are afraid they will find a lump; thus one can go undetected for a long time, making recovery less likely. Some other women do the self-exam, but when they discover a lump, they become so frightened that they do nothing about it. Perhaps knowing a bit more about the realities of breast lumps and the surgery that is performed when they are discovered will help dispel some of the fears surrounding the subject of breast cancer.

There are three kinds of breast lumps: *cysts* (fluid-filled sacs, also called *fibrocystic* or *cystic mastitis*), *fibroadenomas,* and *malignant tumours.* The im-

---

Seminal vesicles: Saclike structures that lie above the prostate, which produce about 70 percent of the seminal fluid.

Prostate: The gland in the male, located below the bladder, that secretes some of the fluid in semen.

Cowper's glands: Glands that secrete a clear alkaline fluid into the male's urethra.

In Focus 4.2

How to Do a Breast Self-Examination

By regularly examining her own breasts, a woman is likely to notice any changes that occur. The best time for breast self-examination (BSE) is 7 to 10 days after your period ends, when your breasts are not tender or swollen. If you are not having regular periods, do BSE on the same day every month.

• Lie down with a pillow under your right shoulder and place your right arm behind your head.
• Use the finger pads of the three middle fingers on your left hand, keeping your hand flat (see Figure 4.15c), to feel for lumps in the right breast.
• Press firmly enough to know how your breast feels. A firm ridge in the lower curve of each breast is normal. If you're not sure how hard to press, talk with your doctor or nurse.
• Making small circles about the size of a dime, move around the breast from the armpit to the breastbone and from the collarbone to below the breast. You can use either the grid or the circular method (see Figure 4.15d). Whichever method you use, feel your entire breast and your nipple

(see Figure 4.15a). Try to remember how your breast feels from month to month so that you notice any abnormal change.
• Repeat the exam on your left breast, using the finger pads of the right hand. (Move the pillow to under your left shoulder.)
• Repeat the examination of both breasts while standing, with one arm behind your head. The upright position makes it easier to check the upper and outer part of the breasts (toward your armpit). This is where about half of breast cancers are found. You may want to do the standing part of the BSE while you are in the shower. Some breast changes can be felt more easily when your skin is wet and soapy.
• For added safety, you can check your breasts for any dimpling of the skin, changes in the nipple, redness, or swelling while standing in front of a mirror right after your BSE each month.
• If you find any changes, see your doctor right away.

Source: Canadian Cancer Society, 2004.

(a)

(b)

(c)

(d)

Figure 4.15   Techniques used in the breast self-exam.

portant thing to realize is that 80 percent of breast lumps are cysts or fibroadenomas and are benign—that is, not dangerous. Therefore, if you find a lump in your breast, the chances are fairly good that it is not malignant; of course, you cannot be sure of this until a doctor has performed a biopsy.

Once you have discovered a lump, you should see a doctor immediately. One of several diagnostic procedures may then be carried out. One is *needle aspiration,* in which a fine needle is inserted into the breast; if the lump is a cyst, the fluid in the cyst will be drained out. If the lump disappears after this procedure, then it was a cyst; the cyst is gone, and there is no need for further concern. If the lump remains, it must be either a fibroadenoma or a malignant tumour.

Other techniques are also available for early detection of breast cancer, specifically mammography. Basically, *mammography* involves taking an X-ray of the breast. This technique is highly accurate, although some errors are still made. The major advantage, though, is that it is capable of detecting tumours that are so small that they cannot yet be felt; thus it can detect cancer in very early stages, making recovery more likely. Nonetheless, mammography involves some exposure to radiation, which itself may increase the risk of cancer. The question is: Which is more dangerous—having mammography or not detecting breast cancer until a later stage? Experts agree that the benefits outweigh the risk for women over 50. The Canadian Cancer Society recommends that women over 50 have a screening mammogram every two years. However, scientists disagree about the effectiveness of mammography screening for women who are between 40 and 49. It is a misconception that mammograms themselves prevent cancer. They only detect tumours, leading to treatment of the cancer.

Most physicians feel that the only definitive way to differentiate between a fibroadenoma and a malignant tumour is to do a *biopsy.* A small slit is made in the breast, and the lump is removed. A pathologist then examines it to determine whether it is cancerous. If it is simply a fibroadenoma, it has been removed and there is no further need for concern.

Mastectomy

Several forms of surgery may be performed when a breast lump is found to be malignant. Radiation therapy, chemotherapy, and hormone therapy may also be used. The most serious surgery is **radical mastec-**

Figure 4.16 Appearance of a breast reconstructed after mastectomy.

tomy, in which the entire breast and the underlying pectoral muscle and the lymph nodes are removed. In *modified radical mastectomy* the breast and lymph nodes, but not the muscles, are removed. In *simple mastectomy* only the breast (and possibly a few lymph nodes) is removed. In **lumpectomy,** only the lump itself and a small bit of surrounding tissue is removed. The breast is thus preserved. Research indicates that in cases of early breast cancer (when the cancer has not spread beyond the breast, e.g., to the lymph nodes), lumpectomy followed by radiation therapy is as effective as radical mastectomy (Henahan, 1984; Veronesi et al., 1981) and is obviously much preferable. Drug therapy (tamoxifen) is also commonly used (Pasacreta & McCorkle, 1998). Women who take tamoxifen may experience menopausal symptoms, sometimes very severe, including sexual side effects such as decreased sexual desire and pain during intercourse related to vaginal dryness (Archibald et al., in press; Kaplan, 1994).

Treatments generally are highly effective and breast cancer deaths have decreased since 1986. If the cancer has not spread beyond the breast, the

---

Radical mastectomy (mast-ECT-uh-mee): A surgical treatment for breast cancer in which the entire breast, as well as underlying muscles and lymph nodes, is removed.
Lumpectomy: A surgical treatment for breast cancer in which only the lump and a small bit of surrounding tissue are removed.

survival rate is more than 94 percent five years after treatment (Canadian Cancer Society, 1995).

Psychological Aspects

A lot more is at stake with breast cancer and mastectomy than technical details about diagnosis and surgery. The psychological impact of breast cancer and mastectomy and other treatments can be enormous (for an excellent review see Meyerowitz, 1980). There seem to be three sources of the trauma: Finding out that one has cancer of any kind is traumatic, and the amputation of the breast and the impact of severe menopausal symptoms are additionally stressful.

The typical emotional response of the mastectomy patient is depression, often associated with anxiety (Compas & Lueken, 2002). These responses are so common that they can be considered normal. The woman must make a number of physical and psychological adaptations, including different positions for sleeping and lovemaking and, for many women, a change to less revealing clothing. It is common for women to have difficulty showing their incisions to their sexual partners. Relationship tensions and sexual problems may increase. Many women experience a fear of recurring cancer and its treatment and of death, as well as concerns about mutilation from mastectomy and a possible loss of femininity. Our culture is very breast-oriented, and a woman who has defined her identity in terms of her beauty and voluptuous figure may have a more difficult time adjusting.

Long-term studies, however, indicate that most women gradually adapt to the stresses they have experienced. One study found that breast cancer survivors did not differ from controls on measures of depression (Cordova et al., 2001). Many women manage to find meaning in the cancer experience, and some show *posttraumatic growth* such as finding new meaning in relationships and appreciating life more.

Educational classes providing relevant information can be very helpful. However, peer support groups such as those offered through the Canadian Cancer Society, although important to many women, have not fared well in tests of their effectiveness in improving mental health (Helgeson et al., 2001). For women who are more severely distressed, cognitive behavioural therapy with a trained therapist can be very effective (Antoni et al., 2001).

Cancer of the Cervix, Endometrium, and Ovaries

Cancers of the cervix, endometrium, and ovaries are also common cancers, accounting for about 12 percent of all new cancers in women. In 2000, 7,087 Canadian women were diagnosed with and 2,440 died of these cancers (National Cancer Institute of Canada, 2004). Other cancers of the female sexual-reproductive organs include cancer of the vulva, vagina, and fallopian tubes; these are all relatively rare.

Approximately 95 percent of cases of cervical cancer are caused by the human papillomavirus, HPV (see Chapter 8) (Janicek & Averette, 2001). Early initiation of heterosexual intercourse during the teenage years is a known risk factor for cervical cancer, as is intercourse with multiple partners. Both early intercourse *and* multiple partners, of course, increase the risk of HPV infection. Research shows that tumour-suppressor genes are active in normal cells, preventing them from becoming cancerous. HPV interferes with the activity of those tumour-suppressor genes (Janicek & Averette, 2001).

It is encouraging to note that the death rate from cervical cancer has decreased 78 percent since the mid-1960s, mainly as a result of the *Pap test* (invented by G. N. Papanicolaou) and more regular checkups. The Pap test is performed during a pelvic examination (described in In Focus 4.3). Because this highly accurate test can detect cancer long before the person has any symptoms, all women over age 18 to 20 should have one annually, and they should begin even earlier if they are sexually active.

There is considerable variation in the incidence of cervical and endometrial cancers across Canada. For example, the incidence of cervical cancer in some Aboriginal groups is 10 times the provincial average, probably because many Aboriginal women do not have access to good health care and regular pelvic exams (Health Canada, 1998c). As with most cancers, the likelihood of a woman having a reproductive tract cancer increases with age, although cervical cancer is relatively common among women in their 20s.

Endometrial and ovarian cancers have multiple symptoms, making diagnosis difficult. Endometrial cancer may be suspected when a woman has vaginal bleeding during times in the menstrual cycle other than her period, or after menopause. Ovarian cancer symptoms—abdominal bloating and cramping, vomiting, and diarrhea—can be (and usually are) indicative of much less serious conditions like a stomach virus or irritable bowel syndrome. Imaging techniques such as pelvic sonogram and MRI, and minimally invasive surgical techniques such as hysteroscopy, can help diagnose these cancers.

Treatment for cervical cancer varies according to how advanced it is when diagnosed. If it is detected very early, it is quite curable with methods such as *cryotherapy*, a nonsurgical technique that uses extreme cold to destroy just the abnormal cells. Another common treatment is *cone biopsy*, in which a segment of the cervix is surgically removed, leaving the cervix largely intact. For women with advanced cervical cancer that has spread beyond a small, localized spot, **hysterectomy** (surgical removal of the uterus) is the usual treatment, although radiation therapy may be an alternative.

For women with endometrial cancer, hysterectomy is the standard treatment. Ovarian cancer is treated by *oophorectomy* (surgical removal of the ovaries), often accompanied by hysterectomy. These surgeries are typically followed by radiation treatments or chemotherapy.

It is important to note some facts about hysterectomy. Although it carries risks similar to those of any major surgery, hysterectomy does not leave a woman "masculinized," with a beard and deep voice. Beard growth is influenced by testosterone, not estrogen or progesterone. And it is the ovaries that manufacture estrogen and progesterone. They are not removed in a hysterectomy except in rare cases when the cancer has spread to them. Women who have their ovaries removed before age 50 can take hormone replacement therapy (HRT) to avoid the effects of premature menopause. Another fallacy about hysterectomy is that it prevents a woman from enjoying—or even having—sex. In fact, though, the vagina is left intact, so intercourse is quite possible (for more detail, see Chapter 12).

Cancer of the Prostate

Cancer of the prostate is the most common form of cancer in Canadian men. In 2000, 18,477 Canadian men were diagnosed with prostate cancer and 3,718

Hysterectomy (his-tuh-REK-tuh-mee): Surgical removal of the uterus.

men died from it (National Cancer Institute of Canada, 2004). About one out of every eight Canadian men is expected to develop prostate cancer at some time in his life. Most cases are not lethal, however, and survival rates are high because it generally affects older men (25 percent of men over 90 have prostate cancer), and because the tumours are small and spread (metastasize) very slowly. On the other hand, a percentage of prostate tumours do spread and are lethal. A prostate cancer gene (HPC1, for Hereditary Prostate Cancer) has been discovered, but it accounts for only about 3 percent of all cases (Pennisi, 1996; Smith et al., 1996).

Early symptoms of prostate cancer are frequent urination (especially at night), difficulty in urination, and difficulty emptying the bladder. These are also symptoms of benign prostate enlargement, which itself may require treatment by surgery or drugs but is not cancer (Oesterling, 1995). These symptoms result from the pressure of the prostate tumour on the urethra. In the early stages, there may be frequent erections and an increase in sex drive; however, as the disease progresses, there are often problems with sexual functioning.

Preliminary diagnosis of prostate cancer is by a rectal examination, which is simple and causes no more than minimal discomfort. The physician (wearing a lubricated glove) simply inserts one finger into the rectum and palpates (feels) the prostate. All men over 50 should have a rectal exam at least once a year; men with a family history of the disease should start having exams at 40. If the rectal exam provides evidence of a tumour, further laboratory tests can be conducted as confirmation. The rectal exam has its disadvantages, though. Some men dislike the discomfort it causes, and it is not 100-percent accurate. A blood test for PSA (prostate-specific antigen) is also available and should be done as well.

Treatment often involves surgical removal of some or all of the prostate, plus some type of hormone therapy, radiation therapy, or anticancer drugs. Because prostate cancer is often a slow-growing cancer, it may be left untreated, particularly if the man is elderly. Surgery may result in erection problems (Perez et al., 2002). Just as research has found that a greater number of sexual partners increases women's risk of cervical cancer, new research indicates that men with a greater number of female partners have an increased risk of prostate cancer (Rosenblatt et al., 2001).

In Focus 4.3

What Is Involved in a Pelvic Exam?

All women over the age of 18 or who are having intercourse should have a checkup every year that includes a thorough pelvic exam. Among other things, such an exam is extremely important in the detection of cervical cancer, and early detection is the key to cure. Some women neglect to have the exam because they feel anxious or embarrassed about it or because they think they are "too young" or "too old"; however, having regular pelvic exams can be a matter of life and death. Actually, the exam is quite simple and need not cause any discomfort. The following is a description of the procedures in a pelvic exam (Boston Women's Health Book Collective, 1992).

First, the health care provider inspects the vulva, checking for irritations, discolorations, bumps, lice, skin lesions, and unusual vaginal discharge. Then there is an internal check for *cystoceles* (bulges of the bladder into the vagina) and *rectoceles* (bulges of the rectum into the vagina), for pus in the Skene glands, for cysts in the Bartholin glands, and for the strength of the pelvic floor muscles and abdominal muscles. The health care provider should also ask the woman a series of questions, including whether she ever loses urine involuntarily, has a foul smelling discharge, or has abnormal bleeding.

Next comes the speculum exam. The *speculum* is a plastic or metal instrument that is inserted into the vagina to hold the vaginal walls apart to permit examination. Once the speculum is in place (it should be prewarmed to body temperature if it is metal), the health care provider looks for any unusual signs, such as lesions, inflammation, or unusual discharge from the vaginal walls, and for any signs of infections or damage to the cervix. The health care provider then uses a small wooden spatula and cytobrush to scrape a tiny bit of tissue from the cervix for the Pap test for cervical cancer. If this is done properly, it should not be painful. Tests for some, but not all, sexually transmitted diseases can also be run.

If the woman is interested in seeing her own cervix, she can ask the doctor to hold up a mirror so that she can view it through the speculum. Women should also be taught how to inspect their own vulva; early detection of diseases would thus be much more likely.

Next, the health care provider does a bimanual vaginal exam. She or he slides the index and middle fingers of one hand into the vagina and then, with the other hand, presses down from the outside on the abdominal wall. The health care provider then feels for the position of the uterus, tubes, and ovaries and for any signs of growths, pain, or inflammation.

Finally, the health care provider may do a recto-vaginal exam by inserting one finger into the vagina and one into the rectum; this provides further infor-

Cancer of the penis is another cancer of the male sexual-reproductive system, but it is rare compared with prostate cancer. It seems to be much more common among uncircumcised men than among circumcised men, suggesting that the accumulation of smegma under the foreskin may be related to its cause. Treatment may consist of surgery or radiation therapy.

Cancer of the Testes

Cancer of the testes is not a particularly common form of cancer. In 2000, 760 men were diagnosed with this form of cancer, and 37 men died from it (National Cancer Institute of Canada, 2004). However, cancer of the testes tends to be a disease of cancer in young men. The mortality rate from cancer of the testes in Canada decreased by 4.5 percent between 1987 and 1996.

mation on the positioning of the pelvic organs and can include a test for colon cancer.

Once again, it is important to emphasize that these are not painful procedures if the woman is relaxed, and that having them performed regularly is extremely important to a woman's health.

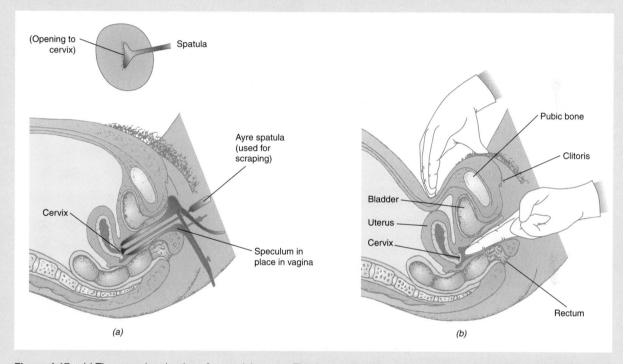

Figure 4.17 *(a)* The speculum in place for a pelvic exam. The Ayre spatula is used to get a sample of cells for the Pap test. *(b)* The bimanual pelvic exam.

The first sign is usually a painless lump in the testes, or a slight enlargement or change in consistency of the testes. There may be pain in the lower abdomen or groin. Unfortunately, many men do not discover the tumour, or if they do, they do not see a physician soon, so that in most cases the cancer has spread to other organs by the time a physician is consulted. When a lump is reported to a physician early, the five-year survival rate is 95 percent. (Lance Armstrong, the great cyclist, was treated for testicular cancer and went on to win the Tour de France multiple times.) However, if the lump is not discovered or the man waits to see a physician and the cancer has progressed to Stage III, the survival rate is 75 percent (American Cancer Society, 2000).

Not every lump in the testes is cancerous. Some lumps are varicoceles; that is, varicose veins. Diagnosis is made by a physician's examination of the testes

In Focus 4.4

How to Do a Testicular Examination

Doctors agree that examination of a man's testicles is an important part of a general physical examination. In addition, the Canadian Cancer Society recommends that men do regular testicular self-examinations every month starting at puberty.

The best time to perform a testicular self-examination is during or right after a bath or shower because the scrotal skin is more relaxed and the contents can be felt more easily. Stand in front of a mirror and hold the penis out of the way. Examine each testicle separately. Check for swelling on the skin of the scrotum. Hold the testicle between the thumbs and fingers with both hands and roll it gently between the fingers. This should not be painful. The normal testicle feels slightly soft with an even consistency and a smooth surface. The epididymis can be felt at the back of the testicle and feels slightly different in consistency. Become familiar with what your scrotum feels like so you will be able to notice any changes. Look and feel for any hard lumps or *nodules* (smooth rounded masses) or any change in the size, shape, or consistency of the testes. Be aware that the testicles contain blood vessels, supporting tissues, and tubes that conduct sperm and that some men may confuse these with cancer. If you have any doubts, ask your doctor.

These are the warning signs of testicular cancer:

1. Any thickening or painless or uncomfortable lump on a testicle, however small (even pea size).
2. A testicular enlargement or swelling.
3. A sensation of heaviness or aching in the lower abdomen or scrotum.

Figure 4.18 The technique used in the testicular self-exam.

4. In rare cases, men with germ cell cancer notice breast tenderness or breast growth.

See a physician promptly if you have any of these symptoms.

Sources: American Cancer Society Web site; Canadian Cancer Society, *An Important Minute in a Man's Life.*

(see In Focus 4.4) and by ultrasound. Final diagnosis involves surgical removal of the entire testis. This is also the first step in treatment. Fortunately, the other testicle remains, so that hormone production and sexual functioning can continue unimpaired. An artificial, gel-filled testicle can be implanted to restore a normal appearance.

The cause of testicular cancer is not known for certain. An undescended testis has a much greater risk of developing cancer.

■ ■ SUMMARY

The external sexual organs of the female are the clitoris, the mons, the inner lips, the outer lips, and the vaginal opening. Collectively these are referred to as the vulva. The clitoris is an extremely sensitive organ and is very important in female sexual response. Clitoridectomy and infibulation are rituals that involve cutting of the clitoris and other parts of the vulva and are practised widely in some African nations and elsewhere. Another external structure is the hymen, which has taken on great symbolic significance as a sign of virginity, although its absence is not a reliable indicator that a woman is not a virgin. The important internal structures are the vagina, which receives the penis during coitus; the uterus, which houses the developing fetus; the ovaries, which produce eggs and manufacture sex hormones; and the fallopian tubes, which convey the egg to the uterus. The breasts of the female also function in sexual arousal and may have great symbolic significance.

The external sexual organs of the male are the penis and the scrotum. The penis contains three spongy bodies which, when filled with blood, produce an erection. Circumcision, or surgical removal of the foreskin of the penis, is a debated practice in Canada but may have some health advantages. The scrotum contains the testes, which are responsible for the manufacture of sperm (in the seminiferous tubules) and sex hormones (in the interstitial cells). Sperm pass out of the testes during ejaculation via the vas deferens, the ejaculatory duct, and the urethra. The seminal vesicles manufacture most of the fluid that mixes with the sperm to form semen. The prostate also contributes secretions.

Breast cancer is the most common form of cancer in women. All women should do a monthly self-exam because the earlier a lump is detected, the greater the chances of complete recovery. The Pap test is used to detect cervical cancer. Prostate cancer is the most common form of cancer in men, but it generally affects older men. Cancer of the testes, although rare, is the most common cancer in men between the ages of 29 and 35. Men should do a monthly testicular self-exam, just as women should do a monthly breast self-exam.

■ ■ QUESTIONS FOR THOUGHT, DISCUSSION, AND DEBATE

1. Form two groups of students to debate the following: *Resolved: Circumcision should not be performed routinely.* You can draw on many resources to provide evidence for your debate, including interviews with doctors and nurses, library materials (books and journal articles on the effects of circumcision), and interviews with parents of infants.

2. You are a gynecologist practising in Toronto. An immigrant woman from Somalia makes an appointment with you. She wants you to perform infibulation on her 8-year-old daughter. She pleads with you, saying that she wants the girl to have the procedure performed under safe, sanitary conditions in a hospital. She firmly believes that she would betray her culture, to which they will return in 2 years, if she does not carry out this ancient custom with her daughter. What should you do?

3. Clitoridectomy and infibulation are practised widely today, particularly in East Africa. Scientific evidence indicates that these practices can cause serious negative health consequences for women and girls. Some argue that people throughout the world should work to eradicate this practice, perhaps with the help of an institution such as the World Health Organization. Others argue that these practices are deeply rooted in the cultures of these countries, and that outsiders have no right to judge it, much less try to stop it. What do you think? Why?

■ ■ ■ SUGGESTIONS FOR FURTHER READING

Boston Women's Health Book Collective. (1996). *The new our bodies, ourselves: A book by and for women.* New York: Simon & Schuster. A good, easy-to-read source on female biology and sexuality.

Gruenbaum, Ellen. (2000). *The female circumcision controversy: An anthropological perspective.* Philadelphia: University of Pennsylvania Press. Gruenbaum tells of her fieldwork in Sudan, where the most severe forms of FGC are practised.

Lamont, J., & Barrett, M. (Eds.). (1994). Sexuality & cancer treatment. *The Canadian Journal of Human Sexuality, 3(2),* 95–183.

Morgentaler, Abraham. (1993). *The male body: A physician's guide to what every man should know about his sexual health.* New York: Simon & Schuster. An authoritative book on men's health.

Olivotto, I., Gelmon, K., & Kuusk, U. (1995). *Intelligent patient guide to breast cancer.* Vancouver: Intelligent Patient Guide. [Available from Intelligent Patient Guide Ltd., 517–750 West Broadway, Vancouver, BC V5Z 1H4.] This book, written by three practising physicians in Vancouver and professors at the University of British Columbia Medical School, describes all aspects of breast cancer.

For Review Questions, Web Resources, and other learning and study tools, visit the *Understanding Human Sexuality* Online Learning Centre at www.mcgrawhill.ca/college/hyde.

CHAPTER 5

Sex Hormones, Sexual Differentiation, and Menstruation

CHAPTER HIGHLIGHTS

This Way

I have AIS, I guess,
because there is a god,
and he or she or both,
peered deep into my heart
to see
that all that I can be
is best expressed
in female form.
The alternative for me
would be XY, and I
would be virilized;
so all that's soft and tender

would instead surrender
to a strand of DNA.
In the lie of X and Y
I came to challenge the
immutability
of "he" and the certainty
of "she." Blended and infused,
a ruse of gender
that upends
a different fate.
Non-functioning receptors
have rescued me
Not a failed mess
But a smashing success of nature!*

One of the marvels of human biology is that the complex and different male and female anatomies—males with a penis and scrotum; females with a vagina, uterus, and breasts—arise from a single cell, the fertilized egg, which varies only in whether it carries two X chromosomes (XX) or one X and one Y (XY). Many of the structural differences between males and females arise before birth, during the **prenatal period,** in a process called *prenatal sexual differentiation.* Further differences also develop during puberty. This process of sexual differentiation—both prenatally and during puberty—will be examined in this chapter. First, however, another biological system, the endocrine (hormonal) system, needs to be considered, paying particular attention to the sex hormones, which play a major role in the differentiation process.

■ Sex Hormones

Hormones are powerful chemical substances manufactured by the *endocrine glands* and secreted directly into the bloodstream. Because they go into the blood, their effects are felt fairly rapidly and at

places in the body quite distant from where they were manufactured. The most important sex hormones are **testosterone** (one of a group of hormones called **androgens**) and **estrogens** and **progesterone.** The thyroid, the adrenals, and the pituitary are examples of endocrine glands. We are interested here in the gonads, or sex glands: the testes in the male and the ovaries in the female. The **pituitary gland** and a closely related region of the brain, the **hypothalamus,** are also important because the hypothalamus

---

Prenatal (pree-NAY-tul) period: The time from conception to birth.
Hormones: Chemical substances secreted by the endocrine glands into the bloodstream.
Testosterone: A hormone secreted by the testes in the male (and also present at lower levels in the female).
Androgens: The group of "male" sex hormones, one of which is testosterone.
Estrogens (ESS-troh-jens): The group of "female" sex hormones.
Progesterone (pro-JES-tur-ohn): A "female" sex hormone secreted by the ovaries.
Pituitary (pih-TOO-ih-tair-ee) gland: A small endocrine gland located on the lower side of the brain below the hypothalamus; the pituitary is important in regulating levels of sex hormones.
Hypothalamus (hy-poh-THAL-ah-mus): A small region of the brain that is important in regulating many body functions, including the functioning of the sex hormones.

---

*Sherri Groveman, an intersex individual with androgen insensitivity syndrome (AIS). In *Hermaphrodites with Attitude*, 1995, p. 2. Retrieved from www.isna.org/library/hwa.

regulates the pituitary, which regulates the other glands, in particular the testes and ovaries. Because of its importance, the pituitary has been called the "master gland" of the endocrine system. The pituitary is a small gland, about the size of a pea, which projects down from the lower side of the brain. It is divided into three lobes: the anterior, the intermediary, and the posterior lobe. The anterior lobe is the one that interacts with the gonads. The hypothalamus is a region at the base of the brain just above the pituitary (see Figure 5.1); it plays a part in regulating many vital behaviours such as eating, drinking, and sexual behaviour,[1] and it is important in regulating the pituitary.

[1] One psychologist summarized the functions of the hypothalamus as being the four F's: fighting, feeding, fleeing, and, ahem, sexual behaviour.

Figure 5.1   The hypothalamus–pituitary–gonad feedback loop in women, which regulates production of the sex hormones.

These three structures, then—the hypothalamus, pituitary, and gonads (testes or ovaries)—function together. They influence such important sexual functions as the menstrual cycle, pregnancy, the changes of puberty, and sexual behaviour.

Sex Hormone Systems in the Male

To learn more about the role of body chemistry in making us male or female, watch the "Hormones and Sexual Differentiation" video in Chapter 5 of your CD.

The pituitary and the testes both produce hormones. The important hormone produced by the testes is *testosterone*. Testosterone, a "male" or masculinizing sex hormone, has important functions in stimulating and maintaining the secondary sex characteristics (such as beard growth), maintaining the genitals and their sperm-producing capability, and stimulating the growth of bone and muscle.

The pituitary produces several hormones, two of which are important in this discussion: **follicle-stimulating hormone (FSH)** and **luteinizing hormone (LH).** These hormones affect the functioning of the testes. FSH controls sperm production, and LH controls testosterone production.

Testosterone levels in males are relatively constant. These constant levels are maintained because the hypothalamus, pituitary, and testes operate in a negative feedback loop (see Figure 5.2). The levels of LH are regulated by a substance called **gonadotropin-releasing hormone (GnRH),** which is secreted by the hypothalamus (FSH levels are similarly regulated by GnRH). The system comes full circle because the hypothalamus is sensitive to the levels of testosterone present, and thus testosterone influences the output of GnRH. This feed-

Follicle-stimulating hormone (FSH): A hormone secreted by the pituitary; it stimulates follicle development in females and sperm production in males.
Luteinizing hormone (LH): A hormone secreted by the pituitary; it regulates estrogen secretion and ovum development in the female and testosterone production in the male.
Gonadotropin-releasing hormone (GnRH): A hormone secreted by the hypothalamus that regulates the pituitary's secretion of gonad-stimulating hormones.

back loop is sometimes called the **HPG axis,** for hypothalamus–pituitary–gonad axis.

This negative feedback loop operates much like a thermostat-furnace system. If a room is cold, certain changes occur in the thermostat, and it signals the furnace to turn on. The action of the furnace warms the air in the room. Eventually the air becomes so warm that another change is produced in the thermostat, and it sends a signal to the furnace to turn off. The temperature in the room then gradually falls until it produces another change in the thermostat, which then turns on the furnace, and the cycle is repeated. This is a *negative* feedback loop because *rises* in temperature turn *off* the furnace, whereas *decreases* in temperature turn *on* the furnace.

The hypothalamus, pituitary, and testes form a

similar negative feedback loop, ensuring that testosterone is maintained at a fairly constant level, just as the temperature of a room is kept fairly constant. The pituitary's production of LH stimulates the testes to produce testosterone. But when testosterone levels get high, the hypothalamus reduces its production of GnRH; the pituitary's production of LH is then reduced, and the production of testosterone by the testes consequently decreases. When it has fallen, the hypothalamus again increases the production of GnRH and the process starts again.

The level of testosterone in men is fairly constant. The traditional assumption of both laypeople and scientists has been that monthly biological and psychological cycles are the exclusive property of women and that men experience no monthly cycles. These assumptions are made, at least in part, because men have no obvious signs like menstruation to call attention to the fact that some kind of periodic change is occurring. Yet their hormone levels do fluctuate—over the day, possibly the month,

> **HPG axis:** Hypothalamus–pituitary–gonad axis, the negative feedback loop that regulates sex-hormone production.

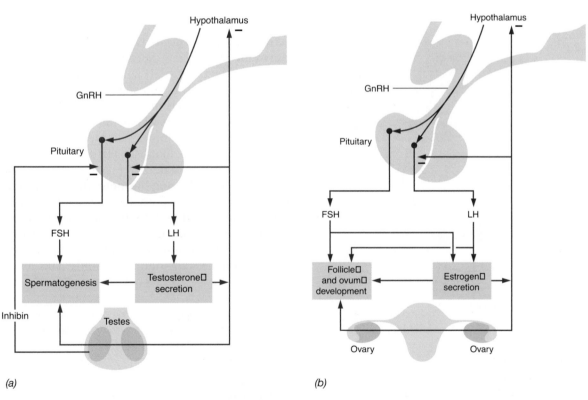

Figure 5.2 Schematic diagram of hormonal control of sex hormones. Note how similar they are in men and women: *(a)* Testosterone secretion and sperm production by the testes. The negative signs indicate that testosterone inhibits LH production, both in the pituitary and in the hypothalamus. *(b)* Estrogen secretion and ovum production by the ovaries (during the follicular phase of the menstrual cycle).

and over the year. In fact, men may be no more or less psychologically changeable than women are. For example, one study found no differences between men and women in day-to-day mood changes—men were no more or less changeable than women (McFarlane et al., 1988; see also McFarlane & Williams, 1994). Undoubtedly there will be increased research on this topic in the next decade.

Although it has been clear for some time that there is a negative feedback loop between testosterone levels and LH levels, it has not been clear what regulates FSH levels. **Inhibin** is a substance produced in the testes (by cells called the Sertoli cells) which serves exactly that function—it acts to regulate FSH levels in a negative feedback loop (Plant et al., 1993).

Interest in inhibin has been intense because it shows great promise, at least theoretically, as a male contraceptive. That is, because inhibin suppresses FSH production, sperm production in turn is inhibited. Future developments in this field should be interesting.

Sex Hormone Systems in the Female

The ovaries produce two important hormones, *estrogen*[2] and *progesterone*. The functions of estrogen include bringing about many of the changes of puberty (stimulating the growth of the uterus and vagina, enlarging the pelvis, and stimulating breast growth). Estrogen is also responsible for maintaining the mucous membranes of the vagina and stopping the growth of bone and muscle, which accounts for the generally smaller size of females as compared with males.

In adult women the levels of estrogen and progesterone fluctuate according to the phases of the menstrual cycle (below) and during various other stages such as pregnancy and menopause. The levels of estrogen and progesterone are regulated by the two pituitary hormones, FSH and LH. Thus the levels of estrogen and progesterone are controlled by a negative feedback loop of the hypothalamus, pituitary, and ovaries, similar to the negative feedback loop in the male (see Figure 5.2b). For exam-

ple, as shown on the right side of Figure 5.2b, increases in the level of GnRH increase the level of LH, and the increases in LH eventually produce increases in the output of estrogen; finally, the increases in the level of estrogen inhibit (decrease) the production of GnRH and LH.

The pituitary produces two other hormones, *prolactin* and *oxytocin*. Prolactin stimulates secretion of milk by the mammary glands after a woman has given birth to a child. Oxytocin stimulates ejection of that milk from the nipple. Oxytocin also stimulates contractions of the uterus during childbirth.

The female sex hormone system functions much like the male sex hormone system. The ovaries and testes produce many of the same hormones, but in different amounts. The ovaries, like the testes, produce inhibin, which in turn forms a negative feedback loop with FSH production (Burger, 1993). The functioning of the female sex hormone system and the menstrual cycle are described in more detail below.

The Menstrual Cycle

It is important to note that humans are nearly unique among species in having a menstrual cycle. Only a few other species of apes and monkeys also have menstrual cycles. All other species of mammals (for example, horses and dogs) have *estrous* cycles. There are several differences between estrous cycles and menstrual cycles. First, in animals that have estrous cycles, there is no menstruation; there is either no bleeding or only a slight spotting of blood (as in dogs), which is not a real menstruation. Second, the timing of ovulation in relation to bleeding (if there is any) is different in the two cycles. For estrous animals, ovulation occurs while the animal is in "heat," or *estrus*, which is also the time of slight spotting. In the menstrual cycle, however, ovulation occurs about midway between the periods of menstruation. A third difference is that female animals with estrous cycles engage in sexual behaviour only when they are in heat; that is, during the estrus phase of the cycle. Females with menstrual cycles are capable of engaging in sexual behaviour throughout the cycle.

The Phases of the Menstrual Cycle

The menstrual cycle has four phases, each characterized by a set of hormonal, ovarian, and uterine changes. Because menstruation is the easiest phase to identify, it is tempting to call it the first phase, and

---

[2]We really should say *estrogens*, because they are a group of hormones. Estradiolis is one of the estrogens. To keep things simple, we will just use the term estrogen.

Inhibin: A substance secreted by the testes and ovaries that regulates FSH levels.

in numbering the days of the menstrual cycle day 1 is counted as the first day of menstruation because it is the most identifiable day of the cycle. However, biologically it is actually the last phase.

Hormones and What Happens in the Ovaries. The first phase of the menstrual cycle is called the **follicular phase** (it is sometimes called the *proliferative phase* or the *preovulatory phase*). At the beginning of this phase, the pituitary secretes relatively high levels of FSH (follicle-stimulating hormone). As the name of this hormone implies, its function is to stimulate follicles in the ovaries. At the beginning of the follicular phase, it signals one follicle (occasionally more than one) in the ovaries to bring an egg to the final stage of maturity. At the same time, the follicle secretes estrogen.

The second phase of the cycle is **ovulation,** during which the follicle ruptures open, releasing the mature egg (see Figure 5.3). By this time, estrogen has risen to a high level, which inhibits FSH production, and so FSH has fallen back to a low level. The high levels of estrogen also stimulate the hypothalamus to produce GnRH, which causes the pituitary to begin production of LH (luteinizing hormone).[3] A surge of LH and FSH causes ovulation.

The third phase of the cycle is called the **luteal phase** (sometimes also called the *secretory phase* or the *postovulatory phase*). After releasing an egg, the follicle, under stimulation of LH, turns into a glandular mass of cells called the **corpus luteum**[4]

Figure 5.3 Ovulation, showing the egg bursting forth from the wall of the ovary.

(hence the names "luteal phase" and "luteinizing hormone"). The corpus luteum manufactures progesterone; thus, progesterone levels rise during the luteal phase. But high levels of progesterone also inhibit the pituitary's secretion of LH, and as LH levels decline, the corpus luteum degenerates. Thus the corpus luteum's output leads to its own eventual destruction. With this degeneration comes a sharp decline in estrogen and progesterone levels at the end of the luteal phase. The falling levels of estrogen stimulate the pituitary to begin production of FSH, and the whole cycle begins again.

The fourth and final phase of the cycle is **menstruation.** Physiologically, menstruation is a shedding of the inner lining of the uterus (the endometrium), which then passes out through the cervix and the vagina. During this phase, estrogen and progesterone levels are low and FSH levels are rising. Menstruation is triggered by the sharp decline in estrogen and progesterone levels at the end of the luteal phase.

What Happens in the Uterus. This brings us to the changes that have been occurring in the uterus while the ovaries and endocrine system were going through the four phases that were just described. During the first, or follicular, phase, the high levels of estrogen stimulate the endometrium (the inner layer) of the uterus to grow, thicken, and form

[3]This statement may seem to contradict one made above, that high estrogen levels cause a decline in LH. Both of these effects occur, but at different times in the menstrual cycle (Molitch, 1995). There are two centres in the hypothalamus, one which produces a negative feedback loop between estrogen and LH, the other which produces a positive feedback loop between the two.

[4]*Corpus luteum* is Latin for "yellow body." The corpus luteum is so named because the mass of cells is yellowish in appearance.

Follicular (fuh-LIK-you-lur) phase: The first phase of the menstrual cycle, beginning just after menstruation, during which an egg matures in preparation for ovulation.
Ovulation: Release of an egg from the ovaries; the second phase of the menstrual cycle.
Luteal (LOO-tee-uhl) phase: The third phase of the menstrual cycle, following ovulation.
Corpus luteum: The mass of cells of the follicle remaining after ovulation; it secretes progesterone.

Menstruation: The fourth phase of the menstrual cycle, during which the endometrium of the uterus is sloughed off in the menstrual discharge.

Figure 5.4   The Keeper menstrual cup, an alternative to sanitary napkins or tampons.

glands that will eventually secrete substances to nourish the embryo; that is, the endometrium proliferates (hence the alternative name for this first phase, the "proliferative phase"). During the luteal phase, the progesterone secreted by the corpus luteum stimulates the glands of the endometrium to start secreting the nourishing substances (hence the name "secretory phase"). If the egg is fertilized and the timing goes properly, about six days after ovulation the fertilized egg arrives in a uterus that is well prepared to cradle and nourish it.

The corpus luteum will continue to produce estrogen and progesterone for about 10 to 12 days. If pregnancy has not occurred, its hormone output declines sharply at the end of this period. The uterine lining thus cannot be maintained, and it is shed, resulting in menstruation. Immediately afterward, a new lining starts forming in the next proliferative phase.

The menstrual fluid itself is a combination of blood (from the endometrium), degenerated cells, and mucus from the cervix and vagina. Normally the discharge for an entire period is only about 60 millilitres or 2 ounces (4 tablespoons). Most commonly the fluid is absorbed with sanitary napkins, which are worn externally, or tampons, which are worn inside the vagina.

Some women use a menstrual cup (brand names *The Keeper* or *The DivaCup*) instead of sanitary napkins or tampons (see Figure 5.4). This is a small reusable device made of flexible rubber or soft medical-grade silicone that has been approved for sale by Health Canada. It has a pull-tab to facil-

itate removal and can be washed in soapy water. Because it is reusable, it is more economical and environmentally friendly.

Recent biological research on the menstrual cycle has led to findings that contradict some previous beliefs (Buffet et al., 1998). First, it turns out that the ovaries—rather than the hypothalamus and pituitary—call the shots in regulating the cycle. Most stages of maturation of the follicle and the egg occur in the ovary under its control, independent of FSH and LH, which are involved in only the last stage of maturation. Levels of FSH and LH are controlled by estrogen and progesterone, which are secreted by the ovaries. Above we discussed the hormone *inhibin*, which is produced by the testes and regulates FSH levels in men. The ovaries also secrete inhibin that, in women as well, suppresses FSH secretion in a negative feedback loop.

Toxic shock syndrome, sometimes abbreviated TSS, is caused by the bacterium *Staphylococcus aureus*. In 1980 a disturbing discovery was made that TSS was associated with tampon use. It was particularly associated with Rely brand tampons, which were withdrawn from the market. Tampon use seems to encourage an abnormal growth of the bacteria. Symptoms of toxic shock syndrome include high fever (39°C or greater) accompanied by vomiting or diarrhea; any woman who experiences these symptoms during her period should discontinue tampon use immediately and see a doctor. Toxic shock syndrome leads to death in approximately 10 percent of cases. It is now recommended that women change tampons frequently, at least every six to eight hours during their periods (although the effectiveness of this is debated), that they not use tampons continuously throughout a menstrual period, and that they minimize use of super-absorbent tampons.

There are no statistics on the number of cases of TSS in Canada, as physicians are not required to report the syndrome. However, the number of cases in the United States has fallen sharply. This is due to public education as well as a change in the chemicals used in tampon manufacture.

Length and Timing of the Cycle.   How long is a normal menstrual cycle? Generally anywhere from 20 to

Toxic shock syndrome: A sometimes fatal bacterial infection associated with tampon use during menstruation.

36 days is considered within the normal range. The average is about 28 days, but somehow this number has taken on more significance than it deserves. There is enormous variation from one woman to the next in the average length of the cycle, and for a given woman there can be considerable variation in length from one cycle to the next.

What is the timing of the various phases of the cycle? In a perfectly regular 28-day cycle, menstruation begins on day 1 and continues until about day 4 or 5. The follicular phase extends from about day 5 to about day 13. Ovulation occurs on day 14, and the luteal phase extends from day 15 to the end of the cycle, day 28. But what if the cycle is not one of those perfect 28-day ones? In cycles that are shorter or longer than 28 days, the principle is that the length of the *luteal* phase is relatively constant. That is, the time from ovulation to menstruation is always 14 days, give or take only a day or two. It is the follicular phase that is of variable length. Thus, for example, if a woman has a 44-day cycle, she ovulates on about day 30. If she has a 22-day cycle, she ovulates on about day 8.

Some women report that they can actually feel themselves ovulate, a phenomenon called *Mittelschmerz* ("middle pain"). The sensation described is a cramping on one or both sides of the lower abdomen, lasting for about a day, which is sometimes confused with appendicitis.

It is also true that ovulation does not occur in every menstrual cycle. That is, menstruation may take place without ovulation. When this happens the woman is said to have an *anovulatory cycle*. Such cycles occur once or twice a year in women in their twenties and thirties and are fairly common among girls during puberty and among women during menopause.

Other Cyclic Changes. Two other physiological processes that fluctuate with the menstrual cycle deserve mention: the cervical mucus cycle and the basal body temperature cycle. The cervix contains glands that secrete mucus throughout the menstrual cycle. One function of the mucus is to protect the entrance to the cervix, helping to keep bacteria out. These glands respond to the changing levels of estrogen during the cycle. As estrogen increases at the start of a new cycle, the mucus is alkaline, thick, and viscous. When LH production begins, just before ovulation, the cervical mucus changes

markedly. It becomes even more alkaline, thin, and watery. Thus the environment for sperm passage is most hospitable just at ovulation. After ovulation, the mucus returns to its former viscous, less alkaline state. If a sample of mucus is taken just before ovulation and is allowed to dry, the dried mucus takes on a fern-shaped pattern. After ovulation, during the luteal phase, the fernlike patterning will not occur. Thus the "fern test" is one method for detecting ovulation. There is also a saliva ovulation test kit sold under the brand name Luna Fertility Indicator.

A woman's *basal body temperature,* taken with a thermometer before getting up in the morning, also fluctuates with the phases of the menstrual cycle. The temperature is low during the follicular phase and takes a dip on the day of ovulation; on the day after ovulation it rises noticeably, generally by 0.3°C or more, and then continues at the higher level for the rest of the cycle. Progesterone raises body temperature, so the higher temperature during the luteal phase is due to the increased production of progesterone during that time (Baker et al., 2002). As the saying goes, "Where there's progesterone, there's heat." This change in basal body temperature is important when a couple are using the fertility awareness method of birth control (Chapter 7) and when a woman is trying to determine the time of ovulation so that she may become pregnant (Chapter 6).

Menstrual Problems

The most common menstrual problem is **dysmenorrhea** (painful menstruation). Almost every woman experiences at least some menstrual discomfort at various times in her life, but the frequency and severity of the discomfort vary considerably from one woman to the next. Cramping pains in the pelvic region are the most common symptom; other symptoms may include headaches, backaches, nausea, and a feeling of pressure and bloating in the pelvis.

Dysmenorrhea is caused by **prostaglandins,** hormonelike substances produced by many tissues of the body, including the lining of the uterus (Deligeor-Oglov, 2000). Prostaglandins can cause

Dysmenorrhea (dis-men-oh-REE-uh): Painful menstruation.
Prostaglandins: Chemicals secreted by the uterus that cause the uterine muscles to contract; they are a likely cause of painful menstruation.

smooth muscle to contract and can affect the size of blood vessels. Women with severe menstrual pain have unusually high levels of prostaglandins. The high levels cause intense uterine contractions, which in turn choke off some of the uterus's supply of oxygen-carrying blood. Prostaglandins may also cause greater sensitivity in nerve endings. The combination of the uterine contractions, lack of oxygen, and heightened nerve sensitivity produces menstrual cramps.

Household remedies for painful menstruation are available and may be helpful to some women. Ibuprofen appears to be the best, and cheapest, painkiller available, and it can help to relieve menstrual pain. A somewhat more provocative remedy suggested by, among others, Masters and Johnson is masturbation. This makes good physiological sense because part of the discomfort of menstruation—the pressure and bloating—results from pelvic edema (a congestion of fluids in the pelvic region). During sexual arousal and orgasm, pelvic congestion increases. After orgasm, the congestion dissipates (see Chapter 9). Thus orgasm, whether produced by masturbation or some other means, should help to relieve the pelvic edema that causes menstrual discomfort. And it's a lot more fun than taking medicine!

Mefenamic acid (an antiprostaglandin drug) is a powerful and effective drug for use in the treatment of menstrual pain. The drug is sold with brand names such as Naprosyn and Anaprox. About 80 to 85 percent of women who take this drug report significant relief from menstrual pain and symptoms such as nausea, vomiting, dizziness, and weakness (Golub, 1992). Interestingly, ibuprofen is also an antiprostaglandin.

Dietary changes and aerobic exercise may also be helpful (Golub, 1992; Hatcher et al., 1998). Caffeine should be avoided; a diet high in carbohydrates and low in protein during the luteal phase is helpful for some.

A menstrual problem that may be mistaken for dysmenorrhea is **endometriosis.** As noted previously the endometrium is the lining of the uterus. Endometriosis occurs when the endometrium grows in a place other than the uterus—for example, the ovaries, fallopian tubes, rectum, bladder, vagina,

vulva, cervix, or lymph glands. Internal bleeding results because endometrial tissue outside the uterus has no way to leave the body. The symptoms vary depending on the location of the growth, but tend to worsen over time. Very painful periods that last an unusually long time, pain during sexual activity, and infertility are the most common symptoms (Ballweg, 1995). Endometriosis is fairly serious and should be treated by a physician. Hormones are generally used in treatment, but if the problem is severe, surgery may be required. Laser surgery is a treatment option.

Another menstrual problem is **amenorrhea,** or the absence of menstruation. It is called *primary amenorrhea* if the girl has not yet menstruated by about age 18. It is called *secondary amenorrhea* if she has had at least one period. Amenorrhea has received considerable attention from physicians because, while rare, it is a symptom of infertility. Some of the causes of amenorrhea include pregnancy, congenital defects of the reproductive system, hormonal imbalance, cysts or tumours, disease, stress, and emotional factors related to puberty and low body fat.

■ Prenatal Sexual Differentiation

Sex Chromosomes

As noted above, at the time of conception the future human being consists of only a single cell, the fertilized egg. The only difference between the fertilized egg that will become a female and the fertilized egg that will become a male is the sex chromosomes carried in that fertilized egg. If there are two X chromosomes, the result will typically be a female; if there is one X and one Y, the result will typically be a male. Thus, while incredibly tiny, the sex chromosomes carry a wealth of information that they transmit to various organs throughout the body, giving them instructions on how to differentiate in the course of development. The Y chromosome, because it is smaller, carries less information than the X.

Occasionally, individuals receive at conception a sex chromosome combination other than XX or XY. Such abnormal sex chromosome complements may lead to a variety of clinical syndromes, such as *Klinefelter's syndrome*. In this syndrome, a genetic male

---

Endometriosis: A condition in which the endometrium grows abnormally outside the uterus; the symptom is unusually painful periods with excessive bleeding.

Amenorrhea: The absence of menstruation.

has an extra X chromosome (XXY). As a result, the testes are abnormal, no sperm are produced, and testosterone levels are low (Winter & Couch, 1995).

The single cell divides repeatedly, becoming a two-celled organism, then a four-celled organism, then an eight-celled organism, and so on. By 28 days after conception, the embryo is about 1 centimetre (less than ½ inch) long, but the male and female embryo are still identical save for the sex chromosomes; that is, the embryo is still in the undifferentiated state. However, by the seventh week after conception, some basic structures have been formed that will eventually become either a male or a female reproductive system. At this point, the embryo has a pair of gonads (each gonad has two parts, an outer cortex and an inner medulla), two sets of ducts (the *Müllerian ducts* and the *Wolffian ducts*), and rudimentary external genitals (the *genital tubercle,* the *urethral folds,* and the *genital swelling*) (see Figure 5.5, top).

Gonads

In the seventh week after conception, the sex chromosomes direct the gonads to begin differentiation. In the male, the undifferentiated gonad develops into a testis at about 7 weeks. In the female, the process occurs somewhat later, with the ovaries developing at around 10 or 11 weeks.

An important gene that directs the differentiation of the gonads, located on the Y chromosome, is called **sex-determining region, Y chromosome (SRY)** (Page et al., 1987; Skaletsky et al., 2003). If SRY is present, testes differentiate and male development occurs (see Figure 5.6 for a summary of all the genes that regulate sexual differentiation). If TDF is not present, female development occurs, making female development the default option. Researchers discovered this gene by studying cases of abnormal development—for example, adult women who had XY sex chromosomes and were infertile. The researchers found that these individuals were missing a section of the Y chromosome, precisely the section containing the SRY. The

[5]Scientists got so excited by this finding of genes on the X chromosome acting on the testes that they started calling them "transsexual genes." Maybe you had to be there.

Sex-determining region, Y chromosome (SRY): A gene on the Y chromosome that causes testes to differentiate prenatally.

X chromosome carries a number of genes that control normal functioning of the ovaries (Winter & Couch, 1995). Surprisingly, a number of genes on the X chromosome affect cells in the testes that manufacture sperm! (Wang et al., 2001).[5]

Prenatal Hormones and the Genitals

Once the ovaries and testes have differentiated, they begin to produce different sex hormones, which then direct the differentiation of the rest of the internal and external genital system (refer to Figure 5.5).

In the female the Wolffian ducts degenerate, and the **Müllerian ducts** turn into the fallopian tubes, the uterus, and the upper part of the vagina. The tubercle becomes the clitoris, the folds become the inner lips, and the swelling develops into the outer lips.

The testes secrete Müllerian Inhibiting Substance (MIS; Vilain, 2000). MIS causes the Müllerian ducts to degenerate, while the **Wolffian ducts,** supported by testosterone, turn into the epididymis, the vas deferens, and the ejaculatory duct. The tubercle becomes the glans penis, the folds form the shaft of the penis, and the swelling develops into the scrotum.

The mechanism by which the internal and external genitals differentiate is the subject of much exciting new research. At least six different genes are involved in prenatal sexual differentiation (Figure 5.6), and a mutation in any one of them can cause an error in development (Vilain, 2000).

By four months after conception, the gender of the fetus is clear from the appearance of the external genitals (Figure 5.5).

Descent of the Testes and Ovaries

As these developmental changes are taking place, the ovaries and testes are changing in shape and position. At first, the ovaries and testes lie near the top of the abdominal cavity. By the tenth week they

Müllerian ducts: Ducts found in both male and female fetuses; in males they degenerate and in females they develop into the fallopian tubes, the uterus, and the upper part of the vagina.
Wolffian ducts: Ducts found in both male and female fetuses; in females they degenerate and in males they develop into the epididymis, the vas deferens, and the ejaculatory duct.

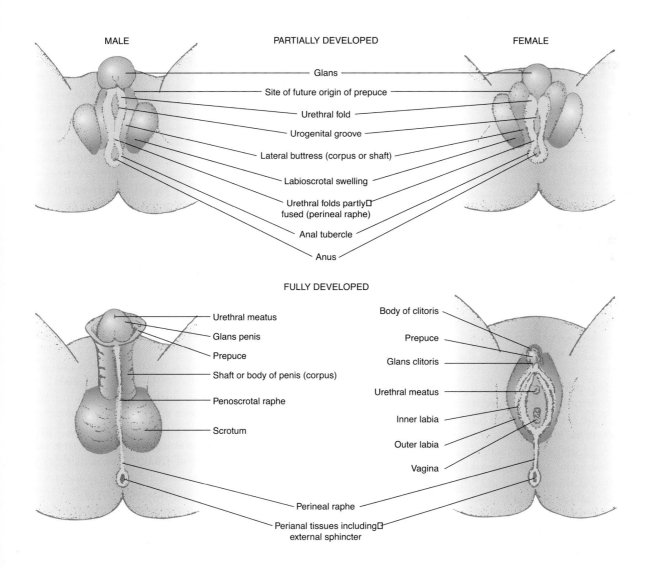

Figure 5.5 Development of the male and female external genitals from the undifferentiated stage. This occurs during prenatal development. Note homologous organs in the female and male.

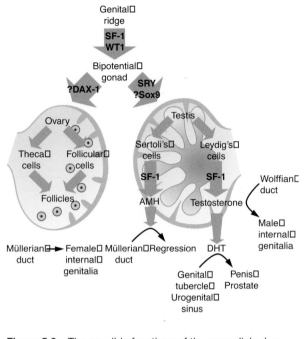

Figure 5.6 The possible functions of the genes linked so far to sexual differentiation in mammals: SRY, Sox9, AMH, WT1, SF-1, and DAX-1 (Marx, 1995b).

have grown and have moved down to the level of the upper edge of the pelvis. The ovaries remain there until after birth; later they shift to their adult position in the pelvis.

The male testes must make a much longer journey, down into the scrotum via a passageway called the *inguinal canal.* Normally this movement occurs around the seventh month after conception. After the descent of the testes, the inguinal canal closes off.

Two problems may occur in this process. First, one or both testes may have failed to descend into the scrotum by the time of birth, a condition known as *undescended testes,* or **cryptorchidism** (Santen, 1995). This occurs in about 2 percent of all males; most frequently, only one testis is undescended, the other being in the normal position. In most of these cases, the testes do descend by puberty, and so only about 1 in 500 adult men has undescended testes. If the testes do not descend

Cryptorchidism: Undescended testes; the condition in which the testes do not descend to the scrotum as they should during prenatal development.

spontaneously, however, the condition must be corrected by surgery or hormonal therapy. The optimum time for doing this is before age 5. Otherwise, if both testes have failed to descend, the man will be sterile because, as discussed in Chapter 4, the high temperature of the testes inside the body inhibits the production of sperm. Undescended testes are also more likely to develop cancer.

The second possible problem occurs when the inguinal canal does not close off completely. It may then reopen later in life, creating a passageway through which loops of the intestine can enter the scrotum. This condition, called *inguinal hernia,* can be remedied by simple surgery.

Brain Differentiation

During the prenatal period, when sex hormones are having a big impact on genital anatomy, they are also acting on the brain (Arnold, 2003). The results of many experiments with animals indicate that, in certain regions, there are differences between male and female brains. The primary sex-differentiated structure is the hypothalamus, in particular a region of it called the *preoptic area* (Collaer & Hines, 1995; Fitch & Bimonte, 2002). In humans, the evidence also indicates that differences exist between male and female brains in the preoptic area, although these differences may develop after birth rather than prenatally (Swaab et al., 1995).

One of the most important effects of this early sexual differentiation is the determination of the estrogen sensitivity of certain cells in the hypothalamus. Estrogen passes into these cells and binds to specific molecules in the nucleus, called *estrogen receptors* (Choi et al., 2001; McEwen, 2001). If testosterone is present during fetal development, these specialized cells in the hypothalamus become insensitive to estrogen. If estrogen is present, these cells become highly sensitive to levels of estrogen in the bloodstream. This sensitivity is crucial to the hypothalamic–pituitary–gonad feedback loop discussed earlier. Male hypothalamic cells are relatively insensitive to estrogen levels, whereas female hypothalamic cells are highly sensitive to them. Male hypothalamic cells have more androgen receptors (Donahue et al., 2000).

New magnetic resonance imaging (MRI) studies are giving us a view into the brains of alive, awake humans, in contrast to earlier techniques that dissected the brains of—well, dead people and animals. The trade-off, at least for now, is that the MRI measures are relatively crude, simple assessments of the volume or size of certain regions. One of these studies found a larger volume of the hypothalamus and amygdala—both being brain regions with high densities of estrogen and androgen receptors—in men compared with women (Goldstein et al., 2001). Regions of the brain that have few estrogen and androgen receptors did not show these gender differences in size. Interestingly, a different MRI technique, the functional MRI or fMRI, has detected increased activation in one region of the hypothalamus in men who were sexually aroused (Arnow et al., 2002).

Homologous Organs

The preceding discussion of sexual differentiation highlights the fact that although adult men and women appear to have very different reproductive anatomies, their reproductive organs have similar origins. When an organ in the male and an organ in the female both develop from the same embryonic tissue, the organs are said to be **homologous.** When the two organs have similar functions, they are said to be **analogous.** Table 5.1 summarizes the major homologies and analogies of the male and female reproductive systems. For example, ovaries and testes are both homologous (they develop from an undifferentiated gonad) and analogous (they produce gametes and sex hormones).

Atypical Prenatal Gender Differentiation

Gender is not a simple matter, a fact that is apparent from the preceding discussion. Most people, however, assume that it is. That is, people typically assume that if a person is female, she will be feminine; will think of herself as a woman; will be sexually attracted to men; will have a clitoris, vagina, uterus, and ovaries; and will have sex chromosomes XX. The parallel assumption is that all males are masculine; think of themselves as male; are sexually attracted to women; have a penis, testes, and scrotum; and have sex chromosomes XY.

Homologous (huh-MOLL-uh-gus) organs: Organs in the male and female that develop from the same embryonic tissue.
Analogous (an-AL-uh-gus) organs: Organs in the male and female that have similar functions.

A great deal of research over the last several decades challenges these assumptions and provides much information about sexuality and gender and their development. Before the results of this research are discussed, however, some background information is necessary.

We can distinguish among the following eight variables of gender (Money, 1987):[6]

1. *Chromosomal gender*   XX in the female; XY in the male
2. *Gonadal gender*   Ovaries in the female; testes in the male
3a. *Prenatal hormonal gender*   Testosterone and MIS in the male but not the female before birth
3b. *Prenatal and neonatal brain differentiation*   Testosterone present for masculinization, absent for feminization
4. *Internal organs*   Fallopian tubes, uterus, and upper vagina in the female; prostate and seminal vesicles in the male
5. *External genital appearance*   Clitoris, inner and outer lips, and vaginal opening in the female; penis and scrotum in the male
6. *Pubertal hormonal gender*   At puberty, estrogen and progesterone in the female; testosterone in the male
7. *Assigned gender*   The announcement at birth, "It's a girl" or "It's a boy," based on the appearance of the external genitals; the gender the parents and the rest of society believe the child to be; the gender in which the child is reared
8. *Gender identity*   The person's private, internal sense of maleness or femaleness

These variables might be subdivided into biological variables (the first six) and psychological variables (the last two). (Gender roles, or the way people of one gender are expected to behave, are discussed in Chapter 14.)

In most cases, of course, all the variables are in agreement in an individual. That is, in most cases the person is a "consistent" female or male. If the person is a female, she has XX chromosomes, ovaries, a uterus and vagina, and a clitoris; she is reared as a female; and she thinks of herself as a

---

[6]The distinction between the terms "gender" and "sex," discussed in Chapter 1, is being maintained here.

Table 5.1   Homologous and Analogous Organs of the Male and Female Reproductive Systems

	Homologous Organs		Analogous Organs	
Embryonic Source	In the Adult Male	In the Adult Female	In the Adult Male	In the Adult Female
Gonad (medulla plus cortex)	Testes (from medulla)	Ovaries (from cortex)	Testes (from medulla)	Ovaries (from cortex)
Genital tubercle	Glans penis	Clitoris	Glans penis	Clitoris
Genital swelling	Scrotum	Outer lips		
Müllerian duct		Fallopian tubes, uterus, part of vagina		
Wolffian duct	Epididymis, vas deferens, seminal vesicles			
Urethral primordia	Prostate, Cowper's glands	Skene's glands, Bartholin glands	Prostate, Cowper's glands	Skene's glands, Bartholin glands

female. If the person is a male, he has the parallel set of appropriate characteristics.

However, as a result of any one of a number of factors during the course of prenatal sexual development, the gender indicated by one or more of these variables may disagree with the gender indicated by others. When the contradictions are among several of the biological variables (1 through 6), the person is called an **intersex** or *pseudohermaphrodite*.[7] Biologically, the gender of such a person is ambiguous; the reproductive structures may be partly male and partly female, or they may be incompletely male or female. Approximately 2 percent of births have an intersex condition (Blackless et al., 2000). Individuals whose assigned gender does not match their gender identity are discussed in Chapter 14.

A number of syndromes can cause intersex, some of the most common being congenital adrenal hyperplasia, progestin-induced pseudohermaphroditism, and the androgen insensitivity syndrome. In **congenital adrenal hyperplasia** (**CAH,** also called "adrenogenital syndrome"), a genetic female develops ovaries normally as a fetus; later in the course of prenatal development, however, the adrenal gland begins to function abnormally (as a result of a recessive genetic

condition unconnected with the sex chromosomes), and an excess amount of androgens is produced. Prenatal sexual differentiation then does not follow the normal female course. As a result, the external genitals are partly or completely male in appearance; the labia are partly or totally fused (and thus there is no vaginal opening), and the clitoris is enlarged to the size of a small penis or even a full-sized one. Hence at birth these genetic females are sometimes identified as males. Long-term follow-ups indicate that CAH girls have a female gender identity and generally function well as girls and women (Wisniewski et al., 2000).

Progestin-induced pseudohermaphroditism is a similar syndrome that resulted from a drug, progestin, which was at one time given to pregnant women to help them maintain the pregnancy if they were prone to miscarriage. (The drug is no longer prescribed because of the following effects.) As the drug circulated in the mother's bloodstream, the developing fetus was essentially exposed to a high dose of androgens. (Progestin and

---

Intersex: An individual who has a mixture of male and female reproductive structures, so that it is not clear at birth whether the individual is a male or a female. Also called a *pseudohermaphrodite*.
Congenital adrenal hyperplasia (CAH): A condition in which a genetic female produces abnormal levels of testosterone prenatally and therefore has male-appearing genitals at birth.

---

[7]The term "hermaphrodite" is taken from Hermaphroditos, the name of the mythological son of Hermes and Aphrodite. The latter was the Greek goddess of love. A true hermaphrodite has both ovarian and testicular tissues.

androgens are quite similar biochemicals, and in the body the progestin acted like an androgen.) In genetic females this produced an abnormal, masculinized genital development similar to that found in CAH.

The reverse case occurs in **androgen insensitivity syndrome (AIS)** (Wisniewski et al., 2000). In this syndrome a genetic male produces normal levels of testosterone; however, as a result of a genetic condition the body tissues are insensitive to the testosterone, and prenatal development is feminized. Thus the individual is born with the external appearance of a female: a small vagina (but no uterus) and undescended testes. The individual whose poem appeared at the beginning of this chapter has AIS.

Intersex persons provide good evidence of the great complexity of sex and gender and their development. Many variables are involved in gender and sex, and there are many steps in gender differentiation, even before birth. Because the process is complex it is vulnerable to disturbances, creating conditions such as intersex. Indeed, the research serves to question our basic notions of what it means to be male or female. In CAH, is the genetic female who is born with male external genitals a male or a female? What makes a person male or female? Chromosomal gender? External genital appearance? Gender identity?

A related phenomenon was first studied in a small community in the Dominican Republic (Imperato-McGinley et al., 1974). Due to a genetic-endocrine problem, a large number of genetic males were born there who, at birth, appeared to be females. The syndrome is called *5-Alpha Reductase Syndrome.* They had a vaginal pouch instead of a scrotum and a clitoris-sized penis. The uneducated parents, according to the researchers, were unaware that there were any problems, and these genetic males were treated as typical females. At puberty, a spontaneous biological change caused a penis to develop. Significantly, their psychological identity also changed. Despite rearing as females, their gender identity switched to male, and they developed heterosexual interests. In their culture, these people are called Guevodoces ("penis at twelve").

Anthropologist Gilbert Herdt (1990) is critical of the research and interpretations about the Guevodoces. The major criticism is that the Western researchers assumed that this culture is a two-gender society, as in Canada, and that people have to fall into one of only two categories, either male or female. Anthropologists, however, have documented the existence of three-gender societies—that is, societies in which there are three, not two, gender categories—and the society in which the Guevodoces grow up is a three-gender society. The third gender is the Guevodoces. Their gender identity is not male or female, but Guevodoce. The 5-Alpha Reductase Syndrome has also been found among the Sambia of New Guinea, who also have a three-gender culture. Again we see the profound effect of culture on our most basic ideas about sex and gender.

■ Sexual Differentiation during Puberty

Puberty is not a point in time, but rather a process during which there is further sexual differentiation. It is the stage in life during which the body changes from that of a child into that of an adult, with secondary sexual characteristics and the ability to reproduce sexually. **Puberty** can be scientifically defined as the time during which there is sudden enlargement and maturation of the gonads, other genitalia, and secondary sex characteristics (such as breasts or a beard), leading to reproductive capacity (Tanner, 1967). It is the second important period—the other being the prenatal period—during which sexual differentiation takes place. Perhaps the most important single event in the process is the first ejaculation for the male and the first menstruation for the female, although the latter is not necessarily a sign of reproductive capability since girls typically do not produce mature eggs until a year or two after the first menstruation.

Androgen-insensitivity syndrome (AIS): A genetic condition in which the body is unresponsive to androgens so that a genetic male may be born with a female-appearing body.

Puberty: The time during which there is sudden enlargement and maturation of the gonads, other genitalia, and secondary sex characteristics, so that the individual becomes capable of reproduction.

In Focus 5.1

Can Gender Be Assigned? The Story of David Reimer

In Winnipeg in 1965, Janet Reimer gave birth to twin boys, Bruce and Brian. Six months later, the boys developed problems urinating, and their doctor suggested that they be circumcised. However, the doctor did not use the standard procedure for circumcision and botched the surgery, burning off Bruce's entire penis. The Reimers were told that Bruce would have to live without a penis. Some months later, Janet Reimer saw a television program describing the pioneering work of Dr. John Money of Johns Hopkins University in Baltimore. Money believed that gender is determined by how a child is raised, not by his or her biology. He argued that his research on intersex individuals (whom he called "pseudohermaphrodites") showed that individuals could be successfully assigned to either gender, providing that assignment is done in infancy and the necessary surgeries and hormone treatments occur. The Reimers consulted Money, who advised them that if Bruce were raised as female and received the appropriate medical treatments, he would likely live a happy and healthy life as a girl and woman.

The decision was made to raise Bruce as female. At the age of 21 months, Bruce's testicles were removed. The Reimers renamed their son Brenda, and following the counsel of Dr. Money resolved not to tell their child the truth. However, despite taking hormones and receiving numerous surgeries, Brenda never really fit in as a girl. She preferred stereotypically male play (e.g., climbing trees) over playing with dolls, and was frequently made fun of by other children for her masculine mannerisms. Brenda even complained of feeling like a boy. When she reached puberty, and was scheduled to have a final surgery to construct a vagina, Brenda refused, indicating she would prefer to die. A psychiatrist suggested to Mr. and Mrs. Reimer that they tell the truth to Brenda, who later commented about this revelation, "Suddenly it all made sense why I felt the way I did."

Within months of learning the truth about his sex, Bruce/Brenda cut his hair, began wearing masculine clothing, and changed his name to David. He underwent a series of surgeries to give him a more male body, including a mastectomy to remove the breasts he had grown as a result of taking estrogen. Although David was much happier with his gender, he struggled with depression, in part because he thought he would not find a partner who would love him for who he was. However, as a young adult, David met and married Jane and became the father of her three children. Yet David continued to battle depression, which worsened in his late thirties following the death of his twin brother. He also experienced marital and work-related difficulties, and failed financial investments. On May 4, 2004, at the age of 38, David committed suicide.

Babies who are born with genitals that are not clearly male or female (intersex individuals) typically are treated like David was, using a protocol that became standard in the 1960s. The treatment, which is based on Money's work, generally involves surgically altering the infant's genitals to make them clearly male or female. In Canada, such procedures are covered under medicare. However, the Intersex Society of North America (ISNA) has argued that intersexuality represents genital *variability*—as opposed to genital abnormality, which is how the medical profession has typically regarded it. The medical standard is that an infant's organ that is 0.9 centimetres or less should be considered a clitoris and 2.5 centimetres or more should be considered a penis, and an infant's gender is assigned accordingly. Intersex activists argue that these cutoffs are arbitrary. What is wrong with a clitoris that is 1.7 centimetres long, for example? Ontario psychologist Morgan Holmes believes that the surgeries are conducted because doctors and parents are uncomfortable with the idea of a child not having genitals that fit a narrow definition of what genitals should look like. He also raised issues related to medical ethics. Should such surgeries and gender assignments be conducted with infants, who cannot give informed consent and who may later prefer another gender than that chosen for them by their parents and doctors? Should parents be encouraged to lie to their

Figure 5.7 David Reimer underwent gender reassignment after a botched surgery when he was six months old.

child, as David Reimer's parents were?

Sex researcher Milton Diamond conducted long-term follow-up studies on several individuals who were treated using Money's standard protocol, including David Reimer. Diamond found that, contrary to Money's published paper describing these individuals as well-adjusted, many of these individuals had significant adjustment problems that they traced directly to the medical "management" of their condition. Diamond has proposed an alternative protocol for dealing with intersex infants in which he urges physicians: (1) to make their most informed judgment about the child's eventual gender identity and counsel the parents to rear the child in that gender; (2) not to perform surgeries that might later need to be reversed; and (3) to provide honest counselling and education to the parents and child as he or she grows up so that the child can eventually make an informed decision regarding treatment.

More systematic follow-up studies on intersex individuals have followed. *Micropenis* is a condition in which a genetic, XY male is born with a very small penis. One study followed up 18 of these individuals in adulthood; 13 had been reared as boys and 5 as girls (Wisniewski et al., 2001). All of the individuals raised as boys reported good or fair erections, but 50 percent were dissatisfied with their genitals. In contrast, 80 percent of the individuals raised as girls were dissatisfied with their genitals and 40 per-

cent had no sexual interest or experience. Whether raised as male or female, all were satisfied with their gender. In this case, it seems that being raised as male resulted in greater satisfaction with their genitals and higher sexual interest. Their satisfaction with their gender supports Money's ideas: gender seems to be partly determined by environment.

Another study examined the success of genital surgery to reduce the size of an "overly large" clitoris or to create or enlarge a vagina, as might happen with CAH girls (Creighton et al., 2001). Of the surgeries done in childhood, 41 percent were judged as having a poor outcome, supporting Diamond's recommendations against these early surgeries. Another study of intersex women—many of them with CAH—who had had clitoral surgery in childhood indicated 39 percent were unable to orgasm, compared with 20 percent of a control group of intersex women who had not had clitoral surgery (Minto et al., 2003). This suggests that early surgery may adversely affect the later sexual functioning of girls born with CAH.

Recognizing these new developments, the American Academy of Pediatrics (2000) issued guidelines for pediatricians on how to care for newborns with genitals that are not clearly male or female. The guidelines specify the factors that should be used to decide which sex a child should be raised as. They include fertility potential and capacity for normal sexual functioning. It should be recognized that much of the treatment of intersex individuals—that is, their assignment to either a female or male gender—comes from society's discomfort with individuals who do not fit into one of only two clearly demarcated categories: female and male. It is only with long-term studies and much consultation with intersex individuals themselves that we will learn how best to treat infants who are born with genital variability.

Sources: American Academy of Pediatrics Committee on Genetics, 2000; CBC News Online, May 10, 2004; Colapinto, June 3, 2004; Creighton & Minto, 2001; Creighton et al., 2001; Diamond, 1996, 1999; Diamond & Sigmundson, 1997; Holmes, 2002; Meyer-Bahlburg, 2004; Money & Ehrhardt, 1972; Wisniewski et al., 2000.

The physiological process that underlies puberty in both genders is a marked increase in level of sex hormones. Thus the hypothalamus, pituitary, and gonads control the changes.

Adolescence is a socially defined period of development that bears some relationship to puberty. Adolescence represents a psychological transition from the behaviour and attitudes of a child to the behaviour, attitudes, and responsibilities of an adult. In Canada it corresponds roughly to the years from age 10 to age 20. Modern Canadian culture has an unusually long period of adolescence (Steinberg, 2002). A century ago, adolescence was much shorter; the lengthening of the educational process has served to prolong adolescence. In some cultures, in fact, adolescence does not exist; the child shifts to being an adult directly, with only a *rite de passage* in between.

Before describing the changes that take place during puberty, we should note two points. First, the timing of the pubertal process differs considerably for males and females. Girls begin the change around 8 to 12 years of age, while boys do so about two years later. Girls reach their full height by about age 16, while boys continue growing until about age 18 or later. Differences between boys and girls in the onset of puberty may create small crises for the adolescent. Many girls are romantically interested in boys long before boys are. Both boys and girls may feel embarrassed when a girl towers over the boy she is dating.

Second, there are large individual differences in the age at which puberty begins. Experiences may also affect the timing of puberty. For example, girls who have been sexually abused experience earlier puberty than do non-abused girls (Turner et al., 1999). There is no "normal" time to begin menstruating or growing a beard. Thus, we give age ranges in describing the timing of the process.

Changes in the Male

A summary of the physical changes of puberty in males and females is provided in Table 5.2. As noted above, puberty begins at about 10 or 11 years of age in boys, about two years later than it does in girls. The physical causes of puberty in boys parallel those in girls. They are initiated by increased production of FSH and LH by the pituitary. At the beginning of puberty, the increase in LH stimulates the testes to produce testosterone, which is responsible for most of the changes of puberty in the male.

The first noticeable pubertal change in males is the growth of the testes and scrotal sac, which begins at around 10 to 13 years of age as a result of testosterone stimulation. The growth of pubic hair begins at about the same time. About a year later the penis begins to enlarge, first thickening and then lengthening. This change also results from testosterone stimulation. As the testes enlarge, their production of testosterone increases even more; thus there is rapid growth of the penis, testes, and pubic hair at ages 13 and 14.

The growth of facial and axillary hair begins about two years after the beginning of pubic-hair growth. The growth of facial hair begins with the appearance of fuzz on the upper lip; adult beards do not appear until two or three years later. Indeed, by age 17, 50 percent of North American males have not yet shaved. These changes also result from testosterone stimulation, which continues to produce growth of facial and chest hair beyond 20 years of age.

Erections increase in frequency and sometimes occur at inopportune times. The organs that produce the fluid of semen, particularly the prostate, enlarge considerably at about the same time the other organs are growing. By age 13 or 14 the boy is capable of ejaculation.[8] By about age 15, the ejaculate contains mature sperm, and the male is now fertile. The pituitary hormone FSH is responsible for initiating and maintaining the production of mature sperm.

Beginning about a year after the first ejaculation, many boys begin having nocturnal emissions, or "wet dreams." For the boy who has never masturbated, a wet dream may be his first ejaculation.

At about the same time penis growth occurs, the larynx ("voice box") also begins to grow in response to testosterone. As the larynx enlarges, the boy's voice drops, or "changes." Typically the transition occurs at around age 13 or 14. Because testosterone is necessary to produce the change in voice, castration before puberty results in a male with a permanently high voice. This principle was used to produce the *castrati*, who sang in the great choirs of Europe during the eighteenth century.

---

[8]Note that orgasm and ejaculation are two separate processes, even though they generally occur together, at least in males after puberty. But orgasm may occur without ejaculation, and ejaculation may occur without orgasm.

Table 5.2 Summary of the Changes of Puberty and Their Sequence

Girls			Boys		
Characteristic	Age Range for First Appearance (Years)	Major Hormonal Influence	Characteristic	Age Range for First Appearance (Years)	Major Hormonal Influence
1. Growth of breasts	7–13	Pituitary growth hormone, estrogens, progesterone, thyroxine	1. Growth of testes, scrotal sac	10–13.5	Pituitary growth hormone, testosterone
2. Growth of pubic hair	8–14	Adrenal androgens	2. Growth of pubic hair	10–15	Testosterone
3. Body growth	9.5–14.5	Pituitary growth hormone, adrenal androgens, estrogens	3. Body growth	10.5–16	Pituitary growth hormone, testosterone
4. Menarche	10–16.5	GnRH, FSH, LH, estrogens, progesterone	4. Growth of penis	11–14.5	Testosterone
			5. Change in voice (growth of larynx)	About the same time as penis growth	Testosterone
5. Underarm hair	About two years after pubic hair	Adrenal androgens	6. Facial and underarm hair	About two years after pubic hair	Testosterone
6. Oil- and sweat-producing glands (acne occurs when glands are clogged)	About the same time as underarm hair	Adrenal androgens	7. Oil- and sweat-producing glands, acne	About the same time as underarm hair	Testosterone

Source: After B. Goldstein (1976), *Introduction to human sexuality.* New York: McGraw-Hill, pp. 80–81. Reprinted by permission of Bernard Goldstein.

They began as lovely boy sopranos, and their parents or the choirmaster, hating to see their beautiful voices destroyed at puberty, had them castrated so that they remained permanent sopranos. Contrary to popular belief, castration in adulthood will not produce a high voice, because the larynx has already grown.

A great spurt of body growth begins in males at around 11 to 16 years of age (Figure 5.8a). Height increases rapidly. Body contours also change. While the changes in girls involve mainly the increase in fatty tissue in the breasts and hips, the changes in boys involve mainly an increase in muscle mass. Eventually testosterone brings the growth process to an end, although it permits the growth period to

continue longer than it does in females.

Puberty brings changes and also problems. One problem is *acne,* which is stimulated by androgens and affects boys more frequently than girls. *Acne* is a distressing skin condition that is caused by a clogging of the sebaceous (oil-producing) glands, resulting in pustules, blackheads, and redness on the face and possibly the chest and back. Generally acne is not severe enough to require medical treatment, although its psychological impact may be great. In order to avoid scarring, severe cases should be treated by a physician, the treatment typically being ultraviolet light, the drug Retin-A, and/or antibiotics. The drug Accutane is highly effective for severe cases. However, it must be used

(a)   (b)

Figure 5.8 There is great variability in the onset of puberty and its growth spurt. All these boys are the same age. Both these girls are the same age.

cautiously because it may have serious side effects, including depression and thoughts of suicide.

Gynecomastia (breast enlargement) may occur temporarily in boys, creating considerable embarrassment. About 80 percent of boys in puberty experience this growth, which is probably caused by small amounts of female sex hormones being produced by the testes. Obesity may also be a temporary problem, although it is more frequent in girls than boys.

In various cultures around the world, puberty rites are performed to signify the adolescent's passage to adulthood. Many aboriginal cultures celebrate this life transition for males and females. In Canada the only remaining vestiges of such ceremonies are the Jewish bar mitzvah for boys and bat mitzvah for girls and, in some Christian churches, confirmation. In a sense, it is unfortunate that we do not give more formal recognition to puberty. Puberty rites probably serve an important psychological function in that they are a formal, public announcement of the fact that the boy or girl is passing through an important period of change. In the absence of such rituals, the young person may think that his or her body is doing strange things and may feel very much alone. This may be particularly problematic for boys, who lack an obvious sign of puberty like the first menstruation (the first ejaculation is probably the closest analogy) to help them identify the stage they are in.

Changes in the Female

The first sign of puberty in the female is the beginning of breast development, generally at around 7 to 13 years of age (Herman-Gibbens et al., 1997). The ducts in the nipple area swell, and there is growth of fatty and connective tissue, causing the small, conical buds to increase in size. These changes are produced by increases in the levels of the sex hormones by a mechanism that will be described below.

As the growth of fatty and supporting tissue increases in the breasts, a similar increase takes place at the hips and buttocks, leading to the rounded contours that distinguish adult female bodies from adult male bodies. Individual females have unique patterns of fat deposits, so there are also considerable individual differences in the resulting female shapes.

Another visible sign of puberty is the growth of pubic hair, which occurs shortly after breast development begins. About two years later, axillary (underarm) hair appears.

Body growth increases sharply during puberty, during the approximate age range of 9.5 to 14.5 years. The growth spurt for girls occurs about two years before the growth spurt for boys (Figure 5.10). This is consistent with girls' general pattern of maturing earlier than boys. Even prenatally, girls show an earlier hardening of the structures that become bones.

Estrogen eventually applies the brakes to the growth spurt in girls; the presence of estrogen also causes the growth period to end sooner in girls, thus accounting for the lesser average height of adult women as compared with adult men.

At about 12 to 13 years of age, the **menarche** (first menstruation) occurs. The girl, however, is not capable of becoming pregnant until ovulation

Menarche (MEN-ar-key): First menstruation.

begins. Typically girls do not ovulate regularly for one to two years after first ovulation (Metcalfe et al., 1983). The first menstruation is not only an important biological event but also a significant psychological one. Various cultures have ceremonies recognizing its importance. In some families, it is a piece of news that spreads quickly to the relatives. Girls themselves display a wide range of reactions to the event, ranging from negative ones, such as fear, shame, or disgust, to positive ones, such as pride and a sense of maturity and womanliness.

Some of the most negative reactions occur when the girl has not been prepared for the menarche, which is still the case surprisingly often. Parents who are concerned about preparing their daughters for the first menstruation should remember that there is a wide range in the age at which it occurs. It is not unusual for a girl to start menstruating in grade 5, and instances of the menarche during grade 4, while rare, do occur.

What determines the age at which a girl first menstruates? One explanation is the *percent body fat hypothesis* (Frisch & McArthur, 1974; Hopwood

(a)

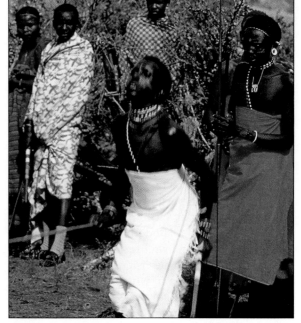

(b)

Figure 5.9 Most cultures celebrate puberty, but cultures vary widely in the nature of the celebration. Canadian Jewish youth celebrate a bar mitzvah (for boys) or bat mitzvah (for girls). The Samburu youth of Kenya celebrate a male circumcision ritual.

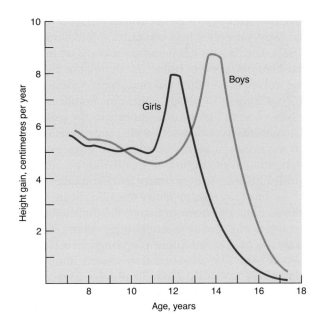

Figure 5.10 The adolescent spurt of growth for boys and girls. Note that girls experience their growth spurt earlier than boys do.

et al., 1990). During puberty, deposits of body fat increase in females. According to the percent body fat hypothesis, the percentage of body weight that is fat must rise to a certain level for menstruation to occur for the first time and for it to be maintained. Thus very thin adolescent girls would tend to be late in the timing of first menstruation. **Leptin,** a protein manufactured in the body, seems to be related to the onset of puberty in girls and in boys, although scientists have not yet sorted out the details (Apter, 2003; Phillip & Lazar, 2003; Wilson et al., 2003). In prepubertal girls and boys, leptin levels rise as body fat increases. Leptin simulates the growth of skeletal bone and the release of LH.

The percent body fat hypothesis also helps to make sense of two related phenomena: the cessation of menstruation in anorexics and the cessation of menstruation in female distance runners. *Anorexia nervosa* is a condition in which the person—most commonly an adolescent girl—engages in compulsive, extreme dieting and exercise, perhaps to

the point of starving herself to death. As anorexia progresses, the percentage of body fat declines and menstruation ceases. It is also fairly common for women who are runners, and all women who exercise seriously to the point where their body fat is substantially reduced, to cease menstruating. For both anorexics and female runners, it seems that when the percentage of body fat falls below a critical value, the biological mechanisms that control the menstrual cycle shut down menstruation.[9]

Before leaving the topic of running, we should note that there is some evidence that serious exercise also affects the male reproductive system. One study of male distance runners found that their testosterone levels were only about 68 percent as high, on the average, as a control group's testosterone levels (Wheeler et al., 1984). There are some reports of male long-distance runners complaining of a loss of sex drive, but it is unclear whether this results from reduced testosterone levels or from the perpetual feelings of fatigue from their intensive training (Wheeler et al., 1984).

Other body changes in girls during puberty include a development of the blood supply to the clitoris, a thickening of the walls of the vagina, and a rapid growth of the uterus, which doubles in size between the tenth and the eighteenth years. The pelvic bone structure grows and widens, contributing to the rounded shape of the female and creating a passageway large enough for an infant to move through during birth.

The dramatic changes that occur during puberty are produced, basically, by the endocrine system and its upsurge in sex hormone production during puberty. The process begins with an increase in secretion of FSH by the pituitary gland. FSH in turn stimulates the ovaries to produce estrogen. Estrogen is responsible for many of the changes that occur; it stimulates breast growth and the growth of the uterus and vagina.

Also involved in puberty are the paired **adrenal glands,** which are located just above the kidneys.

---

[9]On the other hand, programs of moderate, regular aerobic exercise have been shown to reduce menstrual problems such as cramps (Golub, 1992).

Leptin: A protein produced in the body that is related to the onset of puberty.

Adrenal (uh-DREE-nul) glands: Endocrine glands located just above the kidneys; in the female they are the major producers of androgens.

In the female, the adrenal glands are the major producer of androgens, which exist at low levels in females. Adrenal androgens stimulate the growth of pubic and axillary hair and are related to the female sex drive. **Adrenarche**—the time of increasing secretion of adrenal androgens—generally begins slightly before age 8 (Grumbach & Styne, 1998).

■ Psychological Aspects of the Menstrual Cycle

"Why do I get so emotional?" screams the ad for Midol PMS in *Teen* magazine. It is part of the folk wisdom of our culture that women experience fluctuations in mood over the phases of the menstrual cycle. In particular, women are supposed to be especially cranky and depressed just before and during their periods. In France, if a woman commits a crime during her premenstrual phase, she may use the fact in her defence, claiming "temporary impairment of sanity."

What is the scientific evidence concerning the occurrence of such fluctuations in mood, and, if they do occur, what causes them?

Fluctuations in Mood: Do Women Become Extra Emotional?

The term **premenstrual syndrome (PMS)** is used to refer to those cases in which the woman has a particularly severe combination of physical, psychological, and behavioural symptoms premenstrually; these symptoms may include depression, irritability, breast pain, and water retention (Stanton et al., 2002). In the last several decades much research has been done on moods during the premenstrual period and on whether moods fluctuate during the cycle.

Research based on women's daily self-reports throughout the cycle (that is, prospective studies) has found different patterns depending on how the study was conducted. Some studies have found

positive moods around the time of ovulation (that is, mid-cycle), and various symptoms, such as anxiety, irritability, depression, fatigue, and headaches, premenstrually (Golub, 1992). However, the fluctuations are not large. Other prospective studies have found that, on average, women's moods do not change over the menstrual cycle, even though the women later remember having had more pleasant moods at mid-cycle and more unpleasant moods premenstrually (McFarlane et al., 1988).

There have been a number of criticisms made of the research on mood fluctuations during the menstrual cycle (McFarlane & Williams, 1990; Stanton et al., 2002). Two deserve special mention here. First, much of the evidence depends on subjective retrospective reports of mood and symptoms, which are probably not very reliable. Second, the interpretation of the direction of any changes a woman experiences might be questioned. The typical interpretation is that women show a psychological "deficit" premenstrually, as compared with the "normal" state at ovulation and during the rest of the cycle. However, the opposite interpretation might also be made: that women are "normal" premenstrually and experience unusual well-being psychologically at mid-cycle. What defines "normal" or "average" mood, then? Men's moods?

Support for a reinterpretation might come from the statistics on violent crimes committed by women. While it may be true that women are somewhat more likely to commit crimes during the eight premenstrual and menstrual days, even during this period they are far less likely to commit crimes than men are. Thus women might be considered to experience "normal" or typical moods (comparable to men's moods) during the premenstrual and menstrual days and to have feelings of unusual well-being around ovulation. Further, most studies comparing cycles in the moods of women and men have not found differences (Stanton et al., 2002).

Taking into account the criticisms and available evidence, it seems reasonable to conclude the following:

1. Women do, on average, experience some fluctuations in mood over the phases of the menstrual cycle.
2. Present evidence does not clearly indicate how the direction of the shifts should be interpreted—whether women are unusually "low"

Adrenarche (AD-ren-ar-key): A time of increased secretion of adrenal androgens, usually just before age 8.
Premenstrual syndrome (PMS): A combination of severe physical and psychological symptoms, such as depression and irritability, occurring just before menstruation.

premenstrually or unusually "high" around the time of ovulation.

3. There is a great deal of variation from one woman to the next in the size of these shifts and the way they are expressed. Some women experience no shifts or shifts so slight that they are not noticeable, whereas others may experience large shifts. It would be interesting to know how many do show mood fluctuations and how many do not. Unfortunately, the studies that have tried to provide this information themselves show substantial variation; the percentage reporting symptoms ranges between 25 percent and 80 percent in various studies (Stanton et al., 2002). It is important to make a distinction between women who have severe PMS and women who experience no fluctuation or only moderate fluctuations in mood over the cycle.

The American Psychiatric Association has formalized PMS with the diagnosis **premenstrual dysphoric disorder,** or PMDD, in the *DSM-IV* as a severe form of PMS (American Psychiatric Association, 2000). It isn't in the main *DSM,* but rather in an appendix, meaning that it isn't officially "in" yet because there is still controversy around the diagnosis. Symptoms must occur during the last week of the luteal phase and include feeling sad or hopeless, feeling tense or anxious, tearfulness, irritability, difficulty concentrating, and changes in appetite. These have to have occurred most months for the past year and must interfere with the woman's regular behaviour. This new diagnostic category is very controversial, however (Caplan, 1995). Some argue that it represents nothing but a medicalizing and pathologizing of women's experience (Offman & Kleinplatz, 2004; Poulin & Gouliquer, 2003). Others point out that the scientific basis for PMDD is nonexistent, that some studies fail to confirm it, and that PMDD may just reflect a worsening of a woman's preexisting depression (Gallant et al., 1992; Hartlage & Gehlert, 2001; Stanton et al., 2002).

Premenstrual dysphoric disorder (PMDD): A tentative diagnostic category in the DSM-IV, characterized by symptoms such as sadness, anxiety, and irritability in the week before menstruation.

Fluctuations in Performance: Should Women Be Prime Minister?

So far our discussion has concentrated on fluctuations in psychological characteristics such as depression, anxiety, and irritability. However, in some situations performance is of more practical importance than mood. For example, is a female mechanic's work less accurate premenstrually and menstrually? Is a female athlete's coordination or speed impaired during the premenstrual–menstrual period?

Research on performance—such as intellectual or athletic performance—generally shows no fluctuations over the cycle. Research has found no fluctuations in academic performance, problem solving, memory, or creative thinking (Epting & Overman, 1988; Stanton et al; 2002).

In one study, 31 percent of female athletes said they believed that they experienced a decline in performance during the premenstrual or menstrual phases; yet when their actual performance was measured, they showed no deficits in strength (weight lifters) or swimming speed (swimming team members) (Quadagno et al., 1991). Thus there is no reliable evidence indicating that the kinds of performance required in a work situation or an athletic competition fluctuate over the menstrual cycle.

Fluxuations in Sex Drive

Another psychological characteristic that has been investigated for fluctuations over the cycle is women's sex drive or arousability. Observations of female animals that have estrous cycles indicate that sexual behaviour depends a great deal on cycle phase and the corresponding hormonal state. Females of these species engage in sexual behaviour enthusiastically when they are in the estrus, or "heat," phase of the cycle and do not engage in sexual behaviour at all during any other phase. This makes good biological sense, since the females engage in sex precisely when they are fertile.

Human females, of course, engage in sexual behaviour throughout the menstrual cycle. But might some subtle cycling in drive remain, expressed, perhaps, in fluctuations in frequency of intercourse? Studies have yielded contradictory results. Some have found a peak frequency of intercourse around ovulation, which would be biologically functional. But others have found peaks just before and just after menstruation (reviewed by Zillmann et al., 1994).

Of course, one should be cautious about using frequency of intercourse as a measure of a woman's sex drive. Intercourse requires some agreement between partners, and thus reflects not only her desires but her partner's as well. One study assessed both heterosexual women's activity with a partner and self-rated sexual desire (Bullivant et al., 2004). The results indicated that sexual activity initiated by the woman—but not by the man—peaked during the three days before and three days after ovulation. Sexual desire showed the same pattern.

In a sophisticated study, women kept daily diaries of their moods and sexual interest and provided blood samples for hormone assays (Van Goozen et al., 1997). This study assessed testosterone levels, as well as levels of estrogen and progesterone, an important addition because the evidence is strongest for an association between testosterone and sex drive in women. The results indicated that testosterone levels peaked at ovulation. The women seemed to fall into two subgroups, with different patterns of sexual interest. About half the women reported that they suffered from premenstrual symptoms; their sexual interest peaked at ovulation, exactly when testosterone levels are high. The other half of the women said they did not suffer from premenstrual symptoms and their peak in sexual interest occurred premenstrually, perhaps in anticipation of a deprivation during menstruation.

If there is a link between phase of the menstrual cycle and sexual interest, it most likely reflects an association between testosterone levels and sexuality with a peak in sexual interest around the time of ovulation. But with humans, psychological and social factors—such as some couples' dislike of intercourse when the woman is menstruating—play a strong role as well.

What Causes the Fluctuations in Mood: Why Do Some Women Get Emotional?

The answer to the question of what causes mood fluctuations during the menstrual cycle touches off a nature–nurture, or biology–environment, controversy. That is, some investigators argue that the mood fluctuations are caused primarily by biological factors—in particular, fluctuations in levels of hormones—whereas others argue that environmental factors such as menstrual taboos and cultural expectations are the primary cause.

The Biological Explanation

On the biology side, changes in mood appear to be related to changes in hormone levels during the cycle. The fact that depression is more frequent in women premenstrually, at menopause, and postpartum (after having a baby) suggests that there is at least some relationship between sex hormones and depression. The exact hormone–mood relationship is not known, though. Theories of hormonal causes of PMS involving the following factors have been proposed: (1) absolute amount of estrogen; (2) absolute amount of progesterone; (3) the estrogen–progesterone ratio, or balance; (4) hypersensitivity of some individuals to estrogen levels; and (5) withdrawal reactions to either estrogen or progesterone (during all the premenstrual, postpartum, and menopausal periods, hormone levels drop rapidly). Research has not determined which, if any, of these factors is the real cause. Neither is it known exactly what the mechanism is by which hormones influence mood (Golub, 1992). Research does indicate that the estrogen–progesterone system interacts with the production of the neurotransmitters norepinephrine, serotonin, and dopamine, and neurotransmitter levels are linked to mood disorders such as depression (Halbreich, 1996; Mortola, 1998).

Critics of the hormone point of view note that causality is being inferred from correlational data. That is, the data show a correlation between cycle phase (hormonal levels) and mood, but do not show that hormone levels cause the mood shift. They note that medical treatments based on these explanations have not been effective at alleviating symptoms (Gottheil et al., 1999).

A classic study by psychologist Karen Paige (1971) studied mood fluctuations resulting from the manipulation of hormone levels—birth control pills. The spoken stories of 102 married women were obtained on days 4, 10, and 16 and two days before menstruation during one cycle, and they were scored for the amount of anxiety shown in them. The participants fell into three groups: (1) those who were not taking oral contraceptives and never had; (2) those who were taking a combination pill (these provide a steady high dose of both

In Focus 5.2

The Menstrual Experience among Indians in South Africa

Anthropologist Brian du Toit studied women who resided in South Africa but whose ancestors came from India. Most Indian South Africans are Hindu or Muslim. A total of 30 premenopausal and 30 post-menopausal women were interviewed.

Approximately 75 percent of the women reported experiencing premenstrual syndrome (PMS), although they did not use that term. They complained of a heaviness, a bloated feeling, irritability, general crabbiness, or tension associated with headaches—symptoms that are quite similar to those reported by women in Canada.

Despite these symptoms, menstruation was generally viewed by the women in the study as a cleansing process that leaves the body healthy. "Old blood" and impurities are flushed out. The participants saw advantages to menstruation: it means that a woman can have children, it is an indicator of youthfulness, and it has a cleansing function.

When asked why women menstruate, most said that it is somehow related to cleansing the system. Others thought it is the body's preparation for pregnancy. A few believed that it is God's doing—that it is simply the way women were made.

There are various menstrual taboos in this culture. Menstruating women are not supposed to engage in certain religious rituals, although they may engage in kitchen work such as food preparation (which is prohibited in some other cultures). There was unanimous agreement among the women that sexual intercourse should not occur during the flow, but the older women and the younger women had different reasons for this belief. The older women believed that it was dangerous to the man or that a sexually transmitted disease could be contracted through such a practice. The younger women simply thought that it was messy.

This study is interesting because it shows us both cross-cultural similarities (for example, PMS symptoms) and cross-cultural differences (for example, different explanations for the existence of menstruation) between the Indian culture of South Africa and the dominant Canadian culture.

Source: Du Toit, 1994.

estrogen and progestin, a synthetic progesterone, for 20 or 21 days—see Chapter 7 for a more complete discussion); and (3) those who were taking sequential pills (which provide 15 days of estrogen followed by 5 days of estrogen plus progestin, which is a fluctuation similar to the natural cycle but at higher levels). Paige found that the non-pill women experienced statistically significant variation in their anxiety and hostility levels over the menstrual cycle, which was in agreement with findings from previous studies. Women taking the sequential pill showed the same mood change that non-pill women did. This agrees with the predicted outcome, since their artificial hormone cycle is similar to the natural one. Most important, combination-pill women, whose hormone levels are constant over the cycle, showed no mood shifts over the cycle; their hostility and anxiety levels were constant. This study therefore provides evidence that fluctuations in hormone levels over the menstrual cycle cause mood fluctuations and that when hormone levels are constant, mood is constant.

The Cultural Explanation

Those arguing the other side—that the fluctuations are due to cultural forces—note the widespread cultural expectations and taboos surrounding menstruation (for reviews, see Golub, 1992; Stanton et al., 2002; also see In Focus 5.2). In some non-industrialized cultures, women who are menstruating are isolated from the community and may have to stay in a menstrual hut at the edge of town during their period. Often the

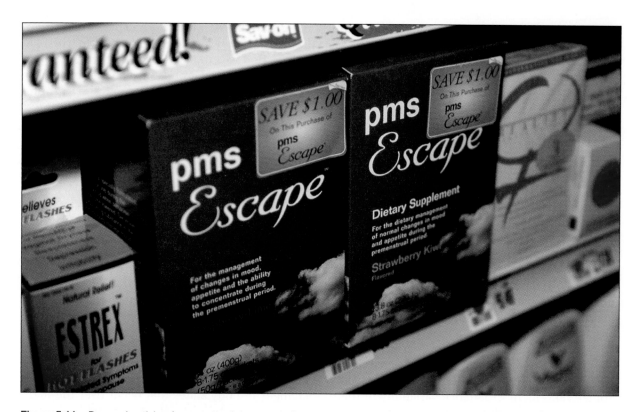

Figure 5.11 Does advertising for menstrual drugs contribute to negative stereotypes about women and PMS?

menstrual blood itself is thought to have supernatural, dangerous powers, and the woman's isolation is considered necessary for the safety of the community. Among the Lele of the Congo, for example:

> A menstruating woman was a danger to the whole community if she entered the forest. Not only was her menstruation certain to wreck any enterprise in the forest that she might undertake, but it was thought to produce unfavorable conditions for men. Hunting would be difficult for a long time after, and rituals based on forest plants would have no efficacy. Women found these rules extremely irksome, especially as they were regularly short-handed and late in their planting, weeding, harvesting, and fishing. (Douglas, 1970, p. 179)

Lest one think that such practices occur only among non-Western people, it should be noted that there is a history of similar practices in Western culture as well. For example, the following passage is from the book of Leviticus in the Bible:

When a woman has a discharge of blood which is her regular discharge from her body, she shall be in her impurity for seven days, and whoever touches her shall be unclean until the evening. . . . And whoever touches her bed shall wash his clothes, and bathe himself in water, and be unclean until the evening; whether it is the bed or anything upon which she sits, when he touches it he shall be unclean until the evening. (Leviticus 15:19–23)

Among the most common menstrual taboos are those prohibiting sexual intercourse with a menstruating woman. For example, the continuation of the passage from Leviticus quoted above is:

> And if any man lies with her, and her impurity is on him, he shall be unclean seven days; and every bed on which he lies shall be unclean. (Leviticus 15:24)

Couples who violated the taboo could be stoned. Orthodox Jews still abstain from sex during the woman's period and for seven days afterward. At the end of this time the woman goes to the *mikvah* (ritual bath) to be cleansed, and only after this cleansing may she resume sexual relations.

Advocates of the cultural explanation argue, then, that women become anxious and depressed around the time of menstruation because of the many cultural forces, such as menstrual taboos, that create negative attitudes toward menstruation. For example, in an Ontario study one-third of the university women sampled, all of whom were in a romantic relationship, had never engaged in sexual activity during menstruation (Remple & Baumgartner, 2003). Furthermore, women's expectations may play a role (Stanton et al., 2002). Our culture is filled with teachings that women are supposed to behave strangely just before and during their periods—for example, drug company ads that ask "Why am I so emotional?" Thus, according to this line of reasoning, women are taught that they should be depressed around the time of menstruation, and because they expect to become depressed, they do become depressed. Researchers in British Columbia have proposed an additional role for expectations (McFarlane et al., 1988). Women (and men) experience variability in their moods. Because of cultural stereotypes about PMS, women attribute their negative mood to hormones when they occur premenstrually. However, they attribute their negative moods at other times in their cycle to other causes (e.g., work or family).

Psychologist Diane Ruble (1977; see also Klebanov & Jemmott, 1992) did a clever experiment to determine whether women's culturally induced expectations influence their reporting of premenstrual symptoms. University students were tested on the sixth or seventh day before the onset of their next menstrual period. They were told that they would participate in a study on a new technique for predicting the expected date of menstruation using an electroencephalograph (EEG), a method that had already been successfully tested with older women. After the EEG had been run (it actually wasn't), the woman was informed of when her next period was to occur, depending on which of three experimental groups she had randomly been assigned to: (1) the woman was told she was "premenstrual" and her period was due in one or two days; (2) the woman was told she was "intermenstrual" or "mid-cycle" and her period was not expected for at least a week to 10 days; or (3) she was given no information at all about the predicted date of menstruation (control group). The women then completed a self-report menstrual distress questionnaire. The results indicated that women who had been led to believe they were in the premenstrual phase reported significantly more water retention, pain, and changes in eating habits than did women who had been led to believe they were around mid-cycle. (In fact, women in these groups did not differ significantly in when their periods actually arrived.) There were no significant differences between the groups in ratings of negative moods, however. This study indicates that, probably because of learned beliefs, women overstate the changes in body states that occur over the menstrual cycle. When they think they are in the premenstrual phase, they report more problems than when they think they are at mid-cycle.

This nature–nurture argument will not be easily resolved, particularly because there is evidence for both points of view. Perhaps the best solution is to say that some women probably do experience mood shifts caused by hormonal and possibly other physical factors and that, for many others, slight biological influences are magnified by psychological and cultural influences. A woman's premenstrual hormonal state may act as a sort of "trigger." It may, for example, provide a state conducive to depression; if the environment provides further stimuli to depression, the woman becomes depressed.

SUMMARY

The major sex hormones are testosterone, which is produced in the male by the testes, and estrogen and progesterone, which are produced in the female by the ovaries. Levels of the sex hormones are regulated by two hormones secreted by the pituitary: FSH (follicle-stimulating hormone) and LH (luteinizing hormone). The gonads, pituitary, and hypothalamus regulate one another's output through a negative feedback loop. Inhibin regulates FSH levels.

Biologically, the menstrual cycle is divided into four phases: the follicular phase, ovulation, the luteal phase, and menstruation. Corresponding to these phases, there are changes in the levels of pituitary hormones (FSH and LH) and in the levels of ovarian hormones (estrogen and progesterone), as well as changes in the ovaries and the uterus. A fairly common menstrual problem is dysmenorrhea, or painful menstruation.

At conception males and females differ only in the sex chromosomes (XX in females and XY in males). As the fetus grows, the SRY gene on the Y chromosome directs the gonads to differentiate into the testes. In the absence of the SRY gene, ovaries develop. Different hormones are then produced by the gonads, and these stimulate further differentiation of the internal and external reproductive structures of males and females. A male organ and a female organ that derive from the same embryonic tissue are said to be homologous to each other.

Intersex conditions are generally the result of various syndromes (such as CAH) and accidents that occur during the course of prenatal sexual differentiation. Currently there is a debate over the best medical treatment of these individuals. The Guevodoces provide an interesting case of gender change at puberty.

Puberty is initiated and characterized by a great increase in the production of sex hormones. Pubertal changes in both males and females include body growth, the development of pubic and axillary hair, and increased output from the oil-producing glands. Changes in the female include breast development and the beginning of menstruation. Changes in the male include growth of the penis and testes, the beginning of ejaculation, and a deepening of the voice.

Research indicates that some, though not all, women experience changes in mood over the phases of the menstrual cycle. For those who experience such changes, their mood is generally positive around the middle of the cycle (i.e., around ovulation), whereas negative moods characterized by depression and irritability are more likely just before and during menstruation. These negative moods and physical discomforts are termed premenstrual syndrome. On the other hand, research indicates that there are no fluctuations in performance over the cycle. There is evidence suggesting that fluctuations in mood are related to changes in hormone levels, but data are also available suggesting that mood fluctuations are related to cultural factors. Research attempting to document whether men experience monthly biological and/or psychological cycles is now in progress.

QUESTIONS FOR THOUGHT, DISCUSSION, AND DEBATE

1. Of the physical changes of puberty, which are the most difficult to cope with?
2. The society in the Dominican Republic in which the Guevodoces are born (see p. 121) is a three-gender society, unlike the two-gender society of the dominant Canadian culture. What would Canada be like if it were a three-gender society? Who would be classified in the third gender? Would their lives be better or worse as a result? Could we have a four-gender society? Who would be classified in the fourth gender? (For further information, see Herdt, 1990.)
3. Are women's fluctuations in mood over the menstrual cycle caused by biological factors or by environmental/cultural factors?
4. Teresa has just given birth to her first baby. The

doctor approaches her with a worried expression and says that her baby's genitals are unusual and some decisions will have to be made. The phallus is too big for a clitoris, but too small for a penis. What should Teresa do? What other information should she obtain from the doctor before making a decision?

5. Your 10-year-old daughter tells you that she has heard about PMS and wonders whether she will get it when she begins her periods. What would you tell her?

■ ■ ■ SUGGESTIONS FOR FURTHER READING

Colapinto, John. (2001). *As nature made him: The boy who was raised as a girl*. Toronto: Harper Perennial Canada. This is the story of David Reimer, the Winnipeg boy who was raised as a girl after a circumcision accident.

Fausto-Sterling, Anne. (2000). *Sexing the body*. New York: Basic Books. The author, a developmental geneticist, has written a provocative book that calls into question our most basic understandings of differentiation of the sexes, both physically and psychologically.

Galub, Sharon. (1992). Periods: *From menarche to menopause*. Newbury Park, CA: Sage. This book, by a well-known researcher in the field, tells you everything you always wanted to know about menstruation (and menopause).

Kessler, Suzanne J. (1998). *Lessons from the intersexed*. New Brunswick, NJ: Rutgers University Press. Kessler, a psychologist, reports on her years of research with intersex individuals and the medical and psychological professionals who treat them, and she proposes new approaches in dealing with the condition.

Larsen, P. Reed et al. (2003). *Williams textbook of endocrinology*. 10th ed. Philadelphia: Saunders. An outstanding endocrinology text, with a particularly good chapter on sexual differentiation.

Steinberg, Laurence. (2002). *Adolescence*. 6th ed. New York: McGraw-Hill. This is the definitive textbook on adolescence, written by a leading researcher.

For Review Questions, Web Resources, and other learning and study tools, visit the *Understanding Human Sexuality* Online Learning Centre at www.mcgrawhill.ca/college/hyde.

CHAPTER 6

Conception, Pregnancy, and Childbirth

CHAPTER HIGHLIGHTS

I remember feeling very sexy. We were trying all these different positions. Now that we were having a baby, I felt a lot looser. I used to feel uptight about sex for its own sake, but when I was pregnant I felt a lot freer.

I thought it would never end. I was enormous. I couldn't bend over and wash my feet. And it was incredibly hot.*

Chapter 5 described the remarkable biological process by which a single fertilized egg develops into a male or a female human being. This chapter is about some equally remarkable processes involved in creating human beings: conception, pregnancy, and childbirth.

■ Conception

Sperm Meets Egg: The Incredible Journey

On about day 14 of an average menstrual cycle the woman ovulates. The egg is released from the ovary into the body cavity. Typically it is then picked up by the fimbriae (long fingerlike structures at the end of the fallopian tube—see Figure 6.1) and enters the fallopian tube. It then begins a leisurely trip down the tube toward the uterus, reaching it in about five days if it has been fertilized. Otherwise, it disintegrates in about 48 hours. The egg, unlike the sperm, has no means of moving itself and is propelled by the cilia (hairlike structures) lining the fallopian tube. The egg has begun its part of the journey toward conception.

The woman's cervix secretes mucus that flushes the passageways to prepare for the arrival of the sperm. Meanwhile, the woman has sexual intercourse, and the man has an orgasm and ejaculates inside the woman's vagina. Alternately, the woman uses assisted insemination to place semen in the vagina.[1] Either way, the sperm are deposited in the vagina, there to begin their journey toward the egg. Actually, they have made an incredible trip even before reaching the vagina. Initially they were manufactured in the seminiferous tubules of the testes (see Chapter 4). They then collected and were stored in the epididymis. During ejaculation they moved up and over the top of the bladder in the vas deferens; then they travelled down through the ejaculatory duct, mixed with seminal fluid, and went out through the urethra.

The sperm is one of the tiniest cells in the human body. It is composed of a *head,* a *midpiece,* and a *tail* (see Figure 6.2). The head is about 5 micrometres long, and the total length, from the tip of the head to the tip of the tail, is about 60 micrometres (about 0.06 millimetre, or 2/1,000 inch). The chromosomal material, which is the sperm's most important contribution when it unites with the egg, is contained in the nucleus, which is in the head of the sperm. The *acrosome,* a chemical reservoir, is also in the head of the sperm. The midpiece contains *mitochondria,* tiny structures in which chemical reactions occur that provide energy. This energy is used when the sperm lashes its tail back and forth. The lashing action (called *flagellation*) propels the sperm forward.

A typical ejaculate has a volume of about 3 millilitres, or about a teaspoonful, and contains about 300 million sperm. Although this might seem to be a wasteful amount of sperm if only one is needed for fertilization, the great majority of the sperm never even get close to the egg. Some of the ejaculate, including one-half of the sperm, will flow out of the vagina as a result of gravity. Other sperm may be killed by the acidity of the vagina, to which they are very sensitive. Others are deformed. Of those that make it safely into the uterus, half swim up the wrong fallopian tube (the one containing no egg).

But here we are, several hours later, with a hearty band of sperm swimming up the fallopian tube

---

*Boston Women's Health Book Collective. (1998). *Our bodies, ourselves for the new century.* New York: Simon & Schuster, pp. 443, 446.

[1]Increasing numbers of Canadian women are becoming pregnant using new reproductive technologies. These are described on pp. 169–173.

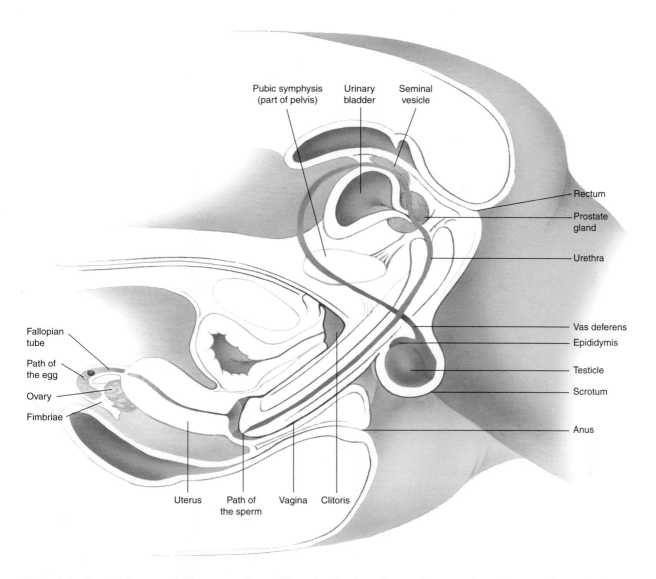

Pubic symphysis (part of pelvis)

Urinary bladder

Seminal vesicle

Rectum

Prostate gland

Urethra

Vas deferens

Epididymis

Testicle

Scrotum

Anus

Fallopian tube

Path of the egg

Ovary

Fimbriae

Uterus

Path of the sperm

Vagina

Clitoris

Figure 6.1 Sexual intercourse in the man-on-top position, showing the pathway of sperm and egg from manufacture in the testes and ovary to conception, which typically occurs in the fallopian tube.

toward the egg, against the currents that are bringing the egg down. Sperm are capable of swimming 1 to 3 centimetres (about 1 inch) per hour, although it has been documented that sperm may arrive at the egg within 1½ hours after ejaculation, which is much sooner than would be expected, given their swimming rate. It is thought that muscular contractions in the uterus may help speed them along. By the time a sperm reaches the egg, it has swum approximately 3,000 times its own length. This would be comparable to a swim of more than 4 kilo-

metres for a human being.

Contrary to the popular belief that conception occurs in the uterus, typically it occurs in the outer third (the part near the ovary) of the fallopian tube. Of the original 300 million sperm, only about 2,000 reach the tube containing the egg. As they approach, a chemical secreted by the egg attracts the sperm to the egg. Chemical receptors on the surface of the sperm respond to the attractant, and the sperm swim toward the egg (Spehr et al., 2003). The egg is surrounded by a thin, gelatinous layer

Acrosome

Head

Nucleus
containing
chromosomes

Midpiece
containing
mitochondria
to provide energy
for swimming

Tail

Figure 6.2   The structure of a mature human sperm.

called the *zona pellucida*. Sperm swarm around the egg and secrete an enzyme called **hyaluronidase** (produced by the acrosome located in the head of the sperm—refer to Figure 6.2); this enzyme dissolves the zona pellucida, permitting one sperm to penetrate the egg.[2] Conception has occurred.

The fertilized egg, called the **zygote,** continues to travel down the fallopian tube. About 36 hours after conception, it begins the process of cell division, by which the original one cell becomes a mass of two cells, then four cells, then eight cells, and so on. About five to seven days after conception, the mass of cells

[2]Thus, while only one sperm is necessary to accomplish fertilization, it appears that it is important for there to be a lot of other sperm present to secrete a chemical that facilitates penetration of the egg. Therefore, maintaining a high sperm count seems to be important for conception.

Hyaluronidase: An enzyme secreted by the sperm that allows one sperm to penetrate the egg.
Zygote: A fertilized egg.

implants itself in the lining of the uterus, there to be nourished and grow. For the first eight weeks of gestation the *conceptus* (product of conception) is called an *embryo;* from then until birth it is called a *fetus.*

Improving the Chances of Conception: Making a Baby

While this topic may seem rather remote to those individuals whose principal concern is probably *avoiding* conception, some couples do want to have a baby. The following are points for them to keep in mind.

The whole trick, of course, is to time intercourse so that it occurs around the time of ovulation. To do this, it is necessary to determine when the woman ovulates. For the vast majority of women, the time of ovulation can best be determined by keeping a *basal body temperature chart.* To do this, the woman takes her temperature every morning immediately upon waking (that means before getting up and moving around or drinking a cup of coffee). She then keeps a graph of her temperature. The most reliable indicator of ovulation is the rise in temperature the day after it occurs. From this, the woman can determine the day of ovulation, and that determination should be consistent with menstruation occurring about 14 days later. Other methods for determining when a woman is ovulating are the cervical mucus and sympto-thermal methods, as well as home tests for the detection of ovulation, described in Chapter 7.

Sperm live inside the woman's body for up to five days (Wilcox et al., 1995). The egg is capable of being fertilized for about the first 12 to 24 hours after ovulation. Allowing the sperm some swimming time, this means that intercourse should be timed right at ovulation or one or two days before.

Assuming you have some idea of the time of ovulation, how frequent should intercourse be? While more may be merrier, more is not necessarily more effective. The reason for this is that it is important for the man's sperm count to be maintained. It takes a while to manufacture 300 million sperm—at least 24 hours. And, as was discussed earlier, maintaining a high sperm count appears to be important in accomplishing the task of fertilizing the egg. For purposes of conceiving, then, it is probably best to have intercourse about every 24 to 48 hours, or about four times during the week in

Figure 6.3 The egg is fertilized by one sperm as many sperm cluster about.

which the woman is to ovulate. Abstaining for more than 48 hours may lead to a low sperm count. (Levitas, 2003).

It is also important to take some steps to ensure that once deposited in the vagina, the sperm get a decent chance to survive and to find their way into the fallopian tubes. Position during and after intercourse is important. For purposes of conceiving, the best position for intercourse is with the woman on her back (man-on-top, or "missionary," position—see Chapter 10). If the woman is on top, much of the ejaculate may run out of the vagina because of the pull of gravity. After intercourse, she should remain on her back, possibly with her legs pulled up and a pillow under her hips, preferably for about a half hour to an hour. This allows the semen to remain in a pool in the vagina, which gives the sperm a good chance to swim up into the uterus. Because sperm are very sensitive to the pH (acidity-alkalinity) of the vagina, this factor also requires some consideration. Acidity kills sperm. Douching with commercial preparations or with acidic solutions (such as vinegar) should be avoided. Finally, lubricants and/or suppositories should not be used; they may kill sperm or block their entrance into the uterus.

■ Development of the Conceptus

For the nine months of pregnancy, two organisms—the conceptus and the pregnant woman—undergo parallel, dramatic changes. The changes that occur in the developing conceptus will be discussed in this section; a later section will be about the changes that take place in the pregnant woman.

Typically the nine months of pregnancy are divided into three equal periods of three months, called *trimesters*. Thus, the first trimester is months 1 to 3, the second trimester is months 4 to 6, and the third (or last) trimester is months 7 to 9.

The Embryo and Its Support Systems

We left the conceptus, which began as a single fertilized egg cell, dividing into many cells as it passed down the fallopian tube, finally arriving in the uterus and implanting itself in the uterine wall.

During the embryonic period of development (the first eight weeks), most of the fetus's major organ systems are formed in processes that occur with amazing speed. The inner part of the ball of cells implanted in the uterus now differentiates into two layers, the endoderm and the ectoderm. Later a third layer, the mesoderm, forms between them. The various organs of the body differentiate themselves out of these layers. The *ectoderm* will form the entire nervous system and the skin. The *endoderm* differentiates into the digestive system—from the pharynx, to the stomach and intestines, to the rectum—and the respiratory system. The muscles, skeleton, connective tissues, and reproductive and circulatory systems derive from the *mesoderm*. Fetal development generally proceeds in a cephalocaudal order. That is, the head develops first, and the lower body last. For this reason, the head of a fetus is enormous compared with the rest of the body.

Meanwhile, another group of cells has differentiated into the *trophoblast*, which has important functions in maintaining the embryo and which will eventually become the placenta. The **placenta** is the mass of tissues that surrounds the conceptus early in development and nurtures its growth.

Placenta (plah-SEN-tuh): An organ formed on the wall of the uterus through which the fetus receives oxygen and nutrients and gets rid of waste products.

Later it moves to the side of the fetus. The placenta has a number of important functions, perhaps the most important of which is that it serves as a site for the exchange of substances between the woman's blood and the fetus's blood. It is important to note that the woman's circulatory system and the fetus's circulatory system are completely separate. That is, with only rare exceptions, the woman's blood never circulates inside the fetus; nor does the fetus's blood circulate in the woman's blood vessels. Instead, the fetus's blood passes out of its body through the umbilical cord to the placenta. There it circulates in the numerous *villi* (tiny fingerlike projections in the placenta). The woman's blood circulates around the outside of these villi. Thus there is a membrane barrier between the two blood systems. Some substances are capable of passing through this barrier, whereas others are not. Oxygen and nutrients can pass through the barrier, and thus the woman's blood supplies oxygen and nutrients to the fetus, providing substitutes for breathing and eating. Carbon dioxide and waste products similarly pass back from the fetal blood to the woman's blood. Some viruses and other disease-causing organisms can pass through the barrier, including those for German measles (rubella) and syphilis. But other organisms cannot pass through the barrier; thus the woman may have a terrible cold, but the fetus will remain completely healthy. Various drugs can also cross the placental barrier, and the woman should therefore be careful about drugs taken during pregnancy (see the section on substances during pregnancy, later in this chapter).

Another major function of the placenta is that it secretes hormones. The placenta produces large quantities of estrogen and progesterone. Many of the physical symptoms of pregnancy may be caused by these elevated levels of hormones. Another hormone manufactured by the placenta is **human chorionic gonadotropin (hCG)**. This is the hormone that is detected in pregnancy tests.

The **umbilical cord** is formed during the fifth week of embryonic development. The fully developed cord is about 55 centimetres (20 inches) long. Normally, it contains three blood vessels: two arteries and one vein. Some people believe that the fetus's umbilical cord attaches to the woman's navel; actually, the umbilical cord attaches to the placenta, thereby providing for the interchanges of substances described above.

Two membranes surround the fetus, the *chorion* and the *amnion,* the amnion being the innermost. The amnion is filled with a watery liquid called **amniotic fluid,** in which the fetus floats and can readily move. It is the amniotic fluid that is sampled when an amniocentesis is performed (see below). The amniotic fluid maintains the fetus at a constant temperature and, most important, cushions the fetus against possible injury. Thus the woman can fall down a flight of stairs, and the fetus will remain undisturbed. Indeed, the amniotic fluid might be considered the original waterbed.

Fetal Development during the First Trimester

In a sense, the development of the fetus during the first trimester is more remarkable than its development during the second and third trimesters. That's because during the first trimester the small mass of cells implanted in the uterus develops into a fetus with most of the major organ systems present and with recognizable human features (see Figure 6.4).

By the third week of gestation, the embryo appears as a small bit of flesh and is about 0.2 centimetres ($\frac{1}{12}$ inch) long. During the third and fourth weeks, the head undergoes a great deal of development. The central nervous system begins to form, and the beginnings of eyes and ears are visible. The backbone is constructed by the end of the fourth week. A "tail" is noticeable early in embryonic development but has disappeared by the eighth week.

From the fourth to the eighth weeks, the external body parts—eyes, ears, arms, hands, fingers, legs, feet, and toes—develop. By the end of the tenth week they are completely formed. Indeed, by the tenth week the embryo has not only a complete set of fingers but also fingernails.

By the end of the seventh week, the liver, lungs, pancreas, kidneys, and intestines have formed and have begun limited functioning. The gonads have also formed, but the gender of the fetus is not clearly distinguishable until the twelfth week.

Human chorionic gonadotropin (hCG): A hormone secreted by the placenta; it is the hormone detected in pregnancy tests.
Umbilical cord: The tube that connects the fetus to the placenta.
Amniotic fluid: The watery fluid surrounding a developing fetus in the uterus.

(a)

(b)

(c)

(d)

Figure 6.4 *(a)* This embryo has divided into four cells and would still be travelling down the fallopian tube. *(b)* The embryo after 4 weeks of development. The major organs are forming; the bright red, blood-filled heart is just below the lower jaw. *(c)* At 9 weeks the human fetus is recognizable as a primate. Limbs have formed and ears are clearly visible. *(d)* By about 3 months the fetus is approximately 8 centimetres long and weighs about 28 grams. Muscles have formed, which move the limbs and body.

At the end of the twelfth week (end of the first trimester) the fetus is unmistakably human and looks like a small infant. It is about 10 centimetres (4 inches) long and weighs about 19 grams (2/3 ounce). From this point on, development consists mainly of the enlargement and differentiation of structures that are already present.

Fetal Development during the Second Trimester

Around the end of the fourteenth week, the movements of the fetus can be detected ("quickening"). By the eighteenth week, the woman has been able to feel movement for two to four weeks. The fetus first opens its eyes around the twentieth week. By about the twenty-fourth week, it is sensitive to light and can hear sounds in utero. Arm and leg movements are vigorous at this time, and the fetus alternates between periods of wakefulness and sleep.

Fetal Development during the Third Trimester

At the end of the second trimester the fetus's skin is wrinkled and covered with downlike hair. At the beginning of the third trimester, fat deposits form under the skin; these will give the infant the characteristic chubby appearance of babyhood. The downlike hair is lost.

During the seventh month the fetus turns in the uterus to assume a head-down position. If this turning does not occur by the time of delivery, there will be a *breech presentation*. Women can do certain exercises to aid the turning (Boston Women's Health Book Collective, 1998). Physicians and midwives can also perform certain procedures to turn the fetus.

The fetus's growth during the last two months is rapid. At the end of the eighth month it weighs an average of 2,500 grams (5 pounds, 4 ounces). The average full-term baby weighs 3,300 grams (7.5 pounds) and is 50 centimetres (20 inches) long.

■ The Stages of Pregnancy

The First Trimester (The First 12 Weeks)

Symptoms of Pregnancy

For most women, the first symptom of pregnancy is a missed menstrual period. Of course, there may be a wide variety of reactions to this event. For the woman who has not planned the pregnancy or who feels that she already has enough children, the reaction may be negative—depression, anger, and fear. For the woman who has been trying to conceive for several months, the reaction may be joy and eager anticipation.

In fact, there are many other reasons besides pregnancy for a woman to have a late period or miss a period. Illness or emotional stress may delay a period, and women occasionally skip a period for no apparent reason.

It is also true that a woman may continue to experience some cyclic bleeding or spotting during pregnancy. This is not particularly a danger sign, except that in a few cases it is a symptom of a miscarriage.

If the woman has been keeping a basal body temperature chart, it can provide a very early sign that she is pregnant. If her temperature rises abruptly at about the time ovulation would normally occur and then stays up for more than two weeks—say, about three weeks—the chances are fairly good that she is pregnant. The increased temperature results from the high level of progesterone manufactured by the corpus luteum and, later, the placenta.

Other early symptoms of pregnancy are tenderness of the breasts—a tingling sensation and special sensitivity of the nipples—and nausea and vomiting (called "morning sickness," although these symptoms may actually happen any time during the day). More frequent urination, feelings of fatigue, and a need for more sleep are other early signs of pregnancy.

Pregnancy Tests

It is important that early, accurate pregnancy tests be available and that women make use of them. This is true for several reasons. A woman needs to know that she is pregnant as early as possible so that she can see a physician or midwife and begin getting good prenatal care. She also needs to know so that she can get the nutrition she requires during pregnancy (see the section on nutrition). And if she does not want to carry the baby to term, she needs to know as soon as possible, because abortions are much safer and simpler when performed in the first trimester than in the second.

A pregnancy test may be done in a physician's office, at a Planned Parenthood or sexual health centre, or at a medical laboratory. The most common pregnancy test is an immunologic test based on detecting the presence of hCG (human chorionic gonadotropin, secreted by the placenta) in the woman's urine. It can be done in a matter of minutes and is very accurate. It involves mixing a drop of urine with certain chemicals, either on a slide or in a tube.

The laboratory tests for pregnancy are 98- to 99-percent accurate. A laboratory test may produce a false negative (i.e., tell the woman she is not pregnant when she really is) if it is done too early or if errors are made in processing. Also, some women simply do not show positive signs in the tests, or do not do so until the second or third test. The modern urine tests are 98-percent accurate 7 days after implantation (just when a period is missed).

A different type of test, called the *beta-hCG radioimmunoassay*, assesses the presence of beta-hCG in a blood sample. It can detect hCG at very low levels, so it can reliably detect pregnancy seven days after fertilization. It is much more expensive than the urine tests and is available only in laboratories associated with hospitals or large clinics.

Home pregnancy tests are also available, sold under such brand names as First Response and ClearBlue. These are urine tests designed to measure the presence of hCG; they cost $13 to $20 depending on whether they contain one test or two tests. Their charm lies in their convenience and the privacy of getting the results. The major problem with them is that they have a very high rate—between 25 and 38 percent—of false negatives (Doshi, 1986; Hart, 1990). This compares with an error rate of 1 to 2 percent for laboratory tests. The home pregnancy tests also have a 16-percent rate of false positives (Hatcher et al., 1994). To guard against false negatives, the manufacturers recommend repeating the test one week later if the results are negative the first time, and some of these kits contain more than one test. The reason that a high rate of false negatives is so serious is that it leads a pregnant woman to think she is not pregnant, and thus she might take substances that would harm the fetus, and she will not begin getting prenatal care; such dangerous conditions as ectopic pregnancy might therefore go undetected. Performing the tests also requires a certain amount of coordination and care. All in all, they are probably not as good an idea as they seem, although they may be improved in the future.

The signs of pregnancy may be classified as *pre-sumptive signs*, *probable signs*, and *positive signs*. Amenorrhea, breast tenderness, nausea, and so on, are presumptive signs. The pregnancy tests discussed previously all provide probable signs. Three signs are interpreted as positive signs, that is, as definite indications of pregnancy: (1) beating of the fetal heart, (2) active fetal movement, and (3) detection of a fetal skeleton by ultrasound. These signs cannot be detected until the fourth month, with the exception of ultrasound, which can be used in the first trimester.

Once the pregnancy has been confirmed, the woman generally is very interested in determining her expected delivery date (called EDC for a rather antiquated expression, "expected date of confinement"). The EDC is calculated using *Nägele's rule*. The rule says to take the date of the first day of the last menstrual period, subtract three months, add seven days, and finally add one year. Thus, if the first day of the last menstrual period was September 10, 2006, the expected delivery date would be June 17, 2007: subtracting three months from September 10 gives June 10, adding seven days yields June 17, and adding one year gives June 17, 2007. In cases where the date when the last menstrual period began is not known, an ultrasound procedure may be used to determine gestational age (Afriat, 1995).

Physical Changes

The basic physical change that takes place in the woman's body during the first trimester is a large increase in the levels of hormones, especially estrogen and progesterone, that are produced by the placenta. Many of the other physical symptoms of the first trimester arise from these endocrine changes.

The breasts swell and tingle. This results from the development of the mammary glands, which is stimulated by hormones. The nipples and the area around them (areola) may darken and broaden.

There is often a need to urinate more frequently. This is related to changes in the pituitary hormones that affect the adrenals, which in turn change the water balance in the body so that more water is retained. The growing uterus also contributes by pressing against the bladder.

Some women experience morning sickness—feelings of nausea, perhaps to the point of vomiting, and of revulsion toward food or its odour. The nausea and vomiting may occur on waking or at other times during the day. Their exact cause is not known. One theory is that the high levels of estrogen irritate the stomach. The rapid expansion of the uterus may also be involved. While these symptoms are quite common, about 25 percent of pregnant women experience no vomiting at all.

Vaginal discharges may also increase at this time, partly because the increased hormone levels change the pH of the vagina and partly because the vaginal secretions are changing in their chemical composition and quantity.

The feelings of fatigue and sleepiness are probably related to the high levels of progesterone, which is known to have a sedative effect.

Psychological Changes

Our culture is full of stereotypes about the psychological characteristics of pregnant women. According to one view, pregnancy is supposed to be a time of happiness and calm. Radiant contentment, the "pregnant glow," is said to emanate from the woman's face, making this a good time for her to be photographed. According to another view, pregnancy is a time of emotional ups and downs. The pregnant woman swings from very happy to depressed and crying, and back again. She is irrational, sending her partner out in a blizzard for kosher dill pickles. One study compared 70 pregnant women (planned pregnancies) with 92 non-pregnant women. The researchers assessed both women's physical and psychological states at three points during the pregnancy (or nine months for the non-pregnant women). On the whole, they found that pregnancy is neither a time of heightened well-being nor heightened emotional turmoil (Striegel-Moore et al., 1996).

Research indicates that the situation is more complex than these stereotypes suggest. A woman's emotional state during pregnancy, often assessed with measures of depression, varies according to several factors. First, her attitude toward the pregnancy makes a difference; women who desire the pregnancy are less anxious than women who do not (Kalil et al., 1993). A second factor is social class. Several studies have found that low income is associated with depression during pregnancy. For example, a study involving interviews with 192 poor, inner-city pregnant women found that they were twice as likely as their middle-income counterparts to be depressed (Hobfoll et al., 1995). This may be due to the economic situation these women face; also, there may be more unwanted pregnancies among low-income women. A third influence is the availability of social support. Women with a supportive partner are less likely to be depressed, perhaps because the partner serves as a buffer against stressful events (Chapman et al., 1997).

During the first trimester, the symptoms that distinguish pregnant from non-pregnant women are nausea, associated with morning sickness, and fatigue (Streigel-Moore et al., 1996). Depression is not uncommon during this time. Women who led very active lives prior to becoming pregnant may find fatigue and lack of energy especially distressing. Depression during the first trimester is more likely among women experiencing other stressful life events, such as moving, changes in their jobs, changes in relationships, or illnesses (Kalil et al., 1993). In this trimester, women's anxieties often centre on concerns about miscarriage.

The Second Trimester (Weeks 13 to 26)

Physical Changes

During the fourth month, the woman becomes aware of the fetus's movements ("quickening"). Many women find this a very exciting experience.

The woman is made even more aware of the pregnancy by her rapidly expanding belly. There are a variety of reactions to this. Some women feel that it is a magnificent symbol of womanhood, and they rush out to buy maternity clothes and wear them before they are even necessary. Other women feel awkward and resentful of their bulky shape and may begin to wonder whether they can fit through doorways and turnstiles.

Most of the physical symptoms of the first trimester, such as morning sickness, disappear, and discomforts are at a minimum. Physical problems at this time include constipation and nosebleeds (caused by increased blood volume). **Edema**—water retention and swelling—may be a problem in the face, hands, wrists, ankles, and feet; it results from increased water retention throughout the body.

By about mid-pregnancy, the breasts, under hormonal stimulation, have essentially completed their development in preparation for nursing.

Edema (eh-DEE-muh): Excessive fluid retention and swelling.

Beginning about the nineteenth week, a thin amber or yellow fluid called **colostrum** may come out of the nipple, although there is no milk yet.

Psychological Changes

While the first trimester can be relatively tempestuous, particularly with morning sickness, the second trimester is usually a period of relative calm and well-being. The discomforts of the first trimester are past, the tensions associated with labour and delivery not yet present. Fear of miscarriage diminishes as the woman feels fetal movement (Leifer, 1980).

Depression is less likely during the second trimester if the pregnant woman has a cohabiting partner or spouse (Hobfoll et al., 1995). Interestingly, women who have had a previous pregnancy are more distressed during this time than women who have not (Wilkinson, 1995). This may reflect the impact of the demands associated with the care of other children when one is pregnant. Research also indicates that feelings of nurturance, or maternal responsiveness to the infant, increase steadily from the prepregnant to the postpartum period (Fleming et al., 1997). This increase does not appear to be related to changes in hormone levels during pregnancy.

Research also indicates that women's beliefs about pregnancy and how they should behave during pregnancy are influenced by culture. A comparison of Indian women giving birth in London with non-Indian women giving birth there found that culture influenced beliefs about diet during pregnancy, and about the amount and type of medical care they should seek (Woollett et al., 1995).

The Third Trimester (Weeks 27 to 38)

Physical Changes

The uterus is very large and hard by the third trimester. The woman is increasingly aware of her size and of the fetus, which is becoming more and more active. In fact, some women are kept awake at night by its somersaults and hiccups.

The extreme size of the uterus puts pressure on a number of other organs, causing some discomfort. There is pressure on the lungs, which may cause shortness of breath. The stomach is also being squeezed, and indigestion is common. The navel is pushed out. The heart is being strained because of the large increase in blood volume. At this stage most women feel low in energy (Leifer, 1980).

One source, *The Journal of Midwifery and Women's Health*, says that the amount of weight gained should range from 11 to 15 kilograms (25 to 35 pounds) depending on the woman's weight prior to the pregnancy. Women who are slim should gain relatively more, while women who are heavy should gain less. The average infant at birth weighs 3,400 grams (7.5 pounds); the rest of the weight gain is accounted for by the placenta (about 450 grams, or 1 pound), the amniotic fluid (about 900 grams, or 2 pounds), enlargement of the uterus (about 900 grams, or 2 pounds), enlargement of the breasts (750 grams, or 1.5 pounds), and the additional fat and water retained by the woman (3.6 kilograms or more, or 8 or more pounds). Physicians recommend limited weight gain because the incidence of complications, such as high blood pressure and strain on the heart, is much higher in women who gain an excessive amount of weight. Also, excessive weight gained during pregnancy can be very hard to lose afterward.

The woman's balance is somewhat disturbed because of the large amount of weight that has been added to the front part of her body. She may compensate for this by adopting the characteristic "waddling" walk of the pregnant woman, which can result in back pains.

The uterus tightens occasionally in painless contractions called **Braxton-Hicks contractions.** These contractions are not part of labour. It is thought that they help to strengthen the uterine muscles, preparing them for labour.

In a first pregnancy, around two to four weeks before delivery the head drops into the pelvis. This is called *lightening, dropping,* or *engagement.* Engagement usually occurs during labour in women who have had babies before.

Some women are concerned about the appropriate amount of activity they should engage in during pregnancy—whether some things constitute "overdoing it." Traditionally, physicians and textbooks warned of the dangers of physical activi-

---

Colostrum: A watery substance that is secreted from the breasts at the end of pregnancy and during the first few days after delivery.
Braxton-Hicks contractions: Contractions of the uterus during pregnancy that are not part of actual labour.

ties and tried to discourage them. It appears now, however, that such restrictions were based more on superstition than on scientific fact. Current thinking holds that for a healthy pregnant woman, moderate activity is not dangerous and is actually psychologically and physically beneficial. Modern methods of childbirth encourage sensible exercise for the pregnant woman so that she will be in shape for labour (see the section on childbirth options later in this chapter). The matter, of course, is highly individual.

Psychological Changes

The patterns noted earlier continue into the third trimester. Psychological well-being is greater among women who have social support (often in the form of a cohabiting partner or husband), have higher incomes or are middle class, and experience fewer concurrent stressful life events. A study conducted in Montreal found that women who reported more anxiety, daily hassles, and stress during pregnancy were more likely to experience pregnancy complications (Costa et al., 1998).

What happens to the relationship of the pregnant woman with her partner? A comparison of women pregnant for the first time with women who had experienced previous pregnancies found that first-time mothers reported a significant increase in dissatisfaction with their husbands from the second to the third trimester (Wilkinson, 1995). Another study included 54 women who were pregnant for the first time and their husbands (Zimmerman-Tansella et al., 1994). Wives who reported that higher levels of affection were exchanged between husband and wife reported lower levels of anxiety and of insomnia in the third trimester.

The Father's Experience in Pregnancy

Physical Changes

Some men experience pregnancy symptoms, including indigestion, gastritis, nausea, change in appetite, and headaches (Kiselica & Scheckel, 1995), referred to as a *couvade syndrome*. These symptoms may be caused by hormonal changes in the male. A longitudinal study of 34 couples collected blood samples from both the men and the women before and after the birth of the infant (Storey et al., 2000). Men and women displayed stage-specific hormone differences, including high levels of prolactin prenatally and low levels of testosterone postnatally. Men with more pregnancy symptoms had higher levels of prolactin prenatally.

In some cultures, this phenomenon takes a more dramatic form, known as *couvades ritual*. In this ritual, the husband retires to bed while his wife is in labour. He suffers all the pains of delivery, moaning and groaning as she does. Couvade is still practised in parts of Asia, South America, and Oceania (Gregersen, 1996).

Psychological Changes

In Canada in the twenty-first century, many men expect to be actively involved in fathering. Men report engaging in many activities in preparation for becoming fathers, including attending parenting classes, planning father–child activities, observing and talking to other fathers, and daydreaming about the baby. Most of these activities, of course, parallel those done by expectant mothers. It has been theorized that men who display this active involvement will do best in the father role after the baby is born (Antle, 1978). In fact, some people claim that there is a "father instinct" (Biller & Meredith, 1975). Recall our discussion in Chapter 2 of the reproductive advantages of a father–infant bond. The likelihood of such a bond depends partly on the father's responsiveness to the infant. In the study of hormonal changes during pregnancy described above, men viewed videotapes with auditory and visual cues from newborns before the blood sample was drawn. Men who showed higher levels of responsiveness had higher levels of prolactin prenatally and lower levels of testosterone postnatally (Storey et al., 2000). Lower levels of testosterone may facilitate paternal behaviour.

Fathers or other partners play an important role in preparing for a baby. The birth or arrival of a first child may require finding a larger home or making physical changes to the present one. There will be visits to medical personnel, tests to be taken, arrangements to be made. Partners who participate in these activities provide support for the pregnant woman and become more involved themselves. Many couples take some form of classes in preparation for childbirth. The classes often specifically address the partner's role in late pregnancy and during labour and delivery. These joint activities contribute to the bond between the

Figure 6.5 Dad changes his daughter's diaper at a course for new fathers, which helps new or prospective fathers adjust to their new role.

partners, which in turn provides a better foundation for the arrival of the new member of the family.

Diversity in the Contexts of Pregnancy

There are lots of family contexts in which women have babies these days besides the traditional one of being married to the baby's father. These include living in a common-law relationship; not living with the baby's father but seeing him regularly; being a single mother-to-be who has no contact with the baby's father; being a single mother-to-be who is pregnant as a result of assisted insemination or other reproductive technologies; and being a woman in a stable relationship with another woman, who is pregnant as a result of assisted insemination or other technologies. Therefore, we use the term "partner" in the following sections.

■ Sex during Pregnancy

Many couples are concerned about whether it is safe or advisable for a pregnant woman to have sexual intercourse, particularly during the latter stages of pregnancy. Traditionally, physicians believed that (1) penile–vaginal intercourse might cause an infection, or (2) sexual activity might precipitate labour prematurely or cause a miscarriage (for a review on sexuality and pregnancy, see Von Sydow, 1999).

Current medical opinion, however, is that—given a normal, healthy pregnancy—intercourse can continue safely until four weeks before the baby is due (Cunningham et al., 1993). There is no evidence that intercourse or orgasm is associated with preterm labour (Sayle et al., 2001). In fact, a study involving interviews with pregnant women at 28 weeks gestation and again following delivery found that recent intercourse and orgasm was associated with reduced risk of preterm birth (Sayle et al., 2001). The only exception is a case where a miscarriage or preterm labour is threatened. Whether and how frequently to engage in sexual activity is a matter for a couple to decide, perhaps in consultation with a physician or midwife.

Table 6.1   Percentage of Women Having Various Frequencies of Coitus at Different Stages of Pregnancy

Number of Acts of Coitus per Week	Baseline Prepregnancy, %	12 Weeks Pregnant, %	24 Weeks Pregnant, %	36 Weeks Pregnant, %
None	0	11	8	36
< 1	7	24	25	26
1–3	54	52	55	33
4 or more	40	14	13	5

Source: R. Kumar, H. A. Brant, & K. M. Robson. (1981). Childbearing and maternal sexuality: A prospective study of 119 primiparas. *Journal of Psychosomatic Research, 25,* 373–383. Copyright 1981 by Elsevier Science Ltd. Reprinted by permission of Elsevier Science, Inc.

Most pregnant women continue to have intercourse throughout the pregnancy (Reamy & White, 1987). The most common pattern is a decline in the frequency of intercourse during the first trimester, no variation in the second trimester, and an even greater decline in the third trimester (see Table 6.1). One study included male partners of pregnant women; the men reported the same pattern (Bogren, 1991). In some cases, the decline in frequency in the third trimester is affected by the partner's perceptions. While some men find their pregnant partner extremely sexy, other men are not attracted to women in the later stages of pregnancy.

During the later stages of pregnancy, the woman's shape makes intercourse increasingly awkward, particularly using the man-on-top position. The side-to-side position (see Chapter 10) is probably the most suitable one for intercourse during the late stages of pregnancy. Couples should also remember that there are many ways of experiencing sexual pleasure and orgasm besides having intercourse—hand–genital stimulation or oral–genital sex may be good alternatives.[3] The best guide in this matter is the woman's feelings. If intercourse becomes uncomfortable for her, alternatives should be explored.

■ Nutrition during Pregnancy

During pregnancy, another living being is growing inside the woman, and she needs lots of energy, protein, vitamins, and minerals at this time. Therefore, diet during pregnancy is extremely important. If the

woman's diet is good, she has a much better chance of remaining healthy during pregnancy and of bearing a healthy baby; if her diet is inadequate, she stands more of a chance of developing one of a number of diseases during pregnancy herself and of bearing a child whose weight is low at birth. Babies with low birth weights do not have as good a chance of survival as babies with normal birth weights. According to a study done in Toronto, mothers in a poor-diet group had four times as many serious health problems during pregnancy as a group of mothers whose diets were supplemented with highly nutritious foods. Those with the poor diets had seven times as many threatened miscarriages and three times as many stillbirths; their labour lasted five hours longer on average (Newton, 1972).

It is particularly important that a pregnant woman get enough protein, folic acid, calcium, magnesium, and vitamin A (Luke, 1994). Protein is important for building new tissues. Folic acid is also important for growth; symptoms of folic acid deficiency are anemia and fatigue. A pregnant woman needs much more iron than usual because the fetus draws off iron for itself from the blood that circulates to the placenta. Muscle cramps, nerve pains, uterine ligament pains, sleeplessness, and irritability may all be symptoms of a calcium deficiency. Severe calcium deficiency during pregnancy is associated with increased blood pressure, which may lead to a serious condition called eclampsia, discussed later in this chapter (Repke, 1994). Deficiencies of calcium and magnesium are associated with premature birth. Sometimes even an excellent diet does not provide enough iron, calcium, or folic acid, in which case the pregnant woman should take supplements.

[3]There is, however, some risk associated with cunnilingus for the pregnant woman, as discussed in Chapter 10.

■ Effects of Substances Taken during Pregnancy

We are such a pill-popping culture that we seldom stop to think about whether we should take a certain drug. The pregnant woman, however, needs to know that when she takes a drug, it not only circulates through her body, but also may circulate through the fetus. Because the fetus develops so rapidly during pregnancy, drugs may produce severe consequences, including serious malformations. Drugs that produce such defects are called **teratogens.**[4] Of course, not all drugs can cross the placental barrier, but many can.

There are a number of drugs and other substances that pregnant women should be cautious in using. A substantial amount of research has documented the risk to a child of maternal drinking during pregnancy. Alcohol consumed by the woman passes through the membrane barrier in the placenta and circulates through the fetus, so it can have pervasive effects on fetal growth and development (Barr et al., 1990; Jacobson et al., 1993, 1994; Streissguth et al., 1999). Health Canada (1996) has identified maternal drinking as one of the leading causes of preventable birth defects and developmental delays in children; according to the National Longitudinal Survey of Children and Youth, 15 percent of pregnant Canadian women drink some alcohol. The effects of prenatal alcohol consumption are dose-dependent; that is, the more alcohol the mother drinks, the larger the number and severity of effects on the child. The most serious effects are a pattern of malformations termed **fetal alcohol syndrome (FAS),** which is characterized by both prenatal and postnatal growth deficiencies, a small brain, small eye openings, joint, limb, and heart malformations, and mental retardation (for a review, see Mattson & Riley, 1998). Research indicates that "risk drinking"

---

[4]"Teratogen" is from the Greek words *teras,* meaning "monster," and *gen,* meaning "cause."

> **Teratogen (ter-AH-teh-jen):** A substance that produces defects in a fetus.
> **Fetal alcohol syndrome (FAS):** Serious growth deficiency and malformations in the child of a mother who abuses alcohol during pregnancy.

(a)

(b)

Figure 6.6   The effects of prenatal exposure to alcohol and other drugs. *(a)* A child born with fetal alcohol syndrome. *(b)* A preterm baby whose mother used crack cocaine during pregnancy.

Table 6.2   Teratogenic Effect of Frequently Used Substances on Prenatal Development

Legal Drugs	Potential Negative Effects
Nicotine	Prematurity, low birth weight, delayed intellectual and behavioural development, risk of pneumonia, bronchitis, laryngitis, inner ear infections; fathers' smoking may transmit risk of cancer to offspring
Alcohol	Fetal alcohol syndrome (physical defects, short stature, mental retardation, hyperactivity, stereotypical behaviours, congenital addiction leading to withdrawal syndrome); father's abuse of alcohol may cause genetic damage that leads to birth defects The combination of parental smoking and drinking may cause miscarriages, prematurity, low birth weight, and sudden infant death syndrome (SIDS)

Illegal Drugs	Potential Negative Effects
Heroin, morphine, methadone	In mother, difficulty conceiving; in infant, prematurity, low birth weight, addiction, withdrawal, death
Marijuana	In mother, difficulty conceiving; in infant, prematurity, low birth weight, high-pitched crying; no long-term effects
Cocaine	In mother, difficulty conceiving; in infant, prematurity, low birth weight, neurological deficits, small head circumference
Lysergic acid diethylamide (LSD)	Chromosomal breakage

Medications/Treatments	Potential Negative Effects
Steroids	Heart and circulatory problems; masculinization of female fetus
Diethylstilbestrol (DES)	In mother, miscarriage; in infant, prematurity, low birth weight; female child may develop cancer of the cervix; male child may have reproductive abnormalities and increased risk of testicular cancer
Reserpine (tranquilizer)	Respiratory problems in infant
Antibiotics	Defective skeletal growth in infant, hearing loss, jaundice
Aspirin	Blood disorders in infant
Some anticonvulsant medications	Cleft lip and palate in infant; failure of blood coagulation
Lithium	Cardiovascular abnormalities
SSRI antidepressant medication	Feeding and breathing difficulties at birth

Source: Adapted from E. Hetherington and R. Parke, *Child Psychology*.

(seven or more drinks per week or five or more drinks on one occasion) poses a serious health threat to the fetus (Centers for Disease Control and Prevention, 2002). However, "safe" limits for alcohol consumption during pregnancy have not been established.

Tobacco use during pregnancy retards fetal growth and increases the risk of infant illness, disability, and death. Maternal smoking is associated with prematurity, low birth weight, cardiovascular anomalies, conditions involving arteries, veins, or the heart, and asthma (Jaakkola & Gissler, 2004; Kai & Pourier, 2001; Woods & Raju, 2001). Results from the National Longitudinal Survey of Children and Youth indicate that 23 percent of Canadian women smoke during pregnancy, although more recent Canadian data suggest that the percentage of women who smoke is lower than this (Health Canada, 2005). Other substances that may produce low birth weight, birth complications, and/or defects in the fetus include steroids, some antihistamines, long-term use of antibiotics, excessive amounts of Vitamin A, D, B$_6$, and K, caffeine, antidepressant medication, lithium, cocaine, and marijuana (see Table 6.2).

As with alcohol, the best rule for the pregnant woman considering using a prescription or over-the-counter drug, herbal product, or other substance is consult your physician. Up-to-date information on the effects of various legal substances is also available from the Motherisk Information Line by telephone at 416-813-6780 or on the Internet at www.motherisk.org.

Dads and Drugs

Most research has focused on the effects of drugs taken by the pregnant woman. However, new theorizing suggests that drugs taken by men before conception may also cause birth defects, probably because the drugs damage the sperm and their genetic contents (Narod et al., 1988). In addition, one study found evidence that a mother's smoking during the first trimester of pregnancy increased her offspring's risk of cancer in childhood; but a father's smoking during the pregnancy in the absence of mother's smoking also increased the risk of childhood cancer (John et al., 1991).

■ Birth

The Beginning of Labour

The signs that labour is about to begin vary from one woman to the next. There may be a discharge of a small amount of bloody mucus (the "bloody show"). This is the mucus plug that was in the cervical opening during pregnancy, its purpose being to prevent germs from passing from the vagina up into the uterus. In about 10 percent of all women the membranes containing the amniotic fluid rupture (the bag of waters bursts), and there is a gush of warm fluid down the woman's legs. Labour usually begins within 24 hours after this occurs. More commonly, the amniotic sac does not rupture until the end of the first stage of labour. The Braxton-Hicks contractions may increase before labour and actually may be mistaken for labour. Typically they are distinct from the contractions of labour in that they are very irregular.

The biological mechanism that initiates and maintains labour is not completely understood. The progesterone-withdrawal theory is the leading hypothesis (Schwartz, 1997). Progesterone is known to inhibit uterine contractions. It has been proposed that some mechanism such as increased production of antiprogesterone reduces the inhibiting effect of progesterone and labour begins.

The Stages of Labour

Labour is typically divided into three stages, although the length of the stages may vary considerably from one woman to the next. The whole process of childbirth is sometimes referred to as *parturition*.

First-Stage Labour

First-stage labour begins with the regular contractions of the muscles of the uterus. These contractions are responsible for producing two changes in the cervix, both of which must occur before the baby can be delivered. These changes are called **effacement** (thinning out) and **dilation** (opening up). The cervix must dilate until it has an opening 10 centimetres (4 inches) in diameter before the baby can be born.

First-stage labour itself is divided into three stages: early, late, and transition. In *early first-stage labour,* contractions are spaced far apart, with perhaps 15 to 20 minutes between them. A contraction typically lasts 45 seconds to a minute. This stage of labour is fairly easy, and the woman is quite comfortable between contractions. Meanwhile, the cervix is effacing and dilating.

Late first-stage labour is marked by the dilation of the cervix from 5 to 8 centimetres (2 to 3 inches). It is generally shorter than the early stage, and the contractions are more frequent and more intense.

The final dilation of the cervix from 8 to 10 centimetres (3 to 4 inches) occurs during the **transition** phase, which is both short and difficult. The contractions are very strong, and it is during this stage that women report pain and exhaustion.

The first stage of labour can last anywhere from 2 to 24 hours. It averages about 12 to 15 hours for a

---

Effacement: A thinning out of the cervix during labour.
Dilation: An opening up of the cervix during labour; also called dilatation.
First-stage labour: The beginning of labour, during which there are regular contractions of the uterus; the stage lasts until the cervix is dilated 8 centimetres (3 inches).
Transition: The difficult part of labour at the end of the first stage, during which the cervix dilates from 8 to 10 centimetres (3 to 4 inches).

(a)   *(b)*

Figure 6.7   Second-stage labour. *(a)* Baby's head crowning and then *(b)* moving out.

first pregnancy and about 8 hours for later pregnancies. (In most respects, first labours are the hardest; later ones are easier.) The woman is usually told to go to the hospital when the contractions are 4 to 5 minutes apart. Once there, she is put in the labour room or birthing room for the rest of first-stage labour.

Second-Stage Labour: Delivery

Second-stage labour (see Figure 6.7) begins when the cervix is fully dilated and the baby's head (or whichever part comes first, if the baby is in some other position; see Figure 6.8) begins to move into the vagina, or birth canal. It lasts from a few minutes to a few hours and is generally much shorter than the first stage.

During this stage, many women feel an urge to push or bear down, and if done properly, this may be of great assistance in pushing the baby out. With each contraction the baby is pushed farther along.

When the baby's head has traversed the entire length of the vagina, the top of it becomes visible at the vaginal entrance; this is called *crowning*. It is at this point that many physicians perform an **episiotomy** (see Figure 6.9), in which an incision or slit is made in the perineum, the skin just behind the vagina; in Canada 24 percent of vaginal deliveries involve an episiotomy (Health Canada, 2003). Most women do not feel the episiotomy being performed because the pressure of the baby against the pelvic floor provides a natural anaesthetic. The incision is stitched closed after the baby is born. The reason physicians give for performing an episiotomy is that if it is not done, the baby's head may rip the perineum; a neat incision is easier to repair than a ragged tear, and the tear may go much deeper and damage more tissue. But the use of the episiotomy has been questioned; critics claim that it is unnecessary and is done merely for the doctor's convenience, while causing the woman discomfort later as it is healing. Midwives reduce the likelihood of vaginal tears during childbirth by massaging the vaginal area and applying ointments (Maticka-Tyndale & Bicher, 1996).

Second-stage labour: The stage during which the baby moves out through the vagina and is delivered.

Episiotomy (ih-pee-see-ah-tuh-mee): An incision made in the skin just behind the vagina, allowing the baby to be delivered more easily.

(a)   (b)   (c)

Figure 6.8 Possible positions of the fetus during birth. *(a)* A breech presentation (4 percent of births). *(b)* A transverse presentation (fewer than 1 percent). *(c)* A normal, head-first or cephalic presentation (96 percent of births).

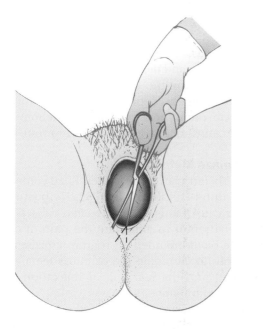

Figure 6.9 Episiotomy. A mediolateral or median cut may be performed.

The baby is finally eased completely out of the mother's body. At this point, the baby is still connected to the mother by the umbilical cord, which runs from the baby's navel to the placenta, and the placenta is still inside the mother's uterus. As the baby takes its first breath of air, the functioning of its body changes dramatically. Blood begins to flow to the lungs, there to take on oxygen, and a flap closes between the two atria (chambers) in the heart. This process generally takes a few minutes, during which time the baby changes from a somewhat bluish colour to a healthy, pink hue. At this point, the baby no longer needs the umbilical cord, which is clamped and cut off about 7 centimetres (3 inches) from the body. The stub gradually dries up and falls off.

To avoid the possibility of transmitting gonorrhea or other eye infections from the mother to the baby, drops of silver nitrate or a similar drug are placed in the baby's eyes (see Chapter 8).

Third-Stage Labour

During **third-stage labour,** the placenta detaches from the walls of the uterus, and the afterbirth (placenta and fetal membranes) is expelled. This stage may take from a few minutes to an hour. Several contractions may accompany the expulsion of the placenta. The episiotomy and/or any tears are sewn up.

Caesarean Section (C Section)

Caesarean section is a surgical procedure for delivery; it is used when normal vaginal birth is impossible or undesirable. Caesarean section may be required for a number of different reasons: if the

Third-stage labour: The stage during which the afterbirth is expelled.
Caesarean section (C section): A method of delivering a baby surgically, by an incision in the abdomen.

baby is too large or if the mother's pelvis is too small to allow the baby to move into the vagina; if the labour has been very long and hard and the cervix is not dilating or if the mother is nearing the point of total exhaustion; if the umbilical cord *prolapses* (moves into a position such that it is coming out through the cervix ahead of the baby); if there is an Rh incompatibility (see p. 166); or if there is excessive bleeding or the mother's or the infant's condition takes a sudden turn for the worse. Another condition requiring a C section is *placenta previa,* in which the placenta is attached to the wall of the uterus over or close to the cervix.

In the Caesarean section, an incision is first made through the abdomen and then through the wall of the uterus. The physician lifts out the baby and then sews up the uterine wall and the abdominal wall.

Caesarian delivery rates increased steadily in Canada in the 1970s and early 1980s, and then again in the last decade. In 2000–01, 21 percent of births were by Caesarian section (Health Canada, 2003). One factor that may be contributing to the increased rates of Caesarian delivery is the fact that increasing numbers of women are having their first child at an older age; women who are older are more likely to require Caesarian delivery. The lowest rate of Caesarian delivery is in Nunavut; the highest is in the Atlantic provinces and British Columbia. The rate of Caesarian delivery in Canada is considerably higher than in most Western European countries. For example, the Caesarean rate is 10 percent of deliveries in the Netherlands, 12 percent of deliveries in Norway, and 10 percent of deliveries in England and Wales (Notzon, 1990). Contrary to popular opinion, it is not true that once a woman has had one delivery by Caesarean she must have all subsequent deliveries by the same method. Vaginal births are possible after Caesareans (Millar et al., 1996), although often the same conditions are present in later deliveries that necessitated the first Caesarean, making it necessary again in the later deliveries. Up to 60 percent of women with a prior Caesarean attempt a subsequent vaginal birth (Lydon-Rochelle et al., 2001).

There is concern about the high Canadian Caesarean rates. Reasons that have been proposed to explain them include the following: (a) Physicians are afraid of malpractice suits. (b) There are more older women giving birth; they may have more difficult labours necessitating Caesareans. (c) Fetal monitors are used increasingly; they can give the physician early warning if the fetus is in distress, necessitating a Caesarean to save the fetus.

Programs in two U.S. hospitals indicate that Caesarean-section rates can be decreased dramatically. In one hospital, prenatal education was expanded, guidelines for Caesareans were tightened, women were encouraged to remain active during labour (for example, to walk at regular intervals), and physicians were given statistics each month about their own deliveries. In May 1988, when the study began, the rate of Caesarean births was 31 percent. For the period January to June 1994, it was 15 percent (Hollander, 1996).

■ Childbirth Options

Pregnant women and their partners can choose from a variety of childbirth options. They can take childbirth classes to prepare mentally and physically for labour and delivery. There are also several options regarding the use of anaesthesia during childbirth. Finally, depending on the province, women can often choose to give birth at home, in a birthing centre, or in a hospital labour room.

The Lamaze Method

English obstetrician Grantly Dick-Read coined the term "natural childbirth" in 1932. He postulated that fear causes tension and tension causes pain. Thus, to attempt to eliminate the pain of childbirth, he recommended a program consisting of education (to eliminate the woman's fears of the unknown) and the learning of relaxation techniques (to eliminate tension).

One of the most widely used methods of *prepared childbirth* was developed by French obstetrician Fernand Lamaze. Classes teaching the Lamaze method or variations of it are now offered in most areas of the country. The **Lamaze method** involves two basic techniques, *relaxation* and *controlled breathing* (see Figure 6.10). The woman learns to relax all the muscles in her body. Knowing how to do this has a number of advantages, including con-

Lamaze method: A method of "prepared" childbirth involving relaxation and controlled breathing.

Figure 6.10 Practice in relaxation and breathing techniques is essential in preparing for a Lamaze childbirth.

servation of energy during an event that requires considerable endurance and, more important, avoidance of the tension that increases the perception of pain. The woman also learns a series of controlled breathing exercises, which she will use to help her during each contraction.

Some other techniques are taught as well. One, called *effleurage*, consists of a light, circular stroking of the abdomen with the fingertips. There are also exercises to strengthen specific muscles, such as the leg muscles, which undergo considerable strain during labour and delivery. Finally, because the Lamaze method is based on the idea that fear and the pain it causes are best eliminated through education, the Lamaze student learns a great deal about the processes involved in pregnancy and childbirth.

One other important component of the Lamaze method is the requirement that the woman be accompanied during the classes and during child-birth itself by her partner or some other person, who serves as "coach." The coach plays an integral role in the woman's learning of the techniques and her use of them during labour. The coach is present during labour and delivery. The coach times contractions, checks on the mother's state of relaxation and gives her feedback if she is not relaxed, suggests breathing patterns, helps elevate her back as she pushes the baby out, and generally provides encouragement and moral support. Aside from the obvious benefits to the mother, this principle of the Lamaze method represents real progress in that it allows the partner to play an active role in the birth of their child and to experience more fully one of the most basic and moving of all human experiences. Some couples also have a *doula* (a Greek word meaning "woman's servant") present during childbirth. The doula does not perform clinical or medical tasks; her role is to provide physical, emotional, and informational support to the woman and her partner during labour and birth.

One common misunderstanding about the Lamaze method is that the use of anaesthetics is prohibited. In fact, the Lamaze method is more flexible than that. Its goal is to teach each woman the techniques she needs to control her reactions to labour so that she will not need an anaesthetic; however, her right to have an anaesthetic if she wants one is affirmed. The topic of anaesthetics in childbirth, which has become quite controversial in recent years, is discussed in the next section.

A number of studies indicate that childbirth training, such as the Lamaze method, has several desirable results. These include reduction in the length of labour, decreased incidence of birth complications, a decrease in the use of anaesthetics, a more positive attitude after birth, increased self-esteem, and a heightened sense of being in control (e.g., Felton & Segelman, 1978; Zax et al., 1975). Lamaze training is associated with increased tolerance for pain and reduced anxiety both before birth and four weeks after birth (Markman & Kadushin, 1986; McClure & Brewer, 1980; Worthington et al., 1983).

There is no doubt that the Lamaze method has improved the childbirth experiences of thousands of women and men. On the other hand, some Lamaze advocates are so idealistic that they may create unrealistic expectations about delivery, especially for women having their first baby

(primiparas). The use of the Lamaze method reduces pain in childbirth but does not eliminate it completely. For primiparas, there is often a discrepancy between their positive expectations for delivery and the actual outcomes (Booth & Meltzoff, 1984). Thus, while the Lamaze method produces excellent outcomes and helps women control pain, childbirth still involves some pain, as well as unexpected complications in some cases.

The Use of Anaesthetics in Childbirth

Throughout most of human history, childbirth has taken place without anaesthetics and in the woman's home or other familiar surroundings. The pattern in North America began to change about 250 years ago when male physicians rather than midwives began to assist during birth. Today almost all births occur in hospitals (Maticka-Tyndale & Bircher, 1996). The next major change came around the middle of the nineteenth century, with the development of anaesthetics for use in surgery. When their use in childbirth was suggested, there was some opposition from physicians, who felt they interfered with "natural" processes, and some opposition from the clergy, who argued that women's pain in childbirth was prescribed in the Bible, quoting Genesis 3:16: "In sorrow thou shalt bring forth children." Opposition to the use of anaesthetics virtually ceased, however, when Queen Victoria gave birth under chloroform anaesthesia in 1853. Since then, the use of anaesthetics has become routine (too routine, according to some) and effective. Before discussing the arguments for and against the use of anaesthetics, let us briefly review some of the common techniques of anaesthesia used in childbirth.

Tranquillizers (such as Valium) or narcotics may be administered when labour becomes fairly intense. They relax the woman and take the edge off the pain. Barbiturates (Nembutal or Seconal) are administered to put the woman to sleep. Scopolamine may sometimes be used for its amnesic effects; it makes the woman forget what has happened, and thus she has no memory afterward of any pain during childbirth. Regional and local anaesthetics, which numb only the specific region of the body that is painful, are used most com-

Primipara: A woman having her first baby.

monly. An example is the pudendal block (named for the pudendum, or vulva), in which an injection numbs only the external genitals. Other examples are spinal anaesthesia (a "spinal"), in which an injection near the spinal cord numbs the entire birth area, from the waist down, and the caudal block and epidural anaesthesia, which are both administered by injections in the back and produce regional numbing from the belly to the thighs (for more information, see Coustan, 1995a). Epidurals are used in 45 percent of vaginal births in Canada.

The routine use of anaesthetics has been questioned by some. Proponents of the use of anaesthetics argue that with modern technology, women no longer need to experience pain during childbirth and that it is therefore silly for them to suffer unnecessarily. Opponents argue that anaesthetics have a number of well-documented dangerous effects on both mother and infant. Anaesthetics in the mother's bloodstream pass through the placenta to the infant. Thus while they have the desired effect of depressing the mother's central nervous system, they also depress the infant's nervous system. Research indicates that babies born under anaesthesia have poor sucking ability and retarded muscular and neural development in the first four weeks of life compared with infants born with no anaesthesia (Boston Women's Health Book Collective, 1998; MacFarlane et al., 1978). Anaesthetics prevent the mother from using her body as effectively as she might to help push the baby out. If administered early in labour, anaesthetics may inhibit uterine contractions, slow cervical dilation, and prolong labour. However, research shows that the negative effects of epidural anesthesia, such as the increased likelihood of the use of instruments during delivery and longer second-stage labour, can be reduced by using low dosages and techniques that allow the woman to move around (Comet, 2001).

Perhaps the best resolution of this controversy is to say that a pregnant woman should participate in prepared childbirth classes and should use those techniques during labour. If, when she is in labour, she discovers that she cannot control the pain and wants an anaesthetic, she should feel free to request it and to do so without guilt; the anaesthetic should then be administered with great caution.

Home Birth versus Hospital Birth

Although in many countries either a physician or a midwife may assist in a home birth, only six provinces (none of the Atlantic provinces) and Nunavut have legislation registering midwives to practise. Midwives are publicly funded in Ontario, B.C., Manitoba, and Quebec. Advocates of home birth argue that the atmosphere in a hospital—with its forbidding machines, regulations, and general lack of "homeyness"—is stressful to the woman and detracts from what should be a joyous, natural human experience. Furthermore, hospitals are meant to deal with illness, and the delivery of a baby should not be viewed as an illness; hospital births encourage the use of procedures such as forceps deliveries and episiotomies that are themselves dangerous. Birth at home is likely to be more relaxed and less stressful; friends and other children are often present. There are some studies that indicate that—for uncomplicated pregnancies—home delivery is as safe as hospital delivery (Hahn & Paige, 1980; for a discussion, see Hoff & Schneiderman, 1985).

On the other side of the argument, if unforeseen emergency medical procedures are necessary, home birth may be downright dangerous for the mother, the baby, or both. Furthermore, hospital practices in labour and delivery have changed radically, particularly with the increased popularity of the Lamaze method; thus, hospitals are not the forbidding, alien environments they once were. Most hospitals, for example, allow partners and loved ones to be present for the entire labour and delivery, and many allow the partner to be present in the operating room during Caesarean deliveries. Many hospitals have created birthing rooms, containing comfortable beds and armchairs, that permit labour and delivery to occur in a relaxed atmosphere and in the position the woman chooses, while being only a minute away from emergency equipment if it is required.

For any home birth, careful medical screening is essential. Only women with normal pregnancies and anticipated normal deliveries should attempt a home birth. A qualified physician or nurse-midwife must be part of the planning. Finally, there must be access to a hospital in case an emergency arises.

(a)

(b)

Figure 6.11 A home birth.

■ After the Baby Is Born: The Postpartum Period

Physical Changes

With the birth of the baby, the woman's body undergoes a drastic physiological change. During pregnancy the placenta produces high levels of both estrogen and progesterone. When the placenta is expelled, the levels of these hormones drop sharply, and thus the postpartum period is characterized by low levels of both estrogen and progesterone. The levels of these hormones gradually return to normal over a period of a few weeks to a few months. Other endocrine changes include an increase in hormones associated with breast-feeding (breast-feeding is discussed in a later section).

In addition, the body undergoes considerable stress during labour and delivery, and the woman may feel exhausted. Discomfort from an episiotomy is common in the first postpartum weeks.

Psychological Changes

On average, Canadian women remain in the hospital for two or three days after parturition; the average length of stay following a Caesarian delivery is 4 to 5 days. However, in 2001–2002, 9 percent of women had a hospital stay of less than two days. For the first two days, women often feel elated; the long pregnancy is over, they have been successful competitors in a demanding athletic event and are pleased with their efforts, and the baby is finally there, to be cuddled and loved.

Following childbirth, many women experience some degree of depression. The depressed mood and other experiences range from mild to severe; the medical literature identifies three types. In the mildest, *postpartum blues* (or "baby blues"), women experience mood swings, with periods of feeling depressed, feeling irritable, and crying alternating with positive moods. The symptoms usually begin a few days after delivery, are most intense one week postpartum, and lessen or disappear by two weeks postpartum. Between 50 and 80 percent of women experience these mild baby blues (Kennedy & Suttenfield, 2001). **Postpartum depression** is more severe, characterized by depressed mood, insomnia, tearfulness, feelings of inadequacy, and fatigue. It usually begins two to three weeks postpartum but may occur anytime after delivery. Between 8 and 15 percent of women will experience it, with symptoms lasting six to eight weeks (O'Hara & Swain, 1996; Morris-Rush & Bernstein, 2002). The more severe disturbance is *postpartum* psychosis, with early symptoms including restlessness, irritability, and sleep disturbance; later ones include disorganized behaviour, mood swings, delusions, and hallucinations. Its onset can be dramatic, within 72 hours of delivery or four to six weeks postpartum. It is very rare, affecting only 1 or 2 women out of 1,000 (Kennedy & Suttenfield, 2001). Postpartum depression and psychosis should be treated; depression improves in response to antidepressant medication, individual psychotherapy, and nurse home visits (Gjerdingen, 2003).

It appears that many factors contribute to this depression. Being in a hospital in and of itself is stressful, as noted previously. Once the woman returns home, another set of stresses faces her. She has probably not yet returned to her normal level of energy, yet she must perform the exhausting task of caring for a newborn infant. For the first several weeks or months she may not get enough sleep, rising several times during the night to tend to a baby that is crying because it is hungry or sick, and she may become exhausted. Clearly she needs help and support from her partner and friends at this time. Some stresses vary depending on whether this is a first child or a later child. The first child is stressful because of the woman's inexperience; while she is in the hospital she may become anxious, wondering whether she will be capable of caring for the infant when she returns home. In the case of later-born children, and some first-borns, the mother may become depressed because she did not really want the baby. Risk factors for more severe depression include personal or family history of psychiatric disorder, unwanted pregnancy, serious complications following birth, and lack of social support (Morris-Rush & Bernstein, 2002).

Physical stresses are also present during the postpartum period; hormone levels have declined sharply, and the body has been under stress. Thus it appears that postpartum depression is caused by a combination of psychological, physical, and social factors.

Fathers, too, sometimes experience depression after the birth of a baby. In one study, 89 percent of the mothers and 62 percent of the fathers had experienced the blues during the three months after the birth (Zaslow et al., 1985). The research indicates that less depressed fathers are more likely to be involved with the infant and the parenting role.

Attachment to the Baby

While much of the traditional psychological research has focused on the baby's developing attachment to the mother, more recent interest has been about the development of the mother's attachment (bond) to the infant. Research shows clearly that this process begins even before the baby is born. Two studies of women expecting their first child found that feelings of nurturance grew during pregnancy, and increased further at birth (Fleming et al., 1997). In this sense, pregnancy is in part a psychological preparation for motherhood.

In the 1970s, pediatricians Marshall Klaus and

Postpartum depression: Mild to moderate depression in women following the birth of a baby.

Table 6.3   Sexual Behaviours within the Previous Month, Reported by Mothers during Pregnancy and the Year Postpartum

	Pregnancy	Postpartum		
Behaviour	2nd Trimester	1 month	4 months	12 months
Intercourse	89%	17%	89%	92%
Mean frequency of intercourse/month	4.97	0.42	5.27	5.1
Fellatio	43%	34%	48%	47%
Cunnilingus	30%	8%	44%	49%
Satisfaction with sexual relationship*	3.76	3.31	3.36	3.53

*Satisfaction with the relationship was rated on a scale from 1 (very dissatisfied) to 5 (very satisfied).

Source: Hyde, J. S., DeLamater, J. D., Plant, E. A., & Byrd, J. M. (1996). Sexuality during pregnancy and the year postpartum; The Journal of Sex Research, 33, 143–151.

John Kennell popularized the idea that there is a kind of "critical period" or "sensitive period" in the minutes and hours immediately after birth, during which the mother and infant should "bond" to each other (Klaus & Kennell, 1976). These ideas have enthusiastically been incorporated into hospital practices, so that in many progressive hospitals the infant is given to the mother to hold immediately after birth. Ironically, scientists later concluded that there is little or no evidence for the sensitive-period-for-bonding hypothesis (e.g., Goldberg, 1983; Lamb, 1982; Lamb & Hwang, 1982; Myers, 1984). That outcome is fortunate. Otherwise, mothers who give birth by Caesarean section (and may therefore be asleep under a general anaesthetic for an hour or more after the birth) and adoptive parents would have to be presumed to have inadequate bonds with their children. We know that, in both cases, strong bonds of love form between parents and children despite the lack of immediate contact following birth. The hospital policy of immediate mother–infant and father–infant contact is still a good one, if only because it is intensely pleasurable and satisfying.

Sex during Postpartum

The birth of a child has a substantial effect on a couple's sexual relationship. Following the birth, the mother is at some risk of infection or hemorrhage (Cunningham et al., 1993), so the couple should wait at least two weeks before resuming intercourse. When coitus is resumed, it may be uncomfortable or even painful for the woman. If she had an episiotomy, she may experience vaginal discomfort; if she had a Caesarean birth, she may experience abdominal discomfort. Fatigue of both the woman and her partner also may influence when they resume sexual activity.

A longitudinal study of the adjustment of couples to the birth of a child collected data from 570 women (and 550 partners) four times: during the second trimester of pregnancy, and at one, four, and twelve months postpartum (Hyde et al., 1996). Data on the sexual relationship are displayed in Table 6.3. In the month following birth, only 17 percent had resumed intercourse. By the fourth month, nine out of ten couples had—the same percentage as reported intercourse during the second trimester. Reports of cunnilingus showed a similar pattern, while reports of fellatio did not indicate a marked decline. Note that although sexual behaviour was much less frequent in the month following birth, satisfaction with the sexual relationship remained high. A major influence on when the couple resumed intercourse was whether the mother was breast-feeding. At both one month and four months after birth, breast-feeding women reported significantly less sexual activity and lower sexual satisfaction. One reason is that lactation suppresses estrogen production, which in turn results in decreased vaginal lubrication; this can make intercourse uncomfortable. This problem can be resolved by the use of vaginal lubricants. Androgen production is also reduced, which may result in reduced sexual desire (La Marre et al., 2003).

■ Breast-Feeding

Biological Mechanisms

Two hormones, both secreted by the pituitary, are involved in lactation (milk production). One, *prolactin,* stimulates the breasts to produce milk. Prolactin is produced fairly constantly for whatever length of time the woman breast-feeds. The other hormone, *oxytocin,* stimulates the breasts to eject milk. Oxytocin is produced reflexively by the pituitary in response to the infant's sucking of the breast. Thus sucking stimulates nerve cells in the nipple; this nerve signal is transmitted to the brain, which then relays the message to the pituitary, which sends out the messenger oxytocin, which stimulates the breasts to eject milk. Interestingly, research with animals indicates that oxytocin stimulates maternal behaviour (Jenkins & Nussey, 1991).

Actually, milk is not produced for several days after delivery. For the first few days, the breast secretes colostrum, discussed earlier, which is high in protein and gives the baby temporary immunity to infectious diseases. Two or three days after delivery, true lactation begins; this may be accompanied by discomfort for a day or so because the breasts are swollen and congested.

It is also important to note that, much as in pregnancy, substances ingested by the mother may be transmitted through the milk to the infant. The nursing mother thus needs to be cautious about using alcohol and other substances.

Physical and Mental Health

The Canadian Pediatric Society and the Public Health Agency of Canada recommend that babies be fed breast milk exclusively for the first six months, and continue breast-feeding after introduction of solid foods up to two years of age and older. This is because breast milk is the ideal food for a baby. It provides the baby with the right mixture of nutrients, it contains antibodies that protect the infant from some diseases, and may help prevent asthma and allergies. It is free from bacteria, and is always the right temperature. Breast-feeding is associated with a reduced risk of obesity at ages 5 and 6 (Von Kries et al., 1999). Researchers in Toronto recently showed that breast milk also helps boost the baby's own immune system (Filipp et al., 2001). Thus there is little question that normally it is superior to cow's milk and commercial formulas. Nonetheless, the vast majority of babies who are not breast-fed grow up healthy.

The percentage of Canadian infants who are breast-fed, at least initially, rose from 38 percent in 1963 to 85 percent in 2003. However, there are large regional differences in breast-feeding rates, ranging from a low of 65 percent in Atlantic Canada to a high of 95 percent in British Columbia. However, about 40 percent of mothers who initiate breast-feeding stop by three months (Health Canada, 2003). Only 19 percent of babies are fed only breast milk for their first six months. Mothers who are younger, single, and have lower education and income levels are less likely to initiate breast-feeding. Immigrant mothers are more likely to breast-feed than are non-immigrants (Health Canada, 1996a). However, individuals from Canada's ethnocultural communities often believe that North American women prefer bottle-feeding over breast-feeding. Thus, they are less likely to breast-feed as they become more acculturated (Agnew, 1997). This pattern is also seen in many Third-World countries, in which urban women are less likely to breast-feed than are rural women, even if they cannot afford to use commercial formula.

A systematic review of programs designed to promote breast-feeding concluded that educational sessions that review benefits, lactation, common problems and solutions, and provide skills training as well as in-person or telephone support programs improve initiation rates and the maintenance of breast-feeding at six months (Guise et al., 2003). There are insufficient data to assess peer counselling programs. Programs that involve only giving out materials at the time the new mother leaves the hospital may actually reduce the likelihood that she will breast-feed. Direct encouragement by a physician or nurse is associated with a much greater likelihood of breast-feeding. The attitudes of the partner are also important. A longitudinal study of 317 first-time mothers and their male partners in Ontario found that male partners' beliefs about breast-feeding affected the women's breast-feeding decisions (Rempel & Rempel, 2004).

Figure 6.12 Breast-feeding.

From the mother's point of view, breast-feeding has several advantages. These include a quicker shrinking of the uterus to its normal size, reduced postpartum bleeding, and more rapid loss of the weight gained during pregnancy. Breast-feeding reduces the likelihood of pregnancy by inhibiting ovulation. It may also reduce the risk of ovarian and breast cancers (Health Canada, 2003). Full breast-feeding, short intervals between feedings, night feedings, and the absence of supplemental feedings are all associated with greater delay in ovulation (Hatcher et al., 2004). However, it is important to note that a woman can become pregnant again before she has a period; recall from Chapter 5 that ovulation precedes menstruation. Research indicates that breast-feeding reduces negative moods and perceived stress (Mezzacappa & Katkin, 2002). Breast-feeding is also associated with reduced risk of breast cancer; the relative risk decreases by 4 percent for every 12 months of breast-feeding (Collaborative Group, 2002).

Some women report sexual arousal during breast-feeding, and a few report having orgasms. Unfortunately, this sometimes produces anxiety in the mother, leading her to discontinue breast-feeding. However, there is nothing "wrong" with this arousal, which appears to stem from activation of hormonal mechanisms. Clearly, from an adaptive point of view, if breast-feeding is important to the infant's survival, it would be wise for Nature to design the process so that it is rewarding to the mother.

The La Leche League is devoted to encouraging women to breast-feed their babies and has helped spread information on breast-feeding. The organi-zation tends to be highly enthusiastic in its advo-cacy of breast-feeding. A few women are physically unable to breast-feed, while some others feel psy-chologically uncomfortable with the idea. This may be due to the prevalence of negative messages in our culture about breast-feeding, particularly in public, as well as the labelling of breasts as sexual organs. And breast-feeding can be inconvenient for the woman who works outside the home, although working women can express their breast milk or supplement morning and evening feeding with for-mula while they are at work.

◼ Problem Pregnancies

Ectopic Pregnancy

An **ectopic pregnancy** (misplaced pregnancy) occurs when the fertilized egg implants somewhere other than the uterus. Most commonly, ectopic pregnancies occur when the egg implants in the fal-lopian tube (tubal pregnancy; Schenker & Evron, 1983). In rare cases, implantation may also occur in the abdominal cavity, the ovary, or the cervix.

A tubal pregnancy may occur if, for one reason or another, the egg is prevented from moving down the tube to the uterus, as when the tubes are obstructed, for example as a result of chlamydia. Early in a tubal pregnancy, the fertilized egg implants in the tube and begins development, forming a placenta and producing the normal hormones of pregnancy. The woman may experience the early symptoms of pregnancy, such as nausea and amenorrhea, and think she is pregnant; or she may experience some bleeding which she mistakes for a period, and think that she is not pregnant. It is therefore quite difficult to diagnose a tubal pregnancy early.

A tubal pregnancy may end in one of two ways. The embryo may spontaneously abort and be released into the abdominal cavity, or the embryo and placenta may continue to expand, stretching the tube until it ruptures. Symptoms of a rupture include sharp abdominal pain or cramping, dull abdominal pain, possibly pain in the shoulder, and vaginal bleeding. Meanwhile, hemorrhaging is occurring, and the woman may go into shock and, possibly, die; thus it is extremely important for a woman dis-playing these symptoms to see a doctor quickly.

Ectopic pregnancy: A pregnancy in which the fertilized egg implants somewhere other than the uterus.

The rate of ectopic pregnancy in Canada has been decreasing since 1992, going from 16 cases per 1,000 reported pregnancies in 1992–93 to 14 per 1,000 pregnancies in 1999–2000 (Health Canada, 2003). The rates vary across Canada, from a low of 9 per 1,000 reported pregnancies in PEI to 26 per 1,000 pregnancies in Nunavut. However, prior to 1992 the rate of ectopic pregnancy in Canada had been increasing, as it still is in a number of other countries. It is thought that high rates are due to: (1) increased rates of sexually transmitted infections (STIs), particularly chlamydia, which lead to blocking of the fallopian tubes; and (2) increased use of contraceptives, such as the IUD and progestin-only methods, that prevent implantation in the uterus but do not necessarily prevent conception. A study of pregnant women in France found that a history of STIs and heavy smoking (more than 20 cigarettes per day) were associated with ectopic pregnancy (Bouyer et al., 2003).

Other Problems

In **pseudocyesis,** or *false pregnancy,* the woman believes that she is pregnant and shows the signs and symptoms of pregnancy without really being pregnant. She may stop menstruating and may have morning sickness. She may begin gaining weight, and her abdomen may bulge. The condition may persist for several months before it goes away, either spontaneously or as a result of psychotherapy. In rare cases it persists until the woman goes into labour and delivers nothing but air and fluid.

Pregnancy may cause a woman's blood pressure to rise to an abnormal level. *Pregnancy-induced hypertension* includes three increasingly serious conditions: (1) hypertension, (2) pre-eclampsia, and (3) eclampsia. Hypertension refers to elevated blood pressure alone. **Pre-eclampsia** refers to elevated blood pressure accompanied by generalized edema (fluid retention and swelling) and proteinuria (protein in the urine). The combination of hypertension and proteinuria is associated with an increased risk of fetal death. In severe pre-eclampsia, the earlier symptoms persist and the woman may also experience vision problems, abdominal pain, and severe headaches. In *eclamp-*

Pseudocyesis: False pregnancy, in which the woman displays the signs of pregnancy but is not actually pregnant.
Pre-eclampsia: A serious disease of pregnancy, marked by high blood pressure, severe edema, and proteinuria.

sia, the woman has convulsions, may go into a coma, and may die (Cunningham et al., 1993).

Pre-eclampsia usually does not appear until after the twentieth week of pregnancy. It is more likely to occur in women who have not completed a pregnancy before. It is especially common among teenagers. The risk of pre-eclampsia rises steadily as pregnancy body mass index increases. For overweight women, a reduction in pre-pregnancy weight may reduce the risk (Bodner et al., 2004). The possibility of pre-eclampsia emphasizes the need for proper medical care before and during pregnancy, especially for teenage and women from ethnocultural minority communities. Hypertension and pre-eclampsia can be managed well during their early stages. Most maternal deaths occur among women who do not receive prenatal medical care.

Certain viruses may cross the placental barrier from the woman to the fetus and cause considerable harm, particularly if the illness occurs during the first trimester of pregnancy. The best-known example is rubella, or German measles. If a woman gets German measles during the first month of pregnancy, there is a 50-percent chance that the infant will be born deaf or have cognitive deficits, cataracts, or congenital heart defects. The risk then declines, so that by the third month of pregnancy the chance of abnormalities is only about 10 percent. While most women have an immunity to rubella because they had it when they were children, a woman who suspects that she is not immune can receive a vaccination that will give her immunity; she should do this well before she becomes pregnant.

Herpes simplex is also *teratogenic,* that is, capable of producing defects in the fetus. Usually the infant contracts the disease by direct contact with the sore; delivery by Caesarean section can prevent this. Women with herpes genitalis also have a high risk of spontaneously aborting.

A woman who is infected with HIV, the virus that causes AIDS, can pass the virus on to her child during pregnancy, delivery, or after birth through her breast milk. In Canada, pregnant women are given the option of being tested for HIV, but testing is not required. It is important that pregnant women know if they are HIV positive. Without treatment, 28 percent of their babies will become infected; however, if the infected mother takes AZT, an antiretrovirus drug, the likelihood of such perinatal transmission is reduced by two-thirds or more (Health Canada, 2002).

Birth Defects

As has been noted, a number of factors, such as substances taken during pregnancy and illness during pregnancy, may cause defects in the fetus. Other causes include genetic defects (for example, phenylketonuria, PKU, which causes cognitive impairment) and chromosomal defects (for example, Down syndrome, which causes cognitive impairment).

Four to five percent of all babies in Canada are born with a birth defect or anomaly. About one-fourth of miscarried fetuses are malformed. The cause of more than half of these defects is unknown (O'Shea, 1995). However, amniocentesis, chorionic villus sampling, and genetic counselling are options to detect genetic defects, provided that abortion is ethically acceptable to the parents.

Amniocentesis involves inserting a fine tube through the pregnant woman's abdomen and removing some amniotic fluid, including cells sloughed off by the fetus, for analysis. The technique is capable of providing an early diagnosis of most chromosomal abnormalities, some genetically produced biochemical disorders, and sex-linked diseases carried by females but affecting males (hemophilia and muscular dystrophy), although it cannot detect all defects. If a defect is discovered, the woman may then decide to terminate the pregnancy with an abortion.

Amniocentesis should be performed between the thirteenth and sixteenth weeks of pregnancy. If a defect is discovered and an abortion is to be performed, it should be done as early as possible (see Chapter 7). Because amniocentesis itself involves some risk, it is generally thought (although the matter is controversial) that it should be performed only on women who have a high risk of bearing a child with a birth defect. A woman is in this category if (1) she has already had one child with a genetic defect; (2) she believes that she is a carrier of a genetic defect, which can usually be established through genetic counselling; and (3) she is over 35, in which case she has a greatly increased chance of bearing a child with a chromosomal abnormality.

Chorionic villus sampling (CVS) (see Figure 6.13) may eventually replace amniocentesis for prenatal diagnosis of genetic defects (Doran, 1990; Kolker,

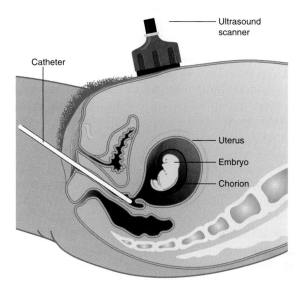

Labels: Ultrasound scanner, Catheter, Uterus, Embryo, Chorion

Figure 6.13 Chorionic villus sampling (CVS) and amniocentesis are both available for prenatal diagnosis of genetic defects. CVS (shown here) is able to detect chromosomal abnormalities and sex-linked diseases.

1989). A major problem with amniocentesis is that it cannot be done until the second trimester of pregnancy; if genetic defects are discovered, there may have to be a late abortion. Chorionic villus sampling, in contrast, can be done in the first trimester of pregnancy, usually around 9 to 11 weeks postconception. Chorionic villus sampling can be performed in one of two ways: transcervically, in which a catheter is inserted into the uterus through the cervix, as shown in Figure 6.13; and transabdominally, in which a needle (guided by ultrasound) is inserted through the abdomen. In either case a sample of cells is taken from the chorionic villi (the chorion is the outermost membrane surrounding the fetus, the amnion, and the amniotic fluid), and these cells are analyzed for evidence of genetic defects. Studies indicate that CVS is as accurate as amniocentesis. Like amniocentesis, it

Amniocentesis (am-nee-oh-sen-TEE-sus): A test to determine whether a fetus has birth defects; done by inserting a fine tube into the woman's abdomen in order to obtain a sample of amniotic fluid.
Chorionic villus sampling (CVS): A technique for prenatal diagnosis of birth defects, involving taking a sample of cells from the chorionic villus and analyzing them.

carries with it a slight risk of fetal loss (due, for example, to miscarriage). According to Health Canada, for both amniocentesis and CVS, the fetal loss rate is between 1 percent and 1.5 percent, but can be as low as 0.04 percent in experenced hands.

Serious ethical questions are raised when amniocentesis and CVS are used to determine gender and are followed by an abortion if the fetus is not the desired gender.

Rh Incompatibility

The Rh factor is a substance in the blood; if it is present, the person is said to be Rh positive (Rh+); if it is absent, the person is said to be Rh negative (Rh–). The Rh factor is genetically transmitted, with Rh+ being dominant over Rh–.

The presence or absence of the Rh factor does not constitute a health problem except when an Rh– person receives a blood transfusion or when an Rh– woman is pregnant with an Rh+ fetus (which can happen only if the father is Rh+). A blood test is done routinely early in pregnancy to determine whether a woman is Rh–. Fortunately, about 85 percent of whites and 93 percent of blacks are Rh+; thus the problems associated with being Rh– are not very common.

If some Rh+ blood gets into Rh– blood, the Rh– blood forms antibodies as a reaction against the Rh factor in the invading blood. During parturition there can be considerable mixing between the mother and fetus, and the blood of an Rh+ baby causes the formation of antibodies in an Rh– woman's blood. During the next pregnancy, some of the woman's blood enters the fetus and the antibodies attack the fetus's red blood cells. The baby may be stillborn, severely anemic, or developmentally delayed. Thus there is little risk for an Rh– woman with the first pregnancy because antibodies have not yet formed; however, later pregnancies can be extremely dangerous.

Fortunately, techniques for dealing with this situation have been developed. An injection of a substance called *Rhogam* prevents the woman's blood from producing antibodies. If necessary, the fetus or newborn infant may get a transfusion.

Miscarriage (Spontaneous Abortion)

Miscarriage, or *spontaneous abortion,* occurs when a pregnancy terminates through natural causes, before the conceptus is viable (capable of surviv-

ing on its own). It is not to be confused with *therapeutic abortion,* in which a pregnancy is terminated by mechanical or medicinal means (what is commonly called *abortion*—see Chapter 7), or with *prematurity,* in which the pregnancy terminates early, but after the infant is viable.

It is estimated that 20 percent of all pregnancies end in spontaneous abortion (Frishman, 1995). This is probably an underestimate, since very early spontaneous abortions may not be detected. The woman may not know that she is pregnant and may mistake the products of the miscarriage for a menstrual period. Thus the true incidence may be closer to 40 percent (Cunningham et al., 1993). Most spontaneous abortions (80 percent) occur during the first trimester of pregnancy.

Most spontaneous abortions occur because the conceptus is defective. Studies of spontaneously aborted fetuses indicate that about 60 percent showed abnormalities that were incompatible with life; for example, many had gross chromosomal abnormalities (Singer, 1995). Thus, contrary to popular belief, psychological and physical traumas are not common causes of miscarriage. In fact, spontaneous abortions seem to be functional in that they naturally eliminate many defective fetuses.

Preterm Birth

A major complication during the third trimester of pregnancy is premature labour and delivery of the fetus. When delivery occurs prior to 37 weeks' gestation, it is considered *preterm.* Because the date of conception cannot always be accurately determined, preterm birth (prematurity) may be defined in terms of the birth weight of the infant; an infant weighing less than 2,500 grams (5½ pounds) is considered to be in the low-birth-weight category. However, this is inappropriate. The principal concern should be the functional development of the infant rather than his or her weight. It is estimated that between 8 and 9 percent of the births in Canada are preterm (Chen & Millar, 1999).

Preterm birth is a cause for concern because the premature infant is much less likely to survive than

---

Miscarriage: The termination of a pregnancy before the fetus is viable, as a result of natural causes (not medical intervention).

the full-term infant. It is estimated that more than half of the deaths of newborn babies in North America are due to preterm birth. Preterm infants are particularly susceptible to respiratory infections, and must receive expert care. Advances in medical techniques have considerably improved survival rates for preterm infants. About 99 percent of infants weighing 2,500 grams at birth survive, as do 64 percent of those weighing 1,000 grams (Cunningham et al., 1993). However, prematurity may cause damage to an infant who survives. A longitudinal study found that low-birth-weight infants scored significantly lower on math and reading tests at age 6 to 14 (Bourdman et al., n.d.).

Maternal factors such as poor health, poor nutrition, heavy smoking, cocaine use, and syphilis are associated with prematurity. Pregnancy-induced hypertension can also lead to preterm birth. Young teenage mothers, whose bodies are not yet ready to bear children, are also very susceptible to premature labour and delivery. The more risks a pregnant women is exposed to, the greater the risk of preterm birth (Ahluwalia et al., 2001).

A particularly serious cause of preterm birth is *abruptio placentae*, the premature separation of the placenta from the wall of the uterus before delivery. In some cases there is partial separation; in other cases there is complete separation. Abruptio placentae is highest in mothers over age 40 and causes between 15 and 25 percent of all stillbirths (Broers et al., 2004).

■ Infertility

Infertility refers to a woman's inability to conceive and give birth to a living child, or a man's inability to impregnate a woman. Health Canada (2003) estimates that 12.5 percent or one in eight Canadian couples experiences infertility. When fertile couples are purposely attempting to conceive a child, about 20 percent succeed within the first menstrual cycle, and about 50 percent succeed within the first six cycles (Hatcher et al., 1994). A couple is considered infertile if they have not conceived after one year of frequent, unprotected

> **Infertility:** A woman's inability to conceive and give birth to a living child, or a man's inability to impregnate a woman.

intercourse (Swerdloff & Wang, 2000). The term "sterile" refers to an individual who has an absolute factor preventing conception.

Causes of Infertility

In about 40 percent of infertile couples, male factors are responsible, and female factors are responsible in an additional 40 percent. In the remaining 20 percent, either both have problems or the cause is unknown (for a detailed discussion, see Liebmann-Smith, 1987).

Causes in the Female

The most common cause of infertility in women is pelvic inflammatory disease (PID) caused by a sexually transmitted infection, especially gonorrhea or chlamydia. Other causes include failure to ovulate, blockage of the fallopian tubes, and "hostile mucus," meaning cervical mucus that blocks the passage of sperm. Less common causes include poor nutrition, eating disorders, exposure to toxic chemicals such as lead or pesticides, smoking, and use of alcohol, narcotics, or barbiturates. Age may also be a factor; fertility declines in women after 35 years of age, the decline being especially sharp after age 40.

Causes in the Male

The most common cause of infertility in men is infections in the reproductive system caused by sexually transmitted infections. Other causes include low sperm count (often due to varicoceles, varicose veins in the testes). Couples concerned about low sperm count may decide to abstain from vaginal intercourse in the hope of increasing the count, but research indicates that this does not work. In men with low sperm counts, the sperm become less motile and begin to show signs of becoming stale after only 24 hours of abstinence (Levitas, 2003). Another cause is low motility of the sperm, which means that the sperm are not good swimmers. Less common causes include exposure to toxic agents such as lead, smoking, alcohol and marijuana use, and use of some prescription drugs (Hatcher et al., 1994). Recent research has shown that exposure to environmental estrogens causes sperm to mature too fast, reducing their fertilizing capacity (Adoya-Osiguwa et al., 2003). Exposure to environmental estrogens comes through contact with substances such as beer and pesticides.

Research also reports that the quality of semen declines with age. As men age, the volume of the semen as well as the number and motility of the sperm declines (Eskanazi et al., 2003). Other research suggests that these declines do not affect rates of success in fertilizing eggs *in vitro* (Paulson et al., 2001).

Combined Factors

In some situations, a combination of factors in both the man and woman causes the infertility. One such factor is an immunologic response. The woman may have an allergic reaction to the man's sperm, causing her to produce antibodies that destroy or damage the sperm. Or her immune system may react to the fetus or placenta. According to one controversial theory, an immune reaction may create the high blood pressure that is associated with pre-eclampsia (Fox, 2002). Immune reactions occur in response to novel cells entering the body; if the body has been exposed to the cells frequently in the past, the reaction is less likely. Frequent prior exposure of a woman to a specific man's semen would reduce the likelihood of rejecting his sperm. So frequent vaginal intercourse without a condom (Robertson & Sharkey, 2001) or oral sex in which the woman swallows the ejaculate (Koelman et al., 2000) prior to the attempt to get pregnant may increase the chances of a successful pregnancy.

Sperm have a chemical sensor that causes them to swim toward the egg, attracted by a chemical on the surface of the egg (Spehr et al., 2003). Researchers have already identified one chemical that disrupts this process by shutting down the receptor. This chemical, or chemicals, that influence the surface of the egg can cause infertility. Finally, a couple may also simply lack knowledge; for instance, they may not know how to time intercourse correctly so that conception may take place.

Psychological Aspects of Infertility

At some point in their lives the vast majority of adults in Canadian society attempt to have a child, and infertility may put significant stresses on a couple (Daniluk, 2001a). Because in our society the male role is defined partly by the ability to father children, the man may feel that his masculinity or virility is in question. Similarly, the female role is defined largely by the ability to bear children and be a mother, so infertility may affect a woman's sense of self-worth, adequacy, and femininity (Daniluk, 1999). Historically, in most cultures fertility has been encouraged—and, indeed, demanded—and not having children has been viewed as selfish; hence, pressures on infertile couples may be high, particularly in traditional cultures. This leads to more psychological stress. The psychological stress is greatest for the partner identified as the source of the infertility and for couples whose infertility remains unexplained (Daniluk, 2001a). Research indicates that, among couples entering fertility treatment programs, women perceive themselves as experiencing greater emotional and social stress than do men (Stanton et al., 2002). Infertility does not significantly reduce relationship satisfaction, but it can lower sexual satisfaction, pleasure, and spontaneity as couples shift from "making love" to "making babies" (Daniluk, 1999, 2001a; Zoldbrod, 1993). As emphasis on population control increases in our society, and being childfree[5] becomes an acceptable and more recognized option, the stress on infertile couples may lessen.

Treatment for infertility also can be long and stressful. British Columbia psychologist Judith Daniluk (2001a) interviewed 65 infertile couples who had received medical intervention for infertility for an average of five years. Couples described their experience with fertility treatments as an emotional rollercoaster. At first they were optimistic that the medical profession, time, and effort could fix the problem; as the process continued, they (particularly the women) experienced a sense of failure every time they began to menstruate and had to accept that the treatment had, once again, not worked. Couples whose attempts to conceive were unsuccessful even after years of medical intervention described being faced with the difficulty of deciding when "enough is enough"—that is, to stop medical interventions, and accept their infertility. They also described the stress in deciding whether to pursue other options to parenthood, a decision that caused conflict between some partners. However, they also described gains

---

[5]Semantics can make a big difference here. Many couples who choose not to have children prefer to call themselves "childfree" rather than "childless."

that had resulted from treatment, including strengthening their relationship and personal growth. Further, all but one couple said that they would do it again.

Treatment of Infertility

There are physicians and clinics that specialize in the evaluation and treatment of infertility. An infertility evaluation should include an assessment of the couple's knowledge of sexual behaviour and conception, and lifestyle factors such as regular drug use. Infertility caused by such factors can be easily treated.

If the infertility problem stems from the woman's failure to ovulate, the treatment may involve the so-called fertility drugs. The drug of first choice is clomiphene (Clomid). It stimulates the pituitary to produce LH and FSH, thus inducing ovulation. The treatment produces a pregnancy in about half the women who are given it. Contrary to media reports, multiple births occur only about 8 percent of the time with Clomid, compared with 1.2 percent with natural pregnancies. If treatment with Clomid is not successful, a second possibility is injections with HMG (human menopausal gonadotropin).

If the infertility is caused by blocked fallopian tubes, delicate microsurgery can sometimes be effective in removing the blockage.

If the infertility is caused by varicoceles in the testes, the condition can usually be treated successfully by a surgical procedure known as varicocelectomy.

Finally, a number of new reproductive technologies, such as in vitro fertilization, are now available for those with fertility problems, as discussed in the next section.

A Canadian study is helpful in putting issues of the treatment of infertility into perspective. Among infertile couples seeking treatment, 65 percent subsequently achieved a pregnancy with *no treatment* (Rousseau et al., 1983). For some couples conception just takes a bit longer. However, for those who meet the medical definition of infertility (unable to conceive after 12 months of unprotected intercourse), only about half will conceive a child with treatment (Daniluk, 2001b). Thus, the risks associated with treatments need to be weighed against the possibility that a pregnancy can be achieved without treatment.

■ New Reproductive Technologies

Reproductive technologies developed in the last three decades mean that there are many ways to conceive and birth babies besides sexual intercourse and pregnancy. These options can be used by infertile couples, single individuals, and same-sex couples. The equality provisions in the Canadian Charter of Rights and Freedoms guarantee that access to new reproductive technologies cannot discriminate on the basis of family status, marital status, sexual orientation, and so on (Law Reform Commission of Canada, 1992).

Assisted Insemination

Assisted insemination (also called *artificial insemination*) involves artificially placing semen in the vagina to produce a pregnancy; thus it is a means of accomplishing reproduction without having sexual intercourse. Assisted insemination in animals was first done in 1776. In 1949, when British scientists successfully froze sperm without any apparent damage to them, a new era of reproductive technology for animals began.

There are 24 assisted insemination programs in Canada. There are two kinds of assisted insemination: assisted insemination by the male partner or husband (AIH), and donor insemination (DI). AIH can be used when the man has a low sperm count. Several samples of his semen are collected and pooled to make one sample with a higher count. This sample is then usually placed in the woman's vagina at the time of ovulation. To increase the number of sperm that reach the fallopian tubes, the sperm can also be washed, concentrated, and injected into the woman's uterus. This is called **intrauterine insemination** or IUI.[6] DI is used

---

[6]After taking a human sexuality course in which this textbook was used, a student contacted me to tell me that her mother had taken part in a pilot study involving IUI. She was born in 1981 and was one of the first, if not the first, babies born in Canada through IUI.

Assisted insemination: Procedure in which sperm are placed into the vagina by means other than sexual intercourse.

Intrauterine insemination: A procedure in which sperm are washed, concentrated, and injected into a women's uterus.

"I ALREADY KNOW ABOUT THE BIRDS AND THE BEES, MOM; I WANT TO KNOW ABOUT ARTIFICIAL INSEMINATION, IN-VITRO FERTILIZATION AND SURROGATE MOTHERING!"

Figure 6.14

when the male partner is sterile or when the woman does not have a male partner. A donor provides semen to impregnate the woman. The success rate is about 60 percent after 6 months for women under the age of 35; it decreases for women who are older. The cost of each donor semen specimen sample is about $400; there are also other expenses associated with DI that can raise the cost substantially.

Sperm Banks

Because it is now possible to freeze sperm, it is possible to store it, which is just what some people are doing: using frozen human *sperm banks.* The sperm banks open up many new possibilities for various life choices. For example, suppose that a couple decide, after having had two children, that they want a permanent method of contraception. The husband then has a vasectomy. A few years later the couple decides that they very much want to have another baby, or the couple has divorced and the man wants to have a baby with a new partner. If the man has stored semen in a sperm bank, they can.

Young men can use sperm banks to store sperm before they undergo radiation therapy for cancer. They can later father children without fearing that they will transmit damaged chromosomes (as a result of the radiation) to their offspring.

Since the mid-1990s sperm banks have gone online, making their services available to millions of people around the world (Springen & Noonan, 2003). There are an estimated 50 sperm banks in Canada and 110 in the United States, and the larger ones have developed Web sites. These sites allow prospective parents to browse through a good deal of information about each potential donor, enabling them to select not only on the basis of height, weight, and eye and hair colour, but also education and family medical history. However, as is often true on the Internet, there is no guarantee that the donor has given accurate information. It is estimated that some 70 percent of the money spent on sperm-bank services in the United States in 2002 ($65 million) was for purchases via the Internet.

Embryo Transfer

With **embryo transfer,** a fertilized, developing egg (embryo) is transferred from the uterus of one woman to the uterus of another woman. Dr. John Buster of UCLA perfected the technique for use with humans, and the first two births resulting from the procedure were announced in 1984 (Associated Press, 1984; Brotman, 1984).

This technique may enable a woman who can conceive but who always miscarries early in the pregnancy to transfer her embryo to another woman who serves as the *surrogate mother;* that is, the person who provides the uterus in which the fetus grows (and whom the media, somewhat callously, have called a "rent-a-womb"). The embryo transfer procedure also essentially can serve as the opposite of assisted insemination. That is, if a woman produces no viable eggs, her male partner's sperm can be used to artificially inseminate another woman (who donates her egg), and the fertilized egg is then transferred from the donor to the mother.

Embryo transfer: Procedure in which an embryo is transferred from the uterus of one woman into the uterus of another.

In Vitro Fertilization

It is possible for scientists to make sperm and egg unite in a dish outside the human body. The scientific term for this procedure is **in vitro fertilization,** or IVF (*in vitro* is Latin for "in glass"). The fertilized egg or embryo can then be implanted in the uterus of a woman and carried to term. This technique can be of great benefit to couples who are infertile because the woman's fallopian tubes are blocked. It can also be used for cases of unexplained infertility, ovulation disorders, endometriosis, or severe male infertility. A process called *intracytoplasmic sperm injection* (ICSI) can be used if the man has no sperm or no healthy sperm in his ejaculate. This involves collecting sperm from the epididymus or testes, injecting a single healthy sperm into the ovum, and then using the fertilized egg for IVF (Pinheiro et al., 1999).

A milestone was reached with the birth of Louise Brown, the first test-tube baby, in England on July 25, 1978. Obstetrician Patrick Steptoe and physiologist Robert Edwards had fertilized the mother's egg with her husband's sperm in a laboratory dish and implanted the embryo in the mother's uterus. The pregnancy went smoothly, and Louise was born healthy and normal. The first IVF children conceived in Canada were born in Vancouver in 1983. IVF is now performed in a number of countries, with 25 clinics in Canada.

According to data from the Canadian Fertility and Andrology Society, on average 20 percent (rates vary considerably from clinic to clinic) of all procedures are successful; that is, they result in a live birth. The success rate is higher when infertility is due to fallopian tube blockage. The procedure is expensive, between $7,000 and $9,000 per attempt. Only Ontario's medicare plan and the armed forces cover IVF, and then only in some cases (Geddes, 1999).

There is also evidence that babies born as a result of IVF are more likely to be low birth weight and have congenital abnormalities. It is not clear whether the increased risk is due to the procedure, or to related factors—for example, mothers are typically older (Kovacs, 2002a). It is also possible to freeze eggs that have been fertilized in vitro, resulting in frozen embryos. This procedure creates the possibility of donated embryos; the birth of a baby resulting from this procedure was first announced in 1984 in Australia. The legal and moral status of the frozen embryo is a difficult question, and some worry about "embryo wastage."

> **In vitro fertilization (IVF):** A procedure in which an egg is fertilized by sperm in a laboratory dish.

(a)

(b)

Figure 6.15   New reproductive technologies. *(a)* With in vitro fertilization, conception is more likely if the egg is scratched, allowing the sperm to enter more easily. *(b)* Vicken Sahakian, MD, medical director of a fertility centre, collects eggs from Deborah, 38. She and her husband, Eric, came in for in vitro fertilization. Out of 13 eggs produced by her, 5 became fertilized and were reintroduced into Deborah.

GIFT

GIFT (for gamete intra-fallopian transfer) is an improvement, in some cases, over IVF. Sperm and eggs (gametes) are collected and then inserted together into the fallopian tube, where natural fertilization can take place, followed by natural implantation.

Yet another improvement is ZIFT (zygote intra-fallopian transfer), which involves fertilizing the egg with sperm in a laboratory dish and then placing the developing fertilized egg (zygote) into the fallopian tube, again allowing natural implantation.

Assisted reproduction is more likely to be successful if the woman is younger (under 34) and if fresh embryos rather than frozen ones are used. Due to ethical concerns related to assisted reproduction, the federal government is planning to outlaw the buying and selling of eggs and sperm (Geddes, 1999).

Cloning

Cloning is the reproduction of an individual from a single cell taken from a "donor" or "parent." The technique, called intracellular nuclear transfer, involves replacing the nucleus of an ovum with the nucleus from a donor, thus producing an embryo that is genetically identical to the donor. Normally, of course, a child has only half of its genes in common with the mother; the other half come from the father. Therefore, children are never genetically identical to either parent. But in cloning, no sperm is necessary and the result is an individual who is genetically identical to the donor.

The first successful cloning was of a mouse, in 1981. In 1997, researchers announced the birth of Dolly, a sheep cloned from a single cell of an adult ewe. In 2000, six cloned piglets were born, significant because pigs are physiologically close to humans (Prather, 2000). Cloning has great potential, for example as a source of organs that could be transplanted to replace failing ones, stem cells, or as an alternative in cases of infertility. But it has great risks as well; fewer than 3 percent of cloning efforts succeed, and those that do sometimes suf-

GIFT: Gamete intra-fallopian transfer, a procedure in which sperm and eggs are collected and then inserted together into the fallopian tube.

fer from grave, unpredictable genetic defects (Kolata, 2001). In 2004, the federal government passed legislation, the Assisted Human Reproduction Act, prohibiting human cloning.

Gender Selection

There is much interest in techniques that will allow couples to choose whether to have a boy or a girl. Such a technology would be useful to parents who have six girls and really want a boy, or for people who would like to have two children, one of each gender. Problems might arise, though. Some scientists fear that the result of being able to choose gender would be a great imbalance in our population, with many more males than females, because many couples prefer their first child to be a boy. This is already beginning to happen in some Asian countries, such as China and India, in which there is a particularly strong preference for sons.

There is a good deal of conventional wisdom about various home methods of increasing the likelihood that a fetus will be male or female. One technique is timing intercourse in relation to ovulation, based on the belief that sperm carrying a Y chromosome swim faster; thus, intercourse at the time of ovulation should increase the chances of a male, whereas intercourse at a time before and remote from ovulation should favour the slow but hardy sperm carrying an X chromosome, resulting in a female. Several studies have tried to test these ideas, relying on indirect measures of time of ovulation (cervical mucus changes, basal body temperature). They suggest that a female is more likely when intercourse coincides with ovulation. Thus, conventional wisdom is wrong. Studies have also investigated the effect of douching; conventional wisdom has it that douching with vinegar will change the vaginal pH, increasing the chances of a boy. Neither of these (or other) "natural" methods will reliably affect the offspring's gender (Kovacs, 2002b).

As usual, entrepreneurs are taking advantage of people's desire to pick the baby's sex, and selling kits that promise results. Some of these kits capitalize on the natural methods, providing the purchaser with thermometers, douching solutions, and other paraphernalia. At least one company is selling kits via the Internet. Again, there is no evidence that these kits will produce the expected results. *Caveat emptor* (buyer beware)!

There are several scientific laboratory procedures that can be used to separate sperm containing male and female chromosomes. Older techniques involved separation based on swimming speed or immunologic characteristics; these work with 70- to 80-percent accuracy. The latest sorting technique, the Micro-Sort method, uses the fluorescence-activated sorter, which can select sperm with an X chromosome with 90-percent accuracy; this technique greatly reduces sperm count and requires assisted reproduction technology (ART). Little data exists on the long-term outcomes of using this procedure (Kovacs, 2002b).

The most reliable method of gender selection is *preimplantation genetic diagnosis* (PGD). This technique involves the removal of eggs from the woman and fertilizing them via IVF. After three days, a cell is taken from each embryo and its chromosomal makeup is determined. An embryo of the preferred type would then be implanted via ART. This method is very invasive to the woman's body and very expensive. The likelihood that the implanted egg would result in the live birth of a healthy infant is the same as for other ART pregnancies.

The Legal and Ethical Challenges of New Reproductive Technologies

The technologies discussed here require expert practitioners and appropriate facilities. Further, these and other procedures raise complex legal and ethical questions (discussed in Chapter 20). The federal government passed legislation in 2004 to regulate the new reproductive technologies and to deal with some of these issues. The Assisted Human Reproduction Act prohibits identifying the sex of an embryo created for reproductive purposes except for medical reasons, paying a woman to be a surrogate mother, paying a donor for sperm or eggs, and buying or selling human embryos. It also created an agency to oversee agencies providing assisted human reproduction services in Canada and to maintain a donor–offspring registry. However, a number of other legal questions remain. One set of questions is to be found in the matter of kinship and parental rights and responsibilities. When a child is born as a result of these techniques, who exactly are the parents? One commentator notes that there can be five: an egg donor, a sperm donor, the donor of a uterus for all or part of the gestation, and the couple who rear the child (Shapiro, 1986, p. 54). This is a particularly thorny question in the case of a surrogate mother who has donated her egg and her uterus for nine months and then is required to give up the child. Do donors have any legal claim to contact with "their" children after birth?

There are also a host of procedural issues. What will the standards of confidentiality be, especially with regard to the identity of non-parent donors? If something goes wrong during one of these procedures—and they are risky—who is liable? Who will take responsibility for a child with a serious disability born through one of these techniques? Should the procedures be covered by medicare? Finally, there is the question of who should pay for treatment of infertility. Investigations of the causes of infertility are covered by medicare. In addition, the provinces fund some costly treatments for infertility such as tubal surgery in women and repair of varicocele in men (Leader, 1999). However, IVF is covered by medicare only for Canadians living in Ontario and who are in the armed forces. Assisted insemination and the drugs used to treat infertility are not covered in any province or territory. This makes most infertility treatments unavailable to the majority of Canadians, who cannot afford them.

■ ■ ■ SUMMARY

Sperm are manufactured in the testes and ejaculated out through the vas deferens and urethra into the vagina. Then they begin their swim through the cervix and uterus and up a fallopian tube to meet the egg, which has already been released from the ovary. When the sperm and egg unite in the fallopian tube, conception occurs. The single fertilized egg cell then begins dividing as it travels down the tube, and finally it implants in the uterus. Various techniques for improving the chances of conception are available.

The placenta, which is important in transmitting substances between the woman and the fetus, develops early in pregnancy. The most remarkable development of the fetus occurs during the first trimester (first three months), when most of the major organ systems are formed and human features develop.

For the woman, early signs of pregnancy include amenorrhea, tenderness of the breasts, and nausea. The most common pregnancy tests are designed to detect hCG in the urine or blood. Physical changes during the first trimester are mainly the result of the increasing levels of estrogen and progesterone produced by the placenta. Despite cultural myths about the radiant contentment of the pregnant woman, some women do have negative feelings during the first trimester. During the second trimester the woman generally feels better, both physically and psychologically.

Despite many people's concerns, sexual intercourse is generally quite safe during pregnancy. Nutrition is exceptionally important during pregnancy because the woman's body has to supply the materials to create another human being. Pregnant women also must be very careful about ingesting substances because some can penetrate the placental barrier and enter the fetus, possibly causing damage.

Labour is typically divided into three stages. During the first stage, the cervix undergoes effacement (thinning) and dilation. During the second stage, the baby moves out through the vagina. The placenta is delivered during the third stage. Caesarean section is a surgical method of delivering a baby.

The Lamaze method of "prepared" childbirth has become very popular; it emphasizes the use of relaxation and controlled breathing to control contractions and minimize the woman's discomfort. Anaesthetics may not be necessary, which seems desirable, since they are potentially dangerous to the infant.

During the postpartum period, hormone levels are very low. Postpartum depression may arise from a combination of this hormonal state and the many environmental stresses on the woman at this time.

Two hormones are involved in lactation: prolactin and oxytocin. Breast-feeding has a number of psychological as well as health advantages.

Problems of pregnancy include ectopic (misplaced) pregnancy, pseudocyesis (false pregnancy), pre-eclampsia and eclampsia, illness (such as German measles), a defective conceptus, Rh incompatibility, spontaneous abortion, and preterm birth.

The most common cause of infertility in men and women is infection related to sexually transmitted infections (STIs).

New reproductive technologies include assisted insemination, frozen sperm banks, embryo transfer, in vitro fertilization, and GIFT (gamete intrafallopian transfer), all of which are now a reality. These procedures are expensive and have low success rates.

■ ■ ■ QUESTIONS FOR THOUGHT, DISCUSSION, AND DEBATE

1. Taking the point of view of a pregnant woman, which would you prefer to have, a home birth or a hospital birth? Why?

2. For readers who are men, what role would you envision for yourself in parenting if you had a child? Do you feel that you are adequately prepared for that role? For readers who are women, what role would you ideally like an imaginary partner to take in the parenting of your imaginary children?

3. A close friend confides in you that she is afraid of pregnancy. She has heard that pregnant women experience unpleasant physical (aches and pains, fatigue, illness) and psychological (crying spells, depression) symptoms. She is especially concerned that pregnancy might have a bad effect on her relationship with her partner. What information would you give her about these fears?

■ ■ ■ SUGGESTIONS FOR FURTHER READING

Agnew, T. (1997). *A multicultural perspective of breast-feeding in Canada*. Ottawa: Minister of Public Works and Government Services Canada. Agnew gives a fascinating account of breast-feeding practices of women from ethnocultural communities both in their countries of origin and after emigrating to Canada.

Dorris, Michael. (1989). *The broken cord*. New York: Harper & Row. The true story of a man and the child he adopted, who turned out to have fetal alcohol syndrome and all the behaviour disturbances that go with it.

Kane, Elizabeth. (1988). *Birth mother: The story of America's first legal surrogate mother*. San Diego: Harcourt Brace Jovanovich. An insightful, first-person account by the woman who was the first to have a contract to bear a child for another couple but later developed serious misgivings.

Laforêt, M. (Ed.). (1993). Sexuality, infertility & assisted reproduction. *The Canadian Journal of Human Sexuality, 2(3)*. This special issue of the journal reviews the literature on the major issues related to infertility and assisted reproduction, and includes a number of personal accounts.

Nilsson, A. L., et al. (1986). *A child is born*. New York: Dell. Contains exceptional photographs of prenatal development.

Zoldbrod, Aline P. (1993). *Men, women and infertility: Intervention and treatment strategies*. New York: Lexington. Explores the impact of infertility on personality, the couple's relationship, and sexuality.

For Review Questions, Web Resources, and other learning and study tools, visit the *Understanding Human Sexuality* Online Learning Centre at www.mcgrawhill.ca/college/hyde.

CHAPTER 7

Contraception and Abortion

CHAPTER HIGHLIGHTS

The Pill, the Patch and the Ring
Drug Interactions
Other Kinds of Pills
The Patch
The Vaginal Ring
Emergency Contraception

Depo-Provera Injections

The IUD

The Diaphragm, the Cervical Cap, the Lea's Shield, and the Contraceptive Sponge
The Diaphragm
The Cervical Cap
Lea's Shield and Contraceptive Sponge

The Male Condom

The Female Condom

Spermicides

Douching

Withdrawal

Fertility Awareness (Rhythm) Methods
The Calendar Method
Standard Days Method
The Basal Body Temperature Method
The Cervical Mucus (Ovulation) Method
The Sympto-Thermal Method
Effectiveness
Advantages and Disadvantages

Sterilization
Male Sterilization
Female Sterilization

New Advances in Contraception
Male Methods
Female Methods

Psychological Aspects: Attitudes toward Contraception

Abortion
Abortion Procedures
Psychological Aspects
Men and Abortion

For a short time I worked in an abortion clinic. One day I was counselling a woman who had come in for an abortion. I began to discuss the possible methods of contraception she could use in the future (she had been using rhythm), and I asked her what method she planned to use after the abortion. "Rhythm," she answered. "I used it for eleven months and it worked!"*

The average student of today grew up in the pill era and simply assumes that highly effective methods of contraception are available. It is sometimes difficult to remember that this has not always been true and that previously contraception was a hit-or-miss affair at best. Contraception is less controversial than it once was. Yet the use of contraceptives was illegal until 1969 when, under Prime Minister Pierre Trudeau, Parliament amended many of the laws pertaining to sexual behaviour.

Prior to 1969, a person who sold, advertised, or published an advertisement about any "means, instructions, medicine, drug or article intended or represented as a method of preventing conception or causing abortion" could be jailed for up to two years. This statute came under the subheading "Offences Tending to Corrupt Morals" and as such was intended to protect the public and preserve social values (Appleby, 1999). The 1969 amendments to the Criminal Code of Canada also allowed abortion under certain restrictive circumstances. The process by which the abortion law was declared unconstitutional by the Supreme Court of Canada in 1988 (abortion is now legal in Canada) is discussed later in this chapter in the section on abortion. Suffice it to say that these contraception and abortion laws are clear examples of the enshrinement in the statute books of the values of another day. They arise from an understanding of reproduction as the only legitimate purpose of sex and the belief in the necessity of vigorous propagation of the species.

Today there are a variety of reasons for an individual's use of contraceptives. Both babies and mothers are healthier if pregnancies are spaced 3 to 5 years apart (Setty-Venugopal & Upadhyay, 2002). Most couples want to limit the size of their family—usually to one or two children. Single persons typically wish to avoid pregnancy. In some cases a couple know, through genetic counselling, that they have a high risk of bearing a child with a birth defect and they therefore wish to prevent pregnancy. And in this era of successful career women, many women feel that it is essential to be able to control when and whether to have children.

At the level of society as a whole, there are also important reasons for encouraging the use of contraceptives. In 2001, there were 37,622 adolescent pregnancies in Canada; 541 of these were girls under 15 years old; adolescent pregnancy is a major social problem. On the global level, overpopulation is a serious problem. In 1900 the world's population was 1.6 billion—and it had taken millions of years to reach that level (Townsend, 2003). By 1950 it had increased to 2.5 billion. In 1999, the world population hit 6 billion, an alarming increase, and experts estimate that it will reach 8.9 billion by 2050. With the resulting destruction of the environment and increased consumption of natural resources, grave concerns arise about the ability of the planet to sustain such a large population, even in the relatively near future. Most experts believe that we must limit the size of the world population (Upadhyay & Robey, 1999). For a summary of contraceptive practices around the world, see Table 7.1.

In this chapter we discuss various methods of birth control, how each works, how effective they are, what side effects they have, and their relative advantages and disadvantages. We also discuss abortion and advances in contraceptive technology.

■ The Pill, the Patch, and the Ring

With **combination birth control pills** (sometimes called *oral contraceptives*) such as Loestrin and

*Paula Weideger. (1976). *Menstruation and menopause*. New York: Knopf, p. 42.

Combination birth control pills: Birth control pills that contain a combination of estrogen and progestin (progesterone).

Table 7.1 Contraception around the World, Reported by Currently Married Women
(The great variations reflect differences among cultures in such factors as availability of medical service, people's education about contraception, and gender roles.)

Region, Country	Voluntary Sterilization		Pill	IUD	Male Condom	Injectables*	Vaginal Methods** & Fertility Awareness	All Methods
	Male	Women						
North America								
United States	11	28	27	1	20	4	4	—
Canada	22	11	21	1	15	1	4	88
Europe								
France	NA	NA	38	21	5	NA	NA	80
Netherlands	9	4	49	3	8	NA	NA	74
Africa (Sub-Saharan)								
Kenya	0	6	9	3	1	12	6	39
Asia								
Bangladesh	1	7	23	1	4	7	5	54
India	2	34	2	2	3	0	3	48
Latin America								
Colombia	1	27	12	12	6	4	7	77
Middle East and North Africa								
Egypt	0	1	10	36	1	6	1	56
Morocco	0	3	38	5	1	<1	3	58

NA: Statistics not available
*Includes injections such as Depo-Provera.
**Includes diaphragm, cervical cap, and spermicides.
Sources: Fisher, Borolitsky, & Morris (2003) U.S.; Bureau of the Census, International Data Base (2004), www.census.gov/ipc/www/idbprint.html; Zlidar et al., 2003.

Orthocept, the woman takes a pill that contains estrogen and progestin (a synthetic progesterone), both at doses higher than natural levels, for 21 days. Then she takes no pill or a placebo for seven days, after which she repeats the cycle.

The traditional 21-on, 7-off pattern is still very common, but variations have been introduced. One is Seasonale, which provides 84 days of combined hormones and 7 days of placebo; this means that the woman has a period only once in three months. Seasonale is not yet available in Canada. However, in some situations physicians may recommend that a woman use certain types of birth control pills in this way for two to three months—that is, not taking the placebo pills from one or two packs before starting the next pack.

How It Works

The pill works mainly by preventing ovulation. Recall from Chapter 5 that in a natural menstrual cycle, the low levels of estrogen during and just after the menstrual period trigger the pituitary to produce FSH, which stimulates the process of ovulation. The woman starts taking the birth control pills on the first day of menstruation. Thus just when estrogen levels would normally be low, they are artificially made high. This high level of estrogen inhibits FSH production, and the message to ovulate is never sent out. The high level of progesterone inhibits LH production, further preventing ovulation.

The progestin provides additional backup effects. It keeps the cervical mucus very thick, making it difficult for sperm to get through, and it changes the lining of the uterus in such a way that even if a fertilized egg were to arrive, implantation would be unlikely.

When the estrogen and progestin are withdrawn (after day 21 in the traditional pill), the lining of the uterus disintegrates, and withdrawal bleeding or menstruation occurs, although the flow is typically reduced because the progestin has inhibited development of the endometrium.

Effectiveness

Before the effectiveness of the pill is discussed, several technical terms that are used in communicating data on contraceptive effectiveness need to be defined. If 100 women use a contraceptive method for one year, the number of them who become pregnant during that first year of use is called the **failure rate** or *pregnancy rate*. That is, if 5 women out of 100 become pregnant during a year of using contraceptive A, then A's failure rate is 5 percent. *Effectiveness* is 100 minus the failure rate; thus contraceptive A would be said to be 95 percent effective. We can also talk about two kinds of failure rate: the *failure rate for perfect users* and the *failure rate for typical users*. The perfect-user failure rate refers to studies of the best possible use of the method—for example, when the user has been well-taught about the method, uses it with perfect consistency, and so on. The failure rate for typical users is just that—the failure rate when people actually use the method, perhaps imperfectly when they forget to take a pill or do not use a condom every time. The good news is that if you are very responsible about contraception, you can anticipate close to the perfect-user failure rate for yourself.

The use of combination pills is one of the most effective methods of birth control. The perfect-user failure rate is 0.1 percent (that is, the method is essentially 100-percent effective), and the typical-user failure rate is 3 percent (Society of Obstetricians and Gynaecologists of Canada, 2000). Failures occur primarily as a result of forgetting to take a pill for two or more days or not taking it at the same time every day. If a woman forgets to take a pill, she should take it as soon as she remembers and take

the next one at the regular time; this does not appear to increase the pregnancy risk appreciably. If she forgets for two days she should consult her clinician for instructions. If she forgets for three or more days, she should switch to some other method of birth control for the remainder of that cycle.

Side Effects

You may have seen reports in the media on the dangerous side effects of birth control pills. Some of these reports are no more than scare stories with little or no evidence behind them. However, there are some well-documented risks associated with the use of the pill, and women who are using it or who are contemplating using it should be aware of them.

Among the serious side effects associated with use of the pill are slight but significant increases in certain diseases of the circulatory system. One of these is problems of blood clotting (thromboembolic disorders). Women who use the pill have a higher chance than non-users of developing blood clots (thrombi). Often these form in the legs, and they may then move to the lungs. A stroke may occur if the clot goes to the brain. The clots may lead to pain, hospitalization, and (in rare cases) death. Symptoms of blood clots are severe headaches, severe leg or chest pains, and shortness of breath. Most cases of clots occur in women over 35 who smoke. For some women, the pill can cause high blood pressure; thus it is important to have regular checkups so that this side effect can be detected if it occurs.

There have been many reports in the media of the pill causing cancer. However, the scientific data do not provide evidence that the pill causes cancer of the cervix, uterus, or breast. The good news is that the pill actually protects women from endometrial cancer and ovarian cancer (Hatcher et al., 2004). However, the pill may aggravate already existing cancer such as breast cancer.

For women who have taken the pill for more than five years, the risk of benign liver tumours increases (Hatcher et al., 2004). These tumours can cause death from bleeding if they rupture. Although these problems are relatively rare, they underline the importance of the doctor giving a thorough examination before prescribing birth control pills and of the woman having regular checkups while using them.

Failure rate: The pregnancy rate occurring using a particular contraceptive method; the percentage of women who will be pregnant after a year of use of the method.

In Focus 7.1

A Brief History of Change: Birth Control and Abortion in Canada

In the 1800s, in Canada and in other Western countries, birth control and abortion early in pregnancy were not illegal. However, laws were passed in the nineteenth century to prohibit the use of birth control as well as the spread of contraceptive information. In the 1892 Canadian Criminal Code, a person who sold, advertised, or published an advertisement about any "medicine, drug, or article" intended to prevent contraception could be jailed for up to two years. Abortion was also made illegal.

The movement toward legalizing birth control in Canada was started by women's groups in British Columbia that recognized the toll that unwanted pregnancies were having on women's health and well-being. They joined together to form the Canadian Birth Control League. This group was influenced by Margaret Sanger, who had founded the American Birth Control League in 1914, thereby launching the birth control movement in the United States. Margaret Sanger's speech to the Canadian Birth Control League in 1923 was particularly influential.

There were a number of other organizations that called for the legalization of birth control during the 1920s and 1930s, including the Saskatchewan section of the United Farmers of Canada, the Seventh Labour Women's Society and Economic Conference, and the National Council of Jewish Women. A. H. Tyler, a Protestant minister who wrote sex education and birth control publications in the 1930s and 1940s, was responsible for the birth control movement in Toronto, and founded the Canadian Voluntary Parenthood League in 1931.

The first birth control clinic in Canada was established in Hamilton, Ontario, by Mary Hawkins in 1932. This clinic, called the Birth Control Society of Hamilton, served hundreds of patients. To allay criticisms by members of the medical profession, a physician was always in attendance. Dr. Elizabeth Bagshaw, one of Hamilton's few female physicians at the time, served the clinic for more than 30 years. The clinic was so successful that the Hamilton hospital began cooperating with the clinic in 1935. By 1937 there were also birth control clinics in Windsor and Kitchener.

In 1936, Dorothea Palmer, an Ottawa social worker, was charged with distributing birth control information in poor neighbourhoods. She was acquitted in 1937, partly through the efforts of the birth control lobby. The court recognized that the provision of birth control information was permissible if it were done in the interest of the "public good." However, the sale and distribution of contra-

---

The pill increases the amount of vaginal discharge and the susceptibility to vaginitis (vaginal inflammations such as monilia—see Chapter 8) because it alters the chemical balance of the lining of the vagina. Women on the pill have an increased susceptibility to chlamydia. In one study women using the pill had a 73-percent-higher rate of acquiring chlamydia and a 70-percent-higher rate of acquiring gonorrhea than did comparison groups of women using sterilization or an IUD (Louv et al., 1989).

The pill may cause some nausea, although this almost always goes away after the first month or two of use. Some brands of pills can also cause weight gain, by increasing appetite or water retention, but this side effect can often be reversed by switching to another brand.

Finally, there may be some psychological effects. About 20 percent of women on the pill report increased irritability and depression, which become worse with the length of time it is used. These side effects are probably related to the progesterone in the pill; switching to a different brand may be helpful. There may also be changes in sexual desire.

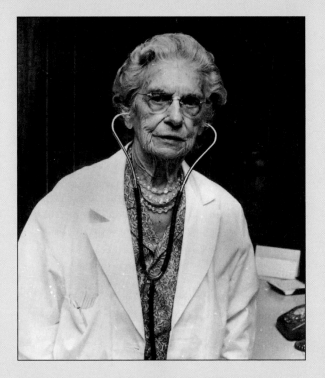

Figure 7.1 Dr. Elizabeth Bagshaw served as a physician for more than 30 years with the clinic run by the Birth Control Society of Hamilton, the first birth control clinic in Canada.

ceptives was still technically illegal until 1969. In fact, as recently as 1960 a Toronto pharmacist was jailed for selling condoms.

In 1967, Pierre Elliott Trudeau, then Minister of Justice, introduced the "Omnibus Bill," making large-scale changes to the Canadian Criminal Code, including the sections related to contraception and abortion. In defending the bill, Trudeau made his now famous statement: "The state has no business in the bedrooms of the nation." The Omnibus Bill was passed in 1969 when Trudeau was prime minister. Among other changes, it made the use of contraceptives legal and allowed abortion under certain restrictive circumstances.

Dr. Henry Morgentaler has been instrumental in bringing changes to Canada's abortion laws through a campaign of civil disobedience. Henry Morgentaler was born in Poland and was interned in two concentration camps before being liberated by U.S. forces. He immigrated to Canada and graduated in medicine from l'Université de Montréal in 1953. He opened his first abortion clinic in Montreal in 1968, moved by the desperation of some of his poor female patients with unwanted pregnancies. In 1988 after a series of court cases, the Supreme Court of Canada, in the "Morgentaler Decision," struck down Canada's abortion law as unconstitutional. (See Chapter 21 for a discussion of the ethical issues surrounding abortion.) Canada currently has no abortion legislation, and abortion is legal in Canada.

Sources: CARAL; Chesler, 1992; Planned Parenthood Federation of Canada.

Some women report an increase in sexual interest (McCoy & Matyas, 1996). But other women report a decrease in sexual desire as well as a decrease in vaginal lubrication (Graham et al., 1995). Once again, switching brands may be helpful.

Because of the side effects discussed previously, women in the following groups should *not* use the pill (Hatcher et al., 2004): those with poor blood circulation or blood-clotting problems; those who have had a heart attack or who have coronary artery disease; those with liver tumours; those with cancer of the breast; nursing mothers (the pill tends to dry up the milk supply, and the hormones may be transmitted through the milk to the baby); and pregnant women. Women over 35 who are cigarette smokers should use the pill only with caution, because the risk of heart attack is considerably higher in this group.

After all this discussion, just how dangerous is the pill? It seems that the answer to this question depends on who you are and on how you look at it. If you have blood-clotting problems, the pill is dangerous to you; if you have none of the contraindications listed above, it is very safe (Hatcher et al., 2004). One's point of view and standard of comparison also matter. While a death rate of 1.6 per 100,000 sounds high, it is important to consider that one alternative to the pill is intercourse with no contraceptive, which can mean pregnancy, with its own set of side effects and death rate. Thus, while the death rate for the pill is 1.6 per 100,000, the death rate for pregnancy and delivery is 12 per 100,000 (Cheng et al., 2003). And while the pill may precipitate diabetes, pregnancy may do so, too. Thus, in many ways the pill is no more dangerous than the alternative, pregnancy, and actually may be safer. Another possible standard of comparison is drugs that are commonly taken for less serious reasons. Aspirin, for example, is routinely used for headaches. Recent reports indicate that Aspirin has side effects, and thus the birth control pill may be no more dangerous than drugs we take without worrying much.

In short, the pill does have some serious potential side effects, particularly for high-risk individuals, but for many others it is an extremely effective means of contraception that poses little or no danger.

Advantages and Disadvantages

The pill has a number of advantages. It is close to 100-percent effective if used properly. It does not interfere with intercourse, as do some other methods—the diaphragm, the condom, and foam. It is not messy. Some of its side effects are also advantages; it reduces the amount of menstrual flow and thus reduces cramps. Indeed, it is sometimes prescribed for the non-contraceptive purpose of regulating menstruation and eliminating cramps. Iron-deficiency anemia is also less likely to occur among pill users. The pill can clear up acne, and has a protective effect against some rather serious things, including pelvic inflammatory disease (PID) and ovarian and endometrial cancer (Hatcher et al., 2004).

The side effects of birth control pills, discussed above, are of course major disadvantages. Another disadvantage is the cost, which is about $20 a month for as long as they are used, although many users (41 percent) do not pay the full cost (Boroditsky et al., 1996). They also place the entire burden of contraception on the woman. In addition, taking them correctly is a little complicated; the woman must understand that they are to be taken at the same time every day, and she must remember when to take them and when not to take them. This effort would not be too taxing for a well-educated woman from a culture that is

familiar with various contraceptives. However, currently available information on the use of birth control pills might be inadequate to meet the needs of a woman from a developing country. Appropriate information and direction on how to use the pill is also important for persons with intellectual disabilities.

One other criticism of the pill is that for a woman who has intercourse only infrequently (say, once or twice a month or less), it represents contraceptive "overkill"; that is, the pill makes her infertile every day of the month (with the side effects of taking it every day), and yet she needs it only a few days each month. Women in this situation might consider a method that is used only when needed, such as the diaphragm or condom.

Finally, it is important to recognize that, although it is an excellent contraceptive, the pill provides absolutely no protection against sexually transmitted infections.

Reversibility

When a woman wants to become pregnant, she simply stops taking pills after the end of one cycle. Some women experience a brief delay (2 or 3 months) in becoming pregnant, but pregnancy rates are about the same as for women who never took the pill.

Drug Interactions

If you are taking birth control pills, you are taking a prescription drug and there may be interactions with other prescription drugs you take (Hatcher et al., 2004). Some anti-tuberculosis drugs, for example, decrease the effectiveness of the pill. There are 30 other drugs that may also interact with the pill; it is important for women to check with their doctor or pharmacist about possible interactions.

The pill may also increase the metabolism of some drugs, making them more potent (Hatcher et al., 2004). Examples include some anti-anxiety drugs, corticosteroids used for inflammations, and theophylline (a drug used for asthma and an ingredient in, for example, Primatene). Therefore, women using the pill may require lower doses of these drugs.

Some over-the-counter drugs may also interact with the pill. St. John's Wort, for example, can decrease the effectiveness of the pill substantailly.

Other Kinds of Pills

To this point, the discussion has centred chiefly on the *combination pill*, so named because it contains both estrogen and progestin. This variety of pill is the most widely used, but there are many kinds of combination pills and several kinds of pills other than combination ones.

Combination pills vary from one brand to the next in the dosages of estrogen and progestin. The dose of estrogen is important because higher doses are more likely to induce blood-clotting problems. Most women do well on pills containing no more than 30 to 35 micrograms of estrogen such as Alesse, Demulen 30, Min-Ovral, and Minestrin (Dickey, 2000). Because of concerns about side effects due to the estrogen in the pill, current pills have considerably lower levels of estrogen than early pills; for example, Ortho 1/35 has one-third the amount of estrogen of the early pill Enovid 10. In January 2005, Yasmin, a new type of contraceptive pill that combines a low dose of estrogen with a synthetic form of progestin (drospirenone), was approved for sale in Canada by Health Canada. High-progestin brands are related to symptoms such as vaginitis and depression. Thus, depending on what side effects the woman wants to avoid, she can choose a brand for its high or low estrogen or progesterone level. (See Hatcher et al., 2004, p. 428 for a list of symptoms related to dosages of estrogen and progestin.)

The **triphasic pill** (e.g., Triphasil, Ortho 7/7/7) contains a steady level of estrogen like the combination pill does, but there are three phases in the levels of progesterone. The idea is to reduce total hormone exposure, although it may be about marketing more than anything else.

Progestin-only pills (Micronor is the only one available in Canada) have also been developed. They are sometimes called *mini-pills*. The pills contain only a low dose of progestin and no estrogen, and were designed to avoid the estrogen-related side effects of the standard pills. The woman takes one beginning on the first day of her period and one every day thereafter; it is important that she takes it at the same time each day. The effects of progestin-only pills that prevent pregnancy include the following: changes in the cervical mucus such that sperm cannot get through, inhibition of implanta-

tion, and inhibition of ovulation (although while taking mini-pills about 40 percent of women ovulate consistently). Progestin-only pills have a typical-user failure rate of 5 percent, which is higher than that of combination pills, although much of the failure occurs during the first six months of use. Their major side effect seems to be that they produce very irregular menstrual cycles. The mini-pill is probably most useful for women who cannot take combination pills—for example, women over 35 who smoke, or women with a history of high blood pressure or blood-clotting problems.

Progestin-only pills are also useful for women who are breast-feeding and cannot use combination pills because they reduce milk production. Neither kind of pill should be used in the first 6 weeks after birth when breast-feeding, because trace amounts of the hormones can reach the infant through the breast milk. After that time, though, progestin-only pills are a good choice.

The Patch

The patch (Ortho Evra) contains the same hormones as combination birth control pills but is administered transdermally—that is, through the skin. The patch itself is thin, beige, and about the size of a double Band-aid. It consists of an outer, protective layer of polyester, an adhesive layer that contains the hormones, and a polyester liner that is removed before applying.

The patch lasts for seven days, so the woman places a new one on once a week for three weeks, and then has a patch-free week. The very first time it is used it takes a couple of days for the hormones to reach effective levels in the bloodstream, so a backup method such as a condom should be used. One advantage of the patch is that women using it do not have to remember to take a pill every day, only to replace the patch every week. In addition, with the patch the hormones enter the body through the skin, rather than going to the stomach and needing to be digested.

The patch is new (it became available in Canada in 2004), so we do not have extensive data on it at this point. Because the hormones are the same as in the pill, the expectation is that the benefits and side effects will be quite similar to those of the pill (Hatcher et al., 2004). A trial over 13 months with real users indicated an actual-user failure rate of less than 1 percent, making it extremely effective,

Triphasic pill: A birth control pill containing a steady level of estrogen and three phases of progesterone, intended to mimic more closely women's natural hormonal cycles.

Figure 7.2 Different types of birth control pills.

somewhat more so than the pill (Audet et al., 2001; Smallwood et al., 2001).

The Vaginal Ring

It's not the latest in body piercing. Rather, the vaginal ring (NuvaRing) is a flexible, transparent ring made of plastic and filled with the same hormones as those in the combination pill, at slightly lower doses. The ring is placed high up in the vagina and remains in place for 21 days. It is removed and the woman goes ring-free for—you guessed it—7 days. She then inserts a new ring. This method requires even less remembering than the patch does.

The ring, too, was only recently introduced, so the scientific data on it are limited. Because the hormones in it are the same as those in the combination pill, the side effects should be the same. Research shows that it is extremely effective at stopping ovulation (Mulders & Dieben, 2001). It is expected to be even more effective than the pill because it removes the problem of missed pills. One study of 2,300 women using it over a year found an actual-user pregnancy rate of less than 1 percent (21 pregnancies), with half the pregnancies resulting from major failures to use the method correctly (Dieben et al., 2002).

Emergency Contraception

Emergency contraception is available in pill form for emergencies involving unprotected intercourse that might result in an unwanted pregnancy, such as from forced intercourse or a condom breaking (Hatcher et al., 2004; Trussell et al., 2000; von Hertzen & Van Look, 1996). The treatment is most effective if begun within 12 to 24 hours, and cannot be delayed longer than 120 hours (5 days) after unprotected intercourse. Regular birth control pills containing levonorgestrel (a progestin) are taken at higher doses—for example, two doses of two tablets each of Ovral, or four tablets each of Lo/Ovral or Levlen, taken 12 hours apart. Plan-B is a product produced specifically for emergency contraception that contains the same important hormone. Nausea is a common side effect, but Gravol can be taken to prevent it.

Emergency contraception may work in any of several ways, depending on when in the cycle it is taken. It may stop ovulation, inhibit the functioning of sperm, prevent fertilization, or inhibit the development of a nourishing endometrium. Its action is almost always to prevent pregnancy, not to cause abortion.

Emergency contraception is between 75- and 89-percent effective (Hatcher et al., 2004). Those statistics underestimate the actual effectiveness, though, because they refer to effectiveness during the most fertile part of the cycle. Actual pregnancy rates are between 0.5 and 2 percent (von Hertzen et al., 2002). That is, emergency contraception is highly effective.

Figure 7.3 NuvaRing, the vaginal contraceptive ring.

The question of whether emergency contraception must be prescribed by a health care professional is controversial. In April 2005, Health Canada approved emergency contraception for use without a prescription. Research in British Columbia, where emergency contraception has been available from pharmacists without a prescription since December 2000, found that this more than doubled its use (Soon et al., 2005). The vast majority of these women used emergency contraception only once during the time period of the study, most often due to birth control failure. It is estimated that if it were readily available, emergency contraception could prevent as many as half of the unintended pregnancies that occur each year (Hatcher et al., 2004).

■ Depo-Provera Injections

Depo-Provera (DMPA) is a progestin administered by injection. The injections must be repeated every three months for maximum effectiveness. Depo-Provera was approved for use as a contraceptive in Canada only in 1997. A study of women in Saskatchewan using Depo-Provera found that most did so because of its convenience; for example, they did not have to worry about forgetting to take the birth control pill (Hampton et al., 2000).

How It Works

Depo-Provera works like the other progestin-only methods, by inhibiting ovulation, thickening the cervical mucus, and inhibiting the growth of the endometrium. Depo-Provera is highly effective, with a typical-user failure rate of 3 percent, making it more effective than the pill.

Advantages and Disadvantages

Depo-Provera has many advantages. It does not interfere with lovemaking. It requires far less reliance on memory than birth control pills do, although the woman must remember to have a new injection every three months. It is available for women who cannot use the combination pill, such as those over 35 who smoke and those with blood pressure problems.

A disadvantage of Depo-Provera is that most users experience amenorrhea (no menstrual periods). Sometimes there is just some spotting. How-

ever, this may be an advantage. It can relieve anemia due to heavy menstrual periods, and Depo-Provera can be used in the treatment of endometriosis.

Side Effects

No lethal side effects of Depo-Provera have been found, although long-term studies have not yet been done (Hatcher et al., 1998).

Reversibility

The method is reversible simply by not getting another injection. Many women are infertile for 6 to 12 months after stopping its use, but then are able to become pregnant at normal rates (Lande, 1995).

■ The IUD

The **intrauterine device,** or **IUD,** is a small piece of plastic; it comes in various shapes. Metal or a hormone may also be part of the device. An IUD is inserted into the uterus by a doctor or nurse practitioner and then remains in place until the woman wants to have it removed. One or two plastic strings hang down from the IUD through the cervix, enabling the woman to check to see whether it is in place.

The basic idea for the IUD has been around for some time. In 1909, Burton Richter reported on the use of an IUD made of silkworm gut. In the 1920s the German physician Ernst Grafenberg reported data on 2,000 insertions of silk or silver wire rings. In spite of its high effectiveness (98.4 percent), his work was poorly received. Not until the 1950s, with the development of plastic and stainless-steel devices, did the method gain much popularity. In the 1980s the use of the IUD in North America was sharply reduced by numerous lawsuits against manufacturers by persons claiming to have been damaged by the device, specifically by the IUD known as the Dalkon Shield, which was taken off the market (Hubacher, 2002). Some companies stopped producing IUDs, and others declared bankruptcy. As a result, only two IUDs are available in Canada today. Both are T-shaped; one contains copper (the Nova-T), the other progesterone (Mirena LNG-IUS). Cur-

Intrauterine device (IUD): A plastic device sometimes containing metal or a hormone that is inserted into the uterus for contraceptive purposes.

rently 106 million women worldwide are using IUDs, 40 million of them in the People's Republic of China, and experts predict a resurgence of enthusiasm for them (Hubacher, 2002).

How It Works

The IUD works by preventing fertilization. It produces changes in the uterus and fallopian tubes, and in this environment sperm that reach the uterus are immobilized and cannot move into the fallopian tube (Treiman et al., 1995). The egg may also move more swiftly through the fallopian tube, reducing the chances of fertilization.

The Mirena releases progesterone directly into the uterus. One effect is to reduce the endometrium. This results in reduced menstrual flow and reduced risk of anemia, thus overcoming two undesirable side effects of other IUDs.

The small amount of copper that is added to the copper T is thought to have an additional contraceptive effect. It seems to alter the functioning of the enzymes involved in implantation. The progestin thickens cervical mucus, disrupts ovulation, and changes the endometrium. The IUD is also used as an emergency contraceptive within 7 days of unprotected intercourse.

Effectiveness

The IUD is extremely effective; it is in the same category as Depo-Provera and the pill (and sterilization) in effectiveness. The pregnancy rate for the copper T is 0.7 percent for the first year of use; after that, the failure rate is even lower. The IUD is effective for 5 to 8 years.

Most failures occur during the first three months of use, either because the IUD is expelled or for other, unknown reasons. Expulsion is most likely in women who have never been pregnant, in younger women, and in women during menstruation. The expulsion rate is about 1 to 7 percent during the first year (Treiman et al., 1995).

Side Effects

The most common side effects of the copper T are increased menstrual cramps, irregular bleeding, and increased menstrual flow. These symptoms occur in 10 to 20 percent of women using it and are most likely immediately after insertion. Mirena, in contrast, reduces menstruation flow and about 20 percent of users stop bleeding altogether. There is no evidence that the IUD causes cancer.

Advantages and Disadvantages

Because insertion of the IUD by a physician is covered by medicare, the initial cost is only about $75—the cost of purchasing the IUD. Thus, the IUD is a cheap means of contraception over a long period of use, since the cost is incurred only once and the copper T lasts 10 years.

The effectiveness of the copper T IUD is a major advantage. The typical-user failure rate is only 0.8 percent, making it more effective than combination birth control pills and approximately as effective as Depo-Provera.

Once inserted, the IUD is perfectly simple to use. The woman has only to check periodically to see that the strings are in place. Thus it has an advantage over methods like the diaphragm or condom in that it does not interrupt intercourse in any way. It has an advantage over the pill in that the woman does not have to remember to use it. The IUD is a method that can be used safely by women after giving birth and while breast-feeding.

Contrary to what some people think, the IUD does not interfere with the use of a tampon during menstruation; nor does it have any effect on intercourse.

Figure 7.4 Copper T IUD (shown enlarged).

Reversibility

When a woman who is using an IUD wants to become pregnant, she simply has a physician remove the device. She can become pregnant immediately.

■ The Diaphragm, the Cervical Cap, the Lea's Shield, and the Contraceptive Sponge

The Diaphragm

The **diaphragm** is a circular, dome-shaped piece of thin rubber with a rubber-covered rim of flexible metal (see Figure 7.5). It is inserted into the vagina and, when properly in place, fits snugly over the cervix. In order for it to be used effectively, a contraceptive cream or jelly (such as Delfen) must be applied to the diaphragm. The cream is spread on the rim and the inside surface (the surface that fits against the cervix). The diaphragm may be inserted up to 6 hours before intercourse; it must be left in place for at least 6 hours afterward and may be left in for as long as 24 hours. Wearing it longer than that is thought to increase the risk of toxic shock syndrome (see Chapter 5).

Use of the diaphragm was the earliest of the highly effective methods of contraception for women. It was popularized in a paper in 1882 by the German researcher Mensinga. In 1925, Margaret Sanger's husband funded the first U.S. company to manufacture them, and they were the mainstay of contraception until about 1960.

How It Works

The primary action of the diaphragm itself is mechanical; it blocks the entrance to the uterus so that sperm cannot swim up into it. The cream kills any sperm that manage to get past the barrier. Any sperm remaining in the vagina die after about eight hours (this is why the diaphragm should not be removed until at least six hours after intercourse).

Effectiveness

The typical-user failure rate of the diaphragm has been estimated to be about 20 percent. Most failures are due to improper use: The woman may not use it

Diaphragm: A cap-shaped rubber contraceptive device that fits inside a woman's vagina over the cervix.

every time, she may not leave it in long enough, or she may not use contraceptive cream or jelly. Even with perfectly proper use, there is still a failure rate. For example, Masters and Johnson found that expansion of the vagina during sexual arousal (see Chapter 9) may cause the diaphragm to slip. To get closer to 100-percent effectiveness, the diaphragm can be combined with a condom around the time of ovulation or throughout the cycle.

Failure rates for the diaphragm and cervical cap are often stated as ranges, for example, 17 to 25 percent. This is done because failure rates for these methods depend so much on the fertility characteristics of the user. For example, a woman under 30 who has intercourse four or more times weekly has twice the average failure rate of a woman over 30 who has intercourse fewer than four times a week.

Because the fit of the diaphragm is so important to its effectiveness, it is important that the woman be individually fitted for one by her physician. She must be refitted after the birth of a child, an abortion, extreme weight gain or loss, or any similar occurrence that would alter the shape and size of the vagina.

(a)   (b)

(c)   (d)

Figure 7.5 The proper use of a diaphragm. *(a)* Spermicide is applied (about 1 tablespoon in centre and around the rim). *(b)* The edges are held together to permit easier insertion. *(c)* The folded diaphragm is inserted up through the vagina. *(d)* The diaphragm is placed properly, covering the cervix. To check for proper placement, feel the cervix to be sure that it is completely covered by the diaphragm.

Side Effects

The diaphragm has few side effects. One is the possible irritation of the vagina or the penis; this is caused by the cream or jelly and can be relieved by switching to another brand. Another side effect is the rare occurrence of toxic shock syndrome that has been reported in women who left the diaphragm in place for more than 24 hours. Therefore, users should be careful not to leave the diaphragm in place for much more than the necessary 6 to 8 hours, especially during menstruation.

Advantages and Disadvantages

Some people feel that the diaphragm is undesirable because it must be inserted before intercourse and therefore ruins the "spontaneity" of sex. People with this attitude, of course, should not use the diaphragm as a means of birth control, because they probably will not use it all the time, in which case it will not work. However, a student told us that she and her partner made the preparation and insertion of the diaphragm a ritual part of their foreplay; he inserts it, and they both have a good time! Couples who maintain this kind of attitude are much more likely to use the diaphragm effectively. Moreover, the diaphragm can be inserted an hour or more before sex.

Some women dislike touching their genitals and inserting their fingers into their vagina. Use of the diaphragm is not a good method for them.

The diaphragm requires some thought and presence of mind on the woman's part. She must remember to have it with her when she needs it and to have a supply of cream or jelly. She also needs to avoid becoming so carried away with passion that she forgets about it or decides not to use it.

A disadvantage is that the cream or jelly may leak out after intercourse.

The cost of a diaphragm is about $50 plus the cost of the contraceptive cream; the office visit is covered by medicare. With proper care, a diaphragm should last about two years, and thus itself is not expensive.

The major advantages of the diaphragm are that it has few side effects and, when used properly, is very effective. For this reason, women who are worried about the side effects of the pill or the IUD should seriously consider the diaphragm as an alternative. There is also evidence of a reduction in the rate of cervical cancer among longtime users of the diaphragm. And the diaphragm provides some protection against sexually transmitted infections such as chlamydia because it covers and protects the cervix.

Reversibility

If a woman wishes to become pregnant, she simply stops using the diaphragm. Its use has no effect on her later chances of conceiving.

The Cervical Cap

The **cervical cap** is also available in Canada. It is similar to the diaphragm but is somewhat different in shape, fitting more snugly over the cervix (see Figure 7.6). Like the diaphragm, it must be fitted by a physician and should be used with a spermicidal cream. It can remain in place for 24 hours, but experts advise against leaving it in longer because of potential problems with odours and increased risk of toxic shock syndrome. Some women are allergic to the latex or to spermicides.

The cervical cap has approximately the same effectiveness as the diaphragm; that is, it has a typical-user failure rate around 18 percent. However, the rate varies considerably depending on whether the woman is nulliparous (has never had a baby) or is parous (has had a baby). The failure rate is 18 percent for nulliparous women, but a whopping 36 percent for parous women.

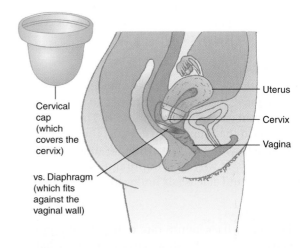

Cervical cap (which covers the cervix)

vs. Diaphragm (which fits against the vaginal wall)

Uterus

Cervix

Vagina

Figure 7.6 The cervical cap.

Cervical cap: A method of birth control involving a rubber cap that fits snugly over the cervix.

The Lea's Shield and the Contraceptive Sponge

There are two female non-prescription barrier methods that have recently been approved for use in Canada. Both are one-size-fits-all and therefore do not need to be fitted by a physician, as the diaphragm and cervical cap do. The **Lea's Shield** is a soft, pliable vaginal barrier contraceptive made of silicone. It is cup-shaped with a one-way valve and a loop that is used for insertion and removal. The valve allows air to escape while it is being inserted, achieving a tighter, suctioned fit.[1] The valve also allows cervical secretions to escape, but does not allow sperm to pass through. It should always be used with a spermicide, as this reduces the failure rate from 12.9 to 8.7 percent. It provides continuous protection for up to 48 hours. It should be left in place for at least 8 hours after the last act of intercourse. It costs about $50.

The **contraceptive sponge,** sold under the names Protectaid and Today's Sponge, is a round, polyurethane foam device that fits over the cervix. It has two slots that can be gripped to make insertion and removal easier. It acts as a barrier to prevent sperm from entering the cervix, and also contains a combination of spermicides. The sponge must be inserted 15 minutes before love-making and provides continuous protection for hours. The sponge must be left in place for at least 6 hours after intercourse. Each sponge can be used only once. Unfortunately, the typical-user failure rate is high, between 21 and 26 percent.

■ The Male Condom

The **male condom** ("rubber," "prophylactic," "safe") is a thin sheath that fits over the penis. (See Figure 7.7.) It comes rolled up in a little packet and must be unrolled onto the penis before use. It may be made of latex ("rubber"), of polyurethane, or of the intestinal tissue of lambs ("skin").

The widespread use of the modern condom, both for contraception and for protection against diseases, dates from about 1843, when vulcanized rubber was developed; however, the use of a sheath to cover the penis has been known throughout most of recorded history.[2] Casanova (1725–1798) was one of the first to popularize it for its contraceptive ability as well as its protective value. Condoms have become increasingly popular because they help protect against sexually transmitted infections, although they may not fully protect against herpes and the human papillomavirus. The polyurethane condom (Avanti, Trojan Supra) is a recent innovation that is helpful to people who are allergic to latex (Walsh et al., 2003).

To be effective, the condom must be used properly. It must be unrolled onto the erect penis before the penis ever enters the vagina—*not* just before ejaculation, since long before then some drops containing a few thousand sperm may have been produced. To be effective in preventing STIs, too, it must be put on before penetration. Condoms come in two shapes: those with plain ends and those with a protruding tip that catches the semen. If a plain-ended one is used, about a centimetre or (½-inch) of air-free space should be left at the tip to catch the ejaculate. Care should be taken that the condom does not slip during intercourse. After the man has ejaculated, he must hold the rim of the condom against the base of the penis as he withdraws. It is best to withdraw soon after ejaculation, while the man still has an erection, in order to minimize the chances of leakage. A new condom must be used with each act of intercourse.

Condoms may be either lubricated or unlubricated. Some further lubrication for intercourse may be necessary. A contraceptive foam or jelly works well and provides additional protection. A sterile, water-based lubricant such as K-Y Jelly may

---

[1]This reminds one of "burping" the lid on a Tupperware container of lettuce, although you probably shouldn't think about this while using it because it isn't very erotic.

[2]Condoms have also been the stimulus for humour throughout history, an example being this limerick:

There was a young man of Cape Horn
Who wished he had never been born
    And he wouldn't have been
    If his father had seen
That the end of the rubber was torn.

Lea's Shield: A soft, pliable barrier contraceptive device that prevents sperm from entering the cervix.

Contraceptive sponge: A round, polyurethane foam contraceptive device containing a combination of spermicides that fits over the cervix.

Male condom: A contraceptive sheath that is placed over the penis.

Figure 7.7   A variety of male condoms.

also be used. Some condoms are coated with a spermicide containing nonoxynol-9. They do not provide extra protection against disease.

How It Works

The condom catches the semen and thus prevents it from entering the vagina. For condoms coated with a spermicide, the spermicide kills sperm and thus provides double protection. Spermicide-coated condoms are not necessarily to be preferred, though. They may create allergies to the spermicide for the man or his partner, and the amount of spermicide is probably not sufficient to be very effective. For couples who want to improve on the effectiveness of the condom, it is probably wiser for the woman to use a contraceptive foam.

Effectiveness

Condoms are actually much more effective as a contraceptive than most people think. The perfect-user failure rate is about 2 percent. The typical-user failure rate is about 18 percent, but many failures result from improper or inconsistent use. Health Canada controls the quality of condoms carefully, and thus the chances of a failure due to a defect in the condom itself are small.

Combined with a contraceptive foam or cream or a diaphragm, the condom is close to 100-percent effective.

Side Effects

The condom has no side effects, except that some users are allergic to latex. For them, non-latex condoms made of polyurethane or other plastics can be used.

Advantages and Disadvantages

One disadvantage of the condom is that it must be put on just before intercourse, raising the old "spontaneity" problem again. If the couple can make an enjoyable, erotic ritual of putting it on together, this problem can be minimized.

(a)   *(b)*

Figure 7.8   Putting on a condom correctly. *(a)* The tip is pinched to keep air out. *(b)* The condom is then rolled down over the erect penis.

Some men complain that the condom reduces their sensation and thus lessens their pleasure in intercourse ("It's like taking a shower with a raincoat on"). This can be a major disadvantage. The reduction in sensation, however, may be an advantage for some; for example, it may help the man who ejaculates more quickly than he or his partner wishes. Polyurethane condoms are thinner and should provide more sensation.

There are several advantages to condoms. They are the only contraceptive currently available for men except sterilization. They are cheap (around $1.50 to $2.50 for three), they are readily available without a prescription at any drugstore and some convenience stores, and they are fairly easy to use, although the man (or woman) must plan ahead so that one will be available when it is needed.

Finally, a major advantage of condoms is that they provide protection against many sexually transmitted infections (Cates, 2001). Over the past several years, some far-right political groups, particularly in the United States, have mounted a campaign to convince the public that condoms are completely ineffective at STI prevention. However, the scientific data say otherwise. Condoms are highly effective protection against STIs that are transmitted mainly through genital secretions (semen, cervical, and vaginal) because they keep the secretions away from the other person. STIs in this category include chlamydia, gonorrhea, trichomoniasis, hepatitis B, and HIV (Hatcher et al., 2004). Condoms also provide some—although not perfect—protection against STIs that are transmitted mainly by skin-to-skin contact, such as herpes, syphilis, and human papillomavirus. They won't protect against these diseases, of course, if the area producing the microbe is not covered by the condom—for example, if herpes blisters are on the scrotum. Latex and polyurethane condoms are the effective ones; animal-skin condoms are much less effective because they have larger pores that allow some viruses, such as HIV, to pass through them. For a more complete discussion of the effectiveness of condoms in STI prevention, see Chapter 8.

Reversibility

The method is easily and completely reversible. The man simply stops using condoms if conception is desired.

Innovations

In the United States the new Mentor brand has an adhesive inner surface, the idea being to reduce the risk of slippage and leakage. The marketing of condoms has also changed dramatically. Promotion efforts are now directed increasingly toward women, and there is a new openness in marketing and purchasing. Condoms can be found packaged in attractive pastel wrappers in the women's health section of drugstores. *Consumer Reports* (February 2005) has reviewed the wide variety of brands now available.

■ The Female Condom

The female condom became available in 1996. It is made of polyurethane and resembles a clear balloon (see Figure 7.9). There are two rings in it, one at either end. One ring is inserted into the vagina much like a diaphragm, while the other is spread over the vaginal entrance. The inside is prelubricated, and additional lubrication may be applied if desired. The penis must be guided into the female condom so that the penis does not slip in between the condon and the vaginal wall. The condom is removed after intercourse, before the woman stands up. The outer ring is squeezed together and twisted to keep the semen inside. A new female condom must be used with each act of intercourse. Only one brand is available in Canada, called Reality Female Condom.

How It Works

The female condom works by preventing sperm from entering the vagina and by blocking the entrance to the uterus. The outer ring also protects the lips at the vaginal entrance from STIs.

Effectiveness

The female condom is new, so we have less data on its effectiveness compared with other methods. The data we have do not look impressive. The typical-user failure rate is 21 percent (Hatcher et al., 2004), which is unacceptably high for many women. The perfect-user failure rate is 5 percent.

Side Effects

There are few if any side effects with the female condom. A few women experience vaginal irritation and a few men experience irritation of the penis as a result of using it.

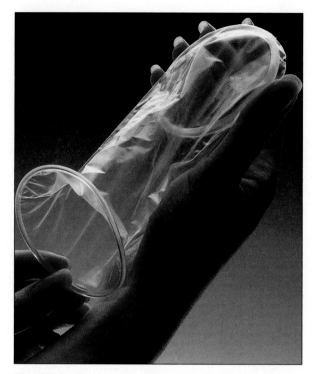

Figure 7.9   The female condom. One ring fits over the cervix, and the other goes outside the body, over the vulva, so that the condom lines the vagina and partly covers the vulva.

Advantages and Disadvantages

The female condom is made of polyurethane, not the latex used in most male condoms. Polyurethane is less susceptible to tearing and does not deteriorate with exposure to oil-based substances in the way that latex does. It does not create the allergic reactions that some people have to latex.

One major advantage is that the female condom is a method that a woman can use herself to reduce her risk of contracting an STI. The polyurethane is impermeable to HIV and to the viruses and bacteria that cause other STIs.

In regard to disadvantages, the spontaneity problem presents itself again. The female condom, at least in its present form (one hopes it will be improved in the near future), is awkward to insert and makes rustling noises while in use. It makes the male condom seem sophisticated and unobtrusive by comparison. Also, it is the least effective of the methods discussed so far in this chapter.

Another disadvantage is the cost, $3 per condom, which is considerably higher than the cost for male condoms.

Reversibility

The method is easily and completely reversible. The woman simply stops using the condom.

■ Spermicides

Contraceptive foams (Delfen, Emko), creams, and jellies are all classified as **spermicides;** that is, sperm killers. They come in a tube or a can, along with a plastic applicator. The applicator is filled and inserted into the vagina; the applicator's plunger is then used to push the spermicide out into the vagina near the cervix. Thus, the spermicide is inserted much as a tampon is. It must be left in for 6 to 8 hours after intercourse. One application provides protection for only one act of intercourse.

Spermicides are not to be confused with the various feminine hygiene products (vaginal deodorants) on the market. The latter are not effective as contraceptives.

How They Work

Spermicides consist of a spermicidal chemical in an inert base, and they work in two ways: chemical and

> **Spermicide (SPERM-ih-side):** A substance that kills sperm.

mechanical. The chemicals in them kill sperm, while the inert base itself mechanically blocks the entrance to the cervix so that sperm cannot swim into it.

Effectiveness

Failure rates for spermicides can be as high as 25 percent (Raymond et al., 2004). Put simply, they are not very effective. Foams tend to be more effective, and creams and jellies less so. Spermicidal tablets and suppositories are also available, but they are the least effective. Spermicides are highly effective only when used with a diaphragm, cervical cap, Lea's Shield, or condom.

Side Effects

Some people experience an allergic reaction—irritation of the vagina or penis—to spermicides. Because we couldn't find any scientific studies on the incidence of these allergies, we surveyed our sexuality classes. We found that, of the students who had used spermicides, about 2 percent of the men reported an allergic reaction, as did 26 percent of the women.

Advantages and Disadvantages

The major advantage of spermicides is that they are readily available, without a prescription, in any

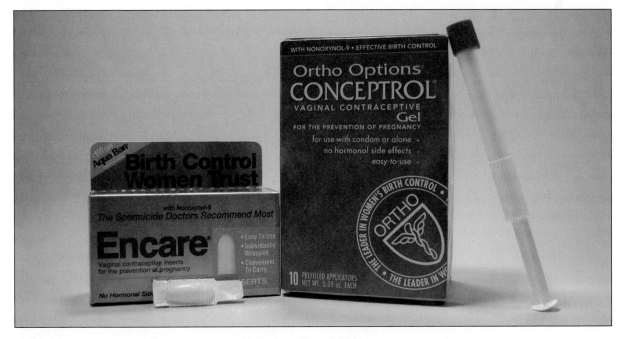

Figure 7.10   Contraceptive foams, creams, and jellies are all spermicides.

drugstore. Thus they can be used as a stop-gap method until the woman can see a physician and get a more effective contraceptive. Their failure rate is so high, though, that we cannot recommend using them by themselves; always combine them with a second method such as a condom.

Spermicides provide no protection against bacterial STIs such as chlamydia and gonorrhea. Neither do they protect against HIV, and there is some evidence that their frequent use increases susceptibility (Hatcher et al., 2004).

Their major disadvantage is that by themselves, they are not very effective. They also interrupt the spontaneity of sex, although only very briefly. Some women dislike the sensation of the spermicide leaking out after intercourse, and some are irritated by the chemicals. Finally, some people find that they taste terrible, and so their use interferes with oral sex.

■ Douching

Some people mistakenly believe that **douching** (flushing the vagina with a liquid) with any one of a variety of solutions is an effective contraceptive technique. A popular rumour among teenagers is that douching with Coca-Cola after intercourse will prevent pregnancy. Unfortunately, while it is true that acidic solutions will kill sperm, it takes only seconds for some of the sperm to reach the cervical mucus; once there, they are free to continue moving up into the uterus, and no douching solution will reach them. The woman would have to be a championship sprinter to get herself up and douched soon enough. And the douche itself may even push some sperm up into the uterus. Douching, therefore, is just not effective as a contraceptive method.

■ Withdrawal

Withdrawal (*coitus interruptus,* "pulling out") is probably the most ancient form of birth control. (A reference to it is even found in Genesis 38:8–9.) Withdrawal is still widely used throughout the world. The man withdraws his penis from his partner's

> **Douching (DOOSH-ing):** Flushing out the inside of the vagina with a liquid.
> **Withdrawal:** A method of birth control in which the man withdraws his penis from his partner's vagina before he orgasms.

vagina before he has an orgasm and thus ejaculates outside the vagina. To be effective as contraception, the ejaculation must occur completely away from the woman's vulva.

Effectiveness

Withdrawal is not very effective as a method of birth control. The failure rate is around 19 percent. Failures occur for several reasons: The few drops of fluid that come out of the penis during arousal may carry enough sperm for conception to occur; if ejaculation occurs outside the vagina but near or on the vulva, sperm may still get into the vagina and continue up into the uterus; and sometimes the man simply does not withdraw in time.

Side Effects

Withdrawal produces no direct physical side effects. However, over long periods of time, worry about ejaculating before withdrawal may contribute to sexual dysfunctions in the man such as premature ejaculation, and also sexual dysfunction in the woman.

Advantages and Disadvantages

The major advantage of withdrawal is that it is the only last-minute method; it can be used when nothing else is available, although if the situation is this desperate, one might consider abstinence or some other form of sexual expression such as mouth–genital sex as alternatives. Obviously, withdrawal requires no prescription and is completely free.

One major disadvantage is that withdrawal is not very effective. In addition, it requires exceptional motivation on the part of the man, and it may be psychologically stressful to him. He must constantly maintain a kind of self-conscious control. The woman may worry about whether he really will withdraw in time, and the situation is certainly less than ideal for her to orgasm.

■ Fertility Awareness (Rhythm) Methods

Fertility awareness (rhythm) methods are the only form of "natural" birth control and are therefore the

> **Fertility awareness (rhythm) method:** A method of birth control that involves abstaining from intercourse around the time the woman ovulates.

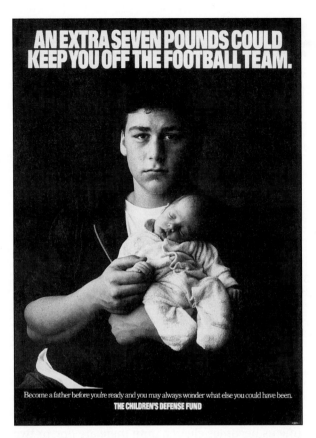

AN EXTRA SEVEN POUNDS COULD KEEP YOU OFF THE FOOTBALL TEAM.

Become a father before you're ready and you may always wonder what else you could have been.
THE CHILDREN'S DEFENSE FUND

Figure 7.11   Male responsibility is a key issue in birth control.

deposited sperm may result in conception), and 2 days are added after it (to allow for long-lasting eggs); thus the couple must abstain from sexual intercourse from day 10 to day 17. Therefore, even for the woman with perfectly regular cycles, 8 days of abstinence are required in the middle of each cycle. Research shows that sperm can live up to 5 days inside the female reproductive tract and eggs live less than a day (Wilcox et al., 1995).

The woman who is not perfectly regular must keep a record of her cycles for at least 6 months, and preferably a year. From this she determines the length of her shortest cycle and the length of her longest cycle. The preovulatory safe period is then calculated by subtracting 18 from the number of days in the shortest cycle, and the postovulatory safe period is calculated by subtracting 11 from the number of days in the longest cycle (see Table 7.2). Thus for a woman who is somewhat irregular—say, with cycles varying from 26 to 33 days in length—a period of abstinence from day 8 to day 22 (a total of 15 days) would be required.

Standard Days Method

The *standard days method* (SDM) is a variation on the calendar method, designed to make it simpler (Hatcher et al., 2004). Proponents of this method say that 80 percent of women have cycle lengths between 26 and 32 days. For those women, the fertile period is very likely to fall between days 8 and 19. Therefore, if a woman knows that she is regular and that her cycle length is between 26 and 32 days, all she needs to do is keep track of the day of the cycle and abstain from days 8 to 19. Of course, abstaining for 12 days each month would not be an enticing prospect for many women.

The Basal Body Temperature Method

A somewhat more accurate method for determining ovulation is the **basal body temperature (BBT) method.** The principle behind this was discussed in Chapters 5 and 6. The woman takes her temperature every day immediately upon waking. During the preovulatory phase her temperature will be at a fairly constant low level. On the day of ovulation it

only methods officially approved by the Roman Catholic Church. They require abstaining from intercourse during the woman's fertile period (around ovulation). There are several fertility awareness methods, in each of which the woman's fertile period is determined in a different way (Kambic, 1999).

The Calendar Method

The **calendar method** is the basic fertility awareness method. It is based on the assumption that ovulation occurs about 14 days before the onset of menstruation. It works best for the woman with the perfectly regular 28-day cycle. She should ovulate on day 14, and almost surely on one of days 13 to 15. Three days are added in front of that period (previously

Calendar method: A type of fertility awareness method of birth control in which the woman determines when she ovulates by keeping a calendar record of the length of her menstrual cycles.

Basal body temperature method: A type of fertility awareness method of birth control in which the woman determines when she ovulates by keeping track of her temperature.

Table 7.2   Determining the Fertile Period Using the Calendar Method*

Shortest Cycle (Days)		Day Fertile Period Begins	Longest Cycle (Days)		Day Fertile Period Ends
22		4	23		12
23		5	24		13
24		6	25		14
25	Minus 18	7	26		15
26	← →	(8)	27		16
27		9	28		17
28		10	29		18
29		11	30		19
30		12	31		20
31		13	32	Minus 11	21
32		14	33 →		(22)
			34		23
			35		24

Example: If a woman's cycles vary in length from 26 days to 33 days, she can be fertile any time between days 8 and 22 of the cycle; so to avoid getting pregnant, she must abstain from sexual intercourse from day 8 to day 22.

*See text "The Calendar Method," for further explanation.

drops (although this does not always occur), and on the day after ovulation it rises sharply, staying at that high level for the rest of the cycle. Intercourse would be safe beginning about three days after ovulation. Some of the psychological stresses involved in using this method have been noted previously. As a form of contraception, the BBT method has a major disadvantage in that it determines safe days only *after* ovulation; theoretically, according to the method, there are no safe days before ovulation. Thus the BBT method is best used in combination with the calendar method, or the cervical mucus method, which determine the preovulatory safe period; the BBT method determines the postovulatory safe period.

The Cervical Mucus (Ovulation) Method

Another fertility awareness method is based on variations over the cycle in the mucus produced by the cervix. This **cervical mucus method** works as explained below.

There are generally a few days just after menstruation during which no mucus is produced and there is a general sensation of vaginal dryness. This

is a relatively safe period. Then there are a number of days of mucus discharge around the middle of the cycle. On the first days, the mucus is white or cloudy and tacky. The amount increases, and the mucus becomes clearer, until there are one or two *peak days,* when the mucus is like raw egg white—clear, slippery, and stringy. There is also a sensation of vaginal lubrication. Ovulation occurs within 24 hours after the last peak day. Abstinence is required from the first day of mucus discharge until four days after the peak days. After that the mucus, if present, is cloudy or white, and intercourse is safe.

The Sympto-Thermal Method

The **sympto-thermal method** combines two fertility awareness methods in order to produce better effectiveness. The woman records changes in her cervical mucus (symptoms) as well as her basal body temperature (thermal). The combination of the two should give a more accurate determination of the time of ovulation.

Recently, home tests for the detection of ovulation have been developed. Most such tests have been designed for use by couples wanting to conceive;

Cervical mucus method: A type of fertility awareness method of birth control in which the woman determines when she ovulates by checking her cervical mucus.

Sympto-thermal method: A type of fertility awareness method of birth control combining the basal body temperature method and the cervical mucus method.

however, a few are now available for contraception (Hatcher et al., 2004). One kind (PG53, PC 2000, and Maybe Baby) involves mini-microscopes to examine saliva or cervical mucus. Others involve temperature computers that work on the BBT method. Hormone computers (e.g., Persona) assess hormone levels in urine. Costs range between $50 and $600. The effectiveness of these tests is not yet well enough researched to recommend them as reliable.

Effectiveness

The effectiveness of the fertility awareness method varies considerably, depending on a number of factors, but basically it is not very effective with typical users (giving rise to its nickname, "Vatican roulette," and a number of old jokes like, "What do they call people who use the rhythm method?" Answer: "Parents"). Although the typical-user failure rate is around 25 percent for all methods, ideal-user failure rates vary considerably. They are 5 percent for the calendar method, 2 percent for BBT, 2 percent for the sympto-thermal method, and 3 percent for the cervical mucus method (Hatcher et al., 2004).

There tend to be fewer failures when the woman's cycle is very regular and when the couple are highly motivated and have been well instructed in the methods. The effectiveness of the fertility awareness method also depends partly on one's purpose in using it: whether for preventing pregnancy absolutely or for spacing pregnancies. If absolute pregnancy prevention is the goal (as it is for many single teenagers), the method is just not effective enough. But if the couple simply wish to space pregnancies further apart than would occur naturally, the method will probably accomplish this. Knowing when the woman's fertile times occur can also improve the effectiveness of other methods of contraception. Combining the sympto-thermal method with use of a condom or diaphragm during fertile days can lead to higher effectiveness with no need for abstinence.

Advantages and Disadvantages

For many Roman Catholic users of the fertility awareness method, its main advantage is that it is considered an acceptable method of birth control by the Roman Catholic Church.

The method has no side effects except possible psychological stress, and it is cheap. It is easily reversible. It also helps the woman become more aware of her body's functioning. The method requires cooperation from both partners, which may be considered either an advantage or a disadvantage.

Its main disadvantages are its high failure rate and the psychological stress it may cause. Periods of abstinence of at least eight days, and possibly as long as two or three weeks, are necessary, which is an unacceptable requirement for many couples. Actually, the fertility awareness method would seem best suited to people who do not have sex frequently.

A certain amount of time, usually several months, is required to collect the data needed to make the method work. Thus one cannot simply begin using it on the spur of the moment.

■ Sterilization

Sterilization, or voluntary surgical contraception (VSC), is a surgical procedure whereby an individual is made permanently sterile; that is, unable to reproduce. Sterilization is a rather emotion-laden topic for a number of reasons. It conjures up images of government-imposed programs of *involuntary* sterilization in which groups of people—possibly persons with severe developmental delay, criminals, or members of some ethnocultured communities—are sterilized so that they cannot reproduce. (The following discussion deals only with voluntary sterilization used as a method of contraception for those who want no more children or who want no children at all.) Some people confuse sterilization with castration, though the two are quite different. This is also an emotional topic because sterilization means the end of one's capacity to reproduce, which is very basic to gender roles and gender identity. The ability to impregnate and the ability to bear a child are very important in cultural definitions of manhood and womanhood. We hope that as gender roles become more flexible in our society and as concern about reproduction is replaced by a concern for limiting population size, the word "sterilization" will no longer carry such emotional overtones.

Most physicians are conservative about performing sterilizations; they want to make sure that the patient has made a firm decision on his or her own and will not be back a few months later wanting to

Sterilization: A surgical procedure by which an individual is made sterile; that is, incapable of reproducing.

have the procedure reversed. The physician has an obligation to follow the principle of "informed consent." This means explaining the procedures involved, telling the patient about the possible risks and advantages, discussing alternative methods, and answering any questions the patient has.

Despite this conservatism, both male sterilization and female sterilization have become increasingly popular as methods of birth control. Sterilization is the most common method of birth control for fertile-aged long-term couples in Canada: 22 percent of men and 17 percent of women. As you would expect, sterilization is more common among couples who are older (Boroditsky et al., 1996).

Male Sterilization

The male sterilization operation is called a **vasectomy,** so named for the vas deferens, which is tied or cut. It can be done in a physician's office under local anaesthesia and requires only about 20 minutes to perform. In the traditional procedure, the physician makes a small incision on one side of the upper part of the scrotum. The vas is then separated from the surrounding tissues, tied off, and cut. The procedure is then repeated on the other side, and the incisions are sewn up. For a day or two the man may have to refrain from strenuous activity and be careful not to pull the incision apart. Now a *no-scalpel vasectomy* procedure has been developed (Hatcher et al., 2004). It involves making just a tiny pierce in the scrotum and has an even lower rate of complications than a standard vasectomy (see Figure 7.12).

Typically, the man can return to having intercourse within a few days. It should not be assumed that he is sterile yet, however. Some stray sperm may still be lurking in his ducts beyond the point of the incision. All sperm are generally gone after 20 ejaculations, but their absence should be confirmed by semen analysis. Until this confirmation is made, an additional method of birth control should be used.

Misunderstandings about the vasectomy abound. In fact, a vasectomy creates no physical changes that interfere with erection. Neither does it interfere in any way with sex hormone production; the testes continue to manufacture testosterone and secrete it into the bloodstream. Nor does a vasectomy in-

> **Vasectomy (vas-EK-tuh-mee):** A surgical procedure for male sterilization involving severing of the vas deferens.

terfere with the process or sensation of ejaculation. As we noted earlier, virtually all the fluid of the ejaculate is produced by the seminal vesicles and prostate, and the incision is made long before that point in the duct system. Thus the ejaculate is completely normal, except that it does not contain any sperm.

How It Works

The vasectomy makes it impossible for sperm to move beyond the cut in the vas. Thus the vasectomy prevents sperm from being in the ejaculate.

Effectiveness

The vasectomy is essentially 100-percent effective; it has a failure rate of 0.1 percent. Failures occur because stray sperm are still present during the first few ejaculations after surgery, because the physician did not completely sever the vas, or because the ends of the vas have grown back together.

Side Effects

The physical side effects of the vasectomy are minimal. In about 5 percent of cases there is a minor complication from the surgery, such as infection of the vas (Hatcher et al., 2004).

Some psychologically based problems may arise. Thus, the man's attitude toward having a vasectomy is extremely important. About 5 percent regret having had a vasectomy (Hatcher et al., 2004).

Reversibility

Quite a bit of effort has been devoted to developing techniques for reversing vasectomies (the surgical procedure for reversal is termed *vasovasostomy*) and to developing vasectomy techniques that are more reversible. At present, with sophisticated microsurgery techniques, pregnancy rates following reversal are around 50 percent (Hatcher et al., 2004). In making a decision about whether to have a vasectomy, though, a man should assume that it is irreversible.

After a vasectomy some men begin forming antibodies to their own sperm. Because these antibodies destroy sperm, they might contribute further to the irreversibility of the vasectomy.

Advantages and Disadvantages

The major advantages of the vasectomy are its effectiveness and its minimal health risks. Once

(a)   (b)   (c)

Reprinted with permission from the Population Information Program

Figure 7.12   The no-scalpel vasectomy. *(a)* The vas (dotted line) is grasped by special ring forceps and the scrotum is pierced by sharp-tipped forceps. *(b)* The forceps stretch the opening slightly. *(c)* The vas is lifted out and then tied off. The other vas is then lifted out through the same small hole and the procedure is repeated.

performed, it requires no further thought or planning on the man's part. As a permanent, long-term method of contraception, it is very cheap. The operation itself is simple—simpler than the female sterilization procedures—and requires no hospitalization or absence from work. Finally, it is one of the few methods that allow the man to assume contraceptive responsibility.

The permanency of the vasectomy may be either an advantage or a disadvantage. If permanent contraception is desired, the method is certainly much better than something like birth control pills, which must be used repeatedly. But if the couple change their minds and decide that they want to have a child, the permanence is a distinct disadvantage. Some men put several samples of their sperm into a frozen-sperm bank so that assisted insemination can be performed if they do decide to have a child after a vasectomy.

Another disadvantage of the vasectomy is the various psychological problems that might result if the man sees sterilization as a threat to his masculinity or virility. However, long-term studies of vasectomized men provide no evidence of such psychological problems (Population Information Program, 1983). In studies done around the world, the majority of vasectomized men say that they have no regrets about having had the sterilization performed, that they would recommend it to others, and that there has been no change or else an improvement in their happiness and sexual satisfaction in marriage. Fewer than 5 percent of vasec-

tomized men report psychological problems such as decreased libido or depression. This rate is no higher than in control samples of unvasectomized men.

Finally, if a couple use the vasectomy as a permanent method of birth control, the woman is not protected if she has intercourse with someone other than her partner. Similarly, the man is not protected from STIs.

The "Vasectomy" video in Chapter 7 of your CD demonstrates how this surgical procedure is performed.

Female Sterilization

Several surgical techniques are used to sterilize a woman including minilaparotomy, laparoscopy and the transcervical approach (tubal ligation or "having the tubes tied" are terms that are also heard). These techniques differ in terms of the type of procedure used (see Figure 7.13). They are performed under local or general anaesthesia, and involve blocking the fallopian tubes in some way so that sperm and egg cannot meet.

In a **minilaparotomy** ("minilap"), a small incision (less than 3 centimetres, or about 1 inch long) is made in the abdomen. Each fallopian tube is in

Minilaparotomy: A method of female sterilization.

The "Tubal Ligation" video in Chapter 7 of your CD demonstrates how this surgical procedure is performed.

turn gently pulled to the opening. Each tube is blocked either by cutting and tying off the ends or by applying a small clip; the tubes are then allowed to slip back into place. With the *laparoscopy*, a very small incision is made in the bellybutton and a magnifying instrument is inserted into the abdomen. The doctor uses it to identify the fallopian tubes and then blocks them by electrocoagulation or by clips. Either procedure takes only about 10 to 20 minutes and does not require that the woman spend the night in the hospital. The newest procedure is the *transcervical approach*, which does not require an incision. Instead, the instruments enter through the cervix and uterus, and a blockage device is placed in the fallopian tubes. Special procedures are also available for women who have just had a baby or an abortion.

The female sterilization procedures do not interfere with the ovaries, and therefore the production of sex hormones continues normally; thus, female sterilization does not bring on premature menopause. Some of the misunderstandings arise from confusion of female sterilization procedures with hysterectomy (surgical removal of the uterus) or oophorectomy (surgical removal of the ovaries, which does impair hormonal functioning). These latter two operations do produce sterility, but they are generally performed for purposes other than sterilization, for example, treatment of cancer.

How It Works

Female sterilization procedures make it impossible for the egg to move down the fallopian tube toward the uterus. They also prevent sperm from reaching the egg.

Effectiveness

These procedures are essentially 100-percent effective. The failure rate of 0.5 percent is due to an occasional rejoining of the ends of the fallopian tubes, and rare cases in which the woman was pregnant before the sterilization procedure was performed.

Side Effects

Occasionally there are side effects arising from the surgery, such as infections, hemorrhaging, and problems related to the anaesthetic. Generally, only 1 percent of women undergoing the surgery experience complications.

Reversibility

Highly refined microsurgery techniques make it possible to reverse female sterilization in some cases. The success rate varies considerably, depending on the method that was used to perform the sterilization. Pregnancy rates range between 38 percent and 82 percent (Hatcher et al., 2004). However, in deciding whether to have sterilization surgery, a woman should assume that it is irreversible. Five years after sterilization, only 7 percent of women regret having had the procedure (Jamieson et al., 2002).

(a)   (b)

Figure 7.13   Two methods for performing a tubal ligation or minilaparotomy. In *(a)* the fallopian tubes are tied off and the loop is cut: the cut ends then scar over. In *(b)* the tubes are tied in two places and the section between is cut and removed.

Advantages and Disadvantages

Female sterilization has some of the same advantages as male sterilization in terms of effectiveness, permanence, and cheapness when used for long-term contraception. One disadvantage is that it offers no protection from sexually transmitted infections.

■ New Advances in Contraception

According to some, a really good method of contraception is not yet available. The highly effective methods either are permanent (sterilization) or have associated health risks (the pill). Other, safer methods (such as the condom and the diaphragm) have failure rates that cannot be ignored. Most of the methods are for women, not men. Because of the limitations of the currently available methods, contraception research continues. Unfortunately, its pace has been slow in the last few years because pharmaceutical companies are wary of lawsuits. There is little incentive for conducting highly innovative research and much incentive for companies to be cautious. Nonetheless, research and innovation continue, even if at a slow pace. Some of the more promising possibilities for the future are discussed below.

Male Methods

Several possibilities for new or improved male contraception are being explored (Gabelnick, 1998; Hatcher et al., 2004; Institute of Medicine, 2004).

New Condoms

Several new models of condoms are being tested. To deal with the problem of allergies to latex, polyurethane condoms have been developed, as noted earlier. They are thinner than latex, so they should provide more sensation. Another model is one that could be put on before erection.

Male Hormonal Methods

The basic idea underlying the development of male hormonal methods is to suppress the production of LH and FSH by the pituitary, so that sperm would not be produced or would not develop properly. Unfortunately, many of the hormone preparations that have been tried shut down sperm production but also shut down the user's sex drive, making them unacceptable to most men. Current drugs being tested involve a combination of a synthetic testosterone and a progestin (such as DMPA, used in the Depo-Provera shot for women); the latter would suppress FSH and LH production. Another group of drugs are GnRH antagonists. By reducing GnRH levels, they would reduce the production of FSH and LH, which would stop spermatogenesis.

Immunocontraceptives

Scientists have been working on a contraceptive vaccine that would induce the individual's immune system to react in a way that would interrupt one of the steps in the fertility system, for example, one of the stages in the production or maturation of sperm. One option is a vaccine targeting sperm antigens. Another is a vaccine for men that would target pituitary FSH, which would block sperm production without stopping the manufacture of testosterone. None of these are in trials yet.

Male Contraceptive Implant

Health Canada has approved a clinical trial for an intra-vas device (IVD) in which two tiny plugs that block sperm are inserted into the vas deferens. Unlike vasectomy, for which reversal is often not successful, these devices could be removed if the man later decided he wanted to father a child.

Female Methods

Microbicides

Microbicides are substances that kill microbes (bacteria and viruses) and, preferably, sperm. Experts had hoped that current contraceptive foams and gels that contain nonoxynol-9 (N-9) would be effective microbicides, but it turns out that N-9 is ineffective and may actually make women more vulnerable to infection. What we need is a microbicide that is highly effective at killing the viruses and bacteria that cause STIs and is effective at killing sperm. Several promising microbicides are in clinical trials now and might be available as soon as 2007 (Hatcher et al., 2004). They include BufferGel, Invisible Condom, Savvy, and PRO 2000. These microbicides could be used by themselves or with a diaphragm or condom.

FemCap

FemCap is a vaginal barrier device similar to the diaphragm and to Lea's Shield. FemCap is shaped like a sailor's cap (see Figure 7.14), is made of silicone, and comes in three sizes. It should be used with a spermicide or one of the new microbicides.

New IUDs

Several new IUDs are under development. One, GyneFix, is similar to the copper T, but without the T—that is, it is frameless. It simply carries copper tubes on a string and would last for at least five years. It has been approved in Europe and is available in China.

Reversible, Nonsurgical Sterilization

This method involves injecting liquid silicone into the fallopian tubes. The silicone hardens and forms a plug. The plugs could later be removed if the woman wished to become pregnant. This method has not yet been approved by Health Canada, but is being studied in the Netherlands. It might also be used to plug the vas in men.

■ Psychological Aspects: Attitudes toward Contraception

It is a favourite old saying among Planned Parenthood workers that contraceptives are only as effective as the people who use them. That is, no contraceptive method is effective if it is not used or if it is used improperly. Thus the user is at least as important as all the technology of contraception.

In 2001, 37,622 teenagers, or one out of every 33 women aged 15 to 19 (most of them single) became pregnant. The rate of teenage pregnancy in Canada (30.6 pregnancies per 1,000 teenagers) is about the same as in England, considerably above France and the Netherlands, and much lower than the United States. Approximately 54 percent of teenage pregnancies are terminated by abortion, 44 percent result in live births (often to single teenagers), and 2 percent end in miscarriage (Dryburgh, 2000). Of the teenagers who give birth, 81 percent choose to keep their baby. The great majority of unwanted pregnancies are the result of failure to use contraceptives responsibly. The Canada Youth Sexual Health and HIV/AIDS Study (CYSHHAS) found that between 5 and 10 percent of high school students in grades 9 and 11 had used no contraceptive method the last time they engaged in sexual intercourse (Council of Ministers of Education, 2003). Recent research in Nova Scotia found similar

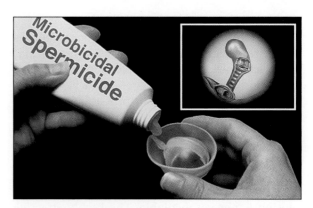

Figure 7.14 FemCap is a new barrier method under development, similar to a diaphragm.

results—12 percent of students in grades 10, 11, and 12 had used no method (Langille et al., 2002). However, only about three-quarters of adolescents engaging in sexual intercourse report always using contraception (Fisher et al., 2004b). Others do not use contraceptives consistently.[3] Research in five Western countries, including Canada, indicates that in all five countries adolescents from low-income families are more likely to become pregnant (Darroch et al., 2001).

If we are to understand this issue and take effective steps to address it, we must understand the psychology of contraceptive use and non-use. Many researchers have been investigating this issue.

Why don't adolescents use contraceptives? The CYSHHAS asked Canadian high school students why they had not used condoms the last time they had sexual intercourse (Council of Ministers of Education, 2003). As shown in Figure 7.15, one important reason for both grade 9 and grade 11 students was that they did not expect to have sex. Another important reason was that they used another method of birth control. Other common reasons were having had too much alcohol or drugs, not wanting to spoil the moment, not having enough money to buy condoms, they or their partner not wanting to use condoms, and feeling that they had a faithful partner. Few students said that

[3]Myths teenagers hold about when a woman can and cannot get pregnant may contribute to their inconsistent use of contraception. For example, when she was in high school, my daughter regularly heard other kids state with certainty that a female cannot get pregnant the first time she has intercourse or if she has intercourse standing up or in water.

they did not know how to use a condom or that they were too embarrassed to talk about condom use. The study did not ask students about some other reasons that adolescents sometimes give for not using contraceptives, such as believing that they could not get pregnant, or wanting to get pregnant. However, research in Quebec has shown that people who avoid thinking about STIs are less likely to use condoms consistently (Klein & Knäuper, 2003).

Social scientists have developed several theories to explain teenagers' use and non-use of contraceptives. These theories tend to fall into one of three other categories: (1) theories that view contraceptive behaviour as a result of a decision-making process; (2) theories that view contraceptive behaviour as the outcome of psychological development; and (3) theories that focus on personality, motivation, and skills, such as William Fisher's work. Let us look at each of these three categories.

An example of a decision-making theory has been formulated by Kristin Luker (1975). She argues that teenage women essentially engage in a cost–benefit analysis—perhaps not a very deliberate one—in which they weigh (1) the costs of contraception (e.g., may be difficult to obtain, partner may not like the idea); (2) the benefits of contraception (not getting pregnant); (3) the costs of pregnancy, which may not seem large for a young woman with few bright hopes for the future; and (4) the benefits of pregnancy (feeling like a woman, having a baby who loves you). The woman also makes some estimate of the probability of getting pregnant, and generally underestimates it. As a result, she engages in contraceptive risk-taking—much like deciding not to fasten one's seatbelt in a car—because the costs of contraception seem to outweigh the benefits, or perhaps because there seem to be benefits to pregnancy.

Developmental models look at the process of psychological development during adolescence (e.g., Jorgensen, 1980; Morrison, 1985). Teenagers may find their values to be firmly in line with their parents' values, but their behaviour increasingly conforms to the norms of their peer group. A conflict between values and behaviour results (Zabin et al., 1984). More specifically, teenagers may hold their parents' conservative values about premarital sex, which prize abstinence and therefore the non-use of contraceptives. Meanwhile, their actual behaviour conforms to that of their peer group and

they engage in premarital intercourse. The hope is that as adolescents mature, their behaviour and values will become more consistent with each other.

William Fisher, a psychologist at the University of Western Ontario, has developed the Information-Motivation-Behavioural Skills (IMB) model to explain the psychological factors that influence sexual health behaviour such as contraceptive use (Fisher & Fisher, 1992, 1998). The first component of this model is *information.* People who lack information about contraceptives and their correct use can scarcely use them effectively. That is, they need accurate, relevant, and understandable information about contraceptives and their correct use. In addition, people need the information to be presented in a way that makes it easy for them to put it into practice. People need basic information about fertility and contraceptives, but they also need specific, practical information about where to acquire contraceptives and how to use them to prevent pregnancy.

The second component of the IMB is *motivation.* People are more motivated to use contraceptives if they have positive attitudes toward the use of contraception, and if they perceive that the use of contraception is socially acceptable. Individuals who believe that contraception interferes with lovemaking or who think that their friends disapprove of sex or of the use of contraceptives will be less likely to practise effective contraception themselves. A person's motivation to engage in contraceptive behaviour is also influenced by his or her emotional responses to sexual cues, called erotophobia-erotophilia (Byrne, 1977, 1983; Fisher et al., 1983). **Erotophobes** don't discuss sex, have sex lives that are influenced by guilt and fear of social disapproval, have intercourse infrequently with few partners, and are shocked by sexually explicit films. **Erotophiles** are just the opposite—they discuss sex, they are relatively uninfluenced by sexual guilt, they have intercourse more frequently with more partners, and they find sexually explicit films to be arousing. Most people are somewhere in between. Research shows that erotophiles are more likely to be consistent, reliable contraceptive users (Fisher et

---

Erotophobia: Negative orientation toward sexuality; feeling guilty and fearful about sex.
Erotophilia: Positive orientation toward sexuality; feeling comfortable with and positive toward sex.

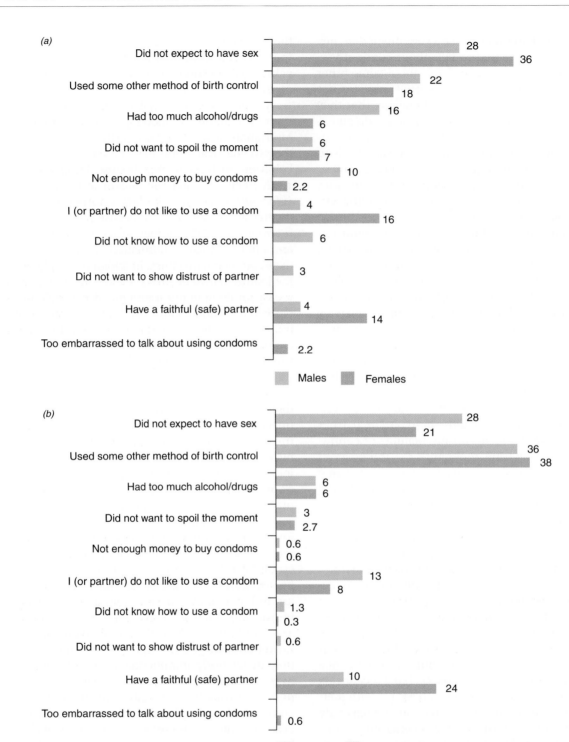

Figure 7.15 Reasons given by high-school students for not using condoms the last time they had intercourse. *(a)* Grade 9 students. *(b)* Grade 11 students.
Source: Councils of Ministers of Education. (2003). *Canadian Youth, Sexual Health and HIV/AIDS Study: Factors influencing knowledge, attitudes and behaviours.* Toronto.

al., 1988). However, extreme erotophiles may also fail to use contraceptives in the heat of the moment (Hynie & Lydon, 1996).

The third component of the IMB is having the *behavioural skills* to engage in the actions needed to use contraceptives effectively. This includes the skills to acquire contraceptives, discuss contraceptive use with a partner, and refuse to engage in sexual intercourse if contraception is not available. Before individuals will engage in these behaviours, they must accept the fact that they are sexually active and that pregnancy (or STIs) can result from intercourse. They also need to set preventing pregnancy as a personal goal (Fisher & Fisher, 1998). Research shows that many people think the chance is zero, or close to it, that intercourse will result in pregnancy, expressing the expectation that "It can't happen to me." People with that expectation are unlikely to use contraceptives.

Research has shown that erotophobes are less likely to engage in a number of the steps essential for effective contraception (Byrne, 1983; Fisher et al., 1988).

1. *Obtaining contraceptive information.* Erotophobes have less sex information than erotophiles do, and when exposed to the same sex information, erotophobes learn less than erotophiles do.
2. *Acknowledging that sex may occur.* Because of their fearfulness, erotophobes are less likely to acknowledge that intercourse may occur, which makes contraceptive planning difficult. Gender-role socialization has made it particularly difficult for women to acknowledge such expectations (Hynie et al., 1995).
3. *Obtaining contraceptives.* Erotophobes have more difficulty going to a doctor or a drugstore to obtain contraceptives. In turn, research has shown that women who are more embarrassed about obtaining contraception are less likely to use it consistently (Herold, 1981).
4. *Communicating with a partner.* Erotophobes have more difficulty talking about sex, and therefore effective communication with their partner about use of contraceptives is unlikely to occur. Each partner may assume that the other will take care of it. An erotophobe may also have more difficulty insisting on contraceptive use with a reluctant partner.
5. *Using contraceptives every time.* Erotophobes may have trouble with actually using the contraceptive. An erotophobic male isn't going to be thrilled about putting on a condom. An erotophobic female won't be thrilled with inserting a diaphragm or thinking about sex every day as she takes her pill.

Although it is generally recognized that fantasy is an important part of sexual expression, *fantasy* may also play an important role in contraceptive behaviour (Byrne, 1983). Most of us have fantasies about sexual encounters, and we often try to make our real-life sexual encounters turn out like the "scripts" of our fantasies. An important shaper of our fantasies is the mass media. Through movies, television, and romance novels, we learn idealized techniques for kissing, holding, lovemaking. But the media's idealized versions of sex almost never include a portrayal of the use of contraceptives. In the popular series *The O.C.*, Seth and Summer have sex for the first time with no evidence of contraception. Ryan and Marissa have sex frequently but never is there a conversation about a condom. There were a number of positive examples of discussion of condoms in the original *Degrassi* series. For example, Caitlin tells Joey that she's ready to have sex with him by slipping a condom into his hand while they are having a nice dinner in a romantic restaurant. More recently, positive examples have come from the series *Sex and the City*. In one sequence, Miranda has "mercy sex" with her ex-boyfriend Steve, who had just undergone treatment for testicular cancer. They don't use a condom and Miranda gets pregnant. After that, she frequently reminds her friends to use a condom, using herself as an example of the consequences if one didn't. These episodes were excellent in showing that negative consequences do occur when contraception is not used, and they provide examples of honest discussions of contraception. If teenagers saw lots of instances of their heroes and heroines behaving responsibly about contraception, it would probably influence their behaviour. But right now that is not what the media give them. However, things may be moving in the right direction: 25 percent of television programs that show or strongly imply sexual intercourse also include a reference to safer sex (Kaiser Family Foundation, 2001). For example, there was the episode of *Friends* in which Monica and Rachel fought over the last condom when both of their boyfriends were staying over.

What are the solutions? Can this research and theorizing on the social psychology of contraceptive use be applied to reducing unwanted teenage pregnancy? The most direct solution would be to have better programs of sex education in the schools. Although all provinces and territories have school programs that include sex education, the extensiveness of these programs varies among and within provinces (Barrett et al., 1997). Sex education programs should include a number of components that are typically missing, including legitimizing presex communication about sex and contraception (Milan & Kilmann, 1987); legitimizing the purchase and carrying of contraceptives; discussing how one weighs the costs and benefits of pregnancy, contraception, and abortion; legitimizing non-coital kinds of sexual pleasure, such as masturbation and oral–genital sex; encouraging males to accept equal responsibility for contraception; and enhancing skills through role playing and other skill-building activities.

The above discussion has focused only on why many adolescents do not use contraceptives consistently. Before leaving this discussion, it is important to note that it is not just single teenagers who have unwanted pregnancies, and many of the same factors discussed above also apply to older individuals. Further, some single teenage mothers make good parents, whereas some single women in their 20s and 30s do not. For example, a Nova Scotia study found no differences between the children of single teenage mothers and those of older single mothers in either parenting skills or the children's educational achievements (Bissell, 2000; Nova Scotia Department of Community Services, 1991). It is poverty and lack of education, rather than age per se, that create difficulties for single mothers (Hardwick & Patychuk, 1999; Maticka-Tyndale, 2001; Singh et al., 2001).

■ Abortion

In the past several decades, **abortion** (the termination of a pregnancy) has been a topic of considerable controversy in North America. Canada currently has no laws related to abortion and so, legally,

Abortion: The termination of a pregnancy.

abortion is treated like any other medical procedure. However, some groups would like to see abortion recriminalized. Opposition to abortion comes from a coalition of antiabortion groups that prefer to call themselves "prolife" and includes the Roman Catholic Church, Evangelical Protestants, and others. Those seeking to preserve the right of women to legal abortions, who call themselves "prochoice," have also organized. The Canadian Abortion Rights Action League (CARAL) has been active in trying first to ensure and then to keep reproductive freedom for Canadian women since 1974.

What do most Canadians think about abortion? A Gallup poll conducted in 2001 using telephone interviews found that 32 percent of Canadians believe that legal abortion should be available to any woman who wants one, whereas 14 percent are opposed to abortion of any kind. The percentage of Canadians favouring legal abortion for any reason is even higher among adolescents—55 percent in one study (Bibby, 2001). The Gallup poll found that men and women did not differ in their attitudes. However, people with more education were more likely to favour legal abortion in all circumstances. Most Canadians take a middle position, believing that abortion should be available under certain circumstances. What are the circumstances in which these middle-of-the-road Canadians feel abortion should be legal? Almost all (96 percent) agreed that a woman should have access to a legal abortion when her health is endangered; 89 percent supported legal abortion if conception is due to rape or incest; 75 percent supported it when the baby is likely to have a serious defect; and 65 percent if it was agreed upon by the woman and her physician. However, only 28 percent were in favour of legalized abortion if the family had a very low income.

Abortion has not always been legal in Canada. For example, changes to the Canadian Criminal Code in 1969 legalized abortion only under certain restricted circumstances. Under this law, many women were not able to get legal abortions. In violation of this law, and as a result of his personal conviction that the law was unjust and harmed women, Dr. Henry Morgentaler began performing abortions in 1970. Dr. Morgentaler was charged several times between 1973 and 1986, and was acquitted by juries in Quebec, Ontario, and Manitoba. In 1988, after this series of court cases, the Supreme Court of Canada struck down Canada's abortion law as unconstitutional, calling it the "Morgentaler Decision." This decision effectively decriminalized abortion in Canada and provided most women with easier access to a legal abortion should they want one. In 1998, more than 110,000 Canadian women obtained legal abortions (Statistics Canada, 2002). Nonetheless, all Canadian women do not have equal access to abortion services.

There are several factors that limit women's access to abortion (Prochoice Forum, 2000). One factor is a lack of availability of abortion services in many areas. As shown in Table 7.3, only a small percentage of hospitals perform abortions. For example, there are no abortion services available on Prince Edward Island, Labrador, and Cape Breton, and only limited services in Newfoundland. There are no free-standing abortion clinics in Saskatchewan or in any of the territories, although women in these areas do have access to hospital abortions. In some provinces, abortions are fully funded by medicare, while in other provinces only hospital abortions are covered and women have to pay between $300 and $550 for a clinic abortion. In general, abortions are more available in urban than in rural areas. Finally, the activities of prolife groups, such as picketing outside abortion clinics or the homes of physicians who provide abortions, has discouraged some physicians from providing abortion services. There is good reason for them to be fearful. At least three Canadian physicians have been wounded in their homes by snipers, and the Toronto Morgentaler clinic was destroyed by a firebomb in 1992. In response to this strategy, the government of British Columbia adopted legislation that creates a "bubble zone" around abortion clinics, doctors' offices, and the homes of abortion providers. Within these zones, it is illegal to protest abortion, try to talk someone out of obtaining an abortion, or intimidate them verbally or physically. However, some protesters continue to demonstrate within the bubble zones.

In other countries, policies on abortion vary widely. It is legal and widely practised in Russia and Japan, parts of eastern and central Europe, and South America. The use of abortion in the developing nations of Africa and Asia is limited because of the scarcity of medical facilities. Table 7.4 gives rates of abortion in various countries.

This section is about methods of abortion and the psychological aspects of abortion; the ethical aspects will be discussed in Chapter 20.

Abortion Procedures

Several methods of abortion are available; which one is used depends on how far the pregnancy has progressed.

Vacuum Aspiration

The **vacuum aspiration method** (also called *vacuum suction* or *vacuum curettage*) can be performed during the first trimester of pregnancy and up to 14 weeks' gestation. It is done on an outpatient basis with a local anaesthetic. The procedure itself takes only about 10 minutes, and the woman stays in the doctor's office, clinic, or hospital for a few hours. It is the most widely used abortion procedure in Canada today, accounting for 97 percent of abortions (Statistics Canada, 1995).

The woman is prepared as she would be for a pelvic exam, and an instrument is inserted into the

> **Vacuum aspiration:** A method of abortion that is performed during the first trimester and involves suctioning out the contents of the uterus.

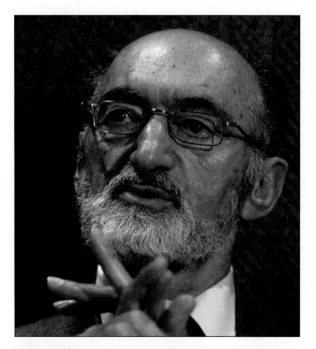

Figure 7.16 Dr. Henry Morgentaler, who was instrumental in decriminalizing abortion in Canada. Legal challenges against Morgentaler began in 1970 and ended in 1988 when the Supreme Court of Canada found that the section of the Criminal Code dealing with abortion was unconstitutional.

Table 7.3 Access to Abortion across Canada

Province	Number of Hospitals Providing Abortions	Number of Clinics Providing Abortions	Health Care Funding for Abortion
Newfoundland/Labrador	2 of a possible 15 (13%)	1	Full funding for hospitals and clinics
Prince Edward Island	0 of a possible 7 (0%)	0	Can request reimbursement for out-of-province hospital abortions; no funding for clinics
Nova Scotia	3 of a possible 33 (15%)	1	Full funding for hospitals; partial funding for clinics
New Brunswick	2 of a possible 30 (7%)	1	Full funding for hospitals; no funding for clinics
Quebec	39 out of a possible 112 (35%)	6 clinics 12 community health centres	Full funding for hospitals and community health centres; partial funding for clinics
Ontario	44 out of a possible 191 (23%)	6	Full funding for hospitals and clinics
Manitoba	2 out of a possible 54 (4%)	1	Full funding for hospitals and clinics
Saskatchewan	2 out of a possible 73 (3%)	0	Full funding for hospitals
Alberta	4 out of a possible 99 (4%)	2	Full funding for hospitals and clinics
British Columbia	20 out of a possible 91 (22%)	3	Full funding for hospitals and clinics
Yukon	1 out of a possible 2 (50%)	0	Full funding for hospitals and travel grants
Northwest Territories	2 out of a possible 2 (100%)	0	Full funding for hospitals and travel grants
Nunavut	0 out of a possible 1 (100%)	0	Full funding for hospitals and travel grants

Source: Canadian Abortion Rights Action League (CARAL), July 2000; Childbirth by Choice Trust, 2003.

vagina; the instrument dilates (stretches open) the opening of the cervix. A tube is then inserted into this opening until one end is in the uterus (see Figure 7.17 on page 210). The other end is attached to a suction-producing apparatus and the contents of the uterus, including the fetal tissue, are sucked out.

Vacuum aspiration has become the most common method of early (first trimester) abortion because it is simple and entails little risk. There are rare risks of uterine perforation, infection, hemorrhaging, and failure to remove all the fetal material.

Dilation and Evacuation

Dilation and evacuation (D and E) is similar to vacuum aspiration, but it must be done in a hospital under a general anaesthetic. It is used especially for later abortions, from 14 to 24 weeks' gestation (Autry et al., 2002). It is somewhat similar to vacuum aspiration, but it is more complicated because the fetus is relatively large by the second trimester.

Induced Labour

During the late part of the second trimester, abortion is usually performed by inducing labour and a mis-

		Table 7.4 Abortion Rates around the World*			

Country	Number of Abortions per Year	Abortion Rate*	Abortion Ratio*
Australia	63,200	16.6	20.4
Bulgaria	119,900	64.7	50.7
Canada	106,418	15.6	23.7
China	10,394,500	38.8	31.4
India[†]	588,400	3.0	2.2
Israel[†]	15,500	16.2	13.5
Italy[†]	191,500	15.3	25.7
Japan[†]	497,800	18.6	27.0
South Korea	528,000	53	43
Sweden	34,700	19.8	24.9
USSR[†]	6,818,000	111.9	54.9
U.S.	1,588,600	28.0	29.7
Vietnam[†]	170,600	14.6	8.2

*"Abortion rate" is the number of abortions per 1,000 women aged 15 to 44. "Abortion ratio" is the number of abortions per 100 known pregnancies.

[†]Data from outside of Canada are from 1989 and are of unknown accuracy.

Sources: Stanley K. Henshaw. (1990). Induced abortion: A world review, 1990. *Family Planning Perspectives, 22*(2), 76–89. Canadian data are from Statistics Canada. (2004). Induced Abortions, 2001.

carriage. The most commonly used version of this method is the saline-induced abortion. A fine tube is inserted through the abdomen into the amniotic sac and saline solution is injected. Within several hours, the solution causes labour to begin. A variation on this technique is the prostaglandin abortion. Prostaglandins (hormonelike substances that cause contractions) are injected and cause labour. Misoprostol can also be used to induce labour for second-trimester abortions (Autry et al., 2002).

Induced labour is used for abortion only if pregnancy has progressed late into the second trimester, and accounts for only 1 percent of abortions in Canada (Statistics Canada, 1995). This method is both more hazardous and more costly than the previous methods.

Hysterotomy

Hysterotomy is a surgical method of abortion that can be done from 16 to 24 weeks after the woman's last menstrual period. Essentially, a Caesarean section is performed, and the fetus is removed. Hysterotomy is more serious and more expensive than the other methods, and there is greater risk of complications. It is done only rarely, but it may be used if the pregnancy has progressed to the late second trimester and the woman's health is such that the induction methods should not be used.

Mifepristone

In 1986 French researchers announced the development of a new drug called **RU-486** or **mifepristone** (Couzinet et al., 1986; Ulmann et al., 1990). It can induce a very early abortion. It has a powerful anti-progesterone effect, causing the endometrium of the uterus to be sloughed off and thus bringing about an abortion (see Figure 7.18 on page 211). It is administered as a tablet followed two days later by a small dose of prostaglandin (misoprostol), which increases contractions of the uterus, helping to expel the embryo. It is used within 10 days of an expected but missed menstrual period. Research shows that it is effective in 92 to 96 percent of cases when combined with prostaglandin (Silvestre et al., 1990; Spitz et al., 1998; Ulmann et al., 1990). It is most effective when the woman has been pregnant less than 49 days. Early research has found little evidence of side effects, although the woman experiences some cramping as the uterine contents are expelled.

In France today, more than half of women who decide to terminate an early pregnancy choose

Hysterotomy: A surgical method of abortion done in the late second trimester.

RU-486 (mifepristone): The "abortion pill."

Figure 7.17 A vacuum aspiration abortion.

RU-486 rather than conventional abortion methods (Jones & Hensha, 2002). RU-486 is also widely used in Britain, Sweden, China, and the United States. RU-486 is not yet available in Canada. However, clinical trials of RU-486 began in in 2000 in Montreal, Sherbrooke, Vancouver, and Toronto—a step needed to secure approval of the drug from Health Canada.

Scientists who developed mifepristone, as well as prochoice groups, prefer not to call it an abortion method, but rather a method for the induction of menstruation or a contragestational drug. It cannot properly be called a contraceptive because it prevents gestation, not conception. Mifepristone and the drug discussed below, methotrexate, are referred to as medical methods of abortion, compared with the more traditional surgical methods.

Methotrexate
Another alternative in drug-induced early abortion involves the use of a combination of the drug

methotrexate, which is toxic to the embryo, with misoprostol, which causes uterine contractions that expel the dead embryo (Hausknecht, 1995). Both of these drugs are already widely used for other purposes, methotrexate for the treatment of cancer and misoprostol for ulcers. As a result, Canadian guidelines for use of these drugs to induce early abortion are being developed. Like mifepristone, they permit the early induction of abortion in a physician's office rather than an abortion clinic or hospital. Methotrexate is also used to treat ectopic pregnancy, which is a life-threatening condition.

Psychological Aspects
The discovery of an unwanted pregnancy triggers a complicated set of emotions, as well as a complex decision-making process. Initially women tend to feel anger and some anxiety. They then embark on the decision-making process studied by psychologist Carol Gilligan (1982). In this process women essentially weigh the need to think of themselves and protect their own welfare against the need to think of the welfare of the fetus. Even focusing only on the welfare of the fetus can lead to conflicting conclusions: Should I complete the pregnancy because the fetus has a right to life or should I have an abortion because the fetus has a right to be born into a stable family with married parents who have completed their education and can provide good financial support? Many women in Gilligan's study showed considerable psychological growth over the period in which they wrestled with these issues and made their decision.

The best scientific evidence indicates that most women do not experience severe negative psychological responses to abortion (Lewis 1997; Major et al., 2000). When women are interviewed a year or so after their abortion, most show good adjustment. Typically they do not feel guilt or sorrow over the decision. Instead, they report feeling relieved, satisfied, and relatively happy, and say that if they had the decision to make over again, they would do the same thing. Nonetheless, some women benefit from talking about their experience, and it is important that postabortion support groups be available (Lewis, 1997). This may be particularly true of women who have had one or more abortions in the past. An Ontario study found that women who are undergoing repeat abortions are significantly more likely to have experienced physical and sexual violence from a male partner and to have a history of child sexual abuse (Fisher, 2005).

Research in this area raises many interesting questions. Women generally show good adjustment after having an abortion, but good adjustment compared with what? That is, what is the appropriate control or comparison group? One comparison group that could be studied is women who requested an abortion but were denied it. It would be important to know the consequences for their adjustment.

One group that has been studied is children who were born because an abortion request was denied. It is impossible to do this research in Canada now because abortion has been legal since 1988. However, in some other countries access to abortion depends upon obtaining official approval. One such country was the former Czechoslovakia. Researchers followed up 220 children born to women denied abortion (the "study group") and 220 children born to women who had not requested abortion; the children were studied when they were 9 years old and again when they were 14 to 16 years old, 21 to 23, 30, and 35 (David et al., 2003). By age 14, 43 children from the study group, but only 30 of the controls, had been referred for counselling. Although there were no differences between the groups in tested intelligence, children in the study group did less well in school and were more likely to drop out. Teachers described them as less sociable and more hyperactive compared with the control group. At age 16, the boys (but not the girls) in the study group more frequently rated themselves as feeling neglected or rejected by their mothers, and felt that their mothers were less satisfied with them. By their early twenties, the study group reported less job satisfaction, more conflicts with co-workers and supervisors, and fewer and less satisfying friendships. Several other studies have found results similar to the Czech one (David et al., 2003). These results point to the serious long-term consequences for some children whose mothers would have preferred to have an abortion.

Men and Abortion

Only women become pregnant, and only women have abortions, but where do men enter the picture? Do they have a right to contribute to the decision to have an abortion? What are their feelings about abortion?

A recent Swedish study surveyed 75 men ranging in age from 18 to 50 who were involved in legal abortion (Kero et al., 1999). The majority were in a long-term relationship with the pregnant woman.

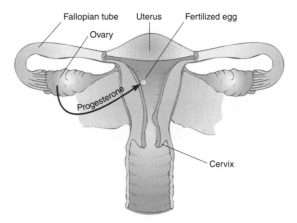

Progesterone, a hormone produced by the ovaries, is necessary for the implantation and development of a fertilized egg.

Taken early in pregnancy, RU-486 blocks the action of progesterone and makes the body react as if it isn't pregnant.

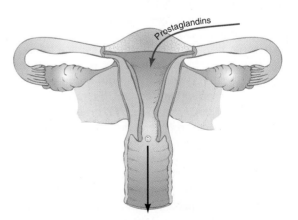

Prostaglandins, taken two days later, cause the uterus to contract and the cervix to soften and dilate. As a result, the embryo is expelled in 97% of the cases.

Figure 7.18 How RU-486, or mifepristone, works.

Among the men, 64 percent indicated that they wanted the woman to have an abortion; 27 percent felt that it was the woman's decision. The main reasons why these men wanted an abortion were related to family planning, such as conflict with life plans (e.g., schooling), feeling unable to offer a child a caring environment, or socio-economic reasons. The second most common reason was feeling that their relationship with the woman was not stable. What were these men's reactions to the

In Focus 7.2

Abortion in Cross-Cultural Perspective

Beliefs about abortion show dramatic variation in different cultures around the world. The following is a sampling from two very different cultures.

Ekiti Yoruba

The Ekiti Yoruba, many of whom have a high school or post-secondary education, live in southwest Nigeria. For them, abortion is not a distinct category from contraception but rather is on a continuum with it (Renne, 1996).

Traditionally in the Ekiti Yoruba culture, the ideal was for a woman to have as many children as possible, spaced at 2- to 3-year intervals. The spacing of children is made possible by a period of sexual abstinence for 2 years postpartum. The Ekiti Yoruba believe that sexual intercourse while a woman is still breast-feeding a baby causes illness or death to the child; men whose children have died in infancy have been blamed for breaking the postpartum sex taboo and causing the death. Because of the high value placed on fertility, use of contraceptives and abortion must be kept secret. Even though condoms, foam, and birth control pills are available at a local clinic, few people take advantage of the service because they would not want others to know that they engaged in such practices. Abortion then becomes the chief method of birth control. Estimates are that between 200,000 and 500,000 pregnancies are aborted each year in Nigeria and that about 10,000 women die each year from botched abortions.

If a woman has an unwanted pregnancy, she generally will consult a local divine healer or herbalist first, in order to "keep the pregnancy from staying." They generally provide pills or substances to insert in the vagina. If the treatment does not work, the woman then goes to a clinic and has a dilation and curettage (D&C; a procedure that is similar to D&E) abortion.

Women who abort generally fall into two categories: single high school or post-secondary stu-dents who want to finish their education, and married women who are pregnant because of an affair. Here is one woman's story:

> In 1991, when awaiting entrance into university, I became pregnant by one boyfriend whom I later decided not to marry in favor of another. Since I did not want my chosen fiancé to know of the pregnancy, I decided to abort it. I first used 3 Bee-codeine tablets, Andrew's Liver Salt, and Sprite, mixing them together and then drinking them. When this did not work, I went to a clinic in a neighboring town for D&C. The abortion cost N80 and was paid for by my boyfriend. There were no aftereffects. (Renne, 1996, p. 487)

The ease with which Ekiti Yoruba people rely on abortion is related in part to their understanding of prenatal development. Many believe that the "real child" is not formed until after the fourth month of pregnancy, and before that the being is lizard-like.

Greece

Birth control for women was legalized in Greece only in 1980, and abortion was not legalized until 1986. Yet Greece has had a sharply declining birth rate since the Second World War, accounted for, in large part, by abortion (Georges, 1996). Among European nations, Greece is unique in its combination of very little use of medical contraception, a low fertility rate, and the highest abortion rate in Europe.

Three powerful institutions—the government, the Greek Orthodox Church, and the medical profession—have exerted a strong pronatalist (in favour of having babies) influence. The Greek Orthodox Church equates abortion with murder and prohibits all methods of birth control except fertility awareness methods and abstinence. The government, for its part, encourages large families by a variety of measures, including paying a monthly subsidy to families with more than three abortion? The most common words the men used to describe their feelings were *anxiety, responsibility, guilt, relief,* and *grief.* That is, more than half the men expressed both positive and negative emotions about the abortion.

Although counselling for women undergoing abortion is a standard procedure, counselling is rarely available for the men who are involved. These findings suggest that many men also need such counselling (see, for example, Cayle & Enright, 1997).

children, making daycare centres widely available, and keeping female methods of contraception illegal (until 1980). Despite all this, Greek women achieved a low fertility rate, which is regarded by the government as a threat to the Greek "race," Greek Orthodoxy, and the military strength of Greece in relation to hostile neighbours, such as the extremely fertile Turks.

Despite the illegality of abortion in Greece until 1986, abortion was widespread and a very open secret. Abortions were not back-alley affairs but rather were performed by gynecologists in private offices. Physicians, as members of a powerful and prestigious profession, were successful at legal evasion. As a result, Greek women did not have to face the life-threatening risks that occur with illegal abortion in other countries. They had access to safe illegal abortion.

Why is there so much reliance on abortion and so little access to contraception in this modern European nation? As noted earlier, the Greek Orthodox Church opposes all medical contraception and the Greek government kept contraception illegal until 1980. But even then, contraception did not become widespread. In 1990, only 2 percent of women of reproductive age were using the pill. Some blame this on the medical profession, which is thought to block access to contraception in order to continue a thriving abortion practice that is more lucrative. Greek women, too, resist contraception. They distinguish between "contraception" (such as birth control pills) and "being careful" (withdrawal and condoms). They reject contraception, but being careful—especially the use of withdrawal—is widespread. Fertility awareness methods are not widely used and would not be very successful if they were, since Greek women commonly believe that they are most fertile for the 4 to 7 days just before and after the menstrual period. The mass media have spread scare messages about the pill, and many women believe that it causes cancer.

How do Greek women, the great majority of whom are Orthodox, deal with the contradiction between their church's teaching—that abortion is murder and that a woman who has had an abortion may not receive communion—and their actual practice of having abortions? First, the Greek Orthodox Church is not as absolutist in its application of doctrines regarding abortion as the Roman Catholic Church is. Some attribute this to the fact that Orthodox priests can be married and are therefore more in touch with the realities of family life. In some cases, women do abstain from receiving communion following an abortion but then later make a confession to the priest. Priests typically are forgiving.

In Greece, motherhood is highly esteemed and idealized, yet abortion is not considered contradictory to the high value placed on motherhood. Good motherhood today is thought to require an intense investment of time and energy in one's children; by definition, then, the good mother limits family size, and abortion is a means to achieve that goal.

Cross-Cultural Patterns

Several patterns emerge from the study of abortion in these quite distinct cultures and other cultures (e.g., Gursoy, 1996; Johnson et al., 1996; Rigdon, 1996; Rylko-Bauer, 1996). First, no matter how strict the prohibitions against abortion, some women in all cultures choose and manage to obtain abortions. Second, the meaning of abortion is constructed in any particular culture based on factors such as beliefs about prenatal development, when life starts, and how much large families are valued. Third, the legality and morality of abortion in any culture is determined in part by political forces, such as the Greek government's desire to expand the size of the Greek population.

Sources: Georges, 1996; Gursoy, 1996; Johnson, Horga, & Andronache, 1996; Renne, 1996; Rigdon, 1996; Rylko-Bauer, 1996.

▨ ▧ ▨ SUMMARY

Table 7.5 provides a comparative summary of the various methods of birth control discussed in this chapter.

Table 7.5 Summary of Information on Methods of Contraception and Abortion

Method	Failure Effectiveness Rating	Failure Rate, Perfect Use, %	Failure Rate, Typical Use, %	Death Rate (per 100,000 Women)	Yearly Costs, $*	Advantages	Disadvantages
Depo-Provera	Excellent	0.3	3		140	Requires less remembering	
Combination birth control pills	Excellent	0.3	8	1.6	0–286	Highly effective; not used at time of coitus; improved menstrual cycles	Cost; possible side effects; must be taken daily
Patch	Excellent	0.3	1.3			Requires less remembering than the pill	
Vaginal ring	Excellent	0.5	5	—	75+		
IUD, Copper T	Excellent	0.6	0.8	1.0	25‡–75‡	Requires no remembering or motivation	May be expelled
Progesterone T	Excellent	0.1	0.1				
Condom, male	Very good	2	18	1.7	75	Easy to use; protection from STIs	Used at time of coitus; continual expense
Condom, female	Good	5	21	2.0	450	Protection from STIs	Awkward
Diaphragm with cream or jelly; Lea's Shield	Good	6–9	20	2.0§	50	No side effects; inexpensive	Aesthetic objections
Cervical cap with spermicide					50	No side effects; inexpensive	—
Parous women	Fair	26	32	2.0§			
Nulliparous women	Good	9	16	2.0§			
Vaginal foam, cream, film	Fair	18	29	2.0§	50	Easy to use; availability	Messy; continual expense
Withdrawal	Good	4	27	2.0	None	No cost	Requires high motivation
Fertility awareness	Poor to fair	2–5	25	2.0§	None	No cost; accepted by Roman Catholic Church	Requires high motivation, prolonged abstinence; not all women can use
Unprotected intercourse	Poor	85	85	9§	None¶		
Legal abortion, first trimester	Excellent	0	0	0.5	0–900**	Available when other methods fail	Expense; moral or psychological unacceptability
Sterilization, male	Excellent	0.10	0.15	0.3	0–100***	Permanent; highly effective	Permanence; expense
Sterilization, female	Excellent	0.5	0.5	1.5	None	Permanent; highly effective	Permanence

*Based on 150 acts of intercourse.
†Based on a cost of $375 for the vaginal ring and use for five years.
‡Based on a cost of $50–$150 for the IUD and the assumption that the IUD will be used for two years.
§Based on the death rate for pregnancies resulting from the method. Of every 100,000 live births, 12 women die (Cheng et al., 2003).
¶But having a baby is expensive.
**All hospital abortions are covered by medicare. Only Newfoundland, Quebec, Ontario, Manitoba, Alberta, and British Columbia cover abortions done in free-standing clinics.
***Although vasectomy is covered by medicare, in some provinces there is an additional fee for those done in doctors' offices.
Source: R. A. Hatcher et al. (2004).

■ ■ QUESTIONS FOR THOUGHT, DISCUSSION, AND DEBATE

1. Do you think you are an erotophobe or an erotophile? In what ways do you think your erotophobia or erotophilia has affected or will affect your use of birth control?

2. Debate the following topic. Resolved: The birth control pill is a safe and effective method of birth control for most women.

3. In Canada, few IUDs are available because of lawsuits against companies that make them and concern over possible health risks. In contrast, in the People's Republic of China they are the mainstay of contraception, with 40 million in use. Which country has the better policy?

4. On your campus, as on all campuses, students probably are inconsistent in their use of birth control or use nothing even though they are engaging in sexual intercourse. Design a program to improve birth control practices on your campus.

5. Knowing that you are taking a human sexuality course and have gained a lot of expertise, Nicole, your best friend, comes to you in a state of crisis. She and her boyfriend had unprotected intercourse last night and she is terrified that she is pregnant. What options would you explain to her, and which one would you recommend?

■ ■ SUGGESTIONS FOR FURTHER READING

Society of Obstetricians and Gynaecologists of Canada. (2000). *Sex sense: Canadian contraceptive guide*. Ottawa. This book was developed by the Society of Obstetricians and Gynaecologists of Canada to provide practical information about all the questions people might have about the various contraceptive options available in Canada. It is user friendly and practical, containing helpful tables and illustrations.

Hatcher, Robert A., et al. (2004). *Contraceptive technology*. 18th ed. New York: Ardent Media. This authoritative book is updated frequently and provides the most recent information on all methods of contraception.

Ulmann, André, Teutsch, Georges, and Philibert, Daniel. (1990 June). RU-486. *Scientific American, 262*, 42–48. An interesting, behind-the-scenes article by three of the French scientists involved in the development of RU-486 (mifepristone).

For Review Questions, Web Resources, and other learning and study tools, visit the *Understanding Human Sexuality* Online Learning Centre at www.mcgrawhill.ca/college/hyde.

CHAPTER 8

Sexually Transmitted Infections

CHAPTER HIGHLIGHTS

Maria and Louis get home after an evening on the town and enter the house hungry for passion. The two embrace, clinging to each other, longing for each other. Louis slowly undresses Maria, hungry for the silky flesh he feels beneath him. As their passion grows, she begins reaching for him, ripping his clothes off as she explores his body with her tongue. As Louis gets more and more excited, Maria rips a condom package open with her teeth and slowly slides the condom over Louis's erect penis. After an hour of incredible lovemaking, Louis, exhausted with pleasure, turns to Maria and says, "You were right, the BEST sex is SAFER sex with LATEX!"*

As noted in Chapter 2, according to the World Health Organization, sexual health is a state of physical, emotional, mental, and social well-being related to sexuality. One aspect of this is the absence of disease, and sexually transmitted infections (STIs) are an example. Not only do STIs affect an individual's physical sexual health, but the psychological aspects of dealing with an STI also may challenge the emotional, mental, and social aspects of one's sexual health and well-being.

The sexual scene is not the same as it was 30 years ago. Genital warts and AIDS pose real threats. We need to do many things to combat these dangers. One is that we must rewrite our sexual scripts, as the quotation above illustrates. We also need to inform ourselves, and the goal of this chapter is to provide you with the important information you need to make decisions about your sexual activity.[1]

Your health is very important, and a good way to ruin it or cause yourself a lot of suffering is to have an untreated sexually transmitted infection (STI). Although in 1997 it appeared that there would be a continuing gradual decline in the rates of many STIs, this trend has not continued; if anything, we are seeing an increase in newly acquired STIs (Patrick et al., 2000). Consequently, it is very important to know the symptoms of the various kinds of STIs so that you can seek treatment if you develop any of them. Also, there are some ways to

prevent STIs or at least reduce your chances of getting them, and these are certainly worth knowing about. Finally, after you have read some of the statistics on how many people contract STIs every year and on your chances of getting one, you may want to modify your sexual behaviour somewhat. If you love, love wisely.

One of the most disturbing things about the STI epidemic in Canada is that it disproportionately affects teens and young adults. For example, of 56,055 new cases of chlamydia that occurred in 2003 in Canada, 37,772 (67 percent) were among people between the ages of 15 and 24. For people in this age group, three infections—human papillomavirus, trichomoniasis, and chlamydia—account for the great majority of cases, although of these only chlamydia is a reportable infection. Worldwide, of the 60 million people who have been infected with HIV, about half became infected between the ages of 15 and 24 (Kiragu et al., 2001). Prevention efforts, including sexuality education for youth, clearly must be accorded a higher priority than they have had in the past.

The STIs are presented in this chapter in the following order. First we look at a group of three diseases—chlamydia, HPV (genital warts), and herpes—that are all quite frequent among university students. Following that is a discussion of HIV infection and AIDS, which is less common among university students but is one of the world's major public-health problems and is generating an enormous amount of research. Next we discuss gonorrhea, syphilis, viral hepatitis, and trichomoniosis. Next comes not an infection but a bug, the pubic louse. After a practical section for you on preventing

---

*From a student essay.

[1]The diagnosis and treatment of sexually transmitted infections is an area of furiously active research. New discoveries are announced almost monthly. Therefore, by the time you read this book, some of the statements in this chapter may have been superseded by newer research.

STIs, the chapter ends with a section about various other genital infections that, for the most part, are not sexually transmitted.

Many statistics throughout this chapter are taken from the Centre for Infectious Disease Prevention and Control (CIDPC) on the Public Health Agency of Canada Web site:

http://www.phac-aspc.gc.ca

Data from the CIDPC are used so frequently throughout the chapter that we do not provide a citation every time. Information on STIs changes quickly, so to get the most up-to-date information, check the Web site. As there is national reporting for some but not all STIs, there are no national data on some of the most common STIs, such as genital herpes and HPV (human papillomavirus).

Some STIs are caused by *bacteria*, some are caused by *viruses*, and a few are caused by other organisms. The distinction between bacterial infections and viral infections is important because bacterial infections can be cured using antibiotics. Viral infections cannot be cured but they can be treated to reduce symptoms. Chlamydia, gonorrhea, and syphilis are all caused by bacteria. Herpes, AIDS, genital warts, and hepatitis B are caused by viruses.

One final note before we proceed: There are a lot of illustrations in this chapter showing the symptoms of various STIs, and some of the photos may make you say "Nasty!" These illustrations are in the chapter not to scare you, but rather to help you recognize the symptoms of STIs. You should know what herpes blisters look like, for example, in case you spot them on a prospective sexual partner and in case they appear on you.

■ Chlamydia

Chlamydia trachomatis is a bacterium that is spread by sexual contact and infects the genital organs of both males and females. **Chlamydia** has become the most prevalent bacterial sexually transmitted infection in Canada. The CIDPC reports that there were 38,628 reported cases in women and 17,383 reported cases in men in 2003. This is a rate of 178.9 cases per 100,000 people in the population and is more than seven times the national rate for gonorrhea. Health Canada has set a national goal of 50 cases per 100,000 population by 2010. Chlamydia is more prevalent in members of higher socio-economic groups and among university students. Adolescent girls have a particularly high rate of infection, more than five times the national rate. When a man consults a physician because of a urethral discharge, his chances of having chlamydia are greater than his chances of having gonorrhea. It is important that the correct diagnosis be made since chlamydia does not respond to the drugs used to cure gonorrhea.

Symptoms

The main symptoms in men are a thin, usually clear discharge and mild discomfort on urination appearing 7 to 14 days after infection. The symptoms are somewhat similar to the symptoms of gonorrhea in the male. However, gonorrhea tends to produce more painful urination and a more profuse, puslike discharge. Diagnosis is made from a urine sample in men and from a sample of cells from the cervix (or urine sample) in women. Tests are then used to detect the bacterium. Unfortunately, 75 percent of the cases of chlamydia infection are **asymptomatic** in women. This means that the woman never goes to a clinic for treatment, and she goes undiagnosed and untreated. The consequences of untreated chlamydia in women are discussed in the next section. Even among men, 50 percent of the cases are asymptomatic.

Treatment

Chlamydia is quite curable. It is treated with azithromycin or doxycycline; it does not respond to penicillin. Poorly treated or undiagnosed cases may lead to a number of complications: urethral damage, epididymitis (infection of the epididymis), Reiter's syndrome,[2] and proctitis in men who have had anal intercourse. Women with untreated or undiagnosed chlamydia may experience serious

---

[2]Reiter's syndrome involves the following symptoms: urethritis, eye inflammations, and arthritis.

Chlamydia (klah-MIH-dee-uh): An organism causing a sexually transmitted infection; the symptoms in males are a thin, clear discharge and mild pain on urination; females are frequently asymptomatic.
Asymptomatic (ay-simp-toh-MAT-ik): Having no symptoms.

complications if not treated: **pelvic inflammatory disease (PID),** and possibly infertility due to scarring of the fallopian tubes (Health Canada, 1998). Chlamydia infection is associated with an increased risk of ectopic pregnancy and with increased rates of prematurity and low-birth-weight babies (Chow et al., 1990; Cohen et al., 1990). A baby born to an infected mother may develop pneumonia or an eye infection.

Prevention?

Scientists doing research on chlamydia have a major goal of developing a vaccine that would prevent infection (Berry et al., 2004; Rasmussen, 1998). Vaccines have been developed that are effective in mice, but certain technical obstacles prevent their use with humans. An effective vaccine for humans should be available in the next decade.

Until a vaccine is available, one of the most effective tools for prevention is screening. The problem with chlamydia is that so many infected people are asymptomatic and spread the disease unknowingly. In screening programs, asymptomatic carriers are identified, treated, and cured so that they do not continue to spread the disease. Nonetheless, reported cases of chlamydia have been increasing each year since 1998. More asymptomatic females are being tested routinely. The development of a urine test for chlamydia to replace the swab test, which is invasive and uncomfortable, particularly for males, has also led to increased screening.

In an innovative program in the U.S., high school girls attending a school health clinic (not necessarily for STIs) collected vaginal swabs themselves, and the swabs were subjected to laboratory tests (Wiesenfeld et al., 2001). Overall, 18 percent of the girls were infected with something: 10 percent had trichomoniasis, 8 percent had chlamydia, and 2 percent had gonorrhea. None had symptoms, so these cases would have gone undetected. About half said that they would never have had a gynecological exam to get a test—yet they agreed to self-collection of vaginal swabs. This method is promising for screening teens.

On an individual level, the best method of prevention is the consistent use of a condom.

Pelvic inflammatory disease (PID): An infection and inflammation of the pelvic organs, such as the fallopian tubes and the uterus, in the female.

■ HPV

HPV stands for human papillomavirus, which causes genital warts. **Genital warts** are cauliflower-like warts appearing on the genitals, usually around the urethral opening of the penis, the shaft of the penis, or the scrotum in the male, and on the vulva, the walls of the vagina, or the cervix in the female; warts may also occur on the anus (Moreland et al., 1996). Typically they appear three to eight months after intercourse with an infected person. The majority of people infected with HPV, however, are asymptomatic.

Infection with HPV is widespread. Although HPV is not a reportable disease and thus there are no national Canadian data, Health Canada estimates that between 20 and 33 percent of women have HPV; between 11 and 25 percent of women have the cancer-causing types of HPV. The disease is highly infectious and although condoms reduce the risk of infection, they do not eliminate it. HPV is transmitted through skin-to-skin contact and the virus is small enough to pass through a condom.

Two studies tested women having routine Pap tests in Newfoundland and Ontario (Ratnam et al., 2000; Sellors et al., 2000). They found that the highest rate of HPV was among women under 25—16 percent of the young Newfoundland women and 24 percent of the young Ontario women had HPV infections.

HPV infection is the single most important risk factor for cervical cancer (Centers for Disease Control, 2001a). In fact, there are 30 distinct types of HPV. One of them, HPV Type 16, accounts for more than 50 percent of the cases of cervical cancer. Type 16 and three other types account for 80 percent of cervical cancers. Due to this increased risk, any woman with recurrent genital warts should have a Pap smear every six months. HPV infections are also associated with cancer of the penis and anus and some forms of respiratory and esophageal cancers (Health Canada, 2000).

New research shows that oral sex can transmit HPV. Individuals infected this way have an increased rate of oral cancers; that is, cancer of the mouth or throat (Herrero et al., 2003; Kreimer et al., 2004).

HPV: Human papillomavirus, the organism that causes genital warts.
Genital warts: A sexually transmitted infection causing warts on the genitals.

(a)

(b)

Figure 8.1   Genital warts *(a)* on the penis, and *(b)* on the vulva.

Diagnosis

Diagnosis can sometimes be made simply by inspecting the warts, because their appearance is distinctive. However, some strains of warts are flat and less obvious. Also, the warts may grow inside the vagina and may not be detected there. However, HPV is a "silent infection" and many individuals with HPV show no obvious signs of infection. Thus, for many women the first indication of HPV is abnormal cells on a Pap test. Men are not routinely tested for HPV. A new test involves analysis of the DNA from a sample of cells taken from the cervix, vagina, or other area of suspected infection and tests directly for the presence of HPV, but it is not routinely available in Canada.

Treatment

Several treatments for genital warts are available (Health Canada, 1998). Podophyllin or bichloro-acetic acid (BCA) can be applied directly to the warts. Typically these treatments have to be repeated sev-

eral times, and the warts then fall off. With cryotherapy (often using liquid nitrogen), the warts are frozen off; again, it is typically necessary to apply more than one treatment. Laser therapy can also be used to destroy the warts. In one study of university women, HPV infection lasted, on average, only eight months (Ho et al., 1998). The duration of infection was longer with older women, and the risk of cervical cancer increases with longer infections.

Vaccine?

As noted, there is a strong association between HPV and cervical cancer. In one study, for example, HPV was found in 93 percent of the 1,000 tissue samples from cervical cancer tumours taken from women in 22 different countries (Bosch et al., 1995). This finding has led researchers to believe that if they developed a vaccine against HPV, the vaccine might also destroy cervical tumours. Several such vaccines are currently being tested (Harper et al., 2004; Reddy et al., 2004; Smyth et al., 2004).

■ Genital Herpes

Genital herpes is a disease of the genital organs caused by the herpes simplex virus (**HSV**). Two strains of HSV are circulating: HSV-1 and HSV-2. In simpler times, HSV-2 caused genital herpes and HSV-1 caused cold sores around the mouth. Today, however, there is more crossing over. In a study of university students in the U.S., cases of genital herpes caused by HSV-1 rose from 31 percent in 1993 to 78 percent in 2001 (Roberts et al., 2003). Genital herpes, then, can be caused by either HSV-1 or HSV-2. Genital herpes is transmitted by sexual intercourse and by oral–genital sex.

There are no national data on the number of Canadians who have herpes. However, experts estimate that more than 20 percent of Canadian adults are infected (Steben & Sacks, 1997). For example, in British Columbia the rate of HSV-2 among women is 17 percent (Patrick et al., 2000). The rate increases with age, reaching 28 percent by age 44. The rate of HSV-2 is lower among women in Ontario than in B.C., reaching 16 percent by age 44. Research shows that infection rates are higher among individuals who have had more sexual partners. Of those who test positive for HSV-2 in their blood, only 10 percent report a history of herpes outbreaks; that is, the great majority are asymptomatic. These persons transmit the disease to others unknowingly.

Symptoms

The symptoms of genital herpes caused by HSV-2 are small, painful bumps or blisters on the genitals. In women, they are usually found on the vaginal lips; in men, they usually occur on the penis. They may be found around the anus if the person has had anal intercourse. The blisters burst and can be quite painful. Fever, painful urination, and headaches may occur. The blisters heal on their own in about three weeks in the first episode of infection. The virus continues to live in the body, however. It may remain dormant for the rest of the person's life.

Genital herpes (HER-pees): A sexually transmitted infection, the symptoms of which are small, painful bumps or blisters on the genitals.
HSV: The herpes simplex virus.

But the symptoms may recur unpredictably, so that the person repeatedly undergoes 7- to 14-day periods of sores. On the average, herpes patients have four recurrences per year (Benedetti et al., 1994). HSV-1 infection tends to be less severe. HSV-2 infection may also be transmitted from a pregnant woman to the fetus. Some infants recover, but others develop a brain infection that rapidly leads to death. (For excellent reviews, see Corey, 1990; Moreland et al., 1996.)

Watch the "Herpes" video in Chapter 8 of your CD to learn more about the challenges of living with this STD.

People with herpes are most infectious when they are having an active outbreak. However, people are infectious even when there is no outbreak or if they have never been symptomatic (Centers for Disease Control, 2001a). Therefore, there may be no "safe" period.

Treatment

Unfortunately, there is not yet any known drug that kills the virus. That is, there is no cure. Researchers are pursuing two solutions: drugs that would cure symptoms in someone who is already infected, and vaccinations that would prevent herpes. The drug acyclovir prevents or reduces the recurring symptoms, although it does not actually "cure" the disease. Acyclovir in capsule form controls symptoms and even suppresses recurrences. Valacyclovir and famciclovir are new drugs that are even more effective at shortening outbreaks and suppressing recurrences (Corey et al., 2004; Sacks, 2004). They also reduce rates of transmission from an infected partner to an uninfected one. Scientists are actively working to create a method for immunization against herpes (Augustinova et al., 2004; Meseda et al., 2004; Milligan et al., 2004).

Long-Term Consequences

Either men or women with recurrent herpes may develop complications such as meningitis or narrowing of the urethra due to scarring, leading to difficulties with urination. However, such complica-

(a)   *(b)*

Figure 8.2   *(a)* Herpes blisters on the penis. *(b)* Herpes infection of the vulva.

tions do not affect the majority of those with herpes. There are two more serious long-term consequences. One is that having a herpes infection increases one's risk of becoming infected with HIV (Mertz, 1993), probably because the open blisters during an outbreak make it possible for HIV to enter the body. Therefore, people who have herpes should be especially careful to use safer sex practices.

The other serious risk involves the transfer of the virus from mother to infant in childbirth, which in some cases leads to serious illness or death in the baby. The risk of transmission to the infant is highest in women who have recently been infected and are having their first outbreak. The risk is less with women who have had the disease longer, and is low if the woman is not having an outbreak (Moreland et al., 1996). C-sections are therefore usually performed on women with an outbreak, but vaginal delivery is possible if there is not an outbreak.

Psychological Aspects: Coping with Herpes
The psychological consequences of herpes need to be taken as seriously as the medical consequences. The range of psychological responses is enormous. At one end of the spectrum are persons with asymptomatic herpes, who are not aware that they have the disease and are happily sexually active—and at the same time possibly unknowingly spreading the disease to others. At the other end of the spectrum are persons who experience frequent, severe, painful recurrences, who feel stigmatized because of their disease, and who believe

that they should abstain from sex in order to avoid infecting others. These difficulties are aggravated by the fact that outbreaks are often unpredictable, and current scientific evidence indicates that people are at least somewhat infectious even when they are not having an active outbreak. A sample of herpes patients reported, not surprisingly, that the disease had the strongest effect on their lives in the area of sexual relations; they reported that it interfered with their sexual freedom, frequency, and spontaneity (Luby & Klinge, 1985). The respondents expressed worries about their ability to establish future intimate relationships, fearing a rejection when the potential partner discovered that they were infected.

On the other hand, many people with herpes are able to cope. For example, in the sample noted above, one-third of the people reported that they had made a successful adjustment to herpes (Luby & Klinge, 1985). In a sample of clinic patients and community volunteers with herpes, 9 percent of the women and 19 percent of the men reported feelings of isolation and loneliness due to the disease (Jadack et al., 1990), but this means that the great majority of HSV-infected people do not! Ironically, the epidemic of herpes in Canada may be a boon to infected persons, because it will become increasingly possible to find a partner who is also infected, so that there are no concerns about transmission. Life goes on.

Psychologists are exploring therapies for herpes patients. One highly effective treatment program consists of a combination of information on herpes, relaxation training, instruction in stress management, and instruction in an imagery technique in which the patient imagines that the genitals are free of lesions and that he or she is highly resistant to the virus (Longo et al., 1988). Patients given six sessions in this program (compared with an untreated control group and a group that participated in a social support group only) showed significantly less depression and anxiety and even had a significant reduction in the average number of herpes outbreaks per year. (See Ebel, 1994, for an excellent book on living with herpes.)

■ HIV Infection and AIDS

In 1981, a physician in Los Angeles reported a mysterious and frightening new disease identified in several gay men. The first AIDS case in Canada was reported in February 1982. Within two years, the number of cases had escalated sharply. In 1990, Ottawa launched the National AIDS Strategy, a major public health effort aimed at understanding and eradicating the disease.

The disease was named **AIDS,** an abbreviation for **acquired immune deficiency syndrome.** As the name implies, HIV destroys the body's natural system of immunity to diseases. Once HIV has damaged an individual's immune system, opportunistic diseases may take over. In the early days of the disease, and for people who do not have access to active antiretroviral drug therapy, the person would then usually die within a few months to a few years. People who do have access to these drugs are living much longer.

A major breakthrough came in 1984 when research teams in the United States (headed by Robert Gallo of the National Institutes of Health) and in France (headed by Luc Montagnier of the Pasteur Institute) simultaneously announced that they had identified the virus causing AIDS. The virus is called **HIV,** for human immune deficiency virus. Another strain of the virus, HIV-2, has been identi-

---

AIDS (acquired immune deficiency syndrome): A sexually transmitted disease that destroys the body's natural immunity to infection so that the person is susceptible to and may die from a disease such as pneumonia or cancer.
HIV: Human immune deficiency virus, the virus that causes AIDS.

---

fied; it is found almost exclusively in Africa. HIV-1 accounts for almost all infections in North America.

An Epidemic?

As of December 2003, 19,344 persons in Canada had been diagnosed as having AIDS and 67 percent of them had died from it. However, these statistics represent only the tip of the iceberg, for they do not count persons who are infected with HIV and do not yet have symptoms of full-blown AIDS, or persons who are infected with HIV but have never been tested for it. At the end of 2003, CIDPC estimated that there were approximately 56,000 Canadians living with HIV, and that one-third of them were unaware of their infection. Experts estimate that 40 million persons worldwide currently are living with HIV, although the majority of them show no symptoms yet and are unaware that they are infected (Centers for Disease Control, 2004).

The hardest-hit part of the world is sub-Saharan Africa. According to UNAIDS, an agency of the United Nations, 3.2 million people in sub-Saharan Africa became newly infected with HIV in 2003 alone. This brought the total number of adults and children living with HIV/AIDS in this region to 26.6 million. In addition, it is estimated that 11 million children in the region have been orphaned by AIDS. In contrast, approximately 1.5 million people in Eastern Europe and Central Asia, 600,000 people in the Middle East and North Africa, 2 million people in Latin America and the Caribbean, 7.4 million people in Asia and the Pacific, and 1.6 million people in high-income countries (North America, Western Europe, Australia, and New Zealand) were living with HIV/AIDS in 2003. HIV infection has caused approximately 20 million deaths worldwide. It is estimated that in the 45 countries most affected by HIV/AIDS, 68 million people will die prematurely as a result of AIDS in the next 20 years. About half of these people will be less than 25 years old when infected and less than 35 when they die. Thus the terms "global epidemic" and "pandemic" (a widespread epidemic) have been used, with reason.

Transmission

When people speak of HIV being transmitted by an exchange of body fluids, the body fluids they are referring to are semen and blood and possible

In Focus 8.1

What Is the Risk of Contracting HIV/AIDS?

Although we are constantly learning more about the relative risks of various behaviours in contracting HIV/AIDS, it is possible to categorize sexual behaviours into high-risk, low-risk, negligible-risk, and no-risk categories. High-risk practices are those that involve an exchange of body fluids and that have been shown in scientific studies to be associated with HIV infection. Low-risk practices also involve an exchange of body fluids but there are only a few reports of infection resulting from these activities, and usually only under certain conditions. Negligible-risk practices involve an exchange of body fluids but there are no confirmed reports of infection from these activities. No-risk practices do not involve the exchange of body fluids and have never been demonstrated to lead to HIV infection.

High Risk

■ Anal or vaginal intercourse without a condom
■ Sharing needles or syringes to inject drugs, steroids, or other substances
■ Sharing sex toys

Low Risk

■ Performing oral sex on a man or a woman without a barrier

■ Anal or vaginal intercourse with a condom
■ Injection of a substance using a used needle or syringe that has been cleaned
■ Wet kissing with exchange of blood

Negligible Risk

■ Performing or receiving oral sex with the use of a barrier
■ Receiving oral sex without the use of a barrier
■ Licking the anus
■ Digital–anal intercourse or digital–vaginal intercourse (fingering someone's anus or vagina)

No Risk

■ Wet or dry kissing with no exchange of blood
■ Solo masturbation or being manually stimulated by a partner without using semen or vaginal fluid as a lubricant
■ Using unshared sex toys
■ Ejaculation on unbroken skin
■ Massage, touch, body rubbing
■ Injection of a substance using a new needle and syringe

Sources: AIDS New Brunswick, 2002; Canadian AIDS Society, 2001, 2004.

---

secretions of the cervix and vagina (not saliva). HIV is spread in four ways: (1) by sexual intercourse (either penis-in-vagina intercourse or anal intercourse[3]); (2) by contaminated blood (a risk for people who receive a blood transfusion if the blood has not been screened); (3) by contaminated hypodermic needles (a risk for those who inject drugs or health care workers who receive accidental sticks); and (4) from an infected woman to her baby during pregnancy or childbirth.

Supporting these assertions, statistics indicate

[3]There is also a chance that mouth–genital sex can spread AIDS, particularly if there is ejaculation by an infected person into the mouth.

that Canadians diagnosed with HIV/AIDS are from the following exposure categories: (1) men who have sex with men (63 percent); (2) people who inject drugs (16 percent); (3) men who have sex with men and use injection drugs (2 percent); (4) heterosexuals who have had sexual contact with an infected person (12 percent); (5) recipients of contaminated blood transfusions (3 percent); and (6) at birth from an infected mother (1 percent). More than 40 percent are between the ages of 30 and 39, indicating that they were likely exposed to HIV in their early 20s (Health Canada, 2000). In Canada in the early years of the epidemic, 11 percent of new cases were women; women accounted for 25 percent of new cases in 2003. Most of these

Figure 8.3*(a)*   The Canadian AIDS Society targets different segments of the population in an effort to educate the public about AIDS. "Keep the Tribe Alive" (above) is an initiative that reaches out to young people. In the photo below, Louise Binder, a woman living with HIV/AIDS, participates in the launch of a campaign to educate women about AIDS stereotypes.

women acquired HIV through heterosexual contact (Gatali & Archibald, 2004). Worldwide, 70 percent of the cases result from heterosexual transmission (Ehrhardt, 1996).

How great is your risk of becoming infected with HIV? In essence, it depends on what your sexual practices are (leaving aside the issues of injection drug use, which are beyond the scope of this book) (Varghese et al., 2002). *The sexual behaviour most likely to spread HIV is anal intercourse, and being the receiving partner puts one most at risk.* This is true for both men and women, regardless of sexual orientation. Penile–vaginal intercourse without a condom is a high-risk activity for contracting HIV as well. Whether you are gay or straight, statistically *the greater your number of sexual partners, the greater your risk of getting infected with HIV.* You may have heard the saying "six degrees of separation." It turns out that it is true for HIV as well. One study found that most people are just a few degrees of sexual separation from someone who is HIV-infected (Liljeros et al., 2001). The greater your number of partners, the greater your chances of connecting with that HIV-positive person. How-

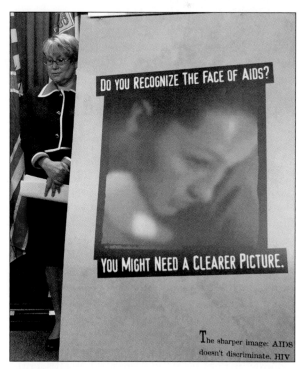

Figure 8.3*(b)*

ever, some people have contracted HIV from their first sexual partner. The risk varies considerably depending on whom you have sex with and whether you use a condom or a dental dam. *Sexual intercourse is riskier if it is with a person who is infected with HIV (seropositive), has engaged in high-risk behaviours (unprotected anal or vaginal sex, injection drug use), is hemophiliac, is from a country where there is a high rate of HIV infection, or if condoms are not used.*

Table 8.1 shows the relative risk of becoming infected from a single act of intercourse with an infected person, using no condom. Perhaps the risk is lower than you thought—researchers in Quebec have shown that a large majority of university students are not aware of the transmissibility of HIV and chlamydia (Knäuper & Kornik, 2004). A study of heterosexual transmission of HIV among 415 Ugandan couples in which one partner was infected at the beginning and one was not indicated that 22 percent of the uninfected became infected over a two-year period (Quinn et al., 2000). The male-to-female transmission rates and female-to-male rates were about equal. The higher the viral count in the infected person, the greater the rate of transmission. Interestingly, none of the circumcised men became infected.

Importantly, condoms are 87-percent effective in protecting against HIV transmission during heterosexual intercourse (Davis & Weller, 1999). This isn't perfect protection, but it's darned good, and far better than no protection. Far-right religious groups have tried to convince the public—especially school children—that condoms are totally ineffective, but the scientific studies say otherwise.

The Virus

HIV is one of a group of retroviruses. Retroviruses reproduce only in living cells of the host species, in this case humans. They invade a host cell, and each time the host cell divides, copies of the virus are produced along with more host cells, each containing the genetic code of the virus. Current research is aimed at finding drugs that will prevent the virus from infecting new cells. At least two strains of HIV are found in North America, HIV-1 and HIV-2.

HIV invades particularly a group of white blood cells (lymphocytes) called T-helper cells, or T4 cells. These cells are critical to the body's immune response in fighting off infections. When HIV reproduces, it destroys the infected T cell. Eventually the

Table 8.1	Risk of Being Infected with an STI as a Result of One Act of Sexual Intercourse with an Infected Person, Using No Condom

	Percentage Risk of Transmission from	
	Male to Female	Female to Male
Gonorrhea	50 to 90%	20%
Genital herpes	0.2%	0.05%
HIV	0.1 to 20%	0.01 to 10%

Source: Stone, K. M. (1994), HIV, other STDs, and barriers, In C. Mauck et al. (Eds.), *Barrier contraceptives: Current status and future prospects,* New York: Wiley, pp. 203–212.

HIV-positive person's number of T cells is so reduced that infections cannot be fought off.

Scientists have pressed hard to understand the functioning of HIV. Major discoveries were announced in 1996 (Alkhatib et al., 1996; Balter, 1996; Feng et al., 1996). Scientists had identified two *coreceptors* for HIV, fusin and CC-CKR-5, which allow HIV to enter T cells. CC-CKR-5 seems to be the important coreceptor in the early stages of the disease and fusin in the later stages. This discovery may lead to advances in treatment if drugs can be used that block these coreceptors.

The Disease

In 1998, the Health Canada Laboratory Centre for Disease Control Expert Working Group on Canadian Guidelines for Sexually Transmitted Disease established the following four broad classes of manifestations of HIV infection:

1. *Primary infection* Initial infection with the virus and development of antibodies to it. Usually people who have been infected show no immediate symptoms or show symptoms that are not specific to HIV, such as a fever or sore throat, but they do develop antibodies in the blood within two to eight weeks after infection.

2. *Asymptomatic infection* During this stage, the person is infected with the virus but shows no symptoms, although lymphadenopathy is frequently present. These symptoms, such as swollen lymph glands and night sweats, are not immediately life-threatening. These asymptomatic carriers can infect other persons.

3. *Progressive infection* During this stage, the person has conditions that indicate that his or her immune system is sufficiently suppressed that it is not able to fight off infections. These include chronic diarrhea, unexplained weight loss, fatigue, and, in women, chronic vaginal infection or precancerous cervical disease, among other symptoms.

4. *AIDS-defining opportunistic infection.* The diagnosis of AIDS is applied when the person is affected by life-threatening opportunistic infections (infections that occur only with severely reduced immunity), such as *Pneumocystis carinii* pneumonia (PCP) and Kaposi's sarcoma (KS), a rare form of skin cancer. The diagnosis is also used when other opportunistic infections or cancers of the lymph tissue are present and the person shows a positive test for HIV antibodies. Neurological problems can occur in AIDS patients because the virus can infect the cells of the brain; symptoms may include seizures and mental problems.

In the past AIDS was defined only by the presence of opportunistic infections such as KS or PCP. However, as many people with HIV do not develop these symptoms until their T4 cell count is very low, the presence of the initial list of opportunistic infections was a poor indicator of the progress of the illness. The list of infections was particularly inadequate for women, who are unlikely to get KS but are likely to get cervical cancer or pelvic inflammatory disease (Stephens, 1991). Therefore, the United States proposed a more recent definition of AIDS that also takes into account the person's T4 cell count (Steinberg, 1993). In contrast, the LCDC added new indicators to the Canadian definition of AIDS but not the T4 cell count (Health Canada, 1993). The normal count is approximately 1,000 cells per cubic millimetre of blood. The early stage of the disease would be defined as beginning with infection and lasts as long as the person keeps feeling well and the T4 cell count stays around 1,000. In the middle stage, the T4 cell count drops by half, to around 500, but the person still may have no outward symptoms. The immune system is silently failing, however. Treatment with AZT, DDI, and other drugs may begin at this time; there is some evidence that these drug treatments (discussed below) are more effective if begun early. In the late stage, the T4 cell count drops to 200 or less and, although the person may initially have no symptoms, he or she becomes increasingly vulnerable to bacterial, viral, and fungal infections. Early in this stage people may show weight loss, develop diarrhea, and experience fatigue and fevers. Later, serious opportunistic infections may develop, including KS, PCP, and toxoplasmosis, a parasitic infection that attacks the brain. According to the later definition, a T4 cell count below 200 is by itself an indication of AIDS.

Diagnosis

The blood test that detects the presence of antibodies to HIV uses the ELISA (for enzyme-linked immunosorbent assay) technique. It is easy and cheap to perform. It can be used in two important ways: (1) to screen donated blood; all donated blood in Canada is now screened with ELISA, so that infections because of transfusions should rarely occur. However, 1,200 Canadians were infected with HIV from tainted blood between 1978 and 1985. A tiny risk remains even with ELISA;[4] and (2) to help people determine whether they are infected (HIV positive) but are asymptomatic carriers. The latter use is important because if people suspect that they are infected and find through the blood test that they are, they should either abstain from sexual activity or, at the very least, use a condom consistently, in order not to spread the disease to others. Only by responsible behaviour of this kind can the epidemic be brought under control.

ELISA is a very sensitive test; that is, it is highly accurate in detecting HIV antibodies (it has a very low rate of false negatives, in statistical language). However, it does produce a substantial number of false positives—the test saying HIV antibodies are present when they really are not. Thus positive results on ELISA should always be confirmed by a second, more specific test.

The other major test, using the Western blot or immunoblot method, provides such confirmation.

---

[4]The risk that ELISA will miss occasional cases of infected blood results from the fact that it detects antibodies to HIV, not HIV itself. It takes six to eight weeks for antibodies to form. Thus if a person donates blood within a few weeks of becoming infected and before antibodies form, ELISA will not detect the infection. Usually ELISA is positive within three months of infection.

It is more expensive and difficult to perform, so it is not practical for mass screening of blood, as ELISA is. However, it is highly accurate (false positives are rare), and thus it is very useful in confirming or disconfirming a positive test from ELISA.

It should be emphasized that both tests detect only the presence of HIV antibodies. They do not predict whether the person will develop symptoms or will progress to the AIDS classification.

One of the drawbacks to the ELISA test is that it involves a long waiting period—more than a week—before test results are known. Two rapid tests have been approved in the U.S.: one for blood and one for oral fluid. Both must be done in clinics, but the results are available in 20 to 30 minutes. The blood test involves a finger stick and detects antibodies to both HIV-1 and HIV-2. The mouth fluid test detects antibodies to HIV-1. A rapid HIV test was piloted in B.C. but was withdrawn because of the risk of false negative results. That is, the test failed to detect the HIV antibodies in some blood samples known to be HIV-positive.

Treatment

There is not yet any cure for AIDS. However, some progress is being made in developing treatments to control the disease. One antiviral drug, **AZT** (azidothymidine, also called zidovudine or ZDV), has been used widely. It has the effect of stopping the virus from multiplying. However, even if the virus is stopped, there is still a need to repair the person's damaged immune system. Unfortunately, AZT has many side effects and cannot be used by some patients, or can be used for only limited periods of time. Therefore there has been a concerted effort to find new drugs that will slow or stop the progression of the disease.

DDI (dideoxyinosine or didanosine) is one such drug. It was released for clinical trials in late 1989 after less testing than usual, owing to the urgency of finding additional drugs to treat HIV-infected persons. Like AZT, DDI slows the progression of the disease by preventing replication of the virus. DDC (dideoxycytidine) is another drug developed in tandem with DDI; it too stops the AIDS virus from replicating. D4T is yet another, similar drug. Col-

lectively, these drugs are called ART, for antiretroviral therapy.

A major breakthrough came in 1996 with the availability of a new category of drugs, *protease inhibitors* (Ezzell, 1996a; Kempf et al., 1995; Vacca et al., 1994). Protease inhibitors attack the viral enzyme protease, which is necessary for HIV to make copies of itself and multiply. Patients take a "drug cocktail" of one of the protease inhibitors (indinavir or ritonavir) combined with AZT and one other anti-HIV drug. This combination is called HAART, for highly active antiretroviral therapy. Within a year of the introduction of HAART, thrilling reports emerged that the HIV count had become undetectable in the blood of persons taking the drug cocktail (Cohen, 1997). Some believed that the cure had been found. The number of deaths due to AIDS began declining.

HIV research, unfortunately, is much like a rollercoaster, with elated highs followed by plunges to the depths. HIV mutated to drug-resistant forms. And, although HIV had become undetectable in the blood of persons treated with the drug cocktail, it was hiding out—in T cells and the lymph nodes and in organs such as the brain, eye, and testes (Cohen, 1998; Finzi et al., 1997; Wong et al., 1997). In short, it is not eradicated by the drug cocktail treatment. Today, HAART is making HIV infection a manageable disease for many persons who are surviving much longer than they would have without this treatment. For others, long-term HAART treatment causes serious side effects, such as diabetes-like problems, brittle bones, and heart disease, which means that they have to stop the treatment or switch to another one (Cohen, 2002). Others simply stop responding to the HAART regimen, and there is concern about the emergence of resistant strains. Nonetheless, in 1998 there were 90 percent fewer deaths due to AIDS in Canada than there had been in 1995.

On another front, progress is also being made with drugs that prevent the opportunistic infections that strike people with AIDS. The drug pentamidine, for example, in aerosol form, is a standard treatment to prevent *Pneumocystis carinii* pneumonia.

Women, Children, Ethnic Minorities, and AIDS

In the early days of the HIV/AIDS epidemic men accounted for most cases in Canada, but the picture has changed considerably and the number

---

AZT: A drug used to treat HIV-infected persons; also called ZDV.

(a)   *(b)*

Figure 8.4   AIDS is a multicultural disease. *(a)* A North American man with AIDS. *(b)* An African woman with AIDS.

of infected women is rapidly rising (Health Canada, 2003). Whereas between 1985 and 1995 women were only 11 percent of positive HIV tests, today 25 percent of individuals who test positive for HIV are women (Gatali & Archibald, 2004). Almost half of these women are under 30 years old. The urgency of addressing the needs of women with HIV infection is thus increasing.

As of 2003, new cases of women with AIDS and HIV infection were most likely to be the result of heterosexual contact (63 percent); injection drug use was the second largest category at 32 percent (Gatali & Archibald, 2004).

Women need far more recognition in AIDS research. For example, intervention programs tailored to their needs should be developed (Deren et al., 1993). Such programs should include sexual assertiveness training, in which women are empowered to insist that their sex partners use condoms. Women also need to be included in clinical trials of drug treatments.

Some of the saddest cases are children with AIDS; these cases are known as pediatric AIDS. Babies born to infected mothers are often, but not always, infected. One bright spot is the finding that using AZT to treat infected women during pregnancy can

substantially reduce the rate of infection in their babies to as low as 5 percent (Harris et al., 2002).

Worldwide, people of colour have borne a disproportionate burden of the cases of AIDS. In Canada, of reported AIDS cases for whom ethnic identity was recorded, 83 percent identified their ethnic background as white, 9 percent as black, 3 percent as Aboriginal, and 2 percent as Asian. Although the annual number of reported AIDS cases has declined among all ethnic groups since 1993, the decline has been lowest among minority groups, resulting in an increase in the proportion of AIDS cases who are black and Aboriginal. For example, the percentage of new cases among blacks went from 5 percent in 1989 to 22 percent in 2003.

The problem is particularly severe among Aboriginals. In 1989, Aboriginals constituted only 1 percent of reported AIDS cases compared to 13 percent in 2003. Recent research suggests that as many as 25 percent of new HIV/AIDS infections in Canada are among Aboriginals, even though Aboriginals make up less than 3 percent of the population (Canadian Aboriginal AIDS Network, 2000). Aboriginals also tend to be infected at an earlier age than non-Aboriginals (Health Canada, 1996a & b). The percentage of Aboriginal women with AIDS is

In Focus 8.2

AIDS in Thailand

Globally, HIV is pandemic; that is, it is an epidemic that has spread around the world. The World Heath Organization estimates that about 40 million persons are infected worldwide, of whom 95 percent are in developing nations. This pandemic is producing serious social and economic strains on many countries, not to mention suffering of individuals.

Asia has generally lagged behind other regions in the spread of HIV. Thailand is a notable exception to the pattern: an epidemic is raging there. In the early 1990s, depending on the region of the country, 40 to 50 percent of injecting drug users were infected, as were 20 to 45 percent of brothel prostitutes. Approximately 1 million of the 60 million people of Thailand are believed to have been infected.

Sociocultural context is the key to understanding why AIDS struck Thailand. Two closely linked factors are Thailand's commercial sex industry and its booming tourism. A large commercial sex industry flourishes in Thailand. It is estimated that approximately half a million young women work as prostitutes, most in the 16 to 24 age group. A wide variety of forms of prostitution exist, catering to every budget, ranging from call girl agencies, executive clubs, and go-go bars to massage parlours, brothels, streetwalkers, and even mobile operations that go out to rural areas.

Why is there such a large commercial sex industry in Thailand? The major factor is economics. Social and income gaps in Thailand are enormous, ranging from rural areas characterized by great poverty to the conspicuous wealth of Bangkok. A young rural girl may go to the city and enter prostitution in order to pay off family debts, for example. Prostitution is very lucrative; it has been estimated that commercial sex workers can earn 25 times as much as young women who work as maids and in other jobs available to them. Another factor is a cultural belief that women are of only two types: virtuous women who are virgins until marriage, and prostitutes. Thailand is also a country that historically practised polygamy and concubinage. And a

---

more than twice as high as in the non-Aboriginal population.

A lack of prevention programs and poor access to testing are two factors that contribute to the increasing rate of HIV in the Aboriginal population. Some Aboriginal people also lack basic AIDS information. In a study of 658 people from First Nations communities in Ontario, 17 percent had not heard of AIDS and overall knowledge of HIV/AIDS was relatively low (Myers et al., 1994). Seventy-one percent of respondents were certain that they would never get AIDS despite the fact that there was extensive unprotected intercourse. Mobility between inner cities and rural/reserve communities is an important factor in the introduction and spread of HIV to unexposed populations (Health Canada, 2000).

There is an urgent need to develop education and prevention programs for Aboriginal and other culturally distinct Canadian communities. These programs must be culturally sensitive. There also should be substantial community involvement in program development and implementation to ensure that the programs are culturally appropriate (Brant, 1990; Health Canada, 1994a–f; Myers et al., 1993, 1999).

Psychological Considerations in AIDS

Psychological issues for those infected with HIV and for AIDS patients are profound. In Focus 8.3 provides a personal view of the psychological struggles of two such people. There are some analogies to people who receive a diagnosis of an incurable cancer, for AIDS is—at least at present—incurable. Many patients experience the typical reactions for such situations, including a denial of the reality, followed by anger, depression, or both. However, the analogy to cancer patients is not perfect, for AIDS is a socially stigmatized disease in a way that cancer is not. Thus the revelation that one man who does not use prostitutes is considered something less than a real man. These cultural factors combine to create great demand for prostitutes. Finally, beginning around the time of the Vietnam War, Thailand became a sex playground for foreign tourists and remains so to the present day.

Tourism provides more clients for prostitutes and therefore provides the incentive for more women to enter prostitution. But tourism also plays a major role in the international spread of HIV, bringing it into Thailand and in turn spreading it to the home countries of the tourists.

Today, Thailand is regarded as a major success story. In 1990 AIDS education was introduced into the schools. In 1991 a "100% condom program" was instituted with the help of the owners of sex parlours and sex workers, encouraging all clients to use condoms. The government supplied 60 million condoms a year to the effort. Research shows that the incidence of extramarital sex and sex with commercial sex workers decreased from 22 percent in 1990 to 10 percent in 1997 (Phoolcharoen, 1998). Officials estimate that, without the condom campaign, 10 percent of adult Thais would have been infected by 2000, whereas only 2 percent were and the rate is not increasing.

Despite the success of these efforts, the epidemic is still serious. Thai officials, working with researchers in the United States and Canada, are therefore considering more daring strategies.

Two promising vaccines against HIV have been developed in the United States, but U.S. officials have decided not to move them into trials in the United States. Thai officials, facing a much more desperate situation, are negotiating to conduct the trials in Thailand. Ironically, the political complications of the democratic process in the United States, combined with a great concern for safety, can slow down developments there—whereas in Thailand, if officials decide to do it, it happens. The strategy would be to vaccinate uninfected volunteers whose sex partners are HIV-positive. Thus, it is possible that Thailand's tragedy will lead to the identification of an effective vaccine that can be used worldwide in stemming the pandemic.

Sources: Balter, 1988; Cohen, 2003a; Ford & Koetsawang, 1991; Phoolcharoen, 1998; Stoneburner et al., 1994.

---

has AIDS must often be accompanied by the announcement that one is gay or drug-addicted or engaged in extradyadic sex (that is, sex outside the relationship). It may make it more difficult for the person to fill the human need for emotional and physical intimacy. Also, as the patient becomes sicker, he or she is unlikely to be able to hold a job, and financial worries become an additional strain.

There is a great need to be sensitive to the psychological needs of AIDS patients. In most cities, support groups for AIDS patients and their families have formed. Social and psychological support from others is essential as people weather this crisis (Pakenham et al., 1994).

Research in Ontario sheds light on the experiences with sexual intimacy of people living with HIV or AIDS (Maticka-Tyndale et al., 2002). The researchers conducted in-depth interviews with 31 men and 4 women living in Windsor who were taking combination anti-viral therapies. Individuals who were living as a couple described a drop in sexual interest soon after diagnosis. For some participants sexual desire returned over time; for others it did not. According to one woman:

> Toward the very beginning, it [sex] was almost non-existent. We were afraid to. Now we're getting back to our regular sexual relationship—protected sex and it's much better than in the beginning. (p. 35)

Some single individuals worried about finding an accepting partner. Others preferred to remain single, often due to concerns about disclosure of their HIV-positive status. As one man said:

> I just don't want to bother … You don't realize what it's like to meet someone and find them attractive physically and all and then have to one day look at them and say, "By the way, I'm HIV-positive." (p. 37)

Finally, participants discussed the negative

In Focus 8.3

What Is It Like to Live with HIV? The Stories of Two HIV-Positive People

Tim Lapp, 44, is a retired chiropractor—retired because he lost his practice when he became too sick with HIV infection to be able to see his patients.

Tim was infected in 1992. Before that, he had been in two long-term relationships and he and his partners got tested regularly for HIV. On a Halloween trip to San Francisco, however, he had sex with a man and they practised safe sex, but the condom broke. He is certain that this incident was the source of his infection. He never saw that man again. He does not blame him, because they conscientiously practised safe sex and the other man did not lie to him. Tim went on, keeping his infection a secret for many reasons.

In 1998 he went on a dream trip to Russia. Not realizing that dairy products there are not pasteurized, he used them and, with his compromised immune system, contracted typhoid fever. He became very sick and was hospitalized. The typhoid fever was cured, but he had a series of serious GI infections over the next year. It was in the midst of all this debilitating illness that he gave up his practice.

Today, Tim is receiving the best treatment available. His T-cell count is 150, its highest in years (it has been as low as 18), and he feels healthy. Protease inhibitors, unfortunately, make him sick so he is not able to take them. Therefore, he is on a drug cocktail minus the protease inhibitors. His current drug combination has worked well for him for two years but just recently has become ineffective, so he will have to switch to different drugs soon. Taking the drugs is not without its problems; about twice a week he vomits four or five times in the morning, but he has learned to accept that.

Tim is in a five-year-long relationship with a man who is an accountant. His partner is HIV-negative, they practise safe sex, and his partner has not become infected. I asked Tim why he has a partner who is uninfected and whether he worries about infecting him. He replied that it is so difficult to find someone whom you love and with whom you are compatible, that they don't want to put up other barriers to forming a relationship such as one another's HIV status. Tim feels that the support he receives from his partner is a large part of the reason he is so healthy now. Tim does extensive volunteer work, especially with the local AIDS support network, serving on the board and coordinating special events.

When I asked Tim what he would say to people reading this book, he replied that he wanted them to know how easy it is to contract the disease. People must use condoms every time they have sex, or all their dreams could go down the drain. He worries that only gay men are careful because they are more aware of the risk, and that others are not careful. Yet he also conveyed a message of hope, because treatments have improved dramatically and, for many, the disease is roughly equivalent to diabetes in that it can be managed. Tim feels today that he can actually look forward to a future.

Janet Conners is an outspoken AIDS activist and educator from Nova Scotia. In 1992, Janet and her

impact of both the symptoms of HIV and the side effects of therapies on sexual intimacy.

Cognitive–behavioural therapy combined with stress-management training has been shown to be effective in improving the quality of life and decreasing anxiety and depression in HIV-infected individuals (Cruess et al., 2002; Lechner et al., 2003). The effectiveness of this therapy is impor-tant for two reasons. First, it improves the quality of life of affected people. Second, research shows that HIV-positive people who do not have symptoms but are depressed die earlier than similar people who are not depressed (Burack et al., 1993). Psychotherapy is therefore likely to have a positive impact on both mental health and physical health. Therapy also needs to focus on improving sexual

Figure 8.5   Canadian AIDS activist Janet Conners.

offer compensation to those people infected with tainted blood. The compensation package for victims of tainted blood and their families in Nova Scotia remains the best of any province in Canada. As an activist, Janet has been vocal in advocating for the rights of people and their families who got HIV through tainted blood. She has advocated equally for other HIV-positive communities including gay HIV-positive men and HIV-positive women. The couple received a human rights award in 1993 for their work in raising awareness about AIDS.

Conners was born in Vancouver and raised in the Fraser Valley and Yellowknife. She was sexually abused by a distant relative as a child, and was physically and emotionally abused by her first husband, whom she married at 22. She has one son from that marriage. Her son, Gus, was 5 years old when she met Randy in 1985. Six weeks later Randy tested positive for HIV. However, doctors downplayed the gravity of the situation and assured the couple that Randy was not going to get sick and that Janet was not going to get infected. He and Janet always used condoms but some of their condoms broke. In 1989, at the age of 33, Janet tested positive for HIV. This changed Janet from a woman providing support to her HIV-positive husband to an AIDS activist. She has been a member of the board of the AIDS Coalition of Nova Scotia, organized fundraisers, provided safe-sex talks in schools, and been engaged in other activities. Along with her husband Randy, she participated in the Krever inquiry into the tainted blood scandal. She also had the difficult task of preparing Gus for the possibility that she would die of AIDS before he became an adult. Randy died in 1994.

Sources: Based on interviews conducted by the authors and newspaper articles.

late husband Randy told the country that Randy, a hemophiliac, had been infected with HIV from tainted blood products and had infected Janet through sexual activity. In 1993 they convinced Nova Scotia's health minister to break with other provinces and

satisfaction among persons living with HIV/AIDS, as this is an important aspect of quality of life (Maticka-Tyndale et al., 2002).

Recent Progress in AIDS Research

As this discussion makes clear, much more research on AIDS is needed. We need better treatments to control this disease, we need a cure for it, and we need a vaccine against it. Those are pretty tall orders, and it is unlikely that any of them will appear in the next few years.

Vaccine.   Researchers have been working hard to develop a vaccine against HIV, but the job has turned out to be much more difficult than expected. The problem is that HIV actually has many forms and, to make matters worse, it mutates rapidly and

In Focus 8.4

What Is Safer Sex?

In this age of AIDS, everyone needs to think about positive health practices that will prevent or at least reduce the chances of infection. Technically, these practices are called "safer sex," there being no absolutely safe sex except no sex. But at least health experts agree that the following practices will reduce the risk of contracting HIV. They also provide protection against other STIs.

1. If you choose to be sexually active (and abstinence is one alternative to consider), have sex only in a stable, faithful, monogamous relationship with an uninfected partner whom you know is uninfected because you both have been tested.
2. If you are sexually active with more than one partner, always use latex condoms and/or dental dams. They have a good track record in preventing many sexually transmitted infections. Laboratory tests indicate that latex condoms are effective protection against HIV and other STIs. Condoms have a failure rate in preventing disease just as they do in preventing pregnancy, but they are still much better than nothing.
3. If there is any risk that you are infected or that your partner is, abstain from sex, always use condoms, or consider alternative forms of sexual expression such as hand–genital stimulation.
4. Do not have sexual intercourse with someone who has had previous partners unless they have been tested.
5. Do not engage in anal intercourse if there is even the slightest risk that your partner is infected.
6. Remember that both vaginal intercourse and anal intercourse transmit HIV and other STIs.

Figure 8.6 Quality control of condoms.

Mouth–genital sex might also, particularly if semen enters the mouth.

7. If you think that you might be infected with HIV, have a blood test to determine whether you are. If you find that you are infected, at the very least use a condom every time you engage in anal or vaginal intercourse or, preferably, abstain from these behaviours. Use a condom or dental dam when you engage in oral sex.
8. If you are a woman and you think that you might be infected with HIV, think carefully before getting pregnant, because of the risk of transmitting the disease to the baby during pregnancy and childbirth.
9. Consider "outercourse" as an alternative to intercourse. Outercourse involves activities like mutual masturbation and erotic massage, which don't transmit diseases.

recombines, creating even more forms (Robertson et al., 1995). In effect, the virus doesn't hold still long enough for a vaccine to take effective aim at it.

One strategy in developing a vaccine is to first develop a vaccine that works with monkeys, which can be infected by an analog to HIV called SIV (simian immunodeficiency virus). It has even been suggested that SIV is the same virus as HIV-2 (Gao et al., 1992). Progress has been made toward developing vaccines that protect monkeys from infection with SIV (Amara et al., 2001; Casimiro et al., 2003).

Yet another strategy involves the development of a vaccine to be administered to people recently infected with HIV. The goal is to boost their immune function so that they can fight off the virus. Vaccines of this type are being developed (Barouch et al., 2000; Rosenberg et al., 2000; Schooley et al., 2000).

Two other strategies involve developing a vaccine that stimulates the body to form resistance (i.e., antibodies) to HIV, or a vaccine that acts at the cellular level by stimulating the production of specialized T cells that are toxic to HIV (Heilman & Baltimore, 1998). Another possibility is a vaccine that combines both. Several of these vaccines have moved into clinical trials with humans (Cohen, 2001).

Research on Nonprogressors.
Some groups of people are being studied for clues to breakthroughs in the war against AIDS. One such group is *nonprogressors* (Buchbinder et al., 1994). Approximately 5 percent of HIV-infected people go for 10 years or more without symptoms and with no deterioration of their immune system. Their T-cell count remains higher than 500. Nonprogressors turn out to have less HIV in their bodies, even though they have been infected for over a decade. Why? One possibility is that these people have unusually strong immune systems that have essentially managed to contain the virus. Another is that they were infected with a weak strain of the virus. Some individuals were infected with a genetically defective strain of HIV that does not replicate; this situation is intriguing because it might be useful in producing a vaccine. Nonprogressors also have particularly high levels of defensins, chemicals secreted by white blood cells (Ganz, 2002). Defensins are known to contribute to the killing of microbes such as HIV.

Chemokines.
Another major scientific advance is the discovery of HIV-suppressor factors or *chemokines* (Balter, 1995; Cocchi et al., 1995; Cohen, 1997). Certain lymphocytes (CD8+ T cells) battle against HIV in the body. They do so by secreting three chemokines (which are molecules), named RANTES, MIP-1α, and MIP-1β. HIV-infected persons who are nonprogressors have high levels of CD8 cells and high levels of chemokines compared with rapid progressors (Haynes et al., 1996). The chemokines can bind to the coreceptor CC CKR 5, blocking HIV from entering cells. Scientists hope that these discoveries may lead to improved treatments for HIV-infected persons and possibly to vaccines that boost the level of chemokines and therefore boost the body's resistance to HIV infection.

People Who Resist Infection.
Another intriguing group are some prostitutes in Nairobi, Kenya, who are repeatedly exposed to HIV because of their work, but have never become infected (Taylor, 1994). Another research group is studying heterosexual couples in the United States in whom the man is HIV-infected but the woman, despite repeated unprotected intercourse, has not become infected. It seems that some people are resistant to HIV infection and that their immune systems are unusual, seeking and destroying the virus. Unravelling this mystery may also yield clues to a vaccine or a cure.

Mutations.
Some researchers believe that HIV's property of rapid mutation could actually be used against it (Chow et al., 1993). They believe that HIV could be forced to mutate to a harmless form. This might be done by exposing the virus to the various drugs used to treat HIV; in response to each, the virus will mutate until eventually it will mutate to a form that cannot replicate itself. This approach, too, holds exciting possibilities.

Microbicides
Microbicides are substances, usually in ointment form, that kill microbes such as HIV. These ointments could be put into the vagina or anus or spread on the penis to battle HIV transmission. The old standby nonoxynol-9 was thought to be effective in killing HIV some years ago, but today we know that it is not only ineffective but also actually makes women more vulnerable to infection by irritating the lining of the vagina (Van Damme et al., 2002). Much effort is now going into developing effective microbicides that will attack HIV as well as other sexually transmitted viruses (Mauck et al., 2001). Some are already in clinical trials, including PRO 2000 Gel and BufferGel (Morrow et al., 2003; Tabet et al., 2003; Van Damme et al., 2002b).

Behavioural Prevention
In the last analysis, prevention is better than cure. Until we have an effective vaccine, our best hope is interventions that aim to change people's behaviour, because it is behaviour (sexual activity, injection drug use) that spreads HIV. The big success story in behavioural prevention is Uganda. In 1991, screening of pregnant women indicated that 21 percent were infected; by 1998 this figure had dropped to 10 percent (Stoneburner & Low-Beer, 2004). In the early 1990s, the Ugandan government

launched a bold and forceful program called ABC—for Abstinence, Be faithful, and use Condoms. It blanketed the country with advertising about the program, which urged unmarried persons to abstain from sex, urged married people to be faithful, and urged everyone to use condoms. The whole emphasis was on behaviour change, with no need for the costly drugs that Uganda couldn't afford. It isn't completely clear which of the three components of the program had the most effect, but in any case the program worked, and the epidemic is under control in that country. Scientists have estimated that this intervention had an effect equivalent to a vaccine with 80-percent effectiveness (Stoneburner & Low-Beer, 2004).

■ Gonorrhea

Historical records indicate that **gonorrhea** ("the clap," "the drip") is the oldest of the sexual diseases. Its symptoms are described in the Old Testament, in Leviticus 15 (about 3,500 years ago). The Greek physician Hippocrates, some 2,400 years ago, believed that gonorrhea resulted from "excessive indulgence in the pleasures of Venus," the goddess of love (hence the term "venereal" disease). Albert Neisser identified the bacterium that causes it, the gonococcus *Neisseria gonorrhoeae,* in 1879.

Gonorrhea has always been a particular problem in wartime, when it spreads rapidly among the soldiers and the prostitutes they patronize. In the twentieth century, a gonorrhea epidemic occurred during the First World War, and gonorrhea was also a serious problem during the Second World War. Then, with the discovery of penicillin and its use in curing gonorrhea, the disease became much less prevalent in the 1950s.

There was a resurgence in the incidence of gonorrhea as contraceptive practices shifted to use of the pill, which (unlike the condom) provides no protection from gonorrhea and actually increases a woman's susceptibility. However, in Canada the reported rate of gonorrhea has declined 93 percent since 1980 due to improved diagnostic services,

> **Gonorrhea (gon-uh-REE-uh):** A sexually transmitted infection that usually causes symptoms of a puslike discharge and painful, burning urination in the male but is frequently asymptomatic in the female.

Figure 8.7   Symptoms of gonorrhea in men include a puslike discharge. About 80 percent of women, however, are asymptomatic.

partner notification, and treatment. In 2003, there were 7,363 reported cases, almost half of which were among 15- to 24-year-olds. Health Canada has set a goal of eliminating gonorrhea by 2010.

Symptoms

Most cases of gonorrhea result from penis-in-vagina intercourse. In the male, the gonococcus invades the urethra, producing *urethritis* (inflammation of the urethra). White blood cells rush to the area and attempt to destroy the bacteria, but the bacteria soon win the battle. In most cases, symptoms appear five to eight days after infection, although they may appear as early as the first day or as late as two weeks after infection (Sherrard & Barlow, 1996). Initially a thin, clear mucous discharge seeps out of the meatus (the opening at the tip of the penis). Within a day or so it becomes thick and creamy and may be white, yellowish, or yellow-green (see Figure 8.7). This is often referred to as a "purulent" (puslike) discharge. The area around the meatus may become swollen. About half of infected men experience a painful burning sensation when urinating (Sherrard & Barlow, 1996). The urine may contain pus or blood, and in some cases the lymph glands of the groin become enlarged and tender.

Because the early symptoms of gonorrhea in men are obvious and often painful, most men seek treatment immediately and are cured. If the disease is not treated, however, the urethritis spreads up the urethra, causing inflammations in the prostate (prostatitis), seminal vesicles (seminal vesiculitis), urinary bladder (cystitis), and epididymis (epididymitis). Pain on urination becomes worse and is felt in the whole penis. Then these early symptoms may disappear as the disease spreads to the other organs. If the epididymitis is left untreated, it may spread to the testicles and the resulting scar tissue may cause sterility.

Asymptomatic gonorrhea (gonorrhea with no symptoms) does occur in males, but its incidence is low (Hook & Handsfield, 1990). In contrast, about 60 to 80 percent of women infected with gonorrhea are asymptomatic during the early stages of the disease. Many women are unaware of their infection unless they are told by a male partner. Therefore, it is extremely important for any male who is infected to inform all his contacts.

The gonorrheal infection in the woman invades the cervix. Pus is discharged, but the amount may be so slight that it is not noticed. When present, it is yellow-green and irritating to the vulva, but it is generally not heavy (it is not to be confused with normal cervical mucus, which is clear or white and nonirritating, or with discharges resulting from the various kinds of vaginitis—discussed in this chapter— which are irritating but white). Although the cervix is the primary site of infection, the inflammation may also spread to the urethra, causing burning pain on urination (not to be confused with cystitis).

If the infection is not treated, the Bartholin glands may become infected and, in rare cases, swell and produce pus. The infection may also be spread to the anus and rectum, either by a heavy cervical discharge or by the menstrual discharge.

Because so many women are asymptomatic in the early stages of gonorrhea, many receive no treatment, and thus there is a high risk of serious complications. In about 20 percent of women who go untreated, the gonococcus moves up into the uterus, often during the menstrual period. From there it infects the fallopian tubes. The tissues become swollen and inflamed, and thus the condition is also called pelvic inflammatory disease (PID)—although PID can be caused by diseases other than gonorrhea. The major symptom is pelvic pain and, in some cases, irregular or painful menstruation. If PID is not treated, scar tissue may form, blocking the tubes and leaving the woman sterile. Indeed, untreated gonorrhea is one of the most common causes of sterility in women. If the tubes are partially blocked, so that sperm can get up them but eggs cannot move down, ectopic pregnancy can result, because the fertilized egg is trapped in the tube.

There are three other major sites for nongenital gonorrhea infection: the mouth and throat, the anus and rectum, and the eyes. If fellatio is performed on an infected man, the gonococcus may invade the throat. (Cunnilingus is less likely to spread gonorrhea, and mouth-to-mouth kissing rarely does.) Such an infection is often asymptomatic; the typical symptom, if there is one, is a sore throat. Rectal gonorrhea is contracted through anal intercourse and thus affects both women in heterosexual relations and, more commonly, men in homosexual relations. Symptoms include some discharge from the rectum and itching, but many cases are asymptomatic. Gonorrhea may also invade the eyes. This occurs only rarely in adults, when they touch the genitals and then transfer the bacteria-containing pus to their eyes by touching them. This eye infection is much more common in newborn infants. The infection is transferred from the mother's cervix to the infant's eyes during birth. For this reason, most provinces require that silver nitrate, or erythromycin or some other antibiotic, be put in every newborn's eyes to prevent any such infection. If left untreated, the eyes become swollen and painful within a few days, and there is a discharge of pus. Blindness was a common result in the preantibiotic era.

Diagnosis

A urine test is available for men. If gonorrhea in the throat is suspected, a swab should be taken and tested. People who suspect that they may have rectal gonorrhea should request that a swab be taken from the rectum, since many physicians will not automatically think to do this.

In females, a sample of the cervical discharge is taken from the cervix and tested. A pelvic examination should also be performed. Pain during this exam may indicate PID. Women who suspect throat or rectal infection should request that samples be taken from those sites as well.

Treatment

The traditional treatment for gonorrhea was a large dose of penicillin, or tetracycline for those who were allergic to penicillin. However, strains of the gonococcus that are resistant to penicillin and tetracycline have become so common that a newer antibiotic, cifixime, must now be used (Health Canada, 1998). It is highly effective, even against resistant strains.

■ Syphilis

There has been considerable debate over the exact origins of **syphilis.** The disease, called "the Great Pox," was present in Europe during the 1400s and became a pandemic by 1500.

The bacterium that causes syphilis is called *Treponema pallidum.* It is spiral-shaped and is thus often called a *spirochete.* In 1906, Wassermann, Neisser, and Bruck described a test for diagnosing syphilis that became known as the *Wassermann test* or *Wassermann reaction.* This test has been replaced by more modern blood tests, but the Wassermann label hangs on.

In 2003, there were only 849 cases of syphilis reported in Canada (the United States has a rate 10 times as high) and two provinces and two territories reported no cases at all. Although the rate of syphilis remains low, there has been an increase in cases in the last few years; for example, there were only 174 reported cases in 2000. The increase is largely due to outbreaks in Vancouver involving sex trade workers, in the Yukon among heterosexuals, and in Calgary, Ottawa, and Montreal among men who have sex with men.

Although syphilis is not nearly as common as gonorrhea, its effects are much more serious if left untreated. In most cases, gonorrhea causes only discomfort and, sometimes, sterility; syphilis, if left untreated, can damage the nervous system and even cause death. There are many cases today of coinfection, in which the person is infected with both syphilis and HIV. Syphilis infection makes one more vulnerable to HIV and vice versa.

Symptoms

The major early symptom of syphilis is the **chancre.** It is a round, ulcerlike lesion with a hard, raised edge, resembling a crater. One of the distinctive things about the chancre is that although it looks terrible, it is painless. It appears about three weeks (as early as ten days or as late as three months) after intercourse with an infected person. The chancre appears at the point where the bacteria

entered the body. Typically, the bacteria enter through the mucous membranes of the genitals as a result of intercourse with an infected person. Thus in men the chancre often appears on the penis or scrotum. In women, the chancre often appears on the cervix, and thus the woman does not notice it and is unaware that she is infected (nature's sexism again). The chancre may also appear on the vaginal walls or, externally, on the vulva (see Figure 8.8).

If oral sex or anal intercourse with an infected person occurs, the bacteria can also invade the mucous membranes of the mouth or rectum. Thus the chancre may appear on the lips, tongue, or tonsils or around the anus. Finally, the bacteria may enter through a cut in the skin anywhere on the body. Thus it is possible (though rare) to get syphilis by touching the chancre of an infected person. The chancre would then appear on the hand at the point where the bacteria entered through the break in the skin.

The progress of the disease once the person has been infected is generally divided into four stages: primary-stage syphilis, secondary-stage syphilis, latent syphilis, and late syphilis. The phase described above, in which the chancre forms, is **primary-stage syphilis.** If left untreated, the chancre goes away by itself within one to five weeks after it appears. This marks the end of the primary stage. However, the disease has not gone away just because the chancre has healed; it has only gone underground.

Beginning one to six months after the original appearance of the chancre, a generalized body rash develops, marking the beginning of **secondary-stage syphilis.** The rash is variable in its appearance, the most distinctive feature being that it does not itch or hurt. Hair loss may also occur during the secondary stage. Usually the symp-

---

Syphilis (SIFF-ih-lis): A sexually transmitted infection that causes a chancre to appear in the primary stage.
Chancre (SHANK-er): A painless, ulcerlike lesion with a hard, raised edge that is a symptom of syphilis.
Primary-stage syphilis: The first few weeks of a syphilis infection, during which the chancre is present.
Secondary-stage syphilis: The second stage of syphilis, occurring several months after infection, during which the chancre has disappeared and a generalized body rash appears.

(a)   *(b)*

Figure 8.8 The chancre characteristic of primary-stage syphilis *(a)* on the labia majora and *(b)* on the penis.

toms are troublesome enough to cause the person to seek medical help. With appropriate treatment at this stage, the disease can still be cured, and there will be no permanent effects.

Even without treatment, the secondary-stage symptoms go away in two to six weeks, leading people to believe mistakenly that the disease has gone away. Instead, it has entered a more dangerous stage.

After the symptoms of the secondary stage have disappeared, the disease is in the latent stage; **latent syphilis** may last for years. Although there are no symptoms in this stage, *T. pallidum* is busily burrowing into the tissues of the body, especially the blood vessels, central nervous system (brain and spinal cord), and bones. After the first year or so of the latent stage, the disease is no longer infectious, except that a pregnant woman can still pass it on to the fetus.

About half of the people who enter the latent stage remain in it permanently, living out the rest of their lives without further complications. The other half, however, move into the dangerous **late syphilis.** In *cardiovascular late syphilis* the heart and major blood vessels are attacked; this occurs 10 to 40 years after the initial infection. Cardiovascular syphilis can lead to death. In *neurosyphilis* the brain and spinal cord are attacked, leading to insanity and paralysis, which appear 10 to 20 years after infection. Neurosyphilis may be fatal.

If a pregnant woman has syphilis, the fetus may be infected when the bacteria cross the placental barrier, and the child gets **congenital syphilis** (meaning present from birth). The infection may cause early death of the fetus (spontaneous abortion) or severe illness at or shortly after birth. It may also lead to late complications that show up only at 10 or 20 years of age. Women are most infectious to their baby when they have primary- or secondary-stage syphilis, but they may transmit the infection to the fetus in utero as long as eight years after the mother's initial infection. If the disease is diagnosed and treated before the fourth month of pregnancy, the fetus will not develop the disease. For this reason, a syphilis test is done as a routine part of the blood analysis in a pregnancy test. In 2001 there were only two cases of congenital syphilis in all of Canada.

Latent (LAY-tent) syphilis: The third stage of syphilis, which may last for years, during which symptoms disappear although the person is still infected.
Late syphilis: The fourth and final stage of syphilis, during which the disease does damage to major organs of the body, such as the lungs, heart, or brain.
Congenital (kun-JEN-ih-tul) syphilis: A syphilis infection in a newborn baby resulting from transmission from an infected mother.

Diagnosis

Syphilis is somewhat difficult to diagnose from symptoms because, as noted above, its symptoms are like those of many other diseases.

The physical exam should include inspection not only of the genitals but also of the entire body surface. Women should have a pelvic exam so that the vagina and the cervix can be checked for chancres. If the patient has had anal intercourse, a rectal exam should also be performed.

If a chancre is present, some of its fluid is taken and placed on a slide for inspection under a dark-field microscope. If the person has syphilis, *T. pallidum* should be present.

The most common tests for syphilis are blood tests, all of which are based on antibody reactions. The VDRL (venereal disease research laboratory test) is one of these blood tests. It is fairly accurate, cheap, and easy to perform.

Treatment

The treatment of choice for syphilis is penicillin. *Treponema pallidum* is actually rather fragile, so large doses are not necessary in treatment. The recommended dose is two shots of benzathine penicillin, of 1.2 million units each, one in each of the buttocks. Latent, later, and congenital syphilis require larger doses.

For those allergic to penicillin the recommended treatment is tetracycline or doxycycline, but these should not be given to pregnant women (Larsen et al., 1996).

Follow-up exams should be performed to make sure that the patient is completely cured.

Elimination of Syphilis?

Health Canada has targeted syphilis for complete elimination in Canada. As an interim and more achievable step, the national goal is fewer than 0.5 cases per 100,000 population. On the surface, the goal may seem odd, given that syphilis is relatively rare compared with other STIs. But syphilis infection makes a person much more vulnerable to HIV infection because of the open sores produced by syphilis, and a person who is HIV-infected and then contracts syphilis may experience immediately life-threatening conditions (Wong & Jordan, 2000). For these reasons, syphilis is more serious than the small rate of infection indicates. Moreover, syphilis is completely curable with a single dose of penicillin, it is easily detectable with inexpensive laboratory tests, and it has not developed resistant strains. Experience since the Second World War indicates that, even when syphilis is effectively treated and brought to a low incidence, it still resurges periodically in epidemics. Therefore, total elimination is the best goal, and this seems feasible.

■ Viral Hepatitis

Viral hepatitis is a disease of the liver. One symptom is an enlarged liver that is somewhat tender. The disease can vary greatly in severity from asymptomatic cases to ones in which there is a fever, fatigue, jaundice (yellowish skin), and vomiting, much as one might experience with a serious case of the flu. There are five types of viral hepatitis: hepatitis A, B, C, D, and E. The one that is of most interest in a discussion of sexually transmitted infections is hepatitis B. Hepatitis C and D (or delta) can also be transmitted sexually, but they are rare compared with B (Shapiro & Alter, 1996).

The virus for hepatitis B (HBV) can be transmitted through blood, saliva, semen, vaginal secretions, and other body fluids. The behaviours that spread it include needle sharing by people who inject drugs, vaginal and anal intercourse, and oral–anal sex. It is most frequently transmitted through intravenous drug use (34 percent), having multiple heterosexual partners (24 percent), and male homosexual sex (7 percent) (Zhang et al., 2001). It has many similarities to AIDS, although hepatitis B is more contagious.

Hepatitis B is more common than most people think because it receives relatively little publicity compared with AIDS and herpes. There are about 700 new cases of hepatitis B in Canada each year. People who have had the disease continue to have a positive blood test for it for the rest of their lives. A Canadian study of men attending STI clinics found that 39 percent of the homosexual/bisexual men tested positive compared with about 9 percent of heterosexual men (Yuan & Robinson, 1994).

Many adults infected with HBV are asymptomatic; their bodies fight off the virus and they are left uninfected, with permanent immunity. Others develop an early, acute (short-term) illness and display a variety of symptoms but recover from the illness. A third group develops chronic (long-term) hepatitis B. They continue to be infectious and may develop serious liver disease involving cirrhosis or cancer. Fortunately, antiviral treatments are now available for those with chronic hepatitis B (Fung & Lok, 2004; Hom et al., 2004; Saltik-Temizel et al., 2004).

The good news is that there is a vaccine against hepatitis B. All provinces except Manitoba have a universal hepatitis B vaccination program for preadolescents (Tepper & Gully, 1997). We urge you to be vaccinated if you are a person who has had a number of partners. You should be tested if there is even a hint that you have been exposed.

■ Trichomoniasis

Trichomoniasis ("trich") is caused by a protozoan, *Trichomonas vaginalis* (Krieger & Alderete, 1999; Swygaard et al., 2004). The organism can survive for a time on toilet seats and other objects so it is occasionally transmitted nonsexually, but it is transmitted mainly through sexual intercourse.

For women, the symptom is an abundant, frothy, white or yellow vaginal discharge that irritates the vulva and has an unpleasant smell. In men, there may be irritation of the urethra and a discharge from the penis, but some men are asymptomatic. It is important that accurate diagnosis be made, because the drugs used to treat trichomoniasis are different from those used to treat other STIs that have similar symptoms, and the long-term effects of untreated trichomoniasis can be serious.

The treatment of choice is metronidazole (Flagyl) taken orally. If left untreated, trich can lead to pelvic inflammatory disease and problems with birth (Swygaard et al., 2004). It also increases susceptibility to HIV infection.

■ Pubic Lice

Pubic lice ("crabs," or *pediculosis pubis*) are tiny lice that attach themselves to the base of pubic hairs and there feed on blood from their human host. They are

Trichomoniasis (trick-oh-moh-NY-us-is): A form of vaginitis causing a frothy white or yellow discharge with an unpleasant odour.
Pubic lice: Tiny lice that attach themselves to the base of pubic hairs and cause itching; also called crabs or *pediculosis pubis*.

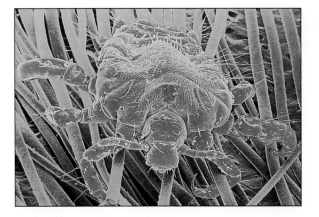

Figure 8.9 A pubic louse, enlarged. The actual size is about the same as the head of a pin.

about the size of a pinhead and, under magnification, resemble a crab (see Figure 8.9). They lay their eggs frequently and live for about 30 days, but they die within 24 hours if they are taken off a human host. Crabs are transmitted by sexual contact, but they may also be picked up from sheets, towels, sleeping bags, or toilet seats. (Yes, there *are* some things you can catch from toilet seats.)

The major symptom of pubic lice is fierce itching in the region of the pubic hair. Diagnosis is made by finding the lice or the eggs attached to the hairs.

Pubic lice are treated with the drugs Nix and Rid, which are available without prescription. Both kill the lice. After treatment, the person should put on clean clothing. Since the lice die within 24 hours, it is not necessary to disinfect clothing that has not been used for longer than 24 hours. However, the eggs can live up to six days, and in difficult cases it may be necessary to boil or dry-clean one's clothing or use a spray such as R and C.

■ Preventing STIs

While most of the literature one reads concentrates on the rapid diagnosis and treatment of STIs, prevention would be much better than cure, and there are some ways in which one can avoid getting STIs, or at least reduce one's chances of doing so. The most obvious, of course, is limiting yourself to a monogamous relationship with an uninfected person or abstaining from sexual activity. If this strat-

In Focus 8.5

Cool Lines about Safer Sex

The popular Web site for teens teenwire.com offers these lines for negotiating safer sex.

Partner	*You*
What's that?	A condom, baby.
What for?	To use when we're making love.
I don't like using them.	Why not?
It doesn't feel as good with a rubber.	I'll feel more relaxed. If I'm more relaxed, I can make it feel better for you.
But we've never used a condom before.	I don't want to take any more risks.
Rubbers are gross.	Being pregnant when I don't want to be is worse. So is getting AIDS.
Don't you trust me?	Trust isn't the point. People carry sexually transmitted infections without knowing it.
I'll pull out in time.	Women can get pregnant and get STIs from pre-cum.
Making love with a rubber on is like taking a shower with a raincoat on.	Doing it without a rubber is playing Russian roulette.
It just isn't as sensitive.	With a condom you might last even longer, and that'll make up for it.
I don't stay hard when I put on a condom.	I can do something about that.
Putting it on interrupts everything.	Not if I help put it on.
I'll try, but it might not work.	Practice makes perfect.
But I love you.	Then you'll help me protect myself.
I guess you don't really love me.	I'm not going to prove my love by risking my life.
I'm not using a rubber, no matter what.	Well, then I guess we're not having sex.
Just this once without it.	It only takes once to get pregnant. It only takes once to get AIDS.
It won't fit.	Condoms come in all different sizes.

Sources: Script for negotiating sex from www.teenwire.com, June 22, 2004. Reprinted with permission from Planned Parenthood ® Federation of America.

egy is unacceptable to you, there are other techniques you might be willing to follow.

The condom, in addition to being a decent contraceptive, gives good protection against HIV, gonorrhea, herpes, syphilis, and other STIs. With the rise of the STI epidemic, the condom is again becoming popular. The key is to eroticize condom use (Ploem & Byers, 1997).

Some simple health precautions are also helpful. Successful prostitutes, who need to be careful about STIs, take such precautions. Washing the genitals before intercourse helps remove bacteria. This may not sound like a romantic prelude to lovemaking, but prostitutes make a sensuous game out of soaping the man's genitals. You can do this as part of taking a shower or bath with your partner. The other important technique is inspecting your partner's genitals. If you see a chancre, a wart, a herpes blister, or a discharge, put on your clothes and leave or, at the very least, immediately start a conversation about STI status (do not fall for the "it's only a pimple" routine). This technique may sound a little crude or embarrassing, but if you are intimate enough with someone to make love with that person, you ought to be intimate enough to look at her or his genitals. Once again, if you are cool about it, you can make this an erotic part of foreplay.

On the other hand, just because a partner has no obvious symptoms like herpes blisters or warts, don't assume that the person is uninfected. We have seen in this chapter how many of these infections—for example, chlamydia, herpes, and warts—can be asymptomatic. The only way to really know is to have a complete battery of tests for STIs, a choice more and more people are making. Not every STI is tested in the standard battery—for example, herpes and HPV usually are not—but it still will catch most infection.

Urinating both before and after intercourse helps to keep bacteria out of the urethra.

Finally, each person needs to recognize that it is his or her ethical responsibility to seek out early diagnosis and treatment. Probably the most important responsibility is that of informing prospective partners if you have an STI and of informing past partners as soon as you discover that you have one. For example, because so many women are asymptomatic for chlamydia, it is particularly important for men to take the responsibility of informing their female partners if they find

that they have the infection. It is important to take care of your own health, but it is equally important to take care of your partner's health.

■ Other Genital Infections

Vaginitis (vaginal inflammation or irritation) is very common among women and is endemic in university populations. Two kinds of vaginitis, as well as cystitis (inflammation of the urinary bladder) and prostatitis, will be considered here. None of these infections are STIs, because they are not transmitted by sexual contact; they are, however, common infections of the sex organs.

A few simple steps can help prevent vaginitis. Every time you shower or take a bath, wash the vulva carefully and dry it thoroughly. Do not use feminine hygiene deodorant sprays; they are unnecessary and can irritate the vagina. Wear cotton underpants; nylon and other synthetics retain moisture, and vaginitis-producing organisms thrive on moisture. Avoid wearing pants that are too tight in the crotch; they increase moisture and may irritate the vulva. Keep down the amount of sugar and carbohydrates in your diet. Wipe the anus from front to back so that bacteria from the anus do not get into the vagina. For the same reason, never go immediately from anal intercourse to vaginal intercourse. Finally, if an attack of vaginitis seems to be coming on, placing some yogurt with active cultures into the vagina can help restore the good bacteria.

Monilia

Monilia (also called *candida, yeast infection, fungus,* and *moniliasis*) is a form of vaginitis caused by the yeast fungus *Candida*. *Candida* is normally present in the vagina, but if the delicate environmental balance there is disturbed (for example, if the pH is changed), the growth of *Candida* can get out of hand. Conditions that encourage the growth of *Candida* include long-term use of birth control pills, menstruation, diabetes or a prediabetic con-

Vaginitis (vaj-in-ITE-is): An irritation or inflammation of the vagina, usually causing a discharge.
Monilia (Moh-NILL-ee-uh): A form of vaginitis causing a thick, white discharge; also called candida or yeast infection.

dition, pregnancy, and long-term use of antibiotics such as tetracycline. It is not a sexually transmitted infection, although intercourse may aggravate it.

The major symptom is a thick, white, curdlike vaginal discharge, found on the vaginal lips and the walls of the vagina. The discharge can cause extreme itching, to the point where the woman is not interested in having intercourse.

Treatment is by the drugs miconzole or clotrimazole, both available over the counter. Flucomazole, a single-dose treatment, is available by prescription.

If a woman has monilia while she is pregnant, she can transmit it to her baby during birth. The baby gets the yeast in its digestive system, a condition known as *thrush*. Thrush can also result from oral–genital sex.

Bacterial vaginosis is another vaginal infection that produces a similar discharge. The distinctive feature is that the discharge has a foul odour.

Cystitis

Cystitis is an infection of the urinary bladder that occurs almost exclusively in women. In most cases it is caused by the bacterium *Escherichia coli*. The bacteria are normally present in the body (in the intestine), and in some cases, for unknown reasons, they get into the urethra and the bladder. Sometimes frequent, vigorous sexual intercourse will irritate the urethral opening, permitting the bacteria to get in.

The symptoms are a desire to urinate every few minutes, with a burning pain on urination. The urine may be hazy or even tinged with red; this is caused by pus and blood from the infected bladder. There may also be backache. Diagnosis can usually be made simply on the basis of these symptoms. A urine sample should be taken and analyzed, though, for confirmation.

Treatment is usually with Bactrim or another antibiotic. The drug may include a dye that helps relieve the burning sensation on urination; the dye turns the urine bright orange-red.

To prevent cystitis or prevent recurring bouts of it, drink lots of water and urinate frequently, especially just before and after intercourse. This will help flush out any bacteria from the bladder and urethra.

Prostatitis

Prostatitis is an inflammation or swelling of the prostate gland. It used to be thought that it was almost always caused by an infection, but it is now known that it can be caused by several different conditions. It can also be caused by gonorrhea or chlamydia. The typical symptoms are fever; chills; pain above the penis or around the scrotum, anus, or rectum; difficulty starting urination; and a need for frequent urination. It may produce sexual dysfunction, typically pain during sexual intercourse. In some cases, prostatitis may be chronic (long-lasting) and may have no symptoms, or only lower-back pain. Antibiotics are used in treatment.

Cystitis (sis-TY-tis): An infection of the urinary bladder in women, causing painful, burning urination.

Prostatitis (pros-tuh-TY-tis): An infection, inflammation, or swelling of the prostate gland.

■ ■ ■ SUMMARY

Sexually transmitted infections (STIs) are at epidemic levels in Canada and worldwide. Three common STIs among college and university students are chlamydia, HPV, and herpes.

Chlamydia is often asymptomatic, especially in women. In men, it produces a thin discharge from the penis and mild pain on urination. It is quite curable with antibiotics. If left untreated in women, the possible complications include pelvic inflammatory disease and possibly infertility.

HPV (human papillomavirus) causes genital warts. Sometimes the warts are obvious, but in other cases they are small and may not be visible. HPV infection increases women's risk of cervical cancer.

Genital herpes, caused by the HSV virus, produces bouts of painful blisters on the genitals. These episodes may recur for the rest of the person's life, although some infected persons experience no or only a few outbreaks. Currently there is no cure, although the drug acyclovir minimizes the symptoms. Herpes infection increases one's risk of HIV infection.

The virus HIV destroys the body's natural immune system and leaves the person vulnerable to certain kinds of infections and cancers that lead to death. The most frequent means of transmission in Canada are men who have sex with men, use of injection drugs, and having heterosexual contact with an infected person. Drugs such as AZT and ritonavir (a protease inhibitor) are used to slow the progression of the disease. More attention needs to focus on the special concerns of HIV-infected women and ethnic minorities. Several strategies for producing a vaccine are being pursued.

The primary symptoms of gonorrhea in the male, appearing five to eight days after infection, are a white or yellow discharge from the penis and a burning pain on urination. The majority of women with gonorrhea are asymptomatic. Gonorrhea is caused by a bacterium, the gonococcus, and is cured with antibiotics. If left untreated, it may lead to infertility.

Syphilis is caused by the bacterium *Treponema pallidum*. The first symptom is a chancre. Penicillin is effective as a cure. If left untreated, the disease progresses through several stages that may lead to death.

Hepatitis B, caused by the virus HBV, is transmitted sexually as well as by needle sharing. Antiviral drugs are available to treat chronic cases. A vaccine is now available and is being administered widely.

Pubic lice are tiny lice that attach to the pubic hair. They are spread through sexual and other types of physical contact. Shampoos are available for treatment.

Techniques for preventing STIs include thorough washing of both partners' genitals before intercourse; urination both before and after intercourse; inspecting the partner's genitals for symptoms like a wart or urethral discharge; and the use of a condom.

Other vaginal infections include monilia, trichomoniasis, and bacterial vaginosis. Cystitis is an infection of the urinary bladder in women, leading to frequent, burning urination. Prostatitis is inflammation of the prostate gland.

■ ■ ■ QUESTIONS FOR THOUGHT, DISCUSSION, AND DEBATE

1. Contact the student health service on your campus and see whether they might be willing to share with you the number of cases of chlamydia, gonorrhea, genital warts, and herpes they diagnose per year; then share the information with your class.

2. Design a program to reduce the number of cases of sexually transmitted infections on your campus.

3. Michael has had a monogamous relationship with Sonya for six months. At her annual pelvic exam, Sonya discovers that she has chlamydia and blows up at Michael for giving it to her. Michael has never been tested for anything. What should Michael and Sonya discuss with each other, what other information do they need, and what should they do?

4. If you were designing an intervention for Aboriginal teenagers to reduce the spread of HIV, how would you make that intervention culturally sensitive? Would the approach be different for women and for men? If you feel that you don't know enough about Aboriginal culture, interview some Aboriginal students or community members to find out more.

■ ■ ■ SUGGESTIONS FOR FURTHER READING

Barrett, Michael (Ed.). (1997). *The Canadian Journal of Human Sexuality: STDs and Sexual/Reproductive Health,* 6(4). Toronto: SIECCAN. This volume of the journal contains a series of articles that summarize our current knowledge about the major STIs and make recommendations for prevention and control of STIs in Canada.

Barrett, Michael (Ed.). (1998). *The Canadian Journal of Human Sexuality: Innovative STD Prevention and Education Programs in Canada,* 7(4). Toronto: SIECCAN. This volume of the journal features articles describing innovative STI prevention programs in Canada.

Ebel, Charles, and Wald, Anna. (2002). *Managing herpes: How to live and love with a chronic STD.* Research Triangle Park, NC: American Social Health Association. People say this is the best herpes book ever.

Gallo, Roe, and McIlvenna, Ted. (2003). *Sexual strategies for pleasure and safety.* Specific Press.

Online **LearningCentre**

For Review Questions, Web Resources, and other learning and study tools, visit the *Understanding Human Sexuality* Online Learning Centre at www.mcgrawhill.ca/college/hyde.

CHAPTER 9

The Physiology of Sexual Response

CHAPTER HIGHLIGHTS

Here are some colors of different people's orgasms: champagne, all colors and white and gray afterward, red and blue, green, beige and blue, red, blue and gold. Some people never make it because they are trying for plaid.*

This chapter is about the way the body responds during sexual arousal and orgasm and the processes behind these responses. This information is very important in developing good techniques of lovemaking (see Chapter 10) and in analyzing and treating sexual problems such as rapid ejaculation or orgasmic dysfunction (see Chapter 19).

First we examine how the body responds physiologically during orgasm. Much of what we know about these processes is based on the classic research of Masters and Johnson. Their research has been criticized, though, so in the next section some alternative models to theirs are presented. Next, we focus on how hormones, the brain, and the spinal cord contribute to sexual behaviour and response. Finally, we consider research on pheromones and their influence on sexual behaviour in animals and in humans.

■ The Four Stages of the Sexual Response Cycle

Sex researchers William H. Masters and Virginia E. Johnson provided one of the first models of the physiology of human sexual response. Their research culminated in 1966 with the publication of *Human Sexual Response,* which reported data on 382 women and 312 men observed in more than 10,000 sexual cycles of arousal and orgasm. (A discussion and critique of the Masters and Johnson research techniques as presented in Chapter 3.) Recent biological research has confirmed many of their findings, while questioning a few and augmenting many. All of this research is the basis for the sections that follow.

Masters and Johnson described four stages of sexual response, which they call *excitement, plateau, orgasm,* and *resolution.* The two basic physiological processes that occur during these

stages are vasocongestion and myotonia. **Vasocongestion** occurs when a great deal of blood flows into the blood vessels in a region, in this case the genitals, as a result of dilation of the blood vessels in the region. **Myotonia** occurs when muscles contract, not only in the genitals but also throughout the body. Let us now consider in detail what occurs in each of the stages.

Excitement

The **excitement** phase is the beginning of erotic arousal. The basic physiological process that occurs during excitement is vasocongestion. This produces the obvious arousal response in the male—erection. Erection results when the corpora cavernosa and the corpus spongiosum fill (becoming engorged) with blood (see Figure 9.1). Erection may be produced by direct physical stimulation of the genitals, by stimulation of other parts of the body, or by erotic thoughts. It occurs very rapidly, within a few seconds of the stimulation, although it may take place more slowly as a result of a number of factors, including age, intake of alcohol, and fatigue.

Research in the last decade—stimulated, in part, by the search for Viagra—has given us much more detailed information about the physiological processes involved in erection (Adams, 1997; Heaton, 2000). Several arteries supply the corpora cavernosa and spongiosum. For an erection to occur, these arteries must dilate (vasodilation), allowing a strong flow of blood into the corpora. At the same time, the veins carrying blood away from the penis are compressed, restricting outgoing blood flow. The arteries dilate because the smooth muscle surrounding the arteries relaxes. Multiple

Vasocongestion (vay-so-con-JES-tyun): An accumulation of blood in the blood vessels of a region of the body, especially the genitals; a swelling or erection results.
Myotonia (my-oh-TONE-ee-ah): Muscle contraction.
Excitement: The first stage of sexual response, during which erection in the male and vaginal lubrication in the female occur.

*Eric Berne. (1970). *Sex in human loving.* New York: Simon & Schuster, p. 238.

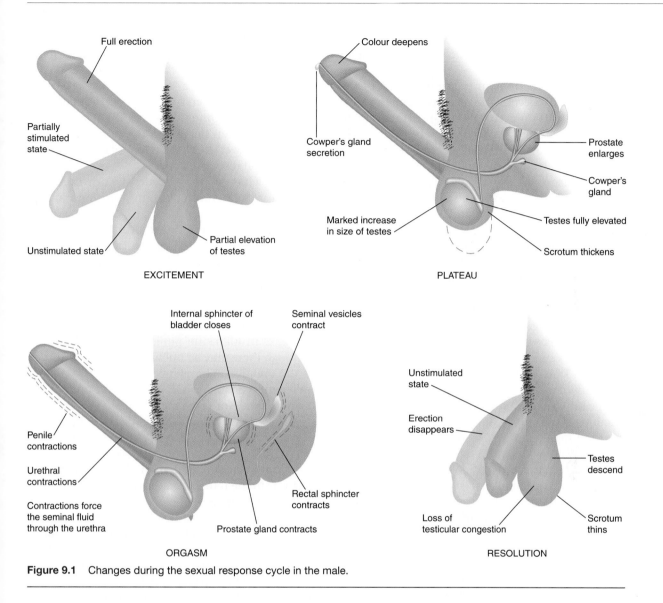

Figure 9.1   Changes during the sexual response cycle in the male.

neurotransmitters are involved in this process including, especially, nitric oxide (NO). Dopamine is involved as well. Viagra acts on the NO system.

Of course erections, nice though they are, would become a pain if they lasted forever, so there is a reverse process—vasoconstriction—that makes an erection go away (as, for example, following orgasm). The neurotransmitters epinephrine and norepinephrine are involved. These processes occur in the resolution phase, discussed below.

An important response of females in the excitement phase is lubrication of the vagina. Although this response might seem much different from the male's, actually they both result from the same physiological process: vasocongestion. Vaginal lubrication results when fluids seep through the semipermeable membranes of the vaginal walls, producing lubrication as a result of vasocongestion in the tissues surrounding the vagina. This response to arousal is also rapid, though not quite so fast as the male's; lubrication usually begins 10 to 30 seconds after the onset of arousing stimuli.[1]

[1]Before the Masters and Johnson research, it was thought that the lubrication was due to secretions of the Bartholin glands, but it is now known that these glands contribute little if anything. At this point, you might want to go back to the limerick about the Bartholin glands in Chapter 4 and see whether you can spot the error in it.

Like the male sexual response, female responding can be affected by factors such as age, intake of alcohol, and fatigue.

During the excitement phase the glans of the clitoris (the tip) swells. This results from engorgement of its corpora cavernosa and is similar to erection in the male. The clitoris can be felt as larger and harder than usual under excitement. The crura of the clitoris, lying deeper in the body (refer to Figure 4.3), also swell as a result of vasocongestion. The vestibular bulbs, which lie along the wall of the vagina, are also erectile and swell during the excitement phase.

Vasocongestion in females results from the same underlying physiological processes as in males. That is, relaxation of the smooth muscles surrounding the arteries supplying the glans and crura of the clitoris and the vestibular bulbs occurs, allowing a great deal of blood flow to the region (Berman et al., 2000). As in the male, nitric oxide is a key neurotransmitter involved in the process (Traish et al., 2002). Estrogen helps the vasodilation.

The nipples become erect; this results from contractions of the muscle fibres (myotonia) surrounding the nipple. The breasts themselves swell and enlarge somewhat in the late part of the excitement phase (a vasocongestion response). Thus the nipples may not actually look erect but may appear somewhat flatter against the breast because the breast has swollen. Many males also have nipple erection during the excitement phase.

In the unaroused state the inner lips are generally folded over, covering the entrance to the vagina, and the outer lips lie close to each other. During excitement the inner lips swell and open up (a vasocongestion response).

The vagina shows an important change during excitement. Think of the vagina as being divided into two parts, an upper (or inner) two-thirds and a lower (or outer) one-third. In the unaroused state the walls of the vagina lie against each other, much like the sides of an uninflated balloon. During the excitement phase, the upper two-thirds of the vagina expands dramatically in what is often called a "ballooning" response; that is, it becomes more like an inflated balloon (see Figure 9.2). This helps accommodate penetration. As part of the ballooning, the cervix and uterus pull up, creating a "tenting effect" in the vaginal walls (Figure 9.2) and making a larger opening in the cervix, which probably allows sperm to move into the uterus more easily.

During excitement a "sex flush" may appear on the skin of both men and women, though more commonly of women. The sex flush resembles blushing; it often begins on the upper abdomen and spreads over the chest. It may also appear later in the sexual response cycle.

Other changes that occur in both men and women include an increase in pulse rate and in blood pressure.

In men, the skin of the scrotum thickens. The scrotal sac tenses, and the scrotum is pulled up and closer to the body (Figure 9.1). The spermatic cords shorten, pulling the testes closer to the body.

Plateau

During the **plateau** phase, vasocongestion reaches its peak. In men, the penis is completely erect, although there may be fluctuations in the firmness of the erection. The glans swells. The testes are pulled up even higher and closer to the body. A few drops of fluid (for some men, quite a few), secreted by the Cowper's gland, appear at the tip of the penis. Although they are not the ejaculate, they may contain active sperm.

In both women and men there is a further increase in the rate of breathing, in pulse rate, and in blood pressure.

In females, the most notable change during the plateau phase is formation of the **orgasmic platform.** This is a tightening of the outer third of the vagina (Figure 9.2). Thus the size of the vaginal entrance actually becomes smaller, and there may be a noticeable increase in gripping during penetration.

Another change is the elevation of the clitoris. The clitoris essentially retracts or draws up into the body.

In short, the processes of the plateau phase are a continuation of the basic processes—vasocongestion and myotonia—of the excitement phase. Both processes continue to build until there is sufficient tension for orgasm.

Plateau: The second stage of sexual response, just before orgasm.
Orgasmic platform: A tightening of the entrance to the vagina caused by contractions of the bulbospongiosus muscle (which covers the vestibular bulbs) that occur during the plateau stage of sexual response.

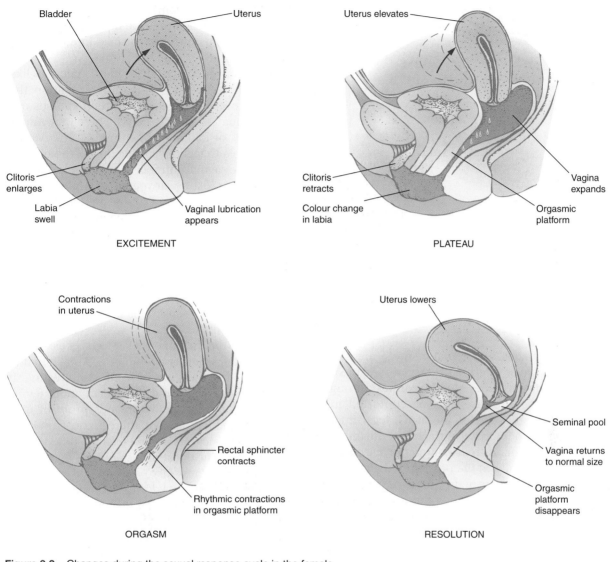

Figure 9.2   Changes during the sexual response cycle in the female.

Orgasm

In the male, **orgasm** consists of a series of rhythmic contractions of the pelvic organs at 0.8-second intervals. Actually, male orgasm occurs in two stages. In the preliminary stage, the vas, seminal vesicles, and prostate contract, forcing the ejaculate into a bulb at the base of the urethra (Figure 9.1).

> **Orgasm:** The third stage of sexual response; an intense sensation that occurs at the peak of sexual arousal and is followed by release of sexual tensions.

Masters and Johnson call the sensation in this stage one of "ejaculatory inevitability" ("cumming"); that is, there is a sensation that ejaculation is just about to happen and cannot be stopped. And, indeed, it cannot be, once the man has reached this point. In the second stage the urethral bulb, muscles at the base of the penis, and the urethra contract rhythmically, forcing the semen through the urethra and out the opening at the tip of the penis. There may also be a difference between ejaculation and the sensation of orgasm (Mah & Binik, 2001).

"Did you comm?"

Figure 9.3   Tom Cheney/Reprinted Courtesy of *Penthouse Magazine.*

In both males and females, there are sharp increases in pulse rate, blood pressure, and breathing rate during orgasm.[2] Muscles contract throughout the body. The face may be contorted in a grimace; the muscles of the arms, legs, thighs, back, and buttocks may contract; and the muscles of the feet and hands may contract in "carpopedal spasms." Generally, in the passion of the moment, one is not really aware of these occurrences, but an aching back or buttocks may serve as a reminder the next day.

The process of orgasm in females is basically similar to that in males. It is a series of rhythmic muscular contractions of the orgasmic platform. The contractions generally occur at about 0.8-second intervals; there may be three or four in a mild orgasm or as many as a dozen in a very intense, prolonged orgasm. The uterus also contracts rhythmically. Other muscles, such as those around the anus, may also contract.

Female orgasm typically leaves no tangible evidence (except for those women who experience ejaculation) and women often do not reach orgasm as quickly as men do. As a result, some women,

particularly young women, may think they are having an orgasm when they are not; they have never had an orgasm, and they mistake intense arousal for orgasm.

Just what does orgasm in the female feel like? The main feeling is a spreading sensation that begins around the clitoris and then spreads outward through the whole pelvis. There may also be sensations of falling or opening up. The woman may be able to feel the contraction of the muscles around the vaginal entrance. The sensation is more intense than just a warm glow or a pleasant tingling. In one study, university men and women gave written descriptions of what an orgasm felt like to them (Vance & Wagner, 1976). Interestingly, a panel of experts (medical students, obstetrician-gynecologists, and clinical psychologists) could not reliably figure out which of the descriptions were written by women and which by men. This suggests that the sensations are quite similar for males and females.

Some of the men in our classes have asked how they can tell whether a woman has really had an orgasm. Their question in itself is interesting. In part it reflects a cultural skepticism about female orgasm. There is usually obvious proof of male orgasm: ejaculation. But there is no consistent proof of female orgasm except that some women do ejaculate. The question also reflects the fact that women sometimes "fake" orgasm. Faking orgasm is a complex issue. Basically, it probably is not a very good idea, because it is dishonest. It also leads the woman's partner to think that his or her technique of stimulation is more effective than it is. On the other hand, one needs to understand the variety of reasons women feel that this is necessary. It is often challenging for women to orgasm, and our culture currently places a lot of emphasis on everyone's having orgasms. The woman may feel that she is expected to have an orgasm, and realizing that it is unlikely to happen this time, she "fakes" it in order to meet expectations. She may also do it to please her partner.[3] But back to the question: How

[2]With all the current attention to aerobics and exercising the heart, we have yet to hear anyone suggest orgasm aerobics. It seems to us that it should work. Kickboxing, watch out. Here comes sexercise!

[3]Indeed, many of the old sex manuals, as well as physicians' textbooks, counselled women to fake orgasm. For example: "It is good advice to recommend to the women the advantage of innocent simulation of sex responsiveness, and as a matter of fact many women in their desire to please their husbands learned the advantage of such innocent deception" (Novak & Novak, 1952, p. 572).

can one tell? There really is not any very good way. From a scientific point of view, a good method would be to have the woman hooked up to an instrument that registers pulse rate; there is a sudden sharp increase in the pulse rate at orgasm, and that would be a good indicator. We doubt, though, that most people have such equipment available, and we are even more doubtful about whether most women would agree to be so wired up. Probably rather than trying to check up on each other, it would be better for partners to establish good, honest communication and avoid setting up performance goals in sex, points that will be discussed further in later chapters.

Resolution

Following orgasm is the **resolution** phase, during which the body returns physiologically to the unaroused state. Orgasm triggers a massive release of muscular tension and of blood from the engorged blood vessels. Resolution, then, represents a reversal of the processes that build up during the excitement and plateau stages.

The first change in women is a reduction in the swelling of the breasts. In the 5 to 10 seconds after the end of the orgasm, the clitoris returns to its normal position, although it takes longer for it to shrink to its normal size. The orgasmic platform relaxes and begins to shrink. The ballooning of the vagina diminishes, and the uterus shrinks.

The resolution phase generally takes 15 to 30 minutes, but it may take much longer—as much as an hour—in women who have not had an orgasm. This latter fact helps to account for the chronic pelvic congestion that Masters and Johnson observed in prostitutes (see Chapter 3). The prostitutes frequently experienced arousal without having orgasms. Thus there were repeated buildups of vasocongestion without the discharge of it brought about by orgasm. The result was a chronic vasocongestion in the pelvis. The mild version of this that occurs in some women who engage in sex but do not have orgasms can be uncomfortable.

In both males and females, resolution brings a gradual return of pulse rate, blood pressure, and breathing rate to the unaroused levels.

Resolution: The fourth stage of sexual response, in which the body returns to the unaroused state.

In men, the most obvious occurrence in the resolution phase is *detumescence*, the loss of erection in the penis. This happens in two stages, the first occurring rapidly but leaving the penis still enlarged (this first loss of erection results from an emptying of the corpora cavernosa) and the second occurring more slowly, as a result of the slower emptying of the corpus spongiosum and the glans.

During the resolution phase, men enter a **refractory period,** during which they are refractory to further arousal; that is, they are incapable of being aroused again, having an erection, or having an orgasm. The length of this refractory period varies considerably from one man to the next; in some it may last only a few minutes, and in others it may go on for 24 hours. The refractory period tends to become longer as men grow older.

Women usually do not enter into a refractory period, making possible the phenomenon of multiple orgasm in women, to be discussed in the next section.

Oxytocin is secreted during sexual arousal, and a surge of prolactin occurs at orgasm in both women and men (Exton et al., 1999; Levin, 2003; Krüger et al., 2002). Some think that prolactin is the off-switch to sexual arousal and that it creates the refractory period in males, although that does not explain why females do not have a refractory period.

Other Findings of the Masters and Johnson Research

A number of other important findings on the nature of sexual response emerged from the Masters and Johnson research, two of which will be discussed here.

Clitoral Orgasm versus Vaginal Orgasm

Some people believe that women can have two kinds of orgasm: **clitoral orgasm** and **vaginal orgasm.** The words "clitoral" and "vaginal" are not

---

Refractory (ree-FRAK-toh-ree) period: The period following orgasm during which the male cannot be sexually aroused.
Clitoral orgasm: Freud's term for orgasm in the female resulting from stimulation of the clitoris.
Vaginal orgasm: Freud's term for orgasm in the female resulting from stimulation of the vagina in heterosexual intercourse; Freud considered vaginal orgasm to be more mature than clitoral orgasm.

meant to imply that the clitoris has an orgasm or that the vagina has an orgasm. Rather, they refer to the locus of stimulation: an orgasm resulting from clitoral stimulation versus an orgasm resulting from vaginal stimulation. The distinction was originated by Sigmund Freud. Freud believed that in childhood little girls masturbate and thus have orgasms by means of clitoral stimulation, or clitoral orgasms. He thought that as women grow older and mature, that is, after the Oedipal stage, they shift their erogenous zone from their clitoris to their vagina. Consequently they shift from having orgasms as a result of clitoral stimulation to having them as a result of heterosexual intercourse; that is, by means of vaginal stimulation. (Perhaps the fact that he was a man influenced him to develop this theory!) Thus he considered vaginal orgasms "mature" and clitoral orgasms "immature" in a developmental sense. Not only did there come to be two types of orgasms, but "mature" has been taken to mean "better," such that many people view one kind of orgasm (orgasms through intercourse alone) as better than the other.

Freud's formulation is of more than theoretical interest. The interpretation of vaginal orgasms as more mature has had an impact on the lives of many women over several decades. Many undertook psychoanalysis and spent countless hours agonizing over why they were not able to achieve the elusive vaginal orgasm and why they enjoyed the "immature" clitoral one so much. Women who could have orgasms only through clitoral stimulation were called "vaginally frigid" or "fixated" at an infantile stage.

According to the results of Masters and Johnson's research, though, the distinction between clitoral and vaginal orgasms does not make sense. This conclusion is based on two findings. First, their results indicate that all female orgasms are physiologically the same, regardless of the site of stimulation. That is, an orgasm always consists of contractions of the orgasmic platform whether the stimulation is clitoral or vaginal. Indeed, they found a few women who could orgasm purely through breast stimulation, and that orgasm was the same as the other two, consisting of contractions of the orgasmic platform and the muscles around the vagina. Thus physiologically there is only one kind of orgasm. (Of course, this does not

mean that psychologically there are not different kinds; the experience of orgasm during intercourse may be quite different from the experience of orgasm during masturbation.) Second, clitoral stimulation is almost always involved in producing orgasm, even during vaginal intercourse. The deep structure of the clitoris (refer to Figure 4.3) ensures that the crura of the clitoris are stimulated as the penis moves through the vaginal entrance. Thus even the purely "vaginal" orgasm results from quite a bit of clitoral stimulation. Clitoral stimulation is usually the trigger to orgasm; the orgasm itself occurs in the vagina and surrounding tissues.

Multiple Orgasm

Traditionally it was believed that orgasmically, women and men can have one orgasm and then enter a refractory period before they can have another. Masters and Johnson, however, discovered that women do not enter into a refractory period, and with continued stimulation they can have **multiple orgasms** within a short period of time. Actually, women's capacity for multiple orgasms was originally discovered by Kinsey in his interviews with women (Kinsey et al., 1953; see also Terman et al., 1938). The scientific establishment, however, dismissed these reports as another instance of Kinsey's supposed unreliability.

The term "multiple orgasm," then, refers to a series of orgasms occurring within a short period of time. They do not differ physiologically from single orgasms. Each is a "real" orgasm, and they are not minor experiences. One nice thing, though, is that the later ones generally require much less stimulation than the first one.

How does multiple orgasm work physiologically? Immediately following an orgasm, both males and females move into the resolution phase. In this phase, males typically enter into a refractory period, during which they cannot be aroused again. But the female usually does not enter a refractory period, perhaps because after orgasm it takes longer for vasocongestion to return to baseline in women than in men (Mah & Binik, 2001). That is, if stimulation continues she can have another orgasm if she chooses to.

Multiple orgasm: A series of orgasms occurring within a short period of time.

Multiple orgasm with a partner is more likely to result from hand–genital or mouth–genital stimulation than from intercourse. Regarding capacity, Masters and Johnson found that women in masturbation might have 5 to 20 orgasms. In some cases, they quit only when physically exhausted. When a vibrator is used, less effort is required, and some women were capable of having 50 orgasms in a row.

It should be noted that some women who are capable of multiple orgasms are satisfied with one, particularly in intercourse, and do not wish to continue. We should be careful not to set multiple orgasm as another of the many goals in sexual performance.

In one sample of adult women, all of whom were nurses (and therefore presumably had a good understanding of the anatomy and physiology involved), 43 percent reported that they usually experienced multiple orgasms (Darling et al., 1991). Among these women, 40 percent reported that each successive orgasm was stronger than the previous one, 16 percent said that each successive one was weaker than the one before, and the remainder said that the orgasms varied or there were no differences in intensity among them. Women who had multiple orgasms were more likely, compared with women who had single orgasms, to have their orgasm before their partner did.

Some men are capable of having multiple orgasms (e.g., Hartman & Fithian, 1984; Zilbergeld, 1992). In one study, 21 men were interviewed, all of whom had volunteered for research on multiply orgasmic men (Dunn & Trost, 1989). Some of the men reported having been multiply orgasmic since they began having sex, whereas others had developed the pattern later in life, and still others had worked actively to develop the capacity after reading about the possibility. The respondents reported that multiple orgasm did not occur every time they engaged in sexual activity. For these men, detumescence did not always follow an orgasm, allowing for continued stimulation and an additional orgasm. Some reported that some of the orgasms included ejaculation and others in the sequence did not. This study cannot tell us the incidence of multiply orgasmic men in the general population, but it does provide evidence that multiply orgasmic men exist.

◼ Cognitive-Physiological Models

Some experts on human sexuality are critical of Masters and Johnson's four-stage model. One important criticism is that the Masters and Johnson model ignores the cognitive and subjective aspects of sexual response (Zilbergeld & Ellison, 1980). That is, Masters and Johnson focused almost entirely on the physiological aspects of the response, ignoring what the person is thinking and feeling emotionally. Desire and passion are not part of the model. This omission would not be a problem except that there can be major discrepancies between physiological response and subjective feelings. People, for example, can feel a high level of sexual desire, yet have no erection or vaginal lubrication.

A second important criticism concerns how research participants were selected and how this process may have created a self-fulfilling prophecy for the outcome (Tiefer, 1991a). To participate in the research, participants were required to have a history of orgasm both through masturbation and through coitus. Essentially, anyone whose pattern of sexual response did not include orgasm—and therefore did not fit Masters and Johnson's model—was excluded from the research. As such, the model cannot be generalized to the entire population. Masters and Johnson themselves commented that every one of their participants was characterized by high and consistent levels of sexual desire. Yet sexual desire is certainly missing among some members of the general population, or it is present sometimes and absent at others. It is not surprising that sexual desire was omitted from Masters and Johnson's model when the participants were preselected to be uniform in their high levels of desire. The research, in short, claims to be objective and universal when it is neither (Tiefer, 1991a).

Another problem with the model is that it omits the subjective qualities of arousal and orgasm. These may be influenced by the context and the quality of the relationship in which sexual activity occurs as well as by a variety of psychological factors (Mah & Binik, 2001). This omission may be particularly problematic in understanding women's sexual response because women tend to emphasize subjective arousal rather than physical arousal (Working Group for a New View of Women's Sexual

Problems, 2001). Women's sense of being aroused is often unrelated to awareness of genital changes (Basson, 2000). Research in Quebec has shown that there are two components to orgasm for both men and women: a sensory dimension, made up of the physical sensations, and a cognitive-affective dimension, consisting of pleasure, satisfaction, emotional intimacy, and feelings of ecstasy (Mah & Binik, 2002).

Once these difficulties with the Masters and Johnson research and model of sexual response were recognized, several alternative models were proposed. We will examine two of them in the following sections. Both of them add a cognitive component to Masters and Johnson's physiological model.

Kaplan's Triphasic Model

On the basis of her work on sex therapy (discussed in Chapter 19), Helen Singer Kaplan (1974, 1979) proposed a **triphasic model** of sexual response. Rather than thinking of the sexual response as having successive stages, she conceptualized it as having three relatively independent phases, or components: *sexual desire*, *vasocongestion* of the genitals, and the reflex *muscular contractions* of the orgasm phase. Notice that two of the components (vasocongestion and muscular contractions) are physiological, whereas the other (sexual desire) is psychological.

There are a number of justifications for Kaplan's approach. First, the two physiological components are controlled by different parts of the nervous system. Vasocongestion—producing erection in the male and lubrication in the female—is controlled by the parasympathetic division of the autonomic nervous system. In contrast, ejaculation and orgasm are controlled by the sympathetic division.

Second, the two components involve different anatomical structures: blood vessels for vasocongestion and muscles for the contractions of orgasm.

Third, vasocongestion and orgasm differ in their susceptibility to being disturbed by injury, drugs, or age. For example, the refractory period following orgasm in the male lengthens with age. Accordingly, there is a decrease in the frequency of orgasm with age. In contrast, for many men the capacity for

Triphasic model: Kaplan's model of sexual response, in which there are three phases: sexual desire, vasocongestion, and muscular contractions.

erection is relatively unimpaired with age, although the erection may be slower to make its appearance. An elderly man may have non-orgasmic sex several times a week, with a firm erection, although he may have an orgasm only once a week.

Fourth, the reflex of ejaculation in the male can be brought under voluntary control by most men, but the erection reflex generally cannot.

Finally, the impairment of the vasocongestion response or the orgasm response produce different disturbances (sexual disorders). Erection problems in the male are caused by an impairment of the vasocongestion response, whereas rapid ejaculation and delayed ejaculation are disturbances of the orgasm response. Similarly, many women show a strong arousal and vasocongestion response, yet have trouble with the orgasm component of their sexual response.

Kaplan's triphasic model is useful both for understanding the nature of sexual response and for understanding and treating disturbances in it. Her writing on the desire phase is particularly useful in understanding problems of low sexual desire, to be discussed in Chapter 19.

Kaplan's model assumes that desire comes before arousal. Vancouver therapist Rosemary Basson (2001) has developed an intimacy-based model of sexual response that does not make this assumption (see Figure 9.4). She argues that people in long-term relationships, particularly women, may not be motivated to engage in sexual activity by their experience of spontaneous sexual desire. Rather they are motivated to engage in sexual activity in order to enhance intimacy, closeness, and commitment with their partner, to enhance their sense of attractiveness, or to share physical sexual pleasure. That is, they begin sexual activity in a sexually neutral state, but are receptive to sexual stimuli that will arouse them. Once sexual activity has begun, the person becomes aroused. This leads them to experience sexual desire and enhanced sexual arousal. Thus, according to Basson, people may begin sexual activity for intimacy reasons, but then continue for sexual as well as intimacy reasons. Basson also acknowledges that, even in long-term relationships, both men and women can and do experience spontaneous sexual desire outside of this intimacy model that may lead to sexual activity with their partner, casual sex, or self-stimulation.

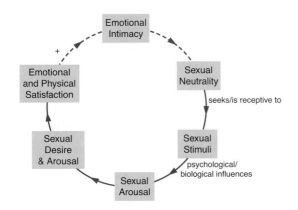

Figure 9.4   Basson's Intimacy model of sexual response.

Walen and Roth: A Cognitive Model

As noted earlier, an important criticism of the Masters and Johnson model is that it ignores the cognitive and subjective aspects of sexual response. In Chapter 2 we discussed the importance of cognitive approaches in understanding the psychology of human sexuality. Susan R. Walen and David Roth (1987) have applied this approach to understanding the sexual response. Their model is shown in Figure 9.5.

Recall from Chapter 2 that according to the cognitive approach, how we feel depends tremendously on what we are thinking: how we perceive what is occurring and how we evaluate it. Thus the first step in the cognitive model is *perception:* the perception of a stimulus as sexual. What we perceive to be sexy stimuli (whether they are visual stimuli, touch stimuli, or odours) depends a great deal on the culture in which we've grown up and on our prior learning. If you've just begun a sexual relationship with someone, the very sight of that person may make you feel turned on, whereas looking at 10 other people in the same room produces no turn-on. To some people, the sight of black leather, high-heeled women's boots may produce instant arousal. According to the model, perception is the first step.

The second step in the cognitive model is *evaluation.* If we feel positive about the sexual stimulus, that will lead to the next step, arousal, but if our evaluation of the stimulus is negative, the arousal cycle stops. For example, if you are a married woman and your husband, with whom you normally have a great sex life, begins to kiss you when his breath smells of a cigarette he has just smoked, your evaluation of the sexual stimulus is likely to be negative and you will not feel aroused.

Let's suppose, though, that the evaluation of the sexual stimulus is positive. Physiological *arousal*— as described in the Masters and Johnson model discussed earlier in this chapter—is the next step. But again, the cognitive approach says that it is not so much what happens physically, but how we perceive it, that counts. So the *perception of arousal,* step 4, is critical. For example, some research shows that women, probably because vaginal lubrication can be a rather subtle response, are sometimes not aware of their own physical arousal (Heiman, 1975, discussed in Chapter 14). Or a man might pay so much attention to whether his technique is pleasing his partner that he fails to perceive his own arousal and thus does not experience as much sexual pleasure as he might. People can create sexual problems for themselves if they set too high criteria for deciding that they are aroused. How much lubrication, or how firm an erection, is "enough"? You can augment your sexual response by perceiving even a little bit of lubrication, or the first stirrings of an erection, or some other sign (such as increased heart rate) as an indication of arousal.

Again, the cognitive approach argues that it is not only the perception of arousal but also a positive evaluation of the arousal that is important if

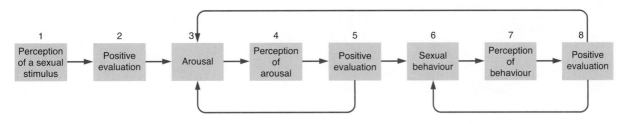

Figure 9.5   Walen and Roth's cognitive model showing the feedback loop that produces a positive sexual experience.

http://www.mcgrawhill.ca/college/hyde

the sexual response cycle is to continue; thus *evaluation* is the next step. As before, if the evaluation is negative, the response cycle stops. An example would be an adult male who feels himself becoming aroused when looking at a child. He realizes that acting on this response is totally inappropriate, evaluates the arousal negatively, and feels anxiety rather than arousal. If the evaluation of the arousal is positive, though—you like the feeling of being turned on in this situation—there is feedback to step 3, so that physical arousal increases further. Essentially, feeling good about being turned on makes you feel even more turned on.

All this propels you to the next step, *sexual behaviour*. Again, cognitive psychologists believe that two further steps—*perception of the behaviour* and a *positive evaluation* of it—are critical for the arousal cycle to continue. If the evaluation is positive, two kinds of feedback occur: the sexual behaviour is likely to continue, and arousal increases.

In sum, the cognitive model of the sexual response cycle stresses the importance of our perception and evaluation of sexual events. It's a testimony to the power of positive thinking, although in a context that Norman Vincent Peale probably didn't intend. As another saying has it, the greatest erogenous zone is the brain.

■ Hormonal and Neural Bases of Sexual Behaviour

Up to this point we have focused on the cognitive and genital responses that occur during sexual activity. We have not yet considered the underlying neural and hormonal mechanisms that make this possible; they are the topic of this section.

The Brain, the Spinal Cord, and Sex

The brain and the spinal cord both have important interacting functions in sexual response. First the relatively simple spinal reflexes involved in sexual response will be discussed; then the more complex brain mechanisms will be considered.

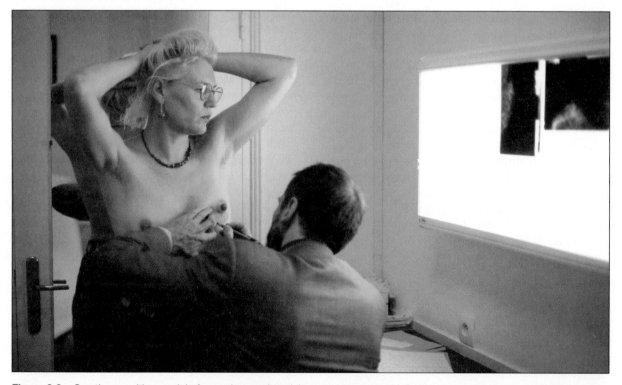

Figure 9.6   Can the cognitive model of sexual arousal explain our response to this? Here a man touches a woman's breast, but it is not sexual. Why not? The context, a medical office, leads us not to perceive the woman's breast as a sexual stimulus, nor the man's touch as sexual.

Spinal Reflexes

Several important components of sexual behaviour, including erection and ejaculation, are controlled by fairly simple spinal cord reflexes (see the lower part of Figure 9.7). A reflex has three basic components: the *receptors,* which are sense organs that detect stimuli and transmit the message to the spinal cord (or brain); the *transmitters,* which are centres in the spinal cord (or brain) that receive the message, interpret it, and send out a message to produce the appropriate response; and the *effectors,* organs that respond to the stimulation. The jerking away of the hand when it touches a hot object is a good example of a spinal reflex.

Mechanism of Erection

Erection is produced by a spinal reflex with a similar mechanism (McKenna, 2000). Tactile stimulation (stroking or rubbing) of the penis (the receptor) or nearby regions such as the scrotum or thighs produces a neural signal that is transmitted to an "erection centre" in the sacral, or lowest, part of the spinal cord (there may also be another erection centre higher in the cord). This centre then sends out a message via the parasympathetic division of the autonomic nervous system to the muscles (the effectors) around the walls of the arteries in the penis. In response to the message, the muscles relax; the arteries then expand, permitting a large volume of blood to flow into them, and erection results. Furthermore, the valves in the veins and the compression of the veins caused by the swelling in the tissue around them reduce the blood flow out of the penis (Adams et al., 1997).

The existence of this reflex is confirmed by the responses of men who have had their spinal cords completely severed, as a result of accidents, at a level above that of the reflex centre (see In Focus 9.1). They are capable of having erections and ejaculations produced by rubbing their genitals, although it is clear that no brain effects can be operating, since signals from the brain cannot move past the point at which the spinal cord was severed. (In fact, these men cannot "feel" anything because neural signals cannot be transmitted up the spinal cord either.) Thus erection can be produced simply by tactile stimulation of the genitals, which triggers the spinal reflex.

Erection may also be produced by conditions other than tactile stimulation of the genitals; for

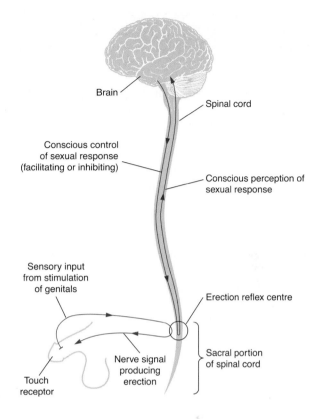

Figure 9.7 Nervous system control of erection. Note both the reflex centre in the spinal cord and brain control.

example, fantasy or other purely psychological factors may produce erection. This points to the importance of the brain in producing erection, a topic that will be discussed in more detail below.

Mechanism of Ejaculation

The ejaculation reflex is much like the erection reflex, except that the ejaculation centre is located higher in the spinal cord, the sympathetic division of the nervous system is involved (as opposed to the parasympathetic division in the erection reflex), and the response is muscular, with no involvement of the blood vessels (Rowland & Slob, 1997). In the ejaculation reflex, the penis responds to stimulation by sending a message to the "ejaculation centre," which is located in the lumbar portion of the spinal cord. A message is then sent out via the nerves in the sympathetic nervous system, and this message triggers muscle contractions in the internal organs that are involved in ejaculation.

In Focus 9.1

How Does Spinal-Cord Injury Affect Sexual Functioning?

It is commonly believed that a person in a wheelchair is sexless. People with physical disabilities are thought not to be interested in sex, much less to be capable of engaging in sexual activity. Contrast those stereotypes with the following ideas:

A stiff penis does not make a solid relationship, nor does a wet vagina. . . .

Absence of sensation does not mean absence of feelings. . . .

Inability to move does not mean inability to please.

(Cole & Cole, 1978, p. 118)

About 10 percent of adults in North America have a physical disability that imposes a substantial limitation on their activities. Given a chance to express themselves, these people emphasize the importance to them of their sexuality and sex drive, which are not necessarily altered by their disability.

Space does not permit a complete discussion of all types of disabilities and their consequences for sexuality. We discuss spinal-cord injury to men and women below.

Paraplegia (paralysis of the lower half of the body on both sides) and quadriplegia (paralysis of the body from the neck down) are both caused by injuries to the spinal cord. Many able-bodied people find it difficult to understand what it feels like to be paralyzed. Imagine that your genitals and the region around them have lost all sensation. You would not know they were being touched unless you saw it happen. Further, there is loss of bladder and bowel control, which may produce embarrassing problems if sexual activity is attempted.

The capacity of a man with a spinal-cord injury to have erections depends on the level of the spinal cord at which the injury (lesion) occurred, and whether the spinal cord was completely or only partially severed. Most men with spinal-cord injuries have normal sexual responses, including erection, elevation of the testes, and increases in heart rate. In most cases, only reflex erections (and not psychogenic erections) are possible; that is, erections produced by direct stimulation of the genitals, even though the man may not be able to feel the sensation. Men with spinal-cord injuries typically are not able to get an erection by erotic thoughts or to ejaculate, although ejaculation may be possible if the cord was only partially severed. Fertility is impaired for almost all men with spinal-cord injury. However, clinicians in Vancouver and elsewhere use special techniques to retrieve sperm from men with spinal-cord injuries and help couples conceive through assisted insemination. In sum, many men with spinal-cord injuries experience the same sexual responses as able-bodied men except that they generally cannot ejaculate, nor can they feel physical stimulation.

Women with spinal-cord injuries experience many of the same sexual responses as able-bodied women, including engorgement of the clitoris and labia, erection of the nipples, and increases in heart rate. Approximately 50 percent of women

Ejaculation can often be controlled voluntarily. This fact highlights the importance of brain influences on the ejaculation reflex (Truitt & Coolen, 2002).

The three main problems of ejaculation are rapid ejaculation, male orgasmic disorder (delayed ejaculation), and retrograde ejaculation. Rapid ejaculation, which is by far the most common problem, and male orgasmic disorder will be discussed in Chapter 19. **Retrograde ejaculation** occurs when the ejaculate, rather than going out through the tip of the penis, empties into the bladder (Kothari, 1984). A "dry orgasm" results, since no ejaculate is emitted. This problem can be caused

Retrograde ejaculation: A condition in which orgasm in the male is not accompanied by an external ejaculation; instead, the ejaculate goes into the urinary bladder.

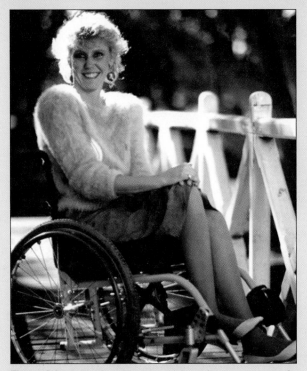

Figure 9.8 In the last 20 years we have become aware of the capacity of people with disabilities for sexual expression. Ellen Stohl, the first woman with a disability to appear in *Playboy* (October 1987), is a quadriplegic, having suffered several broken bones in her neck in an automobile accident. She was completely paralyzed initially, but gradually recovered some use of her arms. She has some sensitivity in her legs and is hypersensitive in the genitals. She enjoys sex very much and is orgasmic.

Because sexuality in our culture is so orgasm-oriented, orgasm problems among people with spinal-cord injuries may appear to be devastating. But many of them report that they have been able to cultivate a kind of "psychological orgasm" that is as satisfying as the physical one. Fantasy is a perfectly legitimate form of sexual expression that has not been ruled out by their injury.

Women with spinal-cord injuries typically have amenorrhea (absence of menstruation) immediately following a spinal-cord injury, although normal menstrual cycling usually returns within six months. After that time, their ability to conceive a baby is normal. Most pregnancies proceed normally, although there is a higher risk of some complications. Vaginal deliveries are usually possible and can be done without anaesthetic because the woman feels no sensation in the pelvic region. The fertility of women with spinal-cord injuries means that contraception is an important consideration for them.

In summary, there are three general points to be made about sexuality and persons with disabilities: (1) They generally do have sexual needs and desires; (2) they are often capable of sexual response quite similar to that of able-bodied people; and, (3) there is a real need for more information—and communication—about what people with various disabilities can and cannot do sexually, as well as how to adapt their sexual script to take their disability into account.

Sources: Bérard, 1989; Beretta, Chelo, & Zanollo, 1989; Komisaruket et al., 1997; McCabe, 2002; McCabe et al., 2003; Rawicki & Itill, 1991; Siosteen et al., 1990; Sipski & Alexander, 1995; Sipski et al., 2001.

with spinal-cord injuries are able to have orgasms from stimulation of the genitals. Some women with spinal-cord injuries develop a capacity for orgasm from stimulation of the breasts or lips.

by some illnesses, by tranquillizers and drugs used in the treatment of psychoses, and by prostate surgery. The mechanism that causes it is fairly simple (see Figure 9.9). Two sphincters are involved in ejaculation: an internal one, which closes off the entrance to the bladder during a normal ejaculation, and an external one, which opens during a normal ejaculation, allowing the semen to flow out through the penis. In retrograde ejaculation, the action of these two sphincters is reversed; the external one closes, and thus the ejaculate cannot flow out through the penis, and the internal one opens, permitting the ejaculate to go into the bladder. The condition itself is quite harmless, although some men are disturbed by the lack of sensation of emitting semen.

Mechanisms in Women

Unfortunately, there is far less research on similar reflex mechanisms in women. We know that sen-

Figure 9.9 How a retrograde ejaculation occurs.

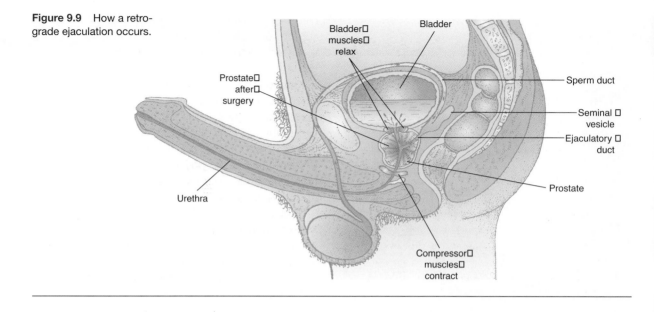

sory input—such as touch—travels along the dorsal nerve of the clitoris and continues within the pudendal nerve to a reflex centre in the sacral portion of the spinal cord (Berman et al., 2000). The clitoris receives both sympathetic and parasympathetic nerve fibres. The vagina, too, is supplied by both sympathetic and parasympathetic nerves. The limbic system of the brain is crucial to both female and male sexual arousal.

Research indicates that *female ejaculation* occurs in some women (Addiego et al., 1981; Belzer, 1981; Perry & Whipple, 1981). The region responsible is the **Gräfenberg spot** (or **G-spot**), also called the *female prostate* or the *Skene's glands* (Schubach, 2002). It is located on the top side of the vagina (with the woman lying on her back, which is the best position for finding it), about halfway between the pubic bone and the cervix (see Figure 9.10). Its ducts open into the urethra. Stroking it produces an urge to urinate, but if the stroking continues for a few seconds more, it begins to produce sexual pleasure. The original researchers, Perry and Whipple, argued that continued stimulation of it produces a *uterine orgasm*, characterized by deeper sensations of uterine contractions than the clitorally induced

vulvar orgasm investigated in the Masters and Johnson research.

In one survey of 1,289 adult women, 40 percent reported having experienced ejaculation at the time of orgasm at least once, and 66 percent reported having an especially sensitive area on the front wall of the vagina (Darling et al., 1990). The most recent biochemical analyses indicate that the female prostate produces *prostate-specific antigen* (PSA) just as the male prostate does (Zaviačič et al., 2000).

Gräfenberg spot (GRAY-fen-berg) or G-spot: A small region on the front wall of the vagina, emptying into the urethra, and responsible for female ejaculation. Also called the *female prostate* or the *Skene's glands*.

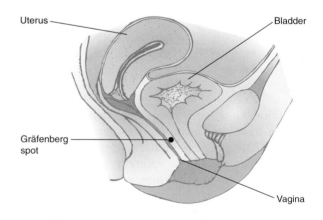

Figure 9.10 The Gräfenberg spot, or G-spot: Hypothesized to produce ejaculation in some women.

Brain Control of Sexual Response

Sexual responses are controlled by more than simple spinal reflexes. Sexual responses may be brought under voluntary control, and they may be initiated by purely psychological forces, such as fantasy. Environmental factors, such as having been taught as a child that sex is dirty and sinful, may also affect one's sexual response. All these phenomena point to the critical influence of the brain and its interaction with the spinal reflexes in producing sexual response (refer to Figure 9.7).

Brain control of sexual response is complex and only partly understood at the present time. It appears that the most important influences come from a set of structures called the **limbic system** (see Figure 9.11). The limbic system forms a border between the central part of the brain and the outer part (the cerebral cortex); it includes the amygdala, the hippocampus, the cingulate gyrus, and the septum. The thalamus, the hypothalamus, the pituitary, and the reticular formation are not properly part of the limbic system, but they are closely connected to it.

Several lines of evidence point to the importance of the limbic system in sexual behaviour. In classic experiments with male monkeys, an electrode was inserted into the brain to deliver electrical stimulation. Stimulation of some areas of the brain produced an erection (MacLean, 1962; Van Dis & Larsson, 1971). In particular, three "erection centres" were found in the limbic system, including one in the septal region. For obvious reasons, little of this research has been done with humans. But in one study, stimulation of the septal region produced orgasm in two humans (Heath, 1972).

A particular region of the anterior portion of the hypothalamus (the medical preoptic area, or MPOA/AH) has been implicated in male sexual behaviour (Paredes & Baum, 1997). If this area of the hypothalamus is given electrical stimulation, male rats increase their sexual behaviour; if this region is lesioned (destroyed), they no longer engage in copulation with females (Paredes & Baum, 1997).

Exciting new research using the brain scanning technique functional MRI confirms the importance of the limbic system in sexual responding. Healthy men were shown erotic or non-erotic films while in the MRI (Park et al., 2001). Several structures in the limbic system—including the cingulate gyrus and thalamus—were activated by the erotic films (see In Focus 9.2).

The brain centres for sex are also close to the olfactory centres. This brings us to the topic of pheromones and their role in sexual behaviour, which will be discussed later in the chapter.

> **Limbic system:** A set of structures in the interior of the brain, including the amygdala, hippocampus, and fornix; believed to be important for sexual behaviour in both animals and humans.

Figure 9.11   The limbic system of the brain, which is important in sexuality.

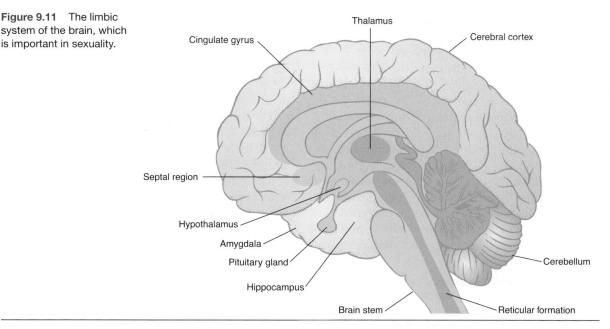

In Focus 9.2

What Happens in the Brain during Sex?

Exciting advances in the technology of neuroimaging are giving us inside views of the human brain during various activities. Methods such as PET (positron emission tomography) and fMRI (functional magnetic resonance imaging) show which regions of the brain "light up" (have neurons most actively firing) while the individual is solving a math problem or thinking about something sad.

Sex researchers have quickly adopted these techniques, with the goal of learning which regions of the brain are most involved in various aspects of sexuality. One of the challenges they have faced is that the subject cannot move while in an MRI scanner, making it difficult to achieve sexual arousal using most of the normal methods. Researchers have solved the problem by showing erotic videos to the person inside the scanner.

In one experiment, heterosexual men viewed erotic video clips, relaxing clips, and sports clips, in random order (Arnow et al., 2002). Meanwhile, their brains were being scanned in an MRI machine and the erection of the penis was measured. One has to admire these men for being able to become aroused while in an MRI scanner! Pictures from the brain scans are shown in Figure 9.12. When the men were exposed to erotic clips and were sexually aroused, as indicated by erection, intense brain activity was found in the right insula and claustrum, striatum (left caudate nucleus and putamen), cingulate gyrus, and—you guessed it—the hypothalamus! The insula is known to be involved in sensory processing, particularly of touch sensations. The cingulate cortex has been demonstrated in other studies to be involved in attentional processes and in guiding responsiveness to new environmental stimuli. Doubtless it was activated because of the men's attention to the erotic film.

Another study used fMRI to assess brain acti-

Hormones and Sex

The sex hormones are another important physiological force that interacts with the nervous system to influence sexual response.

Organizing versus Activating Effects

Endocrinologists generally make a distinction between the organizing effects of hormones and the activating effects of hormones. As discussed in Chapter 5, hormones present during prenatal development have important influences on genital anatomy, creating male or female genitals. Hormone effects such as these are called **organizing effects** because they cause a relatively permanent change in the organization of some structure, whether in the nervous system or in the reproductive system. Typically there are "critical periods" during which these hormone effects may occur.

It has also been known for some time that if an adult male mouse or cat is castrated (has the testes removed, which removes the source of testosterone), it will cease engaging in sexual behaviour (and will be less aggressive). If that animal is then given injections of testosterone, it will start engaging in sex again. Hormone effects such as these are called **activating effects** because they activate (or deactivate) certain behaviours.

The organizing effects of sex hormones on sexual behaviour have been well documented (Keefe, 2002). In a classic experiment, testosterone was administered to pregnant female guinea pigs. The female offspring that had been exposed to testosterone prenatally[4] were, in adulthood, incapable of displaying "female" sexual behaviour (in particular,

[4]Note the similarity of these experiments to John Money's observations of human intersex individuals (Chapter 5).

Organizing effects of hormones: Effects of sex hormones early in development, resulting in a permanent change in the brain or reproductive system.

Activating effects of hormones: Effects of sex hormones in adulthood, resulting in the activation of behaviours, especially sexual behaviours and aggressive behaviours.

vation in both men and women while viewing erotic video segments (Karama et al., 2002). This study found brain activation in roughly the same regions as the study discussed previously. Interestingly, activation of the hypothalamus was observed in men, but not women, during sexual arousal. All other regions responded similarly in women and men. This study also found evidence of activation of the amygdala during sexual arousal. The amygdala is part of the limbic system, which has long been suspected of having a role in sexual responding. The amygdala is known to be involved in emotion, and its activation speaks to the strong emotions—sometimes positive, sometimes negative—that are evoked by sexual stimuli.

These studies are fascinating in themselves as they allow us to view the workings of the brain during sexual responding. As research advances, future studies will help us understand the brain regions and associated neurotransmitters involv-

Figure 9.12   fMRI scans of the brain are opening up exciting opportunities to learn how the brain is involved in sexual response.

ed in sexual dysfunction, which will lead to more effective treatments for these problems. They will also allow us to better understand and treat arousal problems such as those suffered by pedophiles who are aroused by completely inappropriate stimuli—children.

Sources: Arnow et al., 2002; Holstege et al., 2003; Karama et al., 2002; Schultz et al., 1999.

---

lordosis, which is a sexual posturing involving arching of the back and raising of the hindquarters so that intromission of the male's penis is possible) (Phoenix et al., 1959). It is thought that this result occurred because the testosterone "organized" the brain tissue (particularly the hypothalamus) in a male fashion. These female offspring were also born with masculinized genitals, and thus their reproductive systems had also been organized in the male direction. But the important point here is that the prenatal doses of testosterone had masculinized their sexual behaviour. Similar results have been obtained in experiments with many other species.

These hormonally masculinized females in adulthood displayed mounting behaviour, a male[5] sexual behaviour. When they were given testos-

terone in adulthood, they showed about as much mounting behaviour as males did. Thus the testosterone administered in adulthood *activated* male patterns of sexual behaviour.

The analogous experiment on males would be castration at birth, followed by administration of ovarian hormones in adulthood. When this was done with rats, female sexual behaviour resulted; these males responded to mating attempts by other males essentially in the same way females do (Harris & Levine, 1965). Their brain tissue had been organized in a "female" direction during an early, critical period when testosterone was absent, and the female behaviour patterns were activated in adulthood by administration of ovarian hormones.

It thus seems that males and females initially have capacities for both male and female sexual behaviours; if testosterone is present early in development, the capacity for exhibiting female behaviours is suppressed. Sex hormones in adulthood then activate the behaviour patterns that were differentiated early in development.

[5]The term "male sexual behaviour" is being used here to refer to a sexual behaviour that is displayed by normal males of the species and either is absent in females of that species or is present at a much lower frequency. Normal females do mount, but they do so less frequently than males do. "Female sexual behaviour" is defined similarly.

In Focus 9.3

Does Testosterone Cause Sexual Assault?

In March 2000, a 43-year-old man from Quebec who had twice been convicted of sexual assault for molesting children was castrated at his own request to help him control his sexual urges. He said that he felt castration was the only way that he could avoid molesting more children and live a normal life. This case raises an interesting question: Is testosterone the "fuel" that drives men to commit sexual assault? If so, castration would ensure that these men would never commit sexual assault again.

There are two ways to reduce testosterone levels in men. One is physical castration; that is, the surgical removal of the testes, technically known as bilateral orchidectomy. Would surgical castration prevent a man from committing a sexual assault? When the testes are removed, the man is left with little or no natural testosterone in his body. Numerous experiments with other species have demonstrated that the effect of this low level of testosterone is a sharply reduced sex drive and the virtual elimination of sexual behaviour. However, the effects in humans are not so clear because we are not as hormone-dependent as other species. There are documented cases of castrated men continuing to engage in sexual intercourse for years after castra-

tion. Thus, castration may reduce sexual behaviour in humans, but its effects are not completely predictable. Furthermore, testosterone is available artificially, either by pill, injection, or a patch, so that castrated criminals might secretly obtain replacement testosterone.

A man can also undergo chemical castration, which refers to injection of a drug such as Depo-Provera, an anti-androgen drug that sharply reduces the levels of testosterone in the body. As with surgical castration, Depo-Provera does not necessarily reduce sexual behaviour. Further, sex offenders have to voluntarily agree to any treatment. Few sex offenders are willing to take Depo-Provera because it also suppresses normal sexual arousal.

The discussion up to this point has focused on sexual assault as a form of sexual behaviour. Yet many experts believe that sexual assault is better conceptualized as an aggressive or violent crime that happens to be expressed sexually than seen as a sex crime per se. Thus, the scientific question may be restated from "Does castration eliminate sexual behaviour?" to "Does castration eliminate aggressive behaviour?" Here, too, there are numerous experiments documenting—in other species—that

How relevant is this research to humans? Generally the trend is for the behaviour of lower species to be more under hormonal control and for the behaviour of higher species to be more under brain (neural) control. Thus human sexual behaviour is less under hormonal control than rat sexual behaviour; human sexual behaviour is more controlled by the brain, and thus learning from past experiences and cultural conventions, which are stored in the brain, are more likely to have a profound effect (Wallen, 2001).

Let us now consider in more detail the known activating effects of sex hormones on the sexual behaviour of adult humans.

Testosterone and Sexual Desire

Testosterone has well-documented effects on libido, or sexual desire, in humans (Carani et al., 1990; Carter, 1992; Everitt & Bancroft, 1991). In men deprived of their main source of testosterone by castration or by illness, there is a dramatic decrease in sexual behaviour in some, but not all, cases (Feder, 1984). Sexual desire is rapidly lost if a man is given an antiandrogen drug. Thus testosterone seems to have an activating effect in maintaining sexual desire in the adult male. However, in cases of castration, sexual behaviour may decline very slowly and may be present for several years after the source of testosterone is gone; this points to the importance of experience and brain control of sexual behaviour in humans.

aggressive behaviour is greatly reduced by lowering testosterone levels. But once again, the hormone effects are not as clear or consistent in humans. Thus, surgical or chemical castration may be effective in reducing sexual or aggressive behaviours and thus might reduce the chances of the men committing another sexual offence, but such effects cannot be guaranteed. Further, some authorities believe that Depo-Provera is dangerous, possibly increasing the risk of cancer and suicidal depression. Recently, some other drugs that do not have the side effects associated with Depo-Provera—for example, antidepressants such as Prozac—have been shown to have promise as a treatment for sex offenders.

One thing does seem clear. Depo-Provera and other medication should only be a part of the treatment of sex offenders. The treatment should also include intensive psychotherapy designed specifically for sex offenders, such as cognitive-behavioural therapy. In one treatment study combining Depo-Provera and psychotherapy, after three and a half years only 15 percent of the men had repeated their offence, compared with rates as high as 85 percent for men who were only imprisoned.

Sources: Arthur & Driscoll, 2002; Federoff, 1995; Heim, 1981; Rubin, Reinisch, & Haskett, 1981; Wickham, 2001.

Figure 9.13 Sex offenders in a therapy group. Research shows that treatment of sex offenders, whether with the drug Depo-Provera or not, should always include psychotherapy.

It has also been demonstrated that levels of testosterone are correlated with sexual behaviour in boys around the time of puberty (Udry et al., 1985). Boys in grades 8, 9, and 10 filled out a questionnaire about their sexual behaviour and gave blood samples from which their level of testosterone could be measured. Among the boys whose testosterone level was in the highest quartile (25 percent of the sample), 69 percent had engaged in sexual intercourse, whereas only 16 percent of the boys whose testosterone level was in the lowest quartile had. Similarly, of the boys with testosterone levels in the highest quartile, 62 percent had masturbated, compared with 12 percent for the boys in the lowest quartile. These effects were uncorrelated with age, so it wasn't simply a matter of the older boys having more testosterone and more sexual experience. The authors concluded that at puberty, testosterone affects sexual motivation directly.

Research indicates that androgens are related to sexual desire in women also (Hutchinson, 1995; Sherwin, 1991).[6] If all sources of androgens (the adrenals and the ovaries) are removed, women lose sexual desire. Women who have undergone *oophrectomy* (surgical removal of the ovaries, typically because of cancer) report marked decreases

[6]Lest the reader be distressed by the thought that women's considerably lower levels of testosterone might mean that they have lower sex drives, it should be noted that the sensitivity of cells to hormone levels is critical. Women's cells may be more sensitive to testosterone than men's are. Thus for women, a little testosterone may go a long way.

in their sexual desire. If they are treated with testosterone, their sexual desire increases (Shifren et al., 1998, 2000). Moreover, androgens are used successfully in the treatment of women who have low sexual desire (Kaplan & Owett, 1993; Sherwin, 1991). Some physicians are reluctant to use such treatment because of the masculinizing side effects, such as growth of facial hair, but these side effects can be avoided by the use of lower doses. Androgen levels decline with age in women, and research shows that administration of DHEA (a pre-testosterone hormone) to women over age 60 results in their having increased sexual desire (Baulieu et al., 2000; Spourk, 2002).

■ Pheromones

Scientists and laypeople alike are intrigued by the role that pheromones play in sexual behaviour (Cutler, 1999; McClintock, 2000). Pheromones are somewhat like hormones. Recall that hormones are biochemicals that are manufactured in the body and secreted into the bloodstream to be carried to the organs that they affect. **Pheromones,** in contrast, are biochemicals that are secreted outside the body. Through the sense of smell, they are an important means of communication between animals. Often the pheromones are contained in the animal's urine. The dog that does "scent marking" is actually depositing pheromones. Some pheromones appear to be important in sexual communication, and some have even been called "sex attractants."

Much of the research on pheromones has been done with animals and demonstrates the importance of pheromones in sexual and reproductive functioning. For example, pheromones present in female urine have an influence on male sexual behaviour. A classic study demonstrated that male rats can tell the difference between the odour of estrous females and that of females not in estrus and that the males prefer estrous females (LeMagnen, 1952). The hormones estrogen and progesterone are critical to the effect of female pheromones on males (Beach & Merari, 1970). If a female's ovaries are removed, thereby removing estrogen and progesterone, her odours are no longer stimulating to males.

> **Pheromones (FARE-oh-mones):** Biochemicals secreted outside the body that are important in communication between animals and that may serve as sex attractants.

The sense of smell (olfaction) is essential for pheromone effects to occur. Removal of the olfactory bulbs, specifically a region called the *vomeronasal organ*, dramatically reduces the sexual behaviour of males from species such as mice and guinea pigs (Wysocki & Lepri, 1991; Thorne & Amrein, 2003). The vomeronasal organ (VNO), located inside the nose, is a chemoreceptor—that is, it is activated by chemicals such as pheromones. Neuroscientists have even recorded the activity of single neurons in the VNO of mice and found that certain neurons fire when the animal comes into contact with another male, but different neurons fire when he comes into contact with a female (Luo et al., 2003). Activation of the VNO then activates cells in the hypothalamus (Keverne, 1999); as we have seen, the hypothalamus is crucial to sexuality. The VNO is a kind of second olfactory pathway, sometimes called the "accessory" olfactory bulb, that functions in addition to the main sense of smell.

What relevance does all this have for humans? Humans are not, by and large, "smell animals." Olfaction is much less important for us than for most other species. We tend to rely mostly on vision and, secondarily, hearing. Compare this with a dog's ability to gain a wealth of information about who and what has been in a park simply by sniffing around for a few minutes. Does this mean that pheromones have no influence on our sexual behaviour?

It is now clear that human pheromones exist and may play an important role in sexuality (Wyatt, 2003). Indeed, pheromones may be exactly the "body chemistry" that attracts people to each other. Perfumes with musky scents have become popular and presumably increase sexual attractiveness, perhaps because they smell like pheromones. The perfume industry has eagerly tried to capitalize on pheromone research (Berliner et al., 1991). In fact, a perfume called "Pheromone" was introduced to the market.

What scientific evidence is there regarding the existence and effects of pheromones in humans? First, the vomeronasal organ—which, as noted earlier, is related to olfaction and sexual behaviour in other species and essentially seems to function as a pheromone sensor—is present in most humans (Garcia-Velasco & Mondragon, 1991). This makes one wonder whether plastic surgery to create a pretty nose might inadvertently harm the person's sex life.

Androstenol, an odorous steroid that is well documented as a pheromone in pigs, has been iso-

(a)

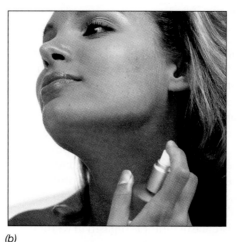

(b)

Figure 9.14 Pheromones. *(a)* Pheromones are a major means of communication between animals. *(b)* Are there human pheromones that are sex attractants?

lated in the underarm sweat of humans (Gower & Ruparelia, 1993). Short-chain fatty acids that are known to be sex-attractant pheromones to male rhesus monkeys have been isolated in human vaginal secretions (Cowley & Brooksbank, 1991). It is clear, therefore, that humans do secrete pheromones.

In one experiment, a synthesized female pheromone was added to women's perfume in one group; a placebo was added to the perfume in the control group (McCoy & Pitino, 2002). The women recorded their sexual behaviour over the next three months. Compared with the control group, pheromone-treated women showed a significantly greater frequency of intercourse, dates, sexual fondling, and kissing. They did not differ in frequency of masturbation. The researchers concluded that the pheromone had increased the women's attractiveness to men. Research has not clearly established that there are male pheromones that affect women's (or men's) sexual behaviour.

Classic research by Martha McClintock (1971) documented the existence of a phenomenon known as **menstrual synchrony:** the convergence, over several months, of the dates of onset of menstrual periods among women who are in close contact with each other (McClintock, 1998; Weller et al., 1995).

> **Menstrual synchrony:** The convergence, over several months, of the dates of onset of menstrual periods among women who are in close contact with each other.

This phenomenon is now thought to be due to pheromones produced by the women.

In perhaps the most dramatic experiment to date in humans, the results indicated that the timing of ovulation could be experimentally manipulated with human pheromones (Stern & McClintock, 1998). Odourless secretions from women's armpits were collected in the late follicular phase; that is, just before ovulation. Recipient women exposed to these secretions showed an accelerated appearance of the LH surge that triggers ovulation. Underarm secretions from the same donors collected later in the menstrual cycle had the opposite effect: they delayed the LH surge of recipients and lengthened the time to menstruation.

The smell of pheromones does not necessarily have to be consciously perceived in order to have an effect (McClintock, 2000). The olfactory system can respond to odours even when they are not consciously perceived. Thus, pheromones that we are not even aware of may have important influences.

If these speculations about the effects of pheromones on human sexual behaviour are correct, our "hyperclean" society may be destroying the scents that attract people to each other. The normal genital secretions (assuming reasonable cleanliness to eliminate bacteria) may contain sex attractants. Ironically, "feminine hygiene" deodorants may destroy precisely the odours that "turn partners on."

Future research on human pheromones should be interesting indeed.

■ ■ SUMMARY

William Masters and Virginia Johnson conducted an important program of research on the physiology of human sexual response. They found that two basic physiological processes occur during arousal and orgasm: vasocongestion and myotonia. They divide the sexual response cycle into four stages: excitement, plateau, orgasm, and resolution.

Their research indicates that there is no physiological distinction between clitoral and vaginal orgasms in women, which refutes an early idea of Freud's. They also provided convincing evidence of the existence of multiple orgasm in women.

Criticisms of Masters and Johnson's model are that (1) they ignored cognitive factors, and (2) their selection of research participants may have led to a self-fulfilling prophecy in their results.

Two cognitive-physiological models are Kaplan's three-component (desire, vasocongestion, and muscular contraction) model, and Walen and Roth's model, which emphasizes cognitive aspects of sexual response (perception and evaluation).

The nervous system and sex hormones are important in sexual response. The nervous system functions in sexual response by a combination of spinal reflexes (best documented for erection and ejaculation) and brain influences (particularly of the limbic system). There is evidence that some women ejaculate. Hormones are important to sexual behaviour, both in their influences on prenatal development (organizing effects) and in their stimulating influence on adult sexual behaviour (activating effects). Testosterone seems to be crucial for maintaining sexual desire in both men and women.

Pheromones are biochemicals secreted outside the body that play an important role in sexual communication and attraction. Much of the evidence is based on research with animals, but evidence in humans is accumulating rapidly.

■ ■ QUESTIONS FOR THOUGHT, DISCUSSION, AND DEBATE

1. Debate the following topic. Resolved: Castration is an appropriate and effective treatment for convicted sex offenders.

2. Do you think that pheromones might play more of a role in human sexual behaviour in cultures that do not stress personal hypercleanliness as much as we do in Canada? If so, what do you think the effects of pheromones would be in those other cultures?

3. Your little sister, Katie, is a second-year university student and is in the fourth month of what looks like it will be a wonderful long-term relationship. Katie and her boyfriend now seem to have a full sexual relationship. As a benevolent older brother/sister, you want Katie to enjoy much sexual pleasure in this relationship. What information from this chapter would you tell Katie about, if you hoped to ensure her sexual satisfaction and sexual pleasure?

■ ■ SUGGESTIONS FOR FURTHER READING

Kaufman, Miriam, Silverberg, Cory, and Odette, Fran. (2003). *The ultimate guide to sex and disability.* San Francisco: Cleis Press. An excellent resource and self-help book with plenty of Canadian content. All three authors are Canadian.

Tiefer, Leonore. (2004). *Sex is not a natural act and other essays.* 2nd ed. Boulder, CO: Westview.

Tiefer is both knowledgeable and a witty writer. This book contains some of her insightful criticisms of the Masters and Johnson model of sexual response.

Wyatt, Tristan. (2003). *Pheromones and animal behaviour.* New York: Cambridge University Press. The definitive book on pheromones.

For Review Questions, Web Resources, and other learning and study tools, visit the *Understanding Human Sexuality* Online Learning Centre at www.mcgrawhill.ca/college/hyde.

CHAPTER 10

Techniques of Arousal and Communication

CHAPTER HIGHLIGHTS

Seeking sexual satisfaction is a basic desire, and masturbation is our first natural sexual activity. It's the way we discover our eroticism, the way we learn to respond sexually, the way we learn to love ourselves and to build self-esteem. Sexual skill and the ability to respond are not "natural" in our society. Sex, like any other skill, has to be learned and practiced.*

We live in the era of sex manuals. We seek out books like *Electrify Your Sex Life*, *The Illustrated Guide to Extended Massive Orgasm*, *The Complete Guide to Sexual Fulfillment*, and *the Multi-Orgasmic Couple*, feature articles and advice columns in magazines, and talk shows like the *Sunday Night Sex Show* with Sue Johanson to get advice on newer and better sexual techniques so that we can produce bigger and longer orgasms in ourselves and our partners. Our fascination with technique has produced both benefits as well as problems. It may turn our attention so much to mechanical techniques that we forget about love and the emotional side of sexual expression. The sex manuals may also set up impossible standards of sexual performance that none of us can meet. On the other hand, we live in a society that has a history of leaving the learning of sexual techniques to nature or to chance, in contrast to some other societies in which adolescents are given explicit instruction in methods for producing sexual pleasure. For human beings, sexual behaviour is a lot more than "doin' what comes naturally"; we all need some means for learning about sexual techniques, and the sex manuals may help to fill that need.

The purpose of this chapter is to provide information on techniques of arousal, while attempting to avoid making sex too mechanical or setting up unrealistic performance standards. It also focuses on skills for communicating in a relationship. As you build a sexual relationship with another person, three components are important: (1) building a loving attachment; (2) building the sexual part of the relationship; and (3) developing good communication. This chapter focuses on items 2 and 3. Love in relationships will be discussed in Chapter 13.

*Betty Dodson. (1987). *Sex for one*. New York: Harmony Books (Crown Publishers), p. 36.

■ Erogenous Zones

While the notion of **erogenous zones** originated in Freud's work, the term is now part of our general vocabulary and refers to parts of the body that are sexually sensitive; stroking them or otherwise stimulating them produces sexual arousal. The genitals and the breasts are good examples. The lips, neck, and thighs are generally also erogenous zones. But even some rather unlikely regions—such as the back, the ears, the stomach, and the feet—can also be quite erogenous. One person's erogenous zones can be quite different from another's. Thus it is impossible to give a list of sure "turn-ons." The best way to find out is to communicate with your partner, verbally and non-verbally.

■ One-Person Sex

It does not necessarily take two to have sex. One can produce one's own sexual stimulation. Sexual self-stimulation is called **autoeroticism.**[1] Two examples are masturbation and fantasy.

Masturbation

Here the term "hand–genital stimulation" will be reserved for stimulation of another's genitals and the term **masturbation** for self-stimulation, either with the hand or with some object, such as a pillow

[1]For those of you who are interested in the roots of words, "autoeroticism" does not refer to sex in the back seat of a car. The prefix "auto" means "self" (as in "autobiography"); hence self-stimulation is autoeroticism.

Erogenous (eh-RAH-jen-us) zones: Areas of the body that are particularly sensitive to sexual stimulation.
Autoeroticism: Sexual self-stimulation; for example, masturbation.
Masturbation: Stimulation of one's own genitals with the hand or with some object, such as a pillow or vibrator.

or a vibrator. Masturbation is a very common sexual behaviour; almost all men and the majority of women in Canada masturbate to orgasm at least a few times during their lives. In response to questions included in the NHSLS of 3,432 Americans, 62 percent of the men and 42 percent of the women reported that they had masturbated in the preceding year (Laumann et al., 1994, Table 3.1). Although there are no national data, our research has found that most Canadian university students (92 percent of the men and 72 percent of the women in one study) have masturbated at least once. Further, 65 percent of Canadians have positive attitudes toward masturbation (refer to Table 1.2 in Chapter 1). The techniques used by males and females in masturbation are interesting in part because they provide information to their partners concerning the best techniques to use in lovemaking.

Techniques of Female Masturbation

Most commonly women masturbate by manipulating the clitoris and the inner lips (Hite, 1976; Kinsey et al., 1953, pp. 158, 189). They may rub up and down or in a circular motion, sometimes lightly and sometimes applying more pressure to the clitoris. Some prefer to rub at the side of the clitoris, while a few stimulate the glans of the clitoris directly. The inner lips may also be stroked or tugged. One woman described her technique as follows:

> I use the tips of my fingers for actual stimulation, but it's better to start with patting motions or light rubbing motions over the general area. As excitement increases I begin stroking above the clitoris

and finally reach a climax with a rapid, jerky circular motion over the clitoral hood. Usually my legs are apart, and occasionally I also stimulate my nipples with the other hand. (Hite, 1976, p. 20)

This finding is in distinct contrast to what many men imagine to be the techniques of female masturbation; the male pictures the woman inserting a finger, a banana, or a similar object into the depths of the vagina (Kinsey et al., 1953). In fact, this is not often done; by far the most common method is clitoral and labial manipulation. Of the women in Kinsey's sample who masturbated, 84 percent used clitoral and labial manipulation; inserting fingers or objects into the vagina was the second most commonly used technique, but it was practised by only 20 percent of the women.

Other techniques used by women in masturbation include breast stimulation, thigh pressure exerted by crossing the legs and pressing them together rhythmically to stimulate the clitoris, and pressing the genitals against some object, such as a pillow, or massaging them with a stream of water while in the shower. A few women are capable of using fantasy alone to produce orgasm; fantasy-induced orgasms are accompanied by the same physiological changes as orgasms produced by masturbation (Whipple et al., 1992).

Techniques of Male Masturbation

Almost all men report masturbating by hand stimulation of the penis. For those interested in speed, an orgasm can be reached in only a minute or two (Kinsey et al., 1948, p. 509).

(a)

(b)

Figure 10.1 *(a)* Male masturbation using hand stimulation of the penis. *(b)* Female masturbation using clitoral stimulation.

Most men use the technique of circling the hand around the shaft of the penis and using an up-and-down movement to stimulate the shaft and glans. Because the penis produces no natural lubrication of its own, some men like to use a form of lubrication, such as soapsuds while showering. The tightness of the grip, the speed of movement, and the amount of glans stimulation vary from one man to the next. Most increase the speed of stimulation as they approach orgasm, slowing or stopping the stimulation at orgasm because further stimulation would be uncomfortable (Masters & Johnson, 1966). At the time of ejaculation, they often grip the shaft of the penis tightly. Immediately after orgasm, the glans and corona are hypersensitive, and men generally avoid further stimulation of the penis at that time (Sadock & Sadock, 1976).

Media and Masturbation

Some men and woman incorporate the use of mass media into their autoerotic activity. Some people masturbate as they view erotic images in magazines, on video or DVD, or on the Internet. In a telephone survey by Harris Interactive of 1,002 American adults, half of the men and one-third of the women reported viewing sexually explicit videos and erotic magazines; 32 percent of the men and 15 percent of the women reported viewing erotic material on Web sites (Adam & Eve, 2004). Some of these viewers used these materials as aids to sexual arousal and masturbation. Up to 10 percent of the male students in our human sexuality classes report that their most recent sexual activity was masturbation while viewing erotic materials.

The Internet plays an important role in another form of autoerotic expression. Some people have specific sexual desires or needs that they are afraid to express in their relationships. They may fear embarrassment and rejection, or risks to their physical or emotional health if they act on these needs and desires. The Internet, because of its anonymity, provides a relatively safe context in which one can explore these needs and desires. A study of 42 men and 62 women recruited in chat rooms found that persons who reported lacking real relationships and expressed fear of disclosing aspects of their sexuality were more likely to use the Internet as an important form of sexual self-expression (McKenna, Green, & Smith, 2001).

Fantasy

Sexual fantasy refers to sexual thoughts or images that alter the person's emotions or physiological state (Maltz & Boss, 1997). Almost all men and women report that they have experienced sexual fantasies (Leitenberg & Henning, 1995). However, many people are uncomfortable with acknowledging that they deliberately think about sex and enjoy doing so (Renaud & Byers, 2001).

The Content of Fantasies

Researchers studied the sexual thoughts and fantasies of heterosexual university students at the University of New Brunswick (Renaud & Byers, 1999). They found that although men think about sex more frequently than women do, for the most part, the content of their sexual fantasies is similar. The most common themes have to do with intimacy and romance. More than 90 percent of students had fantasies about having intercourse with a loved partner, kissing passionately, making love elsewhere than the bedroom such as out of doors, and giving and receiving oral sex. Compared to the women, the men's fantasies more often revolved around themes of anonymous or impersonal sex. The women had romantic fantasies and fantasies about playing a role during sexual activity—such as exposing themselves provocatively or tying their partner up—more often than the men did. In a survey of a national sample of British adults, men were more likely to report fantasies of sex with multiple and anonymous partners, whereas women reported fantasies involving a same-gender or famous male partner (Wilson, 1997). These differences are consistent with predictions based on both evolutionary theory and gender-role socialization.

One study comparing the fantasies of gays and lesbians with those of heterosexual men and women found that the reported contents were very similar, except that the partner was someone of the same gender (Price et al., 1985). However, heterosexuals may fantasize sexual activity with someone of the same gender, and gay and lesbian fantasies may include persons of the other gender.

Sexual fantasy: Sexual thoughts or images that alter the person's emotions or physiological state.

The Nature of Fantasies

Where do sexual fantasies come from? The images may come from past experience, dreams, media portrayals, or stories someone told you. A fantasy may include only one person, either the self or someone else, or it may include other persons of either gender and any sexual orientation. The activity may be dreamlike and sensuous, or explicit and vigorous. Sexual fantasies may represent earlier or childhood experiences, pleasant or abusive (Maltz & Boss, 1997). They may be experienced as positive and pleasant or as negative and unwanted (Byers et al., 1998; Renaud & Byers, 1999).

Positive sexual fantasy can play a variety of functions for the person doing the fantasizing (Maltz & Boss, 1997). These include enhancing self-esteem and attractiveness, increasing one's own sexual arousal (e.g., during masturbation or partnered sex), and facilitating orgasm. In fact, research has shown that people who engage in more frequent sexual fantasies tend to be better adjusted sexually (Renaud & Byers, 2001). A very important role is enabling the person to mentally rehearse future possibilities. Such a rehearsal may enable the person to change behaviour, initiate communication with a partner, or change partners.

Fantasy during Masturbation

More men than women report ever having had sexual fantasies during masturbation. The results of 13 studies indicate that about 87 percent of men and 69 percent of women fantasized during masturbation. Here is an adolescent male's description of one of his favourite fantasies during masturbation:

> We would be riding in the back seat of the car and I would reach over and fondle her breasts. She would reach into my pants and begin to caress my penis and finally suck me off. (Jensen, 1976a, p. 144)

This is the fantasy of one college woman as she imagines seducing her French teacher:

> At exactly 8:00 I knocked on the door. When this guy saw what I was wearing I thought his eyes were going to pop out. Calmly he asked me to come in and sit down . . .
>
> "Please call me Jim." Now I was getting somewhere. . . . I slipped out of my shoes and loosened my dress. When Jim returned I was ready and waiting. . . . Well the man finally got the hint; he reached around and unzipped my dress. While I was slowly undoing his zipper, he buried his head between my breasts. As his mouth slowly descended down my body I could feel the heat rising from between my legs. . . . To add to my desire he started speaking French to me. You didn't have to be fluent to understand this. As his mouth continued to nibble away, his tongue zeroed in on my clit and sent me to a mind boggling orgasm. As my pleasure subsided I began to return the favor. . . . Although I had enjoyed several orgasms by now the night was far from over. Jim then got on top of me and made love to me for what seemed like an eternity. . . . (Moffatt, 1989, pp. 190–191)

The content of male and female sexual fantasies seems to be influenced by cultural stereotypes of male and female sexuality. However, thay are also a good way to experiment with roles outside of cultural stereotypes.

Intrusive Sexual Thoughts

Fantasies can occur at any time and any place, not just during sexual activity. Sometimes sexual thoughts or fantasies become intrusive; that is, unwanted, personally unacceptable, and uncharacteristic of the person. In perhaps the first study of these thoughts, Byers and her colleagues (1998) gave college men and women a list of 20 such thoughts and assessed their frequency. Sexually intrusive thoughts were reported by 84 percent of the participants. The images most frequently reported by men were of having sex in a public place, meeting naked people, and engaging in sex with a person having authority over them. Those most frequently reported by women were of having sex in a public place, having sex with a person having authority over them, and being sexually victimized. Men reported greater physical arousal than women in response to their most intrusive thought. In a follow-up study, Renaud and Byers (2001) found 42 different thoughts that at least one participant selected as their most negative intrusive thought. The thoughts that most often were selected as most negative were having incestuous sexual relations and being embarrassed by sexual performance failure. Students who had more frequent sexual intrusive thoughts were not more poorly adjusted than students who had such thoughts less frequently. However, some people experience negative affect, anxiety, and guilt in response to these unwanted intrusive sexual thoughts (Byers et al., 1998).

Sex Toys

Various sexual devices, such as vibrators and dildos, are used as sex toys by some people in masturbation or by couples as they have sex together.

Both male and female artificial genitals can be purchased. A **dildo** is a rubber or plastic cylinder, often shaped like a penis; it can be inserted into the vagina or the anus. Dildos are used by women in masturbation (although, as was noted in the previous section, this is not very common), by men, by lesbians, by gays, and by heterosexual couples. Artificial vaginas, and even inflatable replicas of the entire body, male or female, can also be purchased.

Some *vibrators* are shaped like a penis but others are not; there are models with a cord that plugs into an electric socket and also battery-operated, cordless models. Women may use them to masturbate, stimulating the clitoral and mons area, or may insert them into the vagina. Men may use them to stimulate the genitals or the anus. They are used either in masturbation or during sex with another person. They can be purchased in "respectable" stores (where they are sometimes euphemistically called "body massagers"), in sex stores, and by mail. Vibrators designed for woman are not recent; they were invented in the 1880s and sold as a medical device (Maines, 1999). Physicians prescribed their use for the treatment of various female "maladies," especially hysteria. Vibrators disappeared from medicinal use after they were used in pornographic films in the 1920s.

Body oils are also popular for sexual use. In fact, their use has been encouraged by experts in the field; for example, sex therapists recommend them for the touching or sensate focus exercises that they prescribe for their patients in sex therapy (see Chapter 19). Oils have a sensuous quality that heightens erotic feelings. Furthermore, if you are being stroked or massaged for any extended period of time, the oil helps ensure that the part of your body that is being stimulated will not end up feeling like a piece of wood that has been sandpapered. Oils can be used either while masturbating

Dildo: A rubber or plastic cylinder, often shaped like a penis.

Figure 10.2   Vibrators and dildos, used for sexual stimulation.

or while having sex with another person. However, be careful not to use oils or Vaseline with latex condoms because they cause the latex to deteriorate. The sex stores sell oils in a variety of exotic scents, but plain baby oil will also do nicely.

■ Two-Person Sex[2]

When many of us think of techniques of two-person sex, the image that flashes across our mind generally reflects several assumptions. One assumption is that one of the people is a male and the other a female—that is, that the sex is heterosexual. This reflects a belief that heterosexual sex is normative. We also tend to assume that the male is supposed to do certain things during the act and the female is supposed to do certain other things, reflecting the sexual scripts of our culture. He, for example, is supposed to take the initiative in deciding what techniques are used, while she is to follow his lead. Although there is nothing particularly evil in these assumptions, they do tend to impose limitations on our own sexual expression and to make people think that their own sexual behaviour is "not quite right." Therefore, we will make an attempt to avoid these assumptions in the sections that follow.

[2]Of course, some people choose to engage in sexual activities with two or more persons at the same time. This is called swinging or *un ménage à trois*. Swinging is discussed in Chapter 12.

Kissing

Kissing (or what we might call, technically, "mouth-to-mouth stimulation") is an activity that virtually everyone in our culture has engaged in. In simple kissing, the partners keep their mouths closed and touch each other's lips. In deep kissing ("French kissing"), both people part their lips slightly and insert their tongues into each other's mouths (somehow these clinical descriptions do not make it sound like as much fun as it is). There are endless variations on these two basic approaches, such as nibbling at the partner's lips or tongue or sucking at the lips; they depend only on your imagination and personal preference. There are also plenty of other regions of the body to kiss: the nose, the forehead, the eyelids, the earlobes, the neck, the breasts, the genitals, and even the feet, to give a few examples.

Touching

Enjoying touching and being touched is essential to sexual pleasure. Sensual touching is important to feelings of closeness and desire. In addition, caresses or massages, applied to virtually any area of the body, can be exciting. The regions that are exciting vary a great deal from one person to the next and depend on how the person is feeling at the moment; thus it is important to communicate what sort of touching is most pleasurable to you. (For specific exercises on touching and being touched, see Chapter 19.)

As noted earlier, one of the best ways to find out how to use your hands in stimulating the genitals of another person is to find out how that person masturbates.

Hand Stimulation of the Male Genitals

As a technique of lovemaking, hand stimulation of the male genitals can be used as a pleasurable preliminary to intercourse, as a means of inducing orgasm itself, or as a means of producing an erection after the man has had one orgasm and wants to continue for another round of lovemaking ("rousing the dead").

Alex Comfort, in *The New Joy of Sex*, recommends the following techniques (see Figure 10.3):

> If he isn't circumcised, she will probably need to avoid rubbing the glans itself, except in pursuit of very special effects. Her best grip is just below the groove, with the skin back as far as it will go, and using two hands—one pressing hard near the root, holding the penis steady, or fondling the scrotum, the other making a thumb-and-first-finger ring, or a whole hand grip. She should vary this, and, in prolonged masturbation, change hands often. (1991, p. 85)

As a good technique for producing an erection he also mentions rolling the penis like dough between the palms of the hands. Firm pressure with one finger midway between the base of the penis and the anus is another possibility.

One of the things that make hand stimulation most effective is for the man's partner to have a playful delight in, and appreciation of, the man's penis. Most men think their penis is pretty important. If the partner cannot honestly appreciate it and enjoy massaging it, hand stimulation might as well not be done.

Hand Stimulation of the Female Genitals

The hands can be used to stimulate the woman's genitals to produce orgasm, as a preliminary method of arousing the woman before intercourse, or simply because it is pleasurable.

Generally it is best, particularly if the woman is not already aroused, to begin with gentle, light stroking of the inside of the thighs and the inner and outer lips, moving to light stroking of the clitoris. As she becomes more aroused, the stimulation of the clitoris can become firmer. There are several rules for doing this, though. First, remember that the clitoris is very sensitive and that this

Figure 10.3   Technique of hand stimulation of the penis.

sensitivity can be either exquisite or painful. Some care has to be used in stimulating it; it cannot be manipulated like a piece of Silly Putty. Second, the clitoris should never—except, perhaps, for some light stroking—be rubbed while it is dry, for the effect can be more like sandpaper stimulation than sexual stimulation. If the woman is already somewhat aroused, lubrication can be provided by touching the fingers to the vaginal entrance and then spreading the lubrication on the clitoris. If she is not aroused or does not produce much vaginal lubrication, saliva works well too. Moisture makes the stimulation not only more comfortable but also more sensuous. Third, some women find direct stimulation of the clitoral glans to be painful in some states of arousal. These women generally prefer stimulation on either side of the clitoris instead.

With these caveats in mind, the clitoris can be stimulated with circular or back-and-forth movements of the finger. The inner and outer lips can also be stroked, rubbed, or tugged. These techniques, if done with skill and patience, can bring the woman to orgasm. Another technique that can be helpful in producing orgasm is for the partner to place the heel of the hand on the mons, exerting pressure on it while moving the middle finger in and out of the vaginal entrance. Another rule should also be clear by now: The partner needs to have close-trimmed nails that do not have any jagged edges. This is sensitive tissue we are dealing with.

Watch the video "Men Talk about Sex" in Chapter 10 of your CD to learn how some men feel about their sex lives.

Watch the video "What Women Want" in Chapter 10 of your CD to learn how some women would like their sex partners to behave toward them.

Other Ways to Stimulate the Genitals

Many couples engage in sexual activities that do not involve penetration or hand stimulaton but nonetheless allow one or both partners to receive genital stimulation. For example, a woman may lie on top of her partner and rub her clitoris against her partner's genitals (when two women do this, it is sometimes called *tribadism*). Alternatively, a man may move his penis between the thighs of his partner, a technique that has been referred to as *interfemoral intercourse*.

The Other Senses

So far, this chapter has been focused on tactile (touch) sensations in sexual arousal. However, the other senses—vision, smell, and hearing—can also make contributions.

Sights

The things you see can contribute to your arousal. Men seem, in general, to be turned on by a variety of visual stimuli, such as an attractive person, or partially dressed or nude bodies. Both men and women respond with physiological arousal to portrayals of partnered sexual activity (Laan & Everaerd, 1995). Just as erotica may be used during autoerotic activity, viewing sexual activity on a video or on the Internet may contribute to partnered sexual activities. Some men, and a few women, have mild fetishes (see Chapter 16 for more detail), and like to see their partner wearing certain types of clothing, such as leather or rubber clothing, or schoolgirl dresses. A good rule here, as elsewhere, is to communicate with your partner to find out what he or she would find arousing.

The decor of the room can also contribute to visual stimulation. Furry rugs, placed on the floor or used as a bedspread, are sensuous both visually and tactilely. Large mirrors, hung either behind the bed or on the ceiling above it, can be a visual turn-on, since they allow you to watch yourself make love. Candlelight is soft and contributes more to an erotic atmosphere than an electric light, which is harsh, or complete darkness, in which case there is no visual stimulation at all.

Perhaps the biggest visual turn-on comes simply from looking at your own body and your partner's body. According to the NHSLS, watching a partner undress is one of the most appealing sexual activities (Michael et al., 1994, Table 12).

Smells

Odours can be turn-ons or turn-offs. The scent of a body that is clean, having been washed with soap and water, is a natural turn-on. It does not need to be covered up with an "intimate deodorant."[3] In a sense, the scent of your skin, armpits, or genitals is your "aroma signature" and can be quite arousing (Comfort, 1991).

A body that has not been washed or a mouth that has not been cleaned or has recently been used for smoking cigarettes can be a real turn-off. Breath that reeks of garlic may turn a desire for closeness into a desire for distance. Ideally, the communication between partners is honest and trusting enough so that if one offends, the other can request that the appropriate clean-up be done.

Sounds

Music—whether your preference is for rock or classical music—can contribute to an erotic atmosphere. Another advantage of playing music is that it helps muffle the sounds of sex, which can be important if you live in an apartment with thin walls or are worried about your children hearing you. Music can also be a turn-off; a funeral dirge is not conducive to joyous sexual activity.

Fantasy during Two-Person Sex

Fantasies are a means of self-stimulation to heighten the experience of sex with another person. Particularly in a long-term, monogamous relationship, sexual monotony can become a problem; fantasies are one way to introduce some variety and excitement without violating an agreement to be faithful to the other person. It is important to view such fantasies in this way, rather than as a sign of disloyalty to, or dissatisfaction with, one's sexual partner.

Fantasies during two-person sex are generally quite similar to the ones people have while masturbating. In one study, 84 percent of males and 82 percent of females reported that they fantasized at least some of the time during intercourse (Cado & Leitenberg, 1990). This kind of fantasizing is quite common.

[3]With the increased popularity of mouth–genital sex, some women worry that the scent of their genitals might be offensive. The advertisements for feminine hygiene deodorant sprays prey upon these fears. These sprays should not be used because they may irritate the vagina. Besides, there is nothing offensive about the scent of a vulva that has been washed; many people, in fact, find it arousing.

Marion, a 32-year-old married woman, reported this fantasy:

I arrive at a party in a large opulent mansion. A servant [gives me a blindfold]. He tells me that I have to put it on and follow him through to the bedroom. He sits me down on the bed and takes off my shoes. Somebody else unzippers my dress and somebody else unfastens my necklace. I feel fingertips gently pinching my nipples through my bra. Somebody else unfastens my bra. Then I feel two people kissing and sucking my breasts. Then somebody's kissing my inner thighs. . . . She clamps her mouth over the crotch of my panties, . . . starts sucking my panties, and slipping her tongue underneath. After a while she pulls my panties to one side and starts licking my pussy. A man works his finger up into my bottom. The girl slides her finger inside my pussy. I'm getting so turned on I can hardly stand it. The girl's licking my clitoris like a hysterical butterfly. My whole body feels as if

Figure 10.4 Erotic sculptures at the Temple of Kandariya Mahadevo, India, built in A.D. 1000.

it's being swept away. I shake with an orgasm. (Masterton, 1993, pp. 107–109)

Here is a man's fantasy:

We're in a group of people around a dinner table . . . a group of several couples. We're playing a card game, strip poker, or a type of elaborate strip poker where anybody who wins gets to have the person who lost do anything they want. And the fantasy is always of Colleen becoming very sexual. All she's interested in is sex. Fucking, sucking, exhibiting herself, that's it. It's mostly a seduction fantasy. She might seduce one of the guys at the table by walking up the stairs and stripping off her clothes as she goes. Then she'll get on her hands and knees and want to fuck there. (Maurer, 1994, pp. 144–145)

Some sexual partners enjoy sharing their fantasies with each other. Describing a sexual fantasy to your partner can be a turn-on for both of you. Some couples act out all or part of a fantasy and find it very gratifying. One man says:

I fantasized about being a fourteen-year-old girl. This is a long-lived fantasy of mine. The girl is pretty, with a petite body, probably five-one, five-two, cute ass, maybe light blond or dark brown pussy hair. Small to medium size breasts. Kind of sweet-looking, virginal. . . . Anyway, Sue got into it, like we were two girlfriends sleeping over and she was a couple years older and she was going to show me some things. I happen to be very sensitive around my nipples, so she'd say, "Oh, you have nice little nipples, you're going to have very pretty breasts." Then she'd massage my crotch like she was massaging a vagina: "Do you like it when I pet you down there?" And she'd show me what to do to pleasure her, how to masturbate her and go down on her. We played around with that for a few months. (Maurer, 1994, p. 231)

Positions of Penile–Vaginal Intercourse

One of the most common heterosexual techniques involves the insertion of the penis into the vagina; this is called **coitus**[4] or *sexual intercourse*. The cou-

[4]From the Latin word *coire*, meaning "to go together."

> **Coitus:** Sexual intercourse; insertion of the penis into the vagina.

ple may be in any one of a number of different positions while engaging in this basic sexual activity. Ancient love manuals and other sources illustrate many positions of intercourse.

Some authorities state that there are only four positions of intercourse. Personally, we prefer to believe that there are an infinite number. Consider how many different angles your arms, legs, and torso may be in, in relation to those of your partner, and all the various ways in which you can intertwine your limbs—that's a lot of positions. We trust that given sufficient creativity and time, you can discover them all for yourself. We would agree, though, that there are a few basic positions and a few basic dimensions along which positions can vary. One basic variation depends on whether the couple face each other (face-to-face position) or whether one partner faces the other's back (rear-entry position); if you try the other obvious variation, a back-to-back position, you will quickly find that you cannot accomplish much that way. The other basic variation depends on whether one partner is on top of the other or whether the couple are side by side. Let us consider four basic positions that illustrate these variations. We'll give you the basic recipes and let you decide on the embellishments.

Man on Top

The face-to-face, man-on-top position ("missionary" position—see Figure 10.5) is probably the one used most frequently by heterosexual couples in Canada. In this position (which used to be called "male-superior," an unacceptable term today) the man and woman stimulate each other until they are aroused, he has an erection, and she is producing vaginal lubrication. Then he moves on top of her as she spreads her legs apart, either he or she spreads the vaginal lips apart, and he inserts his penis into her vagina. He supports himself on his knees and hands or elbows and moves his penis in and out of the vagina (pelvic thrusting). Some men worry that their heavy weight will crush the poor woman under them; however, because the weight is spread out over so great an area, most women do not find this to be a problem at all, and many find the sensation of contact to be pleasurable.

The woman can have her legs in a number of positions that create variations. She may have them straight out horizontally, a position that pro-

Figure 10.5 The man-on-top position of intercourse.

duces a tight rub on the penis but does not permit it to go deeply into the vagina. She may bend her legs and elevate them to varying degrees, or she may hook them over the man's back or over his shoulders. The last approach permits the penis to move deeply into the vagina. The woman can also move her pelvis, either up and down or side to side, to produce further stimulation.

The man-on-top position has some advantages and some disadvantages. It is the best position for ensuring conception, if that is what you want. It leaves the woman's hands free to stroke the man's body (or her own, for that matter). The couple may feel better able to express their love or to communicate other feelings, since they are facing each other. This position, however, does not work well if the woman is in the advanced stages of pregnancy or if either she or the man is extremely obese. Sex therapists have also found that it is not a very good position if the man wants to control his ejaculation; the woman-on-top position is better for this (see Chapter 19).

Woman on Top

There are a number of ways of getting into the woman-on-top position (see Figure 10.6). You can begin by inserting the penis into the vagina while in the man-on-top position and then rolling over. Another possibility is to begin with the man on his back; the woman kneels over him, with one knee on either side of his hips. Then his hand or her hand guides the erect penis into the vagina as she lowers herself onto it. She then moves her hips to produce the stimulation. Beyond that, there are

numerous variations, depending on where she puts her legs. She can remain on her knees, or she can straighten out her legs behind her, putting them outside his legs or between them. Or she can even turn around and face toward his feet.

This position has a number of advantages. It provides a lot of clitoral stimulation, and the woman can control the kind of stimulation she gets; thus many women find it the best position for them to have an orgasm. It is also a good position for the man who wants to delay his ejaculation, and for this reason it is used in sex therapy. This position is also a good one if the man is tired and it seems advisable for the woman to supply most of the movement. Furthermore, the couple face each other, facilitating better communication, and each has the hands free to stroke the other.

Rear Entry

In the rear-entry position, the man faces the woman's back. One way to do this is to have the woman kneel with her head down; the man kneels behind her and inserts his penis into her vagina (see Figure 10.7). (This is sometimes called the "doggie position," because it is the manner in which dogs and most other animals copulate.) Another possibility is for the woman to lie on her stomach, raising her hips slightly so that the man can insert his penis while kneeling over her. Rear entry can also be accomplished when the couple are in the side-to-side position.

In this position the man's hands are free to stimulate the woman's clitoris or any other part of her body. The couple do not face each other, however,

Figure 10.6   The woman-on-top position of intercourse.

and some couples dislike this aspect of the position. A small amount of air may enter the vagina when this position is used, producing interesting noises when it comes out.

Side to Side

In the side-to-side position, the man and woman lie beside each other, either face to face or in a rear-entry position (see Figure 10.8). There are many variations beyond this, depending on where the arms and legs go—so many, in fact, that no attempt will be made to list them. One should be aware, though, that in this position an arm or a leg can get trapped under a heavy body and begin to feel numb, and shifting positions is sometimes necessary.

The side-to-side position is good for leisurely or prolonged intercourse or if one or both of the partners are tired. It is also good for the pregnant and the obese. At least some hands are free to stimulate the clitoris, or whatever.

Other Variations

Aside from the variations in these basic positions that can be produced by switching the position of the legs, there are many other possibilities. For example, the man-on-top position can be varied by having the woman lie on the edge of a bed with her feet on the floor while the man kneels on the floor. Or the woman can lie on the edge of a table while the man stands (don't forget to close the curtains first). Both of these positions produce a somewhat tighter vagina and therefore more stimulation for the penis. Or the man can sit on a chair and insert the penis as the woman sits on his lap, using either a face-to-face or a rear-entry approach. Or, with both partners standing, the man can lift the woman onto his erect penis as she wraps her legs around his back, or she can put one leg over his shoulder (you have to be pretty athletic to manage this one, however).

Mouth–Genital Stimulation

One of the most striking features of the sexual revolution of the last few decades is the increased popularity of mouth–genital, or oral–genital, techniques. There are two kinds of mouth–genital stimulation ("going down on" one's partner): cunnilingus and fellatio.

(a)   *(b)*

Figure 10.13   *(a)* A couple with good body language (good eye contact and body position); *(b)* A couple with poor body language (poor eye contact and body position).

Drawing Your Partner Out

Suppose it is Chris who initiates the conversation rather than Donna. Chris has noticed that Donna doesn't seem to get a lot of pleasure out of sex, and would like to find out why and see what they can do about it. Chris needs to draw Donna out and might begin by saying,

> I've noticed lately that you don't seem to be enjoying sex as much as you used to. Am I right about that? (10)

That much is good because Chris is checking out an assumption. Unfortunately, the question leads to a "yes" or "no" answer, and that can stop the communication. So, if Donna replies "yes," Chris had better follow it up with an *open-ended* question like

> Why do you think you aren't enjoying it more? (11)

If Donna can give a reasonable answer, good communication should be on the way. One of the standard—and best—questions to ask in a situation like this is

> What can we do to make things better? (12)

Body Talk: Non-verbal Communication

Often the precise words we use are not so important as our **non-verbal communication**—the way we say

> **Non-verbal communication:** Communication not through words, but through the body (e.g., eye contact, tone of voice, touching).

them. Tone of voice, expression on the face, position of the body, whether you touch the other person—all are important in conveying the message.

As an example, take the sentence "So you're here." If it is delivered "So *you're* here" in a hostile tone of voice, the message is that the speaker is very unhappy that you're here. If it is delivered "So you're *here*" in a pleased voice, the meaning may be that the speaker is glad and surprised to see you here in Newfoundland, having thought you were in Europe. "So you're here" with a smile and arms outstretched to initiate a hug might mean that the speaker has been waiting for you and is delighted to see you.

Suppose that in Donna and Chris's case, the reason Donna doesn't have more orgasms is that Chris doesn't stimulate her firmly enough or in the spot that feels best to her. During sex, Donna is worried that it is taking her too long to reach orgasm and that Chris is getting tired or bored stimulating her. (Notice that Donna is mind reading again.) As a result, Donna does not enjoy the stimulation she does get as much as she could, and her body language communicates that she's not really into it. Chris already believes that Donna does not really like sex and the response (or rather non-response) of her body confirms these assumptions. Chris reads Donna's body language as communicating that she's not really enjoying having her clitoris stimulated. Although she would like to have an orgasm and for Chris to keep stimulating her, her body is saying "I'm not into this. Let's get it over with." And that's exactly what Chris does. To cor-

In Focus 10.3

How Solid Is Your Relationship?

Good communication enhances a relationship, and a good relationship facilitates good communication. There are several components of a good relationship. Two of these are love and respect. The following self-test assesses the degree of love and respect in a relationship. If you are in an intimate relationship, answer yes or no to each of the following statements. If you agree or mostly agree, answer yes. If you disagree or mostly disagree, answer no. You can either ask your partner to take the test too, or take it a second time yourself, answering the way you think your partner would answer.

1. My partner seeks out my opinion.
   YOU: Yes   No   YOUR PARTNER: Yes   No
2. My partner cares about my feelings.
   YOU: Yes   No   YOUR PARTNER: Yes   No
3. I don't feel ignored very often.
   YOU: Yes   No   YOUR PARTNER: Yes   No
4. We touch each other a lot.
   YOU: Yes   No   YOUR PARTNER: Yes   No
5. We listen to each other.
   YOU: Yes   No   YOUR PARTNER: Yes   No
6. We respect each other's ideas.
   YOU: Yes   No   YOUR PARTNER: Yes   No
7. We are affectionate toward one another.
   YOU: Yes   No   YOUR PARTNER: Yes   No
8. I feel my partner takes good care of me.
   YOU: Yes   No   YOUR PARTNER: Yes   No
9. What I say counts.
   YOU: Yes   No   YOUR PARTNER: Yes   No

rect this situation, Donna might adopt a more active, encouraging approach. She might take Chris's hand and guide it to her clitoris, showing exactly where and how firmly she likes to have it rubbed. She might give Chris verbal feedback, saying "That's good" when Chris touches her in a way that she likes, or "Please don't stop" if she wants oral stimulation to continue.

The point is that in communicating about sex, we need to be sure that our non-verbal signals help to create the impact we intend rather than one we don't intend. It is also possible that non-verbal signals are confusing communication and need to be straightened out. "Checking out" is a technique for doing this that will be discussed in a later section.

Interestingly, research shows that distressed couples differ from non-distressed couples more in their non-verbal communication than in their verbal communication (Gottman et al., 1977; Vincent et al., 1979). For example, even when a person from a distressed couple is expressing agreement with his or her partner, that person is more likely to accompany the verbal expressions of agreement with negative non-verbal behaviour. Distressed couples are also more likely to be negative listeners—while listening, the individuals are more likely to display frowning, angry, or disgusted facial expressions, or tense or inattentive body postures. Contempt is often expressed non-verbally, by sneering or rolling the eyes, for example. In contrast, harmonious relationships are characterized by closer physical distances and more relaxed postures than are

10. I am important in our decisions.
      YOU: Yes   No   YOUR PARTNER: Yes   No

11. There's lots of love in our relationship.
      YOU: Yes   No   YOUR PARTNER: Yes   No

12. We are genuinely interested in one another.
      YOU: Yes   No   YOUR PARTNER: Yes   No

13. I love spending time with my partner.
      YOU: Yes   No   YOUR PARTNER: Yes   No

14. We are very good friends.
      YOU: Yes   No   YOUR PARTNER: Yes   No

15. Even during rough times, we can be empathetic.
      YOU: Yes   No   YOUR PARTNER: Yes   No

16. My partner is considerate of my viewpoint.
      YOU: Yes   No   YOUR PARTNER: Yes   No

17. My partner finds me physically attractive.
      YOU: Yes   No   YOUR PARTNER: Yes   No

18. My partner expresses warmth toward me.
      YOU: Yes   No   YOUR PARTNER: Yes   No

19. I feel included in my partner's life.
      YOU: Yes   No   YOUR PARTNER: Yes   No

20. My partner admires me.
      YOU: Yes   No   YOUR PARTNER: Yes   No

Scoring: If you answered yes to fewer than seven items, it is likely that you are not feeling loved and respected in this relationship. You and your partner need to be more active and creative in adding affection to your relationship.

Source: J. Gottman. (1994). *Why marriages succeed or fail.* New York: Simon & Schuster.

found in distressed couples (Beier & Sternberg, 1977). Once again, it is not only what we say verbally but how we say it, and how we listen, that makes the difference.

Accentuate the Positive

We have been concentrating on negative communications; that is, communications in which some problem or complaint needs to be voiced. It is also important to communicate positive things about the relationship in general and sex in particular (Gottman & Notarius, 2002). If that was a great episode of lovemaking, or the best kiss you've ever experienced, say so. A learning theorist would say that you're giving your partner some positive reinforcement. Social psychologists' research shows

that we tend to like people better who give us positive reinforcements (see Chapter 13). Recognition of the strengths in a relationship offers the potential for enriching it (e.g., Miller et al., 1975). And if you make a habit of positive communications about sex, it will be easier to initiate the negative ones and they will be better received.

Most communication during sex is limited to muffled groans, or "Mm-m's," or an occasional "Faster, John" or "Did you, Michèle?" It might help your partner greatly if you gave frequent verbal and non-verbal feedback, such as "That was great" or "Let's do that again." This would make the positive communications and the negative ones far easier.

Research shows that non-distressed couples make more positive and fewer negative communications than distressed couples (Billings, 1979). In fact, Gottman's (1994) research with married couples found that there is a *magic ratio* of positive to negative communication. In stable marriages, there is five times as much positive interaction—verbal and non-verbal, including hugs and kisses, as there is negative. Not only do happy couples make more positive communications; they are more likely to respond to a negative communication with something positive (Billings, 1979). Distressed couples, on the other hand, are more likely to respond to negative communication with more negative communication, escalating into conflict. We might all take a cue from the happy couples and make efforts not only to increase our positive communications but even to make them in response to negative comments from our partner.

Fighting Fair

Even if you use all the techniques described above, you may still get into arguments with your partner. Arguments are a natural part of a relationship and are not necessarily bad. Given that there will be arguments in a relationship, it is useful if you and your partner have agreed to a set of rules called **fighting fair** (Bach & Wyden, 1969) so that the arguments may help and won't hurt.

Here are some of the basic rules for fighting fair that may be useful to you (Brenton, 1972; Creighton, 1992). Many of them relate to the four destructive communication patterns identified by John Gottman (1999).

1. Edit what you say. Don't make sarcastic or insulting remarks about your partner's sexual adequacy. This generates resentment, opens you to counterattack, and is just a dirty way to fight.
2. Don't bring up the names of former partners, lovers, boyfriends, or girlfriends to illustrate how all these problems didn't happen with them. Stick to the issue: your relationship with your partner.
3. Don't play amateur psychologist. Don't say things like "The problem is that you're a compulsive personality" or "You acted that way because you never resolved your Oedipus complex." You

really don't have the qualifications (even after reading this book) to do so. Even if you did, your partner is likely to think you are biased and so would not be apt to recognize your expertise in the middle of an argument.
4. Don't engage in dumping. Don't store up gripes for six months and then dump them on your partner all at one time.
5. Don't hit and run. Don't bring up a serious negative issue when there is no opportunity to continue the discussion, such as when you're on the way out the door going to work or when guests are coming for dinner in five minutes.
6. Don't focus on who's to blame. Focus on looking for solutions, not on who's at fault. If you avoid blaming, it lets both you and your partner save face, which helps both of you feel better about the relationship.

Checking Out Sexy Signals

One of the problems with verbal and non-verbal sexual communications is that they are often ambiguous. This problem may occur more often with couples who don't know each other well, but it can cause uncertainty and misunderstanding in couples in long-term relationships as well.

Some messages are very direct. Statements like "I want to have sex with you" are not ambiguous at all. Unfortunately, such directness is not common in our society. Two New Brunswick studies show that only a minority of people in opposite-sex relationships—22 percent in dating relationships and 41 percent in long-term relationships—use a direct verbal state-

Figure 10.14   Arguments are not necessarily bad for a relationship, but it is important to observe the rules for "fighting fair," unlike this couple.

Fighting fair: A set of rules designed to make arguments constructive rather than destructive.

ment to initiate sex (Byers & Heinlein, 1989; O'Sullivan & Byers, 1992). The rest use ambiguous verbal or non-verbal messages. Similarly, Ontario researchers found that men and women in same-sex relationships are more likely to initiate sex using non-verbal than using verbal behaviours (Beres et al., 2004). Consider George, who stands up, stretches, and says "It's time for bed." Does he mean he wants to engage in sexual activity or to go to sleep?

Ambiguous messages can lead to feelings of hurt and rejection, or to unnecessary anger and perhaps complaints to third parties. If George wants to have sex but his partner interprets his behaviour as meaning that George is tired, George may go to bed feeling hurt, unattractive, and unloved. A woman who casually puts her arm around the shoulders of a co-worker and gives him or her a hug may find herself explaining to her supervisor that it was a gesture of friendship, not a sexual proposition.

When we confront ambiguous messages, we should check out their meaning. The problem is that most of us are reluctant to do that. Somehow we assume that we ought to know exactly what the other person meant, and that we are dumb or naive if we don't. It is important to recognize that many "sexy signals"—like putting an arm around someone's shoulders, inviting a date to your apartment for coffee, or french-kissing while rubbing your date's (clothed) buttocks—really are ambiguous. Ideally, each of us should be effective communicators, making sure our message clearly matches our intent. It helps to be clear yet also subtle and seductive as messages that are too direct/polite may be a turn-off (Graham et al., 2004). As recipients of ambiguous messages, we need to make an effort to clear them up. In response to an invitation to a woman's apartment for coffee, a man might reply, "I would like some coffee, but I'm not interested in sex this time." Or he might draw her out with a question: "I'd like some coffee; is that all you have in mind?" Check out sexy signals. Don't make any assumptions about the meaning of ambiguous messages.

■ ■ ■ SUMMARY

Sexual pleasure is produced by stimulation of various areas of the body; these are the erogenous zones.

Sexual self-stimulation, or autoeroticism, includes masturbation and sexual fantasies. Women typically masturbate by rubbing the clitoris and surrounding tissue and the inner and outer lips. Men generally masturbate by circling the hand around the penis and using an up-and-down movement to stimulate the shaft. Many people have sexual fantasies while masturbating or having sex with a partner. Common themes are having intercourse with a loved partner, kissing passionately, making love elsewhere than the bedroom, and giving and receiving oral sex. Some people incorporate use of erotic materials into their sexual activity.

An important technique in two-person sex is hand stimulation of the partner's genitals. A good guide to technique is to find out how the partner masturbates. Touching other areas of the body and kissing are also important. The other senses—sight, smell, and hearing—can also be used in creating sexual arousal.

While there are infinite varieties in the positions in which one can have intercourse, there are four basic positions: man on top (the "missionary" position), woman on top, rear entry, and side to side.

There are two kinds of mouth–genital stimulation: cunnilingus (mouth stimulation of the female genitals) and fellatio (mouth stimulation of the male genitals). Both are engaged in frequently today and are considered pleasurable by many people. Lesbians, gays, and straights use similar techniques (e.g., hand–genital stimulation and oral–genital sex). Gays and lesbians, though, seem less goal-oriented, take their time more, and communicate more than heterosexuals do.

Anal intercourse involves inserting the penis into the rectum. This activity and insertion of objects into the anus must be done carefully to avoid injury or transmission of STIs.

An aphrodisiac is a substance that arouses sexual desire. There is no known reliable aphrodisiac, and some of the substances that are popularly thought to act as aphrodisiacs can be dangerous to one's health.

We have a tendency in our culture, perhaps a legacy of the Protestant ethic, to view sex as work and to turn sex into an achievement situation, as witnessed by expressions such as "achieving orgasm." Such attitudes make sex less pleasurable and may set the stage for sexual failures or sexual disorders.

There are clear differences in communication patterns between happy, non-distressed couples and couples who are unhappy, seeking counselling, or headed for separation. Destructive patterns of interaction include criticism, contempt, defensiveness, and withdrawal. A key to sexual satisfaction is self-disclosure of sexual likes and dislikes.

The key to maintaining a good relationship is being a good communicator. Specific tips for being a good communicator include: use "I" language; avoid mind reading; document your points with specific examples; use limited-choice questions; level and edit; be a non-defensive listener; give feedback by paraphrasing; validate the other's viewpoint; draw your partner out; be aware of your non-verbal messages; and engage in positive verbal and non-verbal communication. When you do fight, fight fair. Finally, it is important to check out ambiguous sexy signals to find out what they really mean.

■ ■ ■ QUESTIONS FOR THOUGHT, DISCUSSION, AND DEBATE

1. If you are in a long-term relationship, think about the kind of communication pattern you have with your partner. Do you use the methods of communication recommended in this chapter? If not, do you think that there are areas in which you could change and improve? Would your partner cooperate in attempts to improve your communication pattern?
2. What do you think about sexual fantasizing? Is it harmful, or is it a good way to enrich one's sex-

ual expression? Are your ideas consistent with the results of the research discussed in this chapter?
3. You have been in an intimate relationship for two years. You find you are getting bored with your sexual activity. List five things that could make your sexual relationship more satisfying. How would you communicate your desire to do each of these to your partner?

■ ■ ■ SUGGESTIONS FOR FURTHER READING

Comfort, Alex. (1991). *The new joy of sex: A gourmet guide to lovemaking for the nineties.* New York: Crown. Alex Comfort rewrote his bestseller to maintain the joy of sex while recognizing the risk of AIDS.

Dodson, Betty. (1987). *Sex for one: The joy of self-loving.* New York: Harmony Books (Crown Publishers). An inspiring ode to masturbation.

Gibbons, Boyd. (1986). The intimate sense of smell. *National Geographic Magazine, 170,* 324–361. A fascinating discussion of the sense of smell, including its role in sexual interactions.

Gottman, John. (1994). *Why marriages succeed or fail.* New York: Simon & Schuster. Summarizes the results of 20 years of research on communi-

cation in marriage. The book includes self-assessment questions and specific suggestions to help couples enhance their communication.

Kaufman, Miriam, Silverberg, Cory, and Odette, Fran (2003). *The Ultimate guide to sex and disability.* San Fransisco: Cleis Press. These Canadian authors provide the information that people with disabilities need to create a pleasurable sex life that is right for them.

Tannen, Deborah. (1986). *That's not what I meant: How conversational style makes or breaks relationships.* New York: Ballantine Books. Tannen, a communications expert and author of very popular books, provides excellent tips for improving communication.

For Review Questions, Web Resources, and other learning and study tools, visit the *Understanding Human Sexuality* Online Learning Centre at www.mcgrawhill.ca/college/hyde.

CHAPTER 11

Sexuality and the Life Cycle: Childhood and Adolescence

CHAPTER HIGHLIGHTS

My son Jeremy ... naively decided to wear barrettes to nursery school. Several times that day, another boy insisted that Jeremy must be a girl because "only girls wear barrettes." After repeatedly asserting that "wearing barrettes doesn't matter; being a boy means having a penis and testicles," Jeremy finally pulled down his pants as a way of making his point more convincingly. The boy was not impressed. He simply said, "Everybody has a penis; only girls wear barrettes."*

Stop for a moment and think of the first sexual experience you ever had. Some of you will think of the first time you had sexual intercourse. New Brunswick researchers have shown that we tend to use the terms "having sex" and "sexual intercourse" synonymously (Randall & Byers, 2003). For example, fewer than 15 percent thought that genital fondling and fewer than 25 percent thought that oral sex was having sex. Nonetheless, sex is more than just having sexual intercourse. So, others will remember earlier episodes, like "playing doctor" with the other kids in the neighbourhood, or their first passionate kiss, or orgasms with a partner through manual or oral stimulation. Now think of the kind of sex life you had, or expect to have, in your early twenties. Finally, imagine yourself at 65 and imagine the kinds of sexual behaviour you will be engaging in then.

In recent years, scientists have begun thinking of human sexual development as a process that occurs throughout the lifespan. This process is influenced by biological, psychological, social, and cultural factors. This represents a departure from the Freudian heritage, in which the crucial aspects of development were all thought to occur in childhood. This chapter and Chapter 12 are based on the newer **lifespan,** or "life-cycle," approach to understanding the development of our sexual behaviour throughout the course of our lives. The things you were asked to remember and imagine about your own sexual functioning in the preceding paragraph will give you an idea of the sweep of this approach to development.

*From Bem, S.L. (1989). Genital knowledge and gender constancy in preschool children. *Child Development, 60,* 649–662.

Lifespan development: Development from birth through old age.

■ Data Sources

What kinds of scientific data are available on the sexual behaviour of people at various times in their lives? Most of the data come from surveys in which adults are questioned about their childhood sexual behaviour. Their responses form some of the data to be discussed in this chapter. These responses may be even more problematic than some of the other kinds of data from those studies, though. For example, a 50- or 60-year-old man is asked to report on his sexual behaviour at age 10. How accurately will he remember things that happened 40 or 50 years ago? Surely there will be some forgetting. Thus the data on childhood sexual behaviour may be subject to errors that result from adults being asked to recall things that happened a very long time ago.

An alternative would be to interview children about their sexual behaviour or perhaps even to observe their sexual behaviour. Few researchers have done either, for obvious reasons. Such a study would arouse tremendous opposition from parents, religious leaders, and politicians, who might argue that it is unnecessary, or that it would harm the children who were studied. These reactions reflect in part the widespread beliefs that children are not yet sexual beings and should not be exposed to questions about sex. Such research also raises ethical issues: At what age can a child give truly informed consent to be in such a study?

In a few studies children have been questioned directly about their sexual behaviour. Kinsey interviewed 432 children, aged 4 to 14, and the results of the study were published after his death by Elias and Gebhard (1969). A recent innovation is the use of a "talking" computer to interview children (Romer et al., 1997). The computer is programmed to present the questions through headphones, and the child enters his or her answers using the keyboard. This process preserves confidentiality, even when others are present, because only the child knows the question. This procedure was used to gather data from samples of high-risk youth ages 9 to 15. More children reported sexual experience to the computer than did children in face-to-face interviews.

Many studies of adolescent sexual behaviour and attitudes have also been done. The Canadian Youth, Sexual Health, and HIV/AIDS Study (Council of Ministers of Education, 2003) and its predecessor the Canada Youth and AIDS Study (King et al., 1988) are important national surveys. A series of surveys by Reginald Bibby and Donald Posterski (1992; Bibby, 2001) also provide some information about adolescent sexuality in Canada. In the United States, studies done by Kantner and Zelnik (1972, 1973; Zelnik & Kantner, 1980) are important, as are the sociological studies by DeLamater and MacCorquodale (1979), and by Bancroft, Herbenick, and Reynolds (2002). We can have particular confidence in recent, well-sampled studies of adolescent sexuality.

The studies of child and adolescent sexual behaviour have all been surveys that have used either questionnaires or interviews. No one has made systematic, direct observations of children's sexual behaviour.

■ Infancy (0 to 2 Years)

Before 1890, it was thought that sexuality was something that magically appeared at puberty. Historically, we owe the whole notion that children—in fact, infants—have sexual urges and engage in sexual behaviour to Sigmund Freud.

The capacity of the human body to show a sexual response is present from birth. Male infants, for example, get erections. Indeed, boy babies are sometimes born with erections. Ultrasound studies indicate that reflex erections occur in the male fetus for several months before birth (Masters et al., 1982). And vaginal lubrication has been found in baby girls in the 24 hours after birth (Masters et al., 1982).

The first intimate relationship most children experience is with their mothers. The mother–infant relationship involves a good deal of physical contact and typically engages the infant's tactile, olfactory, visual, and auditory senses (Frayser, 1994).

Figure 11.1   Some activities associated with nurturing an infant are potentially sensuous, because they involve pleasant physical contact.

Most activities associated with nurturing and hygienic care of babies is intimate and sensuous since it involves contact with sensitive organs—lips, mouth, anus, and genitals—that can produce in the infant a physiological response of a sensuous and sexual nature. These activities include (in addition to breast-feeding) toilet training, bathing, cleaning, and diapering. The highly physiological and emotionally charged first encounters of mother and infant play an indispensable part in the development process. (Martinson, 1994, p. 11)

Self-stimulation

Infants are often observed fondling their own genitals. There is some question as to how conscious they are of what they are doing, but at the least they seem to be engaging in some pleasurable, sexual self-stimulation. The rhythmic manipulation of the genitals associated with adult masturbation does not occur until age 2½ to 3 years (Martinson, 1994). Ford and Beach (1951) noted on the basis of their survey of sexual behaviour in other cultures that, if permitted, most boys and girls will progress from absentminded fingering of their genitals to systematic masturbation by ages 6 to 8. In fact, in some cultures adults fondle infants' genitals to

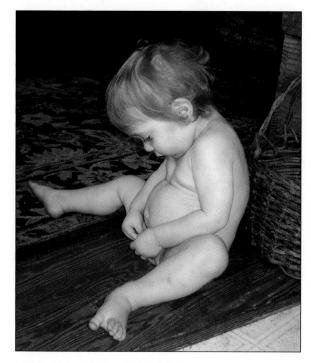

Figure 11.2   Infant self-stimulation.

keep them quiet, a remarkably effective pacifier.

Orgasms from self-stimulation are possible even at this early age, although before puberty boys are not capable of ejaculation. Self-stimulaton is a normal, natural form of sexual expression in infancy. It is definitely not a sign of pathology, as some previous generations believed. Indeed, in one study comparing infants who had optimal relationships with their mothers and infants who had problematic relationships with their mothers, it was the infants with the optimal maternal relationships who were more likely to stimulate their genitals (Spitz, 1949).

Infant–Infant Sexual Encounters

Infants and young children are very self-centred (what the psychologist Jean Piaget called *egocentric*). Even when they seem to be playing with another child, they may simply be playing alongside the other child, actually in a world all their own. Their sexual development parallels the development of their other behaviours. Thus their earliest sex is typically one-person sex—self-stimulation. Not until later do they develop social, two-person heterosexual and/or homosexual sex.

Nonetheless, particularly in later infancy there may be some infant–infant encounters, either affectionate or sexual. In these encounters, children may kiss, hug, pat, stroke, and gaze at each other, behaviours that are part of erotic intimacy later in life.

Non-genital Sensual Experiences

Many of the sensual experiences that infants and young children have are diffuse and not easily classified as some type of activity. For example, as Freud noted, infants delight in putting things in their mouths. Thus sucking at the mother's breast, or sucking on his or her own fingers, may be a sensuous experience for the infant.

Being cuddled or rocked can also be a warm, sensuous experience. Indeed, the infant's experiences in such early intimate encounters might influence her or his reactions to intimacy and cuddling in adulthood. It seems that some infants are cuddlers and some are non-cuddlers (Schaffer & Emerson, 1964). Cuddlers enjoy physical contact, while non-cuddlers show displeasure and restlessness when they are handled or held. As soon as they are old enough to do so, they show resistance to such situations or crawl or walk away from them. Cuddling and non-cuddling seem to be basically different personality patterns. It would be interesting to know whether these patterns remain consistent into adulthood.

Attachment

The quality of the relationship with the parents at this age can be very important to the child's capacity for later sexual and emotional relationships. In psychological terms, an **attachment** (or bond) forms between the infant and the mother, father, or other caregiver. The bond begins in the hours immediately following birth and continues throughout the period of infancy (Coustan & Angelini, 1995), and is facilitated by cuddling and other forms of physical contact. Later, attachments form to other familiar people. These are the individual's earliest experiences with love and emotional attachment. The quality of these attachments—whether they are stable, secure, and satisfying or unstable, insecure, and frustrating—affects the person's capacity for emotional attachments in adulthood. Recent research

Attachment: A psychological bond that forms between an infant and the mother, father, or other caregiver.

with humans (discussed in Chapter 13) indicates that adults' styles of romantic attachment are similar to the kinds of attachment they remember having with their parents in childhood.

Knowing about Boy–Girl Differences

By age 2½ or 3, children know what gender they are (see Chapter 14). They know that they are like the parent of the same gender and different from the parent of the opposite gender and from other children of the opposite gender. At first, infants think that the difference between girls and boys is a matter of clothes or haircuts. But by age 3 there may be some awareness of differences in the genital region and increasing interest in the genitals of other children (Martinson, 1994). At ages 4 to 6 ideas about gender are very rigid, as reflected in the opening vignette. As the child gains experience, these gender beliefs become more flexible (Martin & Ruble, 2004).

■ Early Childhood (3 to 7 Years)

Between the ages of 3 and 7, there is a marked increase in sexual interest and activity, just as there is in activity and interest in general. A recent Swedish survey provides detailed information about the sexual behaviour of children in this age group (Larsson & Svedin, 2002a). Parents and daycare teachers of 89 girls and 96 boys between the ages of 3 and 6 years were asked to rate the frequency of a wide range of sexual behaviour in the child during the preceding six months. In general, the children engaged in more sexual behaviours at home than in the daycare.

Masturbation

Children increasingly gain experience with masturbation during childhood. In a study of 1,114 children ages 2 to 5, the mothers of 60 percent of the boys and of 44 percent of the girls reported that the child touched his or her genitals (Friedrich et al., 1998). In the Swedish study, 43 percent of the girls and 71 percent of the boys had touched his or her own genitals at home; 18 percent of the girls and 28 percent of the boys had used their hand to masturbate (Larsson & Svedin, 2002).

Children also learn during this period that masturbation is something that one does in private.

Figure 11.3   Between the ages of 3 and 7 there is a marked increase in sexual interest.

Other-sex Behaviour

By the age of 4 or 5, children's sexuality has become more social. There is some other sex play. Boys and girls may hug each other or hold hands in imitation of adults. "Playing doctor" can be a popular game at this age (Gundersen et al., 1981). It generally involves no more than exhibiting one's own genitals, looking at those of others, and perhaps engaging in a little fondling or touching. In the Swedish study, 64 percent of the girls and 65 percent of the boys had looked at another child's genitals; 20 percent of the girls and 34 percent of the boys had shown their genitals to other children. As one woman recalled,

> It was at the age of 5 that I, along with my three friends who were sisters and lived next door, first viewed the genitals of a boy. They had a male cousin who came to visit and we all ended up behind the furnace playing doctor. No matter what he would say his symptoms were, we were so fascinated with his penis that it was always the center of our

examinations. I remember giggling as I punched it and dunked it in some red food-colored water that we were using for medicine. This seemed to give him great enjoyment. One girl put hand lotion and a bandage on his penis and in the process he had an erection. We asked him to do it again, but their [sic] was no such luck. (Martinson, 1994, p. 37)

By about the age of 5, children have formed a concept of marriage—or at least of its non-genital aspects. They know that a member of the other gender is the socially appropriate marriage partner, and they are committed to marrying when they get older (Broderick, 1966a, 1966b). They practise marriage roles as they "play house."

Some children first learn about heterosexual behaviour by seeing or hearing their parents engaging in sexual intercourse, or the *primal scene experience*. Freud believed that this experience could inhibit the child's subsequent psychosexual development; some contemporary writers share this belief. Limited empirical data suggest that the experience is not damaging. In surveys, about 20 percent of middle-class parents report that their child observed them when the child was 4 to 6 years of age. Parents report such reactions as curiosity ("Why are you bobbing up and down?"), amusement and giggling, or embarrassment and closing the door (Okami, 1995).

Same-sex Behaviour

During late childhood and preadolescence, sexual play with members of one's own gender may be more common than sexual play with members of the other gender (Martinson, 1994). Generally the activity involves no more than touching the other's genitals (Broderick, 1966a). One girl recalled:

> I encountered a sexual experience that was confusing at kindergarten age. . . . Some afternoons we would meet and lock ourselves in a bedroom and take our pants off. We took turns lying on the bed and put pennies, marbles, etc. between our labia. . . . As the ritual became old hat, it passed out of existence. (Martinson, 1994, p. 62)

Sex Knowledge and Interests

At age 3 or 4, children begin to have some notion that there are genital differences between males and females, but their ideas are very vague. By age 7,

30 percent of North American children understand what the differences are (Goldman & Goldman, 1982). Children generally react to their discovery of genital differences calmly, though of course there are exceptions.

At age 3, children are very interested in different postures for urinating. Girls attempt to urinate while standing. Children are also very affectionate at this age. They enjoy hugging and kissing their parents and may even propose marriage to the parent of the other gender.

At age 4, children are particularly interested in bathrooms and elimination. Games of "show" are also common at this age. They become less common at age 5, as children become more modest. The development of modesty reflects the child's learning of the restrictions that Canadian society places on sexual expression. Often as early as age 3 the child is taught by his or her parents not to display or touch certain parts of his or her body, at least in public. Children are often taught not to touch the bodies of others. Many parents also restrict conversation about sex. These restrictions come at precisely the time the child is becoming more aware of and curious about sexuality. As one young man recalled:

> One of my favorite pastimes was playing doctor with my little sister. During this doctor game we would both be nude and I would sit on her as if we were having intercourse. On one occasion, I was touching my sister's genital area and mother discovered us. We were sternly switched and told it was dirty and to never get caught again or we would be whipped twice as bad. So, we made sure we were never caught again. (Starks & Morrison, 1996)

As a result, children turn to sex play and their peers for information about sex (Martinson, 1994). Cross-cultural data suggest that in less restrictive societies, children continue to show overt interest in sexual activities through childhood and preadolescence (Frayser, 1994). In the rare society that puts no restrictions on childhood sex play, intercourse may occur as young as age 6 or 7. In Canada, first intercourse usually occurs several years later than this.

It is important to remember that children's sex play at this age is motivated largely by curiosity and is part of the general learning experiences of childhood. One man illustrated this well as he recalled:

At the age of six or seven my friend (a boy) and I had a great curiosity for exploring the anus. It almost seemed *more like scientific research.* (Martinson, 1994, p. 59, italics added)

A longitudinal study of the impact of childhood sex play obtained reports from mothers when the child was 6, and assessed the sexual adjustment of the person at age 17 or 18 (Okami et al., 1997). Forty-seven percent of the mothers reported that their child had engaged in interactive sex play. Looking at a range of outcomes, including social relationships and sexual behaviour and "problems," there were no significant differences between males and females whose mothers reported such play, and males and females whose mothers did not report such activity.

■ Preadolescence (8 to 12 Years)

Preadolescence is a period of transition between the years of childhood and the years of puberty and adolescence. Freud used the term *latency* to refer to the preadolescent period following the resolution of the Oedipus complex. He believed that the sexual urges go "underground" during latency and are not expressed. The evidence indicates, however, that Freud was wrong and that children's interest in and expression of sexuality remain lively throughout this period, perhaps more lively than their parents are willing to believe. For many, "sexual awakening" does not occur until the teens, but for others it is a very real and poignant part of preadolescence (Martinson, 1994).

At around age 9 or 10, the first bodily changes of puberty begin: the formation of breast buds in girls and the growth of pubic hair. The growth of pubic hair occurs in response to *adrenarche,* the maturation of the adrenal glands, leading to increased levels of androgens. In three recent studies, one of adolescents and two of adults, the average age at which participants reported first experiencing sexual attraction to another person was at age 10 (McClintock & Herdt, 1996). The samples included gays, lesbians, and heterosexual men and women. This experience may reflect the maturation of the adrenal gland and the increase in testosterone and estradiol (a steroid responsible for the development of female reproductive organs) that result. This research suggests that "adult" sexual development starts as early as age 9 or 10, not at puberty as previously thought.

Masturbation

During preadolescence, more and more children gain experience with masturbation. In a sample of university women, 40 percent recalled masturbating before puberty.[1] The comparable figure for men is 38 percent (Bancroft et al., 2003). Other data, as well as those on adolescents, indicate that boys generally start masturbating earlier than girls do. A study of 269 high-school seniors in Sweden inquired about solitary sexual activities in childhood. Forty-two percent of the boys and 20 percent of the girls reported masturbating to orgasm by age 12; an additional 27 percent of the boys and 18 percent of the girls reported masturbating without orgasm (Larrson & Svedin, 2002).

Interestingly, boys and girls learn about masturbation in different ways. Typically boys are told about it by their male peers, they see their peers doing it, or they read about it; girls most frequently learn about masturbation through accidental self-discovery (Langfeldt, 1981). One man recalled:

An older cousin of mine took two of us out to the garage and did it in front of us. I remember thinking that it seemed a very strange thing to do, and that people who were upright wouldn't do it, but it left a powerful impression on me. A couple of years later, when I began to get erections, I wanted to do it, and felt I shouldn't, but I remembered how he had looked when he was doing it, and the memory tempted me strongly. I worried, and held back, and fought it, but finally I gave in. The worry didn't stop me, and doing it didn't stop my worrying. (Hunt, 1974, p. 79)

Other-sex Behaviour

There is generally little sexual behaviour with the other gender during the preadolescent period, mainly because of the social division of males and females into separate groups. However, children commonly hear about sexual intercourse for the first time during this period. For example, in a sample of adult women, 61 percent recalled having learned about intercourse by age 12 (Wyatt et al., 1988). Children's reactions to this new information are an amusing combination of shock and disbelief—particularly disbelief that their parents would

---

[1]These are cumulative-incidence figures, to use the terminology introduced at the end of Chapter 3.

do such a thing. A university woman recalled:

> One of my girlfriends told me about sexual intercourse. It was one of the biggest shocks of my life. She took me aside one day, and I could tell she was in great distress. I thought she was going to tell me about menstruation, so I said that I already knew, and she said, "No, this is *worse!*" Her description went like this: "A guy puts his thing up a girl's hole, and she has a baby." The hole was, to us, the anus, because we did not even know about the vagina and we knew that the urethra was too small. I pictured the act as a single, violent and painful stabbing at the anus by the penis. Somehow, the idea of a baby was forgotten by me. I was horrified and repulsed, and I thought of that awful penis I had seen years ago. At first I insisted that it wasn't true, and my friend said she didn't know for sure, but that's what her cousin told her. But we looked at each other, and we knew it was true. We held each other and cried. We insisted that "my parents would never do that," and "I'll never let anyone do it to me." We were frightened, sickened, and threatened by the idea of some lusty male jabbing at us with his horrid penis. (From a student essay)

In the study of Swedish high-school seniors, more than 80 percent reported having consensual sexual experiences with another child when they were 6 to 12 years old (Larsson & Svedin, 2002b). The most common activities were talking about sex, kissing and hugging, looking at pornographic videos, and teasing other children sexually. With the exception of kissing and hugging, these activities were more often reported to have occurred when they were 11 and 12 than when they were ages 6 to 10. Turning to the gender of the partner, 57 percent of the boys reported such experiences with girls, 11 percent with another boy, and 33 percent with both boys and girls. For girls, the percentages were 31 with a boy, 29 with a girl, and 40 with both. Thus, sexual experiences are very common, especially at ages 11 and 12, and involve consensual experiences with both boys and girls.

The age at which youth have their first consensual sexual intercourse experience has been declining (see Figure 11.8 later in this chapter). Some boys and girls have their first experience during the preadolescent period. A study of American college students using computer-assisted self-interviewing found that 9 percent of the women and 16 percent of the men reported oral–genital contact, 3 percent of both reported inserting objects in the anus, 18 percent of the women and 22 percent of the men reported inserting objects in the vagina, and 2 percent of the women and 5 percent of the men reported having vaginal intercourse prior to entering high school (Reynolds et al., 2003). Five percent of male adolescents and 1 percent of female adolescents in Canada report that they had engaged in sexual intercourse by the age of 12. The majority of Canadians first engage in intercourse between the ages of 16 and 19 (Maticka-Tyndale, 1997).

For some preadolescents, heterosexual activity occurs in an incestuous relationship, whether brother–sister or parent–child. This topic is discussed in detail in Chapter 17.

Same-sex Behaviour

It is important to understand same-sex sexual activity as a normal part of the sexual development of children. In preadolescence, most children have a social organization that is essentially homosocial, or **gender segregated**. That is, boys play separately from girls, and thus children socialize mainly with members of their own gender. This separation begins at around age 8. According to one study of children's friendship patterns, the segregation reaches a peak at around 10 to 12 years of age. At ages 12 to 13 children are simultaneously the most segregated by gender and the most interested in members of the opposite gender (Broderick, 1966b). Observational research suggests that there is greater segregation at school than in neighbourhood play groups (Thorne, 1993).

Given that children are socializing with other members of their own gender, sexual exploring at this age is likely to be with partners of the same gender. These activities generally involve masturbation, exhibitionism, and the fondling of other's genitals. Boys, for example, may engage in a "circle jerk," in which they masturbate in a group.

Girls do not seem so likely to engage in such group activities, perhaps because the spectacle of

---

Gender-segregated social organization: A general form of social grouping in which males play and associate with other males, and females play and associate with other females; that is, the genders are separate from each other.

them masturbating is not quite so impressive or perhaps because they already sense the greater cultural restrictions on their sexuality and are hesitant to discuss sexual matters with other girls.

A study of psychosexual development among lesbian, gay, and bisexual youth ages 14 to 21 found that the participants reported their first experience of sexual attraction at age 10 or 11 (Rosario et al., 1996). Their first experience of sexual fantasies occurred several months to one year later. The first sexual activity with another person occurred on average at ages 12 or 13. All of the young men and women reported experiencing sexual attraction to and fantasies about a person of the same gender, and one-half also reported them about a person of the other gender.

Dating and Romantic Relationships

Pre- and early adolescence is a period of transition in the nature of social relationships. We noted above the preadolescent activities are often homosocial. Around ages 10 or 11, children begin to spend time in mixed-gender or heterosexual groups. These groups engage in a variety of activities, including "hanging out" in parks or at malls, going to clubs, sporting events, or movies, and later going to parties or dances. A study of 1,284 students in grades 5 through 8 in the U.S. found that the frequency of these mixed-gender activities increased steadily over the four grades (Connolly, Craig, Goldberg, & Pepler, 2004). It is in these mixed-group settings that youth typically first experience dyadic pairings and their first romantic or sexual behaviours. These early behaviours are primarily holding hands, hugging and kissing, and petting above the waist (Williams, Taradash, & Connolly, 2004). Kissing games are popular at parties. One 17-year-old man recalled:

> In sixth and seventh grade it was the Friday night party, where there was a lot of petting and kissing and fondling. In the eighth grade, double dates were real big, watch a movie and fondle. That was pretty much it. (Maurer, 1994, p. 29)

According to the study of the students in grades 5 through 8, *dating*, defined as spending time or going out with a boy or girl whom the youth liked, loved, or had a crush on, emerged in grade 7. A New Brunswick study found that 70 percent of the boys and 77 percent of the girls who were 12 said that they had had a boyfriend or girlfriend (Price

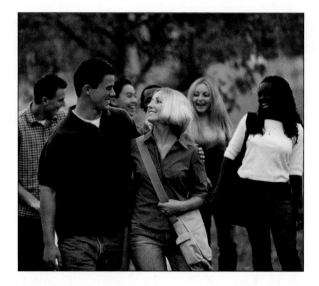

Figure 11.4 Group dating, heterosexual parties, and hanging out emerge during preadolescence, and may include making out.

et al., 2000). At age 13, the figures were 82 percent for the boys and 85 percent for the girls. Many of these relationships are short-lived. For example, the Canadian Youth, Sexual Health, and HIV/AIDS Study (CYSHHAS) found that 25 percent of boys and 23 percent of girls in grade 7 reported having had a steady boyfriend/girlfriend in the last 12 months; however, 34 percent of boys and 34 percent of girls reported having had two or more steady boyfriend/girlfriends within that time period (Council of Ministers of Education, 2003). Some adolescents begin to go out at night with boys and girls, to double date, or to go on dates. However, mixed-gender activities remain very common through grade 8. Another survey of 12- and 13-year-olds in the U.S. found that light sexual activity—that is, holding hands, hugging, and kissing—was reported by about half of the 13-year-olds (Williams et al., 2004). Heavy sexual activity—petting below the waist and intercourse—was reported by fewer than 10 percent of the 13-year-olds; those who reported heavy activity also reported going out on dates alone (without friends). Thus, the progression from mixed-gender activities to dyadic dating is paralleled by a progression in the development of physical intimacy.

Most lesbian and gay youth do not date those they are most attracted to out of very real fear of harass-

In Focus 11.1

What Impact Do the Mass Media Have on Adolescent Sexuality?

A major developmental task of adolescence is learning how to manage physical and emotional intimacy in relationships with others. It is not surprising, therefore, that young people are curious about sex and about sexual intimacy. An increasingly important source of information is the mass media. Although most students identify school as their main source of information on human sexuality, 12 percent of boys and 15 percent of girls in grade 9 indicated that most of their information came from television and movies or books and magazines; 12 percent of the boys and 3 percent of the girls named the Internet as their main source (Council of Ministers of Education, 2003). Whether it is a main source of information, the mass media still provide images and information about sexuality. Further, Canadian youth are influenced by both the Canadian and the U.S. media. Children who watched the TV program *Dawson's Creek* were introduced to Jen, who lost her virginity at age 12. Youth who watch talk shows learn about erection problems, and ways to deal with them. *Da Vinci's Inquest* provides information about erotic dancers, sex workers, and the sex trade. Soap operas deal, sometimes explicitly, with sexual themes like sexual non-responsiveness, menopause, abortion, and extradyadic sex. How much sexual content is there in the mass media? To what extent are children and adolescents exposed to it? And what is the impact of this exposure?

A good deal of research has been devoted to the question of how much sexual content there is in the U.S. media. Content analyses of the media define *sexual material* as verbal references to sexual activity, innuendo, implied sexual activity, and explicit presentations. Looking first at prime-time television, analyses indicate that there has been a 300-percent increase in the number and explicitness of sexual portrayals between 1989 and 1999 (Parents Television Council, 2000). In the 1997–1998 season, there were 5.3 portrayals per hour on the major U.S. networks (Kunkel et al., 1999). The 2000 *Maclean's/ Global Poll* found that 47 percent of Canadians felt that there is too much sexually explicit programming on prime-time TV. Consequences such as pregnancy and sexually transmitted infections are rarely discussed or shown (Kunkel et al., 1996). Turning to movies, adolescents see feature films in theatres, on pay TV, or on videotape or DVD. Many of these films are rated R and contain more frequent and more explicit depictions of sexual behaviour, an average of 17.5 per hour, than depictions of sexual behaviour on prime-time television (Greenberg et al., 1996). Cable movie networks have the largest proportion with sexual content (Fisher et al., 2004). The most frequent portrayals are of unmarried hetero-

ment from their peers. Further, gay and lesbian youth are more likely to be the victims of crime than are their heterosexual peers (Comstock, 1991). Many date partners of the other gender in order to conform to societal expectations (Savin-Williams, 1994).

Of course, these patterns are averages for Canadian preadolescents. There is great variability in the timing of these developments and between youth from different ethno-cultural communities in Canada. In some cultures, boys and girls are married by age 13.

■ Adolescence (13 to 19 Years)

A surge of sexual interest occurs around puberty and continues through adolescence (which is equated here roughly with the teenage years, ages 13 to 19). This heightened sexuality may be caused by a number of factors, including bodily changes and an awareness of them, rises in levels of sex hormones, and increased cultural emphasis on sex and rehearsal for adult gender roles. We can see evidence of this heightened sexuality particularly sexual intercourse, often in a context of alcohol and drug use; only one in four shows with sexual intercourse depicted make reference to safer sex (Kaiser Family Foundation, 2003).

We have already mentioned the variety of sexual situations, most of them problematic, that are included in soap operas. In 1994, each episode of a soap contained an average of 6.6 sexual portrayals, and safer sex was mentioned only infrequently (Greenberg & Bussell, 1996). Finally, there are music videos. The visual elements in many MuchMusic videos are implicitly or explicitly sexual (Brown & Steele, 1995), and frequently combine sexuality with implicit aggression (Sommers-Flanagan et al., 1993). Music videos also objectify women, presenting them in revealing clothing and portraying them as receptive to sexual advances. In addition, although we are starting to see more programs portraying gay and lesbian adults, there are still few positive media images of gay and lesbian adolescents with whom gay and lesbian youth can identify.

There are some differences between Canadian and U.S. television shows. In particular, some topics can be introduced into Canadian television shows that would not be considered acceptable by the U.S. networks (M. Byers, 2001). For example, *Degrassi Junior* (and then *Senior*) *High*, a popular television show of the 1980s and early 1990s, tended to portray youth sexuality in diverse ways and used story lines to explore different sexual choices such as the decision to engage in intercourse, as well as the realistic consequences of sexual behaviour. Some of the female characters became pregnant—in one case a grade 8 character decided to keep her baby and stay in school; in two other cases the characters had abortions, allowing the show to present the abortion debate. Similarly, in *Degrassi: The Next Generation,* one of the female characters became pregnant and had an abortion with no negative psychological consequences. Although these episodes were shown on the Canadian network carrying the show, the American cable station that carries it would not air the abortion episodes. Lest we get too smug as Canadians, it's important to note that the show included very little discussion of gay, lesbian, and bisexual youth (M. Byers, 2001).

Clearly, the mass media are providing a great deal of sexual content. But is anybody watching? Children ages 9 to 13 are heavy TV viewers (Comstock, 1991). During middle and late adolescence, TV viewing declines, and time spent watching music videos, reading magazines, and surfing the Net increases (for a discussion of the sexual material available on the Internet, see Chapter 18).

What effect do these portrayals have? There has been less research on this issue, partly because it is difficult to isolate the effects of media exposure from other influences on adolescents' sexual attitudes and behaviour. Media images can have an immediate effect on the user's emotional state: portrayals may induce arousal, which can influence behaviour or activate thoughts or associations. Media portrayals may have long-term effects in that children may learn schemas and scripts that influ-

in the data on masturbation. But before examining those data, let's consider some theoretical ideas about how hormones and social forces might interact as influences on adolescent sexuality.

Udry (1988) has proposed a theoretical model that recognizes that both sociological factors and biological factors are potent in adolescent sexuality. He studied eighth-, ninth-, and tenth-graders (13 to 16 years old), measuring their hormone levels (testosterone, estrogen, and progesterone) and a number of sociological factors (for example, whether they were in a two-parent family, their parents' educational level, the teenager's response to a scale measuring sexually permissive attitudes, and the teenager's attachment to conventional institutions such as involvement in school sports and church attendance). Thirty-five percent of the males had engaged in sexual intercourse, as had 14 percent of the females.

For boys, testosterone levels had a very strong relationship to sexual activity (including coitus, masturbation, and the extent of feeling sexually ence their later sexual decision-making and behaviour (Kaiser Family Foundation, 1998). One experimental study indicated that teenagers exposed to 15 hours of portrayals of non-marital sexual relationships had more permissive attitudes toward non-marital sex than did teens exposed to portrayals of non-sexual relationships (Bryant & Rockwell, 1994). Another experiment randomly assigned university students to watch clips from TV portraying sexual stereotypes (e.g., women as sex objects) or nonsexual content and assessed the frequency and involvement of their TV viewing. Those who viewed a stereotypic clip and then reported greater frequency and involvement of viewing were more likely to endorse the stereotype (Ward, 2002). Thus, media portrayals reinforce stereotyped views of sexual behaviour and sexual relationships (Brown, 2002). The media may also influence standards of physical attractiveness and contribute to the dissatisfaction with their bodies that many, especially women, feel. For example, research has shown that viewing as little as 30 minutes of television can change women's perceptions of their bodies, which the authors term the "elastic body image" (Myers & Biocca, 1992).

Finally, a one-year longitudinal study of 1,792 adolescents between the ages of 12 and 17 examined the relationship between the extent of sexual content the adolescents watched on television at baseline and their sexual activity over the subsequent year. The study found that the adolescents who watched more sexual content were more likely to advance their sexual activity—that is, engage in breast fondling, genital fondling, and/or intercourse for the first time. The relationship between viewing more sexual content on television and initiating sexual activity held after the researchers controlled for other factors known to be associated with sexual activity, such as the extent of parent monitoring, school grades, and religiosity (Collins et al., 2004). This may mean that watching sexual content on television hastens sexual activity. However, as these results are correlational (see Chapter 3) it may also mean, for example, that youth who are more interested in engaging in sexual activity (and subsequently do so) are also more interested in watching television programs with sexual content.

The evidence that mass media portrayals have an important impact on adolescent sexual knowledge, attitudes, and behaviour is not conclusive. On the other hand, both children and adolescents believe that mass media are an important source of their knowledge. The problem lies in the fact that these portrayals are unrealistic. In sharp contrast to the high rates of non-marital sex portrayed in the media, most sexual activity involves persons who are married or living common-law (see Chapter 12). Many couples in real life, whether married or not, are responsible users of birth control. Many youth and adults use various forms of condoms to prevent STIs. It is unfortunate that these realities are missing from mass media portrayals of sexual behaviour. It is also unfortunate that the media have generally not taken advantage of their opportunity to provide positive sexuality education.

"turned on"). Sexually permissive attitudes, a social variable, were related to sexuality among boys although they had a much smaller effect than testosterone did. For girls, the relationship between testosterone level and sexual activity was not as strong as it was for boys, but it was a significant relationship, and it was testosterone—not estrogen or progesterone—that was related to sexuality. Pubertal development (developing a "curvy" figure) had an effect, probably by increasing the girl's attractiveness. And the effects of testosterone were accentuated among girls in father-absent families. Testosterone level as well as social variables such as permissive attitudes and church attendance influenced the girls' plans about sexuality.

This study shows that testosterone levels have a substantial impact on the sexuality of adolescent boys and girls. Social variables (such as permissive attitudes, father absence for girls, and church attendance) interact with the biological effects, in some cases magnifying them and in some cases suppressing them. Similarly, a study with gay and lesbian youth found that increases in hormone levels with puberty resulted in increases in homo-erotic sexual feelings and behaviours (Savin-Williams, 1995).

Masturbation

According to the Kinsey data, there is a sharp increase in the incidence of masturbation for boys between the ages of 13 and 15. This is illustrated in Figure 11.5. Note that the curve is steepest between the ages of 13 and 15, indicating that most boys begin masturbating to orgasm during that period. By age 15, 82 percent of the boys in Kinsey's study had masturbated. Many girls also begin masturbating in adolescence, but note that the curve on the graph is flatter for them, indicating that many girls do not begin masturbating until later. Thus the increase in their masturbation behaviour is much more gradual than for boys and continues past adolescence.

A study at the University of British Columbia asked students whether they had ever masturbated (Meston et al., 1996). Overall, 80 percent of the males and 48 percent of the females reported masturbating at least once. Asian students were significantly less likely to have masturbated than were non-Asian students. Eighty-five percent of non-Asian males compared to 74 percent of Asian

males had masturbated. The difference between non-Asian and Asian females was even greater— 59 percent compared to 39 percent.

More recent data indicate that children and adolescents begin to masturbate earlier today, and thus the Kinsey data need to be pushed back about one or two years. However, the general shape of the curves still holds (Bancroft et al., 2003).

Boys typically masturbate two or three times per week, whereas girls do so about once per month (Hass, 1979). Interestingly, the frequency of masturbation among boys decreases during periods when they are having sexual intercourse; among girls, however, this situation is accompanied by an increased frequency of masturbation (Sorensen, 1973).

Attitudes toward Masturbation

Attitudes toward masturbation underwent a dramatic change in the twentieth century. As a result, adolescents are now given much different information about masturbation than were earlier adolescents, and this may affect both their behaviour and their feelings about masturbation. For example, a popular handbook, *What a Boy Should Know*, written in 1913 by two doctors, advised its readers:

> Whenever unnatural emissions are produced . . . the body becomes "slack." A boy will not feel so vigorous and springy; he will be more easily tired. . . . He will probably look pale and pasty, and he is lucky if he escapes indigestion and getting his bowels confined, both of which will probably give him spots and pimples on his face. . . .

> The results on the mind are the more severe and more easily recognized. . . . A boy who practices this habit can never be the best that Nature intended him to be. His wits are not so sharp. His memory is not so good. His power of fixing his attention on whatever he is doing is lessened. . . . A boy like this is a poor thing to look at. . . .

> . . . The effect of self-abuse on a boy's characteralways tends to weaken it, and in fact, to make him untrustworthy, unreliable, untruthful, and probably even dishonest. (Schofield & Vaughan-Jackson, 1913, pp. 30–42)

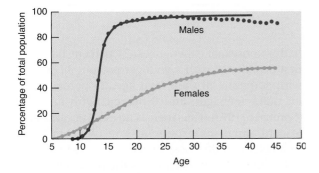

Figure 11.5 Cumulative incidence of males and females who have masturbated to orgasm, according to Kinsey's data. Current data suggest that contemporary youth begin masturbating one or two years earlier.

Masturbation, in short, was once believed to cause everything from warts to insanity.[2]

Attitudes toward masturbation are now considerably more positive, and today few people would subscribe to notions like those expressed earlier. By the 1970s only about 15 percent of young people believed that masturbation is wrong (Hunt, 1974, p. 74). Indeed, masturbation is now recommended as a remedy in sex therapy. As psychiatrist Thomas Szasz said, the shift in attitudes toward masturbation has been so great that in a generation it has changed from a disease to a form of therapy.

While approval of masturbation is now explicit, people can still have mixed feelings about it. Examples of lingering negative attitudes are reflected in questions that teens ask online experts about masturbation, such as "Is it bad?", "How do I stop feeling guilty after I do it?", and "Is it normal?" (Planned Parenthood Federation of America, 2002).

Same-sex Behaviour

About 10 percent of men and 6 percent of women in university report having had a same-sex partner in high school (Bancroft et al., 2003). Of those who have

Figure 11.6 Oshawa high school student Marc Hall and his boyfriend Jean-Paul Dumond walk to their limousine on prom night. Despite the objection by the school board, the Ontario Superior Court granted Hall permission to attend his prom with his boyfriend.

[2]In case you're wondering why boys' advice books were saying such awful things, there is a rather interesting history that produced those pronouncements (Money, 1986). The Swiss physician Simon André Tissot (1728–1797) wrote an influential book, *Treatise on the Diseases Produced by Onanism*, taking the term from the biblical story of Onan (Genesis 38:9). In this work he articulated a degeneracy theory, in which loss of semen was believed to weaken a man's body; Tissot had some very inventive physiological explanations for his idea. The famous American physician of the 1800s Benjamin Rush was influenced by Tissot and spread degeneracy theory in North America. The theory became popularized by Sylvester Graham (1794–1851), a religious zealot and health reformer, who was a vegetarian and whose passion for health foods gave us the names for Graham flour and Graham crackers. To be healthy, according to Graham, one needed to follow the Graham diet and practise sexual abstinence. Then John Harvey Kellogg (1852–1943) of—you guessed it—cornflakes fame entered the story. He was an ardent follower of Graham and his doctrines of health food and sexual abstinence. While experimenting with healthful foods, he invented cornflakes. His younger brother, Will Keith Kellogg, thought to add sugar and made a fortune. John Harvey Kellogg contributed further to public fears about masturbation by writing (during his honeymoon, no less) *Plain Facts for Old and Young: Embracing the Natural History and Hygiene of Organic Life,* which provided detailed descriptions of the horrible diseases supposedly caused by masturbation. These ideas then found their way into the advice books for boys of the early 1900s.

had homosexual experiences, 24 percent had their first experience with a younger person, 39 percent with someone of their own age, 29 percent with an older teenager, and 8 percent with an adult (Sorensen, 1973). Thus there is no evidence that adolescent same-sex experiences result from being seduced by adults; most such encounters take place between peers. In many cases the person has only one or a few same-sex experiences, partly out of curiosity, and the behaviour is discontinued. Such adolescent behaviour does not seem to be predictive of adult homosexual orientation.

Comparing the results reported by Bancroft et al. (2003) with those reported by DeLamater and Mac-

Corquodale (1979), there has been no increase in the incidence of adolescent same-sex sexual behaviour. It seems safe to conclude from various studies, taken together, that about 10 percent of adolescents have same-sex sexual experiences, with the percentages being somewhat higher for boys than for girls.

Alberta sociologist Reginald Bibby (2001) surveyed 3,600 teenagers across Canada, ages 15 to 19. He found that 66 percent of the girls and 41 percent of the boys approve of sexual relations between two people of the same sex. On the other hand, teenagers can be quite naive about same-sex sexual behaviour and societal attitudes toward it. In some cases, they have been taught that sexual activity with the other gender is "bad"; having been told nothing about same-sex sexual activity, they infer that it is permissible. In some cases, sexual relationships naively develop from a same-gender friendship of late childhood and adolescence. One woman recalled:

> I did not even know what homosexuality was. I had never heard the term, although I had read extensively. One day at a friend's house, we were listening to music in her bedroom, she came on to me in a very surprising way. We were good friends and spent much time together, but this particular night was different. Her eyes had a new sparkle, she got very close to me, her touch lingered; she was different than she ever had been before. I was 16 and she was 15. I did not understand, but I knew that I was aroused. We were good church going kids who had never heard anything about this. (Starks & Morrison, 1996, p. 97)

Other-sex Behaviour

Toward the middle and end of the adolescent years, more and more young people engage in heterosexual sex, with more and more frequency. Thus heterosexual behaviour gains prominence and becomes the major sexual outlet.

In terms of the individual's development, the data indicate that there is a very regular progression from kissing, through French kissing and breast and genital fondling, to intercourse and oral–genital contact; this generally occurs over a period of four or more years (Council of Ministers of Education, 2003; DeLamater, 2003). The progression in sexual behaviour is evident from data

on the percentage of youth who have engaged in five different sexual behaviours provided in Table 11.1. Students in grades 9 and 11 were asked whether they had ever engaged in deep kissing, touching above the waist, touching below the waist, oral sex, and sexual intercourse; students in grade 7 were asked only about deep kissing, touching above the waist, and touching below the waist. In grade 7, more than one-third more students had engaged in deep kissing and touching above the waist than had engaged in touching below the waist. In grade 9, almost three times as many students had engaged in deep kissing and more than twice as many had engaged in touching below the waist than had engaged in sexual intercourse. Further, more students had engaged in oral sex than had engaged in sexual intercourse. More than half of grade 11 students had engaged in oral sex and almost half had engaged in sexual intercourse, but more than three-quarters had engaged in touching below the waist. The progression of sexual experience is also evident in the finding that the percentage of students who had engaged in each of the five sexual behaviours was greatest for grade 11 students, intermediate for grade 9 students, and lowest for grade 7 students. To use the terminology introduced in Chapter 2, these behaviours tend to follow a sexual script.

It is interesting to compare youth involvement in sexual activity in the CYSHHAS to the results from the Canadian Youth, Sexual Health, and

Figure 11.7 Sexuality in early adolescence is often playful and unsophisticated.

Table 11.1 Percentage of Canadian Youth Who Have at Least Once Engaged in Various Sexual Behaviours

	Grade 7		Grade 9		Grade 11	
	Boys	Girls	Boys	Girls	Boys	Girls
Deep (open-mouth) kissing	49%	35%	65%	67%	81%	82%
Touching above the waist	46%	34%	67%	64%	81%	81%
Touching below the waist	33%	23%	57%	54%	75%	74%
Oral sex			32%	28%	53%	52%
Sexual intercourse			23%	19%	40%	46%

Source: Council of Ministers of Education (2003). *Canadian youth, sexual health and HIV/AIDS study: Factors influencing knowledge attitudes and behaviours.* Research conducted by Council of Ministers of Education, Canada, with funding provided by Health Canada.

HIV/AIDS Study conducted in 1988 (King et al., 1988). The percentage of students reporting having engaged in deep kissing and sexual touching changed very little over the 14 years between the two studies. However, somewhat fewer students reported having engaged in sexual intercourse in 2003 than in 1988. The earlier survey did not ask about oral sex.

■ Teen Sex

One of the most dramatic changes to occur in sexual behaviour and attitudes in recent decades is in the area of youth sexual behaviour often called premarital sex. Note that the very term "*pre*marital sex" contains some hidden assumptions, most notably that marriage is normative and that proper sex occurs in marriage. Thus, sex among never-married (young) persons is considered *pre*marital—something done before marrying. A more neutral term would be "non-marital sex," although this fails to distinguish between premarital sex, extramarital sex, and postmarital sex and also contains the assumption of marriage. Perhaps we should just call it "adolescent sex" or "teen sex."

How Many Youth Engage in Sexual Intercourse?

On the basis of the data he collected in the 1940s, Kinsey concluded that about 33 percent of all females and 71 percent of all males have had premarital intercourse by the age of 25. According to the NHSLS (Laumann et al., 1994), 70 percent of women and 78 percent of men interviewed reported

engaging in vaginal intercourse before marriage. Thus in the 50 years between these two large-scale surveys, the incidence of premarital intercourse doubled among women, while increasing only slightly among men. Today, most Canadians who marry engage in premarital sex.

As premarital intercourse has become common, and many Canadians choose not to marry, attention has shifted to "teen sex," the incidence of sexual intercourse among teenagers. As shown in Table 11.1, almost half of students have engaged in intercourse by the age of 17 (grade 11). Many sexually experienced youth have had two or more sexual partners (Fisher & Boroditsky, 2000). For example, almost half of the grade 9 and 11 students surveyed in the CYSHHAS who had engaged in sexual intercourse had had two or more partners (Council of Ministers of Education, 2003).

Not only are more teenagers having sex than in the 1940s, but young people today are engaging in intercourse for the first time at younger ages, compared to Canadians born 30 years earlier. Figure 11.8 gives data from the National Population Health Survey conducted by Health Canada based on interviews with more than 35,000 Canadians between the ages of 15 and 59. The figure displays the percentage of men and women who had premarital intercourse by ages 15, 17, and 19 and is based on analyses of National Population Health Survey data by Eleanor Maticka-Tyndale, Michael Barrett, and Alexander McKay (2000b).

First, note that few women or men have intercourse at age 15 or younger, whether born in the early 1940s (3 percent of these women and 13 percent of these men had intercourse by age 15) or in the early

1970s (22 percent of these women and 22 percent of these men had intercourse by age 15). Second, among the oldest group of women only 15 percent had had intercourse by age 17; this percentage increases steadily to 54 percent for women born between 1972 and 1976. For men, 36 percent of the oldest group had had intercourse by age 17; this percentage increases steadily for men born up to 1957 but levels off for men born after 1957. Finally, since the 1940s, there has been an increase in the percentage of men and women who have intercourse by age 19; however, this percentage has stayed steady over the past 20 years for men and over the past 10 years for women. Today 80 percent of men and 75 percent of women have intercourse by age 19.

In short, age of first intercourse has been decreasing. The median age at first intercourse for people who were born between 1942 and 1946 is 18 for men and 20 for women. However, the median age of first intercourse for respondents who were teenagers at the time of the survey (that is, born between 1972 and 1976) is 17 for both males and females. Thus, while the age of first intercourse has decreased for both men and women over the past 30 years, this change has been especially pronounced for women. These trends reflect, in part, the impact of the "sexual revolution" of the 1960s and 1970s, which encouraged greater openness about sexuality

and acceptance of sex between people who are not married and other forms of sexual expression, particularly for women.

For all age groups included in the National Population Health Survey, immigrants to Canada initiated intercourse at later ages than those respondents who were born in Canada did. For example, for the age group that was between 20 and 24 at the time of the survey, 41 percent of immigrant males compared to 60 percent of Canadian-born males had engaged in intercourse by age 17. The difference was even larger for females; 18 percent of immigrant females between the ages of 20 and 24 and 58 percent of Canadian-born females in that age group had engaged in intercourse by age 17 (Maticka-Tyndale et al., 2000b). Rates of sexual intercourse also differ substantially for young people who were born in Canada but who come from different ethnocultural backgrounds. For example, a study at the University of British Columbia found that 36 percent of female

VIDEO

To learn more about social influences on sexual identity, watch the video "Learning to be Straight" in Chapter 11 of your CD.

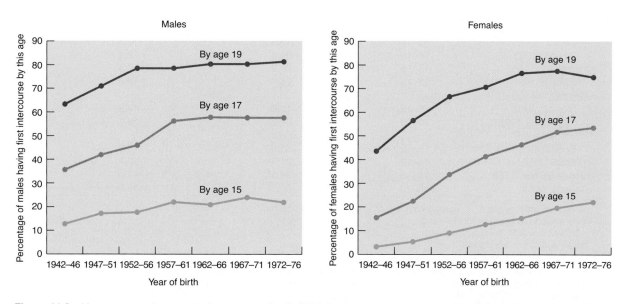

Figure 11.8 Young men and women today are engaging in first intercourse at younger ages than did people born 30 years ago. Graph *(a)* shows data for males while graph *(b)* shows data for females (Maticka-Tyndale et al., © 2000, The Haworth Press, Inc.).

Asian students compared to 69 percent of female non-Asian students had engaged in intercourse. Similarly, 36 percent of Asian males compared to 63 percent of non-Asian males had engaged in intercourse (Meston et al., 1996). Length of residence in Canada or whether the student had been born in Canada did not affect the Asian students' likelihood of having engaged in sexual intercourse. However, British Columbia psychologist Lori Brotto found in a university sample that coitally experienced Asian women who were more acculturated into mainstream Canadian culture reported more sexual experiences than did less acculturated Asian women (Brotto et al., in press).

These ethnocultural differences mirror the substantial variations in patterns of adolescent intercourse in different cultures around the world. Cross-cultural data on unmarried young women are presented in Table 11.2. Most of the data were collected by the Demographic and Health Surveys Program, which interviews women in developing countries. Several interesting points emerge from the data. First, the percentage of young women who report recent intercourse is smaller in Latin and South American countries than in African nations; this is partly due to the greater influence of the Catholic Church in the former. Second, Canada and the United States have some of the highest percentages of 20- to 24-year-old respondents having had premarital intercourse although the time frames are longer for the Canadian and American data (12 months or 3 months versus 4 weeks). Third, there is much less variation in the average age of first intercourse; it is either 16, 17, or 18 in all but one of the countries.

In many countries around the world, the incidence of adolescent intercourse has risen in the last few decades. Around the globe, especially where modernization has been rapid, adolescents are less and less under the influence of family,

Table 11.2	A Global Perspective on Female Adolescent Intercourse		
Country and Year	Age of Respondents (Years)	Percentage Having Had Intercourse (Last Four Weeks)[1]	Median Age of First Coitus (Years)
Africa			
Cameroon, 1998	15–19	33.7	16.3
Kenya, 1998	15–19	19.4	17.3
Nigeria, 1999	15–19	24.6	18.1
Tanzania, 1996	15–19	28.2	17.4
Zambia, 1996	15–19	26.9	16.6
Central America			
Mexico, 1985	15–19	13.0	17.0
Nicaragua, 1998	15–19	21.7	18.1
South America			
Bolivia, 1998	15–19	8.6	19.6
Brazil, 1996	15–19	21.5	18.7
United States, 1999	15–18	36.3[2]	17.4[4]
Canada, 2000	15–19	52.7	16.0

[1]These percentages are of all women, so some of these women are married.
[2]Had intercourse in the last three months.
[3]Had intercourse in the last 12 months.
[4]Mean age of first intercourse.

Source: Data for the United States are from the 1999 Youth Risk Behavior Survey conducted by the Centers for Disease Control and Prevention. The data for other countries are from the Demographic and Health Surveys Program, which collects comparable data from many countries around the world. The results are published in individual volumes for each country by Macro International, Inc., Calverton, MD. The typical reference is: Kenya: Demographic and Health Survey, 1998. Calverton MD: Macro International, 1999. The data for Canada are from the Canadian Community Health Survey, 2000–2001.

community, and religion and more and more responsive to peers and the mass media (Liskin, 1985). On a trip to Ukraine in 1995, we were struck by the prominence of American programs and films on local television.

To summarize, the trends in adolescent sexual intercourse in the last four decades are: (1) both in Canada and in most other countries, more adolescents engaging in sexual intercourse; (2) in Canada, a greater increase in incidence for females, thereby narrowing the gap between males and females; (3) first intercourse occurring at somewhat earlier ages; (4) moderate ethnic-group variations in Canada; and (5) substantial variations from one country to another (Day, 1992; Liskin, 1985).

The increase in adolescent sexual intercourse in general and premarital intercourse in particular reflects two long-term trends. First, the age of menarche has been falling steadily since the beginning of the twentieth century. The average age is about 12.7 years for whites and 12.5 for blacks (Hofferth, 1990). Second, the age of first marriage has been rising. In 1960, men and women who got married for the first time tended to be in their early twenties. In 1998, it was age 27.6 for women and 29.6 for men (Statistics Canada, 2001). The effect is a substantial lengthening of the time between biological readiness and marriage; the gap is typically 12 to 14 years today. Recall that Udry (1988) found that hormone levels are a major influence on the initiation of sexual intercourse. Not surprisingly, many more young people are having sex before they get married now than in 1960.

Factors Associated with Adolescent Sexual Intercourse

Sociologists John DeLamater and Patricia Mac-Corquodale (1979) conducted a large-scale survey to determine what factors are most strongly related to adolescents engaging in intercourse. They found that students with the most liberal attitudes had the most sexual intercourse experience. Attitudes, in turn, appeared to be shaped at first by parents and sometimes by religion. Later, close friends and dating partners become more important influences on adolescent attitudes. The authors con-

Figure 11.9   In South American nations, the percentage of unmarried young women who engage in premarital intercourse is lower than in North America owing to the strong influence of the Catholic Church.

cluded that it is the couple and the nature of their relationship—rather than variables such as social class or religion—that are essential to understanding adolescent sexuality. These findings have been confirmed by later research.

The Canada Youth and AIDS Study examined whether a number of factors were associated with engaging in sexual intercourse (King et al., 1988). Compared to adolescents who had not engaged in sexual intercourse, those who had had sexual intercourse were more likely to drink alcohol on a regular basis and use marijuana. They also had lower educational goals, were less likely to attend religious services regularly, and had poorer relationships with their parents. However, having engaged in intercourse was associated with higher self-esteem and better mental health, particularly for males, as well as with having better relationships with peers. This may reflect the traditional sexual script in Canadian society (see Chapter 14), in which the status of males is enhanced by sexual experience. The CYSHHAS study found that youth were more likely to engage in sexual intercourse if they had a poor relationship with their parents, diagnosis of a learning disability, and perceived their friends to be engaging in sexual intercourse (Council of Ministers of Education, 2003).

It is tempting to make causal inferences from the results of these two studies—to say, for example, that permissive attitudes or drinking alcohol cause increased sexual activity. However, as discussed in Chapter 3, these data are correlational, and causality cannot be inferred from correlation.

First Intercourse

First sexual intercourse is a major transition, with both psychological and social significance. In one study, the researchers analyzed the emotional reactions to first coitus of 1,600 university students (Sprecher et al., 1995). Men reported significantly greater pleasure and significantly less guilt than did women. Both men and women who experienced an orgasm rated the experience as more pleasurable than men and women who did not. Men and women who reported a close relationship with the partner reported stronger emotional reactions than those in casual relationships.

Despite our culture's romanticized high expectations that the first intercourse experience will be like fireworks on Canada Day, it turns out to be much less thrilling than that for most females. For example, the women studied by Sprecher and her colleagues on average gave the experience only a 2.95 on a pleasure scale that ranged from 1 for "not at all" to 7 for "a great deal."

Many people assume that having penile–vagina intercourse for the first time equals losing one's virginity. However, a qualitative study involving in-depth case studies of 61 men and women found that virginity loss is socially constructed (Carpenter, 2001). Many believed that virginity could not be lost by rape, and conversely that behaviours other than vaginal intercourse could constitute loss of virginity. Carpenter identified three distinct interpretations of virginity: as a gift, a stigma, or a process. Each was associated with distinctive individual choices about the transition to nonvirginity. Men and women who viewed virginity as a gift were likely to lose it with a lover or soulmate; those who viewed it as a stigma often lost it with a stranger or non-lover.

Adolescent Sex with a Sex Worker

In the 1940s and 1950s, sex with a sex worker was fairly common among young males, and many received their sexual initiation in this manner. Among the university-educated men under age 35 in one study (Hunt, 1974), 19 percent said they had had their first intercourse with a sex worker as an adolescent. Today, however, having sex with a sex worker as an adolescent is much less common. In the NHSLS of 3432 adults, 3 percent of the men and 0.1 percent of the women reported that their first intercourse had involved a paid partner (Laumann et al., 1994).

Techniques in Adolescent Sex

Paralleling the increase in the incidence of sexual intercourse is an increase in the variety of techniques that are used during sex. One of the most dramatic changes has been the increased use of oral–genital techniques. In the Kinsey sample, 33 percent of the males had experienced fellatio premaritally and 14 percent had engaged in cunnilingus. In a British Columbia study, 64 percent of the non-Asian males had engaged in fellatio and 59 percent had performed cunnilingus, although the rates were lower for the Asian men (Meston et al., 1996). The CYSH found that about 10 percent of high school students had engaged in fellatio and/or

Table 11.3 If two people on a date like each other, do you think it is all right for them to...

	Yes on a first date		Yes, after a few dates		No	
	Males	Females	Males	Females	Males	Females
Hold hands	92%	87%	8%	12%	<1%	1%
Kiss	78	68	21	30	1	2
Neck and pet	43	22	50	63	7	15
Have sex	18	4	50	32	32	64

Source: Reginald W. Bibby (2001). *Canada's teens: Yesterday, today, and tomorrow.* Toronto: Stoddart.

cunnilingus but not in intercourse—perhaps because they know that mouth–genital sex cannot cause pregnancy (Council of Ministers of Education, 2003). Young people today also use a greater variety of positions, not just the traditional man on top position.

Doubtless some of this increased variety in techniques is a result of today's "performance ethic" in sexual relations, which was discussed in Chapter 10. Adolescents and young adults may feel pressured to be gold medallists in the sexual Olympics. One man said:

Sometimes I'm really good; I can make a girl have orgasms until she's about half dead. But if I don't like the girl, or if I'm not feeling confident, it can be hard work—and sometimes I can't even cut the mustard, and that bothers me a lot when that happens. (Hunt, 1974, p. 163)

Attitudes toward Adolescent Sexual Intercourse

Attitudes toward adolescent intercourse have also undergone marked changes, particularly among young people. Sociologist Ira Reiss (1960) distinguished among four kinds of standards for adolescent sexual activity:

1. **Abstinence** Intercourse outside of marriage is considered wrong for both males and females, regardless of the circumstances.
2. **Permissiveness with affection** Intercourse is permissible for both males and females if it occurs in the context of a stable relationship that involves love, commitment, or being engaged.
3. **Permissiveness without affection** Intercourse is permissible for both males and females,

regardless of emotional commitment, simply on the basis of physical attraction.
4. **Double standard** Intercourse outside of marriage is acceptable for males but is not acceptable for females. The double standard may be either "orthodox" or "transitional." In the orthodox case, the double standard holds regardless of the couple's relationship, while in the transitional case, sex is considered acceptable for the woman if she is in love or engaged.

Historically in Canada, the prevailing standard has been either abstinence or the double standard. However, today, particularly among young people, the standard is one of permissiveness with affection—82 percent of youth hold this view (Bibby, 2001). What do adolescents define as affection? That is, at what point in a relationship in which two people like each other is it acceptable to engage in sexual activity? Alberta sociologist Reginald Bibby asked adolescents just this question (Bibby, 2001). As shown in Table 11.3, most adolescents approved of holding hands and kissing on a first date. Male adolescents differed in their attitudes toward the timing of necking and petting and sexual intercourse, with the males approving of them earlier in

Abstinence: A standard in which premarital intercourse is considered wrong, regardless of the circumstances.
Permissiveness with affection: A standard in which premarital intercourse is considered acceptable if it occurs in the context of a loving, committed relationship.
Permissiveness without affection: A standard in which premarital intercourse is acceptable without emotional commitment.
Double standard: A standard in which premarital intercourse is considered acceptable for males but not for females.

In Focus 11.2

How Common Is Casual Sex on Holidays?

Thousands of Canadian university students go to Florida for spring break every year. Spring break involves not only warm weather but also travelling and rooming with a group of friends in a perpetual party atmosphere that includes high alcohol consumption and participating in sexually suggestive contests and displays such as wet T-shirt or hot body contests. Students perceive spring break as a time in which norms, roles, attitudes, and behaviours are more permissive and the usual expectations about behaviour, including sexual behaviour, do not apply. They also perceive that casual sex—sex with a partner whom you meet on spring break and with whom you do not expect to form a relationship—is common. As one female student said, "It's generally expected that lots of people are going to have a great time, and that includes having sex." Of course, perceptions and expectations do not always match reality. Is casual sex as common on spring break as students perceive it to be?

To answer this question, Ontario sociologists Eleanor Maticka-Tyndale and Edward Herold studied sexual behaviour on spring break in Florida. They sent male and female graduate students to Daytona Beach, Florida, in 1996 to administer a 10-minute questionnaire. They used three different methods of recruiting participants. Four hundred and eighty-four participants were recruited on beaches and pool decks; 119 students completed questionnaires on return bus trips home; and 151 students were recruited through the mail. All participants were from

southwestern Ontario. Given the sampling procedure, we cannot be sure that the students who participated were representative of all students on spring break. In fact, the men and women in their sample were more sexually experienced than Canadians of the same age are in general.

The researchers asked participants about their attitudes toward casual sex on spring break, and about whether they had engaged in casual sex while in Florida. The men were more accepting of casual sex and more interested in engaging in casual sex than the women were. For example, whereas 55 percent of the men had intended to engage in intercourse while in Florida, only 11 percent of the women had had these intentions. In contrast, fairly equal numbers of male and female students actually engaged in casual sex—15 percent of the men and 13 percent of the women. Interestingly, a considerably higher percentage—46 percent—had "fooled around" sexually while on spring break; that is, engaged in casual sex that did not include intercourse. The researchers concluded that there are two different distinct sexual scripts for those students who go to Florida without a relationship partner. One sexual script includes no sexual activity. The second script includes either "fooling around" or having intercourse with someone they met in Daytona.

Do students who engage in casual sex use a condom? Almost all respondents who had engaged in sex with a new partner said that they had

the relationship. For example, 43 percent of the males and 22 percent of the females thought it was acceptable to neck and pet on a first date. Similarly, 68 percent of the males but only 36 percent of the females thought it was acceptable to have sex on the first date or after a few dates. These different attitudes may represent a double standard with respect to the timing of initiation of sexual activity within a relationship. Interviews with youth in Nova Scotia

and British Columbia indicate that girls are still more likely to be labelled negatively for their sexual behaviour than boys are (Shoveller et al., 2004). However, one-quarter of female adolescents and one-third of male adolescents report two or more partners in the past year (Maticka-Tyndale, 2001). Some of these individuals are engaging in serial monogamy (see below). Others are engaging in casual sex.

We can see the shift in standards by comparing

Figure 11.10 Students who attend sexually suggestive spring break contests such as this are more likely to also engage in casual sex.

intended to use condoms. Three-quarters of them did use condoms at least once. Apparently condom use is part of the spring break script for casual sex.

What were the characteristics of students who engaged in casual sex? Those students who had intercourse with someone they had just met drank more alcohol, were more likely to frequent dating bars, and were more likely to have participated in spring break activities such as partying, or watching a sexually suggestive contest with someone they had just met. They were also more likely to have intended to engage in casual sex and to have engaged in casual sex on a previous spring break holiday. Females who had casual sex were more likely to have made a pact with their friends to engage in casual sex and to have friends who also engaged in casual sex. Peer influences affected men's intentions to engage in casual sex but not their behaviour.

One consistent gender difference related to sexuality is that men are more accepting of casual sex than women are (See Chapter 14). This gender difference also holds true on spring break despite a relaxation of sexual norms. Many more men than women intended to engage in casual sex. Despite the party atmosphere, participation in casual intercourse is not common—perhaps because women serve as sexual "gatekeepers" in relationships with men and few women intended to have casual sex. On the other hand, many students engage in sexual "fooling around" on spring break.

Egan (2001) found a higher incidence of casual sex among mostly European backpackers and other travellers staying in Canadian youth hostels: than found by Maticka-Tyndale and Herold: 31 percent of the men and 20 percent of the women reported having had casual sex while on their current trip. Travellers who had engaged in casual sex on the current trip were more likely to have had casual sex prior to travel, be on an extended trip (more than 30 days), have engaged in casual sex prior to the trip, and expect to have casual sex on the trip.

Sources: Egan, 2001; Maticka-Tyndale & Herold, 1997, 1999; Maticka-Tyndale, Herold, & Mewhinney, 1998; Mewhinney, Herold, & Maticka-Tyndale, 1995.

data on recent attitudes to those of 25 years before, as shown in Table 11.4. Note that more people approve of premarital sex today than did so in 1975. Two trends are particularly interesting. First, older individuals are less likely to approve of premarital sex than are people under 55. Second, attitudes have become more uniform across Canada, although Prairie residents are still the least likely to approve of premarital sex.

Abstinence

The data presented in Table 11.1 indicate that fewer than one-half of Canadian high-school students have had intercourse. Among those who have not, some will by the time they graduate, but others will remain abstinent. According to a recent survey in the U.S., 74 percent of teens aged 15 to 17 who had not had intercourse said they had "made a conscious decision to wait" (Kaiser Family Foun-

Table 11.4 Percentage of People Agreeing That Premarital Intercourse Is Acceptable in 1975 and 1995

Premarital sex is...

	1975	1995
Not at all wrong	39%	57%
Sometimes wrong	29	23
Almost always wrong	13	7
Always wrong	19	13

Approval of premarital sex

	1975	1995
Nationally	68%	80%
By age		
18–34	90	89
35–54	65	85
55 & over	42	62
By region		
British Columbia	68	80
Prairies	57	71
Ontario	69	78
Quebec	72	88
Atlantic	57	80

Source: Reginald W. Bibby (1995), *Social trends Canadian style*, Toronto: Stoddart, pp. 69 & 76.

dation, 2000). A study of two other samples of American adolescents found that those most likely to abstain had the highest intelligence test scores (Halpern et al., 2000). High intelligence was associated not only with postponing intercourse but also with delaying other partnered sexual activities. One explanation is that smart teens are more committed to long-term educational and career goals and are aware that being involved in a pregnancy or contracting an STI could interfere with or render impossible the achievement of their goals.

Adolescents' Motives for Having Sexual Intercourse

Young people mention a variety of reasons for engaging in physical intimacy (Sprecher & McKinney, 1993). Their motives include expressing love or affection for the partner, experiencing physical arousal or desire, wanting to please the partner, feeling pressure from peers, or wanting physical pleasure. Women are more likely to mention love and affection, whereas men are more likely to mention physical pleasure. In the CYSHHAS, 60 percent of female grade 11 students but only 39 percent of male respondents gave love as the reason for first having sexual intercourse. Curiosity/experimentation was also an important reason given by 21 percent of males but only 14 percent of females (Council of Ministers of Education, 2003).

Adolescent Romantic Relationships

The social forces that have produced changes in premarital sexual behaviour and standards are complex. But among them seems to be a change in courtship stages in which two people establish a special romantic relationship—in the process of meeting, and committing to the relationship. Even the terms have changed. A generation ago we talked about "dating" and "going steady." Now youth say that they are "with" somebody, or that they and their partner are "together" or just that they are "going out." Although these relationships may not last more than a few weeks or months, youth enter their first committed relationship at much younger ages now than in previous generations. Being in an exclusive relationship earlier creates both more of a demand for sexual activity and more legitimacy for it. For many, sexual intimacy is made respectable by being in a committed relationship, regardless how short-term.

Sorensen (1973) found the most common adolescent sexual pattern to be **serial monogamy** without marriage. In such a relationship there is an intention of being faithful to the partner, but the relationship is of uncertain duration. Of those in the sample who had engaged in sexual intercourse, 40 percent were serial monogamists. Though they averaged about four partners, nearly half of them had had only one partner, and about half of them had been involved in their current relationship for a year or more. A more recent Canadian study found that 27 percent of unmarried 15- to 17-year-olds and 82 percent of unmarried 18- to 24-year-olds had experienced sexual intercourse. More than half of these women (53 percent of the younger group

Serial monogamy: A premarital sexual pattern in which there is an intention of being faithful to the partner, but the relationship may end and the person will then move on to another partner.

and 59 percent of the older group) had had more than one intercourse partner within the previous two years (Fisher & Boroditsky, 2000).

A qualitative study of Puerto Rican youth living in New York City explored the concept of serial monogamy (Ascensio, 2002). Most of the youth endorsed monogamy and viewed infidelity as wrong. But many also believed that one was required to be faithful only in a serious relationship, with seriousness not being related to the length of the relationship or whether the couple had engaged in vaginal intercourse. The men were more likely to differentiate between merely a relationship and a "serious" relationship whereas many women defined their relationship as "serious." As a result, men's and women's expectations of fidelity did not always coincide. Both the men and the women expressed greater tolerance for male infidelity. Thus, the attitudes of these young people are complex, reflecting their particular construction of monogamy, fidelity, and the double standard.

As described above, one trajectory for romantic and sexual relationships in adolescence in contemporary Canadian culture start with mixed-gender activities which progress to dyadic dating, and then to a series of special relationships continuing into adulthood. An alternative, increasingly common, pattern is evident in some youth subcultures. Here, many adolescents remain actively involved in mixed-gender social groupings and do not make a transition to primarily dyadic dating relationships. Instead, romantic and sexual activities occur within the context of the group, often during parties. When sexual intimacy occurs, it may involve another member of the group, another friend, or someone met on the Internet. Such relationships are often referred to as *friends with benefits* (Denizet-Lewis, 2004):

> Friends with benefits are an alternative to going steady, being in a relationship. "Being in a real relationship just complicates everything" says Brian, a 16-year-old from New England. "When you're friends with benefits, you go over, hook up, then play video games or something. It rocks." (Denizet-Lewis, 2004 p. 33)

Brian is really describing casual sex, and that is what some adolescents and young adults say they want. Men and women with solid education and career plans want to focus on achieving their goals,

and not get sidetracked by a relationship, an unintended pregnancy, or a life-threatening sexually transmitted infection. Others, however, secretly are looking for a more committed, longer-term relationship, and some admit that they are hurt by the failure of the partner to call them.

These casual encounters are referred to as **hooking up**, a no-strings-attached sexual encounter that usually occurs on one occasion involving people who are strangers or acquaintances (Paul et al., 2000). The term "hooking up" is ambiguous and covers everything from kissing to oral sex or sexual intercourse. That is, hooking up may not involve sexual intercourse; oral sex may occur as one alternative. A study of 555 undergraduates classified each student into one of three groups: no hookup experience, hookup experience without intercourse (HU), and hookup experience including intercourse (HU-Sex). Of interest is the fact that those without hookup experience were much more likely to be in long-term romantic relationships. No hookup persons attained significantly higher scores on a measure of self-esteem. Those who had hookup experience reported an average of 10.8 experiences in their lives. Males were significantly more likely to report hookups involving intercourse. Twenty-eight percent of the HU and 49 percent of the HU-Sex participants reported that they never saw the partner again. The major difference between those in the HU group and those in the HU-Sex group was that the latter experience significantly more symptoms of alcohol intoxication when they drink.

Sexuality and Adolescent Development

Adolescent relationships provide the context in which the individual develops the skills and learns the scripts needed to sustain long-term intimate relationships (O'Sullivan & Meyer-Bahlburg, 2003). Research indicates that the process begins at ages 9 to 12 with a first boyfriend or girlfriend; often there is little direct interaction between the two, but the relationship does provide an opportunity to assume an "adult" role. Later comes group dating, and perhaps mixed-sex social events at school. These situa-

Hooking up: A sexual encounter that usually occurs on one occasion involving people who are strangers or acquaintances.

tions provide an opportunity for conversation and for peers to observe and instruct the person in sexual scripts. In mid to late adolescence, youth begin to spend time in mixed-sex, unsupervised interaction, which provides an opportunity for physical intimacy, leading often to sexual intercourse.

Furman (2002) proposes that this behavioural sequence parallels a developmental one. Early relationships reflect simple interest. Subsequent ones fulfill primarily affiliative and sexual reproductive needs as young people explore their sexual feelings. As the person moves into late adolescence and early adulthood, longer-term relationships become the site of the fulfillment of needs for attachment and mutual care taking. One important consequence of this process is the development of a sexual identity with regard to orientation and sexual attractiveness. Obviously, the timing of this process varies from one person to another, one influence being culture and its associated variation in the degree of parental control over adolescents. Furman points out that many social and cultural arrangements facilitate the emergence of heterosexual relationships and at the same time deter gay and lesbian relationships. Mixed-sex gatherings in adolescence are usually heterosexual, and monitoring by peers would likely result in harassment of same-sex romantic activity. Diamond's (2003) research indicates the relative fluidity of the sexual self-identities of some young women from adolescence to their mid-20s.

Thus, we can see that sexuality is an integral part of adolescent development.

Conflicts

We are currently in an era in which there are tensions between a restrictive sexual ethic and a permissive one. In such circumstances, conflicts are bound to arise. One is between parents and children, as parents hold fast to conservative standards while their children adopt permissive ones.

These conflicts within our society are mirrored in the messages of the mass media.

> We are a nation that is deeply ambivalent about sex. On the one hand, sex is so much a part of the landscape that we almost take it for granted, and the message we get is that everybody else seems to be doing it and we are missing the party if we don't get moving. We should liberate our sexual natures, polish up the hot buttons, follow our hormones, and seek fulfillment somewhere across a crowded room. On the other hand, we hear just how frightening sex can be. Some of that comes from the powerful hold of our puritan heritage, but with a uniquely modern twist. AIDS, urban anonymity, sexual abuse and assault, all make sex a dangerous pastime. And this dovetails nicely with the old morality that coexists with our alleged libertine behavior. (Michael et al., 1994, p. 8)

With such conflicting messages so prevalent, it is no wonder that many young people feel conflicts about engaging in sex.

Young people may also experience conflicts between their own behaviours and their attitudes or standards. Behaviours generally change faster than attitudes do. As a result, people may engage in premarital sex while still disapproving of it. Such individuals are more likely to put themselves at risk for unwanted pregnancy or STIs by having intercourse without using condoms or other contraceptive methods.

Adolescent Condom Use

The CYSHHAS found that 54 percent of grade 9 students and 41 percent of grade 11 students reported using a condom the last time they had sexual intercourse (Canadian Council of Ministers of Education, 2003). Even fewer adolescents use a condom every time they have intercourse despite the fact that condoms provide protection from sexually transmitted infections such as HIV (Calzavara et al., 1998; King et al., 1988; Langille et al., 1994). Condoms are used most frequently at the beginning of relationships or in casual encounters, and adolescents are likely to stop using condoms and switch to the birth control pill as they get to know a partner better (Fisher & Boroditsky, 2000; Maticka-Tyndale, 1997; McMahon, 2004). Despite knowledge about HIV transmission, most teens and young adults see themselves at low risk for contracting HIV infection (Levy et al., 1990, 1992; Maticka-Tyndale, 1992). Further, the CYSHHAS found that two-thirds of grade 7 students and half of grade 9 students think that there is a cure for AIDS. Therefore, adolescents' attitudes toward condoms may be especially important in determining whether they use them (Klein & Knäuper, 2003).

Research by Ontario sociologist Eleanor Maticka-

Tyndale (1992) identified two beliefs that account for why young people do not perceive themselves to be at risk. First, teenagers minimize the seriousness of contracting a sexually transmitted infection such as HIV through their beliefs that medical science will find a cure "in time" should they need one. Second, they believe that by choosing partners who are like themselves and their peers they can ensure that their partners are not infected. The sexual script for an affectionate, trusting relationship does not fit with the idea that a partner can be infected and either not know it or not disclose such information, and so does not include condom use (Hynie et al., 1998). Teenagers are more likely to use condoms when they have positive attitudes toward condoms and when their peer group supports condom use with romantic partners (Fazakas et al., 2001; Ploem & Byers, 1997; Richardson & Beazley, 1997; Tremblay & Frignon, 2004).

Gender roles may make it particularly difficult for adolescent girls to initiate condom use. In an experiment conducted at McGill University, female undergraduates read a fictitious woman's diary entry that described a sexual encounter with a man (Hynie & Lydon, 1995). In one scenario she supplied the condom, in a second one her partner supplied the condom, and in a third scenario they engaged in unprotected sex. The participants in the study rated the behaviour of this woman as more negative and inappropriate and thought that her partner would think of her more negatively when she provided a condom. Thus, although women may understand the importance of condom use, they also perceive that there is a sexual double standard with respect to supplying condoms that may conflict with their desire to be contraceptively prepared. However, more recent research suggests that undergraduates rate both male and female students more positively if they initiated condom use with an exclusive dating partner (Davidson-Harden et al., 2000).

The Information–Motivation–Behavioural Skills model described in Chapter 7 (Fisher & Fisher, 1998) provides a framework to design effective interventions to increase condom use among adolescents.

Adolescent Pregnancy

Research indicates that adolescents are not consistent in using contraceptives to prevent unwanted pregnancy, although the consistency of contraceptive use varies from one ethnic group to another (Boroditsky et al., 1995; Levy et al., 1992). As a consequence, 37,622 teenagers, or about 4 percent of all teenage girls, became pregnant in 2001 in Canada; the rate of teen pregnancy is highest in the four Prairie Provinces and the three Territories. The rate of teenage pregnancy in Canada is about the same as that in Britain and less than half that of the United States but significantly higher than France, Germany, and other northern European countries (Maticka-Tyndale, 2001; Singh & Darroch, 2000). The levels of sexual activity or the ages at which teenagers start engaging in sexual intercourse do not differ across Western countries, so what accounts for the differences in teenage pregnancy rates?

To answer this question, a team of researchers from Sweden, France, Canada, Great Britain, and the United States conducted a large-scale investigation into factors that account for the differences in teenage pregnancy rates in their five countries (Darroch et al., 2001). The lowest rates are in Sweden and France; Canada and Great Britain have intermediate rates; and the U.S. has the highest rate. The authors concluded that there are five primary factors that contribute to these differences.

1. The rates are higher in countries in which teenagers are less likely to use effective contraception.
2. Teenagers from poor and disadvantaged families are less likely to use contraception.
3. National programs that support the transition to adult economic roles and parenthood provide young people with greater incentives and means to delay childbearing.
4. Countries with lower rates have greater societal acceptance of sexual activity among young people.
5. Teenagers are more likely to use contraceptives if they know where to obtain information and services, can reach a provider easily, are assured of receiving confidential, nonjudgmental services, and can obtain contraceptive supplies at little or no cost.

Canada's scores on these five factors was mixed— we scored high on some and intermediate on others compared to the other four countries. Within Canada there are differences in adolescent pregnancy rates from province to province and community to community. For example, researchers in Nova Scotia found that the highest rates of teenage pregnancy in that province were in communities with a higher proportion of single-parent families, lower socioeconomic status, more working women, and lower levels of religious affiliation (Langille et al., in press).

Both the teenage pregnancy rate and the percentage of teen births in Canada have been dropping (Dryburgh, 2000). About 44 percent of these teenagers give birth to a child, and the vast majority choose to keep the baby. Why is teenage pregnancy considered a major social problem in Canada? The reason is that most of these births are to single mothers and from homes with low income (Denton & Scott, 1994). Thus most of these babies will be raised by single mothers and may be associated with tremendous social and economic costs.

A Nova Scotia study that followed pregnant women for up to 10 years after they gave birth gives us important information on the effects of teenage pregnancy on the mother and the child (Bissell, 2000; Nova Scotia Department of Community Services, 1991). This study compared 403 unmarried women to 416 married women, dividing these women into teenage mothers (19 years old or younger) and an older age group (20 or older). The study also included psychological and educational testing with the children. Unmarried mothers of all ages were most dissatisfied with their educational achievement. Women who were still in school prior to the pregnancy were most likely to return to school after the birth. Fifty-two percent of the single teenage mothers lived in poverty, but so did 54 percent of the older unmarried women and 29 percent

of the young married women. The young unmarried mothers made the most economic gains over the 10 years, but they never caught up to the older married group. Eighty-seven percent subsequently married. There were few differences in their children's educational achievement. There were also no differences in the ways in which teenage mothers and older mothers dealt with their children's behaviour.

Grindstaff (1988) used data from the 1981 Canadian census to study 200,000 Canadian women who had married and/or had children before the age of 20. He found that the younger women were at the birth of their first child, the less education they tended to have and the more limited their job opportunities were. However, early marriage was also associated with less successful employment outcomes even if the women delayed having their first child until they were in their early twenties. Thus the negative consequences associated with teenage pregnancy are largely a result of the fact that teenage mothers are more likely to come from socioeconomically disadvantaged backgrounds rather than the age of the mother (Bissell, 2000; Hardwick & Patychuk, 1999; Maticka-Tyndale, 2001; Singh et al., 2001). Two critical factors for successful outcomes for adolescent mothers are finishing high school (and preferably going for even more education) and postponing other births (Furstenberg, 1987). Thus, it is important to have social programs to assist adolescent mothers in finishing high school such as school-based day care as well as effective sex education programs and access to contraception.

■ ■ ■ SUMMARY

A capacity for sexual response is present from infancy. According to recent data, about 40 percent of children have masturbated by the time they reach puberty. Recent studies indicate that children begin masturbating at somewhat earlier ages now than a generation or so ago. Children also engage in some other-sex play, as well as some same-sex activity.

During adolescence there is an increase in sexual activity. According to one theory, this activity is influenced by the interaction of biological factors

(increasing testosterone level) and social and psychological factors (for example, sexually permissive attitudes). By age 15, nearly all boys have masturbated. Girls tend to begin masturbating somewhat later than boys, and fewer of them masturbate. Attitudes toward masturbation are considerably more permissive now than they were a century ago. About 10 percent of adolescents have same-sex experiences to orgasm, with this figure being slightly higher for boys than for girls.

Today the majority of adolescent males and

females have engaged in sexual intercourse. This is a considerable increase over the incidence reported in the Kinsey studies, done 50 years ago. Adolescents today are considerably more likely to use a variety of sexual techniques, including mouth–genital sex. There is variation in the incidence of premarital intercourse among various ethnocultural groups in Canada, and even greater variability from one country to another.

The predominant sexual standard today is one of "permissiveness with affection"; that is, sex is seen as acceptable outside marriage, provided there is an emotional commitment between the partners.

Experiences with sexuality can serve important functions in a person's psychological development. They may be important, for example, in the process of becoming independent of parents and in establishing a viable moral system.

■ ■ ■ QUESTIONS FOR THOUGHT, DISCUSSION, AND DEBATE

1. What challenges do most gay, lesbian, and bisexual youth face in terms of their sexual development that most heterosexual youth do not face? What challenges are similar? How can we change Canadian society to make it easier for gay, lesbian, and bisexual youth?

2. Does "permissiveness with affection" characterize the standard for premarital intercourse among the 18- to 22-year-olds you know?

3. The mother of a 5-year-old child tells you that her son has been masturbating while he watches TV in the family room. She asks you what she should do about his behaviour. What would you tell her?

4. You have been put in charge of designing a program to increase consistent condom use by adolescents. Based on the information provided in this chapter, and on your knowledge of the 18- to 22-year-olds you know, what would you include in the program that you design? How might you need to tailor the program differently for the different ethnocultural groups in Canada?

■ ■ ■ SUGGESTIONS FOR FURTHER READING

Eder, Donna, with Catherine Evans & Stephen Parker. (1995). *School talk: Gender and adolescent culture.* New Brunswick, NJ: Rutgers University Press. A study of adolescent peer groups and relationships in one middle school.

McCormick, Naomi B. (1979). Come-ons and put-offs: Unmarried students' strategies for having and avoiding intercourse. *Psychology of Women Quarterly, 4,* 194–211. An interesting discussion of college students' reported techniques for inviting or avoiding intercourse, and how these techniques relate to gender-role stereotypes.

Starks, Kay, & Eleanor Morrison. (1996). *Growing up sexual* (2nd ed.). New York: HarperCollins. A fascinating view of sexual development with many first-person quotes, based on student autobiographies for a human sexuality course.

Online LearningCentre

For Review Questions, Web Resources, and other learning and study tools, visit the *Understanding Human Sexuality* Online Learning Centre at www.mcgrawhill.ca/college/hyde.

CHAPTER 12

Sexuality and the Life Cycle: Adulthood

CHAPTER HIGHLIGHTS

Grow old along with me!

The best is yet to be.*

Life begins at forty.**

This chapter will continue to trace the development of sexuality across the lifespan. We will look at various aspects of sexuality in adulthood: sex and the single person, cohabitation, common-law and marital sexuality, extramarital sexuality, postmarital sexuality, and sex among older adults. We consider lifestyles involving same-sex partners in Chapter 15. Each of these lifestyles is an option, reflecting the diversity of choices available in Canada today.

■ Sex and the Single Person

Sexual Development

Late adolescence and early adulthood are a time of continued sexual development as the individual moves toward mature, adult sexuality. First, there is a need to deal with issues of sexual orientation and define one's sexual identity. Heterosexuality is the overwhelming norm in our society, and some people slip into it easily without much thought. Others sense that their orientation is gay or lesbian and must struggle with society's **heterosexism** and negative messages about these groups. Others sense that they are attracted to both males and females. Still others feel that their orientation is heterosexual but wonder why they experience homosexual fantasies, thinking that a person's sexual orientation must be perfectly consistent in all areas (research actually shows that heterosexuals sometimes have homosexual fantasies, and vice versa). These struggles over sexual orientation seem to be more difficult for males than for females because heterosexuality is such an important cornerstone of the male role in many societies, including ours (see Chapter 14).

Another step toward maturity is identifying our sexual likes and dislikes and how they vary from occasion to occasion. Learning what one likes and dislikes may occur naturally as the individual experiences various behaviours over time. Alternatively, some people intentionally seek opportunities to engage in novel behaviours or in sexual intimacy with novel partners. Of course, it is not enough to know our likes and dislikes; we must also learn to communicate them to a partner. Learning to communicate with sexual partners is difficult for many persons, perhaps because there are few role models in our society showing us how to engage in direct, honest communication with them.

Two more issues are important in achieving sexual maturity: becoming responsible about sex, and developing a capacity for intimacy. Taking responsibility includes being careful about contraception and sexually transmitted infections, being responsible for yourself and for your partner. Intimacy (see Chapter 13) involves a deep emotional sharing between two people that goes beyond casual sex or manipulative sex.

Our ideas of what constitutes mature sexuality are influenced by the media. Most television shows promote a rather stereotyped and heterosexist view of sex and the single person. Recently there has been an increase in the number of television programs that have sexuality as a major focus, and some of them are tackling topics that never used to be discussed on television. For example, in the early 1990s, the main characters in *Seinfeld* had a competition to see who could go the longest without masturbating. In an episode of *Friends*, Rachel and Monica struggle over who gets the last condom and, by implication, which one of them gets to have sex. *Queer as Folk* and *Will and Grace* introduced gay men and lesbians as central characters. In fact, *Queer as Folk*—popular among gay, lesbian, and heterosexual viewers—was one of the first television shows about the lives of gays and lesbians. It also regularly features scenes of explicit same-sex sexual activity, often emphasizing the use of condoms. *Sex and the*

*Robert Browning. (1864). *Rabbi Ben Ezra*.
**Attributed to Sophie Tucker.

Heterosexism: Belief that heterosexuality is the best and expected way of living.

City introduced single female characters who are not only comfortable with their sexuality but also actively pursue sex for pleasure and talk openly about it. Of course, most single television characters still fit societal stereotypes and, even in the more progressive shows, characters tend to fit the media ideal of young, thin, and attractive. Nonetheless, even though they are isolated examples, these shows expose and challenge the hidden and explicit media messages about sexuality and the single person.

The Never-Married

The term *never-married* refers to adults who have never been married. This group includes those who intend to marry someday and those who have decided to remain single. People are waiting longer to get married. In the 2001 Census, 92 percent of people aged 20 to 24 and 65 percent of those aged 25 to 29 were never-married compared to 56 percent and 21 percent, respectively, in the 1971 Census. Some of these individuals have lived in a common-law relationship with someone of the same or other gender. Most (91 percent) never-married individuals expect to have children (Stobert & Kemeny, 2003).

Most adults in Canada (up to 95 percent) do marry. The average age of first marriage in 2002 was 27.8 years for women and 29.8 years for men (Statistics Canada, 2004), so the typical person who marries spends several adult years in the never-married category. Some of these men and women spend this entire time in one relationship that eventually leads to marriage. According to the NHSLS, among married persons 20 to 29 years old, 46 percent of the men and 65 percent of the women are in this category (Laumann et al., 1994). Other young adults continue the pattern of *serial monogamy* which (as we saw in Chapter 11) characterizes adolescent intimate relationships; they are involved in two or more sexually intimate relationships prior to marriage. According to the NHSLS, among married persons 20 to 29, 40 percent of the men and 28 percent of the women had two or more sexual partners before they married.

The person who passes age 25 without getting married gradually enters a new world. The social structures that supported dating—such as college or university—are gone, and more people of the same age are married.

The attitudes of singles about their status vary widely. Some young men and women decide to live both single and sexually celibate or **chaste** (abstaining from sexual intercourse). Little research has been done on celibacy, and published studies often do not distinguish voluntary from involuntary celibates. One study (Kiernan, 1988) found that such persons were introverted and ambitious, and that celibate women had high educational and occupational status. Research using a questionnaire posted on the Internet (Donnelly et al., 2001) identified three types of involuntary celibates. *Virgins* had never had intercourse, had rarely dated, and often had not engaged in any partnered sexual intimacy; the data suggest that they failed to make the developmental transitions discussed at the end of Chapter 11. *Singles* had had sexual experience but often reported that it was not satisfying; they were unable to find and maintain long-term relationships. Both their residential and work arrangements made it difficult for persons in either group to meet potential partners. Other research suggests that one's competence in romantic relationships in adulthood—being close to and getting along with a partner—is predicted by one's competence in the social and academic domains in late adolescence (Roisman et al., 2004). The third type are *partnered* persons in sexless relationships. Typically the relationship had included sex in the past but the frequency gradually declined over time.

Some young people plan to remain single but not chaste. They find the single lifestyle exciting and enjoy their freedom. The TV series *Sex and the City* (1998 to 2004) undoubtedly contributed to the visibility, if not the popularity, of this lifestyle. A survey of 3,600 Canadian adolescents found that only 88 percent expect to marry (Bibby, 2001). Other men and women are searching for a spouse, some with increasing desperation, as the years go by.

At one extreme, there is the *singles scene*. It is institutionalized in such forms as singles' apartment complexes and singles bars. Health clubs, fitness centres, religious groups, and parties provide opportunities for meeting others. A recent innovation, intended for the busy urban professional, is *speed dating*. Singles attend a dating event involving 15 to 25 other singles. They are given a sticker

Chaste: Abstaining from sexual intercourse; sexually celibate.

with a number on it, and then speak to each of the other attendees for a short and fixed period of time that often depends on the number of attendees, but typically ranges between 4 and 10 minutes. At the end of the evening they indicate their interest in seeing each individual again (yes or no) and wait to see whether there is a match. This process is not without its anxieties. Attendees may find it difficult to remember the characteristics and qualities of the many people they meet, worry about finding something interesting to say in the short period of time allotted, and feel disappointed and despondent if none of the attendees they were interested in indicate interest in them. The singles group, of course, is composed of the divorced and the widowed as well as the never-married. The singles bar is a visible symbol of the singles scene. Most people are there for a similar purpose: to meet that special someone. However, most will settle for a date, and it is fairly well understood that coitus will be a part of the date. The singles bar is somewhat like a meat market; the people there try to display themselves to their best advantage and are judged and chosen on the basis of their physical appearance—and perhaps rejected for not having the type of body considered ideal in our society.

Many singles, however, do not go to singles bars. Some are turned off by the idea; some feel that they cannot compete, that they are too old or not attractive enough; and some live in rural areas where they have no access to such places. An alternative way of meeting people is through singles ads, found in most daily newspapers. As one woman said,

> Most of the men I've dated I've met . . . through personals ads. The reason I prefer guys I meet through ads is because I get to know them before meeting them. I get the chance to really get to know them before I actually see them. (Louis, 1997, p. 10)

Singles ads can also be found on the Internet as part of online dating. There are hundreds of sites where one can post ads or create a personal Web page. Some are general sites. For example, Toronto-based Lavalife.com has three separate streams for individuals seeking either partners of the same or the other gender (labelled "dating," "relationship," and "intimate encounters") and more than 1 million active members—60 percent male and 40 percent female

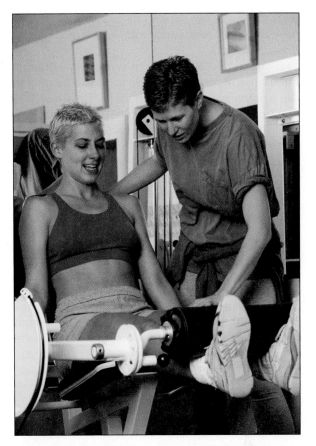

Figure 12.1 Fitness clubs are the current alternative to singles bars for some people who are hoping to meet that special someone.

(*Maclean's*, 2003). There also are smaller sites geared toward individuals with specific interests such as vegetarians, pet lovers, or members of particular religious groups. Internet dating sites have been important in reducing the isolation experienced by some sexual-minority individuals—that is, gay, lesbian, bisexual, intersex, and transgender individuals.

Persons wishing to place ads are encouraged to indicate the type of partner they are searching for as well as their age, ethnicity, height, area of residence, and often a photograph. Those seeking partners can search the ads and home pages on these characteristics. Contacts made online can lead to an offline relationship or to a continuing online one. The relationship may evolve to include **cybersex**, where

Cybersex: The practice of engaging in sexual talk online.

partners engage in sexual talk online for the purposes of sexual pleasure. It may or may not involve masturbation.

A survey of 769 Canadian university students found that 18 percent of the men and 10 percent of the women had used an online dating site in the previous 12 months (Boies, 2002). Researchers in Ontario have shown that, compared to Internet users who are not online daters, Internet dates are more likely to be male, single, divorced, employed, urban, and have higher incomes (Brym & Lenton, 2003). The online daters were not socially isolated, as has sometimes been assumed. They belonged to clubs, socialized with family and friends, and saw themselves as self-confident.

The visibility of online dating, singles bars, singles tours, and other activities geared toward single adults suggests a fun-loving lifestyle with frequent sexual activity. Undoubtedly some single persons live such a life. As Figure 12.2a indicates, 26 percent of the single men and 20 percent of the single women interviewed for the NHSLS reported having sexual intercourse two or more times per week. But the reality is different for other singles; 22 percent of the single men and 30 percent of the single women interviewed did not have sex in the year prior to the interview.

Research in Canada on sexual frequency has not used the same categories as the NHSLS. Nonetheless, the results are similar. As shown in Figure 12.2b, Bibby (1995) found that only 17 percent of single adults reported never engaging in sexual intercourse (compared to about 26 percent in the NHSLS) whereas 42 percent engage in sexual intercourse on a weekly basis or more (compared to about 49 percent in the NHSLS).

■ Cohabitation

In early adulthood, it is common for couples to experiment with various levels of commitment, such as an exclusive dating relationship or living together. Even when living together, there are different levels of commitment, from "living together apart" to "some days and nights" to "all the time." Living together is an important turning point not only because it represents commitment but also because it is a public declaration of a sexual relationship. It is rare for two people who are dating to live together just because it will save on rent. Cohabiting is an opportunity to explore a more serious commitment, at least to some extent.

Cohabitation has become an increasingly common alternative to marriage. Legally in Canada, when two people of the opposite sex or of the same sex live together as a couple for 12 continuous months but are not legally married to each other, they are in a **common-law relationship**. According to the 2001 Canadian Census, 1.2 million couples or 14 percent of Canadians are living in common-law relationships, up from 6 percent in 1981. More than 34,200 couples, or 0.5 percent of couples, are living in same-sex common-law relationships. The rate is highest in Quebec, where 30 percent of couples are common-law. In 1990, 22 percent of people aged 20 to 24 and 39 percent of people aged 25 to 29 had cohabited with a partner at least once (Dumas & Péron, 1992). In fact, common-law relationships are most common among people aged 20 to 24 such that 17 percent of Canadians in that age group are living common-law (Statistics Canada, 1997). Slightly more than half of couples living together eventually marry, although this percentage is lower in Quebec. Two-thirds of these couples marry within two years of starting to live together. However, common-law relationships break up more often than marriages (Statistics Canada, 2004). Further, contrary to what many people think, marriages that are preceded by cohabitation are more likely to end in separation than marriages that are not preceded by cohabitation (Smith, 2003). Of course, since these data are correlational (see Chapter 3), this does not necessarily mean that living together causes divorce. It may be, for example, that more socially conservative couples tend not to live together and also are less likely to divorce. Couples living in common-law relationships can be of the same or different genders.

The popular image of cohabitation is that it involves young, never-married couples without children. However, almost half of common-law couples have children living in the home (Statistics Canada, 2004). Canadians whose first marriage has dissolved often choose common-law over remarriage. This

Common-law relationship: Two people of the opposite or the same gender who live together as a couple but who are not legally married to each other.

accounts for more than one-quarter of common-law relationships in Canada, and is especially true of people in their thirties and forties. People living in common-law relationships "of some permanence" are entitled to most of the same legal rights as married individuals.

With respect to sexual behaviour, Bibby (1995) found that 60 percent of married persons reported having sexual intercourse once a week or more, whereas 71 percent of cohabiting persons had sexual intercourse with that frequency (see Figure 12.2b). Similarly, the NHSLS found that cohabiting men and women reported more frequent sex than did married men and women (see Figure 12.2a). However, notice the wide variation; some cohabitors report having sexual intercourse only a few times per year. It is interesting that on average

cohabiting couples have sex more often than married couples. Cohabitors are concerned about the stability of the relationship (Bumpass et al., 1991); they may have sex more frequently in the hope that it will strengthen the relationship (Blumstein & Schwartz, 1983).

■ Sex in Heterosexual Marriage

In 2000, the Supreme Court of Canada ruled that under the equality provision of the Charter of Rights and Freedoms, gay and lesbian couples (and heterosexual common-law couples) have the same rights and responsibilities as heterosexual married couples. In 2003, courts in Ontario and British Columbia were the first to legalize same-sex marriage, ruling that restricting marriage to one man and one woman vio-

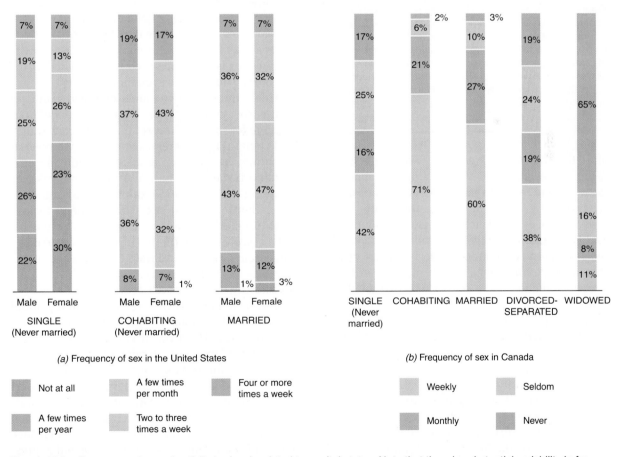

Figure 12.2 Frequency of sexual activity is closely related to marital status. Note that there is substantial variability in frequency within each status as well. U.S. data are from Laumann et al. (1994); Canadian data are from Bibby (1995).

Figure 12.3   Couples Kevin Bourassa (left, glasses) and partner Joe Varnell, and Anne Vautour and partner Elaine Vautour kiss after being married at the Metropolitan Community Church of Toronto in 2001. In June 2005, the House of Commons passed legislation making marriage a right for all Canadians regardless of sexual orientation. Canada is currently one of only three countries in the world to have legalized same-sex marriage.

lates the *Charter of Rights and Freedoms*. In the month following the Ontario ruling, 362 marriage licences were issued to same-sex couples in Toronto alone. In 2004, courts in Quebec, the Yukon, Manitoba, Nova Scotia, Saskatchewan, and Newfoundland and Laborador made the same ruling. In 2005, the federal government introduced legislation to ensure that marriage is a right for all Canadians regardless of sexual orientation. Same-sex weddings in Canada are now sufficiently mainstream that they have even spawned a primetime reality television show, *My Fabulous Gay Wedding*. However, it will probably be a number of years before we have research on sexuality within same-sex marriages.

Given that common-law couples have many of the same rights and responsibilities as married couples, why do people want to marry? Marriage is a psychological turning point for many people. It can also be a sexual turning point (Sarrel & Sarrel, 1984). The decision to get married is a real decision these days, in contrast to previous decades when everyone assumed that they would marry, and the

only question was to whom. Today, most couples have had a full sexual relationship, sometimes for years, before they marry. Some psychological pressures seem to intensify with marriage, and these pressures may result in problems where there were none previously. Marriage is a tangible statement that one has left the family of origin (the family in which you grew up) and shifted to creating one's own family (in which many people become the parents rearing children); for some, this separation from parents is difficult. The pressure for sexual performance may become more intense once people are married as sexual dissatisfactions that were easy to overlook in the early, rose-coloured-glasses phase of the relationship have more and more impact on each individual's sexual satisfaction. And finally, marriage still carries with it an assumption of a lifelong commitment to fidelity or faithfulness, a promise that is hard for some to keep.

In marriage, there is a need to work out issues of gender roles. Who does what? Some of the decisions are as tame as who cooks supper. But who initiates sex is far more sensitive, and who has the right to say no to sex is even more so.

This is the era of two-career couples, or at least dual-earner couples. There are issues here of finding time for sex and for just being with each other.

As a marriage progresses, it can't stay forever as blushingly beautiful as it seemed when the relationship began. The nature of love changes (see Chapter 13), and for some couples there is a gradual disenchantment with sex. Couples need to take steps to avoid boredom in the bedroom. Sexual disorders (see Chapter 19) occur in many marriages, and couples need to find ways to resolve them.

Frequency of Intercourse

According to the 2001 General Social Survey, about 90 percent of Canadians aged 50 to 69 are or have been married. However, it is expected that only 73 percent of men and 78 percent of women aged 30 to 39 will marry at some point in their lives. Of those who divorce, a high percentage—80 percent—remarry (Norton, 1987). In our society, marriage is also the context in which sexual expression has the most legitimacy. Therefore, sex in marriage is one of the commonest forms of sexual expression for adults.

Research in the U.S. shows that the average married couple have coitus two to three times per week

Table 12.1 Marital Coitus: Frequency per Week (Male and Female Estimates Combined), 1938–1949, 1970, and 2003

1938–1949 (Kinsey)		1970 (Westoff)		2003 (Smith)	
Age	Median Frequency per Week	Age	Mean Frequency per Week	Age	Mean Frequency per Week
16–25	2.45	20–24	2.5	18–29	2.1
26–35	1.95	25–34	2.1	30–39	1.7
36–45	1.40	35–44	1.6	40–49	1.4
46–55	0.85			50–59	1.0
56–60	0.55			60–69	0.6
				70+	0.3

when they are in their twenties, with the frequency gradually declining as they get older. The data on this point from three studies are shown in Table 12.1. Several things can be noted from the table. First, the frequency of marital sex has remained about the same from the 1940s to the 2000s. In each survey, people in their twenties reported having intercourse about every three days. Second, the frequency of intercourse declines with age; however, in 2003, among couples in their fifties, the frequency was still once per week. Social characteristics such as race, social status, and religion are generally not related to marital sexual frequency (Christopher & Sprecher, 2000).

Two general explanations have been suggested for the age-related decline in frequency: biological aging, and habituation to sex with the partner (Call et al., 1995). With regard to aging, there may be physical factors associated with age that affect sexual frequency, such as a decrease in vaginal lubrication in females, or increased likelihood of poor health. The habituation explanation states that we lose interest in sex as the partner becomes more and more familiar. Recent data indicate a sharp decline in frequency after the first year and a slow, steady decline thereafter. The decline after the first year may reflect habituation (Call et al., 1995). It is often assumed that this decline in frequency reflects a loss of interest in sex, meaning a decline in quality. However, there is an alternative possibility: that learning about your partner's sexual desires, preferences, and habits results in increased marital sexual quality, if not frequency (Liu, 2003). But analysis of the data on satisfaction with the marital sexual relationship from the NHSLS found a significant decline with length of marriage, controlling for age, consistent with the habituation hypothesis. A third factor is the arrival of children, discussed below.

It is important to note that there is wide variability in these frequencies. For example, 2 percent of couples in their twenties report not engaging in intercourse at all; 6 percent of all married couples had not had sex in the 12 months prior to the interview (Smith, 2003). Research on a sample of 6,029 married couples found that sexual inactivity was associated with unhappiness with the marriage, lack of shared activity, the presence of children, increased age, and poor health (Donnelly, 1993). In contrast, a married couple in Seattle have claimed the world record, having had intercourse more than 900 times in 700 days! Data from the NHSLS and Bibby (1995) also confirm this wide variability, as shown in Figure 12.2.

Sexual Techniques

The NHSLS (Laumann et al., 1994) asked respondents to estimate the duration of their last sexual interaction. As the estimated number of minutes is probably not precise, the researchers focused on whether the duration is 15 minutes or less, or 1 hour or more. Sixteen percent of their married participants reported that sex lasted 15 minutes or less; 9 percent reported that it lasted one hour or more. Participants in the *Maclean's*/CTV poll (1994) reported on the average length of their sexual encounters; 12 percent reported that their sexual encounters lasted 15 minutes or less; 25 percent reported that they lasted more than an hour.

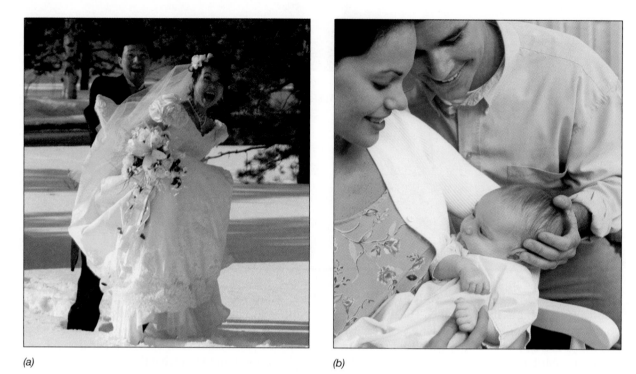

(a)   *(b)*

Figure 12.4   Sexual turning points. (a) Marriage and the commitment it represents is a major turning point. (b) The birth of a baby is a turning point that can have a negative impact on sexual aspects of the relationship, but couples who are aware of this possibility can work to overcome these problems and keep the romance going.

The increased popularity of mouth–genital techniques is one of the most dramatic changes in marital sex to have occurred in the past 50 years. According to Kinsey's data, about half of married women had engaged in oral sex. In the NHSLS data, 74 percent reported that their partners had stimulated their genitals orally, and 70 percent of them had stimulated their partner orally. Similarly, a Montreal study found that almost 80 percent of married and cohabiting respondents had stimulated their partner's genitals orally and that on average this occurred once a week (Samson et al., 1993). Younger respondents were more likely than older respondents to include oral sex in their sexual repertoires. For example, 90 percent of people aged 18 to 34 had stimulated their partner orally compared to only 40 percent of people in the 55 and older age group. People with higher levels of education and incomes were more likely to report engaging in oral sex, showing that there are some social-class differences.

Kinsey did not report data on anal intercourse. According to the NHSLS data, 27 percent of the married men and 21 percent of the married women reported having engaged in this activity (Laumann et al., 1994).

Negotiating Sex

Before any of these techniques are executed, there is typically a "mating dance" between the man and the woman. Sexual scripts are played out in marriages as in other aspects of sex (Gagnon, 1977, pp. 208–209). Some scripts involve direct verbal statements. One person may say, "I'd love to go to bed with you right now." The partner might reply, "What are we waiting for?" or "Not now. Dinner is almost ready." Some scripts are behavioural. One woman said, "We'd get into bed, and he'd roll over to me and kind of bing me in the back end with his penis, so I'd know, Okay, tonight's the night" (Maurer, 1994, p. 180). For other couples, deciding to have intercourse involves preliminary negotiations, which are phrased in indirect or euphemistic language, in part so that the person's feelings can be salvaged if her or his partner is not interested. For example, an individual may say, "I think I'll go take a shower" or "I think I'll go take a nap" (that means "I want to, do you?"). The partner might respond with, "I think I'll take one too" (that means "yes") or "The kids will be home any moment" or "I have a report to finish for tomorrow" (that means "no"). Or conversely, the individual may kiss their partner a bit more passionately than usual after work (that is the offer). The partner may respond with, "I had an exhausting day at work" (i.e. "no") or "I'll meet you upstairs" (i.e. "yes"). To avoid some of the risk of rejection inherent in such negotiations, some couples ritualize sex so they both understand when it will and when it will not occur—Thursday night may be their time, or perhaps Sunday afternoon.

Which of these strategies is used most frequently? A New Brunswick study found that people most frequently use a direct verbal statement to initiate sex (Byers & Heinlein, 1989). The second most frequent strategy is more ambiguous—kissing without saying anything. This study also examined the stereotype that men are more interested in sex than women by having people in long-term relationships keep track for a one-week period of sexual initiations by the man and sexual initiations by the woman. On average the men initiated sex almost twice as often as the women did—about twice a week for the men compared to once a week for the women. Interestingly, the men and the women were equally likely to respond positively to the initiation—about three-quarters of the time. Thus, traditional roles persist in some areas, with men more often having the initiating role. There was also some evidence of liberation. Women initiated sex regularly (and in some couples were the usual initiator), and usually were interested in engaging in sex when their partner suggested it. Contrary to the male stereotype, the men were not always interested in sex and were equally likely to refuse their partner's initiations. There may be differences in how men and women respond when their partner refuses their initiation. According to traditional stereotypes, a woman's refusal could be attributed to her lesser sexual appetite. However, refusals by men go against traditional views of male sexuality. Therefore, a woman may conclude that the man's refusal means that he is not interested in *her* (Blumstein & Schwartz, 1983). Nonetheless, most of the time couples are satisfied with how they resolve disagreements about whether to have sex (Byers & Heinlein, 1989).

Masturbation

Many people masturbate; the NHSLS found that 63 percent of the men and 42 percent of the women reported masturbating in the past year. Seventeen percent of the married men and 5 percent of the married women masturbate at least once a week (Laumann et al., 1994).

Many adults continue to masturbate even though they are married and have ready access to heterosexual sex. This behaviour is perfectly normal, although it sometimes evokes feelings of guilt and may be done secretly. According to the NHSLS, married people were more likely to report that they masturbated than were single people (Michael et al., 1994). Masturbation can serve very legitimate sexual needs in long-term relationships. It feels good whether one is living with a partner or not. It can provide sexual gratification while allowing the partner to remain faithful to a spouse when they are separated or cannot have sex for some reason such as illness.[1]

Masturbation can also be a pleasant adjunct to marital sex. According to a 49-year-old man:

> One of the other things we do a lot is masturbation. We have it developed to a fine art. We rent a porno movie, take a bath, rub each other down with baby oil. My wife and I not only masturbate each other at the same time, but we get pleasure watching each other masturbate individually as well. It's a terrifically exciting thing. (Janus & Janus, 1993, p. 383)

Satisfaction with Marital Sex

Sexual satisfaction is important to most couples. A Canadian survey found that 79 percent of people who are living with a partner feel satisfied with their sex life (Gallup, 1988). Sexual satisfaction is not just physical pleasure, nor is it simply the absence of dissatisfaction or problems. In fact, couples with sexual difficulties may feel sexually satisfied, and couples with no sexual problems may not feel satisfied at all (MacNeil & Byers, 1997). Rather, sexual satisfaction is the overall feeling we are left with after considering the positive and negative aspects (or sexual rewards and costs) of our sexual relationship. Of course, one person's reward may be another person's cost. For example, having sex

---

[1]An old navy saying has it, "If your wife can't be at your right hand, let your right hand be your wife." This saying probably should be updated to refer to both men and women.

every day might be a reward for someone who desires sex every day. It may be a cost for someone who prefers to have sex less frequently, say twice a week. A New Brunswick study found that for men the most frequently identified rewards were feeling comfortable with their partner, feeling good about themselves during and after sex, and having fun during sexual activity. For women the most frequent rewards were being treated well by their partner during sex, feeling comfortable with their partner, and having sex in the context of a long-term relationship (Lawrance & Byers, 1995).

Canadian psychologist Kelli-an Lawrance developed the *interpersonal exchange model of sexual satisfaction*, which identifies four distinct aspects of relationships that influence sexual satisfaction (Lawrance & Byers, 1995). According to this model, we are more sexually satisfied if (1) we perceive ourselves to be getting many sexual rewards and few sexual costs, (2) we perceive that we are getting more rewards and fewer costs than we expect to get, (3) we perceive our own and our partner's rewards and costs to be relatively equal, and (4) we are happy with the non-sexual aspects of the relationship. A longitudinal study of 244 New Brunswick adults living with a partner found that these four components measured at Time 1 predicted sexual satisfaction three months later. Similar results were found in studies involving Canadian dating couples and married Chinese individuals living in Beijing and Shanghai (Byers et al., 1998; Renaud & Byers, 1997). Clearly, our assessment of the rewards and costs in our intimate relationships are associated with our feelings of sexual satisfaction. Our sexual satisfaction is also affected by how we get along outside the bedroom.

In-depth interviews with 52 people, ages 12 to 69, straight, gay, lesbian, and bisexual, identified four factors that differentiate people who are happy with their sex lives (Maurer, 1994). First, there is a sense of calm about, and acceptance of, their sexuality. Second, happy people delight in giving their partners sexual pleasure. Third, these people *listen* to their partners and are aware of the partner's quirks, moods, likes, and dislikes. Fourth, they *talk*, both in and out of bed, even though it is often difficult. These interviews remind us that good communication is essential to a satisfying relationship (see Chapter 10).

Sexual Patterns

Sexual patterns can change during the course of a marriage. After 10 years of marriage they may be quite different from what they were during the first year. One stereotype is that sex becomes duller as marriage wears on, and certainly there are some marriages in which that happens. In a survey of a national sample of adults in the U.S., 23 percent of the sexually active men and women reported that their sexual relationship was often or always "routine." Thirty-eight percent said it was never or hardly ever routine (Kaiser Family Foundation, 1998). As we noted in Chapter 10, a boring sexual relationship can be spiced up by telling each other what you really want to do and then doing it, or by consulting a how-to manual such as *The New Joy of Sex* or *Sex for Dummies*.

There are also relationships in which the sex remains very exciting. A 36-year-old engineer said:

> [Though my wife's career] is tremendously important to her, she manages to look attractive, and to dress chicly, and though she is not what many would call a beautiful woman, she is, to me, a handsome woman. In bed, she is the hottest, most exciting woman I have ever known. We have been married seven years. . . . When we get to bed, and she lets herself go, we get wild together. (Janus & Janus, 1993, p. 191)

Only 7 percent of women and 8 percent of men expect to stay child-free (Stobert & Kemeny, 2003). Having a baby—what researchers call the transition to parenthood—has an impact on a marriage and on the sexual relationship of the couple. According to one 44-year-old mother of three children, "There's the passionate period when you can't get enough of each other, and after a few years it wanes, and after kids it really wanes" (Maurer, 1994, p. 403). Trying to get pregnant and the threat of infertility, which are so much publicized, can be potent forces on one's identity as a sexual being (Daniluk, 2001). Pregnancy itself can influence a couple's sexual interactions, particularly in the last few months (see Chapter 6).

For the first few weeks after the baby is born, intercourse is typically uncomfortable for the woman. While estrogen levels are low—which lasts longer when breast-feeding—the vagina does not lubricate well. Then, too, the mother and sometimes the father feel exhausted with 2 A.M. feedings. The first few months after a baby is born are usually not the peak times in a sexual relationship, and so that, too, must be negotiated between partners. (See Table 12.2.)

Not all couples have children. For example, data from the 2001 General Social Survey indicate that 26 percent of a record number of Canadian women ages 30 to 34 do not have children (Stobert & Kemeny, 2003). Some of these women are delaying childbearing while they complete their education and establish their careers; 20 percent of women in the 30 to 34 age group do not have children but intend to have a child. The average age of first childbirth was 29 years in 1999, up from 24 years in 1969 (Payne, 2004). There is some risk in this strategy; fertility declines with age, so some of these women may be unable to have a child if they want to. Other women in this group have made a decision to remain child-free. According to the GSS, 5 percent of women do not expect to have children. A third group of women are those who chose to adopt; adopting an infant probably has effects on one's relationships and sexual activities similar to those of having a baby.

Some people will experience fundamental changes in their sexual experience at least once over the course of the marriage. The change may result from developing a capacity to give as well as receive sexual pleasure, and to expand our sexual scripts beyond traditional expectations for men and women. A man may outgrow performance anxiety and enlarge his focus to include his partner. A woman may learn that she can take care of her own sexual needs as well as her partner's. Aging may produce change in sexual experience, a topic we consider later in this chapter. There are changes due to illness, such as breast cancer or testicular cancer, which can lead to disaster or triumph depending upon how the couple copes with it.

Sex and the Two-Career Family

In our busy, achievement-oriented society, is it possible that work commitments may interfere with a couple's sex life? One couple, both of whom are professionals, commented to us that they actually have to make an appointment with each other to make love.

Research shows that there is little cause for concern. A longitudinal study followed 570 women and 550 of their husbands for one year following the birth of a baby (Hyde et al., 1998). The women were categorized according to the number of hours worked per week: homemakers, employed part time (6 to 31 hours/week), full time (32 to 44 hours), and high full time (45 or more hours). There actually were no significant differences among the four groups in frequency of sexual intercourse, sexual satisfaction, or sexual desire. It was not the number of hours of work, but rather the quality of work that was associated with sexual outcomes. Women and men

---

Table 12.2   Frequency of Activities to Enhance Sexual Interactions Reported by Adults*

	Very often	Often	Sometimes	Hardly ever	Never	Don't know
Do romantic things like eat by candlelight	8	18	35	30	6	3
Act out fantasies together	4	10	28	39	12	7
Wear sexy lingerie (women**)	9	10	28	35	12	6
Try different sexual positions	11	19	35	23	4	8
Read books or watch videos about improving your sex life	2	3	14	52	26	3
Go out on special evenings or dates or go away on weekends alone	11	22	37	22	5	3

Source: "Sex in the 90s: Kaiser Family Foundation/ABC Television 1998 National Survey of Americans on Sex and Sexual Health," (#1430), The Henry J. Kaiser Family Foundation, September 1998. This information was reprinted with permission of the Henry J. Kaiser Family Foundation. The Kaiser Family Foundation, based in Menlo Park, California, is a nonprofit, independent national health care philanthropy and is not associated with Kaiser Permanente or Kaiser Industries

Notes: *Adults who have ever had intercourse: number of respondents = 1,109
   **Number of female respondents = 564

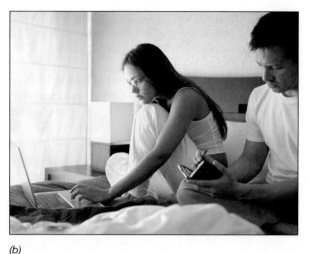

(a)   *(b)*

Figure 12.5   Sex and the two-career family. (a) Research indicates that marital/sexual relationships do not suffer if the woman works outside the home. (b) However, for those working 60 or more hours per week, some experts are concerned because these workaholics literally take their work to bed with them.

who had satisfying jobs reported that sex was better, compared with people who expressed dissatisfaction with their jobs. For women, fatigue was associated with decreased sexual satisfaction, but that was true for both homemakers and employed women; and homemakers reported the same level of fatigue as employed women.

Problems may occur at the extremes, though. Two-profession couples, when both members are committed to working 60 to 80 hours per week, don't have much time for sex. The issue with such couples is not so much having a career as not making time to nurture the relationship. Quality sex requires quality time together.

Maintaining a Long-Term Relationship

Most couples who establish a long-term relationship intend to stay together. However, we know that not all couples succeed. According to Statistics Canada, about 30 percent of first marriages end in divorce. The rate is even higher for first common-law relationships. A good deal of research has looked at differences between non-distressed (happy) couples and distressed (unhappy) couples. What differentiates non-distressed couples from distressed couples?

1. Non-distressed couples have good listening and communication skills. Suggestions for enhancing communication skills are outlined in Chapter 10.

2. Non-distressed couples have effective problem-solving skills. In contrast, distressed couples may discuss problems, but they rarely resolve them. As a result, the same problems tend to come up over and over again.

3. Non-distressed couples have many positive interactions and few negative interactions. For example, they have many enjoyable shared leisure-time activities, are affectionate with each other, and feel good about their communication. In fact, Gottman (1994) found that non-distressed couples have five times as much positive interaction as negative interaction.

4. Non-distressed couples tend to have realistic expectations about what relationships should be like. In contrast, distressed couples may believe that disagreements are destructive, that one must be a perfect sexual partner at all times, or that people who are in love feel intensely passionate about their partner at all times. None of these expectations are realistic.

5. Non-distressed couples tend to interpret their partner's behaviour and the causes of that behaviour positively. For example, if the woman is late for dinner, her partner is likely to assume that it was due to something beyond her control such as heavy traffic. A distressed partner is more likely to see this as an example of her being thoughtless.

6. Non-distressed couples are more likely to share a common view of roles and responsibilities within the relationship. Unhappy couples may disagree on how the relationship should work; for example, they may have different ideas about financial decision-making or how involved each should be with taking care of the children.

Of course, feelings of love and intimacy are also important to maintaining a long-term relationship (see Chapter 13 for a discussion of love in long-term relationships). These feelings often are what motivates couples to work through the problems that inevitably come up. Feelings of equity in the relationship (discussed later in this chapter) are also important.

Relationship satisfaction is one of the key elements contributing to sexual satisfaction (Lawrance & Byers, 1995). Further, dissatisfaction with the marriage and conflict between spouses are associated with susceptibility to infidelity (Buss & Shackelford, 1997b). For example, one woman used her dissatisfaction with her relationship to explain her serious affair. "I'm definitely not looking for more sex. The affair I'm having is for emotional reasons. Freddie [her husband] is very self-centered. He's not an emotional support. He's distant, and we have nothing in common" (Maurer, 1994, p. 391).

Our awareness of the possibility of infidelity sometimes leads us to engage in behaviours designed to preserve the relationship, or *mate retention tactics* (Buss & Shackelford, 1997a). Such tactics may be elicited by our own fear that the partner is losing interest or is dissatisfied, or because we observe some cues to infidelity. Cues thought to be associated with sexual infidelity include physical signs (partner contracting an STI), changes in "normal" sexual behaviour with the partner, increased or decreased sexual interest, and the partner disclosing their infidelity (Shackelford & Buss, 1997). A study of 107 American couples married to a person of the other sex less than one year asked about their use of mate retention tactics. Each partner was given a list of 104 behaviours and was asked how often he or she had performed each in the past year. There were marked gender differences in the reported actions. Men reported greater use of resources display (giving her money) and more frequent submission to the partner. Women reported more frequent use of enhancing their appearance or attractiveness and use of possessive verbal statements. Thus, men's and women's most frequent mate retention strategies fall along traditional gender lines. Unfortunately, these strategies do not address the problems typical of distressed couples listed above.

What does it take to maintain a decades-long relationship? Watch the "Keeping Your Mate" video in Chapter 12 of your CD for some ideas.

■ Extradyadic Sex

Extradyadic sex refers to sexual activity between a person in a committed relationship—gay, lesbian or straight—and someone other than that person's partner. When a person who is married engages in extradyadic sex we call it **extramarital sex**, or adultery. Extradyadic sex can occur under several different circumstances (Pittman, 1993). Sometimes it is *accidental,* unintended and not characteristic of the person; it "just happens." One or both persons may be drunk, or having a bad day, or lonely. More serious is *romantic infidelity,* when the two people fall in love and consider or establish a long-term relationship; this situation can be very destructive to partners, children, and careers. We noted earlier in this chapter that dissatisfaction with the relationship is especially likely to lead to romantic infidelity. A third type is the *open relationship* or *open marriage,* in which the partners agree in advance that each may have sex with other persons. (In contrast, accidental and romantic infidelities begin without the partner's knowledge, and may remain secret.) Finally, there are *philanderers* who repeatedly engage in sexual liaisons outside their committed relationship. These men and women are not motivated by the desire for sexual gratification; they are searching for self-affirmation (Pittman, 1993).

Extradyadic sex: Sexual activity between a person in a serious or exclusive relationship and someone other than his or her steady partner.
Extramarital sex: Sexual activity between a married person and someone other than that person's spouse; adultery.

In Focus 12.1

Have Adults Changed Their Sexual Behaviour in the AIDS Era?

In June 2001, we acknowledged the twentieth anniversary of the AIDS epidemic; in 1981, the first case was diagnosed of an illness caused by what was later named the human immunodeficiency virus. Beginning in 1985, the mass media published and broadcast a steady stream of features about AIDS, including its risks and recommendations for safer sex practices. Public health and community-based groups engaged in large-scale outreach efforts to educate gay men. Perhaps as a result, a recent survey of 2004 Canadians over the age of 15 found that we are generally very knowledgeable about HIV/AIDS (Ekos, 2003). However, has all this publicity and activity had any impact on people's sexual behaviour, or do people continue to engage in high-risk sexual practices? (See Chapter 20 for a discussion of high-risk and safer sex practices.)

In order to assess whether behaviour has actually changed, we need longitudinal research, in which the same people are surveyed or the same questions are asked of comparable samples over time. Unfortunately, there are few such studies; most of the data are from cross-sectional surveys at different points in time.

If you ask adults whether they have changed their behaviour because of AIDS, some say they have. In one sample of single adolescent and adult Canadians, 84 percent said that AIDS had led them to make changes in their sexual behaviour, although the study did not investigate the extent to which their behaviour has changed (Bibby, 1995). Interestingly, only 68 percent said that other adults they knew had made these changes. According to U.S. research, the percentage of people saying that they have changed their behaviour has increased over time (Feinleib & Michael, 2001; Smith, 2003). In the representative sample interviewed by the NHSLS in 1992, 35 percent of the men and 25 percent of the women reported that they had changed their behaviour (Feinleib & Michael, 2001). Men reported reduc-

ing the number of sexual partners (14 percent), increasing condom use (12 percent), and selecting partners more carefully (10 percent). Smaller percentages of women reported these same changes.

In Canada, the number of unmarried men aged 20 to 45 who report having multiple partners has declined (Health Canada, 1998e). According to the National Population Health Survey, in 1994 and 1995, 12 to 19 percent of men and 6 to 7 percent of women had two or more sexual partners within the previous year; in 1997 only 8 percent of men and 6 percent of women reported two or more partners.

Research shows that in the decade 1985 to 1995, gay men showed substantial behaviour change (Ehrhardt et al., 1991). Many gay men reduced their number of sex partners, had fewer anonymous sexual encounters, and engaged less in anal intercourse or used condoms consistently. These changes undertaken by straights and gays contributed to a decline in the number of new cases of AIDS each year from more than 1,000 from 1988 to 1996 to about 580 in 1999 (Health Canada, 2001). Furthermore, several studies suggest that some men and women who are diagnosed with HIV/AIDS become celibate—that is, live without a romantic or intimate relationship (Siegel & Scrimshaw, 2003). This reduces the likelihood of transmission to uninfected persons.

Perhaps because of the decline, and because of the effectiveness of the anti-retroviral therapies in reducing the impact of illness, there has been much less media attention to HIV and AIDS in recent years, and perhaps less effort by public health and medical personnel. There are signs that this recent complacency has led to a slowing or stopping of the gains made earlier. For example, in a survey of 4,803 gay and bisexual men across Canada, 23 percent reported engaging in at least one episode of unprotected anal intercourse within the preceding three months (Myers et al., 1993). This risk-taking behaviour was highest for men who were younger, lived on the Prairies or in small towns in British Columbia, had less than a high school education, were in a monogamous relationship, and used alcohol or drugs prior to sexual activity (Myers et al., 1993; Shaver & Newmeyer, 1996). Perhaps as a result, HIV infections are increasing among gay men in some parts of Canada (Siushansian et al., 2000).

An Ontario study investigated the ways that 102 gay and bisexual men justified engaging in unsafe sex (Adam et al., 2000). Some of the reasons that the men gave were that not using a condom in an ongoing relationship was a way of promoting intimacy and romance; their unsafe sexual behaviour occurred in the heat of the moment and, in some cases, was involuntary; they used the high they got from engaging in risky sex as a way of escaping from negative feelings such as depression; they engaged only in lower–risk sexual behaviour (e.g. fellatio); and, they could determine their partner's HIV status from information they had about him.

Substantial numbers of heterosexuals are not practising safer sex. For example, amongst individuals who reported intercourse with a non-regular partner in the 1994 National Population Health Survey, only 26 percent of the men and 19 percent of the women always used a condom when having sex with a new partner (Health Canada, 1998e). Similarly, national surveys conducted in Britain found that between 1990 and 2000 there was an increase in the percent of individuals reporting a range of behaviours that increase the risk of infection with HIV including increased numbers of opposite-sex partners, same-sex partners, and concurrent (more than one sexual partner at a time) partners, anal sex, and payment for sex (Johnson et al., 2001).

As the number of new AIDS cases has declined, an increasing percentage of those diagnosed are members of ethnocultural minority groups. For example, in 2003, 21.5 percent of Canadians diagnosed with AIDS were black. The problem is particularly severe among members of First Nations. In 1989, Aboriginals constituted only 1 percent of reported AIDS cases; they constituted 13 percent of new cases in 2003 (Health Canada, 2004) even though First Nations individuals make up only 3 percent of the population (Canadian Aboriginal AIDS Network, 2000). Members of First Nations also tend to be infected at an earlier age than are non-Aboriginal Canadians (Health Canada, 1996b, 1996c). The percentage of First Nations women with AIDS is more than twice as high as in the non-Aboriginal population.

Rates of several STIs declined in Canada through 1997 but have recently increased (Patrick et al., 2000). The increase parallels a decline in safe-sex campaigns and sex education programs, suggesting that continuing efforts to increase awareness of the risk of HIV/AIDS and other STIs and the importance of safer-sex practices are very important to efforts to control these illnesses. For example, the CYSHHAS found that adolescents' knowledge about HIV/AIDS prevention had declined in the past 15 years (Council of Ministers, 2003). Research evaluating various intervention programs provides a solid base for designing and implementing such programs. Community-based programs targeting specific groups have demonstrated significant effects on condom use and safer sex (Ross & Williams, 2002). The use of opinion leaders and role models, and the delivery of the intervention by peer educators are associated with the success of such programs. Also important to success is the establishment of ties to the target community and a "buy-in" by the community. Clinic-based programs can also be successful in increasing consistent condom use (Fortenberry, 2002). Extensive, personal counselling can lead to some reduction in the rates of new STIs. Thus, we can further reduce the incidence of HIV/AIDS, but it requires continuing media attention and redoubled efforts by public health and medical personnel, with the active participation of the community.

People engage in extradyadic sexual behaviour for a number of reasons. Some people believe that extradyadic sexual behaviour is acceptable, and they may have an agreement with their partner about the circumstances under which it can occur. Other people, particularly people in long-term relationships, engage in extradyadic sex because they find it particularly exciting. The excitement may be a result of being with a new partner, being found attractive and desirable, or doing something that the individual knows to be forbidden. Finally, some people may engage in extradyadic sex because there are problems in their long-term relationship.

Most of the research on extradyadic sexual behaviour has been on extramarital sex, which we turn to next. However, individuals in dating relationships also engage in extradyadic sexual behaviour, although men are more likely to do so than are women. For example, in one study of university students, 65 percent of the men and 49 percent of the women had experienced extradyadic kissing and fondling; 49 percent of the men and 31 percent of the women had experienced extradyadic sexual intercourse (Wiederman & Hurd, 1999). Many gay couples engaged in extradyadic sexual activity, often by mutual consent (Carballo-Diéguez, 2000).

How Many People Engage in Extramarital Sex?

Extramarital sexual activity is not as common as many people believe. Laumann and his colleagues in the NHSLS (1994) found that about 25 percent of the married men and 15 percent of the married women surveyed reported having engaged in extramarital sex at least once. A *Maclean's*/CTV poll conducted in 1995 found a considerably lower percentage of Canadians who reported having had an affair while married—14 percent of men and 7 percent of women. These differences may reflect cultural differences between Canada and the United States. They may also reflect differences in the methodologies used in the two studies that may have affected participants' willingness to report a behaviour that is generally frowned upon (see Chapter 3).

The incidence of extramarital sex varies from one group to another and one region to another. As shown in Table 1.2 in Chapter 1, the rate of extramarital sexual activity is highest in Quebec.

All these percentages are of persons who had sex with someone other than their spouse while married. At the time of the surveys, some of these people were divorced. Others were remarried, perhaps for the second or third time. We can ask a more specific question: How many people engage in extramarital sex during their first marriage? Data from the NHSLS (1994) indicate that from 10 to 23 percent of the American men had extramarital sex, compared to 6 to 12 percent of the women, depending on the person's age.

There is no indication that extramarital sex is casual or promiscuous. In one Canadian survey, of the respondents who had had extramarital sex, 40 percent had done so with only one partner (Gallup, 1988).

Attitudes toward Extramarital Sex

While, as we have seen, attitudes toward premarital sex have become substantially more permissive during the past several decades, attitudes toward extramarital sex have become, if anything, less accepting. Most people in Canada disapprove of extramarital sex. According to a series of well-sampled surveys conducted by Bibby and his associates (1995), in 1975 50 percent of Canadian adults felt that it is always wrong to have sex with someone other than the marriage partner. In 1995, this zfigure had risen to 60 percent. A 2001 COMPAS poll found that most Canadians feel that an act of unfaithfulness would probably (37 percent) or definitely (44 percent) mean the end of a relationship. Some people view unfaithfulness to a partner in any type of committed relationship as the equivalent of adultery. And some don't limit the term to cases of sexual intimacy. "Adultery is absolutely anything," said one young woman.

One of the best predictors of attitudes toward extramarital sex are attitudes toward premarital sex (Thompson, 1983). That is, the person who has a liberal or approving attitude about premarital sex is more likely to hold a liberal or approving attitude toward extramarital sex. On the other hand, attitudes toward extramarital sex are not very good predictors of extramarital sexual behaviour (Thompson, 1983). That is, the person who approves of extramarital sex is not more likely to actually engage in extramarital sex than the person who disapproves of it. Several other factors are related to attitudes toward sex outside one's primary relationship, including gender (men are more tolerant of it), education (those with more education are more accepting of it), and social class (upper-middle class-persons are more tolerant of it) (Willetts et al., 2004).

Because our society condemns extramarital sex, the individual who engages in it typically has confused, ambivalent feelings. A young married woman describes her feelings:

> I don't like the illicit part of the affair. Mostly, it's a nuisance, because it's very difficult to find time, and I don't like lying to Freddie and sneaking around. If he wouldn't mind, I'd tell him. I don't think he would go for that. He'd show up with a gun. (Maurer, 1994, p. 393)

Swinging

One form of extradyadic sex is **swinging,** in which married couples exchange partners with other couples, or engage in sexual activity with a third person, with the knowledge and consent of all involved.[2]

Swingers may find their partners in several ways. Often they advertise, in tabloid newspapers, in "lifestyle" magazines such as *Maritime Connection,* or on specialized bulletin boards and Web sites on the Internet. The following is an example:

> We are engaged bicouple lookin to meet bim, bif and bicouples for friendship and fun . . . we are into nudism, motorcycling, fishin, volleyball, pool and campin . . . she is 22 5'5 180# 38-d blond blue . . . he is 24 5'10 145# blond green 7" and very thick. email: (www . . . /~gnkfoxx/nefriend.htm)

Swingers may also meet potential partners at swingers' clubs, parties, or resorts. Many of these places advertise in swingers' magazines and newsletters and are listed on specialized Web sites.

Several organizations and many local groups or couples sponsor parties. The date and general location of the party is publicized in magazines and on the Internet. Interested persons call or e-mail a contact person who screens them. If they pass, they are told the exact location of the party, often a private home or a hotel. A fee of $50 or more per couple may be charged for membership or entry to the party. There are estimated to be more than a dozen swinger clubs across Canada, from Dart-

Figure 12.6   A mannequin hangs from the ceiling of this members-only swingers' club in Montreal, which was shut down by police in 1999, only to reopen after owners promised there would be no sex on the premises. Although most swinging occurs in private residences, there are estimated to be more than a dozen swingers' clubs across Canada.

mouth, N.S., to Prince George, B.C. (McClelland, 1999). In 1998, a members-only swing club in Montreal was raided by police and the owner was charged with running a common bawdy house—that is, a place "for the purpose of prostitution or the practice of acts of indecency." The Court eventually ruled that swinging is legal in Canada as long as it takes place in private and that sexual activities that take place in private are "not swinging but an orgy." A CROP poll found that 64 percent of Canadians (76 percent of Quebecers) were accepting of swingers' clubs. That is, swinging passes the community standards of tolerance test (see Chapter 18), but orgies do not.

---

[2]Swinging was originally called "wife-swapping." However, because of the sexist connotations of that term and the fact that women were often as eager to swap husbands as men were to swap wives, the more equitable "mate-swapping" or "swinging" was substituted.

Swinging: A form of extradyadic sex in which married couples exchange partners with each other.

A man who frequently hosts parties describes what happens:

> A lot of people have the idea that swinger parties are big orgies, where everybody jumps on everybody else. It isn't that way. People are selective, like they are anyplace else. [It starts with the eyes.] So if the interest continues from eye contact to talking, and to desire, there's touching. You just go with it. So you go from talking to touching, and at a swinging party you can go from touching to bed. (Maurer, 1994, p. 120)

Swinging may be closed or open. In *closed swinging*, the couples meet and exchange partners, and each pair goes off separately to a private place to have intercourse, returning to the meeting place at an agreed-upon time. In *open swinging*, the pairs get back together for sex in the same room for at least part of the time. In 75 percent of the cases, this includes the women having sex with each other, although two men having sex almost never occurs (Bartell, 1970; Gilmartin, 1975).

What kind of people are swingers? A review of 15 published studies, most of them involving small, convenience samples, concluded that the majority are upper or middle class, above average in education and income, and employed in the professions and in management (Jenks, 1998). Although one might expect them to be politically liberal, in one study only 27 percent described themselves as politically liberal—the rest were moderate or conservative (Jenks, 1985). The evidence indicates that at least two-thirds were raised in a religious home, but as adults they did not attend services and were not affiliated with a denomination.

Why do people become swingers? One of the main reasons is the desire for variety in sexual partners and experiences. Another reason given is pleasure or excitement, in part because exchanging partners is culturally forbidden. A third reason is to meet new people (Bartell, 1970). Researchers have noted that a major aspect of open swinging is the opportunity to be a voyeur, to watch other people engage in sexual activity, which turns some people on (Jenks, 1998).

Swinging appears to involve a small minority of people. Published estimates range from less than 1 to 2 percent, although none of these are current.

Internet Infidelity

The proliferation of Web sites designed to connect people looking for romantic or sexual partners, along with chat rooms and other forms of digital communication, has created new opportunities for people in committed relationships to be unfaithful. A **cyberaffair** is a romantic or sexual relationship initiated by online contact and maintained primarily via online communication (Young et al., 2000). There are some Internet sites set up specifically for people in relationships who wish to have affairs. Once a relationship is established online, contacts can turn into mutual erotic dialogue, which may be accompanied by masturbation. In some cases, the participants arrange to meet face-to-face and may then engage in sexual intimacy.

There has been little empirical study of cyberaffairs. Professionals engaged in relationship and sexual counselling report working with couples whose problems include loss of trust by one person over another's online relationships. Some partners define such a relationship as infidelity even if it did not involve sexual conversation or activity. Note that these can be heterosexual or same-sex couples, who are married, cohabiting, or "committed" to each other. An online survey of Internet users, recruited by a banner that appeared on a major web portal, included questions about cybersex, the practice of engaging in sexual talk online. One-third of 1,828 participants reported engaging in this activity; 46 percent of those reporting the activity—both men and women—said they were also in a committed relationship. Interestingly, those who reported engaging in cybersex reported more offline sexual activity as well (Daneback et al., 2004).

Equity and Extradyadic Sex

Social exchange theories are a type of social-psychological theory that have been used to explain sexuality in close relationships. Unlike most theories that focus on the individual, the social exchange perspective takes the interpersonal context in which most sexual activities occur into account (Byers &

Cyberaffair: A romantic or sexual relationship initiated by online contact and maintained primarily via online communication.

Wang, 2004). One such theory, **equity theory**, has been used to predict patterns of extradyadic sex (Hatfield, 1978).

The basic idea in equity theory is that in a relationship, people mentally tabulate their inputs to it and what they get out of it (benefits or rewards); then they calculate whether these are equitable or not.

According to equity theory, if individuals perceive a relationship as inequitable (if they feel they are not getting what they deserve), they become distressed. The more inequitable the relationship, the more distressed they feel. In order to relieve the distress, they make attempts to restore equity in the relationship. For example, people who feel they are putting too much into a relationship and not getting enough out of it might let their appearance go, or not work as hard to earn money, or refuse to have sex, or contribute to conversations. The idea is that such actions will restore equity.

If these equity processes do occur, they might help to explain patterns of extramarital sex. That is, engaging in extramarital sex would be a way of restoring equity in an inequitable relationship. Social psychologist Elaine Hatfield (1978) tested this notion. Her prediction was that people who felt underbenefited in their marriages (that is, they felt that there was an inequity and that they were not getting as much as they deserved) would be the ones to engage in extramarital sex. Confirming this notion, people who felt they were underbenefited began engaging in extramarital sex earlier in their marriages and had more extramarital partners than did people who felt equitably treated or overbenefited. Apparently, feeling that one is not getting all one deserves in a marriage is related to engaging in extramarital sex. (As an aside, equitable marriages were rated as happier than inequitable ones.)

Equity theory includes rewards and costs of all kinds, as indicated by our examples. However, as noted earlier in this chapter, our perceptions of our *sexual* rewards and costs have a particular impact on our satisfaction (Lawrence & Byers, 1995). For example, people who, during sex, are happy with

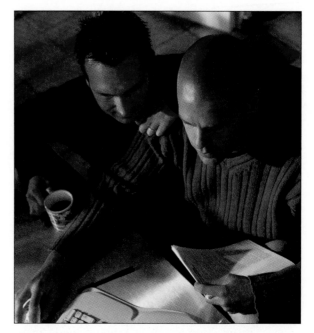

Figure 12.7 Equitable sharing of household tasks—such as budgeting and paying bills—in a marriage. According to equity theory, if a person perceives that the marital relationship is inequitable and feels underbenefited, he or she is more likely to engage in extramarital sex.

their communication with their partner, the level of affection, the frequency of specific techniques such as oral sex, and their ease in reaching orgasm are likely to be sexually satisfied. Individuals with a more favourable balance of sexual rewards to sexual costs are also more satisfied with the relationship in general. Greater sexual satisfaction, in turn is, associated with higher frequencies of affection and sexual behaviour, and fewer sexual concerns and problems.

Clearly, both our perceptions of equity and equality in our intimate relationships as well as our levels of sexual rewards and costs may affect our satisfaction with those relationships and the likelihood that we will become involved in extramarital (or extradyadic) sexuality.

Evolution and Extramarital Sex

Extramarital sex is not unique to North America. In fact, it occurs in virtually every society. When sociobiologists observe a behaviour that occurs in all societies, they are inclined to explain that behaviour in terms of evolutionary processes.

> **Equity theory:** A social exchange theory that states that people mentally calculate the benefits and costs for them in a relationship; their behaviour is then affected by whether they feel there is equity or inequity, and they will act to restore equity if there is inequity.

From an evolutionary perspective, the genes that enable their bearers to produce larger numbers of offspring are more likely to survive from one generation to the next than genes that don't. A man who mates with one woman for life could produce a maximum of 6 to 12 offspring, depending on the length of time infants are breast-fed, post-partum sex taboos, and so on. If that same man occasionally has sex with a second woman (or a series of other women), he could produce 12 to 24 offspring. We think you get the picture. Men who seek out the "other woman" will produce more offspring, who in turn will produce more offspring carrying the genetic makeup that leads to extradyadic liaisons (Fisher, 1992).

What about women? They cannot increase the number of their offspring by increasing the number of their sexual partners. However, there are ways in which having more than one sexual partner might have been biologically adaptive for women in the past (Grailing & Buss, 2000). First, sexual liaisons with other men might have enabled a woman to acquire extra goods and services, that enhanced her offspring's chances for survival. Second, having another partner could serve as "insurance"; if her husband died, she would have another man to turn to for food, shelter, and protection. Third, a woman married to a timid, unproductive hunter could "upgrade her genetic line" by mating with another man. Finally, having children with multiple partners increases the genetic diversity of one's offspring, increasing the chances that some of them will survive. Given the lower status of women in most societies, a married woman who had extramarital liaisons would have had to be careful; if caught she risked death.

Genetic research on species that appear to be monogamous reveals that some of the offspring being raised by a male–female pair were fathered by another male. These tests also reveal that females paired with lesser-quality males engage in extradyadic mating, whereas females paired with high-quality males do not (Morell, 1998). These results provide some support for the sociobiological hypothesis about the adaptive value of female infidelity.

According to this sociobiological perspective, then, extramarital sex occurs because some men and women carry in their genetic makeup something that motivates them to be unfaithful. If there are environments in which extramarital sex is adaptive in contemporary society, people with those genes will have a selective advantage.

Polyamory

Polyamory is "the non-possessive, honest, responsible and ethical philosophy and practice of loving multiple people simultaneously" (Ve Ard & Veaux, 2003). There are several forms of such relationships, including the *intentional family*, involving three or more persons; the *group relationship*, with committed, loving relationships involving three or more partners; and *group marriage*, involving three or more persons. One specific type of *group relationship* is a triad involving a married couple and an additional man or woman, all of whom share sexual intimacy; the third person and one or both members of the couple may be bisexual. Other arrangements involve two or more men and two or more women. Unlike the extramarital affair, there is (ideally) full disclosure of the network of relationships to all participants. Unlike swinging, the emphasis is on long-term intimate relationships.

Research involving in-depth interviews with 20 men and 20 women provided information about participants in one geographic area in the United States (Sheff, 2004). Those interviewed were in their mid-30s to late 50s, usually college educated, and employed in professional occupations; they were overwhelmingly white. Their high social status and access to resources may be a prerequisite for participating in the polyamory lifestyle. The interviewees noted that persons outside the polyamorous community, including members of their family of origin (parents, siblings), often react negatively and with hostility toward community members. Their status insulates them against some potential sanctions.

Women involved in polyamory report expanding their familial, gender, and sexual roles. For example, some of these women rejected monogamy in favour of a network of intimate partner relationships. With respect to gender, the women adopted a much more assertive style in their relationships

---

Polyamory: The "non-possessive, honest, responsible and ethical philosophy and practice of loving multiple people simultaneously."

with men. In the realm of sexuality, the women often recognized their high sex drive, the emotional and sexual value of intimacy with other women, and their bisexual interests or identities. Moving away from traditional roles was reported to be both liberating and frightening; creating new roles was often difficult.

■ Postmarital Sex

From the point of view of developmental psychologists, the sexual relationship in a second union, perhaps following a divorce or the death of one's partner, is especially interesting. In what ways is it the same, and how does it differ, from the sexual relationship in the first marriage? It represents the blending of things that are unique and consistent about the person with things that are unique to the new situation and new partner. As we develop sexually throughout the lifespan, these two strands continue to be intertwined—the developmental continuities (the things that are us and always will be) and the developmental changes (things that differ at various times in our lives, either because we are older or have experienced more, or because our partner or the situation is different).

The Divorced and the Widowed

People who are divorced or widowed from opposite-sex relationships are in a somewhat unusual situation in that they are used to regular sexual expression and suddenly find themselves in a situation in which they no longer have a regular sexual partner. Partly recognizing this dilemma, our society places few restrictions on postmarital sexual activity, although it is not as approved as marital sex. However, divorced and widowed Canadians are least likely to be satisfied with their sex life; 51 percent are satisfied compared to 79 percent of people living with a partner and 75 percent of never-married individuals.

Most divorced women, but fewer widowed women, return to having an active sex life. A Canadian survey found that 25 percent of formerly married respondents had engaged in intercourse in the last 7 days compared to 72 percent of married and 45 percent of never-married participants (Gallup, 1988). An American study found that 77 percent of the widowed had been sexually abstinent in the last year compared with 29 percent of the divorced (Smith, 2003).

The lower incidence of postmarital sex among widows, compared with divorced women, is due in part to the fact that widows are, on the average, older than divorced women; but even when matched for age, widows are still less likely than divorcees to engage in postmarital sex. There are probably several reasons for this (Gebhard, 1968). Widows have the continuing social support system of in-laws and friends, and so they are less motivated to seek new friendships. There is also a belief that a widow should be loyal to her dead husband, and having a sexual relationship with another man is viewed as disloyalty. Many widows believe this or tell themselves that they will "never find another one like him." Widows are more likely to be financially secure than divorced women and therefore have less motivation for engaging in sex as a prelude to remarriage.

Divorced women face complex problems of adjustment (Song, 1991). These problems may include reduced income, a lower perceived standard of living, and reduced availability of social support. Some divorced men face similar problems. These problems may increase the motivation to establish a new long-term relationship.

Widowed and divorced women who have postmarital sex often begin a relationship within one year of the end of the marriage. Evidence from an American survey suggests that these are long-term relationships and that divorced men are more sexually active than divorced women (Stack & Gundlach, 1992). A survey of professional women who held teaching and administrative posts in academic institutions found that divorced women had a larger number of sexual partners and more frequent activity than their never-married counterparts (Davidson & Darling, 1988).

Earlier in this chapter we noted that substantial numbers of men and women cohabit. Like marriages, these relationships break up. What are the similarities and differences between formerly married and formerly cohabiting men and women? To answer this question, Wade and DeLamater (2002) used the NHSLS data to analyze the rate of acquisition of new partners following the dissolution of a relationship. The results indicate that these newly single men and women do not acquire new sexual partners at a high rate, and there were no significant differences between formerly married and formerly cohabiting men and women. Newly single persons acquire new partners at a significantly higher rate than single, never-married persons in the year following a breakup. Men with custody of children and men and women with low incomes have higher rates of new-partner acquisition, perhaps reflecting the impact of familial and economic instability associated with the dissolution. The results suggest that the post-dissolution experience is similar across various demographic groups; given the high rates of breaking up in Canada and the U.S., dissolution may, we suggest, be considered a significant life stage with its own specific characteristics.

Elderly men and women may find the loss of a long-term partner emotionally traumatic, and may find it difficult or impossible establish a new relationship. They may also encounter resistance or hostility from their families, including their adult children, to any effort to find a new partner.

■ Sex and Older Adults

When Freud suggested that young children, even infants, have sexual thoughts and feelings, his ideas met with considerable resistance. When, 50 years later, researchers began to suggest that elderly men and women also have sexual thoughts and feelings, there was similar resistance (Pfeiffer et al., 1968). This section deals with the sexual behaviour of older men and women, the physical changes they undergo, and the attitudes that influence them.

Menopause
Biological Changes
The *climacteric* is a period lasting about 15 or 20 years (from about ages 45 to 60) during which a woman's body makes the transition from being able to reproduce to not being able to reproduce; the climacteric is marked particularly by a decline in the functioning of the ovaries. But climacteric changes occur in many other body tissues and systems as well. **Menopause** (the "change of life," the "change") refers to one specific event in this process, the cessation of menstruation; this occurs, on average, over a two-year period beginning at around age 50 (with a

> **Menopause:** The cessation of menstruation in middle age.

normal menopause occurring anywhere between the ages of 40 and 60).

Biologically, as a woman grows older, the pituitary continues a normal output of FSH and LH; however, as the ovaries age, they become less able to respond to the pituitary hormones. In addition, the brain—including the hypothalamus-pituitary unit—ages (Lamberts et al., 1997; Wise et al., 1996). With the aging of the ovaries, there is an accompanying decline in the output of their two major products: eggs and the sex hormones estrogen and progesterone. More specifically, the ovaries become less capable of responding to FSH by maturing and releasing an egg. The hormonal changes of menopause involve a decline in estrogen and progesterone levels and hormonal imbalance (see Figure 12.8 on p. 358).

Physical symptoms of menopause may include "hot flashes" or "hot flushes," headaches, and dizziness. For some women, a long-range effect of the decline in estrogen levels is *osteoporosis* (porous and brittle bones). The hot flash is probably the best known of the symptoms, particularly in Western cultures. Typically it is described as a sudden wave of heat from the waist up. The woman may get red and perspire a lot; when the flush goes away, she may feel chilled and sometimes may shiver. The flashes may last from a few seconds to half an hour and occur several or many times a day. They may also occur at night, causing insomnia, and the resulting perspiration can soak the sheets. Research in Ontario also showed that women have poorer working memories after menopause. This appears to be due to decreased levels of estrogen; estrogen levels did not affect passive recall (Duff & Hampson, 2000).

Do all women experience these menopausal symptoms? The Massachusetts Women's Health Study (Avis & McKinlay, 1995; McKinlay et al., 1992) followed a large sample of middle-aged women for several years, beginning when they were premenopausal and continuing through menopause to the postmenopausal period. The peak in reporting of hot flashes and night sweats occurred just before the onset of menopause, with 50 percent of women reporting them. About one-quarter of the sample (23 percent) did not report a hot flash at any of the interview times. Furthermore, 69 percent of the women reported not being bothered by the hot flashes and night sweats. So, about one-quarter of women do not experience hot flashes;

50 to 75 percent of women do, but the majority report that they are not bothered by them.

Hormone-replacement therapy (HRT) may be helpful to many menopausal women, particularly for relief of physical discomfort such as hot flashes and some sexual problems such as lack of vaginal lubrication. The treatment today typically includes both estrogen and progesterone, and testosterone may be added as well. The therapy is somewhat controversial, and its benefits need to be weighed against its potential risks. Some research has found that HRT protects women from cardiovascular disease such as heart attack and stroke (Ross & Stevenson, 1993) and from osteoporosis, which may cause a broken hip leading to death in elderly women (Kamel et al., 2001). In contrast, it increases the risk of breast cancer and endometrial cancer (Chen et al., 2002; Rosenberg, 1993; Steinberg et al., 1991). However, a recent U.S. study of the risks and benefits of combined estrogen and progestin that followed 16,608 healthy menopausal women for more than five years found that HRT increased the risk of coronary heart disease, strokes, heart attacks, and breast cancer (Writing Group for the Women's Health Initiative Investigators, 2002). The study found that HRT reduced the risk of colorectal cancer and hip and other fractures. There was no difference in overall mortality. Does this mean that all women should stop HRT? Not necessarily. The trial was of a particular drug; some other formulation of estrogen and progesterone might be fine. The study was investigating long-term use of HRT. Short-term use of HRT for one or two years is probably safe for most women according to the Society of Obstetricians and Gynaecologists of Canada. Moreover, the increase in risk from HRT might seem small to women who are having serious difficulty with menopausal symptoms. Further, other research has found that women using ERT and HRT have a lower rate of mortality than women who did not (Grodstein et al, 1997). Thus, women need to carefully assess, with their doctor, the potential risks and benefits of HRT for them personally. A woman's risk of death between the ages of 50 and 94 is 31 percent from coronary heart disease and only 2.8 percent for breast cancer and 2.8 percent from hip fractures (Brinton & Schairer, 1997). Therefore, HRT protects women against some serious health risks but not others. In short, the picture on ERT and HRT is complex and speaks to the importance of individualized evaluation and treatment for each woman, taking into account her particular pattern of symptoms and how distressed she is by them.

The latest development in HRT is the so-called "designer estrogens" or "tissue-specific estrogens" (Fuleihan, 1997). They are intended to provide the beneficial effects of traditional HRT without increasing the risk of breast and endometrial cancer. It is too soon to know their long-term effects on coronary heart disease, osteoporosis, and cancer. Nonetheless, a short-term, two-year study of raloxifene (one of these drugs) indicated that it increased bone density and lowered total cholesterol levels, yet it did not stimulate the endometrium—precisely the intended effects (Delmas et al., 1997). These drugs hold much promise for the future.

To learn more about how menopause is viewed in various cultures, watch the "Menopause" video in Chapter 12 of your CD.

Sexuality and Menopause

During the climacteric, physical changes occur in the vagina. The lack of estrogen causes the vagina to become less acidic, which leaves it more vulnerable to infections. Estrogen is also responsible for maintaining the mucous membranes of the vaginal walls. With a decline in estrogen, there is a decline in vaginal lubrication during arousal, and the vaginal walls become thinner and less elastic. Because the walls of the vagina are now thinner, they cannot absorb the pressures from the thrusting penis as they once did, and thus nearby structures—such as the bladder and the urethra—may be irritated. As a result, older women may have an urgent need to urinate immediately after intercourse. Furthermore, the vagina shrinks in both width and length, and the labia majora also shrink; thus there is a constriction at the entrance to the vagina, which may make penile insertion somewhat more difficult, and the vagina may be less able to accommodate the size of a fully erect penis. By about five years after menopause, the amount of vaginal lubrication has decreased noticeably. Intercourse can then become somewhat more difficult and painful.

Figure 12.8 Levels of estrogen production in women across the lifespan.

Because of hormonal changes, the contractions of the uterus that occur during orgasm can become painful, to the point where the woman avoids sexual activity. Nonetheless, the woman has the same physical capacity for arousal and orgasm at 80 that she did at 30. For example, researchers in British Columbia examined premenopausal and postmenopausal women's physiological and subjective arousal to an erotic film and found no differences between the two groups (Brotto & Gorzalka, 2002).

Lest these changes sound discouraging, it is important to realize that there are a number of ways to deal with them successfully. Some women's physicians prescribe hormone-replacement therapy for them after menopause; with these added doses of estrogen, the changes described above are minimized or may not occur at all. Also, research indicates that adding testosterone to the therapy will enhance sexual desire and enjoyment (Sherwin, 1991). A simple alternative is to use a sterile lubricant as a substitute for vaginal lubrication. Some women report that sex is even better after menopause.

It also appears that these changes are related in part to sexual activity—or, rather, to the lack of it. A study of 59 healthy women between 60 and 70 years of age found consistent differences between the 39 who were sexually active and the 20 who were not (Bachmann & Leiblum, 1991). All of the women had a male partner. Those who were sexually active reported having intercourse an average of five times per month. They reported having higher levels of sexual desire, greater comfort about expressing their sexual needs, and greater sexual satisfaction. A pelvic exam by a physician who was unaware of which women were sexually active found less genital atrophy in the sexually active women. Sexual problems reported by the women included reduced sexual desire in both self and partner, decreased vaginal lubrication, and erectile difficulties. These are correlational data, so we cannot be sure what is cause and what is effect.

One study analyzed the data from an AARP survey of 1,384 persons age 45 and older (DeLamater & Sill, 2003). The AARP survey, discussed in more detail later in this chapter, included questions about various factors that might affect the frequency of sexual behaviour, including diagnosed physical and emotional illnesses, use of medications, attitudes toward sexuality, and the presence of a sexual partner. Physical limitations such as prior stroke and arthritis, emotional problems such as depression, and use of various medications can interfere with sexual activity. While some men and women reported these conditions, they were relatively uncommon and were not significantly related to the frequency of oral sexual activity or vaginal intercourse. The factors that were significantly related were high scores on an index of sexual desire (frequent sexual thoughts, desire), positive attitudes toward sex for oneself, and the presence of a partner with no limitations related to sexuality. Men and women who reported that their partner had limitations that interfered with sexual expression were significantly more likely to report masturbating.

Some people believe that having a **hysterectomy** means having the end of a woman's sex life. In fact, sex hormone production is not affected as long as the ovaries are not removed (surgical removal of the ovaries is called **oophorectomy** or ovariectomy). The majority of women report that a hysterectomy has no effect on their sex lives. However, approximately one-third of women who have had hysterectomies report problems with sexual response (Zussman et al., 1981). There are two possible physiological causes for these problems. If

Hysterectomy (hiss-tur-EK-tuh-mee): Surgical removal of the uterus.
Oophorectomy (OH-uh-fuh-REK-tuh-mee): Surgical removal of the ovaries.

the ovaries have been removed, hormonal changes may be responsible; the ovaries produce androgens, and they may play a role in sexual response. Alternatively, hysterectomy may change the sexual response if the cervix serves as a trigger for orgasm or if contractions of the uterus contribute to sexual pleasure.

Psychological Changes

Psychological problems that have been associated with menopause include depression, irritability, anxiety, and cognitive symptoms such as inability to concentrate and memory problems.

One authoritative review concluded that menopause does *not* increase the rate of depression (Stanton et al., 2002). And the Massachusetts Women's Health Study found that 85 percent of women were never depressed during the menopausal years, 10 percent were depressed occasionally, and just 5 percent were persistently depressed (Golub, 1992). Research is inconsistent and inconclusive as to whether there are significant cognitive symptoms (Stanton et al., 2002).

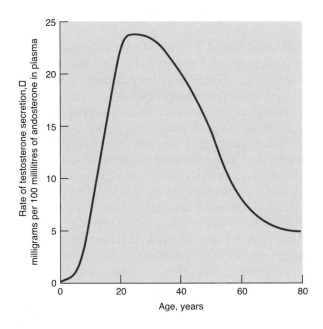

Figure 12.9 Levels of testosterone production in men across the lifespan.

Andropause
Biological Changes

Although people use the term "male menopause," in the technical sense men do not experience a "menopause"; never having menstruated, they can scarcely cease menstruating. However, men do experience a very gradual decline in the manufacture of both testosterone and sperm by the testes, a mild version of the climacteric process in women, although viable sperm may still be produced at age 90 (Schiavi, 1990) (see Figure 12.9). Some refer to this time of life as **andropause**, referring to declining levels of androgens (Lamberts et al., 1997). Others prefer the term ADAM, for *androgen decline in the aging male* (Morales et al., 2000). Some experts argue that a low testosterone syndrome occurs in some older men and that testosterone treatments are beneficial, although this approach is controversial (Jan & Culberson, 2003).

Vascular diseases such as hardening of the arteries are increasingly common with age in men, but good circulation is essential to erection (Riportella-Muller, 1989). A major change is that erections occur more slowly. It is important for men to know that this is a perfectly natural slowdown so that they will not jump to the conclusion that they are developing an erection problem. It is also important for partners to know about this so that they will use effective techniques of stimulating the man and will not mistake slowness for lack of interest.

The refractory period lengthens with age; thus for an elderly man, there may be a period of 24 hours after an orgasm during which he cannot get an erection. (Note that women do not undergo a similar change; most women do not enter into a refractory period and are still capable of multiple orgasm at age 80.) Other signs of sexual excitement—the sex flush and muscle tension—diminish with age.

The volume of the ejaculate gradually decreases, and the force of ejaculation lessens. The testes become somewhat smaller, but viable sperm are produced by even very old men. Ninety-year-old men have been known to father children.

One advantage is that middle-aged and elderly men may have better control over orgasm than

Andropause: The time of declining androgen levels in middle-aged men. The male version of menopause. Also called ADAM (androgen decline in the aging male).

young men; thus they can prolong sexual intercourse and may be better sexual partners.

A study of healthy men, ages 45 to 74, all married, assessed their biological, psychological, and behavioural functioning (Schiavi et al., 1994). Men who reported erectile difficulties were less satisfied with their sexual functioning. Erectile problems, low sexual information, and low marital adjustment were associated with lower general satisfaction. Accurate information is important because it may result in more realistic expectations for sexual performance.

One of the most common physical problems for middle-aged and older men is non-cancerous enlargement of the prostate gland, which is believed to be related to changes in hormone levels. Prostate enlargement occurs in 10 percent of men by age 40, and 50 percent of men who reach age 80. Enlargement of the prostate causes urination problems; there is difficulty in voluntarily initiating urination, as well as frequent nocturnal urination. These symptoms are usually remedied by surgery to remove the part of the gland pressing against the urethra. Unfortunately, complications of the surgery include retrograde ejaculation in about 75 percent of men and erection problems in 5 to 10 percent (Oesterling, 1995). New treatments have recently been developed to avoid these problems, including anti-androgen drugs and laser treatments (Oesterling, 1995). Contrary to a number of myths, prostate enlargement is not caused by masturbation or excessive sexual activity. The infection and inflammation resulting from sexually transmitted diseases, though, can cause prostate swelling.

Some people believe that prostate surgery or removal of the prostate (**prostatectomy**) means the end of a man's sex life. It is true that the volume of the ejaculate will decrease. Prostatectomy can cause damage to the nerves supplying the penis, creating erectile problems. In other cases, retrograde ejaculation may result. Whether there are such problems depends on which of several available methods of surgery is used. Radiation, used in treating prostate cancer, may result in erectile dysfunction. Unfortunately, many men equate sex with sexual intercourse and stop engaging in all

Prostatectomy (pros-tuh-TEK-tuh-mee): Surgical removal of the prostate.

sexual activity if they develop erection difficulties as a result of prostate surgery or radiation.

In sum, the evidence suggests that there need be no time limit on sexual expression for either men or women.

A 73-year-old man reported:

I can't begin to tell you how happy I am. I am married to a wonderful woman who loves me as much as I love her. My children gave me a hard time of it at first, especially because she is a bit younger than me. [My son] was telling me that marrying again and trying to have a lot of sex—imagine that, saying to me *trying* to have sex—could be dangerous to the marriage. So, I said to him with a straight face, "Do you think she'll survive it?" He was so shocked, he laughed. (Janus & Janus, 1993, p. 8)

Psychological Changes

Some authors have argued that declining levels of testosterone in middle-aged and elderly men are associated not only with physical symptoms but also with a number of cognitive, sexual, and emotional symptoms (Urban, 1992). However, research has shown that the amount of testosterone available in the blood was not an important determinant of cognitive, psychological, or sexual functioning or quality of life in a group of men aged 55 to 76 (Tamir, 1982).

Attitudes about Sex and Older Adults

Our society has a negative attitude toward sexual expression among the elderly. Somehow it seems indecent for two 70-year-old people to have sex with each other, and even more indecent for a 70-year-old to masturbate. These negative attitudes become particularly obvious in nursing homes, where staff members may frown on sexual activity among the residents. Somehow what is "virility" at 25 becomes "lechery" at 75.

Cross-cultural research indicates that the sexual behaviour of older adults is related to these cultural expectations (Winn & Newton, 1982). Older adults continue to be sexually active in 70 percent of societies and in precisely those societies where they are expected to be sexually active. Indeed, in 22 percent of societies, women are expected to become more uninhibited about sexuality when they become older.

Why does our society have such negative attitudes toward sex among older adults? In part, these attitudes are due to the fact that ours is a youth-oriented culture. We value youth, and the physical characteristics that are considered "sexy" are youthful ones, such as a trim, firm body and smooth skin. It is therefore hard to believe that someone with old, wrinkled skin could be sexually active. According to one youthful-looking 59-year-old woman:

> No one looks at me today with any kind of sexual interest. I mean, I don't even get the time of day from any man. I'm an older woman. I want men to be aggressive now. I'm not going to approach a man, because I'm afraid to be rejected. So I've just given up. (Maurer, 1994, p. 475)

Our negative attitudes may be a holdover from the belief that sex was for reproductive purposes only—and those past the age of reproduction should therefore not engage in it (Pfeiffer, 1975). The incest taboo may also be involved in our negative attitudes. We tend to identify older people with our parents or grandparents, and find it hard to think of them as sexual beings. This attitude is encouraged by the fact that many parents take great pains to hide their sexual activity from their children.

These attitudes affect the way older people are treated, and older adults whether gay or straight may hold such attitudes themselves (Badeau & Bergeron, 1997). The current generation of older people was raised in a time in which they had little access to accurate sex information and myths about sexuality in older adults were common. Thus, older people today may be particularly affected by their own negative attitudes. For example, a Montreal study found that older men had less tolerant views about sexual expression in older people than did middle-aged men (Libman, 1989). One remedy that has been proposed for these negative attitudes is a "coming out of the closet"; as one 67-year-old commented:

> The common view that the aging and aged are non-sexual, I believe, can only be corrected by a dramatic and courageous process—the *coming-out-of-the-closet* of sexually active older women and men, so that people can see for themselves what the later years are really like. (Brecher, 1984, p. 21)

Various specific misunderstandings may influence sexuality. For example, a man might believe that sex will precipitate a heart attack or, if he has already had a heart attack, that it will bring on another one. Although heart rate accelerates during sexual intercourse, the mean heart rate during orgasm is only 117 beats per minute, which is about that attained during many common forms of daily exercise (Hellerstein & Friedman, 1969). This rate is about the equivalent of climbing two flights of stairs at a moderate pace. Thus the demands of sex on the heart are not unreasonable. A study of 1,775 patients who had had a heart attack questioned them about their activities immediately prior to the attack and in the year prior to the attack (Muller et al., 1996). The results indicate that the increase in risk caused by sexual activity is one chance in one million for a healthy individual. Furthermore, the relative risk is no greater in patients with a history of cardiac disease. Nonetheless, a study of 29 men (their average age was 56) who had been diagnosed with cardiovascular disease found that 41 percent reduced their frequency of sexual activity after diagnosis (Quadagno et al., 1995).

One interesting study of male coronary patients found that two-thirds had a sexual dysfunction (most commonly erectile problems) *before* the heart attack (Wabrek & Burchell, 1980). This puts the incidence of sexual difficulties after a heart attack in a better perspective. The authors suggested that there might be complex interactions among sexual disorders, stress, and heart attacks. That is, severe stress might precipitate both a sexual disorder and a heart attack. Or a sexual difficulty might be the stress that precipitated the heart attack.

Some men also mistakenly believe that sexual activity saps their "vital strength." In some cases men may believe that they can have only a fixed number of orgasms during their lifetime (as a woman is born with a fixed number of ova) and therefore adopt a strategy of saving them now so that they will have some left later on. One woman wrote:

> My husband has reached the age of sixty-five. He has decided that, in order to ensure a longer life and health, he will no longer engage in sex activity. He is convinced that intercourse and the emission of semen are quite debilitating, particularly in his years. (Rubin, 1966, p. 258)

Ideas such as this, as well as factors such as illness or hospitalization, may lead to a period of sexual inactivity. But being sexually inactive is one of the most effective ways of diminishing sexuality. Masters and Johnson emphasized that two factors are critical in maintaining sexual capacity in old age:

1. *Good physical and mental health.* An excellent study confirms this notion (Persson, 1980). A representative sample of 70-year-olds in one town in Sweden were selected, and 85 percent agreed to participate in the detailed interviews. In the entire sample, 46 percent of the men and 16 percent of the women still had sexual intercourse; when only those who were currently married were considered, the figures rose to 52 percent for men and 36 percent for women. For both men and women, those who continued to have sexual intercourse had better mental health as rated by a psychiatrist and more positive attitudes toward sexual activity among the aged.

2. *Regularity of sexual expression.* As was noted earlier, evidence exists that some physical changes of the sex organs in old age are related to sexual inactivity. As the saying goes, "If you don't use it, you lose it." In fact, the results of a longitudinal study suggest that, for men, frequency of orgasm is positively associated with longevity. The study involved 910 men aged 45 to 59. At the beginning of the study, the men completed a standard medical history and a questionnaire that assessed sexual behaviour. Ten years later, the researchers found out who had died, and compared their questionnaire answers with those of the survivors. Men who reported fewer than one orgasm per month at the beginning of the study were more than twice as likely to die as the men who reported two orgasms per month (Smith et al., 1997). Of course, these data are correlational (see Chapter 3) so we cannot conclude that more frequent sexual expression causes men to live longer.

Apparently some older people have caught on to this fact. As one 80-year-old husband said of his relationship with his 75-year-old wife,

My wife and I both believe that keeping active sexually delays the aging process . . . if we are troubled with an erection or lubrication, we turn to oral methods or masturbation of each other. We keep our interest alive by a great deal of caressing and fondling of each other's genitals.

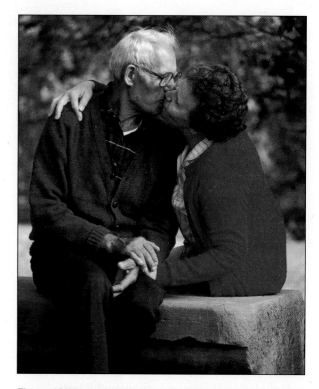

Figure 12.10   In most cultures, older adults continue to be sexually active. This is particularly true in cultures that have positive views of sexuality and aging.

We feel it is much better to wear out than to rust out. (Brecher, 1984, p. 33)

Women's beliefs about menopause may influence their sexuality in the later years. Some believe that menopause means the end of sex. Certainly such attitudes could lead to a diminishing, or even a cessation, of sexual activity. On the other hand, some women who spent their younger years worrying about getting pregnant find menopause to be a liberating experience; their sexual activity may actually increase.

Reformers urge us to change our attitudes about sex and older adults. Nursing homes particularly need to revise their practices and staff need to become more comfortable discussing sexuality with residents. Changes such as knocking before entering a resident's room would help (people masturbate, you know). Other reforms would include making provisions for partners to stay overnight and allowing couples—married or unmarried—to share a bedroom.

Figure 12.11 Romance is important for many nursing-home residents.

Sexual Behaviour of Older Adults

Relationship satisfaction tends to be higher in older couples than in middle-aged couples (Gagnon et al., 1999). This may be because older couples engage in more positive and fewer negative interactions than their younger counterparts, perhaps because they are able to give more attention to their partner after the children have grown up. In turn, relationship satisfaction is closely linked to sexual satisfaction.

Sexual behaviour and sexual interest do decline somewhat with age. For example, a Montreal study found that 27 percent of men and women over 60 reported that sex did not interest them very much, whereas only 5 percent of participants under 60 responded this way (Trudel, 2002). Nonetheless, there are still substantial numbers of older men and women who have active sex lives, even in their eighties. In a sample of healthy 80- to 102-year-olds, 62 percent of the men and 30 percent of the women reported that they still engaged in sexual intercourse (Bretschneider & McCoy, 1988). There does not seem to be any age beyond which all people are sexually inactive.

Some older people do, for various reasons, stop having intercourse after a certain age. For women, this occurs most often in their late fifties and early sixties, while it occurs somewhat later for men (Pfeiffer et al., 1968). Contrary to what one might expect, when a heterosexual couple stop having intercourse, the husband is most frequently the cause; both wives and husbands agree that this is true. For example, a Montreal study found that among older couples, age was not related to sexual frequency (Creti & Libman, 1989). However, couples in which the man lacked confidence in his own sexual response and sexual functioning had sex less frequently than other couples. Thus, the decline in women's sexual expression with age may be directly related to men's decline.

Death of a spouse is more likely to put an end to intercourse for women than it is for men, in part because there are far more older women than older men. Because of both men's earlier mortality and their preference for younger women, older women are more likely to be living alone and to have less access to sexual partners. Men aged 65 and older are much more likely to live with a spouse or partner than are women in that age group. For example, in the 2001 Canadian Census, among those 65 to 74, 48 percent of the women and 65 percent of the men were living with a spouse or partner. Similarly, among those aged 75 to 84, 28 percent of the women and 61 percent of the men were living with a partner. Some innovative solutions have been proposed, such as elderly women forming lesbian relationships.

A Montreal study of 144 married men ranging in age from 51 to 80 and 71 of their female spouses provides some data on how age affects sexual expression (Libman 1989). All participants were in good health and all the men had previously undergone one of two non–life-threatening surgical procedures. The sample was divided into younger (under 65) and older (age 65 and older) groups. The two groups did not differ in their frequency of sexual activity or in their satisfaction with their sex lives— both groups were generally satisfied. However, the older men and women experienced a desire for sex less often and the older men had more concerns about erectile difficulties (erectile difficulties themselves were infrequent in both male age groups, about 15 percent of the time).

The best survey to date on the sexuality of people over age 50 was conducted in the United States by a research firm for the American Association of Retired Persons (1999). The AARP staff designed a questionnaire that focused on the role of sexuality in the lives of older adults. A research firm that maintains a large panel of households selected 3,450 panel members age 45 and older and telephoned them to invite them to participate in the study. A questionnaire was mailed to the 1,709 persons who agreed to participate; 1,384 persons returned completed questionnaires. The result is a volunteer sample, with certain likely biases. Specifically, older adults who are sick or in care facilities, or whose sight has failed so that they cannot read, are highly unlikely to have completed the survey. Thus, we must regard this as a survey of older adults who are above average in health, activity, and intelligence, and who are doubtless more sexually active than some older adults. Nonetheless, it is a very important source of information about sex and older adults, a topic about which there is a shortage of knowledge.

Some statistics from the survey are included in Table 12.3. They are presented by age group; as we would expect, the number of participants declines as age advances. Note that women over 60 are much less likely to have a sexual partner available, so they report much lower frequencies of partnered activities. About 25 percent of the women and 33 percent of the men age 60 to 74 have intercourse at least weekly. More than 25 percent of the women and half the men at all ages report that they always have an orgasm from sexual activity.

In spite of the differences in frequency of activity, men and women were equally likely to report that they were satisfied with their sexual lives. Among 45- to 59-year-olds, 63 and 61 percent reported satisfaction, while among 60- to 74-year-olds, 50 percent said they were satisfied. About 36 percent of men and women aged 75 or older were satisfied. Asked what changes in their lives would increase their satisfaction, men and women 45 to 59 were most likely to say less stress and more free time, while older men said better health for themselves and their partners and women 60 years of age or older said better health for their partner and finding a partner. Thus these results illustrate the fact that among many older couples, it is the health of the man that determines sexual activity, and that for many older women the problem is absence of a partner.

We see, then, that among older people who are healthy and have regular opportunities for sexual expression, sexual activity continues well past 70 years of age.

Table 12.3 Sexual Activity in a Sample of Persons Over Age 45

	45 to 59	60 to 74	75 and Over
Women	(368)	(253)	(119)
Have a sexual partner	77.8%	52.6%	21.4%
Feel sexual desire daily	8.4%	1.6%	0.6%
Have sexual intercourse at least once a week*	49.6%	24.2%	6.6%
Have oral sex at least weekly*	19.5%	2.2%	0.8%
Masturbate once a week or more often*	4.5%	2.0%	0.6%
Always experience an orgasm from sexual activity	31.6%	26.0%	25.0%
Men	(341)	(205)	(90)
Have a sexual partner	84.2%	79.2%	57.9%
Feel sexual desire daily	39.7%	13.9%	3.4%
Have sexual intercourse at least once a week*	54.8%	30.9%	19.1%
Have oral sex at least weekly*	20.1%	6.5%	8.8%
Masturbate once a week or more often*	33.5%	14.2%	5.2%
Always experience an orgasm from sexual activity	76.6%	57.0%	48.1%

*Within the preceding six months

Source: American Association of Retired Persons/Modern Maturity Sexuality Study, Washington, D.C.: AARP, 1999.

■ ■ ■ SUMMARY

Sexuality continues to develop throughout the lifespan. It may be expressed in singlehood, cohabitation, marriage, extradyadic relationships, relationships following divorce, or in a variety of contexts as the individual ages.

Young adults grow toward sexual maturity. Many do so in the context of a single relationship that results in marriage. Others are involved in two or more relationships before they begin to live with or marry someone. Never-married people over 25 may find themselves part of the "singles scene."

Cohabitation is a stage that up to 40 percent of people experience. People in Quebec are more likely to live common-law than are other Canadians. The time couples spend living together varies from a few months to several years. Sixty percent of cohabiting couples marry. Some cohabiting couples have children, either together or with previous partners. Men and women who are living together engage in sexual activity more often, on average, than those who are married or dating.

Marriage represents a major turning point as couples face new responsibilities and problems, and try to find time for each other. Married opposite-sex couples in their twenties engage in sexual intercourse two or three times per week on average, with the frequency declining to two or three times per month among couples over age 60. Perhaps the most dramatic change in marital sex practices in recent decades is the increased popularity of oral–genital sex. Many people continue to masturbate even though they are married. Most people today—both women and men—express general satisfaction with their marital sex life. Sexual patterns in marriage, however, show great variability. There are no data on the sexual activity of married same-sex couples.

Between 14 and 25 percent of heterosexual married men and between 7 and 15 percent of married women engage in extramarital sex at some time. Extramarital sex is disapproved of in our society and is generally carried on in secrecy. In a few cases, it is agreed that both husband and wife can have extramarital sex, as in open marriage, swinging, and polyamory. Equity theory and the sociobiological perspective may be helpful in understanding patterns of extramarital sex.

Virtually all widowed and divorced men return to an active sex life, as do most divorced women and about half of widowed women. A particular set of sexual norms characterizes the divorce subculture.

Research indicates that gay men have modified their sexual practices somewhat in the AIDS era. They have reduced their number of partners and have shifted away from risky sex practices. Among heterosexuals, there is some evidence of a reduction in the number of partners, and slight improvements in condom use. Most heterosexuals do not consider themselves at risk for HIV infection, however, so they are less concerned with safer sex practices.

The climacteric is the period in middle age during which the functioning of the ovaries (both hormone and egg production) declines gradually. One symptom of this process is menopause, the cessation of menstruation. Physical symptoms, such as hot flashes, during this period result from declining levels of estrogen, and may be relieved by hormone-replacement therapy; contrary to popular belief, research does not show an increased incidence of depression at the time of menopause. Changes in sexual functioning across the menstrual cycle and at menopause are most likely related to changes in levels of testosterone.

Men experience a much more gradual decline in the functioning of their gonads. Men and women may experience a psychological transition in middle age.

While sexual activity declines somewhat with age, it is perfectly possible to remain sexually active into one's eighties or nineties. Problems with sex or the cessation of intercourse may be related to physical factors. In women, declining estrogen levels result in a thinner, less elastic vagina and less lubrication; in men, there is lowered testosterone production and increased vascular disease, combined with slower erections and longer refractory periods. Psychological factors can also be involved, such as the belief that the elderly cannot or should not have sex. Masters and Johnson emphasized that two factors are critical to maintaining sexual capacity in old age: good physical and mental health, and regularity of sexual expression. The AARP survey indicates that all sexual behaviours—including opposite-sex intercourse, masturbation, and same-sex behaviours—may continue past age 70.

http://www.mcgrawhill.ca/college/hyde

■ ■ ■ QUESTIONS FOR THOUGHT, DISCUSSION, AND DEBATE

1. What is your response when you see an elderly couple expressing affection physically with each other, perhaps kissing or holding hands? Why do you think you respond that way?

2. What is your opinion about extramarital sex? Is it ethical or moral? What are its effects on a marriage—does it destroy marriage or improve it, or perhaps have no effect?

3. If you are currently in a relationship, in what ways is your relationship characteristic of distressed couples? In what ways is it characteristic of non-distressed couples? What changes can you make to improve your relationship satisfaction?

4. You and your partner are talking about establishing a long-term relationship. Your partner says that his main concern is that living together will lead to a decline in how often you have sex. Is that a realistic concern? If so, what could the two of you do to prevent that from occurring?

5. Among the Yoruba of West Africa, younger women may not travel or engage in trade, but older (postmenopausal) women may. Among the Winnebago of North America, old women sit with men; they are considered to be the same as men. In some cultures, then, women gain in freedom and status after menopause. Does this happen for most women in Canada? Are there variations among ethnic groups in Canada—for example, Aboriginals, blacks, Asians, whites—in the way a postmenopausal woman is viewed and treated? Are there differences between anglophones and francophones? (For more information, see Golub, 1992.)

■ ■ ■ SUGGESTIONS FOR FURTHER READING

Barbach, Lonnie. (1993). *The pause: Positive approaches to menopause.* New York: Dutton. Barbach, a well-known therapist and author, provides many details about menopausal symptoms and positive ways to cope with them.

Brecher, Edward M. (1984). *Love, sex, and aging.* Mount Vernon, NY: Consumers Union. This large-scale survey offers a liberated view of sexuality in the elderly.

Fisher, Helen. (1992). *Anatomy of love: The mysteries of mating, marriage, and why we stray.* New York: Fawcett Columbine. This book presents a provocative, sociobiological account of human sexual behaviour, including extramarital sex.

Golub, Sharon. (1992). *Periods: From menarche to menopause.* Newbury Park, CA: Sage. This book, by a well-known researcher in the field, tells you everything you always wanted to know about menstruation and menopause.

Gould, Terry (1999). *The lifestyle: A look at the erotic rites of swingers.* Toronto: Vintage Canada. This book, written by a Vancouver-based investigative journalist, describes the lifestyle of people who engage in swinging and polyamory.

Maurer, Harry. (1994). *Sex: Real people talk about what they really do.* New York: Penguin Books. Maurer interviewed 52 people of diverse ages, preferences, and orientations about their sexual experiences. He presents lengthy excerpts organized around themes, such as Awakenings, Wild Oats, and the Long Haul.

Sarrel, Lorna, & Sarrel, Philip. (1984). *Sexual turning points: The seven stages of adult sexuality.* New York: Macmillan. This book, written for a general audience, provides an interesting theory of adult sexual development.

Online Learning Centre

For Review Questions, Web Resources, and other learning and study tools, visit the *Understanding Human Sexuality* Online Learning Centre at www.mcgrawhill.ca/college/hyde.

CHAPTER 13

Attraction, Intimacy, and Love

CHAPTER HIGHLIGHTS

> The intimacy in sex is never only physical. In a sexual relationship we may discover who we are in ways otherwise unavailable to us, and at the same time we allow our partner to see and know that individual. As we unveil our bodies, we also disclose our persons.*

Many people believe that there is (or should be) a close connection between love and sex. The sexual standard of today for many is that sex is appropriate if one loves the other person (see Chapter 11). Of course, sex and love do not necessarily go together. Some people have satisfying sexual relationships without emotional involvement; other people are in love with a person with whom they do not have a sexual relationship. Nonetheless, for most people emotional passion and sexual passion are closely linked—without the sexual passion, we might be more likely to think of the person as a friend. People want to express their loving feelings to their romantic partner in a sexual way. Lovemaking, in turn, contributes to their feelings of love. In short, sex is a logical and emotional part of most romantic relationships. Therefore, it is important in a text on sexuality to spend some time considering the emotion we link so closely to sex: love. Unfortunately, much of the research on love has been restricted to studying male–female relationships and has not included same-sex relationships.

This chapter is organized in terms of the way relationships usually progress—if they progress. That is, we begin by talking about attraction, what brings people together in the first place. Then we consider intimacy, which develops as relationships develop. Next, we look at five different views of what love is. Finally we discuss some of the research on love, including cross-cultural research.

■ Attraction

What causes you to be attracted to another person? Social psychologists have done extensive research on interpersonal attraction. The major results of this research are discussed in this section.

*Dr. Thomas Moore, "Soul mates," *Psychology Today*, March–April 1994, downloaded from http://faculty.uccb.ns.ca/pmacintyre/psych365/quotes.htm.

The Girl Next Door

Our opportunities to meet people are limited by geography and time. You may meet that attractive person sitting two rows in front of you in "human sex," as the course is referred to at the University of New Brunswick, but you are unlikely to meet the wealthy, brilliant engineering student who sits in your seat two classes later. You are much more likely to meet and be attracted to the boy next door than the one who lives across town. A 1988 COMPAS poll asked participants where they met their current dating partner. More than half met through friends (33 percent), at school (12 percent), through family (3 percent), or through religious settings (3 percent).

Among those who work in the same place or take the same class, we tend to be more attracted to people with whom we have had contact several times than we are to people with whom we have had little contact (Harrison, 1977). This has been demonstrated in laboratory studies in which the amount of contact between participants was systematically varied. At the end of the session, people gave higher "liking" ratings to those with whom they had had much contact and lower ratings to those with whom they had had little contact (Saegert et al., 1973). This is the **mere-exposure effect;** repeated exposure to any stimulus, including a person, leads to greater liking for that stimulus (Bornstein, 1989).

Birds of a Feather

We tend to like people who are similar to us. We are attracted to people who are approximately the same as we are in age, race or ethnicity, and economic and social status. Similarity on these social characteristics is referred to as **homophily,** the tendency to have

Mere-exposure effect: The tendency to like a person more if we have been exposed to him or her repeatedly.
Homophily: The tendency to have contact with people who are equal in social status.

Table 13.1   Percentage of Relationships That Are Homophilous, by Type of Relationship

TermType of Homophily	Type of Relationship			
	Marriages*	Cohabitations*	Long-Term Partnerships	Short-Term Partnerships
Racial/ethnic	93%	88%	89%	91%
Age[†]	78	75	76	83
Educational[‡]	82	87	83	87
Religious[§]	72	53	56	60

*Percentages of marriages and cohabitational relationships that began in the 10 years prior to the survey.

[†]Age homophily is defined as a difference of no more than five years in partners' ages.

[‡]Educational homophily is defined as a difference of no more than one educational category. The educational categories used were less than high school, high school graduate, vocational training, four-year college, and graduate degree.

[§]Cases in which either partner was reported as "other" or had missing data are omitted.

Source: Laumann et al., 1994, Table 6.4.

contact with people equal in social status. Data on homophily from the NHSLS are displayed in Table 13.1. Note that the greatest homophily is by race, followed by education and age. Couples are least likely to be the same on religion. It is interesting that short-term partnerships are as homophilous as marriages and common-law relationships. One of the reasons for homophily by race is that persons from visible minorities have tended to live in socially and economically separate communities. In communities where different racial groups have co-existed for generations, such as Nova Scotia, there tend to be more interracial relationships.

Social psychologist Donn Byrne (1971) has done numerous experiments demonstrating that we are attracted to people whose attitudes and opinions are similar to ours. In these experiments, Byrne typically has people fill out an opinion questionnaire. They are then shown a questionnaire that was supposedly filled out by another person and are asked to rate how much they think they would like that person. In fact, the questionnaire was filled out to show either high or low agreement with the participant's responses. Participants report more liking for a person whose responses are similar to theirs than for one whose responses are quite different. This is because we get positive reinforcement from that person agreeing with us (Huston & Levinger, 1978). The other person's agreement bolsters our sense of rightness, and we anticipate positive interactions with that person.

Folk sayings are sometimes wise and sometimes foolish. The interpersonal-attraction research indicates that the saying "Birds of a feather flock together" contains some truth. This tendency for men and women to choose as partners people who match them on social and personal characteristics is called the **matching phenomenon** (Feingold, 1988). However, despite the saying that "opposites attract," dissimilar attitudes tend to cause disliking, not liking (Pilkington & Lydon, 1997; Rosenberg, 1986). Nonetheless, we may be attracted to people whose interpersonal styles are dissimilar to our own. In one study, dominant people paired with submissive people reported greater satisfaction with their relationship than dominant or submissive people paired with a similar partner (Dryer & Horowitz, 1997).

Physical Attractiveness

A great deal of evidence shows that, given a choice of more than one potential partner, individuals will prefer the one who is more physically attractive (Hendrick & Hendrick, 1992). For example, in one study snapshots were taken of university men and

Matching phenomenon: The tendency for men and women to choose as partners people who match them, i.e., who are similar in attitudes, intelligence, and attractiveness.

women (Berscheid et al., 1971). A dating history of each person was also obtained. Judges then rated the attractiveness of the men and women in the photographs. For the women there was a fairly strong relationship between attractiveness and popularity; the women judged attractive had had more dates in the last year than the less attractive women. There was some relationship between appearance and popularity for men, too, but it was not as marked as it was for women. Research in Ontario has shown this phenomenon in children as young as 3 to 6 years of age; even young children are more attracted to children with attractive faces (Dion, 1977, 1973).

Physical attractiveness is one aspect of sex appeal; in fact, young men and women typically rate physical appearance as most important (Regan, 2004). Other aspects include general body size (measured in various ways) and certain facial features. Much of the research on attractiveness uses data from samples of white persons. One exception is research on the impact of lightness of skin on ratings of attractiveness among African Americans. Skin tone was strongly associated with the attractiveness ratings given female respondents by both male and female interviewers (Hill, 2002). Light skin was rated as more attractive, perhaps reflecting the use of white skin as the standard.

In general, then, we are most attracted to good-looking people. However, among heterosexuals this effect depends on gender to some extent; physical attractiveness is more important to males evaluating females than it is to females evaluating males (Feingold, 1990). And this phenomenon is somewhat modified by our own feelings of personal worth, as will be seen in the next section. As a final note, a 2001 COMPAS survey asked 400 Canadians to choose whether their perfect partner would have an ordinary face and an extraordinary body or an extraordinary face and an ordinary body. Twice as many women as men choose the extraordinary face—57 percent to 29 percent.

The Interpersonal Marketplace

Although this may sound somewhat callous, whom we are attracted to and pair off with depends a lot on how much we think we have to offer and how much we think we can "buy" with it. Historically, the principle seems to be that women's worth is based on their physical beauty, whereas men's

worth is based on their success. There is a tendency, then, for beautiful women to be paired with wealthy, successful men.

Data from many studies document this phenomenon in heterosexual relationships. In one study, high school yearbook pictures of 601 males and 745 females were rated for attractiveness (Udry & Eckland, 1984). These people were followed up 15 years after graduation, and measures of education, occupational status, and income were obtained. Females who were rated the most attractive in high school were significantly more likely to have husbands who had high incomes and were highly educated (see also Elder, 1969).

In another study, female students were rated on their physical attractiveness (Rubin, 1973, p. 68). They were then asked to complete a questionnaire about what kinds of men they would consider desirable dates. A man's occupation had a big effect on his desirability as a date. Men in high-status occupations—physician, lawyer, chemist—were considered highly desirable dates by virtually all the women. Men in low-status occupations—janitor, bartender—were judged hardly acceptable by most of the women. A difference emerged between attractive and unattractive women, however, when rating men in middle-status occupations—electrician, bookkeeper, plumber. The attractive women did not feel that these men would be acceptable dates, whereas the unattractive women felt that they would be at least moderately acceptable. Here we see the interpersonal marketplace in action. Men with more status are more desirable. But how desirable a man is judged to be depends on the woman's sense of her own worth. Attractive women are not much interested in middle-status men because they apparently think of themselves as being "worth more." Unattractive women find middle-status men more attractive, presumably because they think such men are reasonably within their "price range."

From the Laboratory to Real Life

The phenomena discussed so far—feelings of attraction to people who are similar to us and who are good-looking—have been demonstrated mainly in psychologists' laboratories. Do these phenomena occur in the real world?

Donn Byrne and his colleagues (1970) did a study to find out whether these results would be obtained in a real-life situation. They administered an attitude and personality questionnaire to 420 university students. Then they formed 44 "couples." For half of the couples, both people had made very similar responses on the questionnaire; for the other half of the couples, the two people had made very different responses. The two people were then introduced and sent to the student union on a brief date. When they returned from the date, an unobtrusive measure of attraction was taken—how close they stood to each other in front of the experimenter's desk. The participants also evaluated their dates on several scales.

The results of the study confirmed those from previous experimental work. The couples who had been matched for similar attitudes were most attracted to each other, and those with dissimilar attitudes were not so attracted to each other. The students had also been rated as to their physical attractiveness both by the experimenter and by their dates, and greater attraction to the better-looking dates was reported. In a follow-up at the end of the semester, those whose dates were similar to them and were physically attractive were more likely to remember the date's name and to express a desire to date the person again in the future. Thus in an experiment that was closer to real life and real dating situations, the importance of similarity and physical appearance was again demonstrated.

Attraction Online

Technology has created a new way to meet potential partners—online (Elias, 1997). Some Web sites, such as Toronto-based LavaLife.com, have tens of thousands of "personal ads," and one site claims 500,000 hits per day. Surveys suggest that the people seeking partners online are educated, affluent, 20- to 40-year-olds who don't have the time or the taste for "singles bars." Users say that one advantage of meeting on the Net is that the technology forces you to focus on the person's interests and values. This facilitates finding a person with whom you have a lot in common. Also, in many instances you cannot see the person and so you are not influenced by his or her physical attractiveness (or lack thereof); however, on many sites people are expected to post a picture. A major disadvantage is the risk that the other person may not be honest about his or her interests, occupation, appearance, or marital status. Chat rooms with names like "Women with Other Men" attract people in relationships. Some of the relationships established in these rooms lead to "Divorce, Internet Style" (Quittner, 1997).

Playing Hard to Get

The traditional advice that has been given to girls is that having a boyfriend is important and boys will be more attracted to them if they play hard to get. Is there any scientific evidence that this is true?

In fact, two experiments involving heterosexual men and women provide no support for this strategy; according to these experiments, playing hard to get does not work (Walster et al., 1973). In one of these experiments, university men were recruited for a computer-dating program. They were given the phone number of their date. When they called, the woman was either delighted and accepted the date (easy to get), or reluctant and "busy" (hard to get). After the phone call, the researchers assessed the men's initial impression. The results failed to support the hard-to-get strategy. The men had equally high opinions of the woman whichever strategy she employed. In the face of these and other negative results, the researchers developed a more complex hypothesis. It is the woman who is *selectively hard-to-get* who is most attractive; that is, she is easy to get for *you*, but she is hard to get or unavailable for other men. A computer dating experiment supported this hypothesis; the selectively hard-to-get woman was most popular with men.

Other research looked at the amount of effort needed to establish a relationship, to determine its effect on attractiveness (Roberson & Wright, 1994). Male students were led to believe that it would be easy, difficult, or impossible for them to work with an apparently warm, friendly woman. They were then asked to rate her on two dimensions: how nice she was and how appealing she was as a co-worker. Men who thought she would be difficult to work with rated her as more appealing than did men who thought she would be easy or impossible.

In practical terms, this means that if a woman is going to use hard-to-get strategies, she had better use them in a skillful way. It seems that the optimal strategy would be to give the impression that she has many offers for dates with others but refuses them, while indicating that she is willing to date the young man in question, although it will take some effort on his part to persuade her. On the other hand, the best "strategy" is probably to be honest.

Interestingly, in all the research discussed, it is always the woman who is playing hard to get and the man who is rating her. This reflects cultural gender-role stereotypes, in which it is the woman's role to do things like play hard to get. What we do not know is how men's use of hard-to-get strategies would affect the way women perceive them or the impact of playing hard to get in same-sex relationships.

Two attributes closely related to playing hard to get are (perceived) sexual experience and (perceived) sexual fidelity. Easy-to-get is a phrase at times used to describe people (more often women?) who are believed to have had numerous sexual partners. Research clearly shows that young people with high levels of sexual experience are rated as less desirable or undesirable as partners in romantic or sexual relationships (O'Sullivan, 1995). At the same time, research indicates that chastity or lack of experience is no longer an influence on the ratings of potential partners. So the ideal seems to be limited past sexual experience. In fact, a 2001 COMPAS poll of 400 Canadians found that 40 percent of the men and 49 percent of the women felt their perfect partner should have relatively little past sexual experience. However, 37 percent of the men and 34 percent of the women would want them to have past sexual experience. For example, an Ontario study of 165 university women found that 95 percent were willing to accept a partner who had experienced sexual intercourse with at least one previous partner, and 73 percent were willing to accept a partner with three previous partners. However, only 10 percent of women were willing to accept a partner with 11 or more previous partners (Herold & Milhausen, 1999). Sexual fidelity or exclusiveness is considered an essential characteristic of committed relationships by most people. Research by Cunningham et al. (1996) found that men and women are repulsed by partners who look longingly at others, brag about their sexual prowess, or often discuss prior relationships.

Explaining Our Preferences

The research data are quite consistent in showing that we select as potential partners people who are similar to us in social characteristics—age, race, education—and who share our attitudes and beliefs. Moreover, both men and women prefer physically attractive people, although heterosexual women place greater emphasis on a man's social status or earning potential (Sprecher et al., 1994). The obvious question is, Why? Two answers are suggested, one drawing on reinforcement theory and one drawing on sociobiology (see Chapter 2 for discussions of these theories).

Reinforcement Theory: Byrne's Law of Attraction

It is a rather commonsensical idea—and one that psychologists agree with—that we tend to like people who give us reinforcements or rewards and to dislike people who give us punishments. Social psychologist Donn Byrne (1997) has formulated the law of attraction. It says that our attraction to another person is proportionate to the number of reinforcements that person gives us relative to the total number of reinforcements plus punishments the person gives us. Or, simplified even more, we like people who are frequently nice to us and seldom nasty.

According to this explanation, most people prefer to interact with people who are similar to them because interaction with them is rewarding. People who are similar in age, ethnic background, and education are likely to have similar outlooks on life, prefer similar activities, and like the same kinds of people. These shared values and beliefs provide the basis for smooth and rewarding interaction. It will be easy to agree about such things as how important schoolwork is, what TV programs to watch, and what to do on Friday night. Disagreement about such things would cause conflict and hostility, which are definitely not rewards (for most people, anyway). We prefer pretty or handsome partners because we are aware of the high value placed on physical attractiveness in Canadian society; we believe others will have a higher opinion of us if we have a good-looking partner. Finally, we prefer someone with high social status or earning potential because all the material things that people find rewarding cost money.

These findings have some practical implications (Hatfield & Walster, 1978). If you are trying to get a new relationship going well, make sure you give the other person lots of positive reinforcement. Also, make sure that you have some good times together, so that you *associate* each other with rewards. Do not spend all your time stripping paint off old furniture or cleaning out the garage. And do not forget to keep the positive reinforcements (or "strokes," if you like that jargon better) going in an old, stable relationship.

Figure 13.1 According to Byrne's law of attraction, our liking for a person is influenced by the reinforcements we receive from interacting with them. Shared activities provide the basis for smooth and rewarding interaction.

Sociobiology: Sexual Strategies Theory

Sociobiologists view sexual behaviour within an evolutionary perspective and thus focus on hetero-sexual relationships. Historically, the function of mating has been reproduction. Men and women who selected mates according to some preferences were more successful than those who chose them based on other preferences (Allgeier & Wiederman, 1994). The successful ones produced more off-spring, who in turn produced more offspring, carrying their mating preferences to the present.

Men and women face different adaptive problems in their efforts to reproduce (Buss & Schmitt, 1993). Since women bear the offspring, men need to identify reproductively valuable women. Other things being equal, younger women are more likely to be fertile than older women; hence a preference for youth, which results in young men choosing young women (homophily). Also, sociobiologists assert that men want to be certain about the paternity of offspring; hence, they want a woman who will be sexually faithful—that is, one who is hard to get.

Sociobiologists argue that, other things being equal, a physically attractive person is more likely to be healthy and fertile than someone who isn't—thus the preference for good-looking partners. If attractiveness is an indicator of health, we would expect it to be more important in societies where chronic diseases are more prevalent. Gangestad and Buss (1993) measured the prevalence of seven pathogens, including those that cause malaria and leprosy, in 29 cultures, and also obtained ratings of the importance of 18 attributes of mates. They found that physical attractiveness was considered more important by residents in societies that had a greater prevalence of pathogens. However, one study found that there was no relationship between rated facial attractiveness (based on a photograph) and a clinical assessment of health in a sample of adolescents (169 females, 164 males) suggesting that the assumed link between attractiveness and health is not there. At the same time, the raters ranked more attractive persons as healthier (Kalick et al., 1998).

Women must make a much greater investment than men in order to reproduce. They will be pregnant for nine months, and after the birth they must care for the infant and young child for several years. Thus, women want to select as mates men who are reproductively valuable; hence the preference for good-looking mates. They also want mates who are able and willing to invest resources in them and their children. Obviously, men must have resources in order to invest them; hence, the preference for men with higher incomes and status. Among young people, women will prefer men with greater earning potential; thus, the preference for men with greater education and higher occupational aspirations. This problem of resources is more important than the problem of identifying a reproductively valuable male, so women rate income and earning potential as more important than good looks.

Research provides some evidence that is consistent with this theory. For example, researchers presented a list of 31 tactics to a sample of undergraduate students and asked them to rate how effective each would be in attracting a long-term mate (Schmitt & Buss, 1996). Tactics that communicated sexual exclusivity or faithfulness were judged highly effective in attracting a mate for women. Tactics that displayed resource potential were judged most effective for men. Other research has shown that although there are some differences in the qualities that men and women seek in a long-term partner, there are also many similarities (Stewart et al., 2000). Further, men's and women's values are becoming more similar (Buss et al., 2001).

These two explanations—reinforcement theory and sociobiology—are not inconsistent. We can think about reinforcement in more general terms. Reproduction is a major goal for most adults in every society. Successful reproduction—that is, having a healthy child who develops normally—is very reinforcing. Following the sexual strategies that we have inherited is likely to lead to such reinforcement. Of course, sexual strategies theory is not a good explanation for same-sex attraction.

■ Intimacy

Intimacy is a major component of any close or romantic relationship. Today many people are seeking to increase the intimacy in their relationships. And so, in this section we will explore intimacy in more detail to try to gain a better understanding of it.

Defining Intimacy

Psychologists have offered a number of definitions of intimacy, including the following (Perlman & Fehr, 1987, p. 17):

1. Intimacy's defining features include: "openness, honesty, mutual self-disclosure; caring, warmth, protecting, helping; being devoted to each other, mutually attentive, mutually committed; surrendering control, dropping defenses; becoming emotional, feeling distressed when separation occurs."
2. "Emotional intimacy is defined in behavioral terms as mutual self-disclosure and other kinds of verbal sharing, as declarations of liking and loving the other, and as demonstrations of affection."

Notice that the first definition focuses on intimacy as a characteristic of a person and the second as a characteristic of a relationship. One way to think about intimacy is that certain persons have more of a capacity for intimacy or engage in more intimacy-promoting behaviours than others. But we can also think of some relationships as being more intimate than others.

A definition of **intimacy** in romantic relationships is: "the level of commitment and positive affective, cognitive and physical closeness one experiences with a partner in a reciprocal (although not necessarily symmetrical) relationship" (Moss & Schwebel, 1993, p. 33). The emphasis in this definition is on closeness or sharing, which has three dimensions—affective (emotional), cognitive, and physical. Note, too, that while intimacy must be reciprocal, it need not be equal. Many people have had the experience of feeling closer to another person than that person seems to feel toward them. Finally, note that while intimacy has a physical dimension, it need not be sexual.

In one study, university students were asked to respond to an open-ended question asking what they thought made a relationship one of intimacy (Roscoe et al., 1987). The qualities that emerged, with great agreement, were sharing, sexual interaction, trust in the partner, and openness. Notice that these qualities are quite similar to the ones listed in the definitions given above.

Intimacy and Self-Disclosure

One of the key characteristics of intimacy, appearing in psychologists' and university students' definitions, is self-disclosure; that is, telling personal information about oneself to the other person (Derlega, 1984). Consider the following scenario:

> John is 41 years old and a professor at a university. He has been dating Susan, a 35-year-old junior faculty member, for 3 months. He has felt depressed in the past year. His father died recently after a chronic illness. John has also felt unhappy about his teaching and research efforts. One evening he and Susan talked for several hours about a wide range of topics. They talked most about John's uncertainties and pessimism about taking control over his life. Susan listened patiently as John talked in an open way about himself. She wished to understand him and to be supportive. Susan said she cared about John regardless of the personal problems he was having. John felt grateful and perceived that she understood him. He was much closer to her after their talk. (Derlega, 1984, p. 1)

Intimacy: A quality of relationships characterized by commitment, feelings of closeness and trust, and self-disclosure.

This story illustrates how self-disclosure promotes intimacy in a relationship and makes us feel close to the other person. It also illustrates how important it is for the partner to be accepting in responding to self-disclosure. If the acceptance is missing, we can feel betrayed or threatened, and we certainly will not feel on more intimate terms with the partner.

A study of naturally occurring interactions examined the relationships between self-disclosure, perceived partner disclosure, and the degree of intimacy experienced (Laurenceau et al., 1998). Young people recorded data about every interaction lasting more than 10 minutes, for 7 or 14 days. Data were analyzed for more than 4,000 dyadic (that is, two-person) interactions recorded by 158 participants. Both self-disclosure and partner disclosure were associated with the participant's rating of the intimacy of the interaction. In addition, self-disclosure of emotion was more closely related to intimacy than was self-disclosure of facts.

Self-disclosure and intimacy, then, mutually build on each other. Self-disclosure promotes our feeling that the relationship is intimate, and when we feel that it is, we feel comfortable engaging in further self-disclosure. However, self-disclosure and intimacy don't necessarily increase consistently over time. In some relationships, the pattern may be that an increase in intimacy is followed by a plateau or even a pulling back (Collins & Miller, 1994).

We noted earlier the role of physical attractiveness in initial attraction. Research suggests that physical attractiveness is positively related to self-disclosure. Men and women were randomly paired to create 38 previously unacquainted couples. Each couple was left alone in a room for six minutes. Attractive people self-disclosed more, and people disclosed more to attractive partners (Stiles et al., 1996). This may be because attractive people have greater self-confidence. Self-confidence, in turn, may facilitate the development of intimacy.

Measuring Intimacy

Psychologists have developed some scales for measuring intimacy that can give us further insights. One such scale is the Personal Assessment of Intimacy in Relationships (PAIR) Inventory (Schaefer & Olson, 1981). It measures emotional intimacy in a relationship with items such as the following:

1. My partner listens to me when I need someone to talk to.
2. My partner really understands my hurts and joys.

Another scale measuring intimacy in a relationship includes items such as these (Miller & Lefcourt, 1982):

1. How often do you confide very personal information to him or her?
2. How often are you able to understand his or her feelings?
3. How often do you feel close to him or her?

If you are currently in a relationship, answer these questions for yourself and consider what the quality of the intimacy is in your relationship.

In summary, an intimate relationship is characterized by commitment, feelings of closeness and understanding, and self-disclosure. Another key ingredient is trust, particularly faith that our partner will act in loving and caring ways in the future (Rempel et al., 1985). We can promote intimacy in our relationships by engaging in self-disclosure and being accepting of the other person's self-disclosure. However, we are unlikely to be willing to self-disclose unless we trust our partner.

Figure 13.2 Intimacy occurs in a relationship when there is warmth and mutual self-disclosure.

Figure 13.3 Communicating about love is often difficult.

PEANUTS reprinted by permission of United Feature Syndicate, Inc.

■ Theories of Love

At the beginning of this chapter, we noted that there is a connection between love and sex in our society. In everyday life and in theories of love, this connection lies along a continuum (Hendrick & Hendrick, 2004). At one end are "hookups," short-term sexual relationships on a Saturday night, spring break, or a singles cruise, with little romance (Lambert et al., 2003; Maticka-Tyndale et al., 2003). In theories of love, this is the "love is really sex" view found, for example, in evolutionary theory. At the other end are romantic love relationships in which sex is nonexistent or incidental, as for example in a non-sexual affair. In theories, this is the view found, for example, in Sternberg's theory of love as a story. Toward the middle is the "sex is really love" view, as in the theory of passionate love. In the centre is a relationship that balances the two, and theories that recognize both, such as the triangular theory. In this section, we will consider five views of love: the triangular theory, the attachment theory, the love as a story perspective, the passionate love view, and the love styles perspective.

The Triangular Theory of Love

Robert Sternberg (1986) has formulated a triangular theory of the nature of love. According to his theory, love has three fundamental components: intimacy, passion, and commitment. He calls it a triangular theory because he depicts these three components graphically in a love triangle.[1] As shown in Figure 13.4, the top point is intimacy, the left point is passion, and the right point is decision or commitment.

Three Components of Love

Intimacy. Intimacy is the emotional component of love. It includes our feelings of closeness or bondedness to the other person. The feeling of intimacy usually involves a sense of mutual understanding with the loved one; a sense of sharing

---

[1]This terminology should not be confused with the popular use of the term "love triangle," which refers to a situation in which three people are involved in love, but the love is not reciprocated and so things don't work out quite right. For example, A loves B, B loves C, and C loves A, but A doesn't love C and B doesn't love A. Alas.

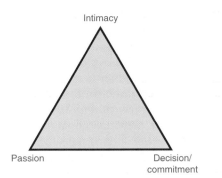

Figure 13.4   The triangle in Sternberg's triangular theory of love.

one's self; intimate communication with the loved one, involving a sense of having the loved one hear and accept what is shared; and giving and receiving emotional support to and from the loved one.

Intimacy, of course, is present in many relationships besides romantic ones. Intimacy here is definitely *not* a euphemism for sex (as when someone asks, "Have you been intimate with him?"). The kind of emotional closeness involved in intimacy may be found between best friends and between parents and children, just as it is between lovers.

Passion.   Passion is the motivational component of love. It includes physical attraction and the drive for sexual expression. Physiological arousal is an important part of passion. Passion is the component that differentiates romantic love from other kinds of love, such as the love of best friends or the love between parents and children. Passion is generally the component of love that is faster to arouse, but in the course of a long-term relationship it is also the component that fades most quickly.

Intimacy and passion are often closely intertwined. In some cases passion comes first, when a couple experience an initial, powerful physical attraction to each other; emotional intimacy may then follow. In other cases, people know each other only casually, but as emotional intimacy develops, passion follows. Of course, there are also cases where intimacy and passion are completely separate. For example, in cases of casual sex, passion is present but intimacy is not.

Decision or Commitment.   The third component is the cognitive component, decision or commit-

ment. This component actually has two aspects. The short-term aspect is the decision that one loves the other person. The long-term aspect is the commitment to maintain that relationship. Commitment is what makes relationships last. Passion comes and goes. All relationships have their better times and their worse times, their ups and their downs. When the words of the traditional marriage ceremony ask whether a person promises to love his or her partner "for better or for worse," the answer "I do" is the promise of commitment.

The Triangular Theory

Sternberg's (1986) triangle metaphor allows us to show how the two people in a couple can be well matched or mismatched in the love they feel toward each other. In Figure 13.5*(a)*, Pat and Robert feel the same levels of intimacy, they both feel equal levels of passion, and they both have the same level of commitment. According to the theory, that is a perfect match. Figure 13.5*(b)* shows a situation in which the couple are slightly mismatched, but not seriously. Figure 13.5*(d)* shows a situation in which there is a severe mismatch. Both partners are equally committed, but Pat feels significantly more intimacy and passion than Robert.

Sternberg's research indicates that when there is a good "match" [as shown in Figure 13.5*(a)* or *(b)*] between the two partners' love, both tend to feel satisfaction with the relationship. When there is a mismatch in the triangles, there is dissatisfaction with the relationship.

Thinking about practical applications of the theory, if a relationship seems to be in trouble, it may be because there is a mismatch of the triangles. One could analyze the love in the relationship in terms of the three components (intimacy, passion, and commitment) to see where the partners are mismatched. It could be that they are well matched for passion, but that one feels and wants more intimacy or commitment than the other person does.

Love in Action

Sternberg also argues that each of the three components of love must be translated into action. The intimacy component is expressed in actions such as communicating personal feelings and information, offering emotional (and perhaps financial) support, and expressing empathy for the other. The

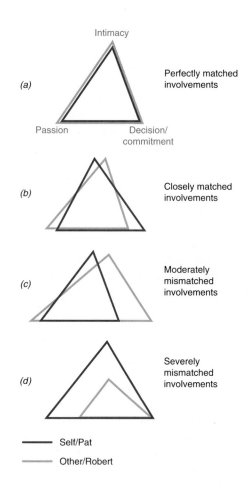

Figure 13.5 Partners can be well matched or mismatched, depending on whether their levels of intimacy, passion, and decision/commitment match.

passion component is expressed in actions such as kissing, touching, and making love. The decision or commitment component is demonstrated by actions such as saying "I love you," getting married, and sticking with a relationship through times when it isn't particularly convenient.

As the great psychoanalyst Erich Fromm wrote in his book *The Art of Loving* (1956), love is something one *does*, not a state one is *in*. Fromm believed that loving is an art, something that one must learn about and practise. And as Sternberg says, "Without expression, even the greatest of loves can die" (1986, p. 132).

Evidence for Sternberg's Triangular Theory of Love

Sternberg has developed a questionnaire, the Sternberg Triangular Love Scale (STLS), to measure the three components in his theory. Several studies have been done on the characteristics of the scale itself (e.g., Sternberg, 1987, 1997; Whitley, 1993). The scale provides good measures of the components, especially of passion and commitment. Scores for the same relationship are stable for up to two months.

Sternberg makes several predictions about how scores ought to change over time. Acker and Davis (1992) recruited 204 adults, ages 18 to 68; 65 percent were married. The average length of the relationship was 9.5 years. As predicted, commitment scores increased as relationships progressed from dating to marriage. Sternberg expects intimacy to decrease over time as familiarity with the partner increases; sure enough, behavioural intimacy (sharing inner feelings, trying to understand the partner) decreased as predicted. However, contrary to prediction, two other measures of intimacy (including Sternberg's) increased. A study of a sample of German adults assessed the relationship between the three components and sexual activity and satisfaction (Grau & Kimpf, 1993). The theory predicts that the amount of passion should be most closely related to sexual activity, but the results indicated that intimacy was most closely related to sexual behaviour and sexual satisfaction.

On the whole, these early results are promising. More refined measures and further research are needed in order to assess the theory more thoroughly.

The Attachment Theory of Love

In Chapter 11 we discussed the earliest attachment that humans experience, the attachment between infant and parent. One hypothesis is that the quality of this early attachment—whether secure and pleasant or insecure and unpleasant—profoundly affects us for the rest of our lives, and particularly affects our capacity to form loving attachments to others when we are adults.

The *attachment theory of love* is based on these ideas (Hazen & Shaver, 1987; Simpson, 1990). According to the most recent formulation proposed by British Columbia psychologist Kim Bartholomew, adults are characterized in their romantic relationships by one of four attachment styles (Bartholomew & Horowitz, 1991). These attachment styles are based on our perceptions of ourselves as well as our expectations of how others will respond toward us. As shown in Figure 13.6, we either see ourselves in a positive way as worthy of love and support or we see ourselves in a negative way as unworthy of love. Similarly, we either see other people in a positive way as trustworthy and available or we see them in a negative way as unreliable and rejecting. As depicted in Figure 13.6, *secure lovers* have a sense of their own lovability and the expectation that other people are generally accepting and responsive. *Preoccupied lovers* have a sense of their own unlovability but a positive evaluation of other people. They try to gain self-acceptance by gaining the acceptance of people they value. They want desperately to get close to a partner but are so worried that the partner does not love them that they may scare them away. *Fearful lovers* have a negative expectation of both themselves and other people. They try to protect themselves against anticipated rejection by others by avoiding romantic relationships. They are uncomfortable feeling close to, trusting, or depending on another person, or having that person feel close to them. Finally, *dismissing lovers* feel themselves to be worthy of love, but have negative views of other people. These people may protect themselves against disappointment by avoiding close relationships and maintaining a sense of independence. Dismissing and fearful lovers are similar in that both avoid intimacy. Preoccupied and fearful lovers are alike in that both depend on acceptance from others to feel good about themselves. Research shows that about 49 percent of adults have a secure attachment style, 12 percent a preoccupied style, 21 percent a fearful style, and 18 percent a dismissing style (Bartholomew & Horowitz, 1991). The research also shows that separation from parents in childhood—perhaps because of divorce or death—is not related to adult attachment styles (Hazen & Shaver, 1987). That is, children of divorced parents are no more or less likely to be secure lovers than are children from intact marriages (a finding that is probably fortunate, given the high divorce rate in Canada). What did predict adult attachment style was the person's perception of the *quality* of the relation-

ship with each parent. Recent research has shown that the quality of friendships in childhood and adolescence also affects adult attachment styles. For example, research using a sample of 191 gay and bisexual men in Vancouver found that both the quality of parental relationships (particularly relationships with fathers) and the quality of peer relationships were associated with adult attachment style (Landott et al., 2004).

This research has some important implications. First, it helps us understand that adults bring to any particular romantic relationship their own personal history of love and attachment. The forces of that personal history can be strong, and one good and loving partner may not be able to change a dismissing lover into a secure lover. This does not mean that people who have insecure attachment relationships with their parents cannot have a secure attachment relationship with their romantic partner. Research in New Brunswick has shown that although people tend to form a particular type of attachment relationship with all of the important people in their lives, some people with insecure attachment relationships with family have secure attachment relationships with their romantic partner (Ross & Spinner, 2001). Second, it helps us understand that conflict in some relationships may be caused by a mismatch of attachment styles. A secure lover who wants a close, intimate relationship is likely to feel frustrated and dissatisfied with a dismissing or fearful lover who is uncomfortable with feeling close. Attachment theory suggests that the important form of similarity is similarity in attachment style (Latty-Mann &

Figure 13.6 Bartholomew and Horowitz's (1991) attachment theory of love. Our attachment style depends on our positive or negative view of ourself and our positive or negative view of others.

In Focus 13.1

What Is Jealousy?

Jealousy—the green-eyed monster—is an unpleasant emotion often associated with romantic and sexual relationships. Intense cases of jealousy may result in violence, including partner abuse, assault, and homicide. As a result, it has been the focus of considerable scholarly work. Several perspectives contribute to our understanding of this emotion.

Jealousy is a cognitive, emotional, and behavioural response to a threat to an interpersonal relationship (Guerrero et al., 2004). The cognitive appraisal perspective suggests that jealousy occurs when an individual *interprets* some stimulus as representing a threat to a valued relationship; in reality, there may or may not be a threat to the relationship. A variety of behaviours by the partner may be interpreted as a threat; in one study, individuals in dating relationships said that having their partner just spend time with another person was one of the top three acts of betrayal (Roscoe et al., 1988). Interaction with someone via the Internet, behaviour or remarks by third parties, or coming home late may arouse suspicion and elicit jealousy from a partner.

There are two types of jealousy that may occur together or separately: emotional and sexual. *Emotional jealousy* occurs when one person believes or knows that the partner is emotionally attached to or in love with another. *Sexual jealousy* occurs when the person believes or knows that the partner wants to engage in or has engaged in sexual intimacy with another. The evolutionary perspective has hypothesized that men are more upset by a (heterosexual) partner's sexual infidelity, whereas women are more upset by a (heterosexual) partner's emotional infidelity. This hypothesis is based on the argument that the male adaptive problem (or concern) in reproduction is uncertainty about paternity, so men are highly vigilant about female sexual fidelity. The female adaptive problem is to obtain enough resources to care for herself and her children, so women are highly vigilant about male romantic fidelity in order to ensure that her partner does not leave her. Research in this area is not without controversy and conflicting findings. However, a careful review of five types of evidence finds little support for this hypothesis (Harris, 2003). A study of both heterosexual and homosexual adults found that men and women were more concerned about the emotional infidelity of a partner (Harris, 2002).

Psychologists Gregory White and Paul Mullen (1989) see jealousy as a constellation including thoughts, emotions, and actions. Two situations, according to their research, activate jealousy. One is a situation in which there is a threat to our self-esteem. For example, in a good relationship, our romantic partner helps us feel good about ourselves—makes us feel attractive or fun to be with, for example. If a rival appears and our partner shows interest, we may think things like "He finds her more attractive than me" or "She finds him more fun to be with than me." We then feel less attractive or less fun to be with—that is, our self-esteem is threatened.

The second situation that activates jealousy is a

Davis, 1996). Third, this theory provides some explanation for jealousy, which is most common among preoccupied lovers (although present among the others) because of their early experience of feeling anxious about their attachment to their parents. Finally, attachment style may help to explain high-risk sexual behaviour. Research in Ontario showed that women who have insecure attachment styles engage in intercourse at a younger age and have more sexual partners than do women with secure attachment styles (Bogaert & Sadava, 2002).

Attachment style affects relationships by affecting the way the partners interact. A study of 128 established couples (average length of relationship 47 months) assessed attachment style, patterns of

Figure 13.7 One situation that activates jealousy is a perceived threat to the relationship.

threat to the relationship. If a rival appears on the scene, we may fear that our partner will separate from us and form a new relationship with the rival. Jealousy is activated because of our negative thoughts and feelings about the loss of a relationship that has been good for us and the loss of all the pleasant things that go along with that relationship, such as companionship and sex.

According to White and Mullen, we go through several stages in the jealousy response, sometimes very quickly. The first is cognitive, in which we make an initial appraisal of the situation and find that there is a threat to our self-esteem or to the relationship. Next we experience an emotional reaction that in itself has two phases. The first is a rapid stress response, the "jealous flash." To use the terminology of the two-component theory of love discussed later in this chapter, this stress response is the physiological component of the jealous emotion. The second phase of emotional response

occurs as we reappraise the situation and decide how to cope with it. In the reappraisal stage, we may shift from seeing the situation as a threat to seeing it as a challenge, for example. The intense initial emotions quiet down and may be replaced by feelings of moodiness.

Attempts to cope with jealousy lead to a variety of behaviours. Some of these are constructive, such as effective communication with one's partner (see Chapter 10). Such a discussion may lead to an evaluation of the relationship, and attempts to change some of the problematic aspects of it. If the problems seem sufficiently serious, a couple may seek help from a mediator or therapist. Other behavioural responses to jealousy are destructive. The threat to one's self-esteem may lead to depression, substance abuse, or suicide. Aggression may be directed at the partner, the third person, or both, and may result in physical or sexual abuse or even murder.

Research suggests that one's attachment style may be an important influence on how one responds to jealousy (Sharpstein & Kirkpatrick, 1997). Undergraduates were asked how they had reacted in the past to jealousy. Those with a secure attachment style reported that they had expressed their anger to the partner and maintained the relationship. Those with a preoccupied or anxious style reported the most intense anger, but they were most likely to say they did not express their anger. People with a fearful or avoidant style were more likely to direct their anger toward the third person.

Sources: Fisher (1992); Guerrero et al. (2004); Reiss (1986); White & Mullen (1989).

accommodation, and satisfaction with the relationship (Scharfe & Bartholomew, 1995). Individuals with a secure attachment reported responding constructively to potentially destructive behaviour by the partner, for example, with efforts to discuss and resolve the problem. People who were fearful of attachment to another responded with avoidance or withdrawal. This may affect relationship

satisfaction. A longitudinal study of university students in Ontario showed that, over a four-month period, participants with a secure attachment style did not change their feelings about the relationship. In contrast, participants with one of the insecure attachment styles reported lower levels of satisfaction and commitment (Keelan et al., 1994).

Love as a Story

When we think of love, our thoughts often turn to the great love stories: Romeo and Juliet, Cinderella and the Prince (Julia Roberts and Richard Gere), King Edward VIII and Wallis Simpson, and *Pygmalion/My Fair Lady*.[2] According to Sternberg (1998), these stories are much more than entertainment. They shape our beliefs about love and relationships, and our beliefs in turn influence our behaviour:

> Zach and Tammy have been married 28 years. Their friends have been predicting divorce since the day they were married. They fight almost constantly. Tammy threatens to leave Zach; he tells her that nothing would make him happier. They lived happily ever after.
>
> Valerie and Leonard had a perfect marriage. They told each other and all of their friends that they did. Their children say they never fought. Leonard met someone at his office, and left Valerie. They are divorced. (Adapted from Sternberg, 1998)

Wait a minute! Aren't those endings reversed? Zach and Tammy should be divorced, and Valerie and Leonard should be living happily ever after. If love is merely the interaction between two people, how they communicate and behave, you're right; the stories have the wrong endings. But there is more to love than interaction; what matters is how each partner *interprets* the interaction. To make sense out of what happens in our relationships, we rely on our love stories.

A **love story** is a story about what love should be like; it has *characters,* a *plot,* and a *theme.* There are two central characters in every love story who play roles that complement each other. The plot details the kinds of events that occur in the relationship. The theme is central; it provides the meaning of the events that make up the plot and gives direction to the behaviour of the principals. The story guiding Zach and Tammy's relationship is the War story. Each views love as war; a good relationship involves constant fighting. The two central characters are warriors, doing battle, fighting for what they believe. The plot consists of arguments, fights,

[2]Notice that all of these stories are heterosexual.

Love story: A story about what love should be like, including characters, a plot, and a theme.

threats to leave—in other words, battles. The theme is that love is war. One may win or lose particular battles, but the war continues. Zach and Tammy's relationship endures because they share this view, and because it fits their temperaments. (Can you imagine how long a conflict-avoider would last in a relationship with either of them?)

According to this view, *falling in love* occurs when you meet someone with whom you can create a relationship that fits your love story. Further, we are satisfied with relationships in which we and our partner match the characters in our story (Beall & Sternberg, 1995). Valerie and Leonard's marriage looked great on the surface but it didn't fit Leonard's love story. He left when he met his "true love"; that is, a woman who could play the complementary role in his primary love story.

Where do our stories come from? Many of them have their origins in the culture, in folk tales, literature, theatre, films, and television programs. The cultural context interacts with our personal experience and characteristics to create the stories that each of us has (Sternberg, 1996). As we experience relationships, our stories evolve, taking into account unexpected events. Each person has more than one story; the stories often form a hierarchy. One of Leonard's stories was "House and Home," where home was the centre of the relationship, and he (in his role of Caretaker) showered attention on the house and kids (not on Valerie). But when he met Sharon, with her aloof air, ambiguous past, and dark glasses, he was hooked—she elicited the "Love Is a Mystery" story, which was more salient to Leonard. He could not explain why he left Valerie and the kids; like most of us he was not consciously aware of his love stories.

It should be obvious from these examples that love stories derive their power from the fact that they are self-fulfilling. We create in our relationships events according to the plot and then interpret those events according to the theme. Our love relationships are literally social constructions. Because our love stories are self-confirming, they can be very difficult to change.

Sternberg and his colleagues have identified five categories of love stories found in North American culture, and several specific stories within each category. They have also developed a series of statements that reflect the themes in each story. People who agree with the statements "I think fights actually make a relationship more vital," and "I actually like to fight with my partner" are likely to believe in the War story. Sternberg and Hojjat studied samples of 43 and 55 couples (Sternberg, 1998). They found that couples generally believed in similar stories. The more discrepant the stories of the partners, the less happy the couple was. Some stories were associated with high satisfaction; for example, the Garden story, in which love is a garden that needs ongoing cultivation. Two stories associated with low satisfaction were the Business story (especially the version in which the roles are Employer and Employee), and the Horror story, in which the roles are Terrorizer and Victim. If you watch *The Simpsons*, what do you think Marge and Homer's love story is?

The Biology of Passionate Love

The three theories considered so far define love as a single phenomenon. A fourth perspective differentiates between two kinds of love: passionate love and companionate love (Berscheid & Hatfield, 1978). **Passionate love** is a state of intense longing for union with the other person and of intense physiological arousal. It has three components: cognitive, emotional, and behavioural (Hatfield & Sprecher, 1986a). The cognitive component includes preoccupation with the loved one and idealization of the person or of the relationship. The emotional component includes physiological arousal, sexual attraction, and desire for union. Behavioural elements include taking care of the other and maintaining physical closeness. Passionate love can be overwhelming, obsessive, all-consuming.

Passionate love can also lead to overly optimistic predictions about the likelihood that the relationship will last. Researchers in Ontario asked university students who were in a dating relationship of between one month and one year, their roommates, and their parents to predict how long the students' dating relationships would last (MacDonald & Ross, 1999). The students described their relationship more positively than did the other two groups, because they tended to focus on the strengths and minimize the negative aspects of the relationship. Students predicted that the relationship would last longer than did parents and roommates. Who was right? The results indicated that roommates were the most accurate about whether the couple would still be together one year later; the students were the least accurate.

By contrast, **companionate love** is a feeling of deep attachment and commitment to a person with whom one has an intimate relationship (Hatfield & Rapson, 1993b). Passionate love is hot; companionate love is warm. Passionate love is often the first stage of a romantic relationship. Two people meet, fall wildly in love, and make a commitment to each other.

Do male and female animals have gender differences in the way they approach sex? Watch the video "The Dance of Life" in Chapter 13 of your CD to find out.

But as the relationship progresses, a gradual shift to companionate love takes place (Cimbalo et al., 1976; Driscoll et al., 1972). The transformation tends to occur when the relationship is between 6 and 30 months old (Hatfield & Walster, 1978).

Some may find this a rather pessimistic commentary on romantic love because it does not fit the societal love story in which people see stars and hear bells when they fall in love, and continue to do so forever after. But it may actually be a good way for a relationship to develop. Passionate love may be necessary to hold a relationship together in the early stages, while conflicts are being resolved. But past that point, most of us find that what we really need is a friend—someone who shares our interests, who is happy when we succeed, and who empathizes when we fail—and that is just what we get with companionate love. However, even when passionate love has evolved to companionate love, it helps to continue to see our partner and our relationship in somewhat idealized ways. An Ontario study found that couples with these positive relationship "illusions" were more satisfied with their relationship (Murray & Holmes, 1997; Murray et al., 1996). Of course, illusions are not sufficient to maintain a relationship if they are not based on common needs and goals.

Passionate love: A state of intense longing for union with the other person and of intense physiological arousal.
Companionate love: A feeling of deep attachment and commitment to a person with whom one has an intimate relationship.

What causes the complex phenomena of passionate and companionate love? Where does the rush of love at first sight come from? Research suggests that it is caused by bodily chemistry and neural activity in the brain. Studies of the prairie vole, a small rodent, have identified specific patterns of neurochemical activity that are associated with mating and pair bonding (preference for a specific partner) (Curtis & Wang, 2003). In female prairie voles, dopamine is released during mating; in both male and female voles, the dopamine appears to enhance the likelihood of pair bonding. Dopamine is associated with euphoria and craving. A surge of dopamine in the human body can produce increased energy, focused attention, and reduced need for food and sleep; these are common experiences of people in the early stages of love.

The frequent presence of the loved one, produced initially by passionate love, triggers the production of two other chemicals, prolactin and oxytocin. The levels of prolactin rise following orgasm in humans and are also related to pair bonding in voles. Oxytocin may contribute to long-term relationships. It has been shown to play an important role in pair-bonding in some animals (McEwen, 1997). In humans it is stimulated by touch, including sexual touching and orgasm, and produces feelings of pleasure and satisfaction. Research by Zak et al. (2003) indicates that levels of interpersonal trust correlate positively with oxytocin as well.

The newest research with humans involves the use of magnetic resonance imaging (MRI) to study brain activity related to love. Bartels and Zeki (2004) recruited young men and women who were in love. While their brain activity was being measured, each participant was shown photos of the romantic partner and of a close friend. The picture of the partner activated specific areas of the brain. Which ones? The areas rich in dopamine pathways were enervated, lending weight to the neurochemical findings that suggest dopamine is important in the experience of love. Furthermore, when measures of levels of brain activity in response to the picture of the lover were correlated with scores on the Passionate Love Scale (discussed in the next section), the scores were positively correlated.

Love Styles

Ontario sociologist John Lee (1973) proposed that there are at least six different styles of loving, which he called love styles. Each love style describes a different way that people express love. Several love styles can be expressed, to a greater or lesser degree, within a single romantic relationship, and the love styles expressed in any given relationship can change over time (Hendrick & Hendrick, 1997). Lee based his theory on interviews, historical accounts, love depicted in literature, and research. He used Greek and Latin words to describe each type of love because Greek and Latin, unlike English, contain different words for different types of love. As you read the list of these six love styles, you may notice that some of them are similar to the types of love proposed by other theories reviewed in this chapter. Lee's six styles are Eros, or romantic passionate love; Ludus, or playful, permissive, game-playing love; Storge, or friendship love; Mania, or possessive, dependent love; Pragma, or practical love; and Agape, or all-giving, selfless love (Hendrick & Hendrick, 1986; Lee, 1973).

Hendrick and Hendrick (1986) developed a scale to measure the six love styles, called the Love Attitude Scale. Their research has found that men are more likely to describe themselves as more game-playing and women as more friendship-oriented, pragmatic, and possessive (Hendrick & Hendrick, 1986, 1995). They also found that love styles are related to relationship satisfaction—in particular, Eros is related to higher and Ludus to lower relationship satisfaction (Hendrick et al., 1988). People who have a similar love style to their partner tend to be more satisfied with their relationship.

■ Research on Love

Measuring Love

So far the discussion has focused on theoretical definitions of various kinds of love. One of the ways psychologists and sociologists define terms is by using an operational definition. In an **operational definition,** a concept is defined by the way it is measured. Thus, for example, in the attraction experiment described earlier in the chapter, one

> **Operational definition:** Defining some concept or term by how it is measured, for example, defining intelligence as those abilities that are measured by IQ tests.

of the ways that attraction was operationally defined was how close people stood to each other (Byrne et al., 1970). Operational definitions are very useful because they are precise and because they help clarify exactly what a scientist means by a complex term such as *love*.

Hatfield and Sprecher (1986a) decided to develop a paper-and-pencil measure of *passionate love*. They wrote statements intended to measure the cognitive, emotional, and behavioural components of passionate love. The respondent rates each statement on a scale from 1 (not true at all) to 9 (definitely true of him or her). If you feel that you are in love with someone, think about whether you would agree with each of the following statements, keeping that person in mind.

1. *Cognitive component:*
   Sometimes I feel I can't control my thoughts; they are obsessively on _____.
   For me, _____ is the perfect romantic partner.
2. *Emotional component:*
   I possess a powerful attraction for _____.
   I will love _____ forever.
3. *Behavioural component:*
   I eagerly look for signs indicating _____'s desire for me.
   I feel happy when I am doing things to make _____ happy.

Hatfield and Sprecher administered their questionnaire to students who were in relationships ranging from casually dating to engaged and living together. The results indicated that scores on the Passionate Love Scale (PLS) were positively correlated with other measures of love and with measures of commitment to and satisfaction with the relationship. These correlations give us evidence that the PLS is valid. Students who got high scores on the PLS reported a stronger desire to be with, held by, and kissed by the partner, and said that they were sexually excited just thinking about their partner. These findings confirm that the scale is measuring passion. Finally, the passionate love scores increased as the nature of the relationship moved from dating to dating exclusively. Hatfield and Sprecher's research is a good example of how to study an important but complex topic—such as love—scientifically.

Love and Adrenaline

Two-Component Theory of Love

Social psychologists Ellen Berscheid and Elaine Walster (1974a) proposed a **two-component theory of love.** According to their theory, passionate love occurs when two conditions exist simultaneously: (1) the person is in a state of intense *physiological arousal,* and (2) the situation is such that the person applies a particular *label*—"love"—to the sensations being experienced. Their theory is derived from an important theory developed by Stanley Schachter (1964).

Suppose that your heart is pounding, your palms are sweating, and your body is tense. What emotion are you experiencing? Is it love—has reading about passionate love led to obsessive thoughts of another person? Is it fear—are you frantically reading this text because you have an exam tomorrow morning? Is it sexual arousal—are you thinking about physical intimacy later tonight? It could be any of these, or it could be anger or embarrassment. A wide variety of emotions are accompanied by the same physiological states: increased blood pressure, a higher heart rate, increased myotonia (muscular tension), sweating palms. What differentiates these emotions is the way we interpret or label what we are experiencing.

Schachter's (1964) two-component theory of emotion says just this; an emotion consists of a physiological arousal state plus the label the person assigns to it (for a critical evaluation of this theory, see Reisenzein, 1983). Berscheid and Walster have applied this to the emotion of "love." They suggest that we feel passionate love when we are aroused and when conditions are such that we identify what we are feeling as love.

Evidence for the Two-Component Theory

Several experiments provide evidence for Berscheid and Walster's two-component theory of love. In one study, male research participants exercised vigorously by running in place; this produced the physiological arousal response of pounding heart and sweaty palms (White et al., 1981). Afterward they

> **Two-component theory of love:** Berscheid and Walster's theory that two conditions must exist simultaneously for passionate love to occur: physiological arousal and attaching a cognitive label ("love") to the feeling.

rated their liking for an attractive woman, who actually was a confederate of the experimenters. Men in the running group said they liked the woman significantly more than did men who were in a control condition and had not exercised. This result is consistent with Berscheid and Walster's theory. The effect is called the **misattribution of arousal;** that is, in a situation like this, the men misattribute their arousal—which is actually due to exercise—to their liking for the attractive woman. An analysis of 33 experiments found that arousal affects attraction even when the source of the arousal is unambiguous (Foster et al., 1998).

A study conducted in North Vancouver suggests that fear can increase a man's attraction to a woman (Dutton & Aron, 1974). An attractive female interviewer approached male passersby either on a fear-arousing bridge (you may be familiar with the Capilano Bridge) or on a non–fear-arousing bridge. The fear-arousing bridge was constructed of boards, attached to cables, and had a tendency to tilt, sway, and wobble; the handrails were low, and there was a 70-metre drop to rocks and shallow rapids below. The "control" bridge was made of solid cedar; it was firm, and there was only a 3-metre drop to a shallow rivulet below. The interviewer asked subjects to fill out questionnaires that included projective test items. These items were then scored for sexual imagery.

The men in the suspension-bridge group should have been in a state of physiological arousal, while those in the control-bridge group should not have been. In fact, there was more sexual imagery in the questionnaires filled out by the men in the suspension-bridge group, and these men made more attempts to contact the attractive interviewer after the experiment than the men on the control bridge. Intuitively, this might seem to be a peculiar result: that men who are in a state of fear are more attracted to a woman than men who are relaxed. But in terms of the Berscheid and Walster two-component theory, it makes perfect sense. The fearful men were physiologically aroused, while the men in the control group were not. And accord-

Figure 13.8   The misattribution of arousal. If people are physically aroused (e.g., by jogging), they may misattribute this arousal to love or sexual attraction, provided the situation suggests such an interpretation.

ing to this theory, arousal is an important component of love or attraction.[3]

Now, of course, if the men (most of them heterosexuals) had been approached by an elderly man or a child, probably their responses would have been different. In fact, when the interviewer in the experiment was male, the effects discussed above did not occur. Society tells us what the appropriate objects of our love, attraction, or liking are. That is, we know for what kinds of people it is appropriate to have feelings of love or liking. For these men, feelings toward an attractive woman could reasonably be labelled "love" or "attraction," while such labels would probably not be attached to feelings for an elderly man.

The physical arousal that is important for love need not always be produced by unpleasant or frightening situations. Pleasant stimuli, such as sexual arousal or praise from the other person, may produce arousal and feelings of love. Indeed, Berscheid and Walster's theory does an excellent job of explaining why we seem to have such a strong tendency to associate love and sex. Sexual arousal is one method of producing a state of physiological

Misattribution of arousal: When one is in a stage of physiological arousal (e.g., from exercising or being in a frightening situation), attributing these feelings to love or attraction to the person present.

[3]According to the terminology of Chapter 3, note that the Dutton and Aron study is an example of *experimental* research.

arousal, and it is one that our culture has taught us to label as "love." Thus both components necessary to feel love are present: arousal and a label. On the other hand, this phenomenon may lead us to confuse love with lust (that is, sexual desire), an all-too-common error.

Cross-Cultural Research

In the past decade, researchers have studied people from other ethnic or cultural groups to see whether attraction, intimacy, and love are experienced in the same way outside North America. Three topics that have been studied are the impact of culture on how people view love, on whom people fall in love with, and on the importance of love in decisions to marry.

Cultural Values and the Meaning of Love

Cross-cultural psychologists have identified two dimensions on which cultures vary (Hatfield & Rapson, 1993a). The first is individualism–collectivism. *Individualistic cultures*, like those of Canada, the United States, and Western European countries, tend to emphasize individual goals over group and societal goals and interests. *Collectivist cultures*, like those of China, Africa, and southeast Asian countries, emphasize group and collective goals over personal ones. Several specific traits have been identified that differentiate these two types of societies (Triandis et al., 1990). In individualistic cultures, behaviour is regulated by individual attitudes and cost–benefit considerations; emotional detachment from the group is accepted. In collectivist cultures, the self is defined by group membership; behaviour is regulated by group norms; attachment to and harmony within the group are valued.

There are different conceptions of love in the two types of cultures. Canadian society, for example, emphasizes passionate love as the basis for marriage (Dion & Dion, 1993b). Individuals select mates on the basis of such characteristics as physical attractiveness, similarity (compatibility), and wealth or resources. We look for intimacy in the relationship with our mate. In Chinese society, by contrast, many marriages are arranged; the primary criterion is that the two families be of similar status. The person finds intimacy in relationships with other family members.

The second dimension on which cultures differ is independence–interdependence. Many Western cultures view each person as independent, and value individuality and uniqueness. Many other cultures view the person as interdependent with those around him or her. The self is defined in relation to others. Canadians value standing up for one's beliefs. The people of India value conformity and harmony within the group.

Dion and Dion (1993a) studied university students in Toronto, representing four ethnocultural groups. Students from Asian backgrounds were more likely to view love as companionate, as friendship, in contrast to those from English and Irish backgrounds. This tendency is consistent with the collectivist orientation of Asian cultures.

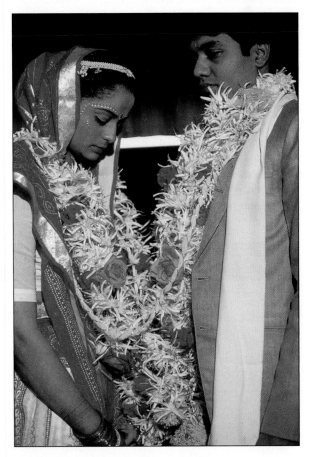

Figure 13.9 Whether a culture is individualistic or collectivistic determines its views on love and marriage. In Canada, which is an individualistic culture, individuals choose each other and marry for love. In India, a collectivistic culture, marriages are arranged by family members to serve family interests.

Cultural Influences on Mate Selection

Buss (1989) conducted a large-scale survey of 10,000 men and women from 37 societies. The sample included people from 4 cultures in Africa, 8 in Asia, and 4 in eastern Europe, in addition to 12 western European and 4 North American ones. Each respondent was given a list of 18 characteristics one might value in a potential mate and asked to rate how important each was to him or her personally. Regardless of which society they lived in, most respondents, male and female, rated intelligence, kindness, and understanding at the top of the list; note that these are characteristics of companionate love. Men worldwide placed more weight on cues of reproductive capacity, such as physical attractiveness; women rated cues of resources as more important. The results support the sociobiological perspective and suggest that there are not large cultural differences.

Many people prefer mates who are physically attractive. We often hear that "beauty is in the eye of the beholder." This saying suggests that standards of beauty might vary across cultures. In one study, researchers had students from varying cultural backgrounds rate 45 photographs of women on a scale ranging from very attractive to very unattractive (Cunningham et al., 1995). The photographs portrayed women from many different societies. Overall, Asian, Hispanic, and white stu- dents did not differ in their ratings of the individual photographs. However, Asian students' ratings were less influenced by indicators of sexual maturity (such as facial narrowness) and expressivity (such as the vertical distance between the lips when the person smiled). In a separate study, black men and white men gave similar ratings to most aspects of female faces, but black men preferred women with heavier bodies than did white men. Again, the results indicate more similarities than differences across cultures, in this case in standards of physical attractiveness.

Love and Marriage

We noted above that individualistic cultures place a high value on romantic love, while collectivist cultures emphasize the group. The importance of romantic love in North American society is illustrated by responses to the question, "If a man (woman) had all the other qualities you desired, would you marry this person if you were not in love with him (her)?" Over time, increasing percentages of North American men and women answer no. The change has been greater for women. Levine and his colleagues (1995) asked this question of men and women in 11 different cultures. We would predict that members of individualistic cultures would answer no, whereas those in collectivist cultures would answer yes. The results are displayed in Table 13.2. Note that, as predicted,

---

Table 13.2   "Would you marry someone you didn't love?"

Cultural Group	Responses (Percent)		
	Yes	Undecided	No
Australia	4.8%	15.2%	80.0%
Brazil	4.3	10.0	85.7
England	7.3	9.1	83.6
Hong Kong	5.8	16.7	77.6
India	49.0	26.9	24.0
Japan	2.3	35.7	62.0
Mexico	10.2	9.3	80.5
Pakistan	50.4	10.4	39.1
Philippines	11.4	25.0	63.6
Thailand	18.8	47.5	33.8
United States	3.5	10.6	85.9

Source: E. Hatfield (1994), *Passionate love and sexual desire: A cross-cultural perspective,* Paper presented at the Annual Meeting, Society for the Scientific Study of Sexuality, Miami. Canada was not included in this study. Data from Robert Levine et al. (1995). "Love and Marriage in Eleven Cultures," *Journal of Cross-Cultural Psychology*, 26, pp. 554–571. Used by permission of Robert Levine. Reprinted in E. Hatfield and R. L. Rapson, *Love and Sex: Cross-Cultural Perspectives*, 1996, Needham Heights, MA: Allyn & Bacon.

many Indians and Pakistanis would marry even though they didn't love the person. In Thailand, which is also collectivist, a much smaller percentage said yes. In the individualistic cultures of Australia, England, and the United States, few would marry someone they did not love.

When we look at the findings of the cross-cultural research on love, attraction, and marriage, the pattern that emerges is one of *cross-cultural simi-* *larities and cross-cultural differences,* a theme we introduced in Chapter 1. That is, some phenomena are similar across cultures; for example, valuing intelligence, kindness, and understanding in a mate. Other phenomena differ substantially across cultures; for example, whether love is a prerequisite for marriage. However, even in Asian societies young people are increasingly seeing love as a basis for marriage (Dion & Dion, 1993a).

■ ■ ■ SUMMARY

For most people—heterosexual, gay, and lesbian—emotional passion and sexual passion are closely linked. Unfortunately, much of the research on love has been restricted to heterosexuals and has not included gays and lesbians.

Research indicates that mere repeated exposure to another person facilitates attraction. We tend to be attracted to people who are similar to us socially (age, race or ethnicity, economic status) and psychologically (attitudes, interests). In first impressions, we are most attracted to people who are physically attractive; we also tend to be attracted to people whom we believe to be "within reach" of us, depending on our sense of our own attractiveness or desirability. Playing hard to get seems to work only if the person does so selectively.

According to reinforcement theory, we are attracted to those who give us many reinforcements. Interaction with people who are similar to us is smooth and rewarding; they have similar outlooks and like the same things we do. According to sexual strategies theory, we prefer young, attractive people because they are likely to be healthy and fertile. Men prefer women who are sexually faithful (hard to get); women prefer men with resources who will invest in them and their children.

Intimacy is a major component of a romantic relationship. It is defined as a quality of a relationship characterized by commitment, feelings of closeness and trust, and self-disclosure.

According to the triangular theory, there are three components to love: intimacy, passion, and decision or commitment. Love is a triangle, with each of these components as one of the points. Partners whose love triangles are substantially dif-ferent are mismatched and are likely to be dissatisfied with their relationship.

According to the attachment theory of love, adults vary in their capacity for love as a result of their love or attachment experiences in infancy. The theory says that there are four types of lovers: secure lovers, preoccupied lovers, fearful lovers, and dismissing lovers.

Love can also be viewed as a story, with characters, a plot, and a theme. People use their love stories to interpret experiences in relationships. Falling in love happens when a person meets someone who can play a compatible role in his or her story.

Love may have a neurochemical component. Passionate love, a state of intense longing and arousal, may be produced by dopamine. Like all chemically induced "highs," passionate love eventually comes to an end. It may be replaced by companionate love, a feeling of deep attachment and commitment to the partner. This type of love may be accompanied by elevated levels of prolactin and oxytocin, which may be produced by physical closeness and touch.

Love styles are descriptions of different ways that people express love. Six major love styles have been identified: Eros, Ludus, Storge, Mania, Pragma, and Agape. Men are more likely than are women to describe themselves as game-playing; women are more likely than men to describe themselves as friendship-oriented, pragmatic, and possessive.

Hatfield and Sprecher have constructed a scale to measure passionate love. Such scales make it possible to do scientific research on complex phenomena like love. Scores on this scale were correlated with measures of commitment to and satisfaction with romantic relationships.

Berscheid and Walster have hypothesized that there are two basic components of romantic love: being in a state of physiological arousal and attaching the label "love" to the feeling. Several studies report evidence consistent with the hypothesis.

Cross-cultural research indicates that individualistic cultures like that of Canada emphasize love as the basis for marriage and encourage intimacy between partners. Collectivist cultures emphasize intergroup bonds as the basis for marriage, and discourage intimacy between partners. Culture influences the importance of various characteristics in choosing a mate; it also affects our standards of beauty and the likelihood that we would marry someone we didn't love.

■ ■ ■ QUESTIONS FOR THOUGHT, DISCUSSION, AND DEBATE

1. If you are currently in love with someone, how would you describe the kind of love you feel, using the various concepts and theories of love discussed in this chapter?

2. Resolved: Selecting mates on the basis of individualistic considerations, such as whether you love the person, contributes to the high rates of divorce and single-parent families.

3. Your best friend has been dating another person exclusively for the past year. One day you ask how the relationship is going. Your friend replies, "I don't know. We get along really well. We like to do the same things, and we can tell each other everything. But I feel like something is missing. How do you know if you are in love?" How would you answer her question?

■ ■ ■ SUGGESTIONS FOR FURTHER READING

Fisher, Helen. (1992). *Anatomy of love*. New York: Fawcett Columbine. Fisher explains sexual anatomy, sexual emotions, mate selection, adultery, and the sexual double standard, among others, using evolutionary perspectives. A provocative book.

Hendrick, Susan, and Hendrick, Clyde. (1992). *Liking, loving and relating*. 2nd ed. Pacific Grove, CA: Brooks/Cole. This textbook explains psychologists' research on interpersonal attraction, love, and the formation and maintenance of relationships.

Lerner, Harriet G. (1989). *The dance of intimacy*. New York: Harper & Row. Lerner, a prominent psychotherapist, gives tips on how to promote intimacy in our relationships.

Sternberg, Robert. (1998). *Love is a story: A new theory of relationships*. New York: Oxford University Press. Sternberg describes his theory and the 27 love stories he has identified. The book includes items from a scale designed to identify which stories a person holds.

For Review Questions, Web Resources, and other learning and study tools, visit the *Understanding Human Sexuality* Online Learning Centre at www.mcgrawhill.ca/college/hyde.

Gender and Sexuality

CHAPTER HIGHLIGHTS

"The majority of women (happily for them) are not very much troubled with sexual feelings of any kind. What men are habitually, women are only exceptionally."*

I can't mate in captivity.†

When a baby is born, what is the first statement made about it? "It's a boy" or "It's a girl," of course. Sociologists tell us that gender is one of the most basic of status characteristics. That is, in terms of both our individual interactions with people and the position we hold in society, gender is exceptionally important. Many people experience consternation in the rare cases when they are uncertain of a person's gender. They may not know how to interact with the person, and may feel flustered, not to mention curious, until they can ferret out some clue as to whether the person is a male or a female. In this chapter we explore gender roles and the impact they may have on sexuality, and transgender (an incongruity between gender identity and physical sex).

■ Gender Roles and Stereotypes

One of the basic ways in which societies codify this emphasis on gender is through gender roles.[1] A **gender role** is a set of norms, or culturally defined expectations, that define how people of one gender ought to behave. A closely related phenomenon is a **stereotype,** which is a generalization about a group of people (for example, men) that distinguishes those people from others (for example, women). Research shows that even in modern North American society, and even among university students, there is a belief that males and females do differ psychologically in many ways, and these stereotypes have not changed much since 1972 (Bergen & Williams, 1991).

Children as young as six are aware of these stereotypes. Researchers in Nova Scotia showed children pictures containing a man and a woman and told them brief stories about the pictures (Edwards & Williams, 1982). Each story described a gender stereotype. The researchers then asked the children which person in the picture the story was about. The children responded with the appropriate stereotype most of the time. More than 85 percent of 8-year-olds identified the woman in the picture as appreciative, gentle, weak, soft-hearted, sentimental, emotional, excitable, and meek and mild. They identified the man in the picture as aggressive, strong, coarse, cruel, loud, and ambitious.

Heterosexuality is viewed as an important part of gender roles (Hyde & Jaffee, 2000). The "feminine" woman is expected to be sexually attractive to men and in turn to be attracted to them. Women who violate any part of this role—for example, lesbians—are viewed as violators of gender roles and are considered masculine (Storms, 1980). Heterosexuality is equally important in the male role.

Gender Schema Theory

In Chapter 2 we discussed gender schema theory, a cognitive approach to understanding gender stereotypes. Recall that according to that theory, a gender schema is the set of ideas (about behaviours, personality, appearance, and so on) that we associate with males and females (Bem, 1981; Martin et al., 2002). Our gender schema influences how we process information. It causes us to tend to dichotomize information on the basis of gender.

---

*Dr. William Acton. (1857). *The functions and disorders of the reproductive organs.*

†Gloria Steinem, in answer to the question why she never married.

[1]The distinction between sex and gender will be maintained in this chapter. Male–female roles—and thus gender roles—are being discussed here.

Gender role: A set of norms, or culturally defined expectations, that define how people of one gender ought to behave.
Stereotype: A generalization about a group of people (e.g., men) that distinguishes them from others (e.g., women).

(a)   *(b)*

Figure 14.1   Children are very interested in achieving adult gender roles.

It also leads us to distort or fail to remember information that is stereotype-inconsistent. Recall that children who were shown pictures of children engaging in stereotype-inconsistent activities such as boys baking cookies recalled, when tested a week later, that they had seen girls baking cookies. Of course, people do not process information using gender schema in every situation. Research in Ontario has shown that both our own gender roles (that is, how traditional we are) and the situation we are in affect how likely we are to process information in terms of gender schema (McKenzie-Mohr & Zanna, 1990).

Gender schema theory points out the extent to which gender stereotypes or gender schemas lead us to gender-dichotomized thinking. It also provides evidence that it is relatively difficult to change people's stereotyped notions because we tend to filter out information that contradicts the stereotypes.

Scripts are cognitive frameworks for how people are expected to behave in social situations. The sexual script that is most pervasive in North America is a heterosexual script, termed the *traditional sexual script* or TSS. The TSS specifies how men and women are expected to behave in (heterosexual) sexual situations (Byers, 1996). Some aspects of the TSS and the underlying gender schema are that:

1. Males are "oversexed" and females are "undersexed." As such, males are seen as having strong sexual needs and being highly motivated to engage in sexual activity at any opportunity. Females are depicted as being sexually reluctant, slow to arouse, and interested in sex only in the context of love and commitment.

2. High sexual experience enhances males' but decreases females' perceived status. That is, for males, sexual experience is perceived as reflecting positive characteristics such as masculinity and attractiveness. In females, highly sexual experience is attributed to undesirable characteristics such as non-selectivity and lack of values. Think of the differences in the values attached to the words used to describe the sexually experienced male ("macho," "stud") compared to those used for the sexually experienced female ("slut," "whore").

3. Males are expected to be "sexperts" and to take responsibility for both their own and their female partner's sexual pleasure and orgasm. Females are expected to be sexually naive. Thus, they may be afraid to share their sexual preferences with their partner out of fear that he will take this as evidence that they have had many sexual partners (something that is evaluated negatively in women). They also may fear that their partner will think they are criticizing him for not being the sexpert he is supposed to be.

4. Males, because of their greater sexual interest, are supposed to be the initiators in sexual situations.

5. In order to avoid being judged negatively by being "too" sexually available, women are expected to be sexual gatekeepers and place limits on sexual activity, particularly with a new

partner. Thus, even when they are interested in engaging in sexual activity, females are expected to offer at least initial token resistance to their partner's sexual advances.

How much evidence is there that heterosexuals follow the TSS? Research conducted in New Brunswick sheds some light on this question (Byers, 1996). Participants in two studies (one of dating relationships, the other of long-term relationships) kept a diary in which they recorded sexual initiations and responses to initiations in their relationships. The results indicated that in heterosexual relationships, men initiate sex more often than women do both in dating and marital/cohabiting relationships. This is consistent with the TSS. However, men are not always the initiators—on average women initiated sex more than once a week. Responses to initiations also did not follow the TSS. The research showed that men and women are equally likely to accept or refuse an initiation—they respond positively about 83 percent of the time in dating relationships and about 74 percent of the time in long-term relationships (Byers & Heinlein, 1989; O'Sullivan & Byers, 1992). Further, when one partner is reluctant to engage in sexual activity, men and women use the same strategies to try to change their partner's mind—most often flirting or touching/stroking the partner (O'Sullivan & Byers, 1996).

These results indicate that some aspects of the TSS, such as the expectation that it is the male role to initiate sex, continue to characterize heterosexual relationships. However, women regularly initiate sexual activity, albeit less frequently than their male partners. Further, research does not support other aspects of the TSS. Women are no more reluctant to engage in sexual activity than men are. To this extent, men's and women's roles in heterosexual sexual interactions appear to be converging. Nonetheless, as discussed in Chapter 17, adherence to the TSS may be a cause of some men's sexual coercion of women in dating relationships (Byers, 1996).

Socialization

Many adult women and men do behave as gender roles say they should. Why does this happen? Psychologists and sociologists believe that it is a result of gender-role socialization. **Socialization** refers to the ways in which society conveys to the individual its norms or expectations for his or her behaviour.

Socialization occurs especially in childhood, as children are taught to behave as they will be expected to in adulthood. Socialization may involve several processes. Children may be rewarded for behaviour that is appropriate for their gender ("What a brave little man he is"), or they may be punished for behaviour that is not appropriate to their gender ("Nice young ladies don't do that"). The adult models they imitate—whether these are parents of the same gender, teachers, or women and men on television—also contribute to their socialization. In some cases, simply telling children what is expected of males and females may be sufficient for role learning to take place. Socialization continues in adulthood, as society conveys its norms of appropriate behaviour for adult women and men. These norms extend from appropriate jobs to who initiates sexual activity.

Who (or what) are society's agents in accomplishing this socialization? Certainly parents have an early, important influence, from buying dolls for girls and footballs or baseball bats for boys to giving boys more freedom to explore. Research indicates that parents treat girls and boys similarly in many ways, with the exception that parents strongly encourage gender-typed activities (Lytton & Romney, 1991).

The peer group also can have a big impact in socializing for gender roles. In an Ontario experiment, children in grades 3 to 6 read stories about boys and girls who engaged in traditionally masculine, traditionally feminine, or a combination of masculine and feminine behaviours. The boys preferred to be friends with the exclusively masculine boy and girls preferred the exclusively feminine girl (Zucker et al., 1995). Teenagers may be particularly effective at exerting pressure for gender-role conformity (Maccoby, 1998).

The media are also important socializing agents. Many people assume that things have changed a lot in the last 20 years and that gender stereotypes are a thing of the past. On the contrary, various media—from television to teen magazines—continue to show females and males in stereotyped roles. For example, an analysis of articles in *Seventeen* magazine over time showed that, in 1955, 43 percent of these articles intended for a female audience

Socialization: The ways in which society conveys to the individual its norms or expectations for his or her behaviour.

focused on personal appearance; in 1995 it was 45 percent (Schlenker et al., 1998). The same study of *Seventeen* showed that in 1955 only 10 percent of the articles were about career development; by 1995 the figure had risen to a staggering 14 percent! In short, the distribution of articles conveys to girls that their appearance is important and a career is not.

An analysis of popular American television situation comedies (sitcoms) from the 1950s to the 1990s indicated that there were small trends toward more egalitarian gender roles, but traditional stereotyping was still common (Olson & Douglas, 1997). *The Cosby Show* of the late 1980s earned the highest ratings for equality of gender roles of spouses and equality of gender roles of children (Olson & Douglas, 1997). But the 1990s series *Home Improvement* earned the lowest scores on equality of gender roles—lower even than the *Father Knows Best* series of the 1950s. More recent television shows, such as *Ally McBeal* and *Sex and the City*, which depict women in high-status careers, also can't seem to get past traditional stereotypes. For example, Ally McBeal was a lawyer who was also very thin and attractive, constantly falling down, and looking for love to "complete" her. *Judging Amy* features a woman who is a judge and a single mother, not a woman in a powerful societal position who is in a happy long-term relationship. Traditional gender roles are still alive on prime time.

Dozens of studies show that gender stereotypes shown on television affect children's stereotyped ideas (reviewed by Signorielli, 1990). For example, 3- to 6-year-olds who view more TV have more stereotyped ideas about gender roles than do children who view less. In a naturalistic experiment in British Columbia, children in a town with little availability of television showed less gender-stereotyped attitudes than children in a town with great availability of television. Television then became more available in the first town; two years later, the children in that town were as stereotyped in their attitudes as the children in the town in which television was available all along.

Although gender roles themselves are universal (Rosaldo, 1974)—that is, all societies have gender roles—the exact content of these roles varies from one culture to the next, from one ethnic group to another, and from one social class to another. Gender roles in the major ethnocultural Canadian communities are described below.

Gender Roles and Ethnicity

Ethnicity refers to a sizeable group of people who share a common and distinct racial, national, religious, linguistic, or cultural origin or heritage. Although people of British and French backgrounds make up the largest ethnic groups in Canada, 28 percent of Canadians report only origins other than British or French (Statistics Canada, 1998a). Between 23 and 41 percent of the population in Toronto, Vancouver, and Montreal were born outside of Canada. Changing immigration patterns since the 1980s have increased the ethnocultural diversity of Canada and have introduced a wide range of attitudes and traditions surrounding gender roles (Barrett et al., 1997). In some ways, the gender roles of members of these communities reflect the values and norms of their country of origin. However, gender roles are also influenced by the majority Canadian culture. For example, in keeping with traditional values, immigrant parents may allow their sons but not their daughters to engage in unsupervised dating. However, the same parents may encourage their daughters to obtain professional degrees and take up careers even though women in their culture traditionally did not work outside the home (Mackie, 1991).

The study *Ethnocultural Communities Facing AIDS* examined sexuality within six Canadian ethnocultural communities (see Chapter 1 for a description of this study). Groups were chosen based on ethnicity, not race. Large, cohesive communities with a large proportion of young people and people who had immigrated to Canada since 1986 were chosen (Cappon et al., 1996). The researchers found a number of cross-cultural similarities in gender roles. Generally men and women in these communities are seen as having distinct roles in that men are expected to be the head of the family and women are expected to be the caregivers. However, economic realities often mean that women must work outside the home, and these role changes often create conflict within the family. There tends to be a double standard with respect to sexual behaviour. Dating and premarital sex are accepted and often encouraged in sons but not tolerated in daughters. Men are expected to be active in sexual relationships, whereas women are expected to be passive and to meet men's needs (Singer, 1996).

There also are differences in gender role expectations between various ethnocultural groups, as

Figure 14.2   Gender roles in Canada's ethnocultural communities reflect aspects of the majority as well as aspects of the minority culture, such as this arranged Hindu marriage in Montreal.

the following descriptions of the Chinese, South Asian, and Caribbean communities in the above study demonstrate (Health Canada, 1994a–f).

The Chinese Community

In 2001 there were 1,029,395 Chinese Canadians, the largest visible minority group. Chinese culture emphasizes responsibility to the family and the community over self-fulfilment and individualism as in the majority Canadian culture. Marriage is highly valued so that couples are reluctant to separate or divorce even when experiencing significant marital problems. In most families, the man is considered the head of the household; the woman is the primary caregiver and is expected to adopt a submissive role with her male partner. It is not acceptable for females to engage in premarital or extramarital sexual activity, and premarital sex is also discouraged for males. However, extramarital sexual activity by men may be accepted, particularly in "astronaut families" in which the man

works away from home in Hong Kong or Taiwan. Today gender roles within the community are becoming more diverse as people move away from their traditional roles. As achievement and education are considered important within the Chinese community, women who were born in Canada may experience conflict between the traditional gender roles of Chinese culture and those of Canadian culture, which increasingly prizes independence and assertiveness in women. Men may also experience conflict between family values and individual achievement.

The South Asian (Indo-Pakistani) Communities

In 2001 there were 917,070 South Asians living in Canada. In South Asian (for example, Indian and Pakistani) communities, religion is a major focus of community life. Hard work, education, and achievement are seen as important. Respect for traditional values, which in some cases includes arranged marriages even for women born in Canada, is also highly

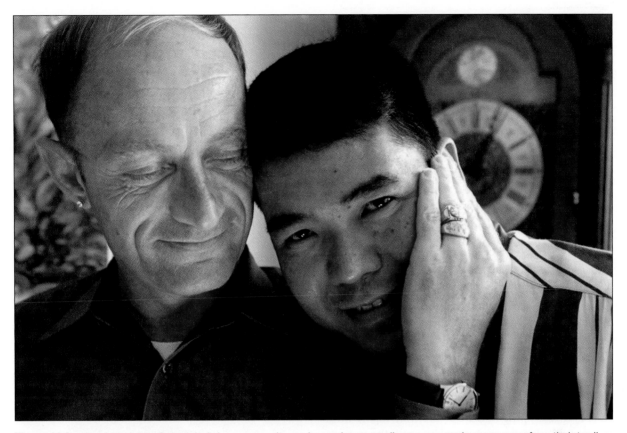

Figure 14.3   Gender roles in Canada's Asian community are becoming more diverse as people move away from their traditional background. This couple was united in a commitment ceremony by a United Church minister.

valued. South Asian men and women tend to be assigned different roles, and women are expected to be submissive to men. Boys tend to be given privileges and freedom, dating is allowed, and it is expected that they will have some sexual experience. However, girls may not be allowed to date because female virginity prior to marriage is highly valued. Men are expected to take the lead in the sexual encounter; women are expected to be passive, submissive, and uninformed about sex. As a result of women's prescribed sexual passivity, some men visit sex workers for casual sex before and during marriage. The women are not supposed to question the behaviour of their husbands or to complain about extramarital sexual activity.

English-Speaking Caribbean Communities

In 2001 there were 662,215 Blacks in Canada, many with roots in the Caribbean. English-speaking Caribbean (for example, Jamaican) communities have a strong sense of family and community. Traditionally, the man was expected to be the provider and the woman was expected to care for the children and the household while also working outside the home. Today there are many single-parent families in the Caribbean communities, usually headed by women. More restrictions are placed on girls than on boys, in part as an attempt to prevent adolescent pregnancy. In adolescence and into adulthood, women's focus is on developing relationships and they may engage in serial monogamy. Both having a male partner and having a child are considered important aspects of the female role and indicators of success. In contrast, young men are more likely to want to have many sexual partners. It also is not uncommon for married and cohabiting men to have multiple partners.

First Nations Communities

In the 2001 Canadian Census, 976,305 people reported Aboriginal ancestry (Statistics Canada, 1998). The Aboriginal peoples constitute an important ethnocultural minority group in Canada. Before contact with Europeans, at least some of the First Nations peoples in North America had relatively egalitarian gender roles (Kinsman, 1996; LaFramboise et al., 1990). That is, their roles were more egalitarian than those of the European culture of the same period. The process of acculturation and adaptation to the majority culture seems to have resulted in increased male dominance among North American Aboriginal peoples.

Among the more than 200 Native languages spoken in North America, at least two-thirds have a term that refers to a third (or more) gender beyond male and female (Tafoya & Wirth, 1996). European anthropologists termed this additional category *berdache*, a term rejected by Native peoples, who prefer the term *two-spirit* (Jacobs et al., 1997). These same anthropologists concluded that the people were homosexuals, transsexuals, or transvestites, none of which are accurate from an Aboriginal point of view (Kinsman, 1996). A man might be married to a two-spirit male, but the marriage would not be considered homosexual because the two are of different genders (Tafoya & Wirth, 1996).

There was also a role of the "manly hearted woman," a role that a woman who was exceptionally independent and aggressive could take on. There was a "warrior woman" role among the Apache, Crow, Cheyenne, Blackfoot, Pawnee, and Navajo tribes (e.g., Buchanan, 1986; House, 1997). In both cases, women could express masculine traits or participate in male-stereotyped activities while continuing to live and dress as women.

In summary, research indicates that gender roles in Canada are not uniform. Different ethnic groups define gender roles differently.

■ Gender Differences in Psychological Functioning

Gender differences in personality and behaviour have been studied extensively by psychologists (e.g., Hyde, 1996). Here we will focus on gender differences in two areas that are particularly relevant to gender and sexuality: aggressiveness and communication styles.

Males and females differ in *aggressiveness*. Males are generally more aggressive than females. This is true for virtually all indicators of aggression (physical aggression such as fighting, verbal aggression, and fantasy aggression) (Hyde, 1984). It is also true at all ages; as soon as children are old enough to perform aggressive behaviours, boys are more aggressive, and males dominate the statistics on violent crimes. The gender difference in aggression tends to be largest among preschoolers, but it gets smaller with age so that gender differences in adults' aggression are small (Hyde, 1984).

Researchers have found that in the U.S. men and women differ in their style of communicating, both verbally and non-verbally. This research was reviewed in Chapter 10, In Focus 10.1. Of particular relevance to sexuality, social psychologists have found

Figure 14.4   Among some First Nations there are three gender roles, the third being known as a "manly hearted woman," or "warrior woman." Chiricahua Tah-des-te was a messenger and warrior in Geronimo's band. She participated in negotiations with several U.S. military leaders and surrendered with Geronimo in 1886.

gender differences in studies of **self-disclosure.** In these studies, people are brought into a laboratory and are asked to disclose personal information either to friends or to strangers. Women are more willing to disclose information than men are in these situations (Dindia & Allen, 1992). Within dating relationships, women self-disclose more about both sexual and non-sexual issues (Byers & Demmons, 1999).

Norms about self-disclosure are changing, though. Traditional gender roles favoured emotional expressiveness for females, but emotional repressiveness and avoidance of self-disclosure for males. There is a contemporary ethic, though, of good communication and openness that demands equal self-disclosure from males and females (Rubin et al., 1980). Research with university students in New Brunswick indicates that traditional gender roles persist in that women are more emotionally expressive than men are both in non-sexual and in sexual situations (Lawrance et al., 1996). However, this research also shows that we are moving toward a norm of greater emotional expressiveness for men. Men were described as ideally equally expressive as women in sexual situations. Thus, the traditional expectation that men should not express their feelings seems to be gradually shifting toward the expectation that they be open and communicative.

There are gender differences in people's ability to understand the non-verbal behaviours of others. The technical phrase for this is "decoding non-verbal cues"—that is, the ability to read others' body language correctly. It might be measured, for example, by one's accuracy in interpreting facial expressions. Research shows that women are better than men at decoding such non-verbal cues and discerning others' emotions (Hall, 1998). Certainly this is consistent with the gender-related expectation that women will show greater interpersonal sensitivity.

What are the implications of these gender differences in communication styles for sexuality? For example, if men are less able to disclose personal information about themselves, consider whether this might not hamper their ability to communicate their sexual needs to their partners.

Self-disclosure: Telling personal information to another person.

■ Gender Differences in Sexuality

In this section, the discussion will focus on areas of sexuality in which there is some evidence of male–female differences. As we will point out, differences do exist, but they are in a rather small number of areas—masturbation, attitudes about casual sex, arousal to erotica, consistency of orgasm during sex, and sex drive. There is a danger in focusing on these differences to the point of forgetting about gender similarities. Keep in mind that men and women are in many ways quite similar in their sexuality—for example, in the physiology of their sexual response (Chapter 9)—as you consider the evidence on male–female differences that follows. Also bear in mind that most of the scientific evidence described here is based on North American samples. Only a few cross-cultural surveys are available. The gender differences discussed in the next sections characterize mainstream North American culture. Gender patterns may be similar or different in other cultures.

Masturbation

In a review of 177 studies of gender differences in sexuality the authors found that the largest gender difference was the incidence of masturbation (Oliver & Hyde, 1993).

Recall that in the Kinsey data, 92 percent of the men had masturbated to orgasm at least once in their lives, as compared with 58 percent of the women. Not only did fewer women masturbate, but in general, those who did masturbate had begun at a later age than the males. Virtually all men said they had masturbated before age 20 (most began between ages 13 and 15), but substantial numbers of women reported masturbating for the first time at age 25, 30, or 35. This gender difference shows no evidence of diminishing, according to more recent studies. The NHSLS, although it did not collect data on lifetime incidence of masturbation, did ask about masturbation in the last year; 63 percent of the men, compared with 42 percent of the women, reported that they had masturbated (Laumann et al., 1994). Similarly, 80 percent of male students but only 48 percent of female students at the University of British Columbia reported masturbating at least once (Meston et al., 1996). The data suggest, then, that there is a substantial gender difference in the incidence of masturbation, with men considerably more likely to have masturbated than women.

Attitudes about Casual Sex

In the review mentioned above, the second largest gender difference noted was in attitudes toward casual sex—that is, sexual intercourse in a situation, such as a "one-night stand," in which there is no emotionally committed relationship between the partners (Oliver & Hyde, 1993). Men are considerably more approving of such interactions, and women tend to be disapproving. Many women feel that sexual intercourse is ethical or acceptable only in the context of an emotionally committed relationship. For many men, that is a nice context for sex, but it isn't absolutely necessary.

In Canada, 68 percent of male adolescents, but only 48 percent of female adolescents, approve of having sex before marriage with someone you like (Bibby, 2001). Further, adolescent females are more likely to believe that sex without love is not satisfying. Gender differences in attitudes toward casual sex were even greater; in the CYSHHAS, 66 percent of grade 11 boys but only 32 percent of grade 11 girls agreed that it was alright to have casual sex (Council of Ministers of Education, 2003).

In the CYSHHAS, the students were also asked about their reasons for first having sexual intercourse. The results indicate significant gender differences. For example, 60 percent of grade 11 girls but only 39 percent of grade 11 boys indicated love for the person as a reason for first having sexual intercourse. In contrast, more boys than girls gave curiosity/experimentation as their main reason—21 percent of the boys and 14 percent of the girls. Nine percent of the boys but only 3 percent of the girls first engaged in sex in order to lose their virginity. In sum, most females emphasize love and commitment, as in the following examples:

> Emotional feelings that were shared, wonderful way to express LOVE!!

> My motives for sexual intercourse would all be due to the love and commitment I feel for my partner.

Contrast those responses with the following typical responses from males:

> Need it.

> To gratify myself.

> When I'm tired of masturbation.

Of course, some males and females gave non-stereotypic responses. For example, one woman wrote:

> To enjoy myself physically, for experimentation, exercise, fun and to get to know someone better. (Carroll et al., 1985, p. 137)

Clearly most males—at least in the college or university years—emphasize physical needs and pleasure as their motives for intercourse, whereas most females emphasize love, relationships, and emotional commitment. No wonder there is some conflict in relationships between women and men!

Arousal to Erotica

Traditionally in our society most erotic material—sexually arousing pictures, movies, or stories—has been produced for a male audience. The corresponding assumption presumably has been that women are not interested in such things. Does the scientific evidence bear out this notion?

Laboratory research shows that men are more aroused by erotic materials, but the gender difference is not large (Murnen & Stockton, 1997). A classic study by psychologist Julia Heiman (1975; for a similar study with similar results, see Steinman et al., 1981) provides a good deal of insight into the responses of males and females to erotic materials. The participants were sexually experienced university students, and Heiman studied their responses as they listened to tape recordings of erotic stories. Not only did she obtain the participants' self-ratings of their arousal, as other investigators have done, but she also got objective measures of their physiological levels of arousal. To do this, she used two instruments: a penile strain gauge and a photoplethysmograph (Figure 14.5). The **penile strain gauge** (which our students have dubbed the "peter meter") is used to get a physiological measure of arousal in the male; it is a flexible loop that fits around the base of the penis. The **photo-**

Penile strain gauge: A device used to measure physiological sexual arousal in the male; it is a flexible loop that fits around the base of the penis.

Figure 14.5 Two devices used to measure physiological sexual response in males and females. The penile strain gauge (left) consists of a flexible band that fits around the base of the penis. The photoplethysmograph (right) is an acrylic cylinder containing a photocell and a light source, which is placed just inside the vagina.

plethysmograph, or photometer, measures physiological arousal in the female; it is an acrylic cylinder, about the size of a tampon, that is placed just inside the entrance to the vagina. Both instruments measure vasocongestion in the genitals, which is the major physiological response during sexual arousal (see Chapter 9).

Research participants heard one of four kinds of tapes depicting heterosexual couples. There is a stereotype that women are more turned on by romance, whereas men are more aroused by "raw sex." The tapes varied according to which of these kinds of content they contained. The first group of tapes was *erotic;* they included excerpts from popular novels giving explicit descriptions of heterosexual sex. The second group of tapes was *romantic;* a couple were heard expressing affection and tenderness for each other, but they did not actually engage in sex. The third group of tapes was *erotic-romantic;*

Photoplethysmograph (foh-toh-pleth-ISS-moh-graf): An acrylic cylinder that is placed inside the vagina in order to measure physiological sexual arousal in the female. Also called a photometer.

they included erotic elements of explicit sex but also romantic elements. Finally, the fourth group of tapes served as a control; a couple were heard engaging in conversation but nothing else. The plots of the tapes also varied according to whether the man or the woman initiated the activity and whether the description centred on the woman's physical and psychological responses or on the man's. Thus the tapes were either male-initiated or female-initiated and either female-centred or male-centred. Three important results emerged from the study:

1. Explicit heterosexual sex (the erotic and erotic-romantic tapes) was most arousing, both for women and for men. The great majority of both men and women responded most strongly, both physiologically and in self-ratings, to the erotic and erotic-romantic tapes. Women, in fact, rated the erotic tapes as more arousing than men did. Neither men nor women responded—either physiologically or in self-reports—to the romantic tapes or to the control tapes (except for a couple of men who were aroused by a discussion of the relative merits of an anthropology major versus premed—ah, well).

2. Both men and women found the female-initiated, female-centred tape to be most arousing. Perhaps the female-initiated plot was most arousing because of its somewhat forbidden or taboo nature.

3. Women were sometimes not aware of their own physiological arousal. Generally there was a high correlation between self-ratings of arousal and objective physiological measures of arousal, for men. When men were physically aroused, they never made an error in reporting this in their self-ratings—it is pretty hard to miss an erection. But when the women were physically aroused, about half of them did not report arousal in their self-ratings (see also Laan et al., 1994). (One might assume that women who were sophisticated enough to volunteer for an experiment of this nature and who were willing to insert a photoplethysmograph into their vagina would not suddenly become bashful about reporting their arousal; that is, it seems likely that these women honestly did not perceive themselves to be aroused.) Research in British Columbia has shown that it is women with sexual disorders, but not other women, whose subjective sense of

sexual arousal does not match their physiological arousal (Palace & Gorzalka, 1992).

In sum, then, Heiman's study indicates that women and men are quite similar in their responses to erotic materials but that women can sometimes be unaware of their own physical arousal.

In statistical terms, Heiman found a low correlation between women's self-reports of arousal and the physiological measures of their arousal. In an interesting follow-up study, one experimental group of women was instructed to attend to their genital signs of sexual arousal ("While rating these slides, I would like you to attend to various changes that may occur in your genital area such as vaginal lubrication, pelvic warmth, and muscular tension"), and a second group was told to attend to non-genital signs of arousal ("While rating these slides, I would like you to attend to various changes that may occur in your body. These are heart rate increase, nipple erection, breast swelling, and muscular tension"), while a control group was given no instructions (Korff & Geer, 1983). Both experimental groups showed high correlations between self-reports and physiological measures of arousal, while the control group showed the same low correlation that Heiman found. This shows that women can be quite accurate in realizing their physical arousal if they are simply told to focus their attention on it. The broader culture, of course, does not give women such instructions, but rather tells them to focus on the environment outside themselves—the love, romance, partner—so that many women have not learned to focus on their body. But the experiment described here shows quite clearly that they can.

To learn more about the plethysmograph and how it works, watch the video "The Plethysmograph" in Chapter 14 of your CD.

Orgasm Consistency

Men are more consistent than women at having orgasms during sex. For example, according to the NHSLS, 75 percent of men, but only 29 percent of women, always have an orgasm during sex with their partner (Laumann et al., 1994, p. 116). The gap is narrower for orgasm consistency during masturbation, but even here men seem to be more effective: 80 percent of men, compared with 60 percent of women, report that they usually or always have an orgasm when masturbating (Laumann et al., 1994, p. 84).

Sex Drive

Evidence from a number of sources indicates that men, on average, have a stronger sex drive than women do (Baumeister et al., 2001; Peplau, 2003). Men think about sex more often and have more frequent and varied fantasies than women do (Renaud & Byers, 1999). Compared with women, men desire more sexual partners and a greater frequency of intercourse. In a study across 52 nations, the gender difference in the preferred number of partners was found in all regions of the globe (Schmitt, 2003). It is important to remember, of course, that these are average differences. For a particular heterosexual couple, it is quite possible that the woman's level of desire would exceed the man's.

■ Why the Differences?

The previous section reviewed the evidence on differences in male and female sexuality. Four differences—the lower percentage of females, compared with males, who masturbate; women's more disapproving attitudes toward casual sex; women's lesser orgasm consistency; and men's greater sex drive—are fairly well documented and in need of explanation. What factors lead to these differences? Many possible explanations have been suggested by a wide variety of scholars.

Are the Differences Bogus?

One possibility is that many of these gender differences, typically documented by self-report, are not true differences. Instead, it could be that people report what is expected of them, shaped by gender norms. Men are expected to want lots of sex, so they exaggerate their desire in self-reports, or women minimize theirs.

A clever study used the bogus-pipeline method to investigate this possibility (Alexander & Fisher, 2003). College students were brought to the lab to fill out questionnaires about their sexual attitudes and behaviours. They were randomly assigned to one of three experimental conditions. In the *bogus-pipeline condition*, the student was hooked up to a fake polygraph or lie-detector machine and told that the machine could detect false answers. People should respond very honestly in this condition. In the *anonymous condition*, the student simply filled out the questionnaire anonymously, as is typical of much sex research, and placed the questionnaire in a locked box when finished. In the *exposure threat condition*, respondents were instructed to hand their completed questionnaires directly to the experimenter, who was an undergraduate peer, and the experimenter sat in full view while the respondents completed their questionnaires, serving as a reminder that this other person would easily be able to see their answers. Figure 14.6 shows the results for reports of the number of sexual partners the respondents had had.

When people were in the bogus-pipeline condition and gave the most honest reporting, men's and women's reports of their number of partners were nearly identical—in fact, women's were slightly higher than men's. In the standard conditions of anonymity used in most sex research, women reported fewer partners than men did. Under a threat that responses would be made public, the largest gap between women and men appeared. In the anonymous condition and the exposure threat condition, differences emerged that were consistent with gender roles. Women confirmed the expectation that they have few partners.

What are the implications of this study? Does it mean that all the differences described in the previous section are bogus? Probably not, but it means that findings of gender differences obtained by self-reports are probably exaggerations of the truth. And it is important to note that findings obtained from physiological measures, such as those used in Heiman's study, are not vulnerable to these reporting biases.

Let's assume that the gender differences discussed in the previous section are real, although perhaps not as dramatically large as the research suggests. How can these differences be explained?

Biological Factors
There has been some speculation that gender differences in sexuality are created by two biological factors: anatomy and hormones.

Anatomy
The male sexual anatomy is external and visible and has a very obvious response: erection. While the male is nude, he can easily see his sexual organs, either by looking down or by looking in a mirror. The female sexual organs, in contrast, are hidden. The nude female looks down and sees nothing except pubic hair (which really is not very informative); she looks in a full-length mirror and sees the same thing. Only by doing the mirror exercise described in Chapter 4 can she get a good view of her own genitals. To make matters worse, the word "clitoris"—but not "penis"—is often missing from books about sexuality, from parents' talk about sex, and from students' knowledge about sexuality (Ogletree & Ginsburg, 2000). Furthermore, the female's genitals do not have an obvious arousal response like the male's erection. As a result, she may be less aware of her own arousal, a notion that is supported by Heiman's research.

The anatomical explanation, then, is that because the woman's genitals are not in plain view and because their arousal response is less obvious than that of the man's genitals, she is less likely to masturbate and less likely to be fully aware of her own sexual response (Baldwin & Baldwin, 1997). If this explanation is correct, or at least part of the answer, could steps be taken to help women become

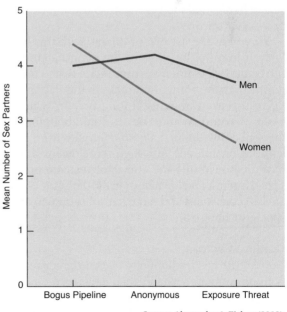

Source: Alexander & Fisher (2003).

Figure 14.6 Mean number of sexual partners reported by men and women in the Bogus Pipeline Study (see text for further details).

more aware of their own sexuality? Perhaps parents could tell their daughters about the mirror exercise at an early age and encourage them to become more aware of their own sexual organs. And parents might want to discuss the idea of masturbation with their daughters.

Hormones

The hormonal explanation rests on the finding that testosterone is related to sexual behaviour. This evidence was reviewed in Chapter 9. Basically, the evidence comes from studies in which male animals are castrated (and thus lose their natural source of testosterone), with the result that their sexual behaviour disappears, presumably reflecting a decrease in sex drive. If replacement injections of testosterone are given, the sexual behaviour returns.

Females generally have lower levels of testosterone in their tissues than males do. Human females, for example, have about one-tenth the level of testosterone in their blood that human males do (Janowsky et al., 1998).

The hormonal explanation, then, is that if testosterone is important in activating sexual behaviour and if females have only one-tenth as much of it as males have, this might result in a lower level of sexual behaviour such as masturbation in women, or a lower "sex drive."

There are at least two problems with this logic. First, it may be that cells in the hypothalamus or the genitals of women are more sensitive to testosterone than the comparable cells in men; thus a little testosterone may go a long way in women's bodies. Second, we must be cautious about making inferences to human males and females from studies done on animals. Although some recent studies have demonstrated the effects of testosterone on sexual interest and behaviour in humans, the effects are less consistent and more complex than in other species (Chapter 9).

Cultural Factors

Our culture has traditionally placed tighter restrictions on women's sexuality than it has on men's, and vestiges of these restrictions linger today. It seems likely that these restrictions have acted as a damper on female sexuality, and thus they may help to explain why some women do not masturbate, why some women have difficulty having orgasms, and why some women are wary about casual sex.

One of the clearest reflections of the differences in restrictions on male and female sexuality is the double standard. As we saw in Chapter 11, the double standard says that the same sexual behaviour is evaluated differently, depending on whether a male or a female engages in it. The sexual double standard gives women less sexual freedom than men (Crawford & Popp, 2003). An example is premarital sex. Traditionally in our culture, premarital intercourse has been less acceptable for females than for males. Indeed, premarital sexual activity might be a status symbol for a male but a sign of undesirable characteristics for a female.

Generally there seems to be less of a double standard today than there was in former times. For example, as the data in Chapter 11 indicate, people now approve of premarital intercourse for females about as much as they do for males. This change in attitudes is reflected in behaviour. A much higher percentage of women report having engaged in premarital intercourse now than in the 1940s. There is much less of a difference between females and males now than there was a generation ago; as reported in Chapter 11, the vast majority of both females and males are now engaging in premarital intercourse. Premarital intercourse remains somewhat more common among males than females in most of Canada. However, research has found that male and female French-speaking college students in Quebec are equally likely to have engaged in intercourse (Levy et al., 1993; Otis et al., 1997).

The decline of the double standard may help to explain why some of the gender differences found in older studies of sex behaviour have disappeared in more recent studies. When cultural forces do not make such a distinction between male and female, males and females become more similar in their sexual behaviour. Yet vestiges of the double standard remain today in regard to casual sex, which is considered less acceptable for women than for men. For example, a Quebec study showed that university women rate females who have sex in an uncommitted relationship more negatively, and believe a male partner will see her more negatively if the woman supplies the condom than if the man supplies the condom (Hynie & Lydon, 1995; Hynie et al., 1997). This suggests that women perceive a double standard.

Gender roles, particularly as prescribed by the traditional sexual script, also contribute to differences in male and female sexuality. For example, the expectation is that in heterosexual relationships males are the initiators and females are the passive objects of men's advances. This makes the man responsible both for his own response and for the woman's response. Women have not been encouraged to be active in producing their own pleasure or bringing about their own orgasms. In keeping with these gender role expectations, research has shown that men are more active in sexual situations than women are (Lawrance et al., 1996).

Further, research in New Brunswick has shown that the cultural sexual script affects perceptions of a partner's sexual preferences (Miller & Byers, 2004). The researchers had 152 heterosexual couples report their actual and ideal duration of foreplay and intercourse, as well as their perceptions of their partner's desired duration of foreplay and intercourse. They found that men's estimates of their partner's ideals were more similar to their estimates of what the average woman would want than they were to the actual preferences stated by their partner. Similarly, women's estimates of their partner's ideals were more similar to their estimates of what the average man would want than they were to their partner's stated preferences. This suggests that people use stereotypes to guide their understanding of their partner's sexual preferences (and possibly the way they make love) more than they use explicit or implicit information provided by the partner.

Marital and family roles may play a part. When children are born, they can act as a damper on the parents' sexual relationship. The couple lose their privacy when they gain children. They may worry about their children bursting through an unlocked door and witnessing them making love. Or they may be concerned that their children will hear the sounds of lovemaking. Generally, though, the woman is assigned the primary responsibility for child rearing, so she may be more aware of the presence of the children in the house and more concerned about the effects on them of witnessing their parents engaging in sex. Once again, her worry and anxiety do not contribute to her having a satisfying sexual experience.

Other Factors

A number of other factors, not easily classified as biological or cultural, may also contribute to differences between male and female sexuality.[2]

[2]Other possible causes of orgasm problems in women are discussed in Chapter 19.

Women get pregnant and men do not. Particularly in the days before effective contraceptives were available, pregnancy might be a highly undesirable consequence of sexuality for a woman. Thinking that an episode of lovemaking might result in a nine-month pregnancy and another mouth to feed could put a damper on anyone's sexuality. Even today, pregnancy fears can be a force for heterosexual women. Many Canadian adolescent females who are sexually active do not use contraceptives or do not use them consistently—32 percent in one study (Fisher et al., 1999; Levy et al., 1992). A woman who is worried about whether she will become pregnant—and, if she is single, about whether others will find out that she has been engaging in sexual activity—is not in a state conducive to the enjoyment of sex, much less the experience of orgasm (although this scarcely explains why more women than men do not masturbate).

Ineffective techniques of stimulating the woman may also be a factor, particularly in heterosexual relationships. The heterosexual techniques of intercourse, with the penis moving in and out of the vagina, may provide good stimulation for the man but not the woman, since she may not be getting sufficient clitoral stimulation. Perhaps the problem, then, is that women are expected to orgasm as a result of intercourse, when that technique is not very effective for producing orgasms in women. Although some lesbians also use ineffective techniques, Masters and Johnson (1979) found that lesbians benefited from stimulating another body like their own.

A relationship probably exists between the evidence that fewer women masturbate than men and gender differences in orgasm consistency. Childhood and adolescent experiences with masturbation are important early sources of learning about sexuality. Through these experiences we learn how our bodies respond to sexual stimulation and what the most effective techniques are for stimulating our own bodies. This learning is important to our experience of adult, two-person sex. For example, Kinsey's data suggested that women who masturbate to orgasm before marriage are more likely to orgasm in intercourse with their husbands;[3] 31 percent of the women who had

[3]Note that this is in direct contradiction to the old-fashioned advice given in manuals that suggested that "getting hooked" on masturbation might impair later marital sexuality; if anything, just the reverse is true.

never masturbated to orgasm before marriage had not had an orgasm by the end of their first year of marriage, while only 13 to 16 percent of the women who had masturbated had not had orgasms in their first year of marriage (Kinsey et al., 1953, p. 407). One woman spoke of how she discovered masturbation late and how this may be related to her orgasm capacity in heterosexual sex:

> I thought I was frigid, even after three years of marriage, until I read this book and learned how to turn myself on. After I gave myself my first orgasm, I cried for half an hour, I was so relieved. Afterwards, I did it a lot, for many months, and I talked to my doctor and to my husband, and finally I began to make it in intercourse. (Hunt, 1974, pp. 96–97)

Not only may women's relative inexperience with masturbation lead to a lack of sexual learning, but it also may create a kind of "erotic dependency" on men. Typically, boys' earliest sexual experiences are with masturbation, which they learn how to do from other boys. More important, they learn that they can produce their own sexual pleasure. Girls typically have their earliest sexual experiences in opposite sex touching and fondling. They therefore learn about sex from boys, and they learn that their sexual pleasure is produced by the male. As sex researcher John Gagnon commented:

> Young women may know of masturbation, but not know *how* to masturbate—how to produce pleasure, or even what the pleasures of orgasm might be. . . . Some young women report that they learned how to masturbate after they had orgasm from intercourse and petting, and decided they could do it for themselves. (1977, p. 152)

Once again, such ideas might lead to a recommendation that girls be given information about masturbation.

Numerous factors that may contribute to shaping male and female sexuality have been discussed. Our feeling is that a combination of several of these factors produces the differences that do exist. The early differences in experiences with masturbation are very important. Although these differences may result from differences in anatomy, they could be eliminated by giving girls information on masturbation. Women may enter into adult sexual relationships with a lack of experience in

the bodily sensations of arousal and orgasm, and they may be unaware of the best techniques for stimulating their own bodies. Put this lack of experience together with various cultural forces, such as the double standard and ineffective techniques of stimulation, and it is not too surprising that there are some gender differences in sexuality.

■ Beyond the Young Adults

One of the problems with our understanding of gender differences in sexuality is that so much of the research has concentrated on heterosexual university students or other groups of young adults (as is true of much behavioural research). For example, the 52-nation study of gender differences in preferred number of partners discussed earlier tested university students at nearly all sites (Schmitt, 2003). Using this population may provide a very narrow view of male–female differences; they are considered during only a very small part of the lifespan. In reality, female sexuality and male sexuality change in their nature and focus across the lifespan. For example, it is a common belief in our culture that men reach their sexual "peak" at around age 19, whereas women do not reach theirs until they are 35 or 40 (Barr et al., 2002). There is some scientific evidence supporting this view. Kinsey (1953) found, for example, that women generally had orgasms more consistently at 40 than they did at 25.

Psychiatrist Helen Singer Kaplan, a specialist in therapy for sexual disorders, advanced an interesting view of differences between male sexuality and female sexuality across the lifespan (Kaplan & Sager, 1971). According to her analysis, the teenage male's sexuality is very intense and almost exclusively genital in its focus. As the man approaches age 30, he is still highly interested in sex, but not so urgently. He is also satisfied with fewer orgasms compared with the adolescent male. With age the man's refractory period becomes longer. By the age of 50, he is typically satisfied with two orgasms a week, and the focus of his sexuality is not so completely genital; sex becomes a more sensuously diffuse experience and has a greater emotional component.

In women, the process is often quite different. Their sexual awakening may occur much later; they may, for example, not begin masturbating until age 30 or 35. While they are in their teens and twenties, their orgasmic response often is slow and inconsistent. However, by the time they reach their mid-thirties, their sexual response has become quicker and more intense, and they orgasm more consistently than during their teens and twenties. They initiate sex more frequently than they did in the past. Also, the greatest incidence of extradyadic sex for women occurs among those in their late thirties. Vaginal lubrication takes place almost instantaneously in women in this age group.

Men, then, seem to begin with an intense, genitally focused sexuality and only later develop an appreciation for the sensuous and emotional aspects of sex. Women have an early awareness of the sensuous and emotional aspects of sex and develop the capacity for intense genital response later. To express this in another way, we might use the terminology suggested by Ira Reiss: **person-centred sex** and **body-centred sex.** Adolescent male sexuality is body-centred, and the person-centred aspect is not added until later. Adolescent female sexuality is person-centred, and body-centred sex comes later.

It is important to remember, though, that these patterns may be culturally, rather than biologically, produced. In some other cultures—for example, Mangaia in the South Pacific (see Chapter 1)—females have orgasms 100 percent of the time during coitus, even when they are adolescents.

■ Transgender

Most people experience their gender identity—that is, their internal sense of femaleness or maleness—as the same as or consistent with their physical sex. However, some individuals experience incongruity between their physical sex and their internal sense of gender. In the medical literature, such a person is described as having **gender dysphoria**. Keeping in mind the distinction between sex and gender, it is important to understand that this is an issue not of sexual behaviour but of gender and gender identity.

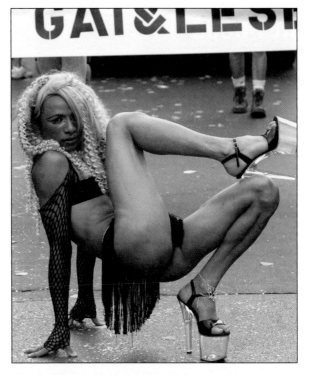

Figure 14.7 A transgender individual.

Transgender, or **trans**, is an all-inclusive term that refers to people who cross the strict lines of the sex they were assigned at birth. It is used to describe a number of different groups of people, including:

- Two-spirit persons: A term used by some Aboriginal people to describe people with alternative gender and sex expressions (discussed earlier in this chapter).
- Intersex persons: Persons born with mixed indicators of biological sex (discussed in Chapter 5).
- Individuals who **cross dress**—that is, dress in clothing traditionally associated with the other sex. They may cross dress for performance reasons (drag queens and drag kings; discussed in Chapter 15), for sexual pleasure (transvestites; discussed in Chapter 16), or simply to express a

---

Person-centred sex: Sexual expression in which the emphasis is on the relationship and emotions between the two people.

Body-centred sex: Sexual expression in which the emphasis is on the body and physical pleasure.

Gender dysphoria (dis-FOR-ee-uh): Unhappiness with one's gender.

Transgender: A category including transsexuals (those who think of themselves as a third gender), transvestites, gender benders, and others.

Cross-dressing: Dressing in the stereotypic clothing of the other gender.

In Focus 14.1

Male Sexuality

Bernie Zilbergeld wrote Male Sexuality, published in 1978, on the basis of his experience as a sex therapist and psychotherapist. The book was much respected and had a large readership over more than a decade. In 1999 Zilbergeld wrote an updated version, *The New Male Sexuality*, to reflect trends in the 1990s, including the release of Viagra.

He argues that the media have taught us a Fantasy Model of Sex, which is ultimately detrimental to men, and to women as well. He captures this idea in his chapter title "It's Two Feet Long, Hard as Steel, Always Ready, and Will Knock Your Socks Off," describing the Fantasy Model of the erect penis and its power over women. The Fantasy Model of Sex creates unrealistic expectations and performance pressures on men.

Zilbergeld discusses a number of cultural myths based on the Fantasy Model. Here are some of them.

Myth 1. We're liberated folks who are very comfortable with sex. The media teach us that we have completely shed our Victorian heritage and everyone is totally comfortable with sex. The men and women in the movies and on TV never have any concerns or problems with sex. The women don't worry about their ability to orgasm. The men don't worry about the size or hardness of their penises. But if all this is true, why do we have such poor sex education in Canada? Why do parents have such difficulty talking about sex with their children? The truth is that, although public manifestations (like the movies) are very open about sex, in our private lives we have all kinds of discomforts and uncertainties about sex.

Myth 2. A real man isn't into sissy stuff like feelings and communicating. Boys are trained into the male role, which discourages the expression of emotions such as tenderness. Communicating about personal feelings becomes difficult if not impossible. As one man said, "What it really comes down to is that I guess I'm not very comfortable with expressing my emotions—I don't think many men are—but I am pretty comfortable with sex, so I just sort of let sex speak for me" (Zilbergeld, 1999, p. 21). Men are crippled in forming emotional relationships, as a result, and sexual interactions are less satisfying than they might be if there were more communication.

Myth 3. All touching is sexual or should lead to sex. For men, touching is a means to an end: sex. For women, touch more often is a goal in itself, as when women hug each other. Men need to learn that sometimes they just need to be held or stroked, and that that can provide more emotional satisfaction than sexual intercourse.

Myth 6. Sex is centred on a hard penis and what's done with it. Adolescent boys have a fixation on their penis and its erections, and this fascination persists throughout life. It creates heavy performance pressure for an erection—and not just any old erection, but a really big one. As Zilbergeld puts it, "Penises in fantasyland come in only three sizes: large, extra large, and so big you can't get [it] through the door." Men need to learn that the penis is not the only sexual part of their bodies, and that many very enjoyable forms of sexual behaviour require no erection at all. That relieves a lot of performance pressure.

Zilbergeld's books are not based on a survey or laboratory research, but rather on his experiences as a sex therapist. His work with people having problems and seeking therapy may bias his views. But his observations are tremendously insightful, and many people not seeking therapy have benefited from his books.

Sources: Zilbergeld, 1978, 1999.

more masculine or feminine side. In fact, most women can identify situations in which they want to dress in more traditionally feminine clothes such as skirts and high heels, and situations in which they want to wear more traditionally masculine clothes, such as suits or jeans.

- People who present both masculine and feminine characteristics.
- **Transgenderists:** Individuals who live part or full time as a member of the other sex.
- **Transsexuals:** Individuals whose physical sex does not match their gender identity.

Many trans individuals describe experiencing an incongruity between their gender identity and their physical sex since early childhood. They may experience particular difficulty when they reach puberty, feeling "betrayed" by their developing body. Further, adolescents are increasingly expected to conform to the gender role expected of their assigned gender. Given the lack of role models, information, and social support, many gender-variant youth are likely to feel confused, isolated, and depressed. According to British Columbia sociologist Aaron Devor, recognizing and accepting oneself as transgender takes place over a number of years. He identified a series of stages in coming to terms with a new gender. In Stage 1, the individual experiences anxiety about their gender and sex, which leads them to question their assigned gender in Stage 2. In later stages, the individual changes genders and sexes—some by undergoing gender reassignment surgery, others through taking hormones or just living as the other gender—and comes to accept and experience themselves as the new gender.

Although many trans individuals regard their physical sex as opposite to their gender identity, others view the binary categories of female and male as restrictive, and see themselves as neither female nor male, both female and male, or another gender altogether (Hill, 2000). In fact, researchers have proposed several alternatives to our current two-gender system. For example, Eyler and Wright (1997) conceptualized gender as occurring along a nine-point continuum with female-based identities on one end, male-based identities on the other, and *bigendered identities* in the middle. They considered people whose feelings and behaviours alternated between male and female as having a bigendered identity. Further, trans activists and

authors such as Aaron Devor (1989), Leslie Feinberg (1996), and Kate Bornstein (1994) have called for the recognition of identities that transcend current gender boundaries, putting forward terms such as "gender outlaw" and "hir" (rather than his and her) and "ze" (rather than he or she) to draw attention to the need for language that is more inclusive of all genders. In fact, Devor coined the term *gender blender*. Other new terms have emerged, including *gender bender* and *gender free* (Bockting, 1999).

Among transsexuals, some choose to present in accordance with their gender identity in only some situations; for example, with a specific group of friends. Others may live in accordance with their gender identity without undergoing physical changes to make their body more in line with their gender. Many choose to alter their physical sex, a process known as sex change, or more recently *gender transition*, or just *transitioning* (discussed below). They may take hormones to bring their physical sex more into alignment with their gender identity. Further, some transsexuals pursue **gender reassignment**, in which their physical anatomy is surgically altered to reflect their gender identity. In the medical literature, individuals who do not pursue surgery are sometimes referred to as non-operative; those who are planning surgery are called pre-operative; and those who have had the surgery are described as post-operative.

We use the terms "male-to-female" and "female-to-male" to identify the direction of the transition and the identity that the transsexual has shown. Thus, those born with male bodies whose identity is female are called **male-to-female transsexuals, transwomen, or MtFs**; those born with female bodies whose gender identity is male are called **female-to-male transsexuals, transmen, or FtMs**.

Transgenderists: People who live part or full time as a member of the other sex.

Transsexual: A person whose physical sex does not match their gender identity.

Gender-reassignment: The surgery done on transsexuals to change their anatomy to match their gender identity.

Male-to-female transsexual (MtF): A person who is born with a male body but who has a female identity and wishes to undergo gender reassignment.

Female-to-male transsexual (FtM): A person born with a female body whose gender identity is male and who wishes to undergo gender reassignment.

In Focus 14.2

Matt: A Transman's Story

Matt is a 29-year-old man who lives in Ottawa. He describes himself as a "different kind of man," in that he was born and raised as a female.

Matt grew up in a small town in Southern Ontario. Unlike his sisters, Matt was not interested in being a Brownie or taking ballet. He had short hair and wore mainly T-shirts. He recalls feeling little pressure to behave like a girl until grades 7 and 8, when he started to feel a need to conform to what was expected of him. Matt remembers thinking that he looked better as a boy than a girl, yet knowing that he would need to change to fit in. He started wearing more feminine clothing and grew his hair. As a teenager, Matt knew he was not interested in boys, yet living in a small town he had no idea of what it meant to be gay.

At 20, Matt moved to Ottawa to attend university. He became involved in the queer community, and gradually began to change how he presented himself. He cut his hair, wore more masculine cloth-ing, and expressed himself in more masculine ways. He felt comfortable with this gender presen-tation. More and more often, Matt was perceived and responded to as male. He recalled that one year he had two jackets. When he wore one of them, he would be perceived as female; when he wore the other, he would be perceived as male. It felt like society was presenting the idea of transi-tioning to him.

The decision to transition was very difficult for Matt. On the one hand, he did not find being a woman aversive, and was concerned about the social consequences of not conforming to his bio-logical gender and the physical consequences of taking testosterone. On the other hand, Matt felt more comfortable presenting as male. There was also the matter of how others responded to his gen-der presentation. Most often, people would initially perceive him as male, but then—often after noticing that Matt had breasts—see him as female. Some

References to transgender individuals are found in much of recorded history, although of course they are not referred to by this term (Devor, 1997). For example, in the early centuries of Christianity, a number of women presented and lived as men. One example is Pelagia, a woman who declined marriage and, presenting as a man, entered a monastery. Pelagia become Pelagius, a man, and was later elected prior of a convent. A woman at the convent became pregnant and accused Pelagius of being the father. Of course this was not possible; however, Pelagius was not in a position to offer his strongest defence. Consequently, he was expelled from the convent and died in disgrace. When he died, it was discovered that he had a female body. However, most of our current understanding of transsexual issues is based on research with MtF transsexuals. This is because they have been more likely than FtM transsexuals to seek sex reassign-ment surgery (Olsson & Moller, 2003). There may be several reasons for this. First, the surgery required to transform male into female genitalia is easier than the surgery required to transform female into male genitalia. Second, transmen often pass as men more readily than transwomen pass as women. Third, our society tends to be much more tolerant of women who cross-dress than men who cross-dress. As such, MtFs may be more strongly motivated to pursue surgery in order to live as their chosen gender. Accordingly, most of the discussion that follows focuses on MtFs.[4]

The Gender Reassignment Process

Gender reassignment, sometimes called *sex change* or, more recently, *gender transition*, is complex and

---

[4]In keeping with the preferences of transgender individuals to use pronouns consistent with their gender identities, we refer to MtF individuals as "her" or "she" and FtM individu-als as "him" or "he."

people were apologetic, which could be uncomfortable for Matt; others were hostile and, in many cases, verbally insulted him. He found public washrooms to be particularly difficult because of how others would respond to him. It was the fear for his physical safety and the stress associated with these daily interactions that prompted Matt to transition: "It took up so much energy not to conform to society's expectation that I present as one gender or the other. I had to choose."

At 25, Matt started taking testosterone. So that the changes would be gradual, he started on a low dose and slowly increased it. He grew facial hair and his voice deepened. Taking the testosterone enabled Matt to be more confident in his interactions with others. He did not have to be constantly vigilant about his personal safety or be concerned about how others would respond to him. Matt has since had a hysterectomy and a double mastectomy and now feels very happy with his body.

Matt feels like his family transitioned with him. Initially, they were concerned that he was transitioning only because he had been influenced by a

friend's example. They worried that he would have difficulty establishing a career, finding a long-term partner, and having a secure and happy future. However, when they recognized that Matt was becoming happier and healthier as he transitioned, they became less concerned. Matt feels his relationship with his parents is much closer than before he transitioned because they have become much more open with each other.

At present, Matt is completing the last year of an accounting diploma. He is in a four-year relationship with a woman, in which he is very happy. He feels that because of his experiences he is much more critical of society's messages about gender and other social categories. He has also developed much closer relationships with others as a result of his personal experiences of discrimination. Matt regards being trans and his decision to alter his body as a function of societal pressure to act a certain way based on sex. He believes that we would all benefit from treating people in accordance with their personality, not their gender presentation.

Source: Based on an interview with Jacqueline Cohen.

proceeds in several stages (Bockting, 1997; Levine et al., 1998; Peterson & Dickey, 1995). Some members of the transsexual community refer to the process as *crossing*. Programs in Montreal and Toronto offer a range of services to transgender individuals. The first step is very careful counselling and psychological evaluation.

It is important to establish that the person is a true transsexual; that is, someone whose gender identity does not match her body type. Some people mistakenly seek sex reassignment; for example, a man who is simply poorly adjusted, unhappy, and not very successful might think that things would go better for him if he were a woman. It is important to establish that the person is a true transsexual or has a core transgender identity before going ahead with a procedure that is irreversible.

Next comes the "real life experience," which is the requirement that the person live as a member of the new gender for a period of one or two years. This is

done to ensure that the person will be able to adjust to the role of the new gender; once again, the idea is to be as certain as possible that the person will not regret having had the operation. Some transsexuals, even before consulting a physician, spontaneously enter this cross-dressing stage in their efforts to become women. Most transgender individuals encounter transphobia, sometimes to the point of violence (Monro, 2000; Lombard et al., 2001).

The next step is hormone therapy. The male-to-female transsexual is given estrogen and must remain on it for the rest of her life. The estrogen gradually produces some feminization. The breasts enlarge. The pattern of fat deposits becomes feminine; in particular, the hips become rounded. Balding, if it has begun, stops. Secretions by the prostate diminish, and eventually there is no ejaculate. Erections become less and less frequent, a phenomenon that pleases the transsexual, since they were an unpleasant reminder of the unwanted penis. The

(a)   *(b)*

Figure 14.8   (a) The appearance of the genitals following male-to-female transsexual surgery. (b) Breast augmentation for the MtF transsexual. Photos courtesy of Dr. Daniel Greenwald.

female-to-male transsexual is given androgens, which bring about a gradual masculinization. A beard may then develop, to varying degrees. The voice deepens. The pattern of fat deposits becomes more masculine. The clitoris enlarges, although not nearly to the size of a penis, and becomes more erectile. The pelvic bone structure cannot be reshaped, and breasts do not disappear except with surgery.

The final step for many people seeking gender reassignment is the surgery itself, which some transgender individuals decide to skip. For the male-to-female transsexual, the penis and testes are removed, but without severing the sensory nerves of the penis. The external genitalia are then reconstructed to look as much as possible like a woman's (see Figure 14.8). The glans of the penis is used to form a clitoris with sexual sensitivity. Next, an artificial vagina—a pouch 15 to 20 centimetres (6 to 8 inches) deep—is constructed. It is lined with the skin of the penis. For about six months afterward, the vagina must be dilated with a plastic device so that it does not reclose. Other cosmetic surgery may also be done, such as reducing the size of the Adam's apple.

The female-to-male change is more complex and generally less successful. In one procedure, a penis and scrotum are constructed from tissues in the genital area and the forearm (see Figure 14.9). The new penis does not have erectile capacity; in some cases a rigid silicone tube is implanted in the penis so that it can be inserted into a vagina, making coitus possi-

ble. Some female-to-male transsexuals choose not to have genital surgery and just go through breast removal and possibly hysterectomy.

An important experience for transgender individual is *passing* (Bockting, 1999). For a MtF, this might mean going into a bank dressed as a woman and having no one notice anything unusual, simply believing she is a woman.

It is important to note that transsexualism as a diagnosis and the means of treating it (hormones and sex-reassignment surgery) are products of modern Western culture. As discussed earlier, some other societies simply consider these individuals to be members of a third gender, and they live comfortably in that category. Examples are the two-spirit people among Native North Americans and the Hijras of India (Jacobs et al., 1997; Nanda, 1997).

What Causes Transsexualism?

Scientists have not found a definite cause of transsexualism. One likely reason is that there may be more than one path to it. As usual, both biological and environmental theories have been proposed.

On the biological side, John Money (1986) has argued that the issue is a critical period during prenatal development. Some event, not yet known, may lead to atypical development of some brain structure—possibly the hypothalamus, corpus callosum, or anterior commissure (Devor, 1997). Other theorists, following this same line of think-

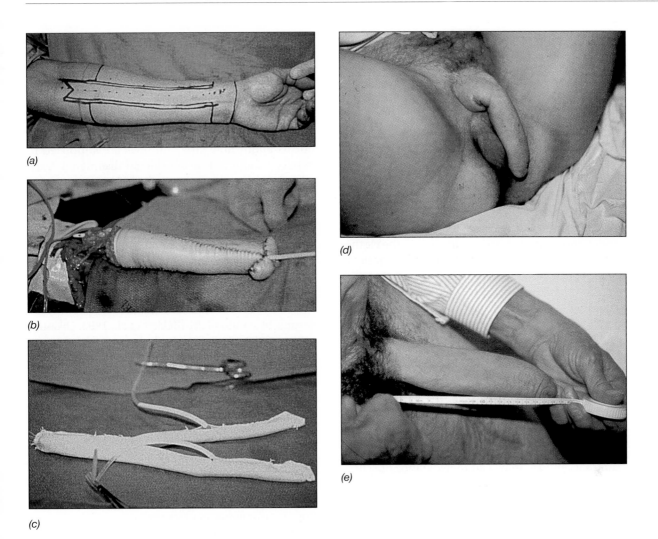

Figure 14.9 Female-to-male transsexual surgery. *(a)* Skin on the forearm marked before transfer to the groin. *(b)* The penis is constructed (blood vessels and nerves shown on the left). *(c)* An inflatable prosthesis, wrapped in Goretex and ready for insertion. *(d)* Penis before insertion of the implant. *(e)* Erect penis. Photos courtesy of Dr. Daniel Greenwald.

ing, have proposed that during prenatal development, the fetus, if it is to become a male, must be both defeminized and masculinized (Pillard & Weinrich, 1987). A failure of either process could produce a person with a male body but a female identity. To understand this distinction between defeminization and masculinization, at least for anatomy, recall from Chapter 5 that in a normally developing male the Müllerian ducts degenerate (defeminization) and the Wolffian ducts thrive (masculinization). If some process failed, though, both might thrive. The same might be true of cells in other brain regions having to do with gender identity. Consistent with this view, two studies have found differ-

ences between MtFs and typical men in the bed nucleus of the *stria terminalis* (BST), part of the limbic system (Kruijver et al., 2000; Zhou et al., 1995). As noted in other chapters, the limbic system is important in sexuality. Also in keeping with biological theories, an Ontario study found that the appearance of boys with gender identity disorder is less masculine and rugged whereas girls with gender identity disorder appear more masculine and rugged than their same-gender peers (McDermid et al., 1998).

On the environmental side, researchers have studied children with gender identity disorders, which might be a forerunner of either homosexuality or transgenderism. Noted sex researcher Richard

Green (1987) concluded that the parents of these children basically treat them as if they were of the opposite gender; for example, dressing boys in girls' clothing and then telling them how cute they look or encouraging girls to engage in rough and tumble play. Clinicians do report instances in which parents of children with gender identity disorder engage in these behaviours. However, not all parents do so (Zucker & Green, 1993).

Gender variation is found in children as young as 2 or 3 years of age. For example, research by Ontario psychologist Kenneth Zucker (1999, 2000, 2002) indicates that some children insist that they are the other gender, show a preference for dressing in the clothes of the other gender, demonstrate an intense desire to participate in the stereotypical play of the other gender, and express dislike for their sexual anatomy. According to the *Diagnostic and Statistical Manual of Mental Disorders*, a diagnostic manual put forward by the American Psychiatric Association (1994), children who express a strong and persistent cross-gender identification as well as discomfort with their own biological sex or gender role have **gender identity disorder (GID)**. This diagnostic category has been very controversial. On the one hand, proponents of the diagnosis argue that cross-gender behaviour will result in social isolation and ostracism that, in turn, may lead to avoidance of school and participation in activities with peers, and may lead to depression, substance abuse, and suicide. Indeed, such advocates present a strong argument to intervene to help the child become more comfortable with his or her biological sex. On the other hand, there are a number of problems with the GID diagnosis. First, longitudinal studies suggest that most children who are diagnosed with GID do not persist in identifying as the opposite to their biological sex in adulthood; rather, many children with GID identify as gay or lesbian in adulthood (Zucker, 2000, 2002). In fact, as discussed in Chapter 15, many gays and lesbians recall engaging in cross-gender behaviours as children. Thus, these behaviours may be part of a normal developmental pathway for gays and lesbians. Second, Canadian psychologist Nancy Bartlett and her colleagues have pointed out that even though the diagnosis of GID is intended for children who experience strong discomfort with

their biological sex, it may also be misused to diagnose children who are dissatisfied with their gender role (Bartlett et al., 2000). As such, it may be more appropriate to regard such children as simply not fitting into the two gender categories prescribed by Canadian culture rather than seeing them as having a disorder. That is, behaviour that violates cultural norms about how girls and boys are supposed to behave should not be considered disordered. Such advocates argue that what is needed is not treatment for the children so much as support groups for the parents to help them accept and provide supportive guidance to their gender-variant children. Clearly both sides are concerned with the welfare of the child. The key question appears to be whether the child benefits from a diagnosis of and treatment for GID.

MtF transsexuals account for the greatest majority of cases seen in clinics, outnumbering FtM transsexuals by a ratio of 2:1 (Bakker et al., 1993; Ollson & Möller, 2003). This may be because male prenatal development is more complex and error-prone, or because preschool boys spend so much more time with their mothers than with their fathers. Alternatively, as about half of gender dysphoric females do not make use of official gender clinics, the numbers may in reality be more equal (Devor, 1996, 1997).

Other Issues

The phenomenon of transsexualism raises a number of interesting psychological, legal, and ethical questions for our contemporary society.

One case that attracted attention was that of Dr. Renée Richards, formerly Richard Raskind, a physician who had her gender reassigned to that of a woman. When she was a man, she was a successful tennis player. In 1976 she attempted to enter a women's tennis tournament. The women players protested that she was not a woman, and she protested that she was. Officials subsequently decided to use the **buccal smear** test for gender, which is also the one used in the Olympics, and is a test of genetic gender. Richards protested that this was not the appropriate test to be used on her. Psychologically she is a female, she has female genitals, and she functions socially as a female, and she feels that these are the appropriate criteria. She does, though, have a

---

Gender identity disorder (GID): A strong and persistent cross-gender identification.

Buccal smear: A test of genetic sex, in which a small scraping of cells is taken from the inside of the mouth, stained, and examined under a microscope.

(a)   *(b)*

Figure 14.10   *(a)* Brandon Teena in the film *Boys Don't Cry*, the true story of a female-to-male transsexual who was murdered because of the ignorance and prejudice of those around him; *(b)* the real Brandon Teena.

male pelvic bone structure and other bone structures that are masculine, and these may have important consequences for athletic performance. The important question raised by this case is: What should the criteria be for determining a person's gender? Should it be chromosomal gender (XX or XY) as tested by the buccal smear? Should it be the gender indicated by the external genitals? Should it be psychological gender identity? In 2000, the International Olympic Committee suspended its use of gender verification for female athletes (Genel, 2000). It seemed not to be accomplishing anything except to embarass some women who turned out to have genetic anomalies.

Another question that might be raised concerns institutions that are all male or all female. In 1999, a MtF transsexual who was receiving hormone therapy at the time of her conviction for murder was given permission by Correctional Services Canada to undergo sex-change surgery and be transferred to a women's prison. Similarly, in 2000 a member of the Canadian Armed Forces was probably the first soldier in the world to undergo a sex-change operation while continuing to serve in the military.

The transsexual also encounters a number of practical problems when undergoing gender reassignment. Official records, such as the social insurance card and birth certificate, must be changed to show not only the new name but also the new gender. In the past, if the person was married before the sex change, the spouse usually must be divorced (Steiner, 1990).

Transsexuals are able to give us, through their personal accounts, new insights into the nature of sex and gender.

Criticisms of Sex-Reassignment Surgery

A number of criticisms of sex-reassignment surgery for transsexuals have been raised. One of these came from a study by Johns Hopkins researcher Jon Meyer (1979). He did a follow-up study of the adjustment of 50 transsexuals, 29 who received surgery and 21 who did not. His conclusion, much publicized, was that there were no significant differences in the adjustment of the two groups. If that is the case, he claimed, then sex-reassignment surgery is unnecessary and should not be done.

Then criticisms of Meyer's study appeared (e.g., Fleming et al., 1980). Meyer's adjustment scale was somewhat peculiar and involved debatable values. After the Meyer study and the criticisms of it, some clinics ceased doing sex-reassignment surgery, but most continue to do it. One study found that 86 percent of people who have sex reassignment surgery are satisfied with the outcome of their surgery (Lief & Hubschman, 1993). In another study of 232 MtFs, none expressed regret at having had the surgery (Lawrence, 2003). Further, according to recent research, the adjustment of transgender individuals—such as reduction in depression—is significantly better following surgery (Abramowitz, 1986; Bodlund & Kullgren, 1996; Green & Fleming, 1990). Further, Ontario psychologist Ray Blanchard has shown that gender reorientation results in greater involvement in love relationships and reduced emotional distress for both FtMs and MtFs (Blanchard et al., 1983; 1985). However, as society becomes increasingly aware of and accepting of the

Figure 14.11   Thailand has a booming medical tourism industry featuring male-to-female gender reassignment surgery.

range of gender presentations, we may see fewer people pursuing interventions such as SRS in order to fit into one of two discrete gender categories.

■ ■ ■ SUMMARY

A gender role is a set of norms, or culturally defined expectations, that specify how people of one gender ought to behave. Children are socialized into gender roles first by parents and later by other forces such as peers and the media.

Gender roles are not uniform in Canada. They vary according to ethnic group and other factors. Gender roles in ethnocultural communities such as the Chinese, South Asian, and Caribbean communities tend to reflect the traditional values of the country of origin. Although most Aboriginal people have adopted gender roles similar to those of the majority Canadian culture, some Aboriginal people traditionally had more egalitarian gender roles in comparison with European culture.

The traditional sexual script specifies how males and females are expected to behave in sexual situations. Research suggests that male and female roles in sexual situations differ in some respects but are converging.

Psychological gender differences have been documented in aggressiveness and communication styles.

The two largest male–female differences in sexuality are in the incidence of masturbation (males having the higher incidence) and attitudes toward casual sex (females being more disapproving). Heiman's study of arousal to erotic materials illustrates how males and females are in some ways similar and in others different in their responses. Males are more consistent at having orgasms, especially during heterosexual intercourse, than females are.

Three sets of factors have been proposed to explain gender differences in sexuality: biological factors (anatomy, hormones); cultural factors (gender roles, the double standard); and other factors (fear of pregnancy, differences in masturbation patterns creating other gender differences).

Most research on gender and sexuality has been done with university-age samples. There is reason to believe that patterns of gender differences in sexuality change in middle age and beyond.

Transsexuals represent an interesting variation in which gender identity does not match anatomy. Generally, their adjustment is good following the gender reassignment. Transgender is a broader category including those who do not seek surgery or who see themselves as being in a third gender category.

■ ■ ■ QUESTIONS FOR THOUGHT, DISCUSSION, AND DEBATE

1. Do you think that transsexual surgery is the appropriate treatment for transsexuals? Why or why not?

2. Recalling from your childhood, do you think you were socialized in a stereotyped masculine or feminine way? What impact do you think those socialization experiences have had on your current sexual attitudes and behaviours?

3. Do you think there is still a double standard for male and female sexuality today? Explain your answer.

4. Dominic is a strong advocate of equality between men and women, yet his 6-year-old daughter's favourite television program shows both the parents and the children in very stereotyped roles. The mother is a secretary and the father is a physician. The teenage daughter is a cheerleader and thinks of nothing else, while the son plays football. What should Dominic do? Why?

■ ■ ■ SUGGESTIONS FOR FURTHER READING

Devor, Holly (1997). *FTM: Female-to-male transsexuals in society.* Bloomington: Indiana University Press. FtMs are the understudied group of transsexuals, and Devor's book fills the gap in an exceptional and fascinating way.

Howey, Noelle (2002). *Dresscodes: Of three girlhoods—my mother's, my father's, and mine*. New York: Picador USA. This is Howey's extraordinary memoir about growing up with a father who proved to be a male-to-female transsexual.

Hyde, Janet S. (2004). *Half the human experience: The psychology of women* (6th ed.). Boston, MA: Houghton Mifflin. We are not in a very good position to give an objective appraisal of this book, but for what it's worth we think it is an interesting, comprehensive summary of what is known about the psychology of women and gender roles.

Zilbergeld, Bernie. (1999). *The new male sexuality* (Revised Edition). New York: Bantam Books. Zilbergeld's original *Male Sexuality* was a great success, and this updated version is every bit as insightful.

For Review Questions, Web Resources, and other learning and study tools, visit the *Understanding Human Sexuality* Online Learning Centre at www.mcgrawhill.ca/college/hyde.

CHAPTER 15

Sexual Orientation: Gay, Lesbian, Bi, or Straight?

CHAPTER HIGHLIGHTS

> The state has no business in the bedrooms of the nation.*
>
> Jeffrey and I met when he responded to an online message I posted, seeking gay teenagers willing to discuss their online lives…. He made it clear that he could allow no overlap between his online gay life and the life he led in the "real world." … He feared that if word of his sexual orientation were to reach his parents, they might refuse to support him or pay for college. From his peers at school he dreaded violence.**

Every summer, cities across North America hold a Gay Pride Day, usually including a parade. This is to commemorate the first time that gay, lesbian, and transgender individuals openly fought back against police harassment; this occurred in June 1969 in The Stonewall, a gay bar in New York City's Greenwich Village. Gay liberation was born. The first gay liberation group in Canada was formed in Vancouver in 1970 (Kinsman, 1996). Eight months later, 200 protesters on Parliament Hill demanded equal rights for gays and lesbians (Smith, 1999). In 1981, 3,000 people rallied in Toronto to protest the arrest of 300 men during police raids on gay bath houses (Kinsman, 1996).

The purpose of this chapter is to try to provide a better understanding of people's sexual orientations, whether homosexual, heterosexual, or bisexual. First, though, several concepts need to be clarified. A distinction has already been made between sex (sexual behavior) and gender (being male or female)[1] and between gender identity (the psychological sense of maleness or femaleness) and sexual orientation (heterosexual, homosexual, or bisexual). To this, the concept of **sexual identity** should be added; this refers to one's self-label or self-identification as heterosexual, gay, lesbian, or bisexual.

There may be contradictions between people's sexual identity (which is subjective) and their actual choice of sexual partners viewed objectively (Math-

ieson & Enicott, 1998). For example, a woman might identify herself as a lesbian yet occasionally have sex with men. Objectively, her choice of sexual partners is bisexual, but her identity is lesbian. More common are persons who think of themselves as heterosexuals but who engage in sex with both male and female partners. A good example of this is the tearoom trade discussed later—the successful, heterosexually married men in gray flannel suits who occasionally stop off at a public rest room to have another male perform fellatio on them. Once again, the behavior is objectively bisexual, in contradiction to the heterosexual identity. Another example is the group of women who claim to have bisexual identities but who have experienced only heterosexual sex. These women claim bisexuality as an ideal they are capable of attaining at some later time. Once again, identity contradicts behaviour.

Given these contradictions, **sexual orientation** is best defined by whom we are sexually attracted to and also have the potential for loving. Thus a **homosexual** is a person whose sexual orientation is toward members of her or his own gender; a **heterosexual** is a person whose sexual orientation is toward members of the other gender; and a **bisexual** is a person whose sexual orientation is

---

*Pierre Trudeau, 1967, when defending his bill to overhaul the Criminal Code of Canada, including statutes that had criminalized consensual homosexual acts.

**Jennifer Egan. (2000). Lonely gay teen seeking same. *The New York Times Magazine*, December 10, 2000, p. 113.

[1]As discussed in Chapter 14, these two gender categories do not fit for some people who would identify as trans.

Sexual identity: One's self-identity as homosexual, heterosexual, or bisexual.
Sexual orientation: A person's erotic and emotional orientation toward members of his or her own gender or members of the other gender.
Homosexual: A person whose sexual orientation is toward members of the same gender.
Heterosexual: A person whose sexual orientation is toward members of the other gender.
Bisexual: A person whose sexual orientation is toward both men and women.

toward both genders. Again, however, a person's attraction may not match their behaviour and/or their sexual identity. The word "homosexual" is derived from the Greek root *homo*, meaning "same" (not the Latin word *homo*, meaning "man"). The term "homosexual" may be applied in a general way to homosexuals of both genders or specifically to male homosexuals. The term **lesbian,** which is used to refer to female homosexuals, can be traced to the great Greek poet Sappho, who lived on the island of Lesbos (hence "lesbian") around 600 B.C. She is famous for the love poetry that she wrote to other women.

However, use of the term "homosexual" to refer to lesbians and gay men is problematic for three main reasons (American Psychological Association, 1991). First, in the past it has been associated with negative stereotypes such as deviance, mental illness, and criminal behaviour, and thus can be used as a derogatory label. Second, it emphasizes sexual behaviour rather than sexual identity. As discussed later in this chapter, many women and men engage in same-sex behaviour, yet do not consider themselves to be lesbian, gay, or bisexual. Third, it is ambiguous because even though it is a general term, it has often been used to refer exclusively to gay men. For these reasons, it is preferable to use the terms *lesbians, gay men, bisexual women*, and *bisexual*. A heterosexual is then referred to as **straight**.

In recent years, some members of the gay, lesbian, and bisexual communities have reclaimed terms that have historically been used as derogatory terms against LGBs. Examples of such terms include "dyke," "fairy," "fag" or "faggot," and "queer." For example, the term "queer" has now been taken back by gay and lesbian activists and scholars, who use it as a proud term encompassing gays, lesbians, and transgender persons. As an umbrella term, it has the advantage of not forcing people to adopt a narrow societally defined label that may not reflect their experience or the fluidity of sexual identity (Bower et al., 2002). Queer theory is prominent in lesbian–gay–bisexual studies. However, although some people are comfortable

---

Lesbian: A woman whose sexual orientation is toward other women.
Straight: Heterosexual.

---

using these terms to refer to themselves, other people are not, perhaps because the terms have been used to belittle them in the past. Thus, while LGBs may use these terms themselves, it is probably not a good idea to impose these terms on them. (In this chapter, we will use the abbreviation "LGB" for lesbians, gays, and bisexuals, because it is awkward to repeat the phrase "gays and lesbians," and even that phrase omits bisexuals.)

■ How Many People Are Gay, Lesbian, Bi, or Straight?

Most people believe that homosexuality is rare. What percentages of people in North America are gay, lesbian, or bisexual? As it turns out, the answer to this question is complex. Basically, it depends on the definition we use.

One source of information we have on this question is Kinsey's research (see Chapter 3 for an evaluation of the Kinsey data). Kinsey found that about 37 percent of all males had had at least one same-sex experience to orgasm in adulthood. This is a large percentage. Indeed, it was this statistic, combined with some of the findings on premarital sex, that led to the furor over the Kinsey report. The comparable figure for females was 13 percent. However, experts agree that, because of problems with sampling, Kinsey's statistics on same-sex experiences were probably inflated (Pomeroy, 1972).

Today, several well-sampled surveys in Canada, the U.S., the U.K., and France have given us improved estimates. Data from the NHSLS (discussed in Chapter 3) and the Canadian Community Health Survey (CCHS) are shown in Table 15.1. The 2003 CCHS surveyed adults aged 18 to 59 and was the first Statistics Canada survey to include a question on sexual orientation. It asked respondents to indicate whether they considered themselves to be homosexual, bisexual, or heterosexual; that is, it assessed sexual identity. Of the men surveyed, 1.3 percent considered themselves to be homosexual; 0.6 percent to be bisexual. Of the women surveyed, 0.7 percent self-identified as homosexual; 0.9 percent as bisexual. These data are similar to the sexual identity question in the NHSLS (Laumann et al., 1994).

The statistics from the NHSLS are more complex,

Table 15.1 The NHSLS and CCHS Statistics on Same-Gender Sex, Identity, and Attraction

	NHSLS		CCHS	
	Men	*Women*	*Men*	*Women*
Partners				
Same-gender partners only, last year	2.0%	1.0%		
Both male and female partners, last year	0.7	0.3		
Same-gender partners only, since age 18	0.9	0.4		
Both male and female partners, since age 18	4.0	3.7		
Sexual Identity				
Heterosexual	96.9	98.6	97.1	98.4
Bisexual	0.8	0.5	0.6	0.9
Homosexual	2.0	0.9	1.3	0.7
Sexual Attraction				
Only opposite gender	93.8	95.6		
Mostly opposite gender	2.6	2.7		
Both	0.6	0.8		
Mostly same gender	0.7	0.6		
Only same gender	2.4	0.3		

Sources: Edward O. Laumann et al. (1994), *The Social Organization of Sexuality: Sexual Practices in the United States.* Reprinted by permission of the University of Chicago Press and Edward O. Laumann; Statistics Canada, 2004.

because the survey asked several questions about sexual orientation and much depends on how *gay, lesbian,* and *bisexual* are defined. Should the definition be based on self-identification alone or also on behaviour? In terms of behaviour, does the definition of gay or lesbian require someone to have had exclusively same-gender sexual experiences, or just some same-gender experiences, or perhaps just to have experienced sexual attraction to members of his or her own gender without ever acting upon it? We will return to this point. What we can say here is that, according to the NHSLS, about 2 percent of men and 1 percent of women are exclusively homosexual in their sexual behavior and in their identity. About 4 percent of both men and women have had at least one same-gender sexual experience in adulthood, and about 4 percent of men and 2 percent of women have experienced sexual attraction to members of their own gender.

These percentages are considerably smaller than Kinsey's. What accounts for the difference? The NHSLS was better sampled; it is generally agreed that Kinsey's unsystematic sampling methods led to overestimates of the incidence of homosexuality. But the NHSLS may not be perfectly accurate, either. The data were collected using face-to-face interviews that may have created problems of concealment, particularly when the questions were about a socially disapproved behaviour such as homosexuality. Therefore, the NHSLS statistics are best seen as minimum estimates.

The NHSLS statistics are comparable to those found in a well-sampled international survey. The results indicated that 6.2, 4.5, and 10.7 percent of males in the United States, United Kingdom, and France, respectively, had engaged in sexual behavior with someone of their own gender in the last five years (Sell et al., 1995). The comparable statistics for women were 3.6, 2.1, and 3.3 percent. These and other surveys confirm that the incidence of same-sex sexual activity among men is higher than the incidence among women. Probably twice as many men as women have a same-sex experience to orgasm in adulthood, and the same ratio is probably true for exclusive homosexuality. What about youth? The CYSHHA survey asked grade 7, 9, and 11 students whether they were attracted to males, attracted to both males and females, or attracted to no one. Somewhat fewer than 3 percent indicated that they are attracted to members of their own gender. Interestingly, 9 percent of grade 7 students but fewer

Figure 15.1   Three ways of conceptualizing homosexuality and heterosexuality.

than 2 percent of grade 9 and 11 students said they were attracted to no one.

After reading these statistics, though, you may still be left wondering how many people are gay, lesbian, and bisexual. As Kinsey soon realized in trying to answer this question, it depends on how you count. A prevalent notion is that like black and white, homosexual and heterosexual are two quite separate and distinct categories. This is what might be called a *typological conceptualization* (see Figure 15.1). Kinsey made an important scientific breakthrough when he decided to conceptualize opposite-sex and same-sex not as two separate categories but rather as variations on a continuum (Figure 15.1, section 2). The black and white extremes of heterosexuality and homosexuality have a lot of shades of gray in between: people who have had both some opposite-sex and some same-sex experience, in various mixtures. To accommodate all this variety, Kinsey constructed a scale running from 0 (exclusively heterosexual) to 6 (exclusively homosexual), with the midpoint of 3 indicating equal amounts of heterosexual and homosexual experience.

Many sex researchers continue to use Kinsey's scale today, but the question remains, When is a person a homosexual? If you have had one same-sex experience, does that make you gay or lesbian, or do you have to have had substantial same-sex experience (say, a rating of 2 or 3 or higher)? Or do you have to have exclusively same-sex experience to be a homosexual? Kinsey dealt with this problem in part by devising this scale, but he also made another important point. He argued that we should not talk about *homosexuality* but rather about *homosexual behaviour.* *Homosexuality,* as we have seen, is exceedingly difficult to define. *Homosexual behaviour,* on the other hand, can be scientifically defined as a sexual act between two people of the same gender. Therefore, we can talk more precisely about people who have engaged in varying amounts of same-sex behaviour or who have had varying amounts of same-sex experience.

Other theorists have suggested that Kinsey's one-dimensional scale is too simple (Sell, 1997; Storms, 1980). The alternative is to form a two-dimensional scheme. The idea here is to have one scale for heteroeroticism (the extent of one's arousal to members of the opposite gender), ranging from low to high, and another for homoeroticism (the extent of arousal to members of one's own gender), ranging from low to high (see Figure 15.1, section 3). Thus if one is high on both

Table 15.2	Attitudes of Adult Canadians toward Homosexuality		
		Percentage of Sample	
Questions and Responses		2000	2002–2004
Percentage who answered "Yes" to the following questions			
Homosexuality is immoral			32
Should homosexuals have equal rights in terms of job opportunities?		92	
Should homosexual couples receive the same tax and employment benefits as heterosexual married couples?		61	
Should homosexuals be allowed to adopt children?		38	46
Do you favour same-sex marriages?		43	53

Sources: Gallup Canada Inc. 2000, 2004; Leger Marketing, 2002.

heteroeroticism and homoeroticism, one is a bisexual; the person high on heteroeroticism and low on homoeroticism is heterosexual; the person high on homoeroticism and low on heteroeroticism is homosexual; and the person low on both scales is asexual. According to a large British study, 1 percent of people report that they have no sexual attraction to men or women (Bogdert, 2004). This scheme allows even more complexity in describing homosexuality and heterosexuality than Kinsey's scale does.

The answer to the original question—How many people are gay, lesbian, and bisexual?—is complex. Probably about 92 percent of men and 95 percent of women are exclusively heterosexual. About 7 to 8 percent of men and 4 to 5 percent of women have had at least one same-gender sexual experience in adulthood. However, fewer than 1 percent claim a bisexual identity. About 2 percent of men and 1 percent of women are exclusively homosexual and/or identify themselves as homosexual. These figures are based on the NHSLS, but adjusted somewhat to allow for concealment by some respondents.

One other statistic that has been popularly cited for decades for the incidence of homosexuality is 10 percent. In fact, one gay and lesbian organization is called the Ten Percent Society. This statistic comes from no single study but rather from an amalgamation of many. It represents the people whose orientation is predominantly homosexual, although they may have had some heterosexual experience. In view of the most recent surveys, the 10 percent figure may be a bit high.

■ Attitudes

Your sexual orientation has implications for the attitudes people have toward you. First, in Canadian culture there is the belief that all people are heterosexual, that heterosexuality is the norm. Furthermore, just as there are stereotypes about other minority groups, there are stereotypes (usually negative) about gays and lesbians. These stereotypes and negative attitudes lead to discrimination and hate crimes against gays and lesbians. In this section we will examine some of the scientific data on these negative attitudes.

Attitudes Toward Gays and Lesbians

Some Canadians disapprove of homosexuality. For example, as shown in Table 15.2, 32.1 percent of Canadians indicated that homosexuality constitutes immoral behaviour. Further, almost all Canadians (92 percent) are in favour of equal rights for gays and lesbians. However, Canadians are more divided on same-sex marriage (53 percent are in favour) and adoption by same-sex couples (46 percent are in favour). Note that Canadians have become more accepting in their attitudes in the last 30 years. For example, in 1995 only 34 percent were in favour of same-sex[2] mar-

---

[2]To be consistent with the definitions of "gender" and "sex" adopted in this book, we should use the terms "same-gender" or "other-gender" when describing sexual behaviour or relationships. However, we have used the term "same-sex" because it is the term most people use—for example, there has been considerable public debate about same-sex marriage.

riage and adoption by same-sex couples. Younger Canadians, those with more education, and those living in Quebec and B.C. are more accepting of homosexuality.

Homophobia may be defined as a strong, irrational fear of homosexuals and, more generally, as fixed negative attitudes and reactions to homosexuals. Some scholars dislike the term "homophobia" because, although certainly some people have anti-gay feelings so strong that they could be called a phobia, what is more common is negative attitudes and prejudiced behaviours. Therefore, some prefer the term **homonegativity**, anti-gay prejudice, sexual prejudice, heterosexism, or heterocentrism (Herek, 2000; Morrison & Morrison, 1999). Another related term is **heterosexism**, the belief that everyone is heterosexual and that heterosexuality is the norm; homosexual people and behaviours are denigrated (Berkeman & Zinberg, 1997).

Homonegativity and heterosexism can have serious emotional consequences for LGB individuals. This may be a particular problem for adolescents establishing their sexual identity. Overt acts of anti-gay prejudice, as well as more subtle negative messages such as those contained in anti-gay humour, can cause significant pain and suffering. Some—but not all—lesbian, gay, and bisexual youth adopt the negative attitudes they see around them, called internalized homonegativity, and this may make it difficult for them to accept their sexual orientation. Cultural homonegativity as well as internalized homonegativity may also affect some LGB individuals' self-esteem. In some cases, LGB youth so devalue their self-worth that they contemplate or attempt suicide.

The most extreme expressions of anti-gay prejudice occur in *hate crimes* against LGBs. Perhaps the most horrifying recent case occurred in Wyoming (Loffred, 2000). Matthew Shepard, a University of Wyoming student, was found tied to a fence, savagely beaten and comatose. Two young men had led Shepard to believe that they, too, were gay and lured him from a bar to ride in their pickup truck, where they began beating him with a revolver. They later tied him to a fence, beat him more, and left him for dead. He died five days later. Similarly, in 2001, Aaron Webster, a prominent photographer and a gay man, was beaten to death in Vancouver by four males wielding baseball bats, a golf club, and a pool cue after they found him naked in an area widely known as a stroll for gay men looking for casual sex.

A survey of Canadian LGBs found high rates of violence (Faulkner, 1997). Seventy-eight percent had experienced verbal assaults, 21 percent had been physically assaulted, 21 percent reported harassment by the police, and 7 percent had been assaulted with a weapon. A study of LGBs in Vancouver found similar results; 74 percent had been verbally abused, 32 percent had been physically assaulted, and 9 percent had been physically and sexually assaulted (*Vancouver Sun*, 1995). LGB university students report a similar pattern of harassment on campus (D'Augelli, 1992). These studies show that hate crimes against and harassment of gays and lesbians are not rare, isolated incidents; instead, they are common, even on supposedly peaceful university campuses. Hate crimes are even more frequent in high schools (O'Conor, 1994; Comstock, 1991). These incidents exact a psychological toll. As one high school student said of verbal harassment, "It's not just name calling. I don't know how schools can isolate it like that. When are they going to see it as a problem? When we're bloody on the ground in front of them?" (Human Rights Watch, 2001).

In 1995, Parliament passed a hate crimes sentencing bill, which specifies longer sentences for hate-motivated crimes; that is, crimes motivated by hate, bias, and prejudice against specific groups. The list of unacceptable hate crimes includes those committed against gays and lesbians. In 2004, Parliament passed a private member's bill introduced by former MP Svend Robinson that bans hate propaganda that targets gays and lesbians. Although this is a step in the right direction of providing some legal protection to LGBs, it may seem like cold comfort to a person who has been the victim of such a crime. Further, police have some discretion in what charges are laid and do not always identify assaults against LGBs as motivated by hate.

Homophobia: A strong, irrational fear of homosexuals; negative attitudes and reactions to homosexuals.
Homonegativity: Negative attitudes and behaviours toward gays and lesbians. Sometimes called anti-gay prejudice or sexual prejudice.
Heterosexism: The belief that everyone is heterosexual and heterosexuality is the norm; homosexuality is denigrated.

Figure 15.2   Svend Robinson became the first openly gay member of Parliament, having come out publicly in 1988. As an MP he worked for gay and lesbian human rights. A Gallup poll conducted in 2000 indicated that 86 percent of Canadians approve of openly gay members of Parliament.

But we should also recognize the other side of the coin. As we can see from the statistics in Table 15.2, most Canadians are tolerant or supportive of LGB individuals. For example, 67 percent of Canadians approve of overt gay and lesbian teachers in middle school, and 86 percent approve of openly gay MPs. Thus while some Canadians are bigots on the issue of homosexuality, most Canadians are not. As one woman said,

> I really don't feel that I've ever been oppressed as a lesbian or suffered any abuse. I've been careful who I've told, but those people have been really accepting. (Jay & Young, 1979, p. 716)

Attitudes Toward Bisexuals

Bisexuals experience a different kind of stigma than do lesbians and gay men. If you are asked to imagine a lesbian or gay couple, you can likely come up with a mental image—two women kissing or two men holding hands or dancing together are easily recognizable as a lesbian or gay couple. Now what do you imagine when you are asked to think of a bisexual couple? The point is that we have few cultural images of bisexuality (Trynka & Tucker, 1995). As such, bisexuality is rarely even recognizable. A study of 22 self-identified bisexual Canadian women found that all participants felt that bisexuality was misunderstood by the straight, lesbian, and gay communities (Bower et al., 2002).

There are a great many negative stereotypes about bisexuals (Herek, 2002). Bisexuals are often thought of as internally conflicted or psychologically immature (Rust, 2000a). They are stereotyped as nonmonogamous, needing both same-sex and opposite-sex partners to satisfy both the "gay/lesbian" and "heterosexual" sides of their sexualities (Spalding & Peplau, 1997). In contrast, research has found that few bisexuals have both female and male partners at the same time (although some do), and bisexuals do not differ from lesbians and gay men in their relationship status and length (Balsam, 2004; Rust, 2000b). Further, few bisexuals report that they "need" both male and female partners to think of themselves as bisexual (Rust, 2001).

Similarly, bisexuals may be viewed with suspicion or downright hostility by the gay and lesbian communities (Bower et al., 2002; Mathieson & Endicott, 1998; Rust, 2002). Bisexual-identified women are often told they are "denying" their true identity, which must be lesbian or heterosexual. Young women who have sexual involvements with other women are often regarded as heterosexuals who are merely experimenting with women because lesbianism is chic (Rust, 2000a). Women who are involved in lesbian communities may be told they are really lesbians who have not yet realized it. Bisexuality is sometimes seen as "fence-sitting," a way to get the "best of both worlds" without having to commit to a particular identity. Some gays even argue that there is no such thing as a true bisexual (Rust, 2002).

In contrast, proponents of bisexuality argue that it has some strong advantages. It allows more variety in one's sexual and human relationships than does exclusive heterosexuality or exclusive homosexuality. The bisexual does not rule out any possibilities and is open to the widest variety of experiences.

Gays, Lesbians, and Bisexuals as a Minority Group

From the foregoing, it is clear that LGB people are the subject of many negative attitudes, just as other minorities are (Meyer, 2003). Like members of other minority groups, they also suffer from job discrimination even though this is illegal. Just as blacks, First Nations peoples, and women have been denied access to certain jobs, so too have homosexuals. Wage discrimination occurs as well. According to research in the U.S., gay men are more educated than straight men, but gay men earn less (Black et al., 2000). Researchers in Ontario assessed university students' attitudes toward English Canadians, French Canadians, Aboriginal peoples, and Pakistanis. Their attitudes were significantly more negative toward homosexuals than toward any of the other groups (Haddock et al., 1993).

Same-sex sexual activity used to be illegal in Canada. For example, in 1967 Everett Klippert was sent to prison as a "dangerous sex offender" after he told police that he had had sex with men over a 24-year period and was unlikely to change. However, consensual same-sex activity was decriminalized in 1969, when, under Prime Minister Pierre Trudeau, Parliament passed a bill introducing widespread changes to laws regulating sexual behaviour in the Criminal Code of Canada. Before 1969, "homosexual offences" included some out-dated and derogatory terms such as "buggery (anal intercourse), attempted buggery, indecent assault on a male by a male or female on a female, acts of gross indecency between men, procuring and attempting to procure acts of gross indecency between males..." (Lahey, 1999, p. 135). These changes to the Criminal Code were a turning point in the recognition and increasing acceptance of LGBs in Canada. However, at that time, the offence of anal intercourse was added to the Criminal Code. Anal sex is illegal only if it involves children or is not done in private. However, the age of consent for anal sex is 18, whereas the age of consent for vaginal intercourse is 14. Further, anal sex is deemed not to be done in private (and therefore illegal) if more than two persons are present. There is no similar provision for vaginal intercourse. This puts gay (and straight) youth who want to experiment sexually with anal intercourse (many gay males do not engage in anal intercourse) in a difficult situation. Thus, the Criminal Code still discriminates against homosexuals in this way. However, recent court rulings have suggested that the higher age of consent for anal intercourse violates the equality provisions of the Charter of Rights and Freedoms.

Activists also argue that there has been more vigorous enforcement of the bawdy-house and obscenity laws against LGBs and homosexual materials. For example, following the 1969 changes to the Criminal Code, police continued to lay "indecent act" and "bawdy-house" charges against men for engaging in consensual sex with other men. Nor were gay men and lesbians legally protected from discrimination (Kinsman, 1996). Before the Charter of Rights and Freedoms, virtually no human rights complaints by gays and lesbians were successful (Lahey, 1999; Smith, 1999). For example, prior to 1992, homosexuality was grounds for dishonourable release from the military (Gouliquer, 2000). In the early 1980s, men and women who were suspected of being gay or lesbian were investigated, interrogated, and sometimes released by the military. However, in 1992 Canadian Forces policy concerning sexual orientation was found to violate the Charter of Rights and Freedoms. LGBs can no longer be denied the right to join the military or serve in the military.

Recent decisions of the Supreme Court of Canada recognize that the equality rights guaranteed in the Canadian Charter of Rights and Freedoms include sexual orientation and that provincial human rights codes must recognize sexual orientation as a prohibited ground for discrimination. In 1996, Parliament amended the Human Rights Act to specifically prohibit discrimination based on sexual orientation (the Act already prohibited discrimination on the basis of other characteristics such as gender, race, and disability). The Act also bars "hate speech" against gays and lesbians. Eight provinces also have amended their human rights codes to prohibit discrimination on the basis of sexual orientation (Greer et al., 1997). This means, among other things, that gays and lesbians cannot be fired because of their sexual orientation, they cannot be refused housing, and they are entitled to adopt children. It also means that couples in same-sex (and other-sex) common-law relationships have the same rights and responsibilities as heterosexual married couples. In fact, Parliament recently passed the Modernization of Benefits and Obligations Act, which amended existing federal statutes to ensure that they apply equally to couples in same-sex and other-sex relationships. The majority of Canadians support such entitlement (refer to Table 15.2 on p. 423). In contrast, in the United States, gays and lesbians do not have legal protection against discrimination, and fewer Americans support equal rights for gays and lesbians. For example, 92 percent of Canadians compared to 84 percent of Americans feel that gays and lesbians should have equal rights in terms of job opportunities.

The most recent area in which gays and lesbians have attained equal rights is marriage. In 2003, courts in Ontario and Quebec were the first to legalize same-sex marriage, ruling that federal laws restricting marriage to one man and one woman violated the Charter of Rights and Freedoms. In 2004, courts in Quebec, Manitoba, Nova Scotia, Saskatchewan, Newfoundland and Labrador, and the Yukon made the same ruling. On June 28, 2005, the House of Commons passed a bill ensuring that marriage is a right for all Canadians regardless of sexual orientation so that all Canadians are treated as equal under the law; the bill was given royal assent and became law less than a month later, on July 20, 2005. Marriage is now defined as "the union of two people to the exclusion of all others." Canada is the fourth country in the world to legalize same-sex marriage.

Canadians are fairly evenly split in their attitudes toward same-sex marriages: A poll conducted in 2004 found that 53 percent are in favour of same-sex marriages (refer again to Table 15.2 on p. 423). Some Canadians oppose gay and lesbian marriages but believe that there should be a legalized relationship other than marriage that is recognized by the state. The attitudes of Canadians on same-sex marriage are similar to those of the British but more liberal than those of Americans. Only 35 percent of Americans are in favour of same-sex marriage, and 59 percent of Americans favour amending the U.S. constitution to ban same-sex marriages. Further, 63 percent of Canadians are in favour of civil unions for same-sex couples compared to 49 percent of Americans (Gallup, 2004).

Discrimination goes hand in hand with stereotypes. One such stereotype is that gay men are child molesters. As with many stereotypes, this one is false. Research shows that the vast majority of child abusers have a heterosexual orientation; only 2 to 3 percent are gay (Jenny et al., 1994).

There is an important way in which LGBs differ from other minorities, though. In the case of most other minorities, appearance is a fairly good indicator of minority-group status. It is easy to recognize a Chinese Canadian or a woman, for example, but one cannot tell simply by looking at a person what his or her sexual orientation is. Thus LGBs, unlike other minorities, can hide their status. There are certain advantages to this. It makes it fairly easy to

Figure 15.3   Michael Stark and Michael Leshner of Toronto. Together for more than 20 years, this couple was instrumental in getting Ontario courts to recognize same-sex marriage. The federal government legalized same-sex marriage in June 2005.

get along in the heterosexual world—to "pass." However, it has the disadvantage of encouraging the person to conceal her or his true identity to avoid homonegativity; this may be psychologically stressful (Meyer, 2003). A study of gay men (all of whom were uninfected with HIV) indicated that those who concealed their identity had a significantly higher incidence of cancer and infectious diseases than those who did not conceal their identity (Cole et al., 1996).

We shouldn't leave this discussion of discrimination and prejudice against LGBs without asking a crucial question (Rothblum & Bond, 1996): What can be done to prevent or end this prejudice? Change must occur at many levels: the individual, the interpersonal, and the organizational levels (e.g., corporations, educational institutions), as well as society as a whole and its institutions (e.g., the federal government). At the individual level, all of us must examine our own attitudes toward LGBs to see if they are consistent with basic values we hold, such as a commitment to equality and justice. Some people may need to educate themselves or attend anti-homonegativity workshops to examine their attitudes. These attitudes, though, were formed as we grew up, influenced by our parents, our peers, and the media. Parents must consider the messages they convey to their children about gays and lesbians. The adolescent peer group is strongly homophobic. What could be done to change it? How can the media change in order not to promote anti-gay prejudices and stereotypes? At the interpersonal level, people must recognize that LGBs are often a hidden minority. Eric, for example, just told a joke that ridiculed gay men. What he didn't know was that one of his three listeners, is gay—just not "out" with him (for obvious reasons). We must examine our interactions with other people, recognizing the extent to which many of us assume that everyone is heterosexual until proven otherwise. At the institutional level, how can education be changed in order to reduce anti-gay discrimination? A strong program of sex education across the grades, with open discussion of sexual orientation, would be a good start (see Chapter 21). In addition, gay–straight alliances can work to combat heterosexism and antigay prejudice in organizations. Such alliances have been established at many high schools and universities across Canada (including the University of Manitoba).

They are open to all students and staff who want to work toward a more inclusive and supportive environment for LGB and trans students.

■ Life Experiences of LGB Individuals

In understanding the lives of lesbians, gays and bisexuals, it is important to recognize that there is a wide variety of experiences. An important aspect of this variability is whether the person is **covert** (in the closet) or **overt** (out of the closet) about his or her sexual identity. As discussed earlier, some people may be heterosexually married and have children, but spend a few hours a month engaging in secret same-sex sexual behaviour or sexual fantasies.[2] Other gays and lesbians, on the other hand, may live almost entirely within an LGB community, particularly if he or she lives in a large city like Toronto or Vancouver where there is a large gay subculture, and may have relatively few contacts with heterosexuals. There are also various degrees of overtness (being "out") and covertness. Many lesbians and gays are out with trusted friends but not with casual acquaintances or in some situations but not others. The lifestyle of gay men differs from that of lesbians, perhaps as a result of the different roles assigned to males and females in our society and the different ways that boys and girls are reared. In addition, there is different discrimination against gay men than there is against lesbians. For example, it is considered quite natural for two women to share an apartment, but if two men over a certain age do so, eyebrows are raised.

The lifestyles of LGBs are thus far from uniform. They vary according to whether one is male or female and overt or covert about ones homosexuality and also according to social class, occupation, personality, and a variety of other factors.

---

[2]Men who secretly have sex with other men while in a sexual relationship with a woman are sometimes said to be on the "down low" or "d" for short.

Covert homosexual: A homosexual who is "in the closet," who keeps his or her sexual orientation a secret.
Overt homosexual: A homosexual who is "out of the closet," who is open about his or her sexual orientation.

Coming Out

In 1992 Toronto's Marc Leduc won a silver medal in boxing for Canada at the 1992 Olympic Games in Barcelona as well as a gold medal at the North American International Boxing Tournament. In the same year, Leduc came out to the public as gay— he felt he could not be open about his sexual orientation until he retired. Similarly, not one of 3,850 men currently playing professional football, basketball, and hockey in North America is openly gay. By the time he was 12, Leduc was aware that he was gay. He was also aware of his love for boxing. As a youth, he was involved in petty crime, used cocaine and speed, and spent six years in jail for robbery.

> I was a problem kid. I think a lot of it snowballed from not dealing with my sexuality, not accepting it. Socially, you're just not accepted. And as an adolescent, you don't feel like a man if you're gay. [told to a reporter]

Since he came out, Leduc has been an advocate for the lesbian and gay communities. He has also appeared in two documentaries on lesbians and gays in sports, *For the Love of the Game* and *The Last Closet*. He is happy to help knock down stereotypes. His earlier life, though, reveals the emotional toll of being in the closet.

As we noted earlier, there are significant variations in the gay experience, depending on whether or not one is out of the closet. The process of coming out of the closet, or **coming out,** involves acknowledging to oneself, and then to others, that one is gay or lesbian (Coleman, 1982). The person is psychologically vulnerable during this stage. Whether the person experiences acceptance or rejection from friends and others to whom he or she comes out can be critical to self-esteem.

Following the period of coming out, there is a stage of exploration, in which the person experiments with the new open sexual identity; during this time the person makes contact with the LGB community and practises new interpersonal skills. Typically, next comes a stage of forming first relationships. These relationships are often short-lived

Coming out: The process of acknowledging to oneself, and then to others, that one is gay or lesbian.

and characterized by jealousy and turbulence, much like many heterosexual dating relationships. Finally, there is the integration stage, in which the person becomes a fully functioning member of society and is capable of maintaining a long-term, committed relationship (Coleman, 1982).

What happens when a high school football player tells his teammates that he is gay? Watch the "Corey Johnson" video in Chapter 15 of your CD to find out.

Of course, before the coming out process can occur, the person must have arrived at a gay identity. Researchers have proposed different models of identity development. Some have suggested that people proceed through a series of stages that occur in a fixed sequence. Others criticize the stage approach for reasons detailed later. Advocates of the stage approach argue that identity development typically proceeds in six stages (Cass, 1979):

1. *Identity confusion*   The person most likely began assuming a heterosexual identity because heterosexuality is so normative in our society. As same-sex attractions or behaviours occur, there is confusion. Who am I?
2. *Identity comparison*   The person now thinks "I *may* be homosexual." There may be feelings of alienation because the comfortable heterosexual identity has been lost.
3. *Identity tolerance*   At this stage the person thinks, "I probably am homosexual." The person now seeks out gay men and/or lesbians and makes contact with the gay subculture, hoping for affirmation. The quality of these initial contacts is critical.
4. *Identity acceptance*   The person now can say "I am homosexual," and accepts rather than tolerates this identity.
5. *Identity pride*   The person dichotomizes the world into gays and lesbians (who are good and important people) and heterosexuals (who are not). There is a strong identification with the gay group, and an increased coming out of the closet.
6. *Identity synthesis*   The person no longer holds an "us versus them" view, recognizing that there are some good and supportive heterosexuals. In

Figure 15.4   Today many Canadian cities have an annual Gay and Lesbian Pride March as part of Gay Pride Week, such as this June 2000 parade in Toronto, watched by 800,000 spectators. In the early 1990s, mayors of Fredericton, Hamilton, London, and Saskatoon refused to declare Gay Pride Week. In each case, the provincial Human Rights Commission found the mayors at fault, fined them, and ordered them to issue gay pride proclamations.

this final stage, the person is able to synthesize public and private sexual identities.

What are the criticisms of this stage approach? First, recent research has found that some people do not go through one or more of these stages, and not everyone goes through the stages in this order (Diamond, 2000; Harvey et al., 2001). Second, the traditional view, particularly based on men, has been that sexual orientation once established does not change. However, there is new evidence that women's sexuality may be more fluid and may be capable of change over time (Baumeister, 2000; Diamond, 1998; Garnets & Peplau, 2001). Thus a woman may change her identify from heterosexual to lesbian if she falls in love with a woman, or vice versa. Third, the stage model suggests that to be fully developed a person must reach the final stage; that is, there is only one positive ending. This may not be accurate. Finally, it does not fit for many individuals who ultimately adopt a bisexual identity (see In

Focus 15.1, about a bisexual woman). As a result, a number of theorists have proposed alternative, non-stage models (Alderson, 2003).

The Internet is having an impact in some crucial aspects (Egan, 2000; McKenna & Bargh, 1998). For a teenage boy who is just realizing that he is gay, the Internet provides boundless information and the opportunity to "chat" with others, while remaining safe in his home and not acknowledging his identity publicly in ways that could be at best embarrassing and at worst dangerous. Interactions with others on the Internet can foster a positive identity and self-acceptance; research in Ontario identified contact with other LGB youth as a particularly important factor in establishing a positive identity (Schneider, 1991).

Bisexual Identity

Bisexual men and women generally begin to think of themselves as bisexual in their early to mid-twenties (Fox, 1995; Weinberg, 1994). There are some gender differences in the sequence of behaviours, though. Bisexual women typically have their first opposite-sex attraction and sexual experiences before their first same-sex ones. Bisexual men, in contrast, are more likely to have same-sex experiences first, followed by opposite-sex ones. What do bisexuals base their identity on? Sexual behaviour, feelings of attraction, or something else?

Research has shown that most bisexual men and women base their sexual identity on their feelings of sexual attraction or capacity to fall in love with either women or men regardless of whether they have expressed these feelings through sexual behaviour (Rust, 2001). Many describe their sexual attractions to women and men as different from each other. Those respondents who have had sexual experiences with both women and men generally reported having these experiences serially over a period of time, often including lengthy monogamous relationships. They indicated they did not cease being bisexual when they became monogamously involved with either a woman or a man, just as heterosexuals do not cease to be straight after a period of celibacy (Rust, 2000a). Some individuals adopt bisexual identities to reflect their politics. They may see bisexuality as a challenge to the importance of gender in defining sexuality, viewing their bisexual identity not as a combination of their attractions to women and men, but an attraction to people regardless of their gender.

Lesbian, Gay, and Bisexual Communities

There is a loose network of lesbian, gay, and bisexual communities around the world (Esterberg, 1996). As one woman put it,

> I have seen lesbian communities all over the world (e.g., Zimbabwe) where the lesbians of that nation have more in common with me (i.e., they play the same lesbian records, have read the same books, wear the same lesbian jewelry) than the heterosexual women of that nation have in common with heterosexual women in North America. (Rothblum, 1994)

These links have been cemented in the past decade by increases in international travel, globalization, and the international reach of the Internet (Puar, 2001).

Distinct LGB communities became visible in Canada in the 1970s in Toronto, Vancouver, and Montreal (Kinsman, 1996). During this period, there was a flourishing of businesses catering to a gay clientele, including bars, clubs, bath houses, restaurants, bookstores, theatres, and social organizations. Many of these establishments also cater to a lesbian and bisexual clientele, although generally there are fewer businesses geared specifically toward lesbians. The lesbian community in particular has been involved in creating a lesbian culture, expressed in music and literature. LGB residential areas grew up close to these commercial establishments, creating LGB neighbourhoods in these cities, although most gays and lesbians do not live in these "gay villages" (Kinsman, 1996).

LGBs tend to be less visible in smaller Canadian communities, but they nonetheless tend to have strong social networks. Some move to large urban centres seeking greater anonymity, acceptance, and perhaps distance from their families.

Several symbols are used as representations of gay, lesbian, and bisexual pride. That is, they are used to indicate that being gay is something to be proud of, not to hide. An upside-down pink triangle, which is what the Nazis used to label gay men, has been reclaimed by the gay community. The lowercase Greek letter lambda is also used. However, perhaps the most easily recognizable symbol is the rainbow flag, used by the gay community since 1978, and a representation of diversity and multiculturalism. A pink, purple, and blue striped flag is used to symbolize bisexual pride, with the pink representing attraction to members of the same gender, the blue representing attraction to people of the other gender, and the purple (the middle stripe) representing attraction to both men and women. Pride celebrations, which celebrate the anniversary of the Stonewall rebellion described earlier, take place in various cities across Canada each summer. The Pride parade, in particular, is considered an important celebration of what it means to be gay, lesbian, or bisexual. The use of slang is another sign of solidarity among LBGs (see Table 15.3 on p. 433).

Gay bars are one aspect of the LGB social life. These are gay-friendly clubs in which drinking, perhaps dancing, talking, socializing with friends, and, sometimes, the possibility of finding a roman-

---

Gay bar: A gay-friendly bar or club frequented by lesbians and gays.

In Focus 15.1

One Woman's Story: Lesbian with Bisexual Tendencies

I am a lesbian with bisexual tendencies. I find myself admitting that I am a bisexual, and then quickly saying, "But I'm involved with a woman." My brief experiences identifying as a single, available bisexual were thrilling, but difficult. During that time I dated a lesbian who decided to stop seeing me partly because she was put off by "that bisexual thing." Similarly, I don't think that the man I saw soon after believed that I wouldn't end up leaving him for a woman. Both of these people also thought that being bisexual means being nonmonogamous. Not for me. One lover is all I can handle.

In my late teens and early twenties I was often in a group of men, one of whom was my lover, arguing about feminism. I wanted a partnership of equals and I just never felt that I could be equal with a man in the eyes of the world.

I began to identify as a lesbian in the late seventies at university. I wanted to be surrounded by women who had the same stake in feminism and leftist politics that I did. Coming out was like dropping backward into a pillow. After several years and a number of relationships with women, I began to admit that I wasn't just interested in feminism or politics, but that I had—and have—strong sexual feelings for women.

Eventually I admitted that I was still attracted to men and had several flirtations. When I did begin to go out with a man again after eight years of love relationships with women, I encountered some surprises. I appreciated the level of understanding of feminist issues I now found in some men.

Then there were my friends' reactions. One said that it was fine if I wanted to see the guy I was dating, but that she didn't ever want to hang out with us together. This is all too familiar to me, having faced the pain of not having my relationships with women accepted, much less welcomed and celebrated, by my family and co-workers. Most of my lesbian friends were supportive, although some appeared concerned. Others revealed that they too had been attracted to men and seemed to take a vicarious pleasure in watching my progress.

At least two otherwise pleasant dinner parties were spoiled by my casual mention of my bisexual tendencies. I brought them up innocent of the inferno of reactions the *bi* word produces. One lesbian attorney argued quite convincingly that I had no right to call myself a lesbian if I ever have sex with men. At a safe distance, I'm not so sure. I think "lesbian with bisexual tendencies" is fairly descriptive.

Sex, after all, is something to be contained. Sex unties all of the nice packages we use to keep ourselves—and to try to keep one another—from slipping off the edge of the cosmos. Our sexual identities tell us how to live. But I need to remember that I can define my own sexual identity. I take courage from some of the bisexual activists I see around me. As a feminist, I want to see more viable alternatives for women. When I acknowledged my attraction to women *and* men, the world became exponentially larger. It's a big, big world, full of interesting and attractive people.

Source: Condensed from Lisa Yost (1991), Bisexual tendencies, In L. Hutchins & L. Kaahumanu (Eds.), *Bi any other name: Bisexual people speak out*, Boston: Alyson.

---

tic or sexual partner are important elements. In large cities, some gays bars cater to either gays or lesbians. However, many gay bars, particularly in smaller Canadian cities, are mixed gender and mixed orientation. This means that they cater to both gay men and to lesbians, as well as to gay-positive heterosexuals. What makes them gay bars is that they are accepting of same-sex relationships. Thus, patrons can be open about their sexual orientation and feel free to socialize and dance with whomever they wish without fearing verbal or physical harassment from other customers. Some gay bars look like any other bar from the outside, while others may have names—for example, The

Table 15.3   Some Slang Terms from LGB Culture

In the closet	Keeping one's sexual orientation hidden, not being open or public
Coming out	Coming out of the closet, or becoming open about one's sexual orientation
Queen	An effeminate gay man
Nellie	An effeminate gay man
Drag queen	A man who dresses in women's clothing ("drag") for fun or performance reasons
Drag king	A woman who dresses in men's clothing ("drag") for fun or performance reasons
Butch	A masculine gay man or a masculine lesbian
Dyke	Slang term for lesbian
Femme	A feminine lesbian
Straight	A heterosexual
Trick	A casual sexual partner
Cruising	Looking for a sexual partner
Tearoom	A public washroom where gay men engage in casual sex

Open Closet—that indicate to the alert that they are gay bars. LGB community dances and parties are other important avenues for socializing, particularly in small centres.

Gay baths are another aspect of some gay men's social and sexual lives. The baths are clubs with many rooms in them, generally including a swimming pool or whirlpool, as well as rooms for dancing, watching television, and socializing; most areas are dimly lit. Once a man has found a sexual partner, they go to one of a number of small rooms furnished with beds, where they can engage in sexual activity. The baths feature casual, impersonal sex, since a partner can be found and the act completed without the two even exchanging names, much less making any emotional commitment to each other.

In many parts of Canada, there are no or relatively few bath houses (Myers et al., 1993). However, there are 15 in Montreal and about six in Toronto. There is some controversy in the gay community about whether they encourage risky sexual practices. Some see the baths as an aspect of gay culture that spreads HIV and will continue to do so, killing thousands; they believe the baths must be closed and the destructive practices they encourage should stop (Rotello, 1997; Signorile, 1997). Others celebrate the liberated sexuality fostered by the baths and see it as an essential part of gay men's lifestyle. Today many bath houses empha-

Gay baths: Clubs where gay men can socialize; features include a swimming pool or whirlpool and access to casual sex.

size safe-sex—for example by supplying condoms and handing out safer sex information.

Certainly in the last three decades the *gay liberation movement* has had a tremendous impact on the gay lifestyle and community. In particular, it has encouraged LGBs to be more overt and to feel less guilty about their behaviour. The gay liberation movement has given rise to a number of provincial and national organizations committed to ending discrimination against LGBs. For example, EGALE, Equality for Gays and Lesbians Everywhere, is a national organization with three objectives. The organization is committed to lobbying for equality, fighting for justice in the courts, and building communication and action networks across Canada. There are also many LGB organizations at the provincial and local levels. Some address social justice issues; others provide community service and education. For example, large Canadian cities and most Canadian universities have pride centres. The Canadian Lesbian and Gay Archives serves as a central clearinghouse for LGB information.

There are thus many places for LGBs to socialize besides bars, including the Metropolitan Community Church (a gay and lesbian church), gay athletic organizations, and gay political organizations.

Among other accomplishments, members of the gay liberation movement have founded numerous gay newspapers and magazines. These have many of the same features as other newspapers: forums for political opinions, human-interest stories, and fashion news. In addition, the want-ads feature advertisements for sexual partners; similar

Figure 15.5 *Queer as Folk*, popular among gay, lesbian, and heterosexual viewers, was one of the first prime-time dramas about the lives of gays and lesbians.

ads for homosexual and heterosexual partners can be found in non-mainstream newspapers in most cities as well as on the Internet. Today there are many regional LGB publications, including *Wayves* published in Halifax, *Swerve* published in Winnipeg, *Perceptions* published in Saskatoon, and *Xtra* published in Toronto, Ottawa (*Capital Xtra*), and Vancouver (*Xtra West*). There are also several publications that list gay-owned or gay-friendly businesses, including information about bars, accommodations, shops, services, and tours. The Canadain Gay, Lesbian, and Bisexual Resource Directory distributes information relevant to LGB communities across Canada through its Web site gaycanada.com.

Gay and Lesbian Relationships

Various surveys indicate that between 45 and 80 percent of lesbians and between 40 and 60 percent of gay men report currently being in a steady romantic relationship (Kurdek, 1995b; Myers et al., 1993). Contrary to stereotypes, a substantial number of lesbians and gay men form long-term, cohabiting relationships. One such relationship is described in In Focus 15.2. In a study of 706 lesbian couples and 560 gay couples, 14 percent of the lesbian couples had been together for 10 or more years, as had 25 percent of the gay male couples (Bryant & Demian, 1990, cited in Kurdek, 1995b).

The 2001 Census was the first Canadian census to provide data on same-sex partnerships. A total of

34,200 same-sex couples indicated that they were living in common-law relationships; of these, 55 percent were male couples and 45 percent were female couples. About 15 percent of the female couples but only 3 percent of the male couples were living with children. A dramatic testimony to the commitment of many gays and lesbians to long-term relationships occurred in 2004, when gay marriage became legal first in Ontario and then in five other provinces and the Yukon. For example, in the month following the Ontario ruling 362 marriage licences were issued to same-sex couples in Toronto alone.

All couples—gay or straight—must struggle to find a balance that suits both persons, in three aspects of the relationship: attachment, autonomy, and equality (Cochran & Peplau, 1985; Kurdek, 1995a). *Attachment* refers to the qualities of closeness and secure love in the relationship. *Autonomy* refers to the quality of independence and individuality for each person. *Equality* refers to the balance of power between the two partners in matters ranging from decisions about finances to the division of household chores. Lesbian couples place a special value on equality in their relationships (Kurdek, 1995a). Attachment and autonomy are, to some extent, in opposition to each other. Some people want a great deal of attachment and little autonomy in their relationship, whereas others want just the opposite. The task is to find a balance that seems reasonable to both people. This task, clearly, is easier if the two partners hold similar values and ideals going into the relationship.

Lesbian and gay couples must negotiate conflicts and issues of power. For both lesbian and gay couples, the areas of conflict, in order of frequency, are finances, driving style, affection and sex, being overly critical, and household tasks (Kurdek, 1995b). This list probably sounds familiar to most heterosexual couples. However, research has shown that, on average, equity in the relationship is more important to gay and lesbian couples than to heterosexual couples. Perhaps as a result, gay and lesbian couples are more positive and less negative with each other when discussing a conflict issue than are heterosexual couples (Gottman et al., 2003a).

In one Quebec study, gay couples, lesbian couples, and heterosexual couples were brought to the laboratory and told to discuss a problem (Julien et al., 2003). Each couple's interactions were videotaped and later coded for both positive and nega-

Figure 15.6   A gay male couple. A large percentage of lesbians and gay men report currently being in a steady romantic relationship.

tive behaviours by each partner. The results showed no differences among lesbian, gay, and heterosexual couples on any of the interaction measures. Other research has shown that the same emotions affect satisfaction and stability in gay, lesbian, and heterosexual relationships (Gottman et al., 2003).

What is striking about all the research on gay and lesbian relationships is how similar all relationships are, regardless of sexual orientation, in their satisfactions, loves, joys, and conflicts (Patterson, 2000; Peplau et al., 1996).

Bisexuality and Relationships

Some bisexuals are in a relationship with a person of the other gender; others are in a same-sex relationship. One study examined 26 married couples in which the husband was bisexual (Wolf, 1985; see also Matteson, 1985). The couples had, on average, been married 13 years, and there had been open disclosure of the man's homosexuality for an average of 5.5 years. By and large, the marriages were

In Focus 15.2

Carolyn and cj: A Same-Sex Couple

Carolyn is 29 and cj is 31. They have been together for eight years. They live in Ottawa, where Carolyn works for the federal government and cj works as a researcher for an online activist organization.

Carolyn has always had close relationships with her parents and younger sister. They were her best friends when she was growing up, and she has many fond memories of working on family craft activities. In school, she was active in almost every non-sports extracurricular club. In middle school she wanted to have a boyfriend, mainly for the social status. In grade 12, she had an impassioned relationship with a young man, and his openness about sexual identity influenced her own ideas on the subject. After this relationship, Carolyn wanted to balance her romantic experiences by having a relationship with a woman. She dated two women before cj and found that she was more able to be herself with women. Carolyn's nuclear family was supportive when she came out to them; they indicated that the gender of her partner was not an issue. She delayed coming out to her extended family, fearing that they would be less supportive. Carolyn identifies as a dyke: For her, the term lesbian assumes an attraction to women only, whereas the term dyke does not negate her past relationship with a man and recognizes her attraction to trans people.

cj's family is also close. She has two brothers and a sister. She had an active childhood and adolescence, spending much of it horseback riding and at the family cottage. Classism was a particular challenge for cj in school. She felt that there were certain expectations of her because she was from an upper-middle-class home. She rejected these expectations and purposefully sought out like-minded friends. Although cj had boyfriends in high school, including a couple of long-term relationships, she now recognizes that she was always attracted to women. In first-year university, cj had crushes on some of the women in her classes, yet did not know how to act on her feelings. She dated one woman before Carolyn. When cj came out to her family, her father was immediately accepting. Her mother found it harder to come to terms with cj's sexual identity, however. Her minister and cj's sister were instrumental in helping her accept her daughter's identity. cj identifies as pansexual, that is, she is not exclusively attracted to women; rather, she is attracted to people regardless of their gender.

cj and Carolyn were both raised in Fredericton, where they attended the same high school. Although they knew each other by name, they travelled in different circles. When cj returned to Fredericton after university, she and Carolyn kept running into each other and had some awkward flirtatious moments. Yet they were not certain of each other's sexual identity or their mutual attraction until they saw each other at a GLBT event. Following this, they went on a coffee date, and within a few months were dating exclusively. Approximately 18 months later, they moved to Ottawa together so that Carolyn could complete a degree in art history and cj could do a Masters in legal studies.

In Spring 2000, three years before same-sex marriage was legalized in Ontario, Carolyn and cj applied for a marriage licence. Although they do not regard marriage as necessary to affirm their relationship, it was important for them to have the legal benefits and protections associated with marriage. They wanted to buy a house together and did not want to wait until same-sex marriage was legalized. So they took the necessary steps to ensure they would have as close to a legal equivalent to marriage as possible.

Most of Carolyn and cj's disagreements relate to household chores. Important aspects of their relationship are having similar politics and values, enjoying discussing such issues, and finding each other interesting. Their trust that the other person will be there to support them is also very important to them.

Source: Based on an interview by Jacqueline Cohen.

happy. When asked to rate the quality of the marriage, 42 percent of the men and 32 percent of the women said it was outstanding. The majority of both husbands and wives said that they remained in the marriage because they valued the friendship of the spouse. Nonetheless, there were some conflicts, as in all marriages. Trust was one issue. One woman said, "I feel more suspicious and jealous at times since he lied in the past" (p. 142). Others, however, commented that their trust had deepened. One factor that seemed most related to positive adjustment in these marriages was communication. The couples expressing the most satisfaction with the marriage were the most likely to have very direct styles of communication and to have communicated about the homosexuality early in the marriage or from the beginning of the marriage. In the AIDS era, a different meaning may be attached to a husband's bisexuality; now it is not just an alternative sexual pattern, but also a potentially dangerous pattern that could infect the wife with HIV.

Lesbian and Gay Families

Increasingly, gay and lesbian couples are creating families that include children. In the past, the courts have tended to grant custody to the non-gay or lesbian parents and have often restricted visitation by the gay or lesbian parent (Barrett et al., 1997). However, legislation in most provinces allows same-sex adoption either by the partner of a parent or of an unrelated child. In provinces where there has not been such legislation, the courts have ruled that provincial acts that prevent same-sex couples from applying to adopt are unconstitutional. The Canadian Charter of Rights and Freedoms prohibits discrimination on the basis of sexual orientation, and this applies to adoption, custody, and access. This legislation appears to recognize the result of research on the effects on children of living in a gay or lesbian family.

It is important to recognize that these families are not all the same. In some, the children were born to one of the partners in a previous heterosexual relationship. In others, the children were adopted or, in the case of lesbian couples, born by means of assisted insemination. Some have even said that a "lesbian baby boom" is underway (Patterson, 1995). Some are single-parent families, with, for example, a lesbian mother rearing her children from a previous heterosexual marriage.

Heterosexuals often make the assumption, based on their homonegativity, that it is better for children to grow up in heterosexual families than in gay or lesbian families. Based on this assumption, they raise three questions about how children fare. First, will they show "disturbances" in gender identity or sexual identity? Will they become gay or lesbian? Second, will they be less healthy psychologically than children who grow up with two heterosexual parents? Third, will they have difficulties in relationships with their peers, perhaps being stigmatized or teased because of their unusual family situation? What has research found?

For a first-person account of what it's like to grow up with two lesbian mothers, watch the video "That's a Family" in Chapter 15 of your CD.

Research on children growing up in lesbian or gay families, compared with those growing up in heterosexual families, dismisses these assumptions. For example, the overwhelming number of children growing up in lesbian or gay households have a heterosexual orientation (Allen & Burrell, 2002; Patterson, 1992).

The adjustment and mental health of children in lesbian and gay families are no different from those of children in heterosexual families (Golombok et al., 2003; Kirkpatrick, 1996; Patterson, 1996).

As for the third concern, about peer relationships, research indicates that children in lesbian or gay families fare about as well in terms of social skills and popularity as children in heterosexual families (Patterson, 1992).

In conclusion, although some people have raised concerns about children growing up in lesbian and gay families based on their negative assumptions, research consistently shows no difference between these children and those in heterosexual families (Allen & Burrell, 2002; Patterson, 1992). As one expert in clinical psychology concluded, "It appears that traditional family structures, including [mother and] father presence and heterosexuality, are not essential for healthy child development. Well-adjusted children of both sexes can be reared in families of

(a)　　　　　　　　　　　　　　　　　　　　　　*(b)*

Figure 15.7　Lesbian and gay parents and their children. In the past, the courts have tended to grant custody to the non-gay or lesbian parent. Recent court decisions prohibit discrimination on the basis of sexual orientation in adoption, custody, or access decisions.

varying configurations with the most crucial ingredient appearing to be the presence of at least one supportive, accepting caregiver" (Strickland, 1995).

■ LGB Sexual Orientation and Mental Health

Some Canadians believe that homosexuality is a kind of mental illness. Is this really true? Do psychologists and psychiatrists agree that LGBs are poorly adjusted or deviant? What are the implications of sexual orientation for a person's adjustment?

Sin and the Medical Model

Actually, the belief that homosexuality is a form of mental illness is something of an improvement over previous beliefs about homosexuality. Before this century, the dominant belief in Europe and North America was that homosexuality was a sin or a heresy. During the Inquisition, people who were accused of being heretics were also frequently accused of being homosexuals and were burned at the stake. Indeed, in those times, all mental illness was regarded as a sin. In the twentieth century, this view was replaced by the **medical model,** in which mental disturbance, and homosexuality in particular, is viewed as a sickness or illness (Bullough & Bullough, 1997).[3] This view is still held by some members of the general public but is not accepted by mental health professionals.

Psychiatrist Thomas Szasz and others are critical of the medical model. In his well-known writing on "the myth of mental illness," Szasz argues that the medical model is now obsolete and that we need to develop a more humane and realistic way of dealing with mental disorders and variations

---

[3]As one gay comedian quipped, "If homosexuality is an illness, hey, I'm going to call in queer to work tomorrow."

Medical model: A theoretical model in psychology and psychiatry in which mental problems are thought of as sickness or mental illness; the problems in turn are often thought to be due to biological factors.

from the norm. He has argued the case particularly for homosexuality (Szasz, 1965). LGB activists have joined in, saying that they do not like being called "sick" and that this is just another form of persecution of gays and lesbians.

Research Results

What do the scientific data say? Once again, the answers provided by the data are complex and depend on the assumptions of the particular investigator and on the research design used, representing progressive sophistication and changing assumptions about the nature of homosexuality.

Studies with Control Groups

Early research compared a group of gays and lesbians in therapy with a group of randomly chosen heterosexuals not in therapy. The question under investigation was "Do homosexuals have more psychological disturbance than heterosexuals?" These studies tended to find more problems of adjustment among the gay and lesbian group than among the heterosexual group (Rosen, 1974). LGBs tended to make more suicide attempts, be more neurotic, and have more disturbed family relationships. There are major problems with this research design. It compared a group of people in therapy with a group of people not in therapy and found, not surprisingly, that the people in therapy had more problems. It, too, was circular in assuming that LGBs were abnormal (in therapy) and that heterosexuals were normal (not in therapy), and then finding exactly that.

Non-patient Research

A major breakthrough came with the third group of studies, which involved non-patient research. In these studies, a group of gays and lesbians not in therapy (non-patients) were compared with a group of heterosexuals not in therapy. The non-patient gays and lesbians were generally recruited through LGB organizations, advertisements, or word of mouth. Such non-patient research has found no differences between the groups (Ross et al., 1988; Rothblum, 1994). That is, gays, lesbians, and heterosexuals were equally well adjusted. This finding is quite remarkable in view of the very negative attitudes that members of the general public tend to hold toward LGBs (Gonsiorek, 1996).

On the basis of these studies, it must be concluded that the evidence does not support the notion that gay men and lesbians by definition are "sick" or poorly adjusted. This position has received official professional recognition by the American Psychiatric Association. Prior to 1973, the APA had listed homosexuality as a disorder in its authoritative *Diagnostic and Statistical Manual of Mental Disorders* (which Canadian psychiatrists also use). In 1973, the APA voted to remove homosexuality from that listing; thus, it is no longer considered a psychiatric disorder by the American or by the Canadian Psychiatric Association. Other countries were slower to make these changes. Homosexuality was removed from the list of mental disorders by the World Health Organization only in 1993, by Japan in 1995, and by China in 2001.

Population Studies

In the last decade a new set of studies has emerged using even better designs that, for example, obtain a random sample of the general population and then compare the gays and lesbians and the heterosexuals in the sample on indices of mental health (Cochran et al., 2003; Meyer, 2003; Wichstrøm & Hegna, 2003). These studies find higher rates of depression among gays and lesbians compared with heterosexuals, and suicide attempts are more common among LGB youth than among heterosexual youth.

Scientists vigorously debate the meaning of the statistics. One controversy concerns how big or meaningful the differences are. For example, in one study 9.1 percent of LGB adolescents had made a suicide attempt, compared with 3.6 percent for heterosexual adolescents (Wichstrom & Hegna, 2003). We could focus on the fact that LGB youth were nearly three times as likely to attempt suicide. Alternatively, we could say that it's a gap of less than 6 percentage points and 90.9 percent of the LGBs had *not* attempted suicide (Savin-Williams, 2001). Should we view the glass as half full or half empty?

Beyond that, scientists agree that higher rates of depression and suicide among LGBs do not indicate that homosexuality per se indicates mental illness. Rather, the higher rates reflect the greater exposure of LGBs to prejudice and hate crimes, and the stress of concealing their true sexual identity (Meyer, 2003).

Can Sexual Orientation be Changed by Psychotherapy?

Conversion therapy or **reparative therapy**—treatments designed to change LGBs into heterosexuals—have been around for more than 100 years (Shidlo et al., 2001; Haldeman, 1994). The latest versions come from far-right religious groups. Many earlier techniques were downright inhumane. They included crude behaviour therapy that involved giving gay men electrical shocks while they viewed slides of nude men, as well as surgeries ranging from castration to brain surgery. All these treatments rested on the assumption that homosexuality was an illness that should be cured.

Investigations of reparative therapies today reveal that many individuals undergoing reparative therapy do so because of pressures from their family. They also identify the personal agonies that people experience as they are forced into, or perhaps choose, to change their orientation. One man, who is now a psychologist, quoted from his diary:

> I am going to meet with the counselor tomorrow. I don't really know what to think. I feel that I need help but I also feel that I'm trying to do away with a part of myself. I know I should look at it as sinful and ugly, like a wart that needs to be burned off. Is it possible that those emotions are what allow me to be a sensitive caring male? Is it possible that God has allowed this in my life to build certain characteristics? Is it really ugly and sinful that I want to hold and be held by a man and that I want to have a relationship with a man that includes sex? It sure sounds ugly on paper. I don't like admitting these things. I really don't. What is it that causes me to think and feel this way? Is it Satanic? Am I possessed? (Ford, 2001, p. 77)

The consequences of reparative therapies can be ugly because they do not actually change people's sexual orientation but do make them feel awfully guilty about it. Thus, reparative therapy itself can create mental health problems. As a result, some gay and bisexual men subsequently seek psychotherapy to help them recover from conversion therapies (Haldeman, 2001).

Conversion therapy: Any one of a number of treatments designed to turn LGBs into heterosexuals. Also called reparative therapy.

Given the evidence discussed earlier in this section supporting the argument that LGBs are not mentally ill, reparative therapies make no sense. In addition, they do not work. Ethical issues are raised as well: Should a person be changed from gay to straight against his or her will? Why do we only try to change people from gay to straight, and not the reverse? By 2000, the scandals associated with conversion therapies had become so great that the American Psychiatric Association issued an official position statement opposing them (American Psychiatric Association, 2000).

■ What Determines Sexual Orientation?

A fascinating psychological question is: Why do people become homosexual, heterosexual, or bisexual? Several theoretical answers to this question, as well as the relevant evidence, are discussed in this section. You will notice that the older theorists and researchers considered it their task to explain homosexuality; more recent investigators, realizing that heterosexuality needs to be explained as well, are more likely to consider it their task to explain sexual orientation.

Biological Theories

A number of scientists have proposed that sexual orientation is caused by biological factors. Interestingly, this is also the view of the majority of Canadians—54 percent believe that homosexuality is something a person is born with and an additional 8 percent believe that it results from a combination of biological factors and environment (Gallup, 2004). The likeliest candidates for these biological causes are genetic factors, prenatal factors, differences in brain structure, and an endocrine imbalance.

Genetic Factors

One study recruited gay and bisexual men who had a twin brother or an adopted brother (Bailey & Pillard, 1991). Among the 56 gay men who had an identical twin brother, 52 percent of the co-twins were themselves gay (in the terminology of geneticists, this is a 52-percent concordance rate). Among the 54 gay men who had a non-identical twin brother, 22 percent of the co-twins were themselves gay. Of the adoptive brothers of gay men, 11 percent were gay. The same research team later repeated the study with lesbians (Bailey et al., 1993). Among the 71 lesbians who had an identical twin, 48 percent of the co-twins were also lesbian. Among the 37 lesbians who had a non-identical twin sister, 16 percent of the co-twins were lesbian. Of the adoptive sisters of lesbians, 6 percent were lesbian. The statistics for women were therefore quite similar to those for men. Later studies using improved methods have found similar results (Kendler et al., 2000; Kirk et al., 2000).

The fact that the rate of concordance is substantially higher for identical twins than for non-identical twins argues in favour of a genetic contribution to sexual orientation. If genetic factors absolutely *determined* sexual orientation, however, there would be a 100-percent concordance rate for the identical twin pairs, and the rates are far from that. The implication is that factors other than genetics also play a role in influencing sexual orientation.

One research group believes that they have discovered a gene, located on the X chromosome, for homosexuality; this research is highly controversial (Hamer et al., 1993; Marshall, 1995). One study, by Hamer, has replicated the finding but others have not (Bailey & Pillard, 1995; Rie et al., 1999).

Prenatal Factors

Another possible biological cause is that homosexuality develops as a result of factors during the prenatal period. As was seen in Chapter 5, exposure to inappropriate hormones during fetal development can lead a genetic female to have male genitals, or a genetic male to have female genitals. It has been suggested that a similar process might account for homosexuality (and also for transsexualism—see Chapter 14).

According to one theory, homosexuality is caused by a variation in prenatal development. There is a critical time of fetal development during which the hypothalamus differentiates and sexual orientation is determined (Ellis & Cole-Harding, 2001). Any of several biological variations during this period will produce homosexuality.

One line of animal research that supports this theory has found evidence that severe *stress to a mother* during pregnancy tends to produce homosexual offspring. For example, exposing pregnant female rats to stress produces male offspring that assume the female mating posture, although their ejaculatory behaviour is normal (Ward et al., 2002). The stress to the mother reduces the amount of testosterone in the fetus, which is thought to produce homosexual rats.

Research with humans designed to test the prenatal stress hypothesis reports mixed results. Some studies find effects like those in the rat studies and others do not (Bailey et al., 1991; Ellis & Cole-Harding, 2001).

Another research group has suggested that prenatal *exposure to abnormally high levels of estrogen* produces human female offspring who are more likely to be lesbian (Meyer-Bahlburg, 1997; Meyer-Bahlburg et al., 1995). To test this hypothesis they studied adult women who had been exposed to DES. DES, or diethylstilbestrol, is a powerful estrogen that was used to prevent miscarriage until 1971, when its use was discontinued because of harmful side effects. More DES-exposed women than controls were rated as homosexual or bisexual (Kinsey ratings of 2 through 6).

Canadians researchers have been leaders in examining prenatal factors that may determine a person's sexual orientation. For example, Ontario psychologists Ray Blanchard and Anthony Bogaert have studied the birth order of gay men. Their research shows that consistently, across many samples, in a number of countries compared with heterosexual men, gay men are more likely to have a late birth order and to have more older brothers but not more older sisters (Blanchard, 1997, 2004; Bogaert, 2003). The researchers find no birth order or sibling effects for lesbians compared with heterosexual women. They believe that they have uncovered a prenatal effect, hypothesizing that, with each successive pregnancy with a male fetus, the mother forms more antibodies against an antigen (H-Y antigen) produced by a gene on the Y chromosome (Blanchard 2001). Because H-Y antigen is known to influence prenatal sexual differentiation, the hypothesis is that the mother's antibodies to this antigen may affect sexual differentiation in the developing fetal brain, and subsequent sexual attraction (Bogaert, 2003). These researchers estimate that between 15 and 30 percent of gay men had their sexual orientation created in this manner (Cantor et al., 2002; Blanchard & Bogaert, 2004).

Other researchers have documented an odd, but potentially important pattern concerning the 2D:4D finger-length ratio. This refers to the ratio of the length of the index finger to the length of the ring finger. In general, men have lower 2D:4D ratios than women; that is, men's index fingers are relatively shorter than their ring fingers, compared with women's. Heterosexual men have a lower 2D:4D ratio than gay men, although heterosexual and lesbian women do not differ on this measure (Lippa, 2003). Similarly, Alberta researcher Martin Lalumière has found that gay men and lesbians are more likely to be left-handed than are heterosexuals; gay men are about 40 percent more likely than straight men to be left-handed, and lesbians are nearly twice as likely as heterosexual women to be left-handed (Lalumière et al., 2000). Both patterns suggest some kind of prenatal effect on the developing brain.

These theories of prenatal influence are intriguing and show much promise for the future.

Brain Factors

Another line of theorizing argues that there are anatomical differences between the brains of gays and straights that produce the differences in sexual orientation. A number of studies have pursued this possibility, all looking at somewhat different regions of the brain (Swaab et al., 1995). A highly publicized study by neuroscientist Simon LeVay (1991) is an example. LeVay found significant differences between gay men and straight men in certain cells in the anterior portion of the hypothalamus. Anatomically, the hypothalamic cells of the gay men were more similar to those of women than to those of straight men, according to LeVay. However, the study had a number of flaws: (1) The sample size was very small: only 19 gay men, 16 straight men, and 6 straight women were included. This small sample size was necessitated by the fact that the brains had to be dissected in order to examine the hypothalamus, so that the brains of living persons could not be studied. (2) All of the gay men in the sample, but only six of the straight men and one of the straight women, had died of AIDS. The groups are not comparable, then. Perhaps the brain differences were caused by the neurological effects of AIDS. (3) Lesbian women were omitted from the study, making them invisible in the research—as they often have been in

psychological and biological research. (4) The gay men were known to have been gay based on records at the time of death; the others, however, were just "presumed" to be heterosexual—if there was no record of sexual orientation, the assumption was that the person had been heterosexual, scarcely a sophisticated method of measurement.

It is difficult to know how much confidence to place in LeVay's findings. Other scientists who looked for this effect found no differences in this region of the hypothalamus as a function of the person's sexual orientation (Byne et al., 2000; Swaab, 2005). Yet animal researchers believe that they have identified a similar region in the hypothalamus of the rat that does seem to be involved in sexual behaviour (Swaab, 2005).

Hormonal Factors

Investigating the possibility that endocrine factors are the cause of homosexuality, many researchers have tried to determine whether the testosterone ("male" hormone) levels of gay men differ from those of straight men. These studies have not found any hormonal differences (Banks & Gartrell, 1995; Gooren et al., 1990).

Despite these results, some clinicians have attempted to cure male homosexuality by administering testosterone therapy (Glass & Johnson, 1944). This therapy fails; indeed, it seems to result in even more same-sex sexual activity than usual. This is not an unexpected result, since, as was seen in Chapter 9, androgen levels seem to be related to sexual responsiveness. As a clinician friend of two of the authors replied to an undergraduate male who was seeking testosterone therapy for his homosexuality, "It won't make you heterosexual; it will only make you horny."

In conclusion, of the biological theories, the genetic theory and the prenatal theory have new suporting evidence, but much more research is needed.

Psychoanalytic Theory
Freudian Theory

Since Freud believed sex to be the primary motivating force in human behaviour, it is not surprising that he concerned himself with sexual orientation and its development (his classic work on the subject is *Three Essays on the Theory of Sexuality*, published in 1910).

As described in Chapter 2, by the end of the phallic stage when the Oedipus complex is resolved, the child comes to love and desire the other-gender parent and comes to identify with the parent of the same gender. Typically children also repress their desire for the same-gender parent during this period. These children become heterosexual. However, there are a number of reasons (at least 17 different routes) why this may not happen, according to Freud. Thus, some children repress their desire for the other-gender parent but not for the same-gender parent. These people become homosexual. Other people do not repress their desire for either parent and become bisexual.

Consistent with Freud's belief that the infant is **polymorphously perverse** was his belief that all humans are inherently bisexual; that is, he believed that all people have the capacity for both opposite-sex and same-sex behaviour. Our attraction to both genders is always there, even if we repress our attraction to one or the other gender. Thus Freud viewed homosexuality as very possible and did not assume that being attracted to members of one's own gender is a sign of psychopathology. However, some neo-Freudians, such as Irving Bieber, have interpreted Freud as saying that the homosexual is fixated at an immature stage of development, and thus that homosexuality is a sign of psychopathology. He originated the notion that male homosexuality is caused by having a dominant mother and a weak or passive father.

Evaluation of Psychoanalytic Theories

Psychoanalytic theories of the genesis of homosexuality clearly operate under the assumption that homosexuality is deviant or abnormal.

Actually, in his later writings Freud came to consider homosexuality to be within the normal range of variation of sexual behaviour; this view, however, appears not to have had much of an impact, compared with that of his earlier writings on the subject. Psychoanalytic theory could thus be criticized for making the abnormality assumption, since, as we have seen, there is no evidence for the notion that homosexuals are poorly adjusted.

The psychoanalytic approach can also be criticized for its confusion of the concepts of "gender

Polymorphousy perverse: Freud's term for the infant's indiscriminate, undifferentiated sexuality.

identity" and "sexual orientation." As previously noted, homosexuals differ from heterosexuals in sexual orientation but not in gender identification: The male homosexual thinks of himself as a man, and the lesbian thinks of herself as a woman. Psychoanalytic theory, however, assumes that gays and lesbians not only make an inappropriate object choice but also have an abnormal gender identification—that the gay man has not identified with his father and has therefore not acquired a masculine identity, and that the lesbian has not identified with her mother and has therefore not acquired a feminine identity. This basic assumption of abnormal gender identification is not supported by the data and is therefore another basis for criticizing psychoanalytic theories.

Perhaps most importantly, the most comprehensive study of the causes of sexual orientation found that parental relationships made little or no difference to a respondent's sexual orientation (Bell et al., 1981).

Learning Theory

Behaviourists emphasize the importance of learning in the development of sexual orientation. They note the prevalence of bisexual behaviour both in other species and in young humans, and they argue that rewards and punishments shape the individual's behaviour into predominant homosexuality or predominant heterosexuality. The assumption, then, is that humans have a relatively amorphous, undifferentiated pool of sex drive which, depending on circumstances (rewards and punishments), may be channelled in any of several directions. In short, people are born sexual, not heterosexual or homosexual. Only through learning does one of these behaviours become more likely than the other. For example, if early sexual experiences are with a same-sex partner and pleasant, the person may become gay. Same-sex sexual activity has essentially been rewarded and therefore becomes more likely.

Another possibility, according to a learning-theory approach, is that a person who has early heterosexual experiences that are very unpleasant might develop toward homosexuality. Heterosexuality has essentially been punished and therefore becomes less likely. This might occur, for instance, in the case of a girl who is sexually assaulted by a male at an early age; her first experience with a male was extremely unpleasant, so she avoids it and turns to homosexuality.

The learning-theory approach treats same-sex sexual activity as a normal form of behaviour and recognizes that both heterosexuality and homosexuality are not necessarily inborn but must be learned.

The evidence on learning theory's explanation of sexual orientation is mixed. A comprehensive study of the influences on sexual orientation in humans disconfirmed some essential arguments. The idea that homosexuality results from early unpleasant heterosexual experiences was not supported by the data. Lesbian women, for example, were no more likely to have been sexually assaulted than were heterosexual women (Bell et al., 1981). Yet recent research using an animal model does point to the importance of early learning. Zebra finches are small birds that are monogamous, mate for life, and are almost invariably heterosexual. If the fathers are removed from the cages, though, so that the young birds grow up without adult males or male–female pairs, in adulthood these birds pair with either males or females (Adkins-Regan, 2002). That is, their behaviour, which is bisexual, is a result of early experience.

In contrast to the bird research, research with humans indicates that children who grow up with a gay or lesbian parent are not themselves more likely as a result to become gay (Allen & Burrell, 2002; Bailey et al., 1995; Golombok & Tasker, 1996). In this sense, then, sexual orientation is not "learned" from one's parents.

Interactionist Theory
Bem: The Exotic Becomes Erotic

Psychologist Daryl Bem (1996) proposed a theory of the development of sexual orientation that encompasses the interaction of biological factors and experiences with the environment. Bem's theory is diagrammed in Figure 15.8.

The theory begins with biological influences, relying on the evidence discussed earlier about biological contributions to sexual orientation (box A in Figure 15.8). However, Bem does not believe that genes and other biological factors directly and magically determine a person's sexual orientation. Rather, he theorized that biological factors exert their influence on sexual orientation through their influence on temperament in childhood (box A to box B). Psychologists have found abundant evi-

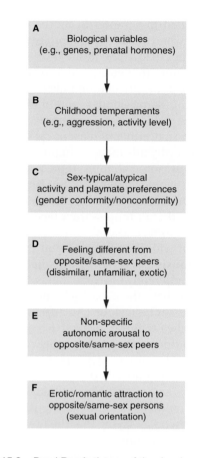

Figure 15.8   Daryl Bem's theory of the development of sexual orientation: The exotic becomes erotic.

dence that two aspects of temperament have a biological basis: aggression and activity level. Moreover, these two aspects of temperament show reliable gender differences. According to Bem, most children show levels of aggression and activity level that are typical of their gender; boys are generally more aggressive and more active than girls. These tendencies lead children to engage in gender-conforming activities (B to C). Most boys play active, aggressive sports, and most girls prefer quieter play activities. These play patterns also lead children to associate almost exclusively with members of their own gender. The boy playing tackle football is playing in a group that consists either entirely or almost entirely of boys. This chain of events will eventually lead to a heterosexual orientation in adulthood.

A minority of children, however, have temperamental characteristics that are not typical of their gender: some boys are not particularly active or aggressive and some girls are. These children are then gender-nonconforming in their play patterns. The boys prefer quieter, less active play and have more girls as friends, and the gender-non–conforming girls prefer aggressive sports and have more boys as friends.

These experiences with childhood play and playmates create a feeling in children that certain other children are different from them and therefore are exotic (box C to D). For the boy who spends most of his time playing active, aggressive sports with other boys, girls are different, mysterious, and exotic. For the gender-nonconforming girl who plays active sports with boys, most girls, too, seem different and exotic to her.

The presence of an exotic other causes a person to feel generalized arousal, whether in childhood, adolescence, or adulthood (box D to E). Those of you who are heterosexual certainly remember many instances in your past when you felt ill at ease and nervous in the presence of a member of the other gender.

In the final link of the model, this generalized arousal is transformed into erotic/romantic attraction. Essentially, the exotic becomes erotic. This transformation may be a result of processes described in Berscheid and Walster's (1974) two-component theory of arousal, discussed in Chapter 13. Generalized arousal can easily be transformed into sexual arousal and attraction if the conditions are right. For heterosexual persons, the exotic people are members of the other gender, with whom they had less contact in childhood and who have become eroticized. For gays and lesbians, the exotic people are members of their own gender, from whom they felt different in childhood and who have become eroticized.

One well-documented phenomenon is that there are considerably more heterosexuals than homosexuals. The theory deals with this fact by recognizing that Canadian society, like most others, is gender polarized. Gender distinctions are emphasized, and gender roles are strong. For most individuals, then, members of the other gender are exotic. It is only in the minority of cases, those whose childhood temperament leads them to be gender-nonconforming, that members of their own gender are exotic.

Certainly one virtue of the theory is that it is designed to explain both homosexual and heterosexual sexual orientations. That is, the essential process is that the exotic becomes erotic, for both heterosexuals and homosexuals. The difference is that, because of childhood temperament and play activities, members of the other gender seem exotic to heterosexuals, whereas members of their own gender seem exotic to gays and lesbians.

One body of evidence that is consistent with Bem's theory indicates that gay men and lesbians, on average, are more likely than heterosexuals to have had a childhood history of gender nonconformity (Bailey & Zucker, 1995; Cohen, 2002). This pattern has been found cross-culturally as well. For example, in one study of lesbians and heterosexual women in Brazil, Peru, the Philippines, and the United States, the lesbians were, as children, significantly more gender-nonconforming than were the heterosexual women (Whitam & Mathy, 1991). The lesbians were significantly more rejecting of gender-typical activities, such as playing with girls' toys and paying attention to women's fashions, and more involved with gender-atypical activities, such as playing with boys' toys and being a tomboy. The consistency of these results is particularly striking given how vastly different these four cultures are. Although this evidence is consistent with Bem's theory, it is also consistent with the biological theories.

At the same time, Bem's theory and evidence have been thoroughly criticized (Peplau et al., 1998; for Bem's response, see Bem, 1998). Two criticisms have been raised: (1) evidence not discussed by Bem contradicts some central propositions of the theory; and (2) the theory reflects male experience and neglects female experience. Regarding the evidence, Bem noted that, in one major study, lesbians (70 percent) were significantly more likely than were heterosexual women (51 percent) to recall feeling somewhat or very different from other girls their age (Bell et al., 1981). The difference is significant, but perhaps more important is the finding that a majority of heterosexual women felt different from other girls. Other girls seemed different or exotic to them. Why didn't they become lesbian, then?

Sociological Theory

Sociologists emphasize the effects of *labelling* in explaining homosexuality. The label "homosexual" has a big impact in our society. For example, one of the biggest insults used by middle school students is calling a classmate a "fag" (McFarland, 2001). The label "homosexual" often has derogatory connotations, reflecting our society's predominantly negative attitudes toward homosexuality.

A clever experiment demonstrated the effects of labelling someone homosexual. Half the participants (all men) were led to believe that a particular member of their group was homosexual. For the other half of the participants (the control group), the man was not labelled. People in the experimental group, in which the man was labelled, rated him as being significantly less clean, softer, more womanly, more tense, more yielding, more impulsive, less rugged, more passive, and quieter (Karr, 1978). Thus labelling a person homosexual does influence perceptions of that person.

But the label "homosexual" may also act as a self-fulfilling prophecy. Suppose that a young boy—possibly because he is slightly effeminate or poor in sports, or for no reason at all—is called "gay." He reacts strongly and becomes more and more anxious and worried about his problem. He becomes painfully aware of the slightest homosexual tendency in himself. Finally he convinces himself that he is gay. He begins engaging in same-sex sexual activity and associates with a gay group. In short, a gay man has been created through labelling.

Recall that in Chapter 2 we discussed Ira Reiss's sociological theory of human sexuality. In his theorizing he addresses the issue of sexual orientation, focusing particularly on gay men. Recognizing the need to explain cross-cultural differences in sexual patterns, he contends that it is male-dominant societies with a great rigidity of gender roles that produce the highest incidence of homosexuality. In such societies, there is a rigid male role that must be learned and conformed to, but young boys have little opportunity to learn it from adult men precisely because the gender roles are rigid, so that women take care of children and men have little contact with them. It is therefore difficult to learn the heterosexual component of the male role. In addition, because the male role is rigid, there will be a certain number of males who dislike it and reject its heterosexual component. Cross-cultural studies support his observations (Reiss, 1986). Societies that have a great maternal involvement with infants and low father involvement with infants and that have rigid gender roles

are precisely those that have the highest incidence of same-sex sexual behaviour in males.

This pattern describes the negative pathway to homosexuality. Reiss argues that there is also a positive pathway. It exists in less gender-rigid societies with more permissiveness about sexuality. In such societies, individuals feel freer to experiment with same-sex behaviour and may find it satisfying. Examples are provided by several First Nations peoples in which three gender roles have been recognized (see Chapter 14).

The Bottom Line

We have examined a number of theories of sexual orientation and the evidence supporting or refuting them. What is the bottom line? Which theory is correct? The answer is, we don't know yet. We do not know what causes sexual orientation. Several theories have strong evidence supporting them, but no one theory accounts for all cases. We believe that a good lesson can be learned from this somewhat frustrating conclusion.

It has generally been assumed not only that gays form a distinct category (which, we have already seen, is not very accurate) but also that they form a homogeneous category; that is, that all gays are fairly similar. Not so. Probably there are many different kinds or "types" of homosexuals and heterosexuals. Indeed, one psychologist has suggested that we should refer not to "homosexuality" but rather to "homosexualities" (Bell, 1974b; Bell & Weinberg, 1978). If this is the case, then one would not expect a single "cause" of sexual orientation but rather many causes, each corresponding to its type. The next step in research, then, should be to identify the various types of LGBs and heterosexuals and the different kinds of development that lead to each.

■ Differences Between Gay Men and Lesbians

Although gay men and lesbians are commonly lumped together in one category and called homosexuals, evidence from a number of sources indicates that there are some important differences between the two groups that go beyond one group being male and the other female.

Women are more likely to be bisexual, and less

likely to be exclusively homosexual, than men are. In the NHSLS data set, 4.1 percent of women and 3.9 percent of men indicated that they were sexually attracted to both women and men, but only 0.3 percent of women and 2.4 percent of men rated themselves as being attracted exclusively to members of their own gender (Rust, 2002).

Some of the theories discussed earlier in this chapter seem to work for gay men or for lesbians but not for both. For example, the birth order effect has been found repeatedly; compared with heterosexual men, gay men are more likely to have a late birth order and an excess of older brothers. Lesbians, however, are no more or less likely to have a late birth order compared with heterosexual women (Blanchard, 1997; Bogaert, 2003). The 2D:4D finger-length ratio effect holds for comparisons of gay men and straight men, but not for comparisons of lesbians and straight women (Lippa, 2003).

We will almost certainly need separate theories to explain the development of sexual orientation in women and in men (Hyde & Jaffee, 2000).

■ Sexual Orientation in Multicultural Perspective

Just as different cultures around the world hold different views of same-sex sexual behaviour (see In Focus 15.3), various Canadian ethnic minority groups have different cultural definitions for same-sex behaviours.

Generally, members of Canadian ethnocultural communities have less tolerance for homosexuality than members of the majority culture do. There tends to be a stigma attached to being a gay man, a denial of the existence of homosexuality within the community, and considerable pressure to conform to community norms. As a result, many LGBs feel forced to stay in the closet with respect to their sexual orientation in order to be accepted within their family and community (Singer et al., 1996).

For example, in both the Caribbean and African communities in Canada, gay and bisexual men may keep their activities secret for fear of being ostracized if they are open about their sexual orientation (Health Canada, 1994b, 1994c). Similarly, because of strong negative attitudes in the community, many gay and bisexual men in the South

Asian community keep their same-sex relationships hidden. They may comply with family pressure to get married to avoid causing conflict in the family. South Asian men who were born in Canada are more likely to be open about their sexual orientation (Health Canada, 1994e).

Members of some ethnic groups, including men from the Caribbean and Latin American communities, may engage in extensive same-sex sexual behaviour while still considering themselves to be heterosexual (Singer et al., 1996). An interesting example of these different cultural definitions comes from a study of Mexican and Mexican American men (Magaña & Carrier, 1991). In Mexico, there is a dichotomizing of same-sex sexual behaviours that parallels traditional gender roles. Anal intercourse, because it most resembles penis-in-vagina intercourse, is the preferred behaviour, and fellatio is practised relatively little. A man adopts the role either of receptive partner or inserting partner and does this exclusively. Those who take the receptive role are considered unmanly, feminine, and "homosexual." Those who take the inserting role are considered masculine, are not labelled "homosexual," and are not stigmatized. Research with Latin American men living in Mon-

Figure 15.9 Ethnicity and sexual orientation. Among Latin American and Caribbean women, warmth and physical closeness are very acceptable, but there are strong taboos against female–female sexual relationships.

In Focus 15.3

Ritualized Homosexuality in Melanesia

Melanesia is an area of the southwest Pacific that includes the islands of New Guinea and Fiji as well as many others. Anthropologists' research on same-sex sexual behaviour in those cultures provides great insight into the ways in which sexual behaviours are the products of the scripts of a culture. This research is rooted in sociological and anthropological theory (see Chapter 2). As such, the analysis focuses on the norms of the society and the symbolic meaning that is attached to sexual behaviours.

Among Melanesians, same-sex sexual behaviour has a very different symbolic meaning from the one it has in Western culture. It is viewed as natural, normal, and indeed necessary. The culture actually *pre*scribes the behaviour, in contrast to Western cultures, in which it is forbidden or *pro*scribed.

Sociologists and anthropologists believe that most cultures are organized around the dimensions of social class, race, gender, and age. Among Melanesians, age organizes the same-sex sexual behaviour. It is not to occur among two men of the same age. Instead, it occurs between an adolescent and a preadolescent, or between an adult man and a pubertal boy. The older partner is always the inserter for the acts of anal intercourse, the younger partner is the insertee.

Ritualized same-sex sexual behaviour serves several social purposes in these cultures. It is viewed as a means by which a boy at puberty is incorporated into the adult society of men. It is also thought to encourage a boy's growth, so that it helps to "finish off" his growth in puberty. In these societies, semen is viewed as a scarce and valuable commodity. Therefore, the same-sex sexual behaviours are viewed as helpful and honourable, a means of passing on strength to younger men and boys. As one anthropologist observed:

> Semen is also necessary for young boys to attain full growth to manhood. . . . They need a boost, as it were. When a boy is eleven or twelve years old, he is engaged for several months in homosexual intercourse with a healthy older man chosen by his father. (This is always an in-law or unrelated person, since the same notions of incestuous relations apply to little boys as to marriageable women.) Men point to the rapid growth of adolescent youths, the appearance of peach fuzz beards, and so on, as the favorable results of this child-rearing practice. (Schieffelin, 1976, p. 124)

In all cases, these men are expected later to marry and father children. This points up the contrast between sexual identity and sexual behaviour. The sexual behaviours are ones that we would surely term "homosexual," yet these cultures are so structured that the boys and men who engage in same-sex sexual behaviours do not form a homosexual identity.

Ritualized same-sex sexual behaviours are declining as these cultures are colonized by Westerners. It is fortunate that anthropologists were able to make their observations over the last several decades to document these interesting and meaningful practices before they disappear.

Source: Gilbert, 1984.

treal also found that men who take the inserting role during anal intercourse with men often consider themselves to be heterosexual (Health Canada, 1994a). In contrast, men who take the receptive role are considered homosexual and are marginalized in the community. This approach differs substantially from that in the gay Canadian majority, where men commonly switch roles and both are considered gay.

Such different definitions of homosexuality are not limited to Latin American cultures. One researcher described the scene in contemporary

Egypt as follows:

> In Egypt, because there was so little sense of homosexuality as an identity, what position you took in bed defined all. Between men, the only sex that counted was anal sex. . . . In the minds of most Egyptians, "gay," if it meant anything at all, signified taking the receptive position in anal sex. On the other hand, a person who took the insertive role—and that seemed to include virtually all Egyptian men, to judge by what my acquaintances told me—was not considered gay. . . . Many of the insults in the Arabic language concern being penetrated anally by another man. (Miller, 1992, p. 76)

As for lesbians, Latin American women and Caribbean women experience conflicts in the complexities of ethnicity and sexual orientation (Espin, 1987; Gonzalez & Espin, 1996; Silvera, 1990). In both cultures, emotional and physical closeness among women is considered acceptable and desirable. However, attitudes toward lesbianism are extremely restrictive. The emphasis on family—defined as mother, father, children, and grandparents in Latin American cultures—and the emphasis on attracting a man and bearing a child in Caribbean cultures makes the lesbian even more of an outsider. Women who are openly lesbian may be stigmatized and ostracized in these communties.

Among the Chinese communities in Canada, two features of the culture shape attitudes toward homosexuality and its expression: (1) a strong distinction between what may be expressed publicly and what should be kept private; and (2) a stronger value placed on loyalty to one's family and on the performance of family roles than on the expression of one's own desires (Chan, 1995). Sexuality is something that must be expressed only privately, not publicly. And having an identity, much less a sexual identity or a gay lifestyle, apart from one's family is almost incomprehensible to traditional Chinese. As a result, a relatively small proportion of LGB members of the Chinese communities in Canada are "out" in their community. Nonetheless, there is an active gay Asian community in Vancouver. However, these individuals often remain in the closet within the Chinese community because of fear of bringing shame to their families (Health Canada, 1994f). As with other ethnocultural communities in Canada, members of the Chinese community who are out tend to be more accultur-

ated—that is, influenced by Canadian culture.

In sum, when we consider sexual orientation from a multicultural perspective, two main points emerge: (1) The very definition of homosexuality is set by culture. In Canada, we would say that a man who is the inserting partner in anal intercourse with another man is engaging in homosexual behaviour, but other cultures (such as Mexico and Egypt) would not agree. (2) Many ethnocultural communities are more disapproving of homosexuality than is the majority Canadian culture. In those cases, LGBs feel conflicts between their sexual identity and loyalty to their ethnic group.

■ A Final Note

As we have seen in this chapter, most theory and research rests on the assumption that sexual orientation is determined by conditions in childhood, or by prenatal or genetic factors. Yet some people have their first heterosexual and then their first homosexual experience in their twenties. It is difficult to believe that these behaviours were determined by some pathological condition at age 5. **Deprivation homosexuality,** or situational homosexuality, is also a good example of the influence of late-occurring experience. A heterosexual man may engage in same-sex sexual behaviour while in prison but return to exclusive heterosexuality after his release. Once again, it seems likely that such a man's same-sex sexual behaviour was determined by his circumstances (being in prison) rather than by some problem years before. Unlike gender identity, which seems to be fixed in the preschool years, sexual identity continues to evolve. This contradicts some scientists' assertion that sexual orientation is determined before adolescence (Bell et al., 1981). We think that when sexual orientation is determined is still an open question. For some it may be determined by genetic factors or experiences early in life, but for others it may be determined in adulthood.

Second, a question is raised as to whether heterosexuality is really the "natural" state. The pattern in some theories has been to try to discover the pathological conditions that cause homosexu-

Deprivation homosexuality: Homosexual activity that occurs in certain situations, such as prisons, when people are deprived of their regular heterosexual activity.

ality (for example, a father who is an inadequate role model or a homoseductive mother)—all on the basis of the assumption that heterosexuality is the natural state and that homosexuality must be explained as a deviation from it. As we have seen, this approach has failed; there appear to be multiple causes of homosexuality, just as there may be multiple causes of heterosexuality. The important alternative to consider is that bisexuality is the natural state, a point acknowledged by Freud, the learning theorists, and sociological theorists (Weinberg et al., 1994). This chapter will close, then, with some questions. Psychologically, the real question should concern not the conditions that lead to homosexuality but rather the causes of exclusive homosexuality and exclusive heterosexuality. Why do we eliminate some people as potential sex partners simply on the basis of their gender? Why isn't everyone bisexual?

■ ■ ■ SUMMARY

Sexual orientation is defined as a person's erotic and emotional attraction toward members of his or her own gender, toward members of the other gender, or both.

Although many Canadians believe that homosexuality is wrong, the vast majority are in favour of equal rights for LGBs and a slim majority favour same-sex marriage. In some cases homonegativity and anti-gay prejudice may be so strong that it results in hate crimes and harassment directed at gays and lesbians.

There are lesbian, gay, and bisexual communities around the world. These communities are defined by a common culture and social life and by rituals such as pride marches.

In surveys, the majority of gay men and lesbians report being in a steady romantic relationship. In these relationships, the couples must find a balance on the dimensions of attachment, autonomy, and equality. Although people with negative attitudes toward LGBs have voiced concerns about the psychological well-being of children who grow up in lesbian and gay families, these concerns are unfounded, according to the available studies.

The most recent well-sampled surveys indicate (when corrected for some underreporting) that about 92 percent of men and 95 percent of women are exclusively heterosexual. About 7 to 8 percent of men and 4 to 5 percent of women have at least one same-sex sexual experience in adulthood, and about 2 percent of men and 1 percent of women are exclusively homosexual. Kinsey devised a scale ranging from 0 (exclusively heterosexual) to 6 (exclusively homosexual) to measure this diversity of experience. A person's sexual identity may be discordant with his or her actual behaviour.

Well-conducted research indicates that homosexuality per se is not a sign of poor adjustment. Research does show somewhat elevated rates of depression and suicide among LGBs, which is almost certainly due to exposure to prejudice and hate crimes. Although some groups claim success in "reparative" therapy to change the sexual orientation of LGBs, there is no scientific evidence that one's sexual orientation can be changed, and many indications that these therapies are psychologically harmful. Most therapists believe that it is extremely difficult to change a person's sexual orientation.

In regard to the causes of sexual orientation, biological explanations include hormone imbalance, prenatal factors, brain factors, and genetic factors. The genetic explanation has some support from the data, and there is new evidence of prenatal factors. According to the psychoanalytic view, homosexuality results from a fixation at an immature stage of development. Learning theorists stress that the sex drive is undifferentiated and is channelled, through experience, into heterosexuality or homosexuality. Bem's interactionist theory proposes that homosexuality results from the influence of biological factors on temperament, which in turn influences whether a child plays with boys or girls; the less familiar (exotic) gender becomes associated with sexual arousal. Sociologists emphasize the importance of roles and labelling in understanding homosexuality. They also note that gender-rigid, male-dominant societies are likely to produce a higher incidence of gay men. Available data do not point to any single factor as a cause of homosexuality but rather suggest that there may be many types of homosexuality ("homosexualities") and heterosexuality with corresponding multiple causes.

Gay men and lesbians differ in some important ways. Women are more likely to be bisexual, and theories that are effective in explaining men's sexual orientation are not supported for women.

Different ethnic groups in Canada, as well as different cultures around the world, hold diverse views of same-sex sexual behaviours.

Bisexuality may be more "natural" than either exclusive heterosexuality or exclusive homosexuality.

■ ■ ■ QUESTIONS FOR THOUGHT, DISCUSSION, AND DEBATE

1. Debate the following topic. Resolved: Homosexuals should not be discriminated against in employment, including such occupations as high school teaching.

2. Do you feel that you are homonegative or homophobic, or do you feel that your attitude toward gays is positive? Why do you think your attitudes are the way they are? Are you satisfied with your attitudes or do you want to change them?

3. Does your university, in addition to prohibiting discrimination on the basis of race and sex, also specifically prohibit discrimination on the basis of sexual orientation? Do you think it should?

4. Imagine that you are a gay man employed at a managerial level in an advertising agency in Calgary. You and your partner have been together for 11 years and intend to stay that way. It is becoming increasingly awkward for you to pretend that you have no partner and that you are straight when you attend parties for the staff or when people ask you how your weekend was. Should you come out to your colleagues at work? Why or why not?

■ ■ ■ SUGGESTIONS FOR FURTHER READING

Besen, Wayne R. (2003). *Anything but straight: Unmasking the scandals and lies behind the ex-gay myth.* Binghamton, N.Y.: Harrington Park Press. Besen, a journalist, conducted investigative reporting on conversion therapies for gays that are led by far-right religious groups.

Herek, Gregory M., Kimmel, Douglas C., Amaro, Hortensia, & Melton, Gary B. (1991). Avoiding heterosexist bias in psychological research. *American Psychologist, 46,* 957–963. This stimulating article on research methodology points out ways in which heterosexist bias can enter research and suggests ways to avoid this bias.

LeVay, Simon. (1996). *Queer science: The use and abuse of research into homosexuality.* Cambridge, MA: MIT Press. Neuroscientist Simon LeVay, whose research was discussed in this chapter, has put together a comprehensive book on scientists' research on homosexuality, focusing particularly on the causes of sexual orientation.

Miller, Neil. (1992). *Out in the world: Gay and lesbian life from Buenos Aires to Bangkok.* New York: Random House. The author travelled around the world, observing gay and lesbian communities. The accounts are fascinating.

Warner, Tom. (2002). *Never going back: A history of queer activism in Canada.* Toronto: University of Toronto Press. This book by one of Canada's leading gay activists chronicles the history of lesbian and gay liberation in Canada.

Online Learning Centre

For Review Questions, Web Resources, and other learning and study tools, visit the *Understanding Human Sexuality* Online Learning Centre at www.mcgrawhill.ca/college/hyde.

CHAPTER 16

Variations in Sexual Behaviour

CHAPTER HIGHLIGHTS

> No kind of sensation is keener and more active than that of pain; its impressions are unmistakable.*

Most laypeople, as well as most scientists, have a tendency to classify behaviour as normal or abnormal. There seems to be a particular tendency to do this with regard to sexual behaviour. Many terms are used for abnormal sexual behaviour, including "sexual deviance," "perversion," "sexual variance," and paraphilias. The term "sexual variations" will be used in this chapter because it is currently favoured in scientific circles.

This chapter will deal with some behaviours that more people might consider to be abnormal, so it seems advisable at this point to consider exactly when a sexual behaviour is abnormal. That is, what is a reasonable set of criteria for deciding what kinds of sexual behaviour are abnormal?

■ When Is Sexual Behaviour Abnormal?

Defining Abnormal

As we saw in Chapter 1, sexual behaviour varies a great deal from one culture to the next. There is a corresponding variation across cultures in what is considered to be "abnormal" sexual behaviour. Given this great variability, how can one come up with a reasonable set of criteria for what is abnormal? Perhaps it is best to begin by considering the way others have defined "abnormal" sexual behaviour.

One approach is to use a *statistical definition.* According to this approach, an abnormal sexual behaviour is one that is rare, or not practised by many people. Following this definition, then, standing on one's hands while having intercourse would be considered abnormal because it is rarely done, although it does not seem very abnormal in other ways. This definition, unfortunately, does not give us much insight into the psychological or social functioning of the person who engages in the behaviour.

In the *sociological approach,* the problem of culture dependence is explicitly acknowledged. A sociologist might define a deviant sexual behaviour as a sexual behaviour that violates the norms of society. Thus if a society says that a particular sexual behaviour is deviant, it is—at least in that society. This approach recognizes the importance of the individual's interaction with society and of the problems that people must face if their behaviour is labelled "deviant" in the culture in which they live.

A *psychological approach* was stated by Arnold Buss in his text entitled *Psychopathology* (1966). He says, "The three criteria of abnormality are discomfort, inefficiency, and bizarreness." The last of these criteria, bizarreness, has the problem of being culturally defined; what seems bizarre in one culture may seem normal in another. However, the first two criteria are good in that they focus on the discomfort and unhappiness felt by the person with a truly abnormal pattern of sexual behaviour and also on inefficiency. For example, a male clerk in a Minneapolis supermarket was having intercourse with willing shoppers in their cars several times a day. This apparently compulsive behaviour led to his being fired. This is an example of inefficient functioning, a behaviour that can reasonably be considered abnormal.

The *medical approach* is exemplified by the definitions included in the *Diagnostic and Statistical Manual of Mental Disorders (DSM-IV-TR)* (American Psychiatric Association, 2000). It recognizes eight paraphilias: fetishism, transvestic fetishism, sexual sadism, sexual masochism, voyeurism, frotteurism, exhibitionism, and pedophilia. The general definition of **paraphilia** is:

> Recurrent, intense, sexually arousing fantasies, sexual urges, or behaviors involving non-human objects (Fetishism, Transvestic Fetishism), the suffering or humiliation of oneself or one's partner

Paraphilia (par-uh-FILL-ee-uh): Recurring, unconventional sexual behaviour that is obsessive and compulsive.

*Marquis de Sade, *Philosophy in the Bedroom.*

(Sexual Sadism, Sexual Masochism), children (Pedophilia), or other non-consenting person (Voyeurism, Frotteurism, Exhibitionism). (*DSM-IV-TR*, p. 566)

Additional diagnostic criteria are stated for each of the specific disorders; these generally include that a) the fantasies, urges, or behaviours have occurred over a period of at least six months, and b) they cause "clinically significant distress or impairment in social, occupational, or other important areas of functioning." These definitions are very influential; they are used in many situations to determine who receives treatment. However, some are also controversial; some authors have argued that these sexual interests do not represent mental disorders and should therefore not be listed in the DSM-IV-TR (Moser, 2001; Moser & Kleinplatz, in press).

Note that most atypical sexual behaviours are not against the law (for example, fetishism and sexual masochism). However, some are. For example, pedophilia, the most serious paraphilia, is against the law because it involves exploitation and force. It is discussed in Chapter 17. Other behaviours do not involve exploitation or force but do violate community standards of taste. In this area we find laws against **indecent exposure**, indecent acts in a public place, and public nudity (refer to In Focus 1.2 for a complete list of sex crimes contained in the Criminal Code of Canada). In addition, there is no provision in the Criminal Code that deals with voyeurism; voyeurism is prosecuted under trespass or loitering provisions. Because these provisions do not adequately deal with people who use cameras to videotape unsuspecting individuals, the federal government is considering adding an offence of "surreptitious viewing and photographing of individuals in a sexual context" to the Criminal Code.

An interesting case that demonstrates how community standards of taste can impact on laws regulating sex crimes arose when Gwen Jacobs walked topless through the town of Guelph in 1991. She was charged with committing an indecent act in a public place. However, in 1996, the Ontario Court of Appeal ruled that women have a right to go topless as long as it is not for commercial gain or sexual purposes.

Indecent exposure: Showing one's genitals in a public place to passersby; exhibitionism.

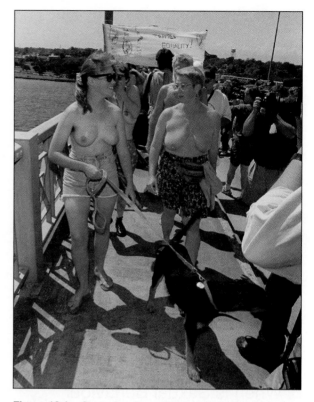

Figure 16.1 Gwen Jacobs and Mary Lou Schloss protested Ontario laws against women going topless in their walk over the Peace Bridge in 1992. In 1996, the Ontario Court of Appeal ruled that going topless is not an indecent act under the Criminal Code.

In this chapter we discuss a number of atypical sexual behaviours, including the seven behaviours that can be diagnosed as paraphilias. As discussed next, all of these behaviours occur along a continuum. Thus, even these seven behaviours can be considered paraphilic only if the person meets the diagnostic criteria listed above; that is, these fantasies, urges, or behaviours are intense, have persisted for six months or longer, and have resulted in significant impairment or distress in important areas of functioning.

The Normal–Abnormal Continuum

Each of the approaches just described provides criteria that attempt to distinguish what is "normal" from "abnormal." While such distinctions may be made in theory, they are often difficult to make in reality. For example, lingerie is often sexually arousing for both men and women. For a woman who is

Figure 16.2   The continuum from normal to abnormal behaviour in the case of fetishes.

wearing a low-cut bra and silk thong panties, the sensuous feel of the material against her skin may be arousing; for a man it might be the sight of the woman wearing the lingerie. At the same time, lingerie is a common sexual fetish object. This is an excellent example of the continuum from normal to abnormal sexual behaviour. That is, normal sexual behaviour and abnormal sexual behaviour—like other normal and abnormal behaviours—are not two separate categories but rather gradations on a continuum. Many people have mild fetishes, finding things such as silk underwear arousing, and that is well within the range of normal behaviour; only when the fetish becomes extreme is it abnormal. Indeed, in one sample of university men, 42 percent reported that they had engaged in voyeurism and 35 percent had engaged in *frottage* (sexual rubbing against a woman in a crowd) (Templeman & Stinnett, 1991). Unfortunately, the researchers did not ask about fetishes. But the point is that many of these behaviours are common even in "normal" populations.

This continuum from normal to abnormal behaviour might be conceptualized using the scheme shown in Figure 16.2. A mild preference, or even a strong preference, for the fetish object (say, silk panties) is within the normal range of sexual behaviour. When the silk panties become a necessity—when the man cannot become aroused and have intercourse unless they are present—we have crossed the boundary into abnormal behaviour. When the man becomes obsessed with white silk panties and shoplifts them at every opportunity, so that he will always have them available, the fetish has become a paraphilia. In extreme forms, the silk panties may become a substitute for a human partner, and the man's sexual behaviour consists of masturbating with the silk panties present. In these extreme forms, the man may commit burglary or even assault to get the desired fetish object, which would certainly fit our definition of abnormal sexual behaviour.

The continuum from normal to abnormal behaviour holds for many of the sexual variations discussed in this chapter, such as voyeurism, exhibitionism, and sadism.

■ Sexual Addictions and Compulsions

Patrick Carnes (1983) advanced the theory that some sexual variations are actually a result of an addictive process much like alcoholism. One definition of alcoholism or other drug dependency is that the person has a pathological relationship with the mood-altering substance. In the case of sexual addiction, the person has a pathological relationship to a sexual event or process, substituting it for a healthy relationship with others. However, there are some differences between chemical addictions that create a physiological dependency and behavioural "addictions." For example, if a person suddenly abstains from an addictive sexual behaviour, there are no physiological withdrawal symptoms as there are from abstaining from using alcohol. A second criticism is that use of the term "addiction" may affect perceptions of these behaviours and thus become an excuse for illegal, destructive behaviour. For example, a sex offender might say: "I'm sexually addicted to forced sex and therefore can't stop myself." Therefore, some experts recommend that we use the term *compulsive sexual behaviour* instead of "sexual addiction" (e.g., Coleman, 1991)

Compulsive Sexual Behaviour

Compulsive sexual behaviour

> is a disorder in which the individual experiences intense sexually arousing fantasies, urges, and associated sexual behaviors that are intrusive, driven, and repetitive. Individuals with this disorder are (a) lacking in impulse control, (b) often incur social and legal sanctions, (c) cause interference in interpersonal and occupational functioning, and (d) create health risks. (Coleman et al., 2001, p. 326)

It can be paraphilic (i.e., involve the sexual behaviours listed in the *DSM-IV-TR*) or nonparaphilic (involve conventional sexual behaviours such as compulsive masturbation or compulsive use of the Internet for sexual purposes) (Coleman et al., 2003). Note that this perspective differs from the addiction approach in emphasizing that the person may experience social and legal sanctions and take health risks. A scale has been developed to measure CSB (Coleman et al., 2001). Forty-two items related to sexual control and other aspects included in the definition above were given to three sample groups: 35 pedophiles, 15 persons with CSB who were not paraphilic, and 42 in a normal control group. Preliminary analyses indicated that 28 of the items were valid. Three factors were identified, which appear to measure *control* (e.g., "How often have you been unable to control your sexual feelings?), *abuse* (e.g., "Have you been forced to have sex?"), and *violence* (e.g., "Have you ever hit, kicked, or beaten any of your sexual partners?"). The scores on the three scales clearly differentiated among the three groups. Pedophiles had higher scores on abuse and lower scores on violence than the other groups. Thus, a measure based on the **compulsive sexual behaviour** model seems to be reliable and to discriminate between groups with different disorders. Coleman et al. (2003) estimate that approximately 5 percent of the population—more men than women—suffer from compulsive sexual behaviour.

The chief distinguishing feature of sexual addictions or compulsions is that the person has lost control of the behaviour. Thus, not all sexual variations are addictions or compulsions. There are also addictions to some behaviours, such as masturbation or Internet sexuality, that in and of themselves are perfectly normal. Thus, for example, the man who masturbates every day in the privacy of his own home while looking at pornographic magazines or at pornography on the Internet is probably not addicted and the behaviour is well within the normal range. However, the man who (and this is based on a client I [ESB] had) rushes from his desk at work several times a day to lock himself in the supply closet to masturbate and can think of little else than the next time he will masturbate even though he has a long-term partner, probably is addicted. The key is the compulsiveness, the lack of control, the obsession (constant thoughts of the sexual scenario), and the obliviousness to danger or harmful consequences.

People who have sexual compulsions or addictions—like alcoholics—often hold faulty beliefs that can contribute to the problem because they involve a denial or distortion of reality. These beliefs allow these people to "justify" their behaviour before engaging in it. For example, they may deny the possibility of sexually transmitted infections. They also engage in self-justification, such as "If I don't have it every few days, the pressure builds up." Like alcoholism, the compulsive behaviour leads to many self-destructive behaviours. The person with a sexual compulsion or addiction may spend money that he or she doesn't have (for example, for payment to prostitutes), may neglect work or family in order to engage in the behaviour (for example, by spending many hours on the Internet), or may risk arrest (for example, for indecent exposure).

According to Carnes's (1983) analysis, each episode of the sexually compulsive behaviour proceeds through a four-step cycle, which intensifies each time it is repeated.

1. *Preoccupation* The person can think of nothing other than the sexual act to which he or she is addicted.
2. *Rituals* The person enacts certain rituals that have become a prelude to the addictive act.
3. *Compulsive sexual behaviour* The sexual behaviour is enacted and the person feels that he or she has no control over it.
4. *Despair* Rather than feeling good after the sexual act is completed, the addict falls into a feeling of hopelessness and despair.

> **Compulsive sexual behaviour:** A disorder in which the person experiences intense sexually arousing fantasies, urges, and associated sexual behaviour.

Interestingly, there is often a history of alcoholism or other types of addictions in the families of people with sexual compulsive behaviour. Sometimes, too, there is a family history of the same sexual compulsive behaviour.

◼ Fetishism

Fetishism is characterized by sexual fantasies, urges, or behaviours involving the use of non-living objects to produce or enhance sexual arousal with or in the absence of a partner. In extreme cases the person is incapable of becoming aroused and having an orgasm unless the fetish object is present. Typically, the fetish item is something closely associated with the body, such as clothing. Inanimate-object fetishes can be roughly divided into two subcategories: media fetishes and form fetishes.

Media Fetishes and Form Fetishes

In a **media fetish,** the material out of which an object is made is the source of arousal. An example would be a leather fetish, in which any leather item is arousing to the person. Media fetishes can be subdivided into hard media fetishes and soft media fetishes. In a hard media fetish, the fetish is for a hard substance, such as leather or rubber. Hard media fetishes may often be associated with sadomasochism (discussed later in this chapter). In a soft media fetish, the substance is soft, such as fur or silk.

In a **form fetish,** it is the object and its shape that are important. An example would be a shoe fetish, in which shoes are highly arousing (see In Focus 16.1). Some shoe fetishes require that the shoes be high-heeled; this fetish may be associated with sadomasochism, in which the fetishist derives sexual satisfaction from being walked on by a woman in high heels. Other shoe fetishes require that the shoes be leather boots that have been worn. Other examples of form fetishes are nylon stockings, garters, and lingerie.

> **Fetishism:** A person's sexual fixation on some object other than another human being and attachment of great erotic significance to that object.
> **Media fetish:** A fetish whose object is anything made of a particular substance, such as leather.
> **Form fetish:** A fetish whose object is a particular shape, such as high-heeled shoes.

Figure 16.3   A common fetish is for leather, often in association with sexual sadism and masochism. This store caters to clientele interested or involved in those activities.

Why Do People Become Fetishists?

Psychologists are not sure what causes fetishes to develop. Here we will consider three theoretical explanations: learning theory, cognitive theory, and the sexual addiction model. These theories can be applied equally well to explaining many of the other sexual variations in this chapter.

According to learning theory (for example, McGuire et al., 1965), fetishes result from classical conditioning, in which a learned association is built between the fetish object and sexual arousal and orgasm. In some cases a single learning trial might serve to cement the association. For example, one adult male recalled:

> I was home alone and saw my uncle's new penny loafers. I went over and started smelling the fresh new leather scent and kissing and licking them. It turned me on so much that I actually ejaculated

In Focus 16.1

A Case History of a Shoe Fetishist

The following case history is taken directly from the 1886 book *Psychopathia Sexualis*, by Richard von Krafft-Ebing, the great early investigator of sexual deviance. It should give you the flavour of his work.

Case 114. X., aged twenty-four, from a badly tainted family (mother's brother and grandfather insane, one sister epileptic, another sister subject to migraine, parents of excitable temperament). During dentition [teething] he had convulsions. At the age of seven he was taught to masturbate by a servant girl. X. first experienced pleasure in these manipulations when the girl happened to touch his member [penis] with her shoe-clad foot. Thus, in the predisposed boy, an association was established, as a result of which, from that time on, merely the sight of a woman's shoe, and finally, merely the idea of them, sufficed to induce sexual excitement and erection. He now masturbated while looking at women's shoes or while calling them up in imagination. The shoes of the school mistress excited him intensely, and in general he was affected by shoes that were partly concealed by female garments. One day he could not keep from grasping the teacher's shoes—an act that caused him great sexual excitement. In spite of punishment he could not keep from performing this act repeatedly. Finally, it was recognized that there must be an abnormal motive in play, and he was sent to a male teacher. He then revelled in the memory of the shoe scenes with his former school mistress and thus had erections, orgasms, and, after his fourteenth year, ejaculation. At the same time, he masturbated while thinking of a woman's shoes. One day the thought came to him to increase his pleasure by using such a shoe for masturbation. Thereafter he frequently took shoes secretly and used them for that purpose.

Nothing else in a woman could excite him; the thought of coitus filled him with horror. Men did not interest him in any way. At the age of eighteen he opened a shop and, among other things, dealt in ladies' shoes. He was excited sexually by fitting shoes for his female patrons or by manipulating shoes that came for mending. One day while doing this he had an epileptic attack, and, soon after, another while practicing onanism in his customary way. Then he recognized for the first time the injury to health caused by his sexual practices. He tried to overcome his onanism, sold no more shoes, and strove to free himself from the abnormal association between women's shoes and the sexual function. Then frequent pollutions, with erotic dreams about shoes occurred, and the epileptic attacks continued. Though devoid of the slightest feeling for the female sex, he determined on marriage, which seemed to him to be the only remedy.

He married a pretty young lady. In spite of lively erections when he thought of his wife's shoes, in attempts at cohabitation he was absolutely impotent because his distaste for coitus and for close intercourse in general was far more powerful than the influence of the shoe-idea, which induced sexual excitement. On account of his impotence the patient applied to Dr. Hammond, who treated his epilepsy with bromides and advised him to hang a shoe up over his bed and look at it fixedly during coitus, at the same time imagining his wife to be a shoe. The patient became free from epileptic attacks and potent so that he could have coitus about once a week. His sexual excitation by women's shoes also grew less and less.

Source: Von Krafft-Ebing, 1886; 1965.

my first load into my pants and have been turned on ever since. (Weinberg et al., 1995, p. 22)

In this case, shoes were associated with sexual arousal as the result of an early learning experience. Another example appears to be the shoe fetishist

described above. This case clearly exemplifies the *DSM-IV-TR* criteria for paraphilia. The youth/man experienced sexual fantasies and urges associated with women's shoes for years, experienced arousal and ejaculation only when they were present, and experienced significant impairment in his academic and social life as a result. There was even an experiment that demonstrated that males could, in the laboratory, be conditioned to become sexually aroused when viewing pictures of shoes (Rachman, 1966).

A second possible theoretical explanation comes from cognitive psychology, discussed in Chapter 2 (Walen & Roth, 1987). According to cognitive theorists, fetishists (or other paraphiliacs) have a serious cognitive distortion in that they perceive an unconventional stimulus—such as black leather boots—as erotic. Further, their perception of arousal (link 4 in the model; refer to Figure 9.5) is distorted. They feel "driven" to the sexual behaviour when aroused, but the arousal may actually be caused by feelings of guilt and self-loathing. Thus there is a chain in which there are initial feelings of guilt at thoughts of the unconventional behaviour, which produces arousal, which is misinterpreted as sexual arousal, which leads to a feeling that the fetish ritual must be carried out; it is, there is orgasm and temporary feelings of relief, but the evaluation of the event is negative, leading to further feelings of guilt and self-loathing, which perpetuates the chain.

A third theory that has been advanced to explain some atypical sexual behaviours, especially those that seem compulsive, is the theory of sexual addiction, discussed earlier in this chapter.

Whatever the cause, fetishism typically develops early in life. In one sample of foot or shoe fetishists, the mean age at which respondents reported first being sexually aroused by feet or shoes was 12 years (Weinberg et al., 1995).

■ Transvestism

Cross-dressing refers to wearing clothes stereotypically associated with the other gender. **Transvestism** ("trans" = "cross"; "vest" = "dressing") refers to cross-dressing for erotic purposes (Moser & Kleinplatz, 2002).

Cross-dressing may be done by a variety of people for a variety of reasons. As discussed in Chapter 14, transgender individuals cross-dress to express a more feminine or masculine side of themselves. Further, transsexuals live as the other gender as part of transitioning. Some gay men—**drag queens**—dress up as women, and some lesbians dress in masculine clothes (drag kings); these practices, though, are basically caricatures of traditional gender roles. **Female impersonators** are men who dress as women, often as part of their jobs as entertainers. For example, Jack Lemmon and Tony Curtis were female impersonators in the classic film with Marilyn Monroe, *Some Like It Hot*. Robin Williams as *Mrs. Doubtfire* and Dustin Hoffman as *Tootsie* won praise from critics and big box office profits for their impersonations of women. Finally, some—perhaps many—adolescent boys cross-dress, usually only once or a few times (Green, 1975). This behaviour does not necessarily mean that the boy will continue to cross-dress throughout his life; it may simply reflect the sexual drives, confusions, and frustrations of adolescence.

In contrast to people who engage in cross-dressing for the reasons discussed above, a transvestite is a heterosexual man who dresses in female clothing to produce or enhance sexual arousal (American Psychiatric Association, 2000).[1] If his fantasies, urges, or behaviours meet the *DSM-IV* diagnostic criteria for paraphilia, the man is said to have a transvestic fetish. The cross-dressing is often done in private, perhaps by a married man without his partner's knowledge.

As a result of such secrecy, no one has accurate data on the incidence of transvestic fetishism. One authority, though, has estimated that more than a million males in the United States get aroused by wearing female clothing at least on occasion (Pomeroy, 1975). This would translate to about 100,000 Canadian men.

Transvestic fetishism is almost exclusively a male sexual variation; it is essentially unknown among women. There may be a number of reasons for this difference, including our culture's tolerance of women who wear masculine clothing and intolerance of men who wear feminine clothing. The phenomenon illustrates a more general point, namely,

---

[1] A common abbreviation for transvestism, used both by scientists and by members of the transvestite subculture, is TV.

Transvestism: The practice of deriving sexual gratification from dressing as a member of the other gender; tranvestic fetishism.

Drag queen: A male homosexual who dresses in women's clothing.
Female impersonator: A man who dresses up as a woman as part of a job in entertainment.

(a)   *(b)*

Figure 16.4   Two examples of cross-dressing: *(a)* Lead actors in several films have portrayed a cross-dresser (e.g., the three leads from *To Wong Foo, Thanks for Everything! Julie Newmar*). *(b)* Men in drag.

that many sexual variations are defined for, or practised almost exclusively by, members of one gender; the parallel practice by members of the other gender is often not considered deviant. Most sexual variations are practised mainly by men.[2]

A common means of studying persons with atypical sexual behaviour patterns is to place ads in specialty newsletters and magazines, and to solicit participants at meetings and conventions attended by such persons. Using these procedures, researchers gathered survey data from 1,032 cross-dressers (Docter & Prince, 1997). The sample did

not include drag queens or female impersonators. The vast majority of the men (87 percent) were heterosexual, 60 percent were married, 65 percent had a university education, and 76 percent reported being raised by both parents through age 18. Sixty-six percent reported that their first cross-dressing experience occurred before age 10. Sexual excitement and orgasm were reported by 40 percent as often or almost always associated with cross-dressing. This indicates that this sample included men who cross-dress for a variety of reasons—not just men who do so to enhance sexual arousal. Almost all (93 percent) preferred complete cross-dressing, but only 14 percent frequently went out in public dressed as a woman.

Another survey was conducted by mailing questionnaires to 1,200 members of a U.S. cross-dressing organization (Bullough & Bullough, 1997). There were 372 questionnaires returned. The median age at which the men began to cross-dress was 8.5; 32 percent reported that they first dressed as a female before they were 6. Most of them reported cross-dressing as children, and 56 percent said they were never caught.

Research indicates that transvestites have four basic motivations (Talamini, 1982):

[2]Several theories have been proposed to explain why there are so many more men than women with paraphilias (Finkelhor & Russell, 1984). Sociobiologists believe that the difference lies in the evolutionary selection of males to inseminate many partners and to be aroused by sexual stimuli devoid of emotional content (Wilson, 1987). Sociologists point to gender role socialization, which teaches males to be instrumental and to initiate sexual interactions. Females, on the other hand, are taught to be nurturing and to empathize with others; for example, with the vulnerability of children (Traven et al., 1990). Moser and Kleinplatz (in press) argue that diagnosis of certain paraphilias, such as transvestism, results from the tendency in our culture to define masculinity very narrowly as well as to pathologize unconventional behaviour.

1. *Sexual arousal* Transvestism appears to result from a conditioned association between sexual arousal and women's clothing. As one male transvestite commented,

   My older sister had beautiful clothes. When I was thirteen I wanted to see what I looked like when I dressed as a woman. We're about the same height. I put some of her lingerie on and I never had such powerful sexual feelings. It's twenty years later and I still dress up. (Talamini, 1982, p. 20)

2. *Relaxation* Cross-dressers report that they periodically need a break from the confining, pressured male role. Dressing up as women allows them to express emotionality and grace, traits that are taboo for men in our society.

3. *Role playing* Just as many actors derive great satisfaction from playing roles in the theatre, so cross-dressers gain a great sense of achievement from being able to pass as women when in public.

4. *Adornment* Men's clothes are relatively drab, whereas women's are more colourful and beautiful. Cross-dressers enjoy this sense of being beautiful.

How do the partner and children of the cross-dresser react to his unusual behaviour? In one sample of 50 heterosexual transvestites, 60 percent of the wives were accepting of their husband's cross-dressing (Talamini, 1982). Most of these women commented that he was a good husband. Some of the wives felt fulfilled being supportive of the husband, and some even helped him in dressing and applying makeup. In the same sample, 13 of the couples had told their children about the cross-dressing. They claimed that the relationship with the children was undamaged and that the children were tolerant and understanding. However, given societal attitudes toward cross-dressing and gender roles, the partner may have problems with it—particularly if she did not know about the cross-dressing before they became involved.

Transvestism is one of the harmless, victimless sexual variations. Like other fetishes, it is a problem only when it becomes so extreme that it is the person's only source of erotic gratification, or when it becomes a compulsion the person cannot control and therefore causes distress in other areas of the person's life.

■ Sadism and Masochism

Definitions

A **sexual sadist** is a person who derives sexual satisfaction from inflicting pain, suffering, or humiliation on another person. The term "sadism" derives from the name of the Marquis de Sade, who lived around the time of the French Revolution. Not only did he practise sexual sadism—several women apparently died from his attentions (Bullough, 1976)—but he also wrote novels about these practices (the best known is *Justine*), thus assuring his place in history.

A **sexual masochist** is a person who is sexually aroused by fantasies, urges, or behaviours involving being beaten, humiliated, bound, or tortured to enhance or achieve sexual excitement. This variation is named after Leopold von Sacher-Masoch (1836–1895), who was himself a masochist and who wrote novels expressing masochistic fantasies. Notice that the definitions of these variations make specific their *sexual* nature; the terms are often loosely used to refer to people who are cruel or to people who seem to bring misfortune on themselves, but these are not the meanings used here. These two are often referred to as a pair since the two behaviours or roles (giving and receiving pain) are complementary.

There are two other styles of interaction that are related to sadism-masochism (S-M). These are bondage and discipline (B-D) and dominance and submission (D-S) (Ernulf & Innala, 1995). **Bondage and discipline** refers to the use of physically restraining devices or psychologically restraining commands as a central aspect of sexual interactions. These devices or commands may enforce obedience and servitude without inducing any physical pain. **Dominance and submission** refers to interaction that involves a consensual exchange

---

Sexual sadist: A person who derives sexual satisfaction from inflicting pain, suffering, or humiliation on another person.
Sexual masochist: A person who derives sexual satisfaction from experiencing pain.
Bondage and discipline: The use of physical or psychological restraint to enforce servitude, from which both participants derive sensual pleasure.
Dominance and submission: The use of power consensually given to control the sexual stimulation and behaviour of the other person.

of power; the dominant partner uses his or her power to control and sexually stimulate the submissive partner. Both B-D and D-S encompass a variety of specific interactions that range from atypical to paraphilic.

Sexual Sadomasochistic Behaviour

Sadomasochism (S-M) is a rare form of sexual behaviour, although in its milder forms it is probably more common than many people think. In fact, discussion of spanking and use of handcuffs during sexual activity has made it to such prime-time television shows as *Friends*, *Sex and the City*, and *Seinfeld*. Kinsey found that about one-quarter of both males and females had experienced definite or frequent erotic response as a result of being bitten during sexual activity (Kinsey et al., 1953). Sadistic or masochistic sexual fantasies are more common; a New Brunswick study found that 65 percent of university students have sexual fantasies of being tied up and 62 percent have fantasies of tying someone up (Renaud & Byers, 1999).

How might you approach your partner about a sexual variation you'd like to try? Watch the "Whipsmart" video in Chapter 16 of your CD for some ideas.

In one study, 178 men who responded to an ad in an S-M magazine or belonged to an S-M support group filled out a questionnaire (Moser & Levitt, 1987). The majority were heterosexual, well educated, and interested in both dominant and submissive roles (switchable). The following are behaviours that the majority of them had both tried and enjoyed: humiliation, bondage, spanking, whipping, fetish behaviour, tying up with ropes, and master-and-slave role playing.

Another study administered questionnaires to 130 men and 52 women who responded to ads placed in S-M magazines; the study focused particularly on the women respondents (Breslow et al., 1985). Thirty-three percent of the males and 28 percent of the females preferred the dominant role; 41 percent of the males and 40 percent of the females preferred the submissive role; and 26 percent of the males and 32 percent of the females were versatile. The majority of these S-M respon-

dents were heterosexual. Men involved in S-M frequently report having been interested in such activity since childhood; women are more likely to report having been introduced to the subculture by someone else (Weinberg, 1994). Women prefer bondage, spanking, and master-slave role playing (Levitt et al., 1994).

Thus, there is a spectrum of activities that constitute S-M. People who become involved in it often have tried a variety of these behaviours and find only some of them satisfying. They develop a script of activities that they prefer to enact each time they engage in S-M. One group of researchers (Santilla et al., 2002) identified 29 individual sexual behaviours associated with S-M. They administered questionnaires to 184 Finnish men and women who were members of S-M clubs. Each participant was asked which of the behaviours he or she had participated in during the preceding year. Four clusters or themes were identified: hypermasculinity (e.g., dildo, enema), administering and receiving pain (e.g., clothespins attached to nipples, caning, hot wax), physical restriction (e.g., handcuffs, straitjackets), and humiliation (e.g., verbal humiliation, face slapping). Further analyses of participation in the behaviours within each cluster identified a continuum in frequency from very common to very rare, with the order of the behaviours suggesting that this continuum reflects a dimension from least to most intense. For example, the humiliation continuum ranges from flagellation (reported by 81 percent; least intense) to verbal humiliation (70 percent) to gagging (53 percent) and face slapping (37 percent), to using knives to make surface wounds (11 percent; most intense). The results suggest that the S-M activities within each cluster are *scripted*, with the less intense behaviours being much more common.

Some observers note that S-M is about play, as in the theatre. S-M sexual activities are organized into "scenes"; one "plays" with one's S-M partners. In addition to the activities such as those discussed above, roles, costumes, and props are an important part of each scene. The roles include slave and master, maid and mistress, and teacher and pupil. The costumes range from simple to elaborate. The props may include tight leather clothing, pins and needles, ropes, whips, and hot wax. In S-M clubs, there are often rules governing the social and S-M interaction, particularly the creation and enactment of scenes. According to one Web site, the rules include no touching of another's body without consent, giving players the room they need to enact a scene, not intruding physically or verbally on a scene in progress, and may include no sexual penetration.

Interestingly, sexual sadists and masochists do not consistently find experiencing pain and giving pain to be sexually satisfying. For example, the masochist who smashes a finger in a car door will yell and be unhappy just like anyone else. Pain is arousing for such people only when it is part of a carefully scripted ritual. As one woman put it,

> Of course, he doesn't *really* hurt me. I mean quite recently he tied me down ready to receive "punishment," and then by mistake he kicked my heel with his toe as he walked by. I gave a yelp, and he said, "Sorry love—did I hurt you?" (Gosselin & Wilson, 1980, p. 55)

Causes of Sexual Sadomasochism

The causes of sexual sadism and masochism are not precisely known. The theories discussed in the section on fetishes can be applied here as well. For example, learning theory points to conditioning as an explanation. A little boy is being spanked over his mother's knee; in the process, his penis rubs against her knee, and he gets an erection. Or a little girl is caught masturbating and is spanked. In both cases, the child has learned to associate pain or spanking with sexual arousal, possibly setting up a lifelong career as a masochist. On the other hand, in one sample of sadomasochists, more than 80 percent did *not* recall receiving erotic enjoyment from being punished as a child (Moser, 1979, cited in Weinberg, 1987). Thus forces besides conditioning may be at work.

Another psychological theory has been proposed to explain sexual masochism specifically, although not sadism (Baumeister, 1988a, 1988b). According to the theory, the masochist is motivated by a desire to escape from self-awareness. That is, the masochistic behaviour helps the individual escape from being conscious of the self in the same way that drunkenness and some forms of meditation do. In an era dominated by individualism and self-interest, why would anyone want to escape from the self? Probably because high levels of self-awareness can lead to anxiety as a result of a focus on pressures on the self, added responsibilities, the need to keep up a good image in front of others, and so on. Sexual masochistic activity allows the person to escape from being an autonomous, separate individual. Sexual masochism may be an unusually powerful form of escape because of its link to sexual pleasure. This theory can also explain why sexual masochism is more common among males than among females (Baumeister, 1988b). According to the theory, the male role is especially burdensome because of the heavy pressures for autonomy, separateness, and individual achievement. Sexual masochism accomplishes an escape from these aspects of the male role. Some men cross-dress while engaging in sexual masochistic activity, a finding that tends to support this theory (Chivers & Blanchard, 1996).

Bondage and Discipline

Sexual bondage, the use in sexual behaviour of restraining devices that have sexual significance, has been a staple of erotic fiction and art for centuries. Current mainstream and adult films and videos portray this activity. In some communities, individuals interested in B-D have formed clubs. There are many B-D sites on the Internet.

We noted earlier the difficulty of gathering data on participation in variant forms of sexual expression. One innovative study downloaded all the messages about bondage mailed to an international computer discussion group (Ernulf & Innala, 1995). Of the messages in which senders indicated their gender, 75 percent were male. Of those indicating a sexual orientation, most were heterosex-

Figure 16.5 Bondage.

ual; 18 percent said they were gay, and 11 percent said they were lesbian. The messages were coded for discussion of what the person found sexually arousing about B-D. Most frequently mentioned (12 percent) was play: "sex is funny, and sex is lovely, and sex is PLAY." Next was the exchange of power (4 percent): "It is a power trip because the active is responsible for the submissive's pleasure." The next most common themes were intensified sexual pleasure, tactile stimulation associated with the use of ropes and cuffs, and the visual enjoyment experienced by the dominant person.

There is a marked imbalance in preferences for the active ("top") and passive ("bottom") roles. Most men and women, regardless of their sexual orientation, prefer to be "bottom." This may be the reason why there are an estimated 2,500 professional dominatrices in the United States.

Dominance and Submission

Sociologists emphasize that the key to S-M is not pain, but rather dominance and submission (D-S) (Weinberg, 1987). Thus it is not an individual phenomenon, but rather a social behaviour embedded in a subculture and controlled by elaborate scripts.

Sociologists feel that to understand D-S one must understand the social processes that create and sustain it (Weinberg, 1987). There is a distinct D-S subculture, involving magazines (such as *Corporal*), clubs, and bars. It creates culturally defined meanings for D-S acts. Thus a D-S act is not a wild outbreak of violence, but rather a carefully controlled performance with a script (recall the concept of scripts in Chapter 2). One woman reported that:

> we got into dominance and submission. Like him giving me orders. Being very rough and pushing me around and giving me orders, calling me a slut, calling me a cunt. Making me crawl around . . . on all fours and beg to suck his cock. Dominance-submission is more important than the pain. I've done lots and lots of scenes that involve no pain. Just a lot of taking orders, being humiliated. (Maurer, 1994, pp. 253, 257)

Within the play, people take on roles such as master, slave, or naughty child. Thus men can play the submissive role in D-S culture, even though it contradicts the male role, because it is really not they who are the naughty child, just as an actor can

play the part of a murderer and know that he is not a murderer.

One interesting phenomenon, from a sociological point of view, is the social control over risk taking that exists in the D-S subculture (Weinberg, 1987). That is, having allowed oneself to be tied up or restrained and then whipped, one could be seriously injured or even murdered, yet such outcomes are rare. Why? Research shows that complex social arrangements are made in order to reduce the risk (Lee, 1979). First, initial contacts are usually made in protected territories such as bars or meetings, that are inhabited by other people involved in D-S who play by the same rules. Second, the basic scripts are widely shared, so that everyone understands what will and will not occur. When the participants are strangers, the scenario may be negotiated before it is enacted. Third, as the activity unfolds, very subtle non-verbal signals are used to control the interaction (Weinberg, 1994). By using these signals, the person playing the submissive role can influence what occurs. Thus, as two people enact the master and slave script, the master is not in complete control and the slave is not powerless. So it is the *illusion* of control, not actual control, that is central to D-S activity for both the master and the slave.

■ Voyeurism

There are two types of **voyeur** ("Peeping Tom").[3] In **scoptophilia,** sexual pleasure is derived from observing sexual acts and the genitals; in *voyeurism*, technically, the sexual pleasure comes from viewing nudes, often while the voyeur is masturbating. The most recent strategy of voyeurs is to secretly install small video cameras so that they can observe women using the washroom or changing their clothes.

The Criminal Code of Canada does not include

---

[3]"Voyeur" comes from the French word *voir*, meaning "to see." "Peeping Tom" comes from the story of Lady Godiva; when she rode through town nude to protest the fact that her husband was raising his tenants' taxes, none of the townspeople looked except one, Tom of Coventry.

Voyeur: A person who becomes sexually aroused from secretly viewing nudes.
Scoptophilia: A sexual variation in which the person becomes sexually aroused by observing others' sexual acts and genitals.

a specific crime of "voyeurism." Instead, voyeurs who are arrested are typically charged with trespassing or with invasion of privacy.

Voyeurism provides another good illustration of the continuum from normal to abnormal behaviour. For example, many men and women find it arousing to watch a man or woman undress and "dance"—otherwise there would be no strip clubs—and this is certainly well within the normal range of behaviour. Some women are "crotch watchers," much as men are breast watchers (Friday, 1973, 1975). However, voyeurism can also be a paraphilia.

Peepers are typically men who want the woman they view to be a stranger and do not want her to know what they are doing (Yalom, 1960). The element of risk is also important; while one might think that a nudist camp would be heaven to a peeper, it is not, because the elements of risk and forbiddenness are missing (Sagarin, 1973).

Voyeurs may or may not be dangerous (Tutuer, 1984). Potentially dangerous voyeurs can be identified by the following characteristics: (1) They enter the confines of a building or other structure in order to view their subject, and (2) they draw the attention of their subject to the fact that they are watching (Yalom, 1960).

A study of 561 males who sought treatment for paraphilias included 62 voyeurs (Abel & Rouleau, 1990). One-third reported that their first experience occurred before they were 12 years old. One-half said they recognized their interest in peeping prior to age 15. These men estimated that, on average, they had peeped at 470 persons.

In one study of arrested (male) voyeurs, it was found that they were likely to be the youngest child in their family and to have good relationships with their parents but poor ones with their peers (Gebhard et al., 1965). They had few sisters and few female friends. Few were married. These studies, however, point out one of the major problems with the research on sexual variations: much of it has been done only on people who have been arrested for their behaviour or sought treatment. The "respectable" person with a paraphilia who has the behaviour under somewhat better control or who is skilled enough or can pull enough strings not to get caught is not studied in such research. Thus the picture that research provides for us of these variations may be very biased.

■ Exhibitionism

The complement to voyeurism is **exhibitionism** ("flashing"), in which the person derives sexual pleasure from exposing his genitals to others in situations where this is clearly inappropriate. In the Criminal Code this is referred to as indecent exposure. The pronoun "his" is used advisedly, since exhibitionism is primarily associated with men. When a man exposes himself, his behaviour is likely to be considered offensive. On the other hand, a man who notices that a woman wearing a skirt is not wearing underwear is more likely to be turned on than offended. Here again, whether a sexual behaviour is considered abnormal depends greatly on whether the person doing it is a male or a female. Homosexual exhibitionism is also quite rare; so the prototype we have for exhibitionism is a man exposing himself to a woman. Research in New Brunswick found that in 1996, 6 percent of male sex offenders were convicted for exhibitionism (Byers et al., 1997). Many of the men convicted for exhibitionism, 48 percent in one Canadian study, commit another offence involving indecent exposure within the next few years (Marshall et al., 1991). In addition, 6 percent of the exhibitionists in an Ottawa study were subsequently convicted of a hands-on sexual offence such as sexual touching or sexual assault (Greenberg et al., 2002). According to one survey, 33 percent of university women have been the objects of indecent exposure (Cox, 1988).

According to the study of males seeking treatment for paraphilias (Abel & Rouleau, 1990), 15 percent of the exhibitionists had exposed themselves at least once by age 12; one-half had done so by age 15. According to other research (Blair & Lanyon, 1981), exhibitionists generally recall their childhoods as being characterized by inconsistent discipline, lack of affection, and little training in appropriate forms of social behaviour. An analysis of 10 studies of the social skills of sexual offenders (rapists, molesters, incest offenders, pedophiles, and exhibitionists) found that sexual offenders possess fewer social skills than non-offenders (Emmers-Sommer et al., 2004).

In adulthood, exhibitionists do not seem to be

Exhibitionist: A person who derives sexual gratification from exposing his genitals to others in situations in which this is inappropriate.

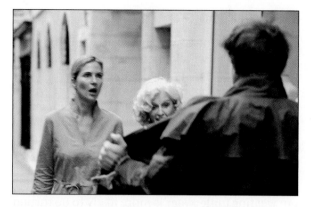

Figure 16.6 Exhibitionism.

psychiatrically disturbed (Blair & Lanyon, 1981). However, they generally are timid and unassertive and lacking in social skills. They also seem to have trouble recognizing and handling their own feelings of hostility. Many are married, but they do not seem to be gratified with heterosexual sex.

The causes of exhibitionism are not known, but a social learning-theory explanation offers some possibilities (Blair & Lanyon, 1981). According to this view, the parents might have subtly (or perhaps obviously) modelled such behaviour to the person when he was a child. In adulthood, there may be reinforcements for the exhibitionistic behaviour because the man gets attention when he performs it. In addition, even if he is married, the man may lack the social skills to form an intimate adult relationship (Marshall, 1989). As a result he receives little reinforcement from interpersonal sex.

The learning-theory approach has been used to devise some programs of therapy that have been successful in treating exhibitionists. For example, exhibitionists may be shown photos of scenes in which they typically engaged in exhibitionism; while experiencing arousal to the scene, an unpleasant-smelling substance is placed at their nostrils (Maletzky, 1997). After 11 to 19 twice-weekly sessions of this conditioning and some self-administered home sessions, all but one of the men passed a temptation test in which they were placed in a naturalistic situation with a volunteer female and managed not to flash at her. Therapists typically also apply a variety of cognitive techniques. For example, most exhibitions have a number of cognitive distortions such as "Many girls find this amusing" or "These women are older than me

and therefore cannot be harmed." The therapist would help the man identify and alter these cognitions as one focus of therapy (Maletzky, 1997).

Many women, understandably, are alarmed by exhibitionists. But since the exhibitionist's goal is to produce shock or some other strong emotional response, the woman who becomes extremely upset is gratifying him. Probably the best strategy for a woman to use in this situation is to remain calm and make some remark indicating her coolness, such as suggesting that he should seek professional help for his problem.

A study of 62 female sex offenders in Great Britain identified five women who had exhibited themselves (O'Connor, 1987). One 21-year-old woman stripped off her clothes and masturbated in public on several occasions. A 25-year-old single woman exposed her genitals and invited passersby to have sex with her. A 40-year-old woman entered private residences, took off her clothes, and invited any male present (including one child) to have sex with her. Two women were arrested while urinating in public. All five women had histories of unusual behaviour and had been diagnosed with alcohol or psychiatric problems. Their atypical sexual behaviours appear to reflect these problems, rather than sexual motivations.

Notice that both voyeurism and exhibitionism are considered problematic behaviour when the other person involved is an unwilling participant. A man who derives erotic pleasure from watching his partner undress or a woman who is aroused by exhibiting her body in new lingerie to her partner are not engaging in criminal or paraphilic behaviour.

■ Hypersexuality

We turn now to several variations that are not explicitly listed in the *DSM-IV-TR*; however, each of these also may vary from atypical through compulsive to paraphilic, depending on their frequency, duration, and consequences.

Hypersexuality includes nymphomania and satyriasis, conditions in which there is an extraordinarily high level of sexual activity and sex drive; the person is apparently insatiable and, at the extreme, sexuality overshadows all other concerns and interests. When it occurs in women, it is called nymphomania; in men it is called *satyriasis* (or Don

Figure 16.7   Historical painting of a satyr, which gives the name to satyriasis, a sexual variation in which a man has an excessive, insatiable sex drive.

Juanism).[5] While this definition seems fairly simple, in practice it is difficult to say when a person has an abnormally high sex drive. As was seen in Chapters 11 and 12, there is a wide range in the frequencies with which people engage in coitus; therefore, the range we define as "normal" should also be broad. In real life, **"nymphomania"** or **"satyriasis"** is often defined by the spouse who thinks his or her partner wants sex "too" frequently.

Because these two terms are imprecise, some researchers prefer the term hypersexuality. **Hypersexuality** refers to an excessive, insatiable sex drive in either a man or a woman. It leads to compulsive sexual behaviour in the sense that the person feels driven to it even when there may be very negative consequences (Goldberg, 1987). The person is also never satisfied by the activity, and she or he may not be having orgasms, despite all the sexual activity. Such cases meet the criteria for abnormal behaviour discussed at the beginning of this chapter: The compulsiveness of the behaviour leads it to become extremely inefficient, with the result that it impairs functioning in other areas of the

person's life. While most people use sexuality sites on the Internet in healthy ways, some people feel driven toward online sexual pursuits. Compulsive cybersex use is discussed below.

A study of 100 male patients with paraphilias or related disorders focused on creating an operational definition of hypersexuality (Kafka, 1997b). The results supported the use of the criterion of seven or more orgasms per week for a minimum duration of six months. The men reported an average of 7.4 to 8.0 orgasms per week in the preceding six months; the modal time per day the men spent in unconventional sexual activity was one to two hours. The most common unconventional behaviours were compulsive masturbation (67 percent of the sample), protracted promiscuity (56 percent), and dependence upon pornography (41 percent). The most common paraphilias were exhibitionism, voyeurism, and pedophilia.

This research provides a useful operational definition for men, but note that the suggested criterion should not be applied to women. The criterion

[5]Satyriasis is named for the satyrs, who were part-human, part-animal beasts in Greek mythology. A part of the entourage of Dionysus, the god of wine and fertility, they were jovial and lusty and have become a symbol of the sexually active male.

Nymphomania (nim-foh-MANE-ee-uh): An excessive, insatiable sex drive in a woman.
Satyriasis (sat-ur-EYE-uh-sis): An excessive, insatiable sex drive in a man.
Hypersexuality: An excessive, insatiable sex drive in either men or women.

HOT COUPLES
SWM, 35, 6'1", 210lbs., brown hair, blue eyes. Seeks hot couple or single ladies for exotic fun. Does your lady need more fantasies fulfilled? Age/weight unimportant. Ad# 6240

FIRST TIMER
W couple, late 30s. Seeking Bi-SWF, 25-40, for occassional erotic adventures. Must be height/weight proportionate, drug/disease-free. Ad# 6250

BI-KER BABE
Wanted! Couple 30s, who like to ride. She's: sensuous, lewd. He's: fine, driving and lasting. You're: lovely in leather or lace. On bikes, bars, or candlelight dining, friends sharing what we like best. We're open! Ad# 6256

Figure 16.8 Advertising for partners. Many newspapers and magazines carry such "personal ads." © Tribune Media Services, Inc. All rights reserved. Reprinted with permission.

is stated as the number of orgasms per week. Some women rarely or never experience orgasms; in fact, their anorgasmia might cause them to engage in compulsive sexual behaviour. Another problem is that women who are orgasmic are capable of multiple orgasms during a single session of activity (see Chapter 9). A woman who engages in sexual activity three times a week could experience seven or eight orgasms, which would not be atypical or abnormal. Once again, we see that a person's gender is very important in defining abnormality. A valid criterion for hypersexuality in men thus may not be valid for women.

One study of highly sexual women recruited participants from volunteers at presentations about the topic, and via newspaper ads in alternative newspapers (Blumberg, 2003). The term *highly sexual* refers to women who desire sexual stimulation to orgasm six or seven times per week, or who think of themselves as highly sexual and their sexuality frequently strongly affects their lives. Forty-four women were interviewed, ranging in age from 20 to 82, from such diverse occupations as janitor and corporate CEO; 41 of the 44 were white. Twenty-five percent were married; 48 percent were separated or divorced. The preferred weekly frequency of sexual episodes—again, not orgasms—ranged from 3 to 70. The women reported that the internal demand for sexual

excitement and satisfaction was too strong to be ignored; for many of them, it shaped their daily lives. This demand led to challenges in the areas of their feelings about themselves, their relationships with partners, and their relationships with female friends. Some of the women found it impossible to form a single relationship that could fulfill their needs, leading to multiple partners or the frequent forming of new relationships. The researcher believes that neither the term *sexual addiction* nor *compulsive sexual behaviour* should be applied to this behaviour. These women did not feel that their behaviour was out of control, and they did not report an increase in frequency of behaviour or the impact of it on their lives over time.

■ Asphyxiophilia

Asphyxiophilia is the desire to induce in oneself a state of oxygen deficiency in order to create sexual arousal or to enhance sexual excitement and orgasm (Zaviačič, 1994). A variety of techniques are used, including temporary strangulation by a rope around the neck, a pillow against the face, or a

Asphyxiophilia: The desire to induce in oneself a state of oxygen deficiency in order to create sexual arousal or to enhance excitement and orgasm.

plastic bag over the head or upper body. Obviously, this is very dangerous behaviour; a miscalculation can lead to death.

Little is known about asphyxiophilia. Most of the deaths attributed to the practice involve men. There were 118 recorded deaths due to asphyxiophilia in Alberta and Ontario (the only provinces that record this information) between 1974 and 1987; only one was female (Hucker & Blanchard, 1992). The average age of death was 26 but ranged from 10 to 56 years. Such cases are often obvious to the trained investigator. Characteristics that distinguish these deaths from intentional suicides include a male who is nude, cross-dressed, or dressed with genitals exposed, and evidence of sexual activity at the time of death (Hucker & Blanchard, 1992). Pornography or other props such as mirrors are often present (Zaviačič, 1994).

Recently, some cases have been identified involving women (Byard et al., 1993). A review of eight fatal cases among women found that only one involved unusual clothing, and none involved pornography or props. Two of the cases were initially ruled homicide, one suicide, and five accidental death. The investigators suggest that death due to asphyxiophilia may be much more common among women than we realize, because these deaths are less often recognized for what they are by investigators.

Men and women engage in asphyxiophilia in the belief that arousal and orgasm are intensified by reduced oxygen. There is no way to determine whether this is true. If the experience is more intense, it may be due to heightened arousal created by the risk rather than by reduced oxygen. Some believe that certain women may experience an orgasm accompanied by urethral ejaculation; this belief has been identified as one reason women engage in asphyxiophilia. Again, there is no evidence.

There is probably a range, from those who try this activity once out of curiosity to those who engage in it repeatedly and compulsively. Obviously, practitioners don't want to kill themselves; most include a self-release mechanism, but these safeguards sometimes fail.

■ Cybersex Use and Abuse

A major concern in recent years has been whether the use of the Internet to access sexually oriented materials, chat rooms, and bulletin boards can become compulsive, addictive, or paraphilic. Recall that compulsive behaviour involves (a) a lack of impulse control, (b) a tendency to lead to social and legal sanctions, (c) interference in interpersonal and occupational functioning, and (d) the creation of health risks. Addictive behaviour involves preoccupation, ritual, loss of control, and despair. Paraphilias are behaviours defined as lasting six months or more and causing significant distress. This concern has been raised by therapists and clinicians, who report cases of Internet use leading to job loss, relationship difficulties leading to divorce, and other adverse consequences (Galbreath et al., 2002).

If we think about Internet sexual behaviour as falling on a continuum from healthy and normal to unhealthy and abnormal, most people who use the Internet for sexually related activities are cybersex users, not cybersex abusers, addicts, or compulsives (Cooper et al., 1999a, 1996b). However, the Internet is thought to be especially likely to be involved in leading to addictive or compulsive behaviour because it is characterized by the three A's: anonymity, accessibility, and affordability (if you aren't poor). Unlike face-to-face behaviours such as cruising for a partner or buying or renting X-rated videos, Internet users are anonymous. The Net is available 24/7, and its use is relatively cheap—you can download almost any kind of sexual material for as little as $2.95, and often for free. The latter enhances its appeal; even if your ideal partner is 5'1", weighs 140 lbs, has red hair and green eyes, and dresses in black leather with an opening exposing the genitals, you can find him or her online.

British psychologist Mark Griffith (2000, 2001) has argued that cybersex becomes an addiction or compulsion when it has the following six characteristics. These characteristics are similar to those proposed by Carnes (1983) for sexual addictions more generally:

1. *Salience* Cybersex becomes the most important activity in the person's life and he or she becomes preoccupied with thinking about it.
2. *Mood modification* The person reports that cybersex alters his or her negative mood by producing either an arousing "buzz" or "high" or a calming feeling of "escape" or "numbing" and thus is used as a coping strategy.

3. *Tolerance* The person requires greater and greater amounts of cybersex to achieve the former changes in mood. As a result, he or she spends more and more time engaging in Internet sex.

4. *Withdrawal symptoms* The person experiences unpleasant feelings and physical effects when he or she stops engaging in cybersex or suddenly decreases its use.

5. *Conflict* As a result of spending a great deal of time on the Internet the person experiences conflicts with the significant people in his or her life (e.g., not spending time with his or her partner), with other activities (such as job, social life, school), or within him- or herself.

6. *Relapse* If the person begins to engage in cybersex again after a period of not doing so, he or she quickly returns to his or her most extreme pattern of use.

Research on Internet use has utilized convenience samples of persons who respond to invitations on Web sites and agree to complete an online questionnaire. Obviously, such samples consist of persons with access to computers who possess basic online skills. Thus, these samples may underrepresent lower-income and minority persons, although though they may be representative of people engaging in cybersex. Early research found that almost one-half of the participants spent less than one hour per week in online sexual pursuits (Cooper et al., 1999). Of concern was the 8 percent who reported spending 11 or more hours per week in such activity. These heavy users were more likely to go online both at home and at work and to report that their online sexual behaviour interfered with their lives. A study based on more than 40,000 users assessed the relationship between the frequency and duration of Internet use and mental health. The results indicated that the number of months that had passed since participants first went online was positively associated with a history of mental health problems and treatment, as well as with current behavioural difficulties involving alcohol, gambling, food, and sex. Spending more hours per week online was associated with a history of mental health problems and treatment (Mathy & Cooper, 2003).

Research using a sexual compulsivity scale sought to determine what percentage of users were compulsive users (Cooper et al., 2000). The study found that 83 percent of the participants were not problematic users. Eleven percent attained moderate scores on the scale, 4.6 percent were *sexually compulsive*, and 1 percent were *cybersex compulsives*—that is, they attained the highest scores on compulsivity and spent more than 11 hours per week in online sexual pursuits. Persons in the cybersex compulsive group were more likely to be male, to be single and dating, and to report that they were bisexual; they reported spending 15 to 25 hours per week in online sexual pursuits. Twenty-one percent of the respondents reported that their online activities had jeopardized at least one area of their life; the most common being personal relationships. The researchers concluded that bisexuals, and perhaps other sexually marginalized groups, may be especially at risk for online sexual compulsivity.

■ Other Sexual Variations

The sexual variations discussed below are too rare to have had much research devoted to them; they are nonetheless interesting.

Saliromania is a disorder found mainly in men; there is a desire to damage or soil a woman or her clothes or the image of a woman, such as a painting or statue. The man becomes sexually excited and may ejaculate during the act.

Coprophilia and **urophilia** are both variations having to do with excretion. In coprophilia the feces are important to sexual satisfaction. In urophilia it is the urine that is important. The urophiliac may want to be urinated on as part of the sexual act. Insiders refer to urination as "golden showers."

Frotteurism is the seventh paraphilia identified by the *DSM-IV-TR*. It is defined as sexual fantasies, urges, or behaviours involving touching or rubbing one's genitals against the body of a nonconsenting person. It must occur over a period of at least six

---

Saliromania: A desire to damage or soil a woman or her clothes.

Coprophilia (cop-roh-FILL-ee-uh): Deriving sexual satisfaction from contact with feces.

Urophilia (YUR-oh-fill-ee-uh): Deriving sexual satisfaction from contact with urine.

Frotteurism: Rubbing one's genitals against the body of a nonconsenting person.

months and cause marked distress or interpersonal difficulty. Milder forms of this activity are common. A man may approach a woman from the rear and press his penis against her buttocks; or a woman may approach a man from the side and rub her genitals against his leg or hip. The target may be unaware of it if it occurs in a crowded elevator or subway train, or in the crush of a crowd at a sports event or concert. We noted earlier that 35 percent of a sample of college men reported having engaged in this activity.

Necrophilia is sexual contact with a dead person. It is a very rare form of behaviour and is considered by experts to be psychotic and extremely deviant. Necrophiliacs derive sexual gratification from viewing a corpse or actually having intercourse with it; the corpse may be mutilated afterward (Thorpe et al., 1961).

Zoophilia is sexual contact with an animal; this behaviour is also called *bestiality* or *sodomy*, although the latter term is also sometimes used to refer to anal intercourse or even mouth–genital sex between humans. About 8 percent of the men in Kinsey's sample reported having had sexual experiences with animals. Most of this activity was concentrated in adolescence and probably reflected the experimentation and diffuse sexual urges of that period. Not surprisingly, the percentage was considerably higher among boys on farms; 17 percent of boys raised on farms had had animal contacts resulting in orgasm. Kinsey found that only about 3 to 4 percent of all females have had some sexual contact with animals. Contemporary therapists report cases of men and women engaging in sexual activity with household pets. Activities include masturbating the animal, oral–genital contact, and intercourse. A preference for sexual contact with animals over humans is extremely rare (Earls & Lalumière, 2002).

Researchers posted a questionnaire online and recruited participants through a letter to members of a network of people with sexual interests in animals (as we said, you can find anything on the Web—that's accessibility). Those who volunteered were asked to refer others who had interests similar to those assessed by the questionnaire (Williams & Weinberg, 2003). Data were obtained from 114 men, all white, with a median age of 27; 64 percent were single, never married, and 83 percent had at least some college education. These characteristics undoubtedly reflect in part the fact that the sample was obtained via the Web. Ninety-three percent defined themselves as "zoophiles" and said this identity involved a concern for the animal's welfare and an emphasis on consensual sexual activity. They compared themselves favourably with "bestialists," whom they said were not concerned about an animal's welfare. Given a list of possible reasons for sexual interest in animals, the two most common were a desire for affection and pleasurable sex. The type of sexual contact reported by the men varied by the type of animal. Receiving oral sex and receiving anal intercourse were the most frequent activities with dogs, whereas performing vaginal and anal intercourse were most frequent with horses. Only one man preferred sheep. Many of the men had not had a human partner of either sex in the preceding year. The researchers suggest that a preference for sexual activity with animals can be explained by learning theory in that the rewards offered by sex with animals are immediate, easy, and intense, and thus extremely reinforcing. They suggested that the respondents' choice of animal is explained by their early conditioning; most men preferred the type of animal they first had sex with.

■ Prevention of Harmful Sexual Variations

For many of the variations discussed in this chapter, there is a continuum from normal to abnormal. People whose behaviour falls at the normal end enjoy these activities at no expense to self or others. Some may need reassurance that there is nothing wrong with engaging in these behaviours. People whose behaviour falls at the abnormal end are cause for concern.

Some people who engage in sexual variations find them highly distressing, causing them significant unhappiness. Their sexual interests (for example, in the case of a person with a sexual compulsion or addiction) may interfere with having healthy relationships or completing their day-to-day responsi-

Necrophilia: Deriving sexual satisfaction from contact with a dead person.
Zoophilia: Sexual contact with an animal; also called bestiality or sodomy.

bilities. Yet they may find these sexual interests extremely difficult to change or control. Other sexual variations—for example, pedophilia—cause significant harm to other people. Thus it is important to develop programs to prevent these types of harmful sexual variations (Qualls et al., 1978). In preventive medicine, a distinction is made between primary prevention and secondary prevention. Applied to the sexual variations, primary prevention would mean intervening in home life or in other factors during childhood to help prevent problems from developing, or trying to teach people how to cope with crises or stress so that problems do not develop. In secondary prevention, the idea is to diagnose and treat the problem as early as possible once it has started, so that difficulties are minimized.

It would be highly advantageous to do primary prevention of harmful or distressing sexual variations—that is, to head them off before they even develop. Unfortunately, this is proving to be difficult, for a number of reasons. One problem is the diagnostic categories. The categories for the diagnosis of sexual variations are not nearly so clearcut in real life as they may seem in this chapter, and multiple diagnoses for one person are not uncommon. That is, a given man might have engaged in incest, pedophilia, and exhibitionism. If it is unclear how to diagnose sexual variations, it is going to be rather difficult to figure out how to prevent them. If one is not sure whether there is a difference between chicken pox and measles, it is rather difficult to start giving inoculations.

An alternative approach that seems promising—rather than figuring out ways to prevent each separate variation—is to analyze the *components of sexual development*. Disturbance in one or more of these components in development might lead to different sexual variations. Two such components are arousal to appropriate stimuli and formation of relationships with others (Bancroft, 1978). Thus, for example, a disturbance in attachment relationships in childhood might lead to exhibitionism or to compulsive cybersex. The idea would then be to try to ensure that as children grow up, their development in each component is healthy. Ideally, harmful sexual variations should not occur then. However, this task is made more difficult by the fact that we have little scientific knowledge about either what constitutes unusual sexual behaviours among

children or what components of development lead to harmful sexual variations (Moser et al., 2004).

Interest in developing preventive programs targeting children partly stems from the number of youth charged with sexual offences. For example, in 2003 in Canada there were 392 youth charged with sexual assault and 268 youth charged with other sexual offences in youth court (many more youth were charged with other crimes such as physical assault and theft than were charged with sexual offences). Research with 45 adolescent sex offenders in Toronto indicated that 42 percent showed equal or more arousal to film clips of children than to film clips of adults—that is, had pedophilic interests (Seto et al., 2003). One study of American adolescents incarcerated for sexual offences found that 46 percent committed their first offence before the age of 12 (Burton, 2000). Childhood victimization was positively associated with later sexual aggression by the youth, suggesting that social learning can help explain the development of sexual offending.

We have a long way to go in preventing harmful sexual variations, to say the least.

■ Treatment of Sexual Variations

Some of the sexual variations discussed in this chapter—such as the mild fetishes—are well within the normal range of sexual expression. There is no need for treatment. Others, however, fall into the abnormal range, causing personal anguish to the individual and possibly causing harm to unwilling victims. Treatments are needed for this category of variations. Many different treatments have been tried, each based on a different theoretical understanding of the causes of sexual variations. We will look at four categories of treatments: medical treatments, cognitive–behavioural therapies, skills training, and AA-type 12-step programs.

Medical Treatments

Inspired by the notion that sexual variations are caused by biological factors, various medical treatments for sexual variations have been tried over the last century. Some of them look today like nothing other than cruel and unusual punishment. Nonetheless, people would love to have a "pill" that would cure some of these complex and painful or dangerous paraphilias, so the search for such treatments continues.

Surgical castration has never been commonly used in Canada as a treatment for various kinds of uncontrollable sexual urges, although it was used extensively in Europe. However, a few sex offenders in Canada do "voluntarily" undergo surgical castration, as was discussed in In Focus 9.3. Such treatments are based on the notion that removing a man's testosterone by removing the testes will lead to a drastic reduction in sex drive, which will in turn erase urges to commit sex offences. However, as we saw in Chapter 9, a reduction in testosterone levels in humans does not always lead to a reduction in sexual behaviour (Federoff & Moran, 1997). Surgical castration cannot be recommended as a treatment for sex offenders either on humanitarian grounds or on grounds of effectiveness.

Hormonal treatment involves the use of drugs to reduce sexual desire. Sexual arousability is heavily dependent on maintaining the level of androgen in the bloodstream above a given threshold. Two ways to reduce this level are to administer (1) drugs that reduce the production of androgen in the testes ("chemical castration"), or (2) antiandrogens that bind to androgen receptors in the brain and genitals, blocking the effects of androgen. The use of either should produce a sharp decline in sexual desire. Several drugs have been tried in the past 40 years. The most commonly used in Canada is *medroxyprogesterone acetate* (MPA), which binds to androgen receptors. The drug is given by injection, often weekly. A review of the literature shows that the use of MPA results in reduced sexual interest and a lower level of sexual fantasies, along with decreased erections and ejaculation (Miner & Coleman, 2001). However, "the drop-out rate is extremely high and re-offense rates have been found to exceed 65 percent of those who discontinue antiandrogen treatment" (p. 8). Recently, clinicians have started using leuprolide acetate, a synthetic analog of gonadotropin-releasing hormone (GnRH; see Chapter 5); its continued use suppresses androgen production and reduces sexual fantasies and drive. It has fewer side effects than MPA. Systematic studies of its effectiveness have not been published.

The use of alternative, *psychopharmacological treatment* increased dramatically in frequency in the 1990s. Here, psychotropic medications are administered to offenders. These medications influence patients' psychological functioning and behaviour by their action on the central nervous system. The newness of the drugs being used means there is little research on the effectiveness of this technique.

There is a great deal of interest in the use of the newer antidepressant known as selective serotonin reuptake inhibitors (SSRIs). Case reports indicate that SSRIs reduce paraphilic fantasies and urges (Raymond et al., 2002). They appear to change the compulsive sexual behaviour rather than sexual desire (Bradford, 2000; Federoff, 1994). As these drugs have been successfully used to treat nonsexual compulsive behaviours, their success with paraphilias suggests that these conditions may be a type of obsessive-compulsive disorder (Miner & Coleman, 2001).

Both hormonal and psychopharmacological treatment should be used as only one element in a complete program of therapy, which would include counselling and treatment for other emotional and social deficits (Bradford, 2000). For example, Eli Coleman (Coleman et al., 2003) recommends that in addition to psychopharmacological treatment, individuals with compulsive sexual behaviour should: (1) receive psychotherapy to deal with issues from the families-of-origin and learn to better deal with their stress, anxiety, and depression that can trigger the compulsive sexual behaviour; (2) participate in group therapy in order to learn from others with similar problems and overcome feelings of shame and guilt; and (3) receive couple therapy that is aimed at improving the couple's intimacy and sexual functioning. The best results are obtained with men who are highly motivated to change their behaviour and therefore comply with the prescribed treatment regimen. If the man with the paraphilia stops taking the drug or participating in other aspects of treatment, the program will fail. Unfortunately, one of the limitations of research on the effectiveness of these treatments is the dropout rate, which was 46 percent in one study.

Cognitive–Behavioural Therapies

Compared to other therapeutic approaches, cognitive–behavioural therapy is effective at reducing recidivism among sex offenders (Hanson et al.,

2002; Marshall et al., 1991). Cognitive programs are used extensively to treat incarcerated sex offenders in Canadian prisons (Byers et al., 1997). Comprehensive programs include (Abel et al., 1992; Hanson & Harris, 1997; Marshall & Barbaree, 1990):

1. Behaviour therapy to reduce inappropriate sexual arousal and enhance appropriate arousal.
2. Social skills training.
3. Modification of distorted thinking; challenging the rationalizations that the person uses to justify the undesirable behaviour.
4. Relapse prevention; helping the person identify and control or avoid whatever triggers the behaviour.
5. Finding other, less problematic ways of meeting the needs and desires fulfilled by the behaviour.

One technique that is often used is *covert sensitization*. It involves pairing aversive imagery (thoughts) with fantasies of the target behaviour. In the treatment of an exhibitionist, for example, he repeatedly practises a vivid fantasy in which, just as he imagines getting ready to expose himself, he experiences waves of nausea and vomiting. The details, of course, are individualized to the person and his particular problem. Reports indicate that this approach has been effective in some cases of sexual sadism, exhibitionism, and pedophilia (Barlow et al., 1969; Walen & Roth, 1987).

Another approach is *orgasmic reconditioning* (Marquis, 1970; Walen & Roth, 1987). With this method, the patient is told to masturbate to his usual paraphilic fantasies. Then, just at the moment of orgasm, he switches to an acceptable fantasy. After practising this for some time, he becomes able to orgasm regularly while having an acceptable fantasy. He then is told to move the fantasy progressively to an earlier phase of masturbation. Gradually he becomes conditioned to experiencing sexual arousal in the context of acceptable behaviour.

One program designed for female offenders combined cognitive–behavioural with psychodynamic techniques, and relied on one-on-one rather than group therapy (Traven et al., 1990). Male offenders typically deny responsibility for their behaviour, so the initial stage of treatment may focus on acknowledging one's behaviour and its consequences. Women in this program readily acknowledged what they had done and were overwhelmed by guilt and shame, so the initial stage focused on self-esteem. Thus, different treatment programs may be needed for men and women with paraphilias.

Skills Training

According to yet another theoretical understanding, persons with paraphilias engage in their behaviour because they have great difficulty forming relationships, and so do not have access to appropriate forms of sexual gratification. Many of these people do not have the skills to initiate and maintain conversation. They may find it difficult to develop intimacy (see Chapter 13) (Keenan & Ward, 2000). Such people may benefit from a treatment program that includes social skills training. Such training may include how to carry on a conversation, how to develop intimacy, how to be appropriately assertive, and identifying irrational fears that are inhibiting the person (Abel et al., 1992). These programs may also include basic sex education.

If a person needs to learn and practise sexual interaction skills, one approach would be to have him interact with a trained partner. This is the basis for a very controversial practice, the use of *sex surrogates* as part of a treatment program. The surrogate works with the therapist, interacting socially and sexually with the client to provide opportunities for using the newly acquired information and skills. Some therapists believe that the use of surrogates is ethical, but others see it as a type of prostitution. Just as the definition of "abnormal" depends on one's point of view, so does the definition of "sex therapy."

AA-Type 12-Step Programs

Sexual addictions theory argues that many people who engage in compulsive, inappropriate sexual patterns are addicted to their particular sexual practice. The appropriate treatment, according to this approach, is one of the 12-step programs modelled on Alcoholics Anonymous. Several groups have adapted the AA program for sexual addictions, among them Sexaholics Anonymous (SA), Sexual Addicts Anonymous (SAA), and Sex and Love Addicts Anonymous (SLAA). These groups can usually be found by calling the local phone number for Alcoholics Anonymous or by looking

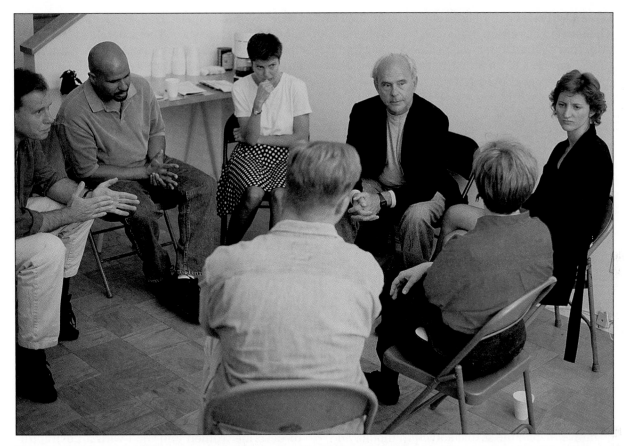

Figure 16.9 The centrepiece of 12-step programs such as Sex Addicts Anonymous are group meetings in which participants confront their addiction with the support of other group members.

up their Web sites on the Internet. Some of the programs are run by group members, whereas others are affiliated with professional health care facilities.

Twelve-step programs combine cognitive restructuring, obtaining support from other members who have the same or similar problem behaviours, and enhancing spirituality. This last aspect involves increasing one's awareness of a "higher power" who can be relied on to help one recover. The first step in the process of recovery is admitting that one is sexually addicted, that the behaviour is out of control, and that one's life has become unmanageable. These are hard admissions to make for someone who has spent years denying the existence of a problem. There are frequent meetings with a support group, and there is a strong emphasis on building feelings of self-worth. AA for alcohol or drug addiction demands that the addict abstain from contact with the substance. Simi-

larly, programs for sexual addicts adopt a definition of "sexual sobriety." They cannot adopt an abstinence model, however, because sexual expression is a basic human need. Thus, they attempt to differentiate addictive sexual behaviour from healthy sexual behaviour. For some groups, although not all, only marital sex (and not other partnered sex or masturbation) is considered to fit the definition of sexual sobriety.

AA-based groups are generally unwilling to cooperate with researchers, believing that to do so would prevent group members from concentrating on recovery. As a result, there is little research data on the effectiveness of these programs.

What Works?

What is needed is carefully controlled research on the effectiveness of various approaches to the treatment of sexual variations (Miner & Coleman, 2001).

Research to date has tended to apply one method to a heterogeneous group of people. It is likely, however, that each method will be more effective with some paraphilias than with others. Research involving drugs should systematically assess side effects; some drugs have severe side effects on some people, especially if used more than six months. Research should consider the relative likelihood of relapse; some people with paraphilias pose grave danger to themselves (e.g., asphyxiophiliacs) or to others if they resume their problematic behaviour.

■ ■ ■ SUMMARY

It seems reasonable to define "abnormal sexual behaviour" as behaviour that is uncomfortable for the person, inefficient, bizarre, or physically or psychologically harmful to the person or others. The American Psychiatric Association defines paraphilias as recurrent, intense, sexually arousing fantasies, urges, or behaviours that are obsessive and compulsive. A behaviour is compulsive if the person is obsessed with it, feels compelled to engage in it, and has experienced personal, relationship, medical, or legal difficulties as a result of it. Some of these behaviours are against the law, but most are not.

Four theoretical approaches have been used in understanding the paraphilias: learning theory, cognitive theory, the sexual addiction model, and sociological theory. Several explanations have been proposed for the fact that there are many more males than females with paraphilias.

A fetishist is a person who becomes erotically attached to some object other than another human being. Most likely, fetishism arises from conditioning, and it provides a good example of the continuum from normal to abnormal behaviour.

The transvestite derives sexual satisfaction from dressing as a member of the other gender. Like many other sexual variations, transvestism is much more common among men than among women. Survey data suggest that many men who later become transvestites begin cross-dressing in childhood.

Three styles of sexual interaction involve differences in control over sexual interactions. Dominance and submission involve a consensual exchange of power, and the enacting of scripted performances. Bondage and discipline involve the use of physical restraints or verbal commands by one person to control the other. Both D-S and B-D may occur without genital contact or orgasm. Sexual sadism and masochism involve deriving sexual gratification from giving and receiving pain. Both are recognized as paraphilias if they become compulsive.

The voyeur is sexually aroused by looking at nudes. The exhibitionist displays his or her sex organs to others. Both are generally harmless.

Nymphomania and satyriasis are terms used to describe women and men with an extraordinarily high sex drive. Both terms are ambiguous and subject to misuse. The term hypersexuality is potentially more precise, particularly if it is defined behaviourally.

Other sexual variations include asphyxiophilia, zoophilia, and necrophilia. A recent concern is cybersex abuse, which is facilitated by the anonymity, accessibility, and affordability of the Net.

The possibility of programs to prevent sexual variations is being explored.

Four types of programs to treat sexual variations are: medical treatments including hormonal and psychopharmacological interventions, cognitive–behavioural therapies, social skills training, and AA-type 12-step programs. We need careful research to determine which programs work best in the treatment of given behaviours.

■ ■ ■ QUESTIONS FOR THOUGHT, DISCUSSION, AND DEBATE

1. What do you think of the idea about preventing sexual variations presented in this chapter? Do you think the schools or some other agency should institute a program to screen children, trying to detect those with characteristics that might indicate they would develop a sexual variation later in life, and then give therapy to those children?

2. Of the sexual variations in this chapter, which seem to you to be the most abnormal? Why? Do the ones you have chosen fit the criteria for abnormality discussed at the beginning of the chapter?

3. A common phenomenon in medical school is for medical students to think they have contracted one of the diseases they are studying. The analogous phenomenon would be for students who read this chapter to think that they have one or more of the paraphilias. Did you notice yourself becoming sexually aroused as you read about one (or more) of the variations? If so, do you think you are abnormal? Why, or why not?

4. Most persons who seek treatment or are arrested for atypical or paraphilic behaviours are white men. Do you think that this is an accurate picture of our society, or are we just unaware of non-whites who engage in these behaviours? Based on the data presented and the causes discussed, would you expect black, Asian, or Aboriginal men to engage in these behaviours? Why, or why not?

■ ■ ■ SUGGESTIONS FOR FURTHER READING

Griffin-Shelley, Eric. (1991). *Sex and love: Addiction, treatment, and recovery.* Westport, CT: Praeger. This book describes the addiction model as it is applied to sex and love. It also describes treatment programs.

Wilson, Glenn D. (Ed.). 1987. *Variant sexuality: Research and theory.* Baltimore: Johns Hopkins University Press. The chapters in this book review different theoretical explanations for sexual variations, from genetics and sociobiology to cross-cultural perspectives.

Online **Learning**Centre

For Review Questions, Web Resources, and other learning and study tools, visit the *Understanding Human Sexuality* Online Learning Centre at www.mcgrawhill.ca/college/hyde.

CHAPTER 17

Sexual Coercion

CHAPTER HIGHLIGHTS

Eboni's basic education about sex came from what she saw and the direct experiences that she had. When she was 5, she and her brother were wrestling with their uncle. Suddenly her uncle locked her brother out of the room and began taking off Eboni's clothes. He held her down on the bed and began to penetrate her but stopped abruptly. Eboni was frightened of him from then on. She didn't really understand what he intended to do or why he wanted to do it, but she knew that his behavior was unexpected and strange.

… Eboni's grandmother and father insisted that she not talk to strangers or take money from them. Eboni understood why—she knew that being molested meant being raped. But strangers were not the predators.*

This chapter is about sexual activity that involves coercion and is not between consenting adults; specifically, we will consider sexual assault; child sexual abuse; and sexual harassment at work, in education, and by professionals. All these topics have been highly publicized in the last 20 years, and much good scientific research on them has appeared.[1]

■ Sexual Assault

In the last two decades, there has been a movement toward seeing crimes involving force in sexual relations as crimes of violence and victimization rather than as sex crimes. In 1983, the Criminal Code of Canada was amended to accommodate this different understanding and to protect the victims. Prior to 1983, the Criminal Code had four statutes that prohibited forced sexual activity: rape, attempted rape, indecent assault against a female, and indecent assault against a male. At that time, the legal definition of rape was heterosexual intercourse by a man with a woman who was not his wife (see Table 17.1). The rape law was criticized on a number of grounds. First, rape was limited to forced heterosexual intercourse. Second, it defined the assailant as male and the victim as female. Thus, women could not be charged with rape, and men

*Wyatt, 1997, pp 72–73.

[1] Portions of this chapter are excerpted from J. S. Hyde. (1996). *Half the human experience: The psychology of women,* 5th ed. Boston: Houghton Mifflin.

could not be victims of rape. Third, husbands could not be charged with raping their wives, meaning that a woman could not legally refuse her husband's demands (Hughes, 2001). Fourth, the victim's prior sexual activities could be considered as evidence of her consent and of the credibility of her testimony, effectively putting her past on trial. In addition, the law had a number of provisions that made the criminal justice system unresponsive to sexual assault complaints. It specifically required corroboration that the crime of rape actually took place. The judge was obliged to inform the jury that they should not convict only on the basis of the complainant's testimony (Los, 1994). Finally, rape complaints that were not made immediately after the attack were invalidated. These provisions meant that it was extremely difficult to get a conviction if there was no physical evidence (such as physical injury) or when the complaint was not filed immediately. In fact, the majority of complaints of rape did not result in a conviction (Clark & Lewis, 1977; Siegel & McCormick, 1999).

In 1983, the Criminal Code was amended so that the offences of rape and indecent assault were replaced with three gender-neutral crimes of sexual assault. These crimes depend on the amount of force used to carry out the assault and the degree of injury sustained by the victim, not on the nature of the forced sexual activity. The purpose of these changes was to de-emphasize the sexual nature of the offence, to stress their violent nature, to encourage victims to report these crimes to the police, and to improve the court procedure so as to reduce trauma to victims and increase the rate

Table 17.1 The Offence of "Rape" in the Criminal Code of Canada in 1968. This offence was replaced with three sexual assault offences in 1983.

A male person commits rape when he has sexual intercourse with a female person who is not his wife,

a. Without her consent, or
b. With her consent if the consent
    (i) Is extorted by threats or fear of bodily harm
    (ii) Is obtained by impersonating her husband, or
    (iii) Is obtained by false and fraudulent representations as to the nature and quality of the act.

of convictions (Roberts & Gebotys, 1992). The three levels of sexual assault parallel the three levels of physical assault in the Criminal Code: (simple) sexual assault, sexual assault with a weapon causing serious injury or endangering the life of the victim or causing bodily harm, and aggravated sexual assault (refer to In Focus 2.2 for a description of these statutes).

Sexual assault[2] includes a wide range of non-consensual sexual experiences ranging from unwanted touching to forced oral, anal, or vaginal intercourse and sexual violence causing serious physical injury or disfigurement to the victim. In keeping with the equality provisions of the Charter of Rights and Freedoms, the law is written in gender-neutral terms so that either men or women can be the victim of a sexual assault and can be charged with sexual assault, and the statute no longer discriminates against married people. The crucial point is that the activity is non-consensual—that is, the victim did not consent to it. The Criminal Code also defines "consent" for the purposes of sexual assault offences. Consent must be actively established. Silence, inaction, or ambiguous conduct is not consent. Consent is not considered to be obtained if the complainant is unable to give consent because of being drunk or unconscious, if the complainant shows by his or her actions that he or she is not in agreement, or if the complainant consents to engage in sexual activity and then changes his or her mind. Children under 14 cannot be considered to have consented to sexual activity as this is considered child sexual abuse (discussed later in this chapter).

There were also some provisions that related to court proceedings, such as limiting the questioning of victims in sexual assault trials about their sexual history (often referred to as the "rape shield laws") and no longer requiring corroboration of the victim's testimony. However, due to court challenges, there are now some conditions under which the judge can allow the victim's sexual history to be admitted as evidence. Advocacy groups such as the Women's Legal Education and Action Fund (LEAF) argue that many judges are still influenced by myths and stereotypes about sexual assault, such as the mistaken belief that many women make false allegations about sexual assault, and thus, contrary to the will of Parliament, judges frequently permit sexual history evidence (Busby, 1999).

Incidence Statistics

In 1993, Statistics Canada conducted the Violence Against Women Survey, a nationwide survey of 12,300 women aged 18 and over. They used the definition of sexual assault in the Criminal Code of Canada to determine its incidence. Thirty-nine percent of women reported having been sexually assaulted by a man since the age of 16; 5 percent (corresponding to 572,000 women) in the previous 12 months. Only 6 percent of the women had reported the assault to the police. Victims of sexual assault by a stranger are most likely to report the incident to authorities (Renner & Wackett, 1987).

[2]Although many Canadians still use the term "rape" in everyday conversation—usually meaning forced sexual intercourse—in keeping with the Canadian Criminal Code we have chosen to use the term "sexual assault" in this chapter, except when studies specifically used the term "rape."

Sexual assault: Any non-consensual sexual activity ranging from unwanted touching, to forced oral, anal, or vaginal intercourse, to sexual violence in which the victim is wounded or maimed or his or her life is endangered or when the victim is incapable of giving consent.

There has been no Canadian national survey of the incidence of sexual assault against men. However, the NHSLS conducted in the United States showed that men are victims of sexual aggression, although much less frequently than women are. According to the NHSLS, 1 percent of men reported having been victims of forced sex with a woman, compared to 22 percent of women who reported having been the victims of forced sex with a man (Laumann et al., 1994). It is more common for a man to have been forced to have sex by another man (1.9 percent of men) than by a woman (1.3 percent of men).

In 1999, the Canadian General Social Survey asked both women and men under age 65 about their experiences of sexual aggression: 1.8 percent of the women but only 0.3 percent of the men reported that someone had touched them against their will in the previous 12 months. Respondents in married or common-law relationships were asked about forced sexual activity by their partner within the last five years: 0.7 percent of the women and 0.2 percent of the men reported that their partner had forced them to engage in unwanted sexual activity by threatening them, holding them down, or hurting them in some way. The sexual assault provisions of the Criminal Code of Canada apply equally to men and to women as victims. However, data from 166 police departments across Canada in 2000 indicate that 98 percent of adult victims who reported the assault to the police were women (Brzozowski, 2004).

The following discussion starts with sexual assault by men against women, because this is the most common type of sexual assault.

Sexual Assault of Women by Acquaintances

Sexual assault by someone who is known to the victim, often called "date rape" or sexual assault by an aquaintance, is much more frequent than sexual assault by a stranger (Renner & Wackett, 1987; Statistics Canada, 1994). Studies in this area typically ask respondents about a range of unwanted sexual activity due not only to threats or physical force, but also to verbal coercion such as continual arguments and pressure. Thus, some but not all of these unwanted experiences would meet a legal definition of sexual assault.

How many people report these types of unwanted sexual experiences? A national survey found that 28 percent of female university and college students had experienced sexual coercion in the past year (DeKeseredy & Kelly, 1993). Similarly, 19 percent of middle and high school girls in New Brunswick reported having had a sexually coercive experience with a boyfriend that they found highly upsetting (Price et al., 2000). Many women do not recognize that what happened to them was sexual assault because it occurred in a dating situation, often after the couple had engaged in consensual sexual activity at a lower level (e.g., kissing). Nonetheless, research in Ontario has demonstrated that sexual coercion by a dating partner is associated with higher depression, lower self-esteem, and more negative sexual self-perceptions (Offman & Matheson, 2004).

To learn more about sexual coercion, watch the "Behind Closed Doors" video in Chapter 17 of your CD.

Miscommunication may contribute to sexual assault in dating relationships. Research has shown that many men still hold to the traditional view in dating relationships that a woman who says "no" really means "yes" (Byers et al., 1987; Osman, 2003). This myth is too often reinforced in films that portray women as enjoying sex resulting from sexual coercion by men. Men need to learn that "no" means "no." Consider this example of miscommunication and different perceptions in a case of sexual assault by an acquaintance:

Bob: Patty and I were in the same statistics class together. She usually sat near me and was always very friendly. I liked her and thought maybe she liked me, too. Last Thursday I decided to find out. After class I suggested that she come to my place to study for midterms together. She agreed immediately, which was a good sign. That night everything seemed to go perfectly. We studied for a while and then took a break. I could tell that she liked me, and I was attracted to her. I was getting excited. I started kissing her. I could tell that she really liked it. We started touching each other and it felt really good. All of a sudden she pulled away and said "Stop." I figured she didn't want me to think that she was "easy" or "loose." A lot of girls think they have to say "no" at first. I knew once I showed her what a good time she could have, and that I would respect her in the morning, it would be OK. I just ignored her protests and eventually she stopped struggling. I think she liked it but afterward she acted bummed out and cold. Who knows what her problem was?

Patty: I knew Bob from my statistics class. He's cute and we are both good at statistics, so when a tough midterm was scheduled, I was glad that he suggested we study together. It never occurred to me that it was anything except a study date. That night everything went fine at first, we got a lot of studying done in a short amount of time, so when he suggested we take a break I thought we deserved it. Well, all of a sudden he started acting really romantic and starting kissing me. I liked the kissing but then he started touching me below the waist. I pulled away and tried to stop him but he didn't listen. After a while I stopped struggling; he was hurting me and I was scared. He was so much bigger and stronger than me. I couldn't believe it was happening to me. I didn't know what to do. He actually forced me to have sex with him. I guess looking back on it I should have screamed or done something besides trying to reason with him but it was so unexpected. I couldn't believe it was happening. I still can't believe it did. (Hughes & Sandler, 1987, p. 1)

Several explanations have been proposed for why sexually aggressive men misperceive women's communications. The first proposes that aggressors lack competence in "reading" women's negative emotions. The second suggests that sexually aggressive men fail to make subtle distinctions between women's friendliness and seductiveness. The third proposes that they have a "suspicious schema" and automatically doubt that women are communicating truthfully and accurately, particularly when the woman rejects a sexual advance. Research supports the third explanation (Malamuth & Brown, 1994). These findings have important implications for prevention and treatment programs for sexual aggressors. They suggest that the programs that use cognitive therapy to get the man to change his suspicious schema are likely to be most effective. Such programs might be used as part of a comprehensive program with convicted sex offenders, or as prevention programs with high school or university men who have been identified as potential sexual aggressors.

A frightening problem today is the emergence of the so-called "date-rape drugs." There are three major types: Rohypnol, GHB, and ketamine. Numerous cases have been reported of men who slipped the drug into a woman's drink and then sexually assaulted her. Rohypnol (row-HIP-nawl; "roofie," "roachie," "La Rocha," "forget pills," "pasta," "peanuts," "whiteys," "ropes") is the drug name for flunitrazepam. The drug causes drowsiness or sleep and the man sexually assaults the woman while she is asleep. The drug also causes the woman not to remember the event the next day. GHB ("liquid G," "G," "Georgia home boy," "easy lay," "grievous bodily harm"), the drug name for gamma hydroxyl butyrate, produces similar effects to alcohol but can cause hallucinations in larger doses and when mixed with alcohol can lead to loss of consciousness. Ketamine ("K," "vitamin K," "special K") causes a combination of amnesia and hallucinations. Ecstasy ("Adam," "XTC," "bean," "E," "M," "roll") is also sometimes used as a date rape drug. Several strategies for avoiding this situation have been suggested, including, especially, not accepting a drink from a stranger, and never leaving your drink unattended.[3]

Spousal Sexual Assault of Women

The Criminal Code of Canada definition of sexual assault includes non-consensual sex with a spouse or common-law partner. How common is **spousal sexual assault**? The Violence Against Women Survey found that 8 percent of respondents had been sexually assaulted by a current or former spouse (Statistics Canada, 1993).

One phenomenon that emerges from the research is an association between non-sexual and sexual violence in long-term relationships—

---

[3]An enterprising U.S. company claims to have developed a coaster that detects Rohypnol and other drugs. Customers put a drop of their drink on the coaster and if it changes colours, the drink contains one of the drugs. Although a good idea, it does not detect all the drugs. Further, it is another preventive strategy that focuses on women taking responsibility for their own safety rather than on educating and punishing potential aggressors.

Spousal sexual assault: The sexual assault of a person by his or her current or former marital or common-law spouse.

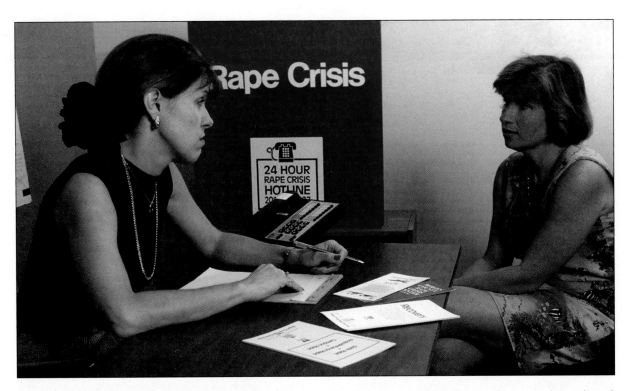

Figure 17.1   Sexual assault crisis counselling. Many women experience severe emotional distress after a sexual assault, and it is important that crisis counselling be available to them.

that is, the man who batters his female partner is also likely to force her to have sex (CDC, 2004).

A man might sexually assault his female partner for many motives, including anger, power and domination, sadism, or a desire for sex regardless of whether she is willing (Russell, 1990). In some cases the man is extremely angry, perhaps in the middle of a family argument, and he expresses his anger toward his partner by sexually assaulting her. In other cases, power and domination of the female partner seem to be the motive; for example, the woman may be threatening to leave him. Finally, some sexual assaults appear to occur because the man is sadistic—enjoys inflicting pain—and is psychiatrically disturbed.

The Impact of Sexual Assault on Women

A large number of studies have investigated the psychological reactions of women following sexual assault (e.g., Burgess & Holmstrom, 1974a, 1974b; Frazier et al., 2004; Koss, 1993). This research shows that sexual assault is a time of crisis for a woman and that the effects on her adjustment

may persist for a year or more. This is true of both women sexually assaulted by a stranger as well as those sexually assaulted by an acquaintance or date (Koss, 1993; Neville & Heppner, 1999).

Emotional reactions immediately after a sexual assault can be severe (Burgess & Holmstrom, 1974a). The high levels of distress generally reach a peak three weeks after the assault and continue at a high level for the next month. There is then gradual improvement beginning two or three months after the assault (Koss, 1993; Rothbaum et al., 1992). Many differences between assaulted and non-victimized women disappear after three months, except that assaulted women continue to report more fear, anxiety, self-esteem problems, and sexual problems. These effects may persist for 18 months or longer (Koss, 1993).

Some women experience self-blame (Cairns, 1993). A woman may spend hours agonizing over what she did to bring on the sexual assault or what she might have done to prevent it: "If I hadn't worn that tight sweater...."; "If I hadn't worn that short skirt ... "; "If I hadn't been dumb enough to walk

In Focus 17.1

A Sexual Assault Victim Tells Her Story

During my second year at university, I realized that I wanted to socialize more. I broke up with my home-town honey, began attending college parties, started drinking, and dated other guys at my school. I was a virgin and didn't want to be any-more. I met my second boyfriend in physics. "G" was a football player and a big, handsome man, the best-looking man I'd ever met. We began to date and at first it was wonderful. He even carried me home once from a party, and I thought, "This is the one." Our first attempt at intercourse was difficult and I began to beg him to stop, but he just kept try-ing until he was successful and there was blood everywhere. It was awful.

I continued to date G, but he began to act very differently. When he drank, he became extremely violent, and on different occasions I watched him break a vending machine, put his foot through the soft top of a Porsche, and pull a toilet out of a wall at a university residence. He was unhappy with the way he was treated on the football team, and I tried to console him. He became angrier and paranoid. He demanded to know where I was at all times and accused me of cheating on him. I wanted to break up with him, especially since sex was rough and not always consensual, but I was scared of him. I

tried avoiding him but he always found me.

One night, G arrived very drunk at a party I was attending. He threatened a guy who was there talk-ing to me. I tried to sneak out of the party. He noticed I left and ran out after me. Another guy slowed me down to try to persuade me to let him drive me home since I had been drinking. G accused me of trying to pick this guy up and threat-ened the guy, who even volunteered to drive both of us home. But G wouldn't let him and said I would take him home. I didn't want trouble so I drove him to his dorm. He claimed he was too drunk to walk to his dorm, so I tried to help him into his room. When I turned around to leave, he sprang up and locked me in. He attacked me. I tried fighting him, but he wouldn't listen or stop. He hit my head into the wall several times and tried to force me to perform oral sex. I bit him, and that made him more angry. He then tried to force anal sex, and I fought as hard as I could. I finally started crying, and he stopped when he lost his erection. The rest of the night, I felt completely trapped in his dorm room. I lay awake all night and tried to leave, but he would wake up and stop me. I've never forgotten how scared I felt that entire night. He got up that morning and show-ered and acted as if nothing had happened. He was

on that dark street . . . "; "If I hadn't been stupid enough to trust that guy . . . " This is an example of a tendency on the part of both the victim and oth-ers to *blame the victim* and excuse the perpetrator.

Researchers are finding increased evidence of the damage to women's *physical health* that may result from sexual assault (Golding, 1999; Heise, 1993; Koss et al., 1991; Koss & Heslet, 1992). Women may suffer physical injuries, such as cuts and bruises, and vaginal pain and bleeding. Women who have been forced to have oral sex may suffer irritation or damage to the throat; rectal bleeding and pain are reported by women forced to have anal intercourse. A sexually assaulted woman may

contract a sexually transmitted infection such as HIV/AIDS or herpes. In about 5 percent of cases involving forced intercourse, pregnancy results (Koss et al., 1991). Women who have been sexually or physically assaulted at some time in the past visit their physician twice as often per year as non-victimized women (Koss et al., 1991).

Experts argue that many sexual assault victims experience **post-traumatic stress disorder** (e.g.,

Post-traumatic stress disorder (PTSD): Long-term psychological distress suffered by someone who has experienced a terrifying event.

in all my classes for the rest of my university career.

I began to drink very heavily afterward. I told my roommate, J, and another woman on my floor, D. I never thought to report it, since he was my "boyfriend." A week later, D was assaulted by another student. She went to the campus police afterward. They took her to the head of student housing. He told her it was not their problem or the police's but her drinking problem.

A year and a half later, I began to hear voices. It was a male voice calling me a fucking bitch, whore, and other names. I thought I was going crazy and became very depressed. I decided I must be schizophrenic and decided to kill myself.

Soon after, I was shopping in a feminist bookstore. I saw this title staring right at me, *I Never Called It Rape*. I started reading it right there in the store, and I began crying and thinking, "This is what happened to me." I spoke with a faculty member, who arranged for immediate counselling.

The first time I went to see the counsellor, I couldn't even speak. I sat in her office and cried for the entire hour. She kept saying, "It's not your fault, it's not your fault." I couldn't believe it. Later we discussed how most of the times G and I had sex had actually been sexual assault, including the first and the last. I participated in a "Take Back the Night March." One male residence threw bottles at us.

I went through medical school and residency.

During my first year of residency, I was assaulted again, this time by a man in a stairwell during a New Year's Eve party at a hotel. I started screaming "You're raping me, you're raping me!" He stopped and I got away! But I didn't go to the ER, I just went home and crawled in bed. My old shame came back. I began to drink heavily again. One night I drank all night and never showed up to work that next morning. I finally rolled into my director's office, depressed, hung over, and still smelling of alcohol, and my boss said I had to stop and straighten up right away or he wouldn't let me back for the next year. So I stopped drinking. I also made two very good friends around the same time. Through their support, I really turned my life around.

Three years later, I moved to a different city. I was living alone for the first time and had a great deal of anxiety. I joined a Sexual Assault Survivors Support Group. Then in the spring, I was invited to speak at my old university for Career Day for high school students, so I went back there 10 years after the incidents. I was finally successful in my career, had strong, loving relationships with my friends and parents, and was happy. I look back at what happened now and think that I really survived a lot. I feel it helps me to be a better physician because I can empathize with how bad life can be for people.

Source: Based on an interview conducted by Janet Hyde.

Koss, 1993). Post-traumatic stress disorder (PTSD) is an official diagnosis that was originally developed to describe the long-term psychological distress suffered by war veterans, most of whom are men. Symptoms can include persistently re-experiencing the traumatic event (flashbacks, nightmares), avoiding stimuli associated with it (avoiding certain locations or activities), and hyperarousal (sleep difficulties, difficulty concentrating, irritability). According to a cognitive–behavioural view of PTSD, people who have experienced a terrifying event form a memory schema that involves information about the situation and their responses to it (Foa et al., 1989).

Because the schema is large, many cues can trigger it and therefore evoke the feelings of terror that occurred at the time; the schema is probably activated at some level all the time. Schemas also affect how we interpret new events, so that the consequences are far-reaching and long-lasting (see In Focus 17.1).

It is important to recognize that sexual assault affects many people besides the victim. Most women routinely do a number of things that stem from fears of sexual assault. For example, a single woman is not supposed to list her full first name, but rather her first initial or a man's name, in the telephone book, so as not to reveal that she lives

In Focus 17.2

What Should I Do after a Sexual Assault?

If You Have Been Sexually Assaulted

Tell someone you trust. Sexual assault is a traumatic violation of the person. Especially in the beginning it is helpful to be with someone who will listen to your feelings and help you carry out your decisions. If you can't tell a friend or a family member, call a sexual assault crisis line. This will help you know that you are not alone.

Decide whether to report the assault to the police. This is your decision. If you decide to report, call the police as soon as possible and preserve evidence of the crime. Do not wash, change your clothes, bathe, shower, or douche until you have a medical exam. Save anything that was involved as it may be needed as evidence.

Seek medical attention. Whether or not you decide to report the assault to the police, it is important that you see a doctor to treat any physical injuries and check for STIs and/or pregnancy. If pregnancy seems likely, emergency contraception can be used (see Chapter 7). If you have made a police report, the hospital will use a sexual assault forensic kit to collect evidence such as scrapings, semen, blood, and hair. It is important that this be done within 24 hours of the assault.

Understand that it is normal to experience a wide range of emotions. Emotions such as anger, sadness, detachment, depression, fear, and being out of control are normal responses to sexual assault. It will take time to recover. Taking control over the little things in your life, and later the bigger things, can be one step on the road to recovery.

Understand that the assault was not your fault. You may feel guilty or that the attack was somehow your fault. Sexual assault is a crime, and it was not your fault.

If Someone You Know Has Been Sexually Assaulted

Believe them. A sexual assault survivor may fear not being believed. Accept their version of the facts and be supportive. Sexual assault survivors react differently; no emotional reaction may indicate that they are in shock.

---

alone. Many women, when getting into their car at night, almost reflexively check the backseat to make sure no one is hiding there. Most university women avoid walking alone through dark parts of the campus at night. In the Violence Against Women Survey (Statistics Canada, 1993), 60 percent of women reported feeling worried when walking alone in their neighbourhood after dark. The point is that most women experience the fear of sexual assault, if not sexual assault itself (Burt & Estrep, 1981; Senn & Dzinas, 1996), and this fear restricts their activities.

Spouses or partners of victims may also be profoundly affected. At the same time, they can provide important support for the woman as she recovers (see In Focus 17.2).

New research in psychology indicates that not everyone who experiences a serious traumatic event develops PTSD. Some, in fact, display **posttraumatic growth**—that is, positive life changes and psychological development following exposure to trauma (Tedeschi et al., 1998). Research with sexual assault victims—or, more accurately, sexual assault survivors—confirms that some do report positive life changes, such as an increased ability to take care of themselves, a greater sense of purpose in life, and greater concern for others in similar situations (Frazier et al., 2004).

Causes of Sexual Assault against Women

To provide a perspective for the discussion that

Post-traumatic growth: Positive life changes and psychological development following exposure to trauma.

Listen to them. Find somewhere to be alone with them, and let them talk. Be patient. Let them tell their story at their own speed and in their own way. They may need to talk at odd hours, or a great deal in the beginning.

Comfort them. Try to calm and ground them if they are anxious or upset. Do this in a soothing, not a disapproving, way. They may not want to be held or touched, but you can still nurture them by offering tea, a blanket, a comfortable chair, a favourite object, and so on.

Tell them it was not their fault. Do not judge. Avoid questions that seem to blame them for their actions. Avoid "why" questions such as "Why didn't you fight harder?" or "Why did you go to their room?" Let them know that it was the aggressor's fault, not theirs.

Provide security. Help them feel safe by offering to find them a secure place to sleep and companionship when they return home.

Encourage action. Suggest calling a sexual assault crisis centre. A sexual assault crisis worker is experienced in talking to survivors, and can understand the survivor's needs and offer useful resources. Medical assistance also may be impor-tant, depending on the nature of the assault. If they agree to medical assistance, go with them to the hospital, clinic, or doctor's office. Stay during the examination if they want you to.

Let them make the decisions. A sexual assault survivor needs to regain their feeling of control. You can help with this by giving referrals and resources, but letting them make the decisions.

Help them decide whether to report the assault. If they decide to report the assault, encourage them to preserve any evidence. They should not take a shower or remove their clothes until they talk to the police.

Recognize your own limitations. Take time out when you need it. Recognize when you have reached the limits of your abilities. Help them create a network of support and referrals. Put aside your feelings and deal with them elsewhere. If you have strong feelings, talk to another friend or a local hotline.

Source: Condensed from Hughes and Sandler (1987) and from materials developed by the Fredericton Sexual Assault Crisis Centre.

---

follows, we can distinguish among four major theoretical views of the nature of sexual assault (Albin, 1977; Baron & Straus, 1989):

1. *Victim-precipitated sexual assault* This view holds that a sexual assault is always caused by a woman "asking for it." Sexual assault, then, is considered basically the woman's fault. This view represents the tendency to "blame the victim."
2. *Psychopathology of sex offenders* This theoretical view holds that sexual assault is an act committed by a psychologically disturbed man. His deviance is responsible for the crime occurring.
3. *Feminist* Feminist theorists and learning theorists view sexual assault as the product of gender-role socialization in our culture, which reinforces and legitimizes male aggression in general and sexual coercion specifically. Femi-nists also have theorized about the complex links between sex and power: In some assaults, men use sex to demonstrate their power over women; in other assaults, men use their power over women to get sex. Feminists also point to the eroticization of violence in our society. Gender inequality is both the cause and the result of sexual assault in this view.
4. *Social disorganization* Sociologists believe that crime rates, including sexual assault rates, increase when the social organization of a community is disrupted. Under such conditions the community cannot enforce its norms against crime.

You personally may subscribe to one or more of these views. It is also true that researchers in this area have generally based their work on one of these theoretical models, which may influence their research. You should keep these models in mind as you read the rest of this chapter.

What do the data say? Research indicates that a number of factors contribute to sexual assault, ranging from forces at the cultural level to factors at the individual level. These factors include the following: cultural values, sexual scripts, early family influences, peer-group influences, characteristics of the situation, miscommunication, sex and power motives, and masculinity norms and men's attitudes. The data on each of these factors are considered below.

Cultural values can serve to support sexual assault. Cross-culturally, in preliterate societies, sexual assault is significantly more common in cultures that are characterized by male dominance, a high degree of general violence, and an ideology of male toughness (Sanday, 1981).

Sociologists Larry Baron and Murray Straus (1989), experts in violence research, did an extensive study to test the last two theories, feminist theory and social disorganization theory. Both theories deal with sexual assault as a result of cultural context. Baron and Straus collected extensive data on each of the 50 states in the United States, seeing them as representing variations in cultural context (think, for example, of the different cultures of Louisiana, New York, and North Dakota). To test feminist theory, they collected data on the extent of gender inequality in each state (for example, the gap between men's and women's wages); they also examined the feminist hypothesis that use of pornography encourages sexual violence, by collecting data on the circulation of pornographic magazines in each state. They also obtained measures of social disorganization, such as the number of people moving into or out of the state, the divorce rate, and even the number of tourists flowing into the state. Their data gave strong support to three conclusions: (1) Gender inequality is related to sexual assault (the states with the greatest gender inequality had the highest rape rates); (2) pornography provides ideological support for sexual assault (the states with the highest circulation of pornographic magazines tended to have the highest rape rates); and (3) social disorganization contributes to sexual assault (the states with the greatest social disorganization tended to have the highest rape rates). This research emphasizes how important cultural context is in creating a social climate that encourages or discourages sexual assault.

Sexual scripts play a role in sexual aggression as well (Byers, 1996). Adolescents quickly learn society's expectations about dating and sex through culturally transmitted sexual scripts. These scripts support sexual assault when they convey the message that the man is supposed to be oversexed and be the sexual "aggressor." By adolescence, both girls and boys endorse scripts that justify sexual aggression. A New Brunswick study of almost 1,700 middle and high school students found that about 11 percent of boys believe that it is acceptable for boys to be sexually coercive with a girlfriend (Price & Byers, 1999). Research has shown that middle school, high school, and university men who hold these beliefs are more likely to be sexually aggressive (Byers & Eno, 1991; Price et al., 1999).

Early family influences may play a role in shaping a man into becoming a sexual aggressor. Specifically, young men who are sexual aggressors are more likely to have been sexually abused themselves in childhood (Friedrich et al., 1988; Koss et al., 1994).

The peer group can be a powerful factor in men's sexually aggressive behaviour. For example, a national study of 1,300 Canadian male college and university students found that men who had abusive friends were more likely to have used sexual aggression (DeKeseredy & Kelly, 1993; DeKeseredy & Schwartz, 1999). It may be that aggressive friends encourage men to be sexually aggressive. It also may be that sexually aggressive men choose friends who have similar attitudes.

Characteristics of the situation play a role. Sexual assault is more likely to occur in secluded places or at parties at which excessive alcohol is used (Koss et al., 1994). Another situational factor is social disorganization, as noted earlier. An extreme example is war, in which sexual assault of women is common (Brownmiller, 1975). In the 1990s we saw graphic examples of this in the war in the former Yugoslavia. Bosnian women—Croats and Muslims—were frequently sexually assaulted by the attacking Serbs.

Miscommunication between women and men is a factor. In the section on sexual assault in dating relationships we saw a case in which the man and the woman had totally different understandings of what had occurred. Because many people in Canada find it difficult to discuss sex directly, they try to infer sexual interest from subtle non-verbal cues, a process that is highly prone to errors (Abbey, 1991). Specifically, men are likely to interpret a woman's friendly behaviour as carrying a sexual message that she did not intend.

Sex and power motives are involved in sexual assault. Feminists have stressed that sexual violence is an expression of power and dominance by men over women (Brownmiller, 1975; Clark & Lewis, 1977). Current theory emphasizes that sexual motives and power motives are both involved and interact with each other. For example, using phallometric assessment, researchers in Ontario examined differences in physiological arousal to consenting and nonconsenting sexual scenarios between a group of men convicted of sexual assault, a group of men convicted of nonsexual crimes, and a group of men from the community. The violent non-sexual criminals and men from the community were more aroused by hearing about consensual sex than by hearing about forced sex. However, the sex offenders showed little difference in their arousal to consenting and sexual assault scenarios (Lalumière et al., 2003). Research by Ontario psychologists Howard Barbaree and William Marshall (1991) has identified a number of processes that may be involved. For example, sexually aggressive and non-aggressive men may differ in their ability to suppress sexual arousal when it occurs under inappropriate circumstances. Hostile aggression may inhibit sexual arousal in non-aggressive men but not in sexually aggressive men.

Finally, *masculinity norms and men's attitudes* are another factor (Abram et al., 2003; Koss et al., 1994), as we will see in the next section. Supporting the feminist theoretical view, research shows that men who have more hypermasculine attitudes are more likely to have a history of sexual aggression (Murnen et al., 2002).

Thus, research has supported the theories that propose that socialization, social inequality, and social disorganization contribute to sexual assault. However, research has not found that women cause their own sexual assault (victim-precipitated theory) or that most men who commit sexual assault have psychological disorders. The very commonness of sexual assault, especially in dating relationships, argues against the psychopathology of sexual offenders. Hypermasculinity is a far more common cause than psychopathology.

Men Who are Sexually Aggressive against Women

There is no "typical" sexually aggressive man. Men who commit sexual assault against women vary tremendously in occupation, education, marital status, previous criminal record, and motivation for committing sexual assault. One thing we do know about sexually aggressive men is that they tend to be repeat offenders. In one study of men who admitted to rape on a survey but had never been prosecuted, the majority had committed the crime more than once (Lisak & Miller, 2002). Those who were repeat offenders averaged about six rapes each.

A massive program of research by Neil Malamuth, Mary Koss, and their colleagues identified four factors that predispose men to engage in sexual coercion of women (Malamuth, 1998; Malamuth et al., 1991):

1. *A violent home environment* A boy who grows up in a hostile home environment has a higher likelihood of engaging in sexual aggression against women. Factors that create a hostile home environment include violence between the parents or abuse directed toward the child, whether battering or sexual abuse.
2. *Delinquency* Being involved in delinquency is itself made more likely by coming from a hostile home. But the delinquency in turn increases the likelihood of engaging in sexual coercion— the boy associates with delinquent peers who, for example, encourage hostile attitudes and rationalizations for committing illegal acts and reward a tough, aggressive image.
3. *Sexual predatory orientation* The male, often in the context of the delinquent peer group, develops a heavy emphasis on sexual conquests to bring him self-esteem and status with the peer group. For example, Alberta sex researcher Martin Lalumière and his colleagues found that sexually coercive men highly value having many new partners and engaging in casual sex (Lalumière et al., 1996; Lalumière & Quinsey, 1996). Coercion may seem to them a reasonable way of making conquests.
4. *A hostile masculine personality* This personality constellation involves deep-seated hostility toward women together with negatively defined, exaggerated masculinity—masculinity defined

In Focus 17.3

Sexual Assault in the Canadian Armed Forces

In May 1998, *Maclean's* magazine carried the stories of 13 women who had come forward to report that they had been victims of sexual assault while members of the Canadian Armed Forces. One woman had been sexually assaulted by a fellow sailor while a male friend looked on. Another woman was sexually assaulted by an officer while privates guarded the doors. Many of the women had feared that there would be reprisals against them if they reported what had happened. Others felt that the military hierarchy had discounted their claims and failed to prosecute their assailants. Male and female military members who had witnessed assaults also feared they would experience reprisals if they reported the assaults.

The *Maclean's* article brought the problem of sexual harassment and sexual assault in the military to the public's attention and led to the establishment of a sexual-assault hotline for members of the Armed Forces. It also raised questions about how military culture contributes to the sexual assault of women.

An effective military must be ready for combat at all times, and strong bonds between members facilitate combat readiness. According to research by New Brunswick sociologist Deborah Harrison, some of the strategies used to maintain military bonding also promote and condone violence against women. For example, male military members are instilled with a feeling of exclusivity and separateness from civilians by being encouraged to adopt dehumanizing attitudes toward members of socially marginalized groups such as women, gay men, and lesbians. Women are stereotyped, objectified, and put down. Sexual harassment is tolerated and condoned. This is a culture that does not welcome the inclusion of women, and in fact it has only been since 1987, as a result of a Canadian Human Rights Tribunal decision, that Canadian women have become eligible to serve in combat positions.

In keeping with military bonding, members are expected to stick together by covering up for their peers' mistakes, including covering up abuse when it occurs. In fact, in units devoted to combat, violence against women may be specifically tolerated and fostered. In these units, women are commonly referred to as "bitches," "sluts," "cunts," and "whores." Male soldiers often make lewd sexual innuendoes toward their female peers.

Military culture socializes men to have sexist attitudes toward women and creates an environment in which sexual harassment and sexual assault are likely to occur and unlikely to be reported. In order to counteract violence against women, the military has adopted a sexual harassment policy and instituted awareness training for all members. Although there is some evidence that sexual harassment has recently decreased, sexual harassment remains a problem in the Canadian Armed Forces. For example, a 1998 survey of 1,099 members of the Canadian Forces found that 14 percent of the women reported experiencing sexual harassment during the previous 12 months; most (93 percent) occurred in the workplace. This compared to 26 percent of the women in a similar survey conducted in 1992. In both 1992 and 1998, 3 percent of the men surveyed reported experiencing sexual harassment (DND/CF Human Resources, 1999).

Sources: Davis Thomas, 1998; Harrison, 2000; *Maclean's*, May 25, June 1, June 8, and December 14, 1998.

as rejecting anything feminine such as nurturance, and emphasizing power, control, and "macho" characteristics.

Perhaps surprisingly, this research was not based on convicted sex offenders but rather on a national representative sample of U.S. male university students.

Similarly, research in Ontario using a community sample of men between the ages of 19 and 82 found that childhood abuse and having a large number of sexual partners in adolescence increased the likelihood of using sexual coercion (Senn et al., 2000). In addition, the researchers found that men who had trouble expressing their feelings were more likely to have used sexual coercion. In contrast, empathy for other people's feelings seems to attenuate or reduce a man's likelihood of being sexually aggressive (Dean & Malamuth, 1997). That is, a man who has several of the risk factors listed above, but who also is sensitive to others' feelings and needs and is not self-centred, is not likely to use sexual coercion, compared with a man who has the risk factors and lacks empathy and is self-centred (Baumeister et al., 2002). These research findings have important implications for programs of therapy for convicted sex offenders. Empathy training should be emphasized, as it is in the most modern programs (Marshall, 1993; Pithers, 1993).

Ethnicity and Sexual Assault against Women

We have seen how cultural context can promote or inhibit sexual assault. The cultural heritages of various ethnocultural groups in Canada provide different cultural contexts for people of those groups, so it is important to consider the incidence of sexual assault in Canadian ethnocultural communities. Participants in three of the communities that participated in the *Ethnocultural Communities Facing AIDS* study were asked whether they had ever been coerced or forced to have sex with someone against their will. The incidence of sexual coercion differed markedly from one community to the other. In the English-speaking Caribbean communities, 37 percent of the women and 19 percent of the men reported that they had experienced sexual coercion, compared to 8 percent of the women and 1 percent of the men in the Latin American communities and 5 percent of

the men from the South Asian communities (Maticka-Tyndale et al., 1996). Interestingly, in the English-speaking Caribbean communities, people who had been in Canada longer were more likely to indicate that they had experienced sexual coercion. This suggests that sexual coercion is a more common experience in Canada than it is in the Caribbean.

Historical factors may also affect the meaning of sexual assault. Many recent Canadian immigrants are refugees from countries such as Bosnia, where invading military forces instituted systematic campaigns of sexual violence against women (Valentich, 1994). Similarly, sexual assault has a highly charged meaning in the history of African Americans (Wyatt, 1992). In the period following the American Civil War, an African American man convicted of rape or attempted rape of a white woman was typically castrated or lynched. In sharp contrast, there was no penalty for a white man who raped a black woman.

Sexual Assault against Men

The sexual assault provisions in the Criminal Code of Canada apply equally to men and to women as victims. However, in 2000 only 1.5 percent of adults convicted of sexual assault were women. Some authors believe, based on self-report studies, that there are more women sex offenders than indicated by police reports (Denov, 2003). Research shows that men who have been sexually assaulted experience symptoms of PTSD, as women do (Sarrell & Masters, 1982). It is important for counsellors and others in helping professions to recognize the possibility of male victims of sexual assault.

It is possible for a woman to force a man to engage in intercourse; research shows that men may respond with an erection in emotional states such as anger and terror. In a study of 115 men who had been sexually assaulted, 7 percent had been assaulted by a woman or group of women and an additional 6 percent by both a man and a woman (King & Woollett, 1997). Forced vaginal intercourse occurred in only two of the cases.

Research in New Brunswick has investigated males' and females' experiences of unwanted sexual activity due to pressure or force (Byers & O'Sullivan, 1998; O'Sullivan et al., 1998). The results showed that sexual coercion of men by women is not rare—19 percent of men had experienced unwilling sexual activity in the previous year; 9 percent of women reported having used sexual coercion. Further, 14 percent of the men who had experienced sexual coercion were extremely upset by the incident. In a study of New Brunswick middle school and high school students, 4 percent of the boys had experienced unwanted sexual activity that they found upsetting (Price et al., 2000). Although both these studies showed that females are more likely to experience sexual coercion than males are, the results indicate that sexual coercion of males by females is not that infrequent and that these experiences are very upsetting for some males, and that men who have been sexually assaulted can experience symptoms of PTSD.

Some of the same factors that contribute to sexual aggression by men also contribute to sexual aggression by women. They occur in similar heterosexual dating situations, and men and women use similar strategies to influence their partner to engage in the unwanted sexual activities, most often verbal forms of pressure or ignoring requests to stop (O'Sullivan & Byers, 1999). Sexual scripts play a role as well. Research in Ontario has shown that many women believe the stereotype that men are always interested in sex (Clements-Shreiber et al., 1998). Thus, they may not believe that when a man says "no" he really means "no." For example, in a study of sexual coercion in a sample of university students, 58 percent of the men (and 78 percent of the women) reported being the objects of sexual persistence after they had refused sexual advances (Struckman-Johnson et al., 2003). Sexual persistence included using any of a number of tactics to have sexual contact with the respondent despite their initial refusal of their sexual advances. The persistence tactics assessed included persistent kissing and touching, the perpetrator taking off his or her own clothes, telling lies, and using physical restraints. One man said,

> At a party, she came up and began talking to me. I was already drinking some at the time. While playing cards, she talked me into finishing several of her drinks and beers. She said there was another party and convinced me to go. I was too drunk to drive so she drove us. The "party" seemed to lack other people. After about a half-hour of kissing/making out, I was tired and wanted to go home. She said no and told me she wanted to have sex. I said no, but she continued to kiss me and try to talk me into it. When she produced a condom, I gave in. (Struckman-Johnson et al., 2003, p. 83)

Having recognized that some men are sexually coerced by women, it is important to note that the great majority of male victims of forced intercourse are sexually assaulted by men, not women, often in prison (Calderwood, 1987).

Sexual Assault in Prison

According to a study of 516 men and women prisoners in U.S. prisons, 22 percent of the men and 7 percent of the women had been the objects of sexual coercion (Struckman-Johnson et al., 1996). Prison staff were the perpetrators in 18 percent of the cases, fellow prisoners in the remainder. Among the male victims, 53 percent had been forced to have receptive anal sex, sometimes with multiple male perpetrators, and 8 percent were forced to have receptive oral sex. The men reported severe emotional consequences. Inmates offered a number of suggestions for ending prison sexual violence. The most frequent was to segregate the most vulnerable: those who are young, non-violent, new in prison, white. Many also favoured allowing conjugal visits.

Sexual assault in prison is a particularly clear example of the way in which sexual assault is an expression of power and aggression; prisoners—most of whom would identify as heterosexual—use it as a means of establishing a dominance hierarchy.

Preventing Sexual Assault

Strategies for preventing sexual assault need to be aimed at both men and women. Although most programs are aimed at teaching women ways to avoid victimization, it is perhaps more important to develop programs for men. To eliminate sexual assault of women, our society would need to make a radical change in the way it socializes males (Hall & Barongan, 1997). If little boys were not so pressed to be aggressive and tough, and were encouraged to express their feelings and to be nurturant, perhaps there would be no sexually aggressive men. If adolescent boys did not have to demonstrate that they are hypersexual, perhaps there would be no sexually aggressive men.

We also need prevention programs aimed at changing attitudes that contribute to sexual assault.

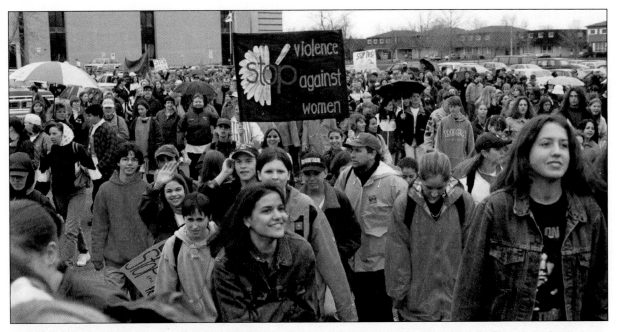

Figure 17.2 Young people today are challenging stereotypes about female weakness and passivity. This photo shows a protest by more than 800 students in Welland, Ontario, against violence against women.

In an innovative prevention program at the University of New Brunswick, Men Against Sexual Aggression, male university students conduct workshops to help other university men examine their attitudes about women in romantic relationships. The goal of the program is not only to change individual men's attitudes but also to foster a climate in which sexually coercive behaviour is seen as unacceptable. By using male peers to make the presentation, the program hopes to avoid the perception of "male bashing" that can result in a backlash that increases attitudes and statements justifying men's use of sexual coercion. An infamous example is the response of some men to a "No means No" campaign at Queen's University in Kingston—they hung banners out of the windows of male residences that read "No means more beer" and "No means tie her up."

Unfortunately, until large changes are made in society, we still need to teach women to be vigilant. These strategies fall into two categories: (1) avoiding situations in which there is a high risk of sexual assault; (2) if the first strategy has failed, knowing some self-defence techniques if a sexual assault attempt is actually made. Here are some ways to avoid high-risk situations (Hughes & Sandler, 1987, p. 3):

Set sexual limits.   No one has a right to force you to do something with your body that you don't want to do. If you don't want to be touched, for example, you have a right to say, "Don't touch me," and to leave if your wishes are not respected.

Decide early if you would like to have intercourse. The sooner you communicate your intentions firmly and clearly, the easier it will be for your partner to understand and accept your decision.

Do not give mixed messages; be clear.   Say "yes" when you mean "yes" and "no" only when you mean "no."

Be forceful and firm.   Do not worry about being polite if your wishes are being ignored.

Do not do anything you do not want to do just to avoid a scene or unpleasantness.   Do not be assaulted because you are too polite to get out of a dangerous situation or because you are worried about hurting your date's feelings. If things get out of hand, be loud in protesting, leave, and go for help.

Be aware that alcohol and drugs are often related to sexual assault by dating partners.   They compromise your ability (and that of your date) to make responsible decisions.

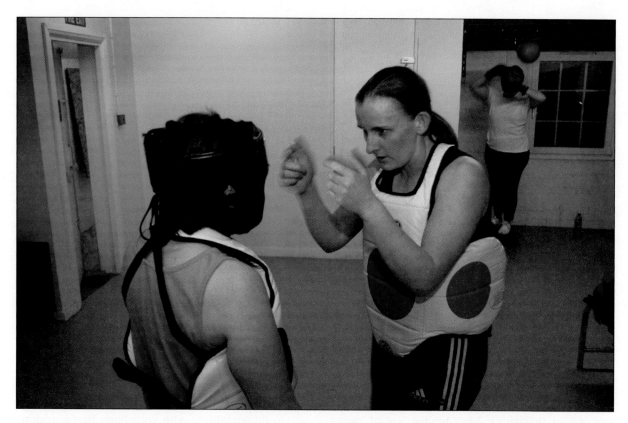

Figure 17.3 Self-defence classes for women. Many experts believe that all women should take such classes to gain the skills necessary to defend themselves in the case of an attempted sexual assault.

Trust your gut-level feelings. If the situation feels risky to you, or if you feel you are being pressured, trust your feelings. Leave the situation or confront the person immediately.

Be careful when you invite someone to your home or you are invited to your date's home. These are the most likely places for sexual assaults to occur.

If this first set of strategies—avoiding sexual assault situations—does not work, self-defence strategies are needed. Always remember that the goal is to get away from the attacker and run for help.

Many universities, YM-YWCAs or YM-YWHAs, and other organizations offer self-defence classes for women, and we believe that every woman should take at least one such course. Many techniques are available and the exact method the woman chooses is probably not too important. Research shows that fighting back—fighting, yelling, fleeing—increases a woman's likelihood of thwarting a sexual assault attempt (Ullman & Knight, 1993; Zoucha-Jensen & Coyne, 1993). However, changes also need to be made to the ways females are socialized so that they are more comfortable being assertive and using self-defence.

Finally, to prevent sexual assault of men by women, we need to combat the cultural stereotype that men are always interested in sex. This belief may make it difficult for men to clearly and repeatedly refuse a sexual invitation, and may make women less likely to believe men when they do say no. However, for men and women to be honest and open about their sexual interests, they will first need to become more comfortable talking about sex and less reliant on nonverbal communication.

Sexual assault prevention programs have been attempted over the past several decades. Often they are designed for a mixed audience of male and female first-year university students. Sadly and frustratingly, evaluations of these programs typically show only small changes in attitudes that do not last long, and no changes in actual sexual assault rates (Breitenbecher, 2000; Rozee & Koss, 2001). Experts in the field are trying to develop more effective prevention programs for both women and men; we need to put our best energies into these efforts (Lonsway & Kothari, 2000; Rozee & Koss, 2001).

■ Child Sexual Abuse

In this section we discuss the broad category of child sexual abuse and one specific subcategory, intrafamilial sexual abuse—sexual abuse that occurs within the family.

There are currently several statutes related to the sexual exploitation of children in the Criminal Code of Canada, including sexual assault, sexual interference, invitation to sexual touching, and sexual exploitation (refer to In Focus 2.2). These offences apply to any type of sexual contact with a child by a man or a woman, showing pornography to a child, having a child witness sexual intercourse, or using a computer to facilitate committing a sexual offence against a child. Making, possessing, and distributing child pornography is also illegal and is discussed in Chapter 18.

The laws that seek to prevent the sexual exploitation of children and young people were amended in 1985. Prior to 1985, there was an offence for sexual intercourse with a female under 14. There were also offences for sexual intercourse with a female 14 to 16 and for seduction of a female 16 to 18 "of previously chaste character" (Mohr & Roberts, 1994). Many of the criticisms of the repealed rape law also applied to the laws pertaining to sexual exploitation of children. For example, in most cases they applied only to girls (Busby, 1999). In contrast, the current provisions are gender-neutral and based on a combination of age, whether the accused is in a position of trust, and the specific activities that occurred. For example, the age of consent is normally 14. This means that a person accused of engaging in sexual activity with someone under 14 cannot defend themselves on the basis that the child agreed to the sexual activity. However, if the child is 12 or 13, consent can be used as a defence if the defendant is less than two years older than the complainant. The age of consent for anal intercourse is 18 and thus is higher than for vaginal intercourse, although the Supreme Court has ruled that this constitutes discrimination against gay youth. The age of consent is also higher if the adult is in a position of trust or authority with a child, such as a teacher or sports coach. Under the sexual exploitation provision, it is an offence for a person in a position of trust to have sex with a child who is under 18 years old, whether or not the child consents to it.

Finally, the Criminal Code includes a law against incest. This statute prohibits sexual intercourse with a person who is your parent, child, brother, sister, grandparent, or grandchild. Most prosecutions are cases involving children and adult relatives. The nearly universal taboo against incest seems to have as its purpose the promise to children that the home will be a place where they can be free from sexual pressure and the prevention of the alleged genetic problems of inbreeding.

Patterns of Child Sexual Abuse

How common is child sexual abuse in Canada? The 1983 National Population Survey (often called the Badgley Report) found that 18 percent of women and 8 percent of men had experienced unwanted sexual contact (touching or intercourse) by age 16 (Bagley, 1989). A recent survey of 9,953 individuals aged 15 and over living in Ontario found that 11 percent of the females and 4 percent of the males reported that they had experienced severe sexual abuse as children (threats, touching, or intercourse) (MacMillan et al., 1997). Similarly, in the United States the NHSLS found rates of 17 percent for women and 12 percent for men (Laumann et al., 1994). It seems clear that child sexual abuse is not rare, and that girls are more often its victims than boys are. Most cases are never reported. In the National Population Survey, only about 20 percent of the victims had told anyone.

How many of these incidents get reported to the authorities? The Canadian Incidence of Reported Child Abuse and Neglect study investigated child abuse cases that were reported to child welfare

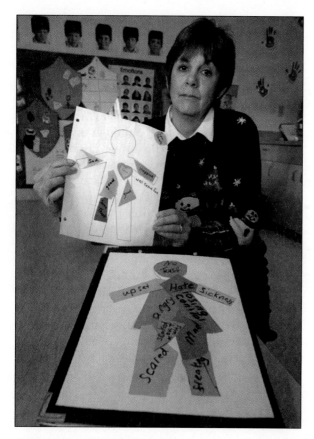

Figure 17.4 A counsellor holds art depicting the "before" and "after" feelings of an abused child. On the limbs of the "after" image words such as "mad," "hate," "scared," "upset," and "angry" are written.

services across Canada (Trocmé et al., 2001). They found that there were an estimated 2.2 reported cases of child sexual abuse per 1,000 children in Canada. Only 38 percent of these reports were substantiated. In the rest of the cases, either the abuse had not occurred or there was not enough evidence to substantiate that it had occurred. Of those complaints that were substantiated, most involved touching and fondling of the genitals (68 percent), attempted or completed sexual activity (35 percent), or adults exposing their genitals (12 percent).

The great majority of perpetrators of child sexual abuse are men. According to the NHSLS, for girls almost all the reported cases involved sexual contact with men; for boys, some cases involved men and some women, although cases involving men were considerably more common. A number of factors probably account for this great imbal-

ance. Men in our culture are socialized more toward seeing sexuality as focused on sexual acts rather than as part of an emotional relationship. The sexual script for men involves partners who are smaller and younger than themselves, whereas women's sexual script involves partners who are larger and older than they are.

In the great majority of cases, both for boys and girls, the sexual activity involves only touching of the genitals (Laumann et al., 1994). However, for girls, 10 percent of cases involved forced oral sex, 14 percent of cases involved forced vaginal intercourse, and 1 percent involved forced anal sex. For boys, 30 percent of cases involved forced oral sex and 18 percent involved forced anal sex.

Reports from 166 police departments in 2000 provide information regarding reported cases of sexual assault of children and youth in Canada (Brzozowski, 2004). Most (81 percent) of the child and youth victims of sexual assault were girls. Some of the sexual abuse was of children at very young ages; 2 percent were of children under 3 years old and 43 percent were of children between 3 and 11 years old. Table 17.2 shows the relationship between these adults and their victims. Notice that sexual assault by a stranger is least common, accounting for only 16 percent of sexual assaults of girls and 12 percent of sexual assaults of boys. In contrast, 29 percent of the girls and 35 percent of the boys were sexually assaulted by a family member; 39 percent of these by a parent, 32 percent by a sibling, and 28 percent by extended family (Brzozowki, 2004). The extended family group includes, among others, grandparents and other blood relative, step-parents, adoptive parents, and foster parents.

Of particular concern is sexual abuse of children by a person in a position of trust or authority. One of the most publicized cases of this type of abuse was that of eight Roman Catholic priests and 10 lay members of the Christian Brothers of Ireland in Canada who were convicted of sexually abusing 77 boys at Mount Cashel Orphanage in St. John's, Newfoundland, in the 1970s. A number of priests in other parts of Canada and in the United States have also been convicted of child sexual abuse. Many First Nations children attending residential schools and Aboriginal and non-Aboriginal boys in youth detention centres were also sexually abused by persons charged with their care.

Table 17.2 Categories of People Who Were Accused of Child Sexual Assault in 2000

Perpetrators	Percentage of Victims	
	Girls	Boys
Acquaintance	49%	48%
Family	29	35
Stranger	16	12
Unknown	6	4

Acquaintance includes any relationship in which the perpetrator and victim were familiar with each other, but were not related or in a legal guardianship arrangement.

Source: Brzozowski (2004).

Patterns of Intrafamilial Sexual Abuse

Incest is defined in the Criminal Code of Canada as sexual contact between blood relatives. Of particular concern is sexual abuse of children by an adult family member, often called **intrafamilial sexual abuse**. Intrafamilial abuse includes child sexual abuse by a relative and by a non-relative who is the child's caregiver; for example, between stepfather and stepdaughter.

The overwhelming majority of cases of intrafamilial child sexual abuse go unreported to authorities and unprosecuted. Nonetheless, court statistics (see Table 17.2) show that in 2000 family members were accused of 30 percent of the sexual assaults against children (Brzozowski, 2004). Data from the NHSLS based on adult recollections of incidents of sexual abuse in childhood, most of which were never reported, also show that a large percentage of cases are perpetrated by family members. Researchers found that 54 percent of the women and 20 percent of the men reported that the perpetrator was a family member.

Psychological Impact on the Victim

Many therapists who are experienced with cases of child sexual abuse feel that the effects on the victim

Intrafamilial sexual abuse: Sexual contact between a child and an adult who is the child's relative or caregiver, such as a stepfather.

are serious and long-lasting. Consider the following case:

A 25-year-old office worker was seen in the emergency room with an acute anxiety attack. She was pacing, agitated, unable to eat or sleep, and had a feeling of impending doom. She related a vivid fantasy of being pursued by a man with a knife. The previous day she had been cornered in the office by her boss, who aggressively propositioned her. She needed the job badly and did not want to lose it, but she dreaded the thought of returning to work. It later emerged in psychotherapy that this episode of sexual harassment had reawakened previously repressed memories of sexual assaults by her father. From the age of 6 until midadolescence, her father had repeatedly exhibited himself to her and insisted that she masturbate him. The experience of being entrapped at work had recalled her childhood feelings of helplessness and fear. (Herman, 1981, p. 8)

In a major review of studies of children who were sexually abused (either by family members or by nonrelatives), the researchers concluded that there is strong evidence of a number of negative effects on these children, compared with control groups of non-abused children (Kendall-Tackett et al., 1993; but see Rind et al., 1998). Sexually abused children are significantly more likely to have symptoms of anxiety, posttraumatic stress disorder (PTSD), depression, poor self-esteem, health complaints, aggressive and antisocial behaviour, inappropriate sexual behaviour, school problems, and behaviour problems such as hyperactivity. Victims had more severe symptoms when (1) the perpetrator was a member of the family; (2) the sexual contact was frequent or occurred over a long period of time; and (3) the sexual activity involved penetration (vaginal, oral, or anal). The child's gender did not seem to be a factor; that is, there were no differences in symptoms between boys and girls. However, the researchers noted that gender was not investigated in many studies, probably because so few boys appeared in most samples. Research in Quebec has shown that sexually abused children experience more PTSD symptoms than do children who have experienced other life stressors, such as an orthopedic problem (Collin-Vézina & Hébert, in

(a)   (b)

Figure 17.5   Sexual abuse outside the family is most often perpetrated by a person in a position of trust such as (a) the sexual abuse of Sheldon Kennedy by his junior hockey coach; (b) the sexual and physical abuse of Aboriginal children attending native residential schools run by several different Christian churches—the subject of an Edmonton-to-Ottawa walk for justice by Robert Desjarlais in June 2000.

press; Tremblay et al., 2000). The trauma of sexual abuse may also trigger early puberty. Note that although children who have experienced sexual abuse are more likely to experience each of these symptoms, some of these children do not experience any severe negative consequences.

Research has demonstrated that many of the negative effects of child sexual abuse persist into adulthood. Canadian research has shown that adults who were sexually abused as children display more depression, anxiety, eating disorders, and alcohol and drug dependence, compared with controls (Gold, 1986; Lemieux & Byers, 1996; Runtz & Roche, 1999). The risk of these difficulties is greater if attempted or completed intercourse occurred, if the abuse was by a relative, and if the victim told someone and received a negative response from that person (Bulik et al., 2001; Kendler et al., 2000). Adult survivors of child sex-

ual abuse are also more likely to experience sexual assault as an adult as well as sexual disorders such as fears of sex (sexual aversion), lack of sexual desire, and lack of arousal (Leonard & Follette, 2002; Loeb et al., 2002). Women who were sexually abused as children are also more likely to be preoccupied with sex, younger at the time of their first voluntary intercourse, and more likely to be teen mothers (Noll et al., 2003). Their sexuality is ambivalent—they experience both sexual aversion and a preoccupation with sex.

In most cases child sexual abuse is psychologically damaging and may lead to symptoms such as depression and PTSD. Several factors affect the psychological consequences for children; they are more severe when the perpetrator is a close family member who is an adult, and when there is extensive sexual contact that involves penetration. In addition, two Canadian studies have shown that adjustment is affected by both the abused child's coping style as well as whether the child feels supported by his or her parents (Runtz & Schallow, 1997; Tremblay et al., 1999). Further, some women who were objects of child sexual abuse perceive some benefit from the adverse life experience. They believe that it made them better at protecting their own children from abuse and made them stronger people (McMillen et al., 1995). This is another example of posttraumatic growth.

The Offenders

In 2000, Carl Toft came up for parole after serving eight years of a 13-year sentence for molesting more than 200 boys at the New Brunswick Training Centre. Critics argued that he should be denied parole because, by his own admission, he is not cured. Many child molesters abuse more than one child. In particular, child sexual abusers who abuse boys outside the family are likely to have multiple victims (Abel et al., 1987).

What do the data say about child sexual abusers? Are they likely to repeat the offence? Are there effective treatments for them?

Pedophilia involves an adult who has a sexual preference for prepubescent children, generally age 13 or younger (American Psychiatric Association, 2000). To meet the official criteria for diagnosis as a paraphilia (see Chapter 16), the person must have intense sexually arousing fantasies, sexual urges, or behaviours, over a period of at least six months, that involve sexual activity with a prepubescent child. Not all pedophiles are child molesters—that is, have sex with children. Not all child molesters are pedophiles—that is, have a sexual preference for prepubescent children.

Pedophiles fall into a number of categories, depending on the gender of the children they are attracted to and other factors. In one study of 678 pedophiles, all of them men, 27 percent were attracted to boys, 47 percent to girls, and 25 percent to both (Blanchard et al., 1999). Child molesters also differ in whether their victims are their biological children, stepchildren, children they know, or children they do not know (Guay et al., 2001). Pedophiles who molest children tend to be

Pedophilia: Child molesting; an adult having sexual activity with a prepubescent child.

repeat offenders and their patterns of preference tend to be stable over time.

Pedophiles score low on measures of heterosocial competence (Dreznick, 2003). That is, they lack the interpersonal skills to function well in adult heterosexual relationships. Canadian research shows that pedophiles have poorer cognitive functioning than controls and are more likely than controls to have had accidents involving head injury and unconsciousness before the age of 6 (Blanchard et al., 2002; Cantor et al., 2004). This suggests that problems with early brain development and/or some injury to the developing brain may create this disorder.

Two Ontario researchers attempted to answer the question of recidivism (repeat offending) by sex offenders by conducting a review of research conducted in six different countries including Canada, most of whom had received treatment (Hanson & Bussière, 1998). They found that the recidivism rate was only about 13 percent for child molesters within four to five years after the offence. This is no doubt an underestimate of the actual rates of reoffending, because so much child sexual abuse goes unreported (Hanson, 2000). Further, recidivism is much higher for sex abusers who have not received treatment (and participation in treatment is voluntary) and for certain subgroups of child molesters. For example, it was higher among those who had committed previous sexual offences, had begun sexual offending at an early age, and had targeted male victims. The strongest predictor of recidivism was phallometric measures of sexual deviance (recall the penile strain gauge discussed in Chapter 14). Offenders are shown slides of children and their arousal (erection) is measured. Several Canadian studies have found that men who show greater sexual arousal to children as measured through phallometric assessment are more likely to commit another sexual offence (Firestone et al., 2000; Proulx et al., 1997; Rice et al., 1991; Seto et al., 2000). Ontario researchers have also demonstrated that the recidivism rate is higher for extrafamilial offenders than for intrafamilial offenders (Firestone et al., 1999, 2000; Greenberg et al., 2000). Therefore, depending on the particular case, there may be a very low or very high risk of repeating the offence, and we know some of the factors that predict which category a particular offender might belong in.

In Focus 17.4

False Memory Syndrome? Recovered Memory?

One of the nastiest professional controversies today concerns the issue of what some call recovered memory and others false memory syndrome. The issue is sexual abuse or other severe trauma in childhood and whether the child victim can forget (suppress) the memory of the event and later recover that memory.

On one side of the argument, the *recovered memory* side, psychotherapists see adult clients who display serious symptoms of prior trauma, such as severe depression and anxiety. Sometimes these clients have clear memories of being sexually abused in childhood and have always remembered the events but have never told anyone until they told the therapist. In other cases, the client doesn't remember that any abuse occurred but, during the process of therapy, or sometimes spontaneously before therapy, something triggers the memory and the client then recalls the sexual abuse. Psychotherapists are understandably outraged about the psychological trauma that results from childhood sexual abuse.

On the other side, some psychologists believe that these memories for events that had been forgotten and then are remembered are actually *false memories*; that is, the events never occurred. They argue that unscrupulous or overzealous therapists may induce these memories by hypnotizing clients or strongly suggesting to clients that they had been abused in childhood.

What do the data say? First, there is evidence from laboratory studies that information associated with unpleasant emotions is more likely to be forgotten (e.g., Bootzin & Natzoulas, 1965). Research directly on the issue of child sexual abuse also provides support for the idea that forgetting does occur in some cases. In one study, 129 women who were known to have been sexually abused as children—they had been brought to a hospital for treatment at the time and the abuse had been medically verified—were interviewed 17 years later; 38 percent did not remember their prior abuse (Williams, 1994). The possible flaw in this study is that some of the respondents may have remembered but not have reported it to the interviewer. However, they were reporting many other intimate sexual experiences, so it seems likely that they would report accurately about this one, too. In a study of adult women who reported to a researcher that they had been victims of child sexual abuse, 30 percent said that they had completely blocked out any memory of the abuse for a full year or more (Gold et al., 1994). In another, similar study, 19 percent of adult women who reported child sexual abuse said that they forgot the abuse for a period of time (Loftus et al., 1994). In a national survey of a sample of psychologists, 24 percent reported being the victims of child sexual abuse; of those, 40 percent reported a period of forgetting (Feldman-Summers & Pope, 1994).

Abuse was more likely to have been forgotten

Canadian researchers have been leaders in the development of assessment and treatment strategies for child sexual abusers (Bradford & Greenberg, 1996; Hall, 1995; Marshall & Barbaree, 1988; Marshall & Pithers, 1994). Among the treatments in use in Canada are antiandrogen drugs, hormones, SSRIs (explained below), and cognitive–behavioural

therapy. Cyproterone acetate (CPA) is an antiandrogen drug—that is, it reduces the action of testosterone in the body with the hope that the sexually aggressive behaviour will be sharply reduced—that has been used in the treatment of child sexual abusers. Research indicates that CPA greatly reduces pedophiles' sexual arousal to chilwhen it was more severe. Therefore, the evidence seems to indicate that in from 19 to 40 percent of cases memories of childhood sexual abuse are forgotten for a period of time and then remembered again. In fact, it has been theorized that amnesia for traumatic events of this kind, particularly when the child has been betrayed by someone like a parent, is an adaptive response that helps the child survive in a terribly distressed family situation (Freyd, 1996).

The other question is, can memories of events that did not occur be "implanted" in someone? In one study, the researcher was able to create false memories of childhood events in 25 percent of the adults given the treatment (Loftus, 1993). Certain conditions seem to increase the chances that people will think they remember things that did not actually occur, including suggestion by an authority figure and suggestion under hypnosis.

Two recent studies shed additional light on this debate. One was a study of women admitted to a hospital unit specializing in the treatment of trauma-related psychological disorders (Chu et al., 1999). Among those reporting childhood sexual abuse, 26 percent had partial amnesia for it and 27 percent had complete amnesia for a period of time before recalling it. These patients also displayed dissociative symptoms. *Dissociative amnesia* is an inability to recall important personal information, usually of a traumatic nature (American Psychiatric Association, 2000). The great majority of those who suffered child sexual abuse had been able to corroborate the occurrences by some method such as medical records. Importantly, most of them first remembered the abuse while at home, and about half were not involved in any kind of treatment or counselling at the time they remembered, ruling out the possibility of suggestion by a therapist.

In another study, normal participants' brains were scanned using fMRI (functional magnetic resonance imaging) while they were suppressing unwanted memories (Anderson et al., 2004). Neural systems underlying suppression were clearly identified and included a region in the prefrontal cortex and the hippocampus. From this study we can see that suppression of memories is not just hocus-pocus, but has a real basis in the brain.

What is the bottom line? There is evidence that some people do forget childhood sexual abuse and remember it later. There is also evidence that some people can form false memories based on suggestions made by another person. It seems likely that most of the cases of recovered memory of child sexual abuse are true, but that some are false and the product of suggestion. It is also probably true that false accusations of past child abuse are made, often by a well-intentioned "victim" who is highly suggestible to press reports of other cases or who has been misled by an overly zealous therapist. As a result, an accused person who is actually innocent may be arrested. There are errors of justice on both sides. Nonetheless, there are many more cases of unreported and unpunished perpetrators than of falsely convicted persons.

Sources: Anderson et al., 2004; Bootzin & Natsoulas, 1965; Chu et al., 1999; Feldman-Summers & Pope, 1994; Freyd, 1996; Gold, Hughes, & Hohnecker, 1994; Loftus, 1993; Loftus, Polonsky, & Fullilove, 1994; Williams, 1994.

dren (Bradford & Greenberg, 1996). Medroxyprogesterone acetate (MPA) is a hormone that has a similar antiandrogen effect and is used in the treatment of sex offenders. Its effects are similar to those of CPA but, for a variety of technical reasons, CPA seems to be the preferred drug. Results with a new anti-GnRH drug are quite promising (Rosler & Witztum, 1998). By blocking the action of GnRH, pituitary and gonadal functioning is inhibited, again reducing levels of testosterone. A relatively new class of antidepressants (the SSRIs, which include Prozac and Zoloft) are also proving to be successful in the treatment of sex offenders (Bradford & Greenberg, 1996). Their use is based on the assumption that sex offending can be a particular kind of obsessive-compulsive disorder, and such disorders generally respond well to these antidepressants. Cognitive–behavioural therapy makes use of a number of techniques, including cognitive restructuring, masturbation reconditioning [the man learns to experience arousal to appropriate persons (adults) rather than inappropriate persons (children)], role-playing, desensitization, and stress management (Barbaree & Seto, 1997; Marshall & Pithers, 1994).

A review of studies assessing the effectiveness of the various treatments found that overall, the recidivism rate was 27 percent for untreated sex offenders and 19 percent for treated sex offenders, a significant improvement (Hall, 1995). Hormonal treatments and cognitive–behavioural therapy were equally effective. Cognitive–behavioural therapy has advantages, though, because offenders often refuse or discontinue hormone treatment as it reduces both normal and deviant sexual arousal (Barbaree & Seto, 1997). Between 30 and 100 percent of men who start hormonal treatment later drop out. A program for sex offenders in Kingston, Ontario, is an example of a successful comprehensive cognitive–behavioural treatment program. This program reduced recidivism from 35 percent among untreated sex offenders to less than 10 percent among treated offenders (Marshall, 1992; Marshall & Eccles, 1991).

Mandatory Notification of the Release of Sex Offenders

Many Canadians are concerned that sex offenders who are released into the community after serving their sentence will reoffend; that is, commit another sexual assault or molest another child. Media coverage of high-profile cases in which offenders have reoffended after their release adds to public fears and has resulted in a call from some people for mandatory public notification of the release of sex offenders. They argue that if people are aware that there is a released sex offender in their community, they can protect themselves and their children from sexual violence.

Since 1994, organizations (but not individuals) have been able to have potential employees and volunteers screened by police to ensure that they do not have a prior conviction for child sexual abuse. In addition, in December 2004 the federal government, with unanimous support of the provinces and territories, implemented the National Sex Offender Registry. All convicted sex offenders are required to register. This registry is available only to law enforcement officials and is intended to help them investigate unsolved crimes of a sexual nature. This information is not available to the general public. However, some people argue that there should be a comparable registry of child molesters available to the public (Canadian Centre for Justice Statistics, 1999).

Most authorities raise a number of concerns related to establishing a national registry of sex offenders available to the public. These include problems related to misidentification of innocent people and sex offenders' rights to privacy if they do not pose a risk to the public. They also fear that some citizens may take the law into their own hands. Finally, public notification may drive sex offenders underground so that it becomes more difficult for police to keep track of them (Federoff & Moran, 1977). The issue of public warnings about the release of sex offenders pits the rights of the community to be informed about the risk of significant harm against the privacy rights of the offender (Canadian Centre for Justice Statistics, 1999). Therefore, at present community notification is restricted to offenders who are believed to pose an immediate risk to the public. Nonetheless, police are left with a great deal of discretion in determining which offenders pose such a risk, leaving the issue open to continued public debate.

Preventing Child Sexual Abuse

With increasing awareness of the prevalence and potential negative consequences of child sexual abuse, most elementary schools in Canada have implemented a sexual abuse prevention program (these often go by names such as "personal safety"). The goal of these programs is to empower children to resist people who attempt to abuse them sexually as well as to provide them with the skills they will need to do so. Most programs share certain concepts (Hébert et al., 2001; Hébert & Tourigny, 2004). For example, they help children to distinguish between good touches and bad touches, as well as to recognize potentially abusive situations. They teach them strategies to deal assertively with potential abuse, such as yelling "No." They emphasize the importance of the child telling a trusted adult about the abuse or attempted abuse. Finally, they reassure children that they are not to blame in the event that sexual abuse does occur. However, the programs differ in their length, the way the program is delivered (e.g., video, puppets, books, etc.) and who delivers it (teachers, parents, police officers) (Hébert & Tremblay, 2000; Hébert et al., 2001). A few programs offer concurrent programs for parents to assist them in talking to their own children about sexual abuse. Researchers in Quebec evaluated the impact of such a parent workshop (Hébert et al., 2002). They found that the workshop had a positive impact on parents' knowledge as well as on their reactions to a hypothetical situation involving child sexual abuse compared to parents who did not attend the workshop. However, only 20 percent of the invited parents chose to attend the workshop.

How effective are these programs? Do children learn the concepts? Do they remember them? A review of studies on the effectiveness of child sexual abuse prevention programs found that these programs do increase elementary school children's knowledge (Hébert & Tourigny 2004). Further, in role-play situations, the children are better able to identify potentially abusive situations and implement the skills that they learned. Older children tend to show greater gains than younger children do. However, the gains are sometimes small and tend to decrease over time. This suggests that children will need to have booster sessions—that is, have sexual abuse prevention skills reviewed regularly—if they are to retain their skills. Longer programs and programs that allow children to practise and role play their self-protection skills, rather than relying only on instruction, tend to be more effective. For example, evaluation of child abuse prevention programs in Quebec and Calgary found that the children who received the program increased their knowledge and skills at the end of the program more than a control group (Hébert et al., 2001; Tutty, 1997).

There are some concerns that are often raised about child abuse prevention programs. First, are children able to put the skills they learn into practice (Finkelhor & Daro, 1997)? That is, how many children actually use the skills they learned in a

sexual abuse prevention program when faced with a sexual abuser, particularly when the abuser is a family member? Second, will the program have negative effects on the children, such as increasing their anxieties or their fear of appropriate physical affection (Reppucci et al., 1999)? Although some children do show these types of responses, according to parental reports most children do not (Hébert et al., 2001; Tutty, 1997).

■ Sexual Harassment

Under Canadian federal and provincial law, sexual harassment is a form of sex discrimination and therefore is illegal. The issue is a powerful one—it can interfere with a person's ability to do a job or obtain a service. It may force a victim out of a job, but it can also force a perpetrator from a job.

Canadian courts and human rights tribunals have used the following definition of sexual harassment developed by the U.S. Equal Employment Opportunity Commission (Aggarwal, 1992):

> Unwelcome sexual advances, requests for sexual favors, and other verbal or physical conduct of a sexual nature constitute sexual harassment when
>
> A. Submission to such conduct is made either explicitly or implicitly a term or condition of an individual's employment or academic advancement,
>
> B. Submission to or rejection of such conduct by an individual is used as the basis for academic or employment decisions affecting that individual, or
>
> C. Such conduct has the purpose or effect of unreasonably interfering with an individual's work or academic performance or creating an intimidating, hostile, or offensive working or educational environment.

According to the New Brunswick Human Rights Commission, sexual harassment is any "vexatious comment or conduct of a sexual nature, that is known or ought reasonably to be known to be unwanted"; that is, that a reasonable person should have known was unwelcome. Sexual harassment can be divided into two categories: sexual coercion and sexual annoyance (Aggarwal, 1992). The key ingredient for sexual coercion is that compliance with the sexual advances has some direct link to employment or educational status or opportunity, or to receipt of a public service. This is termed "quid pro quo harassment" (*quid pro quo* meaning "I'll do something for you if you do something for me"). Sexual annoyance or environmental harassment is sexually related behaviour that creates a hostile, intimidating work environment so that the person cannot work effectively, such as constant lewd innuendoes, verbal intimidation, or practical jokes that cause embarrassment.

Sexual harassment can occur at work and in education, as well as in other contexts such as psychotherapy or on the street.

Sexual Harassment at Work

Sexual harassment at work may take a number of different forms. A prospective employer may make it clear that sexual activity is a prerequisite to being hired. Stories of such incidents are rampant among actors. Once on the job, sexual activity may be made a condition for continued employment, for a promotion, or for other benefits such as a raise. Or it can involve creating a hostile work environment. Here is one case:

> I work at a family-owned restaurant. Because I am a bartender, it is often just me behind the bar. On numerous occasions, I have caught one of the owners staring at my backside as I am getting things out of the refrigerator behind the bar. He has also blatantly stared at my legs, if I am wearing a skirt, while I am trying to speak with him. This owner also enjoys standing at the end of the counter so he partially obstructs the walkway that allows me to move from behind the bar. When I try to get out and say "Excuse me," he leans forward on the counter so I have to squeeze between him and the wine rack. He has also shown me how to clean the nozzle used to foam milk for coffee drinks, but does so in a fashion that looks much like someone manually stimulating a certain piece of the male anatomy, and then looks at me with a grin on his face. There have been times when the dishwasher wasn't working and he made comments to the male bartender, as I was standing right there, such as, "Be gentle with her... you have to go slowly so you don't hurt it... it needs lubrication." He has walked up behind me and blown on my neck.

All of the comments and actions are very unnerving. (From a student essay)

It is clear how psychologically damaging such environments are to the victim.

Surveys indicate that sexual harassment at work is far more common than many people realize. An Angus Reid-Southam News telephone survey in 1991 found rates of 37 percent for women and 10 percent for men (Aggarwal, 1992). A more recent survey of 1,990 Canadian women between the ages of 18 and 65 found that 56 percent had experienced sexual harassment in the last year; the overall lifetime rate was 77 percent (Crocker & Kalemba, 1999). The preponderance of harassers are male.

Both women and men victims report that harassment has negative effects on their emotional and physical condition, their ability to work with others on the job, and their feelings about work (Tangri et al., 1982). However, men are more likely to feel that the overtures from women ended up being reciprocal and mutually enjoyable. Women, on the other hand, are more likely to report damaging consequences, including being fired or quitting their job (Gutek, 1985). There is evidence linking the experience of sexual harassment to depression and PTSD (Fitzgerald, 1993).

Why does sexual harassment at work occur? According to a theory proposed by psychologists Susan Fiske and Peter Glick (1995), it results from a combination of gender stereotyping and men's ambivalent motives. Stereotypes of women in Canadian culture are complex and include three distinct clusters: "sexy," "non-traditional" (e.g., feminist), and "traditional" (e.g., mother). Many men have ambivalent motives in their interactions with women because they desire both dominance and intimacy. Fiske and Glick argue that there are four types of harassment of women by men. With the first, *earnest harassment,* the man is truly motivated by a desire for sexual intimacy, but he won't take "no" for an answer and persists with unwelcome sexual advances. He stereotypes women as sexy. With the second type, *hostile harassment,* the man's motivation is domination of the woman, often because he perceives her as being competitive with him in the workplace. He holds the stereotype of women as non-traditional and therefore competitive with him. His response to rejection by

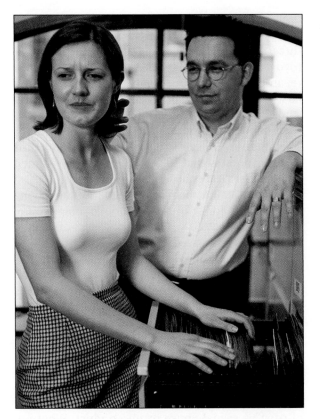

Figure 17.6 This man has positioned himself so that the woman cannot avoid contact, and if he is her supervisor, she may be hesitant to protest.

a woman is increased harassment. The third and fourth types of harassment involve ambivalent combinations of the two basic motives, dominance and a desire for intimacy. In the third type, *paternalistic-ambivalent harassment,* the man is motivated by a desire for sexual intimacy but also by a paternalistic desire to be like a father to the woman. This type of harassment may be particularly insidious because the man thinks of himself as acting benevolently toward the woman. Finally, the fourth type, *competitive-ambivalent harassment,* mixes real sexual attraction and a stereotype of women as sexy with the man's hostile desire to dominate the woman, which is based on his belief that she is non-traditional and competitive with him. This theory gives us an excellent view of the complex motives that underlie men's sexual harassment of women.

Social psychologists have developed a clever method for studying sexual harassment experi-

mentally in the laboratory, called the Computer Harassment Paradigm (Maass et al., 2003). In one study, university men were first exposed to a female confederate of the experimenters, who expressed either strong feminist beliefs (intentions to get a high-level career in an area usually reserved for men, and involvement in an organization for women's rights), or traditional beliefs. The men then had the opportunity to harass the woman by sending her pornographic material on a computer (she did not actually receive it). The men exposed to the feminist sent significantly more pornography than did men in the control group. However, not all men in the feminist-threat condition responded with harassment; those who did so were mainly men who identified strongly with the male role. The findings of this experiment are consistent with the type of harassment known as hostile environment harassment.

Sexual harassment at work is more than just an annoyance. Particularly for women, because they are more likely to be harassed by supervisors, it can make a critical difference in career advancement. For the woman who supports her family, being fired for sexual non-compliance is a catastrophe. The power of coercion is enormous.

Sexual Harassment in Education: An A for a Lay

Sexual harassment on campus is not rare (Pyke, 1996). For example, a 1989 survey at the University of Prince Edward Island found that 29 percent of the female students reported that they had been personally sexually harassed by a faculty member (Mazer & Percival, 1989). Harassment ranged from sexual teasing and jokes to unwanted touching and offers of favours for sex. More than 85 percent of male and female students had experienced sexual harassment in class, most commonly sexual jokes and faculty remarks that put down women, men, gay men, or lesbians. Women report dropping courses, changing majors, or dropping out of university as a result of sexual harassment (Fitzgerald, 1993).

Many Canadian universities have sexual harassment policies and have set up reporting and grievance procedures for dealing with sexual harassment cases.

Sexual harassment is not confined either to universities or to teachers harassing students. One survey of 14- and 15-year-olds in the Netherlands found that 24 percent of the girls and 11 percent of the boys had been the objects of sexual harassment (Timmerman, 2003). Of those cases, 73 percent represented harassment by peers and 27 percent harassment by teachers (or other school-related adults such as a tutor or principal). Of the teachers who were harassers, 90 percent were men. The psychological consequences were more severe when the harassment was done by a teacher than by a peer. An Ontario study of 1,213 youth in grades 6 to 8 found that 36 percent of boys and 21 percent of girls reported have perpetrated sexual harassment; 42 percent of boys and 38 percent of girls reported have experienced sexual harassment (McMaster et al., 2002). The two most common sexually harassing behaviours were homophobic name-calling and sexual comments, jokes, gestures, and looks.

Sex between Professionals and Patients

There is another category of coercive and potentially damaging sexual encounters—those between a psychotherapist and a client, or between other professionals, such as physicians, and a patient. Professional associations, such as the Canadian Psychological Association (1991), state clearly in their codes of ethics that such behaviours are unethical. Nonetheless, professional sexual misconduct does occur, and can be extremely damaging.

One survey of a sample of licensed Ph.D. psychologists found that 5.5 percent of the male and 0.6 of the female psychologists admitted having engaged in sexual intercourse with a client during the time the patient was in therapy, and an additional 2.6 percent of male and 0.3 percent of female therapists had intercourse with clients within three months of the termination of therapy (Holroyd & Brodsky, 1977). These are probably best regarded as minimum figures because they are based on the self-reports of the therapists and some might not be willing to admit such activity even though the questionnaire was anonymous. The Ontario College of Physicians and Surgeons (1991) estimated that 10 percent of Ontario women had been sexually abused by a physician.

Experts regard this kind of situation as having the potential for serious emotional damage to the client (Pope, 2001). Like the cases of sexual harassment discussed earlier, it is a situation of unequal power, in which the more powerful person, the therapist, imposes sexual activity on the less powerful person, the client. The situation is regarded as particularly serious because people in psychotherapy have opened themselves up emotionally to the therapist and therefore are extremely vulnerable emotionally. Some provinces, such as Ontario and New Brunswick, have passed legislation that defines sexual contact between a patient or client and any health professional in a position of trust as sexual abuse or misconduct. What are the responses of professionals accused of sexual misconduct? According to two Quebec therapists, they generally fall into three groups: deniers, rationalizers, and repentants. Deniers refuse to acknowledge that the sexual activities occurred. Rationalizers tend to avoid responsibility for their behaviour by minimizing its impact. Those in the repentant group take full responsibility for their action, are sincerely sorry that it occurred, and take steps to ensure that it will not occur again.

▨ ■ ■ SUMMARY

In the Criminal Code of Canada, sexual assault is any activity to which the victim did not consent, ranging from unwanted touching to forced oral, anal, or vaginal intercourse. There are three levels of sexual assault, depending on the amount of force used, not on the nature of the sexual activity. The law is gender-neutral in that it applies equally to men and women as victims. The Violence Against Women Survey found that 39 percent of Canadian women reported having been sexually assaulted. Other surveys have found that some men report having experienced sexual coercion, although a smaller percentage of men than women report these experiences. Victims may experience posttraumatic stress disorder (PTSD) as a result of the assault. Sexual assault by a dating or romantic partner is more common than many people realize. There are four major theoretical views of sexual assault: victim-precipitated, psychopathology of sex offenders, feminist, and social disorganization. The incidence of sexual assault differs markedly between the various ethnocultural communities in Canada.

Approximately 18 percent of women and 8 percent of men report that they had experienced unwanted sexual contact with an adult or older adolescent by age 16. There are currently several statutes related to the sexual abuse of children in the Criminal Code of Canada, including sexual assault, sexual interference, invitation to sexual touching, and sexual exploitation. Most sexual abuse of children is committed by a relative or by a family friend. Sexually abused children are more likely than other children to have symptoms such as anxiety, PTSD, depression, and health complaints. More severe psychological consequences are likely to occur when the perpetrator is a close family member who is an adult (sibling incest seems less harmful) and when the sexual contact is extensive and involves penetration. Pedophiles are more likely to be attracted to girls than to boys. Some types of child molesters have a low rate of recidivism, but certain types are highly likely to repeat their offence. Drugs such as MPA and CPA are effective treatments for sex offenders, as is cognitive-behavioural therapy. There is controversy over whether the public should be notified about the release of all sex offenders.

There is a controversy among professionals over whether adults can recover memories of child sexual abuse that they had forgotten (recovered memory), or whether these are cases of false memory syndrome, in which the supposedly remembered incidents never actually occurred.

Most schools offer child abuse prevention programs. Their goals are to provide children with the knowledge and skills to resist people who attempt to abuse them.

Sexual harassment, whether on the job or in education, involves unwelcome sexual advances when there is some coercion involved, such as making the sexual contact a condition of being hired or receiving an A grade in a course. In another form of sexual harassment, the work or educational environment is made so hostile, on a sexual and gender basis, that the employee cannot work effectively. Surveys show that sexual harassment at work is fairly common. In severe cases it can lead to damaging psychological consequences, such as PTSD for the victim. In education, the data indicate that about one-third of female students have been individually harassed by professors, although many more have experienced sexual harassment in class. This abuse can lead to negative consequences for the student, such as being forced to change majors or drop out of school. Sex between psychotherapist and client also carries the potential for psychological damage to the client.

■ ■ ■ QUESTIONS FOR THOUGHT, DISCUSSION, AND DEBATE

1. On your campus, what services are available for sexual assault victims? Do these services seem adequate, given what you have read in this chapter about victim responses to sexual assault? What could be done to improve the services?

2. Find out what procedures are available on your campus to deal with incidents of sexual harassment of a student by a professor.

3. Apply the four theoretical views of sexual assault to child sexual abuse.

4. Angie was sexually assaulted last night at a party, by a man she had met previously in one of her classes. Should she report it to the police?

5. Under Canadian law, sexual harassment is a form of sex discrimination. Sexual harassment involves repeated unwelcome sexual advances or a requirement of sex in return for something like being hired or getting a raise, or an environment that is so sexually hostile that the person has difficulty working. Discrimination based on sexual orientation is also prohibited. Do you think there is a sexual orientation parallel to sexual harassment? That is, do you think that homosexual harassment exists? If yes, how would you define it?

◼ ◼ ◼ SUGGESTIONS FOR FURTHER READING

Brady, Katherine. (1979). *Father's days.* New York: Dell paperback. This autobiography of an incest victim is both moving and insightful.

Byers, E. S., & O'Sullivan, L. F. (Eds.). (1996). *Sexual coercion in dating relationships.* New York: Haworth. This monograph presents a series of research articles on various aspects related to sexual coercion in dating relationships.

Cruise, David, & Griffiths, Alison. (1997). *On South Mountain: The dark secrets of the Goler clan.* Toronto: Viking. The horrific tale of child sexual abuse within the Goler family of Nova Scotia. In 1984, 14 members of the Goler family were convicted of 100 counts of sexually abusing children in their family.

Koss, Mary B., et al. (Eds.). (1994). *No safe haven: Male violence against women at home, at work, and in the community.* Washington, DC: American Psychological Association. An excellent collection, with chapters by experts on rape and sexual harassment.

Lalumière, Martin L., Harris, Grant T., Quinsey, Vernon L., & Rice, Marnie E. (2005). *The causes of rape: Understanding individual differences in male propensity for sexual aggression.* Washington, American Psychological Association. These well-known Canadian researchers provide a comprehensive review of research on why some men rape.

Raine, Nancy V. (1998). *After silence: Rape and my journey back.* New York: Crown. Raine, a professional writer, provides an intense account of the aftermath of being raped.

 Online **Learning Centre**

For Review Questions, Web Resources, and other learning and study tools, visit the *Understanding Human Sexuality* Online Learning Centre at www.mcgrawhill.ca/college/hyde.

Sex for Sale

CHAPTER HIGHLIGHTS

> If one thing became clear during the public hearings across Canada, it was that there is no consensus on the subject of prostitution in this country...[Opinions range] from those who would have the law eliminate prostitution entirely to those who would legalize or decriminalize it.*

The exchange of sexual gratification for money is a prominent feature of many contemporary societies and one that involves large amounts of money. In this chapter, we consider two ways in which sex can be bought and sold: commercial sex worker and pornography. Both involve complex legal issues and public controversy, but also attract a steady stream of eager customers.

■ Commercial Sex Work

Sex workers are individuals who work as prostitutes, escorts, erotic dancers, phone sex workers, in non-therapeutic massage parlours, and as pornographic models and actors. According to Ontario sociologist Eleanor Maticka-Tyndale and her colleagues, what is common to all these types of activities is that they involve the sale of a service to "satisfy a sexual fantasy, produce sexual excitement or arousal, and/or provide sexual satisfaction to the customer" (Maticka-Tyndale et al., 2000b, p. 88).

Prostitutes/commercial sex workers ("hookers") engage in partnered sexual activity or interactions in return for money, material gifts, or some other form of payment such as drugs. As social critics have pointed out, some dating and living arrangements and long-term relationships, including certain marriages, also fall in this category.

Although prostitution per se—that is, the buying and selling of sex—has never been illegal in Canada, various activities related to prostitution are criminal offences (Shaver, 1996). The Criminal Code of Canada prohibits stopping cars, impeding the flow of traffic, or communicating in public for the purposes of engaging in prostitution or obtaining the sexual services of a prostitute. These are often called "communication offences." The statute clearly states that a prostitute can be a person of either gender and that both prostitutes and their customers can be charged. In addition, cities attempt to control sex work through by-laws pertaining to zoning, traffic, and licensing of businesses.

Enforcement of these statutes has largely been aimed at street prostitutes and their customers in order to make prostitutes less visible and less of a nuisance. Prostitution is considered a minor offence punishable usually by a fine or by a short jail term for repeat offenders. Keeping or being found in a **common bawdy-house** (the legal term for a place in which prostitution occurs), procuring (pimping), and living on money made from prostitution are also illegal, and the maximum sentences for these offences are significantly higher than for the communication offences (refer to In Focus 2.1). It is also illegal to keep a common bawdy-house for performance of "indecent acts," although what is considered indecent is determined by community standards. One criticism of the current law is that although prostitution is legal, there are no clear guidelines on where it can take place. Further, these laws are difficult to enforce, and the probability of arrest is low. For example, in 1987, prostitutes in Montreal were arrested 1.8 times on average in a 10-month period and fined $480. Thus, the laws do little to discourage women from entering prostitution.

How are the prostitution laws enforced? The answer is with great inconsistency (Gemme, 1998; Shaver, 1993, 1994, 1996). Almost all charges are for communication offences involving street prostitution—people working within massage parlours, escort services, brothels, and call operations rarely get charged. More prostitutes than customers are

*P. Fraser et al. (1985), *Pornography and Prostitution in Canada*, vol. II, Report of the Special Committee on Pornography and Prostitution, Ottawa: Minister of Supply and Services Canada.

Prostitute/commercial sex worker: A person who engages in sexual acts in return for money or drugs and does so in a fairly non-discriminating fashion.
Common bawdy-house: A place kept, occupied, or used by one or more persons to engage in prostitution or indecency.

charged and their sentences are more severe. In addition, more men who pay for sex with women are charged than men who pay for sex with men, in part because male police officers do not like to pose as a prostitute to entrap clients. Thus charges are disproportionately laid against female prostitutes. As Quebec sociologist Frances Shaver concluded:

> The women and men involved are both culpable under the law—as are all persons engaged in any form of prostitution—nevertheless, the enforcement patterns penalize women more often and more severely than men; they penalize prostitutes more than customers, procurers, or pimps; and they penalize on-street prostitution more than off-street prostitution. (Shaver, 1993, p. 165)

According to a 2002 Leger Marketing Poll, 69 percent of Canadians believe that prostitution is immoral; however, fewer Canadians believe prostitution is immoral than believe that shoplifting (89 percent) or having an extramarital affair (81 percent) are immoral. Men, individuals who had higher incomes, and those with university educations were less likely to see prostitution as immoral. Further, Canadians have varying views on whether prostitution should be illegal (Fraser Committee, 1985). Some people argue that prostitution is a victimless crime, and that since both parties in prostitution are consenting, prostitution should not be illegal. The argument against the criminalization of prostitution assumes that if prostitution-related activities were legal, they could be regulated and the problems of crime, public offence, and the spread of sexually transmitted infections associated with prostitution might be avoided. Under decriminalization, prostitution is viewed as a personal choice and therefore a private matter between adults rather than a crime. The law could still be involved to ensure that people, particularly children, are not forced into prostitution and to penalize pimps and other people who profit from the work of prostitutes.

Quebec sexologist Robert Gemme argues that in addition to eliminating the legal consequences of prostitution, we also need to remove the negative effects that result from the social stigma attached to prostitution—thus the term "sex worker." From this perspective, prostitution is sex-work (emphasis on the word "work") and is a trade to be regulated like any other trade. Thus, prostitutes should be entitled to all the benefits and protection given to other workers, such as freedom from harassment, proper pay, humane living and working conditions, the right to be treated with respect, and worker compensation (MacDonald & Jeffrey, 2000; Lewis et al., in press). Thus, in several Canadian cities there are movements to unionize sex workers.

Other Canadians do not favour decriminalizing the activities related to prostitution. They argue that the activities of prostitution have turned some areas of large cities into unpleasant and possibly dangerous places for many citizens, since prostitution brings with it added traffic, loitering, noise, illegal drugs, and exposure of children and residents to discarded condoms and needles. Thus, they want better enforcement of current laws to contain prostitution in non-residential areas in order to reduce visibility and the nuisance aspects of prostitution (Duchesne, 1999). Still other Canadians want stronger laws and stiffer sentences imposed by the courts.

Venues for Female Sex Workers

There are a number of settings or venues in which commercial sexual activity occurs. The nature of the venue or of the social or sexual context influences the type of sex worker and client found there (e.g., race, social class), the activity that occurs, and its associated risks. The discussion that follows focuses on female workers and their male clients, but keep in mind that there are male, female, gay, lesbian, bisexual, and transgender sex workers and clients.

The **call girl** (notice the diminutive "girl") works out of her own residence, making appointments with clients by a landline or cell phone. She is often from a middle-class background and may be a university graduate. She dresses expensively and lives in an upscale neighbourhood. A call girl in a medium-size city may charge a minimum of $100 per hour and more if she engages in atypical activities; call girls in major metropolitan areas charge $200 or more per hour. A call girl can earn a great deal of money. But she also has heavy business expenses: an expensive residence, an extensive wardrobe, bills for makeup and hairdressers, high medical bills for maintaining her health, and tips for porters and landlords.

Call girl: The most expensive and exclusive category of sex workers.

A call girl may have a number of regular customers and may accept new clients only on referral. Because she makes dates by telephone, she can exercise close control over whom she sees and over her schedule. She usually sees clients in her residence, which also allows her to control the setting in which she works. In addition to sexual gratification, she may provide other services, such as accompanying clients to business and social gatherings. Call girls have considerable autonomy, and their physical and health risks are reduced by the setting in which they work.

Another venue for commercial sex work is the **brothel**. In the 1800s and early 1900s there were many successful brothels in North America. They varied from storefront clipjoints, where the customer's money was stolen while he was sexually occupied, to elegant mansions where the customer was treated like a distinguished dinner guest. Brothels declined in number after World War II. In the past 20 years, they have been replaced by **in-call services,** which employ women working regular shifts in an apartment or condo, servicing clients who come to the apartment. In major cities the charge is $150 or $200 per hour; in exchange, the client can participate in standard sexual activity including fellatio, cunnilingus, and vaginal intercourse. Many in-call services also require initial contact by telephone, although others advertise their location in specialized media or even telephone books. A sex worker in this setting generally has less autonomy than a call girl; there is usually a manager or madam (see below) who determines the conditions of work, the fees to be charged, and collects a substantial percentage of each fee. In-call workers have less choice of clients and may be expected to service several per shift. Brothels and in-call services are illegal in Canada under the Criminal Code provision that it is illegal to be involved in a "common bawdy-house."

Another contemporary setting for commercial sex is the **massage parlour.** Some massage parlours provide legitimate massage therapy. In oth-

ers, the employees sell sexual services (Perkins & Bennett, 1985); these often advertise "sensual massage" or "erotic massage," making it pretty clear which type of parlour they are. Some parlours offer a standard list of services and prices; others allow the masseuse or masseur to decide what she or he will do with a particular client, and possibly how much of a "tip" is required for that activity. Massage parlours vary greatly in decor and price. Some are located in "professional" buildings, expensively decorated, and provide food and drinks in addition to sexual gratification. Charges may range from $100 to $300 or more. Such parlours may accept charge cards, with the business listed on the monthly statement as a restaurant. At the other end of the scale, storefront parlours, often located in "commercial sex districts," offer no amenities and charge rates of $40 to $100.

Another venue for a sex business is the *escort service.* These services have revealing names such as Alternative Lifestyle Services, First Affair, All Yours, Versatile Entertainment, and Hubbies for Hire. Most escort services employ both men and women who will engage in sexual activity; like massage parlours, the service may have a standard menu, or the escort may have the autonomy to decide what activities he or she will do with a client. Prostitution in this setting is referred to as an **out-call service,** since the escorts go to the clients. This is obviously a more risky business in that the escort cannot control the setting in which the services are provided. Escorts are usually required to telephone the service when they arrive and when they leave the client's location. This not only contributes to their safety but also allows the service to monitor how long the escort spent with the clients, and therefore the amount owed the service. Several Canadian cities license escorting, including Calgary, Edmonton, Winnipeg, and Windsor. The bylaw in Windsor differs from that in other Canadian cities because it allows escorts to work out of their own homes instead of requiring them to set up offices in specially zoned areas of the city. This was an attempt to treat escorts the same as other independent business people (Maticka-Tyndale et al., in press).

Brothel (BRAH-thul): A house of prostitution where prostitutes and customers meet for sexual activity.
In-call service: A residence in which prostitutes work regular shifts, selling sexual services on an hourly basis.
Massage parlour: A place where massages, as well as sexual services, can generally be purchased.

Out-call service: A service that sends a prostitute or sex worker to a location specified by the client to provide sexual services.

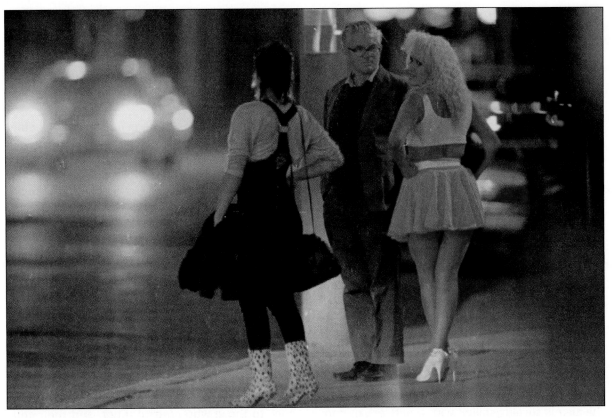

Figure 18.1   Sex for sale on Jarvis Street in Toronto.

In most communities, the most visible sex worker is the **streetwalker.** She sells her wares on the streets of cities. She is generally less attractive and less fashionably dressed than the call girl, and she charges correspondingly less for services, perhaps as little as $20 for a "quickie." She is more likely to impose strict time constraints on the customer. In one study, female street prostitutes in Montreal earned between $1,800 and $2,000 per week. Because her mode of operation is obvious, she is most likely to be arrested; 95 percent of prostitution-related charges in Canada are for street prostitution (Wolff & Geissel, 1994). Because streetwalkers have relatively little control over the conditions in which they work, they are at greater risk of disease and of violence at the hands of their customers, pimps (see below), and even police officers. In one study of 30 female sex workers in Montreal, 14 had been sexually assaulted and 22 had been physically assaulted in the previous 12 months (Shaver, 1996). In Vancouver, more than 50 women, many of them prostitutes, were murdered between 1983 and 2001.

Child or juvenile prostitutes also work as street prostitutes. About one-half of prostitutes enter the trade when they are under 16 years old (Badgley, 1984). There has been an increasing demand in recent years for child prostitutes. In 1988, Parliament passed specific legislation prohibiting purchasing sexual services from someone under 18 years old. The Federal/Provincial/Territorial Working Group on Prostitution has recommended that youths involved in prostitution be treated as persons in need of assistance and not as offenders (Canadian Centre for Justice Statistics, 1999).

Research on commercial sex workers in a large Canadian city has found that the same person may work in several different venues over time (Lewis et al., 2004). For example, in areas with cold winters, people who work on the streets in the summer and fall may work in in-call services or bars during the

Streetwalker: A lower-status prostitute or sex worker who walks the streets selling sexual services.

winter. Women also may move back and forth between an escort service and working as a call girl.

The Role of Third Parties

Many people associate prostitutes with a **pimp** ("The Man"), portrayed as her companion-master. If she has a pimp, she supports him with her earnings, and in return he may provide her with companionship and sex, bail her out of jail, and provide her with food, shelter, clothing, and drugs. If he keeps an eye on her when she is working, he may provide some protection against theft and violence because a prostitute is scarcely in a position to go to the police if she is robbed by a customer. But the same pimp also may exercise considerable control over her and engage in verbal, physical, and sexual abuse toward her if she fails to do what he tells her. In Canada, a majority of adult prostitutes work without a pimp (Badgley, 1984; Shaver, 1994). However many child prostitutes do have a pimp.

Another third party in commercial sex work is the **madam**, a woman who manages or owns an in-call service, out-call service, brothel, or escort service. A madam is usually experienced and skilled at managing sex workers and businesses. Sometimes she also is socially skilled with a network of contacts in the community. The most celebrated madam of the 1990s was Heidi Fleiss, dubbed the "Hollywood Madam" by the media. She was convicted of pandering for supplying call girls for rich and famous clients associated with the entertainment industry. Her customers reportedly paid from $200 for a "quick hit" to $1,500 for an entire night with one of the attractive and stylish young women who worked for her (Fleming & Ingrassia, 1993). In 1995, she was fined $1,500 and sentenced to three years in prison.

In other venues there may be other third parties. Massage parlours employ managers who are on the premises at all times and may exercise close control of their employees. The importance of these third parties is that they reduce the autonomy of the sex workers they supervise, and may coerce them to perform activities or work with clients that they do not want to. There is sharp disagreement among observers over the extent to which a sex worker can exercise choice with regard to his or her activities. Some argue workers choose who they serve and what acts they perform; others argue that they have little choice if they need the money. The reality depends, in part, on the involvement of the third parties in the worker's daily life.

Although there is disagreement about whether call girls, in-call workers, and streetwalkers have autonomy or are coerced to participate in commercial sex work, everyone agrees that girls and women caught up in sex trafficking are forced to engage in it. **Sex trafficking** refers to the recruitment and control of persons, by threat or use of force or deception, for purposes of sexual exploitation (Hynes & Raymond, 2002). Typically, girls and young women are recruited in Third World or developing countries, by ads or by people who promise them a good job (as a dancer, nanny, secretary), education, or a husband in a developed country. Recruiters may even supply forged travel documents, often for a price. When the women arrive in the destination country, they find themselves captives; often their travel documents are taken away, the money earned by their activity goes to those who control them, and their controllers threaten physical harm to the women or their families if they disobey or run away. The women often work in bars, brothels, and massage parlours, and may be moved every few weeks. One woman interviewed in the U.S. reported having 10 to 30 customers per day. The United Nations estimates that tens of thousands of young women and girls are trafficked each year; half are children, with most of these victims ending up in Germany, the U.S., and Italy. Thousands of these women are brought to Canada every year to work in the sex trade; some are kept as virtual prisoners (McClelland, 2001). Clearly, these women are being exploited because third parties control every detail of their lives.

The Career of a Sex Worker

The first step in a sex worker's career is entry. Women enter sex work for a variety of reasons (Vanwesenbeeck, 2001). For sex workers in western countries the most important one is eco-

---

Pimp: A prostitute's companion, protector, and master.
Madam: A woman who manages a brothel, in-call, out-call, or escort service.

Sex trafficking: The recruitment and control of persons for sexual exploitation.

nomics. Some women, for various reasons, are attracted by a desire for money, material goods, and an exciting lifestyle. These women are attracted by the image of the call girl, a status that some of them are fortunate enough to attain. For some women—for example, a poor but attractive woman—prostitution can be a means of upward economic mobility. Other women enter out of economic necessity, in order to survive. A poorly educated single mother may have no alternative means of earning a living. Some women become prostitutes in order to support a drug addiction.

Force or coercion is another factor. Some women report being coerced physically or psychologically by a husband or lover into selling sex for money. As noted above, coercion is a major factor in sex trafficking. Another category of reasons involves gaining power. For example, a woman who serves as a call girl to famous politicians may think of herself as having access to real political power. Some women become involved in prostitution through a family member or friend who is already a sex worker and can teach them the ropes (Miller, 1986).

On entering prostitution, most women go through an apprenticeship in which they learn the skills of the profession. The apprentice learns sexual techniques, especially fellatio, since many customers want oral sex. She learns how to hustle, to successfully negotiate her services and price with potential customers. She learns how to maintain control over the interaction so that she can protect herself as much as possible from being hurt or robbed by clients (and many sex workers are hurt or robbed). She learns values, like "the customer is always right," and fairness to other "working girls."[1] Women who are recruited into the life by a pimp may be trained by one of his more experienced "wives." Some women are trained by an experienced madam, in exchange for a large percentage of their fees (Heyl, 1979).

There has been relatively little research on the "mid-career" sex worker. We have noted that a sex worker may work in several different venues over time. A woman might move from in-call to out-call as she becomes more experienced at managing clients. She might move from the street into work in bars or at truck stops in response to changes in the weather or her health. Sex workers who are addicted to drugs

---

[1]A 1986 film entitled *Working Girls* provides a realistic look at an in-call service.

may be forced to work long hours and service many customers in more than one venue in order to support their habit. Again, some of these changes may result from coercion or exploitation by a pimp or a sex trafficker.

"Squaring up" or "leaving the life" refers to giving up sex work. Financially and psychologically it is a difficult thing to do, particularly for the woman with no job skills. As Gwen wrote:

> When you can't understand why a woman can't leave the sex trade or why she goes back or why she can't just get a job, I want you to remember that her life is not like yours. I want you to remember that your experiences are as foreign to her as hers are to you. She can no more become a bureaucrat tomorrow than you can become a sexually exploited youth tonight. (Field & Rabinovitch, 2003)

Recognizing this, some analysts call for comprehensive programs that provide education and job training, shelters, and counselling for women (and men) who want to leave commercial sex work (Hynes & Raymond, 2002). For example PEERS, which stands for Prostitutes, Empowerment, Education, and Resource Society, has branches in several Canadian cities including Victoria, B.C., and Moncton, N.B., and provides support, training, and resources to help male and female sex workers leave the trade.

Prostitutes who are in long-term relationships may return full-time to their previous lifestyle, often as homemakers. Single prostitutes may leave the sex trade upon meeting a partner.

The major hazards associated with being a prostitute are being a victim of a "bad trick" (that is, physical or sexual assault or even murder), drug addiction, sexually transmitted infections, and arrest by police (Badgley, 1984; Church et al., 2001). However, there are variations across the country in how vigorously laws pertaining to prostitution are enforced as well as in the sentences (fines compared to prison terms) given to women who are convicted of prostitution-related offences (Wolff & Geissel, 1994).

Sex Workers' Well-Being

There are a variety of images of the contemporary sex worker: young, attractive, autonomous, healthy, "the happy hooker"; young, brazen, aggressive, "the tough chick"; not-so-young, bruised emotionally and physically, a victim. Which one is valid?

According to a landmark study (Vanwesenbeeck,

1994), all these images are accurate. In the first phase, researchers recruited 90 prostitutes and former prostitutes in the Netherlands and conducted extended interviews with them about their daily lives. Two years later, 100 women who had been working for at least one year were recruited for a study of "sex and health"; these women were interviewed and completed several measures of coping style and well-being. The samples included women who worked on the street, in windows, in clubs and brothels, for escort services, and in their own homes. The results indicated that one-fourth of the women were doing well. They had few physical or psychosocial complaints, used problem-focused coping strategies, and were satisfied with their lives. Another quarter were at the opposite end. They complained of headaches, backaches, anxiety, and depression; their coping strategies involved dissociation (seeing problems as unrelated to the self) and denial, and they were dissatisfied with prostitution. The remaining women were in the middle.

The risks to a woman and thus her well-being varied according to the venue in which she worked. In the Netherlands, where sex work has been legalized, women who worked in windows and on the streets were at greater risk. Similarly, research in Canada has found that working the streets is associated with greater risk of arrest and of violence by clients (Lewis et al., in press; Shaver, in press). This obviously influences physical and mental health. Women who worked in windows or on the streets worked faster, had more clients, and earned less per customer than those working in in-call and out-call services. In a more recent study of indoor sex workers in the Netherlands (Venicz & Vanwesenbeeck, 2000), workers reported having an average nine-hour workday; more than one-third worked more than 40 hours per week, and half had taken no holidays in the past year. A major source of stress is the fact that a worker cannot predict or control the pace of work. Workers reported that, on average, they kept one-half of what clients paid them. Risks are especially high for women who are being trafficked because they are at risk of suffering abuse and injury by both clients and masters, experiencing illness and infection, and facing medical neglect (Hynes & Raymond, 2002).

There is also the risk of exposure to sexually transmitted infections, especially HIV/AIDS. Prostitutes infected with HIV are often workers who are also injecting drugs; research indicates that it is the injecting that is the greatest risk. In the Western world, studies show that the sex worker's risk of HIV infection is greater in his or her private sex life than in the sex work. The risk varies greatly in other parts of the world, with high rates of HIV/AIDS in some cities and countries but low rates in others (Vanwesenbeeck, 2001).

It has been suggested that the high levels of violence and of psychological distress found among sex workers are not due to the nature of the sex work per se, but instead reflect the stigma associated with sex work (Vanwesenbeeck, 2001). Prostitutes are at risk of rape because of attitudes such as the view that you can't rape a prostitute so no harm is done if you do force them to have sex (Miller & Schwartz, 1995). The risk of arrest and mistreatment by law enforcement personnel, and the resulting anxiety and distress, reflect the fact that some aspects of sex work are illegal.

Sex workers use a variety of cognitive and behavioural strategies to cope with the risks of their work. Some use drugs and alcohol to increase their confidence and decrease their guilt. Others use a strategy of shutting down their feelings and focusing narrowly on the task. The consequences of this distancing are often referred to as *depersonalization* (not, of course, an experience unique to sex work). Some emphasize the rewarding aspects of the work; perhaps that it supports their children. Many sex workers use as a coping technique the careful management of time and place, locating their sex work in a specific physical and temporal place separated from their private sexual and familial relationships (also not unique to sex work). Sex workers also may use the network of contacts with other sex workers as a source of support; workers on one "stroll" worked together to protect a pregnant colleague by giving her all the customers who wanted a "blow job" and protecting her from clients known to be rough (Anderson, 2004).

The Role of Early Abuse
The study of women working in the Netherlands found that, in addition to their work venue, having a history of victimization and trauma as children or adolescents before they entered prostitution was associated with poorer well-being (Vanwesenbeeck, 1994). Much of the research literature prior to 1990 reported that a high percentage of prostitutes had been physically or sexually abused as children, which was then often taken as the cause of their entry into sex work (Vanwesenbeeck, 2001). It was

often suggested that their childhood abuse leads to feelings of stigmatization that in turn results in early sexual activity and/or drug use, running away from home, and a drift into sex work. There is no doubt that some men and women do enter commercial sex work via this path. But the research upon which this is based utilized samples of streetwalkers, women in jail, or former prostitutes located through social service agencies. These respondents are not representative of all sex workers, so these results cannot be generalized. Further, according to Quebec sociologist Frances Shaver (in press), much of this research has failed to use an appropriate comparison group—that is, a comparison group that is similar to the group of prostitutes in age and socioeconomic status. We don't, in fact, know how important a history of abuse might be in any individual's entry into sex work. Clearly, any adult who has experienced childhood victimization may have poor well-being.

Customers

At the time of the Kinsey research, about 69 percent of all white males had had some experience with sex workers (Kinsey et al., 1948). In 1992 the NHSLS asked all respondents whether they had had sex with someone they paid or who paid them (Laumann et al., 1994). Only 17 percent of men and 2 percent of women reported that they had had sex with such a partner since age 18. Thus, the use of prostitutes has declined dramatically in the past 50 years. This likely reflects the increased frequency of non-marital and casual sexual activity during this same period (see Chapters 11 and 12).

Prostitutes refer to their customers as "johns." About 50 percent of the clients are occasional johns; they may be businessmen who seek only occasional contacts with prostitutes, perhaps while on business trips. Nearly 50 percent are repeat clients who seek a regular relationship with one particular prostitute or a small group of them (Freund et al., 1991). The remainder are compulsive johns, who use prostitutes for their major sexual outlet. They are driven to them and cannot stay away (see Chapter 16).[2] About half of these men are married (Lowman, 1995).

[2]Some Canadian cities have implemented programs designed to increase johns' awareness of the risks of street prostitution. Instead of receiving criminal charges, the johns attend a full-day seminar that provides information on community concerns, health risks, and sexual addictions and compulsions (Symbaluk & Jones, 1999).

A study of the clients of male and female prostitutes in Atlanta found that the two groups of men were very similar. On the average, they were 35 years old and had completed one or two years of university. The men reported having had an average of four sexual partners during the preceding month, of whom 2.5 were paid. The clients of male prostitutes had been using prostitutes for six years, the clients of female prostitutes for seven and a half years (Boles & Ellifson, 1994). The participants were recruited through newspaper ads, so they are probably not a representative sample.

Research in Quebec indicates that men use the services of prostitutes for a variety of reasons (Gemme et al., 1984). Some have long-term partners but want sex more frequently than their partner does or want to engage in practices—such as fellatio—that they feel their partner would not be willing to do. Some use prostitutes to satisfy their exotic sexual needs, such as being whipped or having sex with a woman who pretends to be a corpse. The motivation for the single man or the one who is away from home for a long period of time (for example, during a war) may simply be loneliness or release of sexual tension. Others, particularly adolescents, may have sex with prostitutes to prove their manhood or gain sexual experience. Finally, for some men it is a way to engage in discreet same-sex activity.

Male Sex Workers

Although under the Criminal Code of Canada a prostitute can be either male or female, male prostitutes are less likely to be charged than are female prostitutes (Shaver 1994, 1996). Overall, 25 percent of sex workers in Canada are male (Fraser, 1985). Most male prostitutes serve a male clientele—97 percent of clients of Canadian sex workers are male (Badgley, 1984). However, some sell their services to women or to both women and men.

Male prostitutes serving a female clientele work in three settings. These male prostitutes virtually never work in the street, in contrast to female streetwalkers and male *hustlers* (see below). This reflects gender-role socialization; female clients are unlikely to cruise the streets and pick up a prostitute, because they have been taught to let the male take the initiative and because women are not supposed to be that interested in sex, especially not interested enough to be willing to pay for it. Some male prostitutes work for escort services and provide companionship and sexual gratification on an out-call basis. Some men work in massage parlours, under the same conditions as female employees. A third type is the **gigolo**, a male who provides companionship and sexual gratification on a continuing basis to a woman in exchange for money. A gigolo often, though not always, has only one client at a time. The demand for gigolos reflects the fact that women, like men, desire sexual gratification on a continuing basis and will pay for it when circumstances require or allow them to do so. On the other hand, most women prefer their sexual activity to be part of an ongoing relationship.

Hustlers are male sex workers who cater to men. Interestingly, some of them consider themselves to be straight, not gay. In one study of male sex workers in Canada, 23 percent reported that they were heterosexual (Badgley, 1984). They may have strict rules for their customers to follow, such as only permitting the customer to perform fellatio on them.

Parallel to patterns of heterosexual prostitution, there are male escort services for a more upscale male clientele (Salamon, 1989).

Male hustlers seem to fall into three main categories (Allen, 1980). First are the full-time street and bar hustlers, who operate much as female streetwalkers do except that they rarely have a pimp (Lowman, 1991). They tend to be younger than sex workers, and there is some market for "chickens" (young boys) as sex workers. They are less likely to experience violence from pimps or customers. Increasingly, male sex workers are working from indoor locations by using telephones, and working as licensed escorts and masseurs rather than as street prostitutes, particularly in small Canadian cities (Allman, 1999). Second are full-time call boys or kept boys. They tend to have a more exclusive clientele and to be more attractive and more sexually versatile than the streetwalkers. Surprisingly, by far the largest group is the third: part-time hustlers, who are typically students or individuals employed in another occupation. They generally work at prostitution only when they need money. The part-time hustlers are notable because unlike those in the other groups, they are less likely to come from dysfunctional families. They also have the best long-term chance for acquiring an education and a stable job and achieving a good social adjustment.

In one study of male sex workers in Montreal between the ages of 16 and 29, the main reason for engaging in sex work, stated by 88 percent, was money, although some said they engaged in sex work as a way to meet people (Earls & David, 1989). Many of these young men came from troubled home environments, often leaving home at an early age. The majority (78 percent) reported using drugs on a regular basis.

Transgender Sex Workers

Some transgender individuals work as prostitutes. These are genetic males who may or may not live full-time as women. They are typically taking estrogen, which feminizes their body including giving them breasts. Transgender sex workers serve a male clientele. A study of 46 women, 46 men, and 48 transgender individuals working as street prostitutes found that the transgender sex workers were more similar to the female sex workers than to the male sex workers in keeping regular hours and spending less time with each client (Weinberg et al., 1999). Few of the transgender sex workers reported never enjoying sexual activities with clients; in this way they were more similar to the male than to the female sex workers in the study. The transgender sex workers typically provided oral sex, hand jobs, and receptive anal intercourse. More than half never or rarely told their customers that they were male; they would deceive their customers by restricting services (e.g., to oral sex), taping or tucking their penis back between their legs, and providing an excuse not to remove their skirt or panties (e.g., having their period).

Sex Tourism

An increasingly important type of commercial sex is **sex tourism**, which refers to varieties of leisure travel that have as their purpose the purchase of sexual services (Wonders & Michalowski, 2001). Sex tourism is made possible by three large-scale social forces: the migration of men and women from less developed nations, or from rural to urban areas, in search of jobs; the commodification of sexual inti-

---

Gigolo (JIG-uh-loh): A male who provides companionship and sexual gratification on a continuing basis to a woman in exchange for money.
Hustler: A male sex worker who sells his services to men.
Sex tourism: Leisure travel with the purpose of purchasing sexual services.

macy making all types of sex a commodity or service for sale; and increased travel for recreational purposes. All three of these forces are tied to increasing globalization, the movement of information and people freely across national boundaries.

The migration of people in search of economic opportunities provides a large group of young men and women in search of work. In some locales, they are aggressively recruited into sex work by pimps or persons with ties to sex trafficking. In other places, they enter into the life more or less voluntarily, often because there are few other opportunities for persons of their racial or ethnic background. In Amsterdam, where the attitude toward sex work can be described as regulated tolerance, a few individuals control much of the commercial sex work, recruiting foreign migrants to work in windows and brothels. In Havana, Cuba, commercial sex work is decentralized, with many men and women working independently. They contact potential clients in hotels, bars, and on the street, hoping to connect with someone who will employ them for several days. In some countries, sex tourism is the most rapidly growing economic sector and a major source of hard currency; in such places, governments have little incentive to attempt to reduce or eliminate it. One estimate places the value of the global sex industry at $20 billion per year.

The tourists who can purchase sexual services are obviously wealthy enough to travel, which in turn often means they are citizens of developed countries and members of the middle and upper classes in their home societies. The sex workers are often from a different national and ethnic background. One of the attractions for the tourist is sex with this "dark-skinned other," perhaps someone from a group stereotyped as sexually free and uninhibited. The encounter is appealing because it is a sharp contrast to the tourist's usual sexual experience (Frank, 2003). Unfortunately, one such appeal for men is sex with a young girl, and in some Asian cities girls as young as 12 and 13 are available in brothels tightly controlled by their managers.

■ Pornography

A debate over pornography has been raging for more than four decades. Religious fundamentalists and some feminists (strange bedfellows, indeed!) agree that some kinds of pornography should be made illegal, while civil liberties groups and some other feminists argue that freedom of expression, guaranteed in the Charter of Rights and Freedoms, must be preserved and therefore pornography should not be restricted by law. Meanwhile, Joe Brown stops at his local video store, buys *Wall to Wall Sex, v. 46,* and drives home for a pleasurable evening's entertainment. Here we will examine what the issues are, paying particular attention to social scientists' research on the effects of pornography on people who are exposed to it. First, we need to clarify some terminology.

Terms

We can distinguish among pornography, obscenity, and erotica. Pornography comes from the Greek words *porneia,* which means, quite simply, "prostitution," and *graphos,* which means "writing." In general usage today, **pornography** refers to magazines, films, and so on that are intended to be sexually arousing (Malamuth, 1998).

The Criminal Code of Canada uses the term "obscenity," not pornography. It is a crime to sell or possess for the purposes of distribution any material that is "obscene." It is also illegal to present an "immoral, indecent or obscene" play, film, or other live performance. **Obscenity** refers to "any publication a dominant characteristic of which is the undue exploitation of sex." Because "undue exploitation" is rather vague, the courts have used the **community standards of tolerance test** to determine whether material is obscene. Community standards of tolerance do not refer to what Canadians would look at themselves; they refer to what Canadians would accept other Canadians being exposed to. Using the community standards of tolerance test means that standards can change over time as societal attitudes change. For example, some experts estimate that 30 percent of all Canadian periodical sales are of magazines that would have been illegal 30 years ago (Robertson, 1992).

Pornography: Sexually arousing art, literature, or films.
Obscenity: Something that is offensive according to accepted standards of decency; the legal term for pornography.
Community standards of tolerance test: The test used by courts to determine whether something is obscene based on what Canadians would accept other Canadians being exposed to.

In the debate over pornography, some make the distinction between pornography (which is unacceptable to them) and erotica (which is acceptable to them). According to this distinction, sexually explicit material that depicts sex coupled with violence, that is degrading or dehumanizing (usually to women), or that includes children is *pornography* (Russell, 1980). In contrast, **erotica** depicts explicit sex that is not violent and is neither degrading nor dehumanizing. According to this definition, a movie of a woman being sexually assaulted would be pornography, whereas a movie of two mutually consenting adults who are both enjoying having intercourse together would be considered erotica.

In keeping with this distinction, the Supreme Court of Canada in the *Butler* case ruled in 1992 that sexually explicit material depicting adults that does not depict sex with violence, and that is not degrading or dehumanizing, is not obscene. This decision divided pornography into three categories: (1) explicit sex with violence, (2) explicit sex without violence but in which people are treated in a way that is degrading or dehumanizing, and (3) explicit sex that is neither degrading nor dehumanizing. The Court ruled that the first category, sex with violence, constitutes "undue exploitation of sex" and thus fits the definition of obscenity in the Criminal Code. The Court indicated that the third category (erotica) is generally accepted in Canadian society (unless it involves children) and thus is not obscene. However, explicit sex that is degrading or dehumanizing may or may not be obscene depending on the risk of harm involved and whether the material has artistic merit. While the Supreme Court decision gave a good deal of guidance to the courts, there is still ambiguity in the law. For example, what exactly constitutes degrading or dehumanizing sex? What criteria should be used to determine whether material has artistic merit? Should material depicting sadomasochistic activity in which partners consensually participate in some types of pain rituals be considered obscene (MacDonald, 2000)?

Another complication is that Canada Customs officials have the power to refuse to allow books, magazines, videotapes, and other materials "deemed to be obscene" to enter Canada without having to lay criminal charges or have the materials reviewed by the courts. In 1994 the Little Sisters Bookstore and Art Emporium in Vancouver challenged the right of Customs officials to do so. They argued that Customs officials specifically target gay and lesbian bookstores and that they deem material that does not include violence or degradation to be obscene just because it depicts gay or lesbian sex. Ultimately the Supreme Court of Canada upheld the Customs Act but criticized Customs inspectors for unfairly targetting the store.

Beyond these definitions by experts and by the court, it is interesting to see what typical Canadians find acceptable. Research shows that there is a great diversity in what people consider pornographic. A well-sampled study of 2,018 Canadians showed that although 31 percent of Canadians feel that all sexually explicit material is obscene, 42 percent do not, and the beliefs of the remainder are somewhere in between (Peat et al., 1984). Most respondents, 66 percent, agreed that everyone has the right to view sexually explicit material in private. Younger people and men tended to find sexually explicit material more acceptable, as do people living in Quebec. Sex combined with violence is seen as the least acceptable. The same poll showed that the majority of Canadians have been exposed to various kinds of sexually explicit material.

Types of Pornography

Pornography is a multibillion-dollar business in North America. Included in this business are a number of products: magazines directed to various audiences, films, X-rated videocassettes and DVDs, live sex shows, telephone sex, the latest technological advance, computer porn, and child pornography. Some of this activity is legal (e.g., publishing *Penthouse*); some of it is illegal (e.g., producing films featuring children engaged in sex); and the legality of the rest is hotly debated. It is impossible to obtain precise data on the economics of pornography in Canada. However, it is estimated that Americans spend between $4 billion and $10 billion per year on pornography (*Forbes*, 2001; ABC News, 2004).

Magazines

A large chunk of the Canadian pornography market consists of U.S. magazines, ranging from *Playboy* and *Penthouse*—soft-core—to *Hustler* and hundreds of

---

Erotica: Sexually arousing material that is not degrading or demeaning to women, men, or children.

other less well-known hard-core magazines, although now even soft-core magazines may contain some "hard-core" pictures. The soft-core magazines mushroomed in the 1970s. In the 1990s the market was large and included both general magazines and those catering to specialized tastes. In 2004 in Canada, *Playboy* had a circulation of 90,325 copies per issue, and *Penthouse* a circulation of 49,544 copies per issue. Each of the other pornography magazines had a circulation of less than 25,000.

Much pornography is designed for the heterosexual male reader. In the 1970s, however, *Playgirl* appeared, featuring "beefcake" (that is, muscular men in minimal clothing) in an attempt to attract heterosexual women. There is also a large variety of printed material designed for gay men, lesbians, people interested in interracial sex, swingers, and other groups.

Hard-core magazines have a no-holds-barred approach to what they present. Photographs may include everything from vaginal intercourse to anal intercourse, sadomasochism, bondage, and sex with animals. A study of the titles of magazines and books found in "adult" bookstores in the United States revealed that 17 percent were about a paraphilia or sexual variation (Lebeque, 1991). Of those, 50 percent featured sadomasochism. An additional 21 percent dealt with incest.

Here, again, the profit is great. The markups may be as high as 600 percent, and it is estimated that there are approximately 20,000 stores in the United States selling hard-core magazines, mostly to repeat customers. Yet more profit comes from customers who have regular subscriptions for pornographic magazines by mail.

Films, Videos, and DVDs

Although sexually explicit movies were made as early as 1915, only in the last four decades have these films been slick and well produced. The *hard-core film* industry began to emerge in a big way around 1970. Two films were especially important in this breakthrough. *I Am Curious, Yellow,* appearing in 1970, showed sexual intercourse explicitly. In part because it was a foreign film with an intellectual tone, it became fashionable for people, including married couples, to see it. The other important early film was *Deep Throat,* appearing in 1973. With its humour and creative plot, it was respectable and popular among the middle class. Linda Lovelace,

Figure 18.2 Porn magazines designed for a male audience. They run the gamut from the relatively tame *Playboy* to the raunchier and more sexually explicit *Hustler*.

the female star, gained national recognition and later appeared on the cover of *Esquire*.

After the success of *Deep Throat,* many more full-length, technically well-made hard-core films soon appeared. *Deep Throat* had made it clear that there were big profits to be made. It cost $24,000 to make, yet by 1982 it had yielded $25 million in profits.

Loops are short (10-minute) hard-core films. They are set up in coin-operated projectors in private booths, usually in adult bookstores. The patron can enter and view the film in privacy and perhaps masturbate while doing so (Jewksbury, 1990).

In the early 1980s, X-rated *videocassettes* for home viewing began to replace porn theatres. For example, *Deep Throat* became available on cassette in 1977, and by 1982, 300,000 copies had been sold (Cohn, 1983). Cable and satellite television have also entered the arena, with porn channels thriving in some areas of the country. The latest advance is the DVD.

Many hard-core films, X-rated videocassettes, and DVDs are made for a heterosexual audience. In the United States, "adult videos" earn $4 billion per year and account for more than 700 million video rentals annually (Rich, 2001). Based on an informal survey, an adult video distributor estimated that in 1998 more than 38,000 adult videos were rented each day in Ontario, resulting in an annual revenue of more than $52 million. There are no national data available. These videos portray couples engaging in both fellatio and cunnilingus, and vaginal intercourse in various settings and bodily positions.

In Focus 18.1

Behind the Scene: Making X-rated Videos

Dave Cummings bounces out of bed. He's working today, so he goes through his routine; he showers, shaves extremely close to get a smooth face, trims his fingernails and his pubic hair, applies lotion to his groin, and finishes with hand lotion. He dresses casually, and drives to a large, expensive home in Beverly Hills rented for the shoot. When he arrives, he greets the other performers, mostly young women and men in their 20s and 30s. In this group, Dave is "odd man out." He is 59 years old, balding, and looks like your doctor, not the typical male performer in an X-rated video. It is that appearance that gets him work. Dave provides the realism in the video; he is believable as a doctor, lawyer, judge, or schoolteacher in roles where a hard-bodied, bronzed guy in his 20s is not credible (Kikuras, 2004).

Dave points to one of the most important qualifications for a male actor in the world of X-rated videos: the ability to perform sexually. Many videos are budgeted to be shot in three days. The script calls for six to nine episodes of sex, each requiring one or more erect penises; the majority are to end with visible ejaculation. In other words, these videos place a premium on male sexual performance, perhaps not surprising in a performance-oriented culture (see Chapter 10). It costs money and frustrates everyone involved if a male actor has a long refractory period (see Chapter 9). To make it in the industry, a man has to demonstrate that he is up to the demands. Dave is lucky; he has good genes and stamina. In his own words, he can "get it up, keep it up, not come before [I am] told to, and can climax on cue." In years past, a man without Dave's talents would not last in this line of work. But a pharmaceutical breakthrough—Viagra—changed all that. Many male porn actors routinely use Viagra or similar medications, which enable them to get it up and keep it up. As a result, there are hundreds of men competing for the available jobs.

One consequence of this competition is pressure to perform acts and take risks that the actor might prefer to avoid. Even in this era of widespread knowledge of HIV/AIDS, condom use is rare in the porn industry; some viewers don't like to see them, some directors and producers don't allow them, some actors and actresses don't like the resulting hassle or change in sensation. The risk became very real in May 2004 when it was announced that five performers had positive HIV tests. Darren James was exposed to HIV while in Brazil. Three

A content analysis of 50 videos produced between 1979 and 1988 identified several changes over that 10-year period (Brosius et al., 1993). There were increases in portrayals of sexual activity within casual relationships, sexual activity involving a male and a female superordinate (e.g., his boss), encounters in which the female persuades the male to engage in sexual activity, and fellatio. Portrayals of males having sex with a co-worker or prostitute, however, declined in frequency. Less often, films and videos show sexual activity involving three or more people, or two women (Davis & Bauserman, 1993). There are also increasing numbers of adult videos made for a gay audience.

A rapidly expanding part of the porn industry is the "amateur" video. The development of the home-video camera has enabled anybody with a willing partner, friends, or neighbours to produce home-made porn. Such videos cost virtually nothing to make, and distributors are eager to purchase them. These films account for at least 20 percent of all adult videos made in the United States ("The Sex Industry," 1998).

In the 1990s, a number of companies began marketing videos designed to educate people about various aspects of human sexuality. With names like the "Better Sex" video series, these include explicit portrayals of a wide variety of consenting heterosexual activities. As such, these are erotica, infected actresses, Lara Roxxx, Jessica Dee, and Miss Arroyo had worked with James after he returned from Brazil; all three women had engaged in "double anal" scenes with James and another actor. Anal intercourse is a prime route for transmission of HIV (see Chapter 8). As of June 2, 2004, 54 adult video performers who may have been exposed were quarantined (Miller & Kernes, 2004).

Another consequence of the competition is low pay. Men may be paid as little as $500 for a video. The industry is built primarily around women. It is the women who achieve a kind of stardom, whose names appear in the publicity and on the video boxes, and whose bodies are featured in the videos. Relatively new performers may be paid $350 to $1,000 for a film featuring conventional sex. Engaging in unconventional or rough sex brings a higher fee. Needless to say, there are no royalties paid to the performers. The typical film is budgeted at $5,000 to $35,000 (Huffstutter & Frammolino, 2001). A typical release sells 1,000 to 2,000 copies; it is only the rare hit that brings in $1 million (Forbes, 2001). Thus, there is constant pressure to keep costs to a minimum.

We noted that there are a variety of pathways into commercial sex work. Dave Cummings voluntarily entered the industry at age 54. Once he had demonstrated his prowess, he found himself in continuing demand. In fact, he is now producing his own line of videos. Cummings says he does it because he enjoys sex, and for the opportunity to have sex with lots of attractive young women. A 21-year-old starlet, Sienna, drifted into performing in adult videos. She had worked in a fast-food outlet and bagel shop; she saw an ad in the newspaper for "nude modelling" and tried it. For the first year she did still photo shoots, $350 to $400 for a few hours. Then she moved to working for an Internet company, engaging in masturbation while clients watched her via the Net. After a few months she thought, "If I'm gonna do this, I might as well do porn and make more money." Sienna says she may leave the industry soon; "I've just been pounded so much in these movies that I'm starting to get tired" (Petkovich, 2004). Some performers report being coerced into performing for stills or movies, through the use of alcohol, drugs, or physical force by others on camera.

As a result of the development of video technology that enables both the producer to produce and the purchaser to buy X-rated videos cheaply, an estimated 11,000 are produced every year (ABC, 2004).

not pornography. They often include commentary by a psychologist or sex therapist reassuring viewers that the activities portrayed are normal. These series are advertised in national magazines and some daily newspapers.

The continuum noted in magazines from the subtle to the explicit also exists in video. The subtle end is found in *music videos*. The sexual content of many videos shown on MuchMusic is unmistakable. One team of researchers analyzed 40 MTV videos, coding the content at 30-second intervals. They found that in these videos, men engaged in significantly more aggressive behaviour, women engaged in significantly more implicitly sexual behaviour, and women were the object of implicit, explicit, and aggressive sexual advances (Sommers-Flanagan et al., 1993). Some singers dress and portray themselves in a sexualized way to boost sales.

Live Sex Shows

Live sex shows are yet another part of the sex industry. Female strip shows have a long tradition in our culture, and male strippers catering to a female audience also have become common. In 1997, there were about 2,478 licensed exotic dancers in Toronto alone (Maticka-Tyndale et al., 1999). Dancers perform stage shows, table dances, and lap dances either in public or in private areas of clubs. An Ontario study found

Figure 18.3 The sexual content of many music videos played on MuchMusic is unmistakable.

that lap-dancers made between $10 and $20 per dance, although customers pay more for dances in private rooms (Lewis & Maticka-Tyndale, 1998). Dancers earn only a small wage for dancing on stage and are typically expected to offer table dances or lap dances if requested. Lap dances can be performed either in public or in private areas of the club. In the private areas the stripper allows the patron to touch her body, excluding her genitals, as she dances. Most often she will gyrate in his lap and rub herself against him. Some strip clubs also offer VIP rooms in which a greater level of sexual activity takes place, although not all strippers provide these services. Typically this involves fellatio and manual stimulation to ejaculation as well as a lap dance. The price is typically between $100 and $150.

The question of whether lap-dancing is legal or constitutes an "indecent performance," particularly when done in a private room, has not been fully settled by the courts. However, in general, the courts have ruled that the community's level of tolerance can be placed quite high when activities occur in private. This is complicated by the fact that lap-dancing is safest for dancers if it is done in a public area of the club where they are less likely to be assaulted or forced to go beyond "dancing" (Lewis & Maticka-Tyndale, 1998; Maticka-Tyndale et al., 2000b). There is also more protection for the cus-

tomer in these public areas from pressure to engage in activities beyond watching the dancer. Some cities, such as Toronto, have enacted bylaws that prohibit physical contact, including touching, between patrons and persons providing services in adult entertainment parlours as a way of restricting table dancing and lap-dancing.

Telephone Sex

Telephone sex provides another example of enlisting technology to sell sexual titillation. A 1991 study of a sample of prerecorded messages identified several patterns (Glascock & LaRose, 1993). The typical recording was of a female voice describing a series of sexual activities in which the caller was a participant. Callers to 900 and long-distance numbers were much more likely to hear fantasies involving masturbation, vaginal intercourse, and oral sex. Few of the descriptions included violence or rape. More frequent were descriptions of activities in which the woman dominated and degraded the man.

There are also phone sex services that provide live conversation. In some cases, large numbers of chat-line workers may be in the same location talking to callers. Prices are typically $5–$10 per minute. In other cases, the phone sex worker takes calls at his or her home. Some phone sex workers are students who need money for tuition and books. One such student, after reading an advertisement for phone sex operators in a Winnipeg newspaper, set up a 1-900 line in her home (Schroeder, 2000). Callers were charged $1.30 per minute.

Most callers are men; most chat-line workers are women. The men typically masturbate duing the conversation. A male described one conversation:

> I say, "When you give a guy a blow job, what's your favorite way to do it?" She says, "Well, I love being on my knees, cause being on my knees with him standing is so submissive." I said, "Do you like looking at his cock in his pants, does that really turn you on?" She says, "I love that." I say, "I would love to be standing in front of you." She says, "Oh, that would really turn me on." "Do you like having your breasts played with when you're giving a blow job?" "Yes, I like it very much. I also like to be fingered." "How many fingers do you like inside you?" "I love two fingers." "And why do you like blowing a guy so much?" "Because I'm getting him excited and I know I can't wait for him to fuck me." "Do you like to fuck for a

Figure 18.4   The newest innovation in the porn business is computer porn.

long time?" "Yes, I get lost in it." So then I said, "Well, I've really been thinking about you on top of me, and while you're riding me, I'll be spanking you." She said, "Oh God, I love that." I was masturbating and I came. It was great. (Maurer, 1994, 349–350)

Electronic Pornography

In the past 15 years the World Wide Web and Internet have made available a wide variety of pornographic services for every computer attached to a modem, whether at work, at school, or at home. These services include online chats or conversations, exchanging messages with like-minded persons via discussion groups, access to sexually arousing stories, photographs, videos, and films, and access to a broad array of goods and services via specialized Web sites.

Chat Rooms

Chat rooms, or Internet relay chat groups, provide a location where individuals can meet and carry on conversations electronically. These rooms are often oriented toward persons with particular sexual interests, often captured by their names. An Internet resource guide had links to 153 sex-oriented chat rooms in June 2004. The conversations often involve graphic descriptions of sexual activities or fantasies typically through instant messaging. Some people also make use of webcams or cell phone cams as part of the interaction. Some people have left relationships, including marriages, for someone they knew only through electronic conversation. In this context, an interesting feature of these chats can be that the other person cannot see you. This allows you to present yourself in any way you desire, to rehearse or try out a broad range of identities.

Doug is a midwestern college junior. He plays four characters . . . One is a seductive woman. One is a macho, cowboy type whose self-description stresses that he is a "Marlboros-rolled-in-the-T-shirt sleeve kind of guy." The third is a rabbit of unspecified gender . . . a character he calls Carrot. (Turkle, 1995, p. 13)

Doug would not describe the fourth character, beyond saying it was furry. Remember that the character you are chatting with may not be who she or he seems to be.

The telephone sex conversation reproduced above could have taken place electronically, with the words displayed on a computer screen or through audio connections instead of spoken over a phone line. However, unlike telephone sex, customers can actually see the performers as well as communicate with them either through text messaging or audio connections so as to direct the sexual activity they are viewing. On some sites, customers can also control the video camera from their home computer. Sexual activities run the full range from masturbation to couple activity to unusual sexual interests.

News Groups

People can also log on to sex-oriented news or discussion groups, read messages posted by others, and post messages themselves. The messages may include personal information, or they may be a story or a file containing pornographic pictures in digital format. Stories can be printed by the user; picture files can be downloaded and viewed through a "plug-in." Often, the messages are simply advertisements for or links to sex-oriented Web sites that sell pornographic material. The June 2004 resource guide mentioned previously had links to 706 sex-oriented news groups. A research team at Carnegie-Mellon University studied Usenet activity in 1994 (Rimm, 1995). Only 3 percent of all groups included sexually explicit content, but they were accessed much more frequently than were non-sexual groups.

Commercial Bulletin Boards

There are numerous commercial bulletin boards that contain sexually explicit photographs in digital form. The aforementioned June 2004 Internet resource guide listed 45 sex-oriented bulletin boards. Users may log on to these bulletin boards and download images for a fee. Each image is listed in an electronic catalogue with a short description. The Carnegie-Mellon researchers studied the content of these images by classifying 5.5 million image descriptions. Table 18.1 displays the results. Hard-core images (sample description: "Girl with big tits gets fucked by guy") made up 38 percent of the

Table 18.1 Total Surveyed "Adult" Usenet Files and Downloads by Classification

Classification	Total Files	Total Downloads
Hard-core	133,180 (45.6%)	2,102,329 (37.9%)
Soft-core	75,659 (25.9%)	760,009 (13.7%)
Paraphilia	63,232 (21.6%)	1,821,444 (32.8%)
Pedophilia	20,043 (6.9%)	864,333 (15.6%)

Source: M. Rimm, (1995), Marketing pornography on the information superhighway, *Georgetown Law Journal, 83,* Table 5, p. 1891.

downloaded images. Another 33 percent were images of paraphilias ("Girl with big tits gets fucked by horse"). Of particular concern is the popularity of pedophilic images, which accounted for 15.6 percent of the downloaded images. Such images are illegal and not readily available elsewhere. The researchers concluded: "The 'adult' BBS market is driven largely by the demand for paraphilic and pedophilic imagery. The availability of, and the demand for, vaginal sex imagery is relatively small" (Rimm, 1995, p. 1890). Canadian and U.S. authorities continue to debate what, if anything, can be done to regulate the flow of these materials on computer networks.

Adult Web sites

Adult Web sites sell a variety of pornographic services and sexual materials. The June 2004 Internet resource guide had links to 647 such sites, with names like Bizar, Honey's Hot Horny Spot, House of Sin, IIISome, and Smutland. Each site typically includes thousands of pornographic photos organized by content, pornographic videos that can be viewed on your computer screen, stories, links to live sex shows, and links to live video cameras in places such as men's and women's locker rooms. Some also sell videos, CD-ROMs, sex aids such as dildos, and other sexual devices and costumes. Some also include "interactive" sex shows, where the viewer can request that the actors perform specific acts. Many of these sites specialize, featuring "teenagers" (if the actors are under 18, the material violates the law), black, Asian, or Latina women, gays, lesbians, pregnant women, and on and on. Each site charges a daily, weekly, or monthly "membership fee" for

Figure 18.5   While there are differences between men and women in their response to pornography, some women enjoy watching a stripper as much as some men do. The final scenes of *The Full Monty* portray the pleasure both the male performers and the female audience experience.

access; the fee can usually be paid by supplying a valid credit card number.

Electronic porn is cause for concern, for several reasons. One is that the large and ever-increasing number of chat rooms, news groups, and Web sites facilitate a person becoming dependent on or addicted to (see Chapter 16) this type of sexual content. None of these involves face-to-face social interaction, which is central to most sexual relationships; the risk is that they become a substitute. However, only a small percentage of people who use the Internet for sexual activities (1 percent in one study) develop a sexual addiction or compulsion (Griffiths, 2001). There is also a great deal of concern that children will access these materials. For example, children may unwittingly link to a pornographic site by typing in an ambiguous term. Some parents try to counter this by installing software filters. All sites include a printed notice that one must be over 18 to access the site, and that one who is offended by sexually explicit material should not enter the site. This "honour system" is not an effective control. It is true that to access a Web site or download photographs from bulletin boards the user must supply a valid credit card number, but this is not a major deterrent for many adolescents. To date, there has been little guidance from Canadian courts on the issues involved in computer pornography.

Finally, the Internet facilitates the distribution of child pornography, which is illegal in Canada. Existing Canadian laws governing child pornography apply to the Internet, and some law enforcement agencies seek out and arrest offenders. However, this material can be easily transferred across borders, and may be legal in the country where it originated, making enforcement of the child pornography laws difficult (Canadian Centre for Justice Statistics, 1999).

Child Pornography

Child pornography, or kiddie porn, features photographs or films of sexual acts involving children.

Child pornography: Pictures or films of sexual acts involving children.

http://www.mcgrawhill.ca/college/hyde

In Focus 18.2

Ernie: A Pedophile and Child Pornographer

In a study of child sexual abuse and child pornography, the investigators reported the following description of one offender:

Contact was made with Ernie, a northern Indiana man, and arrangements were made to meet with him to share child pornography collections. Ernie arrived at a motel room carrying a small suitcase containing approximately 75 magazines and a metal file box containing twelve super-8-mm movies. The metal box was also filled with numerous photographs. Ernie then began to discuss his collection. He described himself as a pedophile and showed a series of instant photographs he had taken of his 7-year-old niece while she slept. The pictures revealed Ernie's middle finger inserted into the young girl's uncovered genitals, and he described how he had worked his finger up into her. Other photographs featured the girl being molested in various ways by Ernie while she remained asleep.

Despite the fact that he had engaged in numerous incidents of child molestation, Ernie had not been discovered because his victims remained asleep. He had molested and exploited both males and females, his own children, grandchildren, and neighbourhood children. In order to photograph the uncovered genitals of his sleeping victims, Ernie had devised a string and hook mechanism. The hook was attached to the crotch of the underpants, and he would uncover his sleeping victims' genitals as he photographed them with an instant-developing camera.

Ernie displayed his collection with the pride of a hobbyist. He exhibited photographs he had reproduced from magazines; he had reproduced these same photographs repeatedly and had engaged in a child pornography business from his residence.

While displaying his magazines and films, Ernie was arrested. A search warrant was obtained for his residence, and material seized from his one-bedroom apartment filled two pickup trucks. Numerous sexually explicit films, photographs, magazines, advertisements, and children's soiled underwear were confiscated. The panties had been encased in plastic, the child's school photograph featured with the panties. Also confiscated were nine cameras and a projector.

Several months passed before investigators found proof that Ernie had processed, through a central Indiana photographic lab, approximately 1,500 photographs per week. It is believed that Ernie sold these pictures at $2 each, grossing an estimated $3,000 per week.

Source: Burgess, 1984.

It is viewed as the most reprehensible part of the porn industry because it produces such an obvious victim, the child model. Children, by virtue of their developmental level, cannot give truly informed consent to participation in such activities, and the potential for doing psychological and physical damage to them is great.

In 1993, a specific statute prohibiting people from possessing, making, or distributing child pornography, defined as any depiction of a person under the age of 18 engaging in explicit sexual activity, was added to the Criminal Code of Canada. These statutes use the term "pornography" rather than obscenity as with the adult provisions, and they specifically prohibit the making, sale, or possession of child pornography. The purpose of these laws is to protect children from harm by ensuring that they are not involved in the making of pornography and by preventing child sexual abuse by users of child pornography. Child pornography is defined as any material that shows a child's genitals for a sexual purpose or depicts a child engaged in sexual activity. A child is defined as anyone under the age of 18. These statutes also outlaw "pseudo-child pornography;" that is, pornography that uses adults but makes them look like children.

There are several ways in which the child pornography offences differ from offences governing adult pornography. Displaying or offering to sell pornography to persons under 16 is an offence, whether or not these materials would be viewed as obscene under the Criminal Code. In addition, the sentences for child pornography offences are greater than for obscenity offences. Finally, it is an offence to be in the possession of child pornography, whereas adult pornography is an offence only when possession is for the purposes of sale or distribution.

In 2001, the Supreme Court upheld the law criminalizing the possession of child pornography with two narrow exceptions. It ruled that possessing private works of imagination that have artistic merit and photographic depictions of oneself are legal. Thus, it is legal to write or draw sexually explicit depictions of children for one's own personal pleasure. In response to this ruling, the government has proposed amendments to the child pornography legislation that will strengthen it; for example, people using the artistic merit defence will have to show that they have a legitimate purpose for possessing the child pornography.

Again, the profit motives are strong. An advertisement in the magazine *Screw* offered $200 for little girls to appear in porn films, and dozens of parents responded. A reporter covering the scene said:

> Some parents appeared in the movie with their children; others merely allowed their children to have sex. One little girl, age 11, who ran crying from the bedroom after being told to have sex with a man of 40, protested, "Mommy I can't do it." "You have to do it," her mother answered. "We need the money." And of course the little girl did. (Anson, 1977)

Some major, well-known films could easily be classified as kiddie porn. *Taxi Driver* featured Jodie Foster as a 12-year-old prostitute. And *Pretty Baby* launched the career of Brooke Shields, playing the role of a 12-year-old brothel prostitute in New Orleans. Shields herself was 12 years old when the film was made.

A major study of offenders (the people who produce child pornography) and victims profiled the offender as follows: All of the 69 offenders studied were male. They ranged in age from 20 to 70, with an average age of 43. And 38 percent had an already established relationship with the child before the illicit activity began—they were family friends or relatives, neighbours, teachers, or counsellors (Burgess, 1984). For a profile of one child pornogra-

Figure 18.6   Sex in advertising. Many advertisers, including Calvin Klein, use sexual images to sell products.

pher, see In Focus 18.2. Interpol, the International Criminal Police Organization, has an office in Ottawa and tracks Internet child pornography cases in Canada. In 2001, it identified 500 cases.

Advertising

Let's close our discussion of pornography by considering a mating of sex and money that all of us encounter every day—*sex in advertising*. Both subtle and obvious sexual promises are used to sell a wide variety of products. A muscular young man wearing low-slung jeans and no shirt sells Calvin Kleins. Abercrombie & Fitch catalogues feature photos of nude young people in bed or in pools. Perfumes promise that they will make women instantly sexually attractive. One brand of coffee seems to guarantee a warm, romantic, sensuous evening for the couple who drink it.

How much sexual content is there in advertising? One study analyzed the sexual content of magazine advertising in 1964 and 1984 (Soley &

Kurzbard, 1986). The percentage of ads with sexual content had not increased over that 20-year period, although the illustrations had become more explicit. In 1984, 23 percent of ads contained sexual content. And in those ads, female models were considerably more likely (41 percent) than male models (15 percent) to be shown partially clad or nude. Sexually provocative behaviour is another aspect of sex found in magazine advertising; in ads portraying heterosexual couples, the percentage engaging in sexual contact (passionate kissing, simulated intercourse) increased from 21 percent in 1983 to 53 percent in 1993 (Reichert, 2002).

Television advertising uses not only bodily display or nudity and sexually suggestive interaction but also context (a Caribbean beach, a bed or bedroom) and language including double entendre (a message with two meanings, one being sexual) and talk about sexual activity. Some advertisers, such as Victoria's Secret and Calvin Klein, cultivate a sexually suggestive image. A study of prime-time commercials broadcast on NBC found that 12 percent of the female models and 2 percent of the male models were dressed to be sexually suggestive. Network promotional ads were more likely to include sexual content. Sexual contact increased from 12 percent in 1990 to 21 percent in 1998. A review of the research on the effects of advertising concludes that sexual information attracts attention, and viewers are more likely to remember the sexual image; paradoxically, however, they are less likely to remember the brand name (Reichert, 2002). Beyond the effects of ads on brand images and purchasing, there is concern that continuing exposure to ads that contain gender stereotyped ideas and images, such as thin, attractive females and taut, buff males, may affect attitudes toward one's body. Male and female college students were shown either 20 sexist ads, 15 sexist ads, and 5 neutral ads, or no ads. The results indicated that exposure to the sexist ads was associated with dissatisfaction with one's own body among *both* men and women (Lavine et al., 1999).

The Customers

What is known about the consumer of pornography? Studies consistently find that the typical customer in a pornographic bookstore is an educated, middle-class male between the ages of 22 and 34 (Mahoney, 1983). That is, the use of the materials sold in such stores is "typical" or "normal" (in the statistical sense) among males. But the range is wide. The manager of one store said,

> We get everyone in here from millionaires to scum of the earth. The blue-collar and white-collar men come for the tapes. Married couples come in for things to help their sex life. The gay crowd cruises the booths in back. Groups of women come in for gag items. ("Porn Shop," 1994)

Women purchase and watch pornographic videos. Research conducted in Australia in 1999 reported that 65 percent of X-rated videos were purchased by a woman or a heterosexual couple. In data from 280 women, 20 percent said they selected the video, 50 percent said both selected it, 18 percent said the partner selected it with both their preferences in mind, and 9 percent said the partner selected it (Contessini, 2003). Female interest in erotica was recognized 20 years ago by Candida Royalle, then a film star; she became a producer and director and has made more than a dozen films directed toward women. A growing number of men and women are attempting to market to women, producing what is called "female empowered" adult entertainment, including films, cable TV programs, sex-toy stores, and Web sites.

Surveys also suggest that many students use sexually explicit materials. In one survey, 59 percent of males and 36 percent of females said they went to X-rated movies or read pornographic books (Houston, 1981). Similarly, researchers in Ontario found that 63 percent of women had read erotic novels, 45 percent had read *Playboy*-type magazines, 36 percent had read *Playgirl*-type magazines, and 39 percent had watched an X-rated video in the last year (Lawrance & Herold, 1988).

Repeat customers are a crucial part of the success of the porn business. "There are people who come in here three to five times a day for their fix. Before work. At lunch. After work. Late at night. Their addiction isn't to the perversion of it, just the pornography" ("Porn Shop," 1994).

Computer porn attracts a more varied clientele. Chat rooms and news groups attract both men and women of diverse ages (assuming that those who describe themselves are doing so accurately). Some of these people are married. Depending on

Figure 18.7 Candida Royalle (left), a former porn star, now produces and directs soft-core films geared toward a female audience.

the focus of the room or group, participants may be from diverse racial or ethnic backgrounds. For the most part, bulletin boards and adult Web sites probably attract the same types of clients as adult bookstores—middle-aged, middle-class, white men. However, Nielson/NetRatings found that one-quarter of visitors to adult Web sites were women (Navano, 2004).

Feminist Objections to Pornography

Some—though not all—feminists are very critical of pornography (e.g., Griffin, 1981; Lederer, 1980; Morgan, 1978). Why would feminists, who prize sexual liberation, be opposed to pornography?

There are four basic reasons why some feminists object to pornography. First, they argue that pornography debases women. In the milder, soft-core versions it portrays women as sex objects whose breasts, legs, and buttocks can be purchased and then ogled. In the hard-core versions women may be shown being urinated upon or being chained. This scarcely represents a respectful attitude toward women.

Second, pornography associates sex with violence toward women. As such, it contributes to sexual assault and other forms of violence against women and girls. Robin Morgan has put it bluntly: "pornography is the theory and rape is the practice" (Morgan, 1980, p. 139). This is a point that can be tested with scientific data, producing evidence that will be covered in the next section.

Third, pornography shows, indeed glamorizes, unequal power relationships between women and men. A common theme in pornography is men forcing women to have sex, so the power of men and subordination of women are emphasized. Consistent with this point, feminists do not object to sexual materials that portray women and men in equal, humanized relationships—what we have termed *erotica.*

Finally, they object to the structure of the pornography industry. Anti-pornography feminists believe that many models and actors in the pornography industry are physically, sexually, and emotionally abused in doing their work.

Feminists also note the intimate relationship between pornography and traditional gender roles. Pornography is enmeshed as both cause and effect. That is, pornography in part results from traditional gender roles that make it socially acceptable for men to use and require hypersexuality and aggressiveness as part of the male role. One study of androgyny and the use of pornography among university students found that the likeliest users of pornography are traditionally gender-typed, masculine males and androgynous females (Kenrick et al., 1980). In turn, pornography may serve to perpetuate traditional gender roles. By seeing or reading about dominant males and submissive, dehumanized females, each new generation of adolescent boys is socialized to accept these roles. On the other hand, the female-oriented videos discussed above attempt to equalize the power relationships between the male and female characters and are often filmed from the woman's point of view.

The Effects of Violent Pornography[3]

Some of the assertions summarized above—for example, that using violent pornography may predispose men toward committing violent crimes against women—can be tested using the methods of social science. A number of social psychologists have been collecting data for 20 years to test such assertions.

Four questions can be asked about the effects of using pornography. First, does it produce sexual arousal? Second, does it affect users' attitudes, particularly about sexual and non-sexual violence toward women? Third, does it affect the sexual behaviour of users? Fourth, does it affect the aggressive or criminal behaviour of users, particularly aggressive behaviour toward women?

More than 40 studies have examined the effect of sexually explicit material on sexual arousal. This research consistently finds that exposure to *material that the viewer finds acceptable* does produce arousal (Davis & Bauserman, 1993). Exposure to portrayals that the viewer finds objectionable produces a negative reaction. Most people disapprove of paraphilic behaviours (see Chapter 16), sexual

[3]Note that this discussion refers to violent pornography. There are many other sexually explicit images that are not of concern.

assault, and sexual activity involving children, so they react negatively to hard-core and child pornography. The one exception is that men who report, before they view pornography, that they would commit sexual assault under some circumstances are aroused by portrayals of forced intercourse.

There are gender differences in self-reports of response to sexually explicit materials. Men report higher levels of arousal to such portrayals than do women (Malamuth, 1998). The differences are larger in response to pornography than to erotica, and the difference is much larger among university students than among older persons (Murnen & Stockton, 1997). This difference between men and women is often attributed to the fact that most erotica and pornography is male-oriented. The focus is almost exclusively on sexual behaviour, with little character development or concern for relationships. There is limited foreplay and afterplay; the male typically ejaculates on some part of the woman's body (the "cum shot") rather than inside her. Former porn film star Candida Royalle produces videos made for women. An experiment found that male university students responded positively to and were aroused by videos made for men and for women; females reported negative responses to the videos intended for men and positive responses and sexual arousal to the videos designed for women (Mosher & MacIan, 1994).

What about the effect of pornography on attitudes? The research indicates that a single exposure to stories, photographs, or videos has little or no effect. Massive exposure (such as viewing videos for five hours) does lead to more permissive attitudes. In this situation, viewers become more tolerant of the behaviour observed and less in favour of restrictions on it (Davis & Bauserman, 1993). What about attitudes toward aggression against women? Some studies show that exposure to portrayals of forced intercourse lead men to be more tolerant of sexual assault, but other studies do not find a relationship between exposure and attitudes (Fisher & Grenier, 1994). Men exposed to portrayals of sexual aggression against women do not report a greater willingness to sexually assault a woman (Davis & Bauserman, 1993).

With regard to sexual behaviour, the research shows that, in response to erotic portrayals of consenting heterosexual activity, both men and women may report an increase in sexual thoughts and fantasies and in behaviours such as masturbation and

(a)

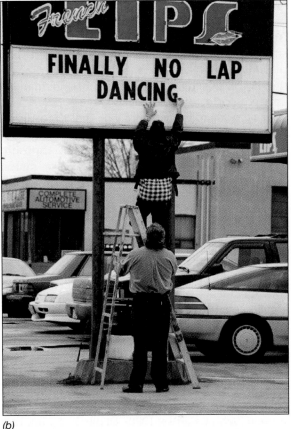

(b)

Figure 18.8   Canadians are divided in their opinions about lap-dancing and its legality is still being debated in Canada's courts. A Quebec court ruled that it was not obscene if not performed in the public area of a club, such as the Montreal nightclub shown in *(a)*. But an earlier Ontario ruling declared lap-dancing in private areas of a club would be considered prostitution—leading employees of a Toronto nightclub to change their sign in *(b)*.

intercourse. Exposure to portrayals of behaviour the person has not personally engaged in does *not* lead to an increase in these behaviours (Davis & Bauserman, 1993).

Finally, there has been great interest in whether exposure to portrayals of sexual aggression (which almost always involve men behaving aggressively toward women) increases aggressive behaviour. In laboratory studies, a number of studies have shown that males who are insulted or provoked by a woman and have been exposed to violent pornography are significantly more aggressive toward the woman in the experimental situation compared with men exposed to sexually explicit but non-violent material. If the comparison group is men exposed to non-sexual violent films, many studies find no difference between the two, but some find that exposure to sex-

ual violence increases aggression toward a woman more than exposure just to violence (Davis & Bauserman, 1993). Research in Ontario suggests that men with lower IQs may be more influenced by violent pornography than men with higher IQs (Bogaert et al., 1999). However, few men (5 to 6 percent in one Ontario study) choose to watch violent pornography when given the opportunity (Bogaert, 1993, 2001).

Ontario psychologists William Fisher and Guy Grenier have questioned the extent to which these laboratory studies capture the relationship between pornography and aggression in the "real world" (Fisher & Grenier, 1994). They point out that, in these laboratory studies, the men are told by the experimenter to send some level of shock to the female confederate. Although they can choose the level of shock to administer, they are not given the opportunity to engage in a non-aggressive response. However, in a real-life situation, a man could choose to speak to a woman who angered him or to walk away from the situation, instead of engaging in an aggressive response. The researchers found that when given the choice, 86 percent of the men chose not to make an aggressive response (Fisher & Grenier, 1994).

In sum, then, we can conclude that exposure to sexually explicit material that the viewer finds acceptable is arousing to both men and women. Exposure to aggressive pornography does increase males' aggression toward women under certain laboratory conditions. The extent to which these results are generalizable to a real-life situation is not known, however. Exposure to aggressive pornography may also affect males' attitudes, making them more accepting of violence against women. (For an excellent review, see Linz, 1989.) However, researchers in Ontario have concluded that men who are already predisposed to sexual aggression are the most likely to be affected by pornography; men who are not predisposed toward violence are unlikely to be affected (Seto et al., 2001).

What about the effects of pornography on women? Researchers in Ontario found that exposure to violent and dehumanizing pornography, but not to erotica, has a negative emotional impact on women (Senn & Radtke, 1990). Of particular interest is that women who reported having had more forceful sexual experiences in the past were particularly negative in their evaluations of pornography but not of erotica. It may be that, for these women, violent sexual images bring back painful memories.

What Is the Solution?

These are disturbing conclusions. What is the solution? Should pornography be censored or made illegal? Or would this only make it forbidden and therefore more attractive, and still available on the black market? Or should all forms of pornography be legal and readily available, and should we rely on other methods—such as education of parents and students through the school system—to abolish its use? Or should we adopt some in-between strategy, making some forms of pornography—such as child pornography and violent porn—illegal, while allowing free access to erotica? Note that the 1992 Supreme Court decision in the *Butler* case adopted this latter approach.

Our own opinion is that legal restrictions of sexually explicit material depicting adults—known less politely as censorship—are probably not the solution. We agree with the view of Donnerstein and his colleagues that a better solution is education (Donnerstein et al., 1987; Linz et al., 1987). In their experiments, they have debriefed male participants at the conclusion of the procedures. They then convey to the participants that media depictions are unreal and that the portrayal of women enjoying forced sex is fictitious. They dispel common myths about sexual assault, especially any that were shown in the film used in the experiment. Participants who have been debriefed in this way show less acceptance of myths about sexual aggression and more sensitivity to victims of sexual assault than participants shown a neutral film (Donnerstein et al., 1987). Subsequently, some researchers introduced *pre*briefing of participants in research involving exposure to sexually explicit materials. The typical briefing (pre or post) consists of a short audiotape or a printed handout pointing out that the material is fictional. It reminds participants that women do not enjoy forced sex and that sexual assault is a serious crime. Researchers identified 10 studies that included pre- or post-debriefing, and measures of the effects of exposure to the material. All 10 found that there were no negative effects of exposure accompanied by an educational briefing; in six of the studies, participants were less accepting of rape myths at the conclusion of the study than at the beginning (Allen et al., 1996). This research provides solid evidence that education can eliminate at least negative effects on attitudes.

■ ■ ■ SUMMARY

Commercial sex is a major industry in Canada, and increasingly around the world. Two prominent aspects of it are sex work and pornography. Although sex work is not illegal in Canada, various activities related to it are. It is also a crime to see or distribute any material that is "obscene." Obscenity is determined using the community standards of tolerance test. Possession of child pornography is also illegal.

Commercial sex workers engage in partnered sexual activity in return for payment, such as money, gifts, or drugs. There are several venues in which they work in Canada, including their own homes, in-call services, out-call services, and massage parlours. The working conditions, risks, and income of a sex worker depend on the setting. Third parties who may be involved include a pimp, madam, or manager; the involvement of these people generally limits a worker's autonomy. Sex trafficking involves exploitation and is a major problem. Research suggests that a female sex worker's well-being depends upon the risk level of the setting in which she works, the reasons she entered sex work, and whether she experienced victimization as a child or adolescent.

Data indicate that the use of sex workers has declined substantially in North America in the past 50 years. About one-half of the clients of female sex workers are occasional johns; the other 50 percent are repeat clients. Some men rely on sex workers for their sexual outlet.

Some male sex workers serve a female clientele. They may work as escorts, employees of massage parlours, or gigolos. More common are hustlers who cater to a male clientele.

Distinctions are made among pornography (sexually arousing art, literature, or film), obscenity (material offensive to Canadians), and erotica (sexual material that shows men and women in equal, humane relationships). Pornographic magazines, films, and videocassettes, both soft-core (erotica) and hard-core, are a multibillion-dollar business. Electronic porn has mushroomed in the past 20 years; people can discuss explicit sexual activity online, read sexually arousing stories, download sexually explicit images, or purchase a variety of goods and services at adult Web sites. Children—often runaways—are the star-victims in child pornography.

Some feminists object to pornography on the grounds that it debases women, encourages violence against women, and portrays unequal relationships between men and women.

Social-psychological research indicates that exposure to portrayals that the viewer finds acceptable is arousing to both men and women. Men are more likely to report arousal than women. Massive exposure leads to more favourable attitudes toward the behaviour observed. Some studies find that exposure to violent pornography creates more tolerant attitudes toward violence against women but others find no such effect. Exposure of heterosexuals to portrayals of consenting heterosexual activity leads to an increase in sexual thoughts and behaviour. Exposure to portrayals of sexual or non-sexual violence toward women increases men's aggression against women in the laboratory. Education about the effects of pornography is probably the best solution to the problems created by violent and dehumanizing pornography.

■ ■ QUESTIONS FOR THOUGHT, DISCUSSION, AND DEBATE

1. What is your position on the issue of censoring pornography? Do you think that all pornography should be illegal? Or should all pornography be legal? Or should some kinds—such as child pornography and violent pornography—be illegal, but not other kinds? What reasoning led you to your position?

2. In Canada, sex work is not illegal but many of the activities associated with sex work, such as communicating for the purposes of sex work, are illegal. Some people argue that we should have stricter laws and tougher sentences to deter the exchange of sex for money. Other people argue that sex work should be decriminal-

ized as it is a private matter between consenting adults. Based on what you know about sex workers and their clients, what approach would you suggest? Should the act of sex work be a criminal offence? If sex work-related activities were legal, in what ways should the sex trade be regulated, if at all?

3. Many of the streetwalkers in major cities are black or Asian women. Adult Web sites often prominently display photographs, stories, and videos about "interracial sex." Yet most of the customers of both sex workers and adult Web sites are white males. Why are white men attracted by materials featuring women from other ethnic groups?

■ ■ ■ SUGGESTIONS FOR FURTHER READING

Albert, Alexa. (2001). *Brothel: Mustang Ranch and its women.* New York: Random House. This book is based on a qualitative study of Mustang Ranch. It includes the stories of some of the women who work there, their attitudes, their circumstances, and their sense of professionalism.

Bullough, Vern, & Bullough, Bonnie. (1987). *Women and prostitution: A social history.* Buffalo, NY: Prometheus Books. A fascinating history of the oldest profession, from ancient Greece and Rome, through medieval times, India, and China, to the present.

Rimm, Marty. (1995). Marketing pornography on the information superhighway. *Georgetown Law Journal, 83,* 1849–1925. This article reports the findings of the first systematic study of computer pornography.

Vanwesenbeeck, Ine. (1994). *Prostitutes' well-being and risk.* Amsterdam: VU University Press. An excellent empirical study of the determinants of psychological well-being among prostitutes.

Online **LearningCentre**

For Review Questions, Web Resources, and other learning and study tools, visit the *Understanding Human Sexuality* Online Learning Centre at www.mcgrawhill.ca/college/hyde.

CHAPTER 19

Sexual Disorders and Sex Therapy

CHAPTER HIGHLIGHTS

> Telling it in plain words
> Makes me see how I feared the wrong thing.*

Many people experience sexual problems and concerns from time to time that go away without treatment. When a problem with sexual response causes significant psychological distress or interpersonal difficulty it is called a sexual disorder. The term *sexual dysfunction* is also used. Examples are a man's difficulty getting an erection and a woman's difficulty to orgasm.

This definition seems fairly simple. As we will see, however, in practice it can be difficult to determine exactly when something is a sexual disorder. In addition, there is a tendency to think in terms of only two categories, people with a sexual disorder and "normal" people. In fact, there is a continuum. Most of us have had, at one time or another, a sexual problem that went away in a day or a few months without treatment. In one New Brunswick study, 59 percent of the men and 68 percent of the women reported experiencing a sexual problem in the previous 18 months, but none had sought treatment (MacNeil & Byers, 1997). These cases represent the shades of grey that lie between absolutely great sexual functioning and long-term difficulties that require sex therapy.

Long-term sexual difficulties can cause a great deal of psychological distress to individuals troubled by them, not to mention to their partners, and many of these people seek out treatment. Until the 1960s, the only available treatment was long-term psychoanalysis, which is costly and wasn't particularly effective. A new era in understanding and treatment was ushered in with the publication, in 1970, of *Human Sexual Inadequacy* by Masters and Johnson. This book reported on the team's research on sexual disorders, as well as on their rapid-treatment program of behavioural therapy. Since then, many additional developments have taken place in the field, including cognitive–behavioural therapy and medical (drug) treatments.

*Margaret Avison (1982), The Agnes Cleves Papers, In *Winter Sun/The Dumbfounding: Poems 1940–66*, Toronto: McClelland & Stewart.

Sex disorders and treatments for them are the topics of this chapter. First we will consider the kinds of sexual disorders. Following that, we will review the causes of these disorders, and then the treatments for them.

■ Sexual Disorders

In this section we will consider the four categories of **sexual disorders**: desire disorders (hypoactive sexual desire, sexual aversion), arousal disorders (erectile disorder, female sexual arousal disorder), orgasmic disorders (rapid ejaculation, male orgasmic disorder, female orgasmic disorder), and sexual pain disorders (dyspareunia, vaginismus). Notice that the first three categories correspond to components of the sexual response cycle discussed in Chapter 9. They are presented in Table 19.1. Each disorder can be seen to vary along two dimensions (Wincze & Carey, 1991). It can be **lifelong**, often called a primary sexual disorder; or it can be **acquired**, called a secondary sexual disorder. A primary sexual disorder occurs when the individual has always had that disorder. A secondary sexual disorder occurs when the individual currently has the problem but did not have the problem in the past. Sexual disorders can also be either *generalized,* that is, occurring in all situations, or *situational.* A **situational sexual disorder** is when the disorder occurs in some situations but not in others. Sexual disorders can occur with a partner of the same or other gender.

Sexual disorder: A problem with sexual response that causes a person mental distress.
Lifelong sexual disorder: A sexual disorder that has been present since the person began sexual functioning.
Acquired sexual disorder: A sexual disorder that develops after a period of normal functioning.
Situational sexual disorder: A sexual disorder that a person has in some situations but not in others.

Table 19.1 Sexual Disorders That Correspond to Each Phase of the Sexual Response Cycle. Sexual pain disorders may affect any or all phases of the sexual response cycle.

Type of Disorder	Men	Women
Desire	Hypoactive sexual desire disorder Sexual aversion disorder	Hypoactive sexual desire disorder Sexual aversion disorder
Arousal	Erectile disorder	Female sexual arousal disorder
Orgasmic	Premature ejaculation Male orgasmic disorder	Female orgasmic disorder
Sexual Pain	Dyspareunia	Dyspareunia Vaginismus

Source: American Psychiatric Association (2000).

Desire Disorders

Hypoactive Sexual Desire

Sexual desire, or *libido,* refers to an interest in sexual activity, leading the individual to seek out sexual activity or to be pleasurably receptive to it (Kaplan, 1995). The term **hypoactive sexual desire** (HSD; the prefix *hypo* means "low") is used to describe inhibited sexual desire—that is, when an individual does not have spontaneous thoughts or fantasies about sexual activity and is not interested in sexual activity (Basson et al., 2001; Rosen & Leiblum, 1995). It is also sometimes termed *inhibited sexual desire* or *low sexual desire.* This disorder is found in both women and men.

People with HSD typically avoid situations that will evoke sexual feelings. That is, they do not initiate sex and are not receptive when their partner initiates. If, despite their best efforts, they find themselves in an arousing situation, they experience a rapid "turn-off" so that they feel nothing. The turn-off may be so intense that they report negative, unpleasant feelings; they may even report *sexual anaesthesia,* that is, no feeling at all, even though they may respond to the point of having an orgasm.

The identification of low sexual desire as a sexual disorder arose from the study of persons whom traditional sex therapy had failed to help. Typically, these patients had been misdiagnosed as having disorders connected to the excitement or the orgasm phases of the sexual response cycle. Therapists came to realize that they were seeing an increasingly frequent disorder of desire (e.g., Kaplan, 1979; LoPiccolo, 1980). Similarly, 39 per-

cent of Canadian women report diminished sexual desire (Fisher et al., 1999). Surveys of the general population indicate that lack of interest in sex is common. In the NHSLS, 15 percent of men and 30 percent of women reported experiencing it (Laumann et al., 1994).

Like other sexual disorders, HSD poses complex problems of definition. There are many circumstances when it is perfectly normal for a person not to experience sexual desire. For example, one cannot be expected to find every potential partner a turn-on.

It is also often true that the problem is not the individual's absolute level of sexual desire, but a discrepancy between the partners' levels (Zilbergeld & Ellison, 1980). That is, if one partner wants sex considerably less frequently than the other partner does, there is a conflict. This problem is termed a **discrepancy of sexual desire.**

Among those seeking therapy for HSD, some gender differences appear (Donahey & Carroll, 1993). Women usually report HSD in their early thirties, whereas men usually do so in their mid to late forties. However, a Canadian study found no differences in the prevalence of diminished sexual desire among women of different ages (Fisher et al., 1999). Thus, it may simply be that this result

Hypoactive sexual desire (HSD): A sexual disorder in which there is a lack of interest in sexual activity; also termed *inhibited sexual desire* or *low sexual desire.*
Discrepancy of sexual desire: A sexual problem in which the partners have considerably different levels of sexual desire.

reflects men's and women's willingness to seek professional help, but not necessarily the percentage of men and women who experience HSD at different ages. Women with HSD were also more likely than men with HSD to be dissatisfied with the quality of their relationship, particularly with the expression of affection. It is likely that when women's emotional needs are not being met by their partners, their sexual desire decreases.

Sexual Aversion Disorder

In sexual aversion disorder, the person has a strong aversion involving anxiety, fear, or disgust to sexual interaction and actively avoids any kind of genital contact with a partner (American Psychiatric Association, 2000). This problem causes great difficulty in the person's relationships. The prevalence of this disorder in the general population has not been documented in well-sampled studies, but experts believe that it is rare (Heiman, 2002a). It is fairly common, though, in persons who have panic disorder (Figueira et al., 2001).

Arousal Disorders
Erectile Disorder

Erectile disorder is the inability to have an erection or maintain one. Other terms for it are *erectile dysfunction* and *inhibited sexual excitement.* Although erectile disorder used to be called "impotence" (a term many laypeople still use), many professionals prefer not to use this term because of the negative connotations associated with it. One result of erectile disorder is that the man cannot engage in sexual intercourse. Using terminology discussed earlier, cases of erectile disorder can be classified as either *lifelong erectile disorder* or *acquired erectile disorder* depending on whether the man has ever been able to have and maintain an erection that is satisfactory for penetration in the past.

According to the NHSLS, about 10 percent of men have experienced an erection problem within the last 12 months (Laumann et al., 1999). This statistic varies a great deal by age: it is only 7 percent for 18- to 29-year-olds, but 18 percent for 50- to 59-year-olds. Another American survey found rates of 19 percent in men aged 50 to 59, and 39 percent in men 60 and older (Carson et al., 2002). Studies in Germany and France have found similar rates (Braun et al., 2000; Giuliano et al., 2002). Erectile disorder is the most common of the disorders

among men who seek sex therapy, particularly since the introduction of Viagra.

Psychological reactions to erectile disorder may be severe. For many men, it is one of the most embarrassing things they can imagine. Depression may follow from repeated episodes. It may also cause embarrassment or worry to the man's partner.

Female Sexual Arousal Disorder

Female sexual arousal disorder refers to a lack of response to sexual stimulation (American Psychiatric Association, 2000). The disorder involves both a subjective, psychological component and a physiological element (Basson et al., 2000). It is defined partly by the woman's own subjective sense that she does not feel aroused and partly by difficulties with vaginal lubrication. However, researchers in British Columbia have shown that many women who report subjective sexual arousal difficulties did not differ from control women in their physiological arousal to an erotic film. That is, they did get physiologically aroused while viewing the film, just as the control women did (Brotto et al., 2004). In contrast, the women who reported physiological arousal difficulties (without subjective arousal difficulties) did get less aroused. This suggests that there may be different subtypes of female sexual arousal disorder.

Difficulties with lubrication are common; they were reported by 19 percent of the women in the NHSLS (Laumann et al., 1994). These problems become particularly frequent among women during and after menopause and this is not a sexual disorder: as estrogen levels decline, vaginal lubrication decreases. The use of sterile lubricants is an easy way to deal with this problem. The absence of subjective feelings of arousal is more complex to treat.

Orgasmic Disorders
Premature Ejaculation

Premature ejaculation (or PE, if you want to be on familiar terms with it) occurs when a man has an

Erectile (eh-REK-tile) disorder: The inability to have or maintain an erection.
Female sexual arousal disorder (FSAD): A sexual disorder in which there is a lack of response to sexual stimulation.
Premature (rapid) ejaculation: A sexual disorder in which the man ejaculates too soon and feels he cannot control when he ejaculates.

orgasm and ejaculates sooner than desired—that is, too soon. In extreme cases, ejaculation may take place so soon after erection that it occurs before penetration can occur. In other cases, the man is able to delay the orgasm to some extent, but not as long as he would like or not long enough to meet his partner's preferences. Some experts prefer the terms *early ejaculation* or *rapid ejaculation* as having fewer negative connotations (Grenier & Byers, 1995, 2001).

While the definition given above—having an orgasm and ejaculating too soon—seems simple enough, in practice it is difficult to specify when a man is a premature ejaculator (Grenier & Byers, 1995, 2001; Metz et al., 1997). What should the precise criterion for "too soon" be? Should the man be required to last for at least 30 seconds after stimulation begins? For 12 minutes? For 2 minutes after penetration? The definitions used by authorities in the field vary widely. One source defines "prematurity" as the occurrence of orgasm less than 30 seconds after the penis has been inserted. Another group has extended this to 1½ minutes; for a third, the criterion is ejaculation before there have been 10 pelvic thrusts. Masters and Johnson defined premature ejaculation as the inability to delay ejaculation long enough for the woman to have an orgasm at least 50 percent of the time. This last definition has merit because it stresses the importance of the interaction between the two partners; however, it carries with it the question of how easily the woman is stimulated to orgasm. It also assumes that all men have female partners. Psychiatrist and sex therapist Helen Singer Kaplan (1974; see also Grenier & Byers, 2001; McCarthy, 1989) believed that the key to defining premature ejaculation is the absence of voluntary control of orgasm; that is, the real problem is that the man with premature ejaculation has little or no control over when he orgasms. Another good definition is self-definition: if a man finds that he has become greatly concerned about his lack of ejaculatory control or that it is interfering with his ability to form intimate relationships, or if a couple agree that it is a problem in their relationship, then it may reasonably be called premature ejaculation.

Poor ejaculatory control is a common problem in the general male population. Our research has shown that 24 percent of Canadian men report having a current problem with climaxing too early (Grenier & Byers, 2001). Although the average time to ejaculation after penetration reported by the men in this study was about 8 minutes, 7 percent reported ejaculating within 1 minute and 17 percent reported ejaculating within 2 minutes. Further, 23 percent of the men felt that they had a sexual difficulty or problem due to early ejaculation. However, not all of these men ejaculated quickly; some were concerned because they had unrealistic expectations about how long intercourse should last. It might be some relief for them to know that their female partners were less likely to see their rapid ejaculation as a problem—only 10 percent of the partners felt the man had a problem related to rapid ejaculation (Byers & Grenier, 2003). Further, PE was associated with lower sexual satisfaction for the men but not for their partners, and it was not associated with relationship satisfaction for either partner. In another study, 53 percent of university men reported limited ejaculatory control; 59 percent were very concerned about ejaculating sooner than they wanted to (Grenier & Byers, 1997). Very few of these men had ever sought therapy for the problem.

Like erectile disorders, premature ejaculation may create a web of related psychological problems. Because the ability to postpone ejaculation and "satisfy" a partner is so important in our concept of a man who is a competent lover, rapid ejaculation can cause a man to become anxious about his sexual competence. Furthermore, the partner may become frustrated because she or he is not having a satisfying sexual experience either. So the condition may create friction in the relationship.

The negative psychological effects of early ejaculation are illustrated by a young man in one of our sexuality classes who handed in an anonymous question. He described himself as a premature ejaculator and said that after several humiliating experiences during intercourse with dates, he was now convinced that no woman would want him in that condition. He no longer had the courage to ask for dates, so he had stopped dating entirely. He wanted to know how the women in the class would react to a man with such a problem. The question was discussed in class, and most of the women agreed that their reaction to his problem would depend a great deal on the quality of the relationship they had with him. If they cared deeply for him, they would be sympathetic and patient and help him overcome the difficulty. The point is, though, that the early ejaculation had created problems so severe that the young man not only had stopped having sex but also had stopped dating.

Men have developed (mostly ineffective) home remedies for dealing with rapid ejaculation such as doubling up on condoms and using desensitizing creams. Perhaps the most common is to think of something else. We had university men in New Brunswick report the thoughts they used to delay ejaculation (Grenier & Byers, 1997). These thoughts fell into five categories: sex negative (thinking of an unattractive TV personality); sex positive (thinking "we're in no hurry" or visualizing a past episode of prolonged intercourse); non-sexual and negative (thinking of a sad event, unpaid debts); sex neutral (counting backwards from 100); and sexually incongruous (thinking of your grandmother, reciting the Lord's Prayer). We recommend the sex positive alternative because it not only delays ejaculation but also allows both partners to remain in the moment.

Male Orgasmic Disorder

Male orgasmic disorder (also sometimes called *delayed or retarded ejaculation*) is the opposite of premature or *delayed* ejaculation. The man is unable to orgasm or it is greatly delayed, even though he has a solid erection and has had more than adequate stimulation (Apfelbaum, 2000). The severity of the problem may range from only occasional problems with orgasming to a history of never having experienced an orgasm. In the most common version, the man is incapable of orgasm during intercourse but may be able to orgasm as a result of hand or mouth stimulation.

Male orgasmic disorder is far less common than premature ejaculation. In the NHSLS, 8 percent of the male respondents had had a problem in the last 12 months with being unable to orgasm (Laumann et al., 1999). The incidence varies only slightly as a function of age: it was 7 percent for 18- to 29-year-olds and 9 percent for 50- to 59-year-olds. Among men seeking sex therapy, it constitutes about 3 to 8 percent of the cases (Rosen & Leiblum, 1995b).

Male orgasmic disorder is, to say the least, a frustrating experience for a man. One would think that any partner would be delighted to have intercourse with a man who has a long-lasting erection that is not terminated by orgasm. In fact, though, some people react negatively to this condition, seeing their partner's inability to have an orgasm as a personal rejection. Some men, anticipating these negative reactions, have adopted the practice of faking orgasm. In some cases, the man's orgasmic disorder can create painful intercourse because intercourse goes on too long.

Female Orgasmic Disorder

Female orgasmic disorder is the inability to orgasm. This condition goes by a variety of other terms, including *orgasmic dysfunction, anorgasmia,* and *inhibited female orgasm.* Laypersons may call it "frigidity," but sex therapists reject this term because it has derogatory connotations and is imprecise. "Frigidity" may refer to a variety of conditions ranging from total lack of sexual arousal to arousal without orgasm. Therefore, the term "female orgasmic disorder" is preferred.

Like other sexual disorders, cases of female orgasmic disorder may be classified into *lifelong* and *acquired* depending on whether the woman has ever had orgasms in the past (American Psychiatric Association, 2000). A common pattern is *situational orgasmic disorder,* in which the woman has orgasms in some situations but not others. For example, she may be able to have orgasms while masturbating, but not while being stimulated by a partner.

Orgasmic disorders are common among women. Twenty-one percent of Canadian women report that they do not usually have an orgasm during intercourse (Fisher et al., 1999). Younger women were more likely to report infrequent orgasms than were older women. Female orgasmic disorder accounts for 25 to 35 percent of the cases of women seeking sex therapy (Spector & Carey, 1990).

Once again, though, these definitions become more complicated in practice than in theory. Consider the case of the heterosexual woman who orgasms as a result of masturbation or hand or mouth stimulation by a partner but who does not orgasm in vaginal intercourse. Is this really a sexual disorder? The notion that it is a disorder can be traced to sexual scripts and beliefs that there is a "right" way to have sex—with the penis inside the

---

Male orgasmic disorder: A sexual disorder in which the male cannot have an orgasm, even though he is highly aroused and has had a great deal of sexual stimulation.
Female orgasmic disorder: A sexual disorder in which the woman is unable to have an orgasm.

vagina—and a corresponding "right" way to have orgasms. Because this pattern of situational orgasmic disorder is so common, some experts consider it to be well within the normal range of female sexual response (Wincze & Carey, 2001). Perhaps the woman who orgasms as a result of hand or mouth stimulation, but not penile thrusting, is simply having orgasms when she is adequately stimulated and is not having them when she is inadequately stimulated.

Nonetheless, there should be room for self-definition of disorders. If a woman has situational orgasmic disorder, is truly distressed that she is not able to orgasm during vaginal intercourse, and wants therapy, then it may be appropriate to do so even if she does not meet the criteria for having a disorder. The therapist, however, should be careful to explain to her the problems of definition raised above, in order to be sure that her request for therapy stems from her own dissatisfaction with her sexual responding rather than from an overly idealistic sexual script. Therapy in such cases probably is best viewed as an attempt to enrich the client's experience rather than to fix a problem.

Sexual Pain Disorders
Painful Intercourse

Painful intercourse, or **dyspareunia,** refers simply to genital pain experienced during intercourse (America Psychiatric Association, 2000). It is usually thought of as a female sexual disorder, but males occasionally experience it as well. In the NHSLS, 14 percent of the women reported pain during sex, compared with 3 percent of the men (Laumann et al., 1994). Similarly 14 percent of Canadian women reported pain during intercourse (Fisher et al., 1999). While complaints of occasional pain during intercourse are fairly common among women, persistent dyspareunia is not very common. In women, the pain may be felt in the vagina, around the vaginal entrance and clitoris, or deep in the pelvis. The pain may also differ in quality and in intensity (Pukall et al., 2003). Some women describe a burning sensation, others a sharp pain or an aching feeling. Most of these women also experience pain in non-sexual situations affecting the vulva, such as sports or inserting a tampon (Binik et al., 2000; Meana et al., 1997). In men, the pain is felt in the penis or testes. To put it mildly, dyspareunia decreases one's enjoyment of the sexual experience and may even lead one to abstain from sexual activity.

Quebec psychologist Yitzchak Binik and his colleagues have criticized the notion of sexual pain disorders (Binik et al., 2001, 2002; Meana et al., 1997; Pukall et al., 2000). They point out that just because pain interferes with sexual activity such as intercourse, this does not make it a sexual disorder. They use the analogy of lower back pain that interferes with work. Although lower back pain may prevent a person from working, this pain is classified by its location (that is, lower back pain) rather than by the activity it interferes with (that is, work pain). Further, the pain associated with intercourse often also occurs in non-sexual situations, such as inserting a tampon or physical exercise. Thus they argue that painful intercourse should be reclassified and treated as a pain disorder that interferes with sexual activity rather than as a sexual disorder.

Painful intercourse may be related to a variety of physical factors, to be discussed below.

Vaginismus

Vaginismus (the suffix "-ismus" means "spasm") is a spastic contraction of the outer third of the vagina; in some cases it is so severe that the entrance to the vagina is closed, and penetration is impossible (Leiblum, 2000). Vaginismus and dyspareunia may be associated (Binik et al., 2000; Reissing et al., 1999). That is, if attempted intercourse is painful, one result may be spasms that close off the entrance to the vagina. Ontario researcher Elke Reissing found that women diagnosed with vaginismus had greater muscle tension, lower muscle strength, and greater fear and avoidance of intercourse than did women with other forms of dyspareunia and control women. However, contrary to the diagnostic criteria not all women diagnosed with vaginismus had muscle spasms (Reissing et al., 2004).

Vaginismus is not a very common sexual disorder in the general population. It is, however, relatively common among women seeking sex therapy,

Dyspareunia (dis-pah-ROO-nee-uh): Painful intercourse.

Vaginismus (Vaj-in-IS-mus): A sexual disorder in which there is a spastic contraction of the muscles surrounding the entrance to the vagina, in some cases so severe that penetration is impossible.

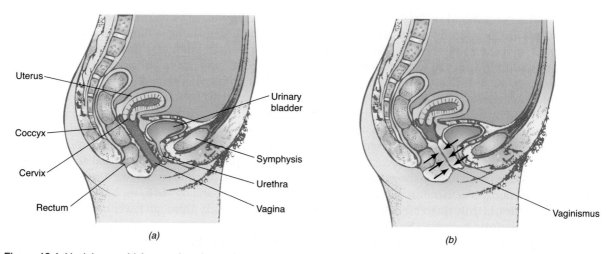

Figure 19.1 Vaginismus. *(a)* A normal vagina and other pelvic organs, viewed from the side, and *(b)* vaginismus, or involuntary constriction of the outer third of the vagina.

accounting for 12 to 17 percent of the cases (Spector & Carey, 1990). Women may be particularly likely to seek treatment for it when it makes intercourse impossible and they are interested in conceiving a child (Binik et al., 2000).

■ What Causes Sexual Disorders?

There are many causes of sexual disorders, varying from person to person and from one disorder to another. Several categories of factors may be related to sexual disorders: physical factors (organic factors and drugs), individual psychological factors, combined cognitive and physiological factors, and interpersonal factors. Each of these categories is discussed below.

Physical Causes

Physical factors that cause sexual disorders include **organic factors** (physical factors such as diseases) and drugs. Organic factors that have been implicated in various disorders are discussed first, followed by a discussion of the effects of drugs.

Erectile Disorder

Perhaps 50 percent or more of cases of erectile dis-

> **Organic factors of sexual disorders:** Physical factors, such as disease or injury, that cause sexual disorders.

order (ED) may be due to organic factors or to a combination of organic and other factors (Buvat et al., 1990; Richardson, 1991).

Diseases associated with the heart and the circulatory system are particularly likely to be associated with the condition, since erection itself depends on the circulatory system (Gajewski, 1999). Any kind of vascular pathology (problems in the blood vessels supplying the penis) can produce erection problems. Erection depends on having a great deal of blood flowing into the penis via the arteries, with simultaneous constricting of the veins so that the blood cannot flow out as rapidly as it is coming in. Thus damage to either these arteries or the veins may produce erectile disorder.

Erectile disorder is associated with diabetes mellitus, although the exact mechanism by which diabetes or a prediabetic condition may cause erectile disorder is not known (Bancroft & Gutierrez, 1996). In fact, erectile disorder may in some cases be the earliest symptom of a developing case of diabetes. Of course, not all diabetic men have erectile disorders; indeed, the majority do not. One estimate is that 35 percent of men with diabetes have an erectile disorder (Weinhardt & Carey, 1996).

Hypogonadism—an underfunctioning of the testes so that testosterone levels are very low—is associated with ED (Morales & Heaton, 2001). ED is also associated with a condition called hyperprolactinemia in which there is excessive production of prolactin (Johri et al., 2001).

Any disease or injury that damages the lower part of the spinal cord may cause erectile disorder, since that is the location of the erection reflex centre (see Chapter 9). Erectile disorder may also result from severe stress or fatigue. Finally, some—though not all—kinds of prostate surgery may cause the condition (Libman & Fichten, 1987; Libman et al., 1989).

With erectile disorders, as with most sexual disorders, it is important to recognize that the distinction between organic causes and psychological causes is too simple (Buvat et al., 1990). Many sexual disorders result from a complex interplay of the two causes. For example, a man who has circulatory problems that initially cause him to have erection problems is likely to develop anxieties about erection, which in turn may create further difficulties. This notion of dual causes has important implications for therapy. Many people with such disorders require both medical treatment and psychotherapy.

Premature Ejaculation

Rapid ejaculation is more often caused by psychological than physical factors. However, for some men early ejaculation may be due to a malfunctioning of the ejaculatory reflexes (Grenier & Byers, 1995). These men have a physiological hypersensitivity that results in faster ejaculation. (See Chapter 9 for a discussion of ejaculation.) Physical factors may also be involved in cases of acquired disorder in which the man at one time had ejaculatory control but later lost it. A local infection such as prostatitis may be the cause, as may degeneration in the related parts of the nervous system, which may occur in neural disorders such as multiple sclerosis.

An intriguing explanation for early ejaculation comes from the sociobiologists (Hong, 1984). Their idea is that rapid ejaculation has been selected for in the process of evolution—what we might call "survival of the fastest." Monkeys and apes (and humans) who copulated and ejaculated rapidly, the argument goes, would be more likely to survive and reproduce in that the female would be less likely to get away, and the male would be less likely to be attacked by other sexually aroused males while he was copulating. In fact, the average time from intromission (insertion of the penis into the vagina) to ejaculation among chimpanzees is rapid—about 7 seconds (Tutin & McGinnis, 1981). However, primates engage in lengthy courtship and foreplay behaviours that would not be predicted by sociobiologists (Bixler, 1986). Nonetheless, according to sociobiologists, the genes for rapid ejaculation are still around.

Male Orgasmic Disorder

Male orgasmic disorder, or retarded ejaculation, may be associated with a variety of medical or surgical conditions, such as multiple sclerosis, spinal cord injury, and prostate surgery (Rosen & Leiblum, 1995). Most commonly, though, it is associated with psychological factors.

Female Orgasmic Disorder

Orgasmic disorder in women may be caused by severe illness, general ill health, or extreme fatigue. Injury to the spinal cord can cause orgasm problems (Sipski et al., 2001). However, most cases are caused by psychological factors.

Painful Intercourse

Although dyspareunia in women is often caused by organic factors, the *experience* of sexual pain is influenced by psychological factors (Bergeron et al., 1997). Organic factors include:

1. *Disorders of the vaginal entrance* Irritated remnants of the hymen; painful scars, perhaps from an episiotomy or sexual assault; or infection of the Bartholin glands.

2. *Disorders of the vagina* Vaginal infections; allergic reactions to spermicidal creams or the latex in condoms or diaphragms; a thinning of the vaginal walls, which occurs naturally with age or chemically-induced menopause; or scarring of the roof of the vagina, which can occur after hysterectomy.

3. *Pelvic disorders* Pelvic infection such as pelvic inflammatory disease, endometriosis, tumours, cysts, or a tearing of the ligaments supporting the uterus.

Sexual pain in men can also be caused by a variety of organic factors. For an uncircumcised man, poor hygiene may be a cause; if the penis is not washed thoroughly with the foreskin retracted, material may collect under the foreskin, causing infection. Phimosis, a condition in which the fore-

Table 19.2 Drugs That May Impair or Improve Sexual Response

Drug	How It Affects Sexual Functioning	Common Medical Uses
1. Psychoactive Drugs		
Antianxiety drugs/tranquillizers		Anxiety, panic disorders
Buspirone	Enhanced desire, orgasm	
Benzodiazepines (Librium, Valium, Ativan)	Decreases hypoactive desire, improves premature ejaculation	
Antidepressants I: Tricyclics and MAO inhibitors	Desire disorders, erection problems, orgasm problems, ejaculation problems	Depression
	May treat hypersexuality, premature ejaculation	
Antidepressants II: Serotonin Reuptake Inhibitors (Paxil, Prozac, Zoloft)	Desire disorders, erection problems, orgasm problems	Depression, obsessive-compulsive disorder, panic disorders
Lithium	Desire disorders, erection problems	Bipolar disorder
Antipsychotics Thorazine, Haldol	Desire disorders, erection problems, orgasm problems, ejaculation problems	Schizophrenia
2. Antihypertensives		High blood pressure
Reserpine, Methyldopa	Desire disorders, erection difficulties, orgasm delayed or blocked	
ACE inhibitors (Vasotec)	Erection difficulties	
3. Substance Use and Abuse		
Alcohol	At low doses, increases desire	
	At high doses, decreases erection, arousal, orgasm	
	Alcoholism creates many disorders and atrophied testicles, infertility	
Nicotine	Decreases blood flow to penis, creates erectile disorder	
Opioids		
Endogenous: Endorphins	Sense of well-being and relaxation	
Heroin	Decrease in desire, orgasm, ejaculation, replaces sex	
Marijuana	Enhances sexual pleasure but not actual "performance"; chronic use decreases desire	

Sources: Crenshaw & Goldberg, 1996; Segraves & Balon, 2003.

skin cannot be pulled back, can also cause sexual pain. An allergic reaction to spermicidal creams or to the latex in condoms may also be involved. Finally, various prostate problems may cause pain on ejaculation.

Vaginismus

Vaginismus is sometimes caused by painful intercourse, and therefore by organic factors that cause that condition. More frequently, though, it is caused by individual psychological factors or interpersonal factors (Rosen & Leiblum, 1995).

Drugs

Some drugs may have side effects that cause sexual disorders (Segraves & Balon, 2003). For example, some drugs used to treat high blood pressure increase problems with erection in men and decrease sexual desire in both men and women. Although it would be impossible to list every drug effect on every aspect of sexual functioning, a list of some of the major drugs that may cause sexual disorders is provided in Table 19.2. Here we will consider the effects of alcohol, illicit drugs, and prescription drugs.

Figure 19.2   Alcohol and cocaine are popular recreational drugs that many people believe enhance sexual experience. Research shows, though, that high levels of alcohol suppress sexual arousal, and repeated use of cocaine is associated with loss of sexual desire, orgasm disorders, and erection problems.

Alcohol

The effects of alcohol on sexual responding vary considerably. We can think of these effects as falling into three categories: (1) short-term pharmacological effects, (2) expectancy effects, and (3) long-term effects of chronic alcohol abuse. In regard to the last category, alcoholics, particularly in the later stages of alcoholism, frequently have sexual disorders, typically including erectile disorder, orgasmic disorder, and loss of desire (Segraves & Balon, 2003). These sex problems may be the result of any of a number of organic effects of long-term alcoholism. For example, chronic alcoholism in men may cause disturbances in sex hormone production because of atrophy of the testes. Chronic alcohol abuse, too, generally has negative effects on the person's interpersonal relationships, which may contribute to sexual disorders.

What about the person who is not an alcoholic, but rather has had one or many drinks on a particular evening and then proceeds to a sexual interaction? As noted above, there is an interplay of two effects: expectancy effects and actual pharmacological effects (George & Stoner, 2000). Many peo-ple have the expectation that alcohol will loosen them up, making them more sociable and sexually uninhibited. These expectancy effects in themselves produce increased physiological arousal and subjective feelings of arousal. Expectancy effects, though, interact with the pharmacological effects and work mainly at low doses, that is, when only a little alcohol has been consumed. At high dosage levels, alcohol acts as a depressant and sexual arousal is markedly suppressed, in both men and women.[1]

Illicit or Recreational Drugs

There is a widespread belief that *marijuana* has aphrodisiac properties. Little scientific research has been done on its actual effects, and most of what has been done is old and based on small samples. Therefore, we can provide only tentative ideas about the effects of marijuana on sexual functioning. In surveys of users, many respondents report

---

[1]Some refer to the resulting erection problems as "whisky dick" or "brewer's droop."

that it increases sexual desire and makes sexual interactions more pleasurable. In regard to potential negative effects, one early study indicated that long-term marijuana use lowers testosterone levels and sperm count in males (Kolodny et al., 1974). Chronic users report decreased sexual desire (Segraves & Balon, 2003). In community studies, marijuana use has been associated with orgasmic disorder (Johnson et al., 2004).

Among drug users, *cocaine* is reported to be one of the drugs of choice for enhancing sexual experiences. It is said to increase sexual desire, enhance sensuality, and delay orgasm. Chronic use of cocaine, however, is associated with loss of sexual desire, orgasmic disorders, and erectile disorders (Segraves & Balon, 2003). The effects also depend on the means of administration—whether the cocaine is inhaled, smoked, or injected. The most negative effects on sexual functioning occur among those who regularly inject the drug.

Recently MDMA, or "Ecstasy," has increasingly been used in connection with sexual activity; in fact, it is sometimes called the "love drug." Users report that it enhances sexual desire, sexual arousal, female sexual desire, and orgasmic intensity (Zemishlany et al., 2001). However, it is reported to interfere with erection for some men, and to delay orgasm in both men and women.

Stimulant drugs, notably *amphetamines*, are associated with increased sexual desire and better control of orgasm in some studies (Segraves & Balon, 2003). Injection of amphetamines itself causes a physical sensation that is described by some as a total-body orgasm. In some cases, though, orgasm becomes difficult or impossible when using amphetamines.

Crystal methamphetamine ("ice") is the hot new recreational drug. This drug is of particular concern because, while high on it, people have a tendency to engage in risky sexual behaviours (Semple et al., 2004; Urbina & Jones, 2004; Wohl et al., 2002). One study of heterosexual, HIV-negative adults using meth indicated that, over a two-month period, they averaged 22 acts of unprotected vaginal sex and nine different sex partners (Semple et al., 2004). Crystal meth can also lead to paranoia, hallucinations, and violent behaviour (Brecht et al., 2004). We cannot recommend it.

The *opiates* or narcotics, such as morphine, heroin, and methadone, have strong suppression effects on sexual desire and response (Segraves & Balon, 2003). Long-term use of heroin, in particular, leads to decreased testosterone levels in males.

Prescription Drugs

Table 19.2 on p. 546 provides a partial list of prescription drugs that can affect sexual responding.

Some *psychiatric drugs*—that is, drugs used in the treatment of psychological disorders—may affect sexual functioning (Segraves & Balon, 2003). In general, these drugs have their beneficial psychological effects because they alter the functioning of the central nervous system. But these CNS alterations in turn affect sexual functioning. For example, the drugs used to treat schizophrenia may cause delayed orgasm or "dry orgasm" in men—that is, orgasm with no ejaculation. Tranquillizers and antidepressants often improve sexual responding as a result of improvement of the person's mental state. However, there may also be negative effects. Many of the antidepressants, for example, are associated with arousal and delayed orgasm problems in men as well as women. On the other hand, they are sometimes used to treat premature ejaculation precisely because they delay orgasm. A few antidepressants—most notably bupropion (Wellbutrin)—have few sexual side effects and are becoming popular for that very reason.

The list of other prescription drugs that can affect sexual functioning is long, so we will mention just two examples. Some of the antihypertensive drugs (used to treat high blood pressure) can cause erection problems in men (Segraves & Balon, 2003). Most of the research on antihypertensive drug effects has been done with men, so we have less knowledge of their effects on women, although sexual problems have been reported among women using antihypertensive drugs. Some of the drugs used to treat epilepsy appear to cause erection problems and decreased sexual desire, although epilepsy by itself also seems to be associated with sexual disorders.

Psychological Causes

The psychological sources of sexual disorders can be separated into predisposing factors and maintaining or ongoing causes (Wincze & Carey, 1991).

Predisposing factors are people's prior life experiences—for example, things that happened in childhood—that now inhibit the sexual response. **Maintaining factors** are ongoing life circumstances, personal characteristics, and characteristics of lovemaking that help explain why the problem continues.

Maintaining Psychological Causes

The following eight factors are frequently maintaining psychological causes of sexual disorder: (1) myths or misinformation; (2) negative attitudes; (3) anxieties such as fear of failure; (4) cognitive interference; (5) individual psychological distress such as depression; (6) behavioural or lifestyle factors; (7) failure to engage in effective, sexually stimulating behaviour due to failure of the partners to communicate; and (8) relationship distress.

Myths or *misinformation* can be a source of sexual dysfunction. Many people have beliefs about lovemaking that are incorrect, or are unaware of sexual information (such as the effects of aging on the sexual response) that is important to sexual functioning. For example, some couples seek sex therapy because of a woman's failure to orgasm; the therapist soon discovers that neither partner is aware of the location of the clitoris, much less its fantastic erotic potential. Misinformation can lead to a sexual script that does not fully enhance sexual arousal and pleasure or to anxiety and worry. These cases can often be cleared up by simple educational techniques.

A second possible source of sexual dysfunction is *negative attitudes* about sexual activity, one's own body, or one's partner's body. For example, the beliefs that "good" people do not enjoy sex or that one is ugly or fat may result in anxiety or other negative feelings during sexual activity that may affect sexual functioning.

Masters and Johnson theorized that *anxiety* during intercourse can be a source of sexual disorders. Anxiety may be caused by negative or traumatic experiences in the past such as child sexual abuse. However, anxiety also may be caused by fear of failure—that is, fear of being unable to perform. But anxiety itself can block sexual response in some people. Often anxiety can create a vicious circle of self-fulfilling prophecy in which fear of failure produces a failure, which produces more fear, which produces another failure, and so on. For example, a man may have one episode of erectile dysfunction, perhaps after drinking too much at a party. The next time he has sex, he anxiously wonders whether he will "fail" again. His anxiety is so great that he cannot get an erection. At this point he is convinced that the condition is permanent, and all future sexual activity is marked by such intense fear of failure that erectile disorder results. The prophecy is fulfilled.

Cognitive interference is a fourth maintaining cause of sexual disorders. "Cognitive interference" refers to thoughts that distract the person from focusing on the erotic experience. The problem is basically one of attention and of whether the person is focusing his or her attention on erotic thoughts and feelings or on distracting thoughts (Will my technique be good enough to please her? Will my body be beautiful enough to arouse him?). **Spectatoring,** a term coined by Masters and Johnson, is one kind of cognitive interference. The person behaves like a spectator or judge of his or her own sexual "performance." People who do this are constantly (mentally) stepping outside the sexual activities in which they are engaged, to evaluate how they are doing, mentally commenting, "Good job," or "Lousy," or "Could stand improvement." These ideas on the importance of cognition in sexual disorder derive from the cognitive theories of sexual responding discussed in Chapters 2 and 9.

Sex researcher David Barlow (1986) ran an elegant series of experiments to test the ways in which anxiety and cognitive interference affect sexual functioning. He studied men with and without sexual disorders, particularly erectile disorder, whom he calls the "functionals" and the

---

Predisposing factors: Experiences that people have had in the past—for example, in childhood—that now affect their sexual response.
Maintaining factors: Various ongoing life circumstances, personal characteristics, and lovemaking patterns that inhibit sexual response.

Cognitive interference: Negative thoughts that distract a person from focusing on the erotic experience.
Spectatoring: Masters and Johnson's term for acting as an observer or judge of one's own sexual performance; hypothesized to contribute to sexual disorders.

"dysfunctionals." He found that functionals and dysfunctionals respond very differently to stimuli in sexual situations. For example, anxiety (induced by the threat of being shocked) *increases* the arousal of functional men, but *decreases* the arousal of dysfunctional men while watching erotic films. Similarly, demands for performance (e.g., the experimenter says the research participant must have an erection or he will be shocked) increase the arousal of functionals but are distracting to (create cognitive interference in) and decrease the arousal of dysfunctionals. When both self-reports of arousal and physiological measures of arousal (the penile strain gauge) are used, dysfunctional men consistently underestimate their physical arousal, whereas functional men are accurate in their reporting.

From these laboratory findings, Barlow constructed a model that describes how anxiety and cognitive interference act together to produce sexual disorders such as erectile disorder. When dysfunctionals are in a sexual situation, there is a performance demand. This causes them to feel negative emotions such as anxiety. They then experience cognitive interference and focus their attention on non-erotic thoughts, such as thinking about how awful it will be when they don't have an erection. This increases arousal of their autonomic nervous system. To them, that feels like anxiety, whereas a functional person would experience it as sexual arousal. For the dysfunctionals, the anxiety creates further cognitive interference, and eventually the sexual performance is dysfunctional—they don't manage to get an erection. This leads them to avoid future sexual encounters or, when they are in one, to experience negative feelings, and the vicious cycle repeats itself.

It is important to note that anxiety produces sex problems only in some men. For the majority of men, who function well sexually, anxiety does not impair sexual responding, at least in the lab. The same is true for women (Elliott & O'Donohue, 1997).

A fifth possible cause of sexual disorders is individual *psychological distress*. That is, sexual disorder may be one symptom of a more general psychological disorder. For example, individuals who are depressed often experience low sexual desire or have difficulty becoming aroused (Araujo et al., 1998; Frohlich & Meston, 2002). Emotions such as anger and sadness (as well as anxiety, as we

saw earlier) can interfere with sexual responding (Araujo et al., 2000).

Behavioural and lifestyle factors can also affect sexual functioning. Smoking, alcohol consumption, and obesity are all behaviours that are associated with higher rates of sexual disorders (Derby et al., 2000; Segraves & Balon, 2003). However, these behaviours are quite modifiable. A study of middle-aged and older men showed that regular physical exercise reduced the risk of erectile disorder (Derby et al., 2000). A stressful lifestyle, such as a difficult work environment, long work hours, or a lack of privacy in the home, may also affect sexual functioning. Surprisingly, couples often fail to recognize how their lifestyle impacts on their sexual functioning.

The last two maintaining factors relate to the couple's interactions and relationship. Sexual disorders may be caused by *failure to engage in effective sexually stimulating behaviour*. Sometimes this is a result of simple ignorance—that is, myths and misinformation. More often poor technique is due to the failure of the partners to communicate with each other about their sexual preferences. We often expect our partners to read our minds (which most of us are not particularly good at) to determine what we like and don't like. In fact, a survey of more than 3,000 Canadian men and women found that only 28 percent had had even one serious discussion about sex in their relationship in the previous year (Auld et al., 2002). Two New Brunswick researchers examined whether sexual self-disclosure does, in fact, enhance sexual functioning (MacNeil & Byers, 2005). They had 74 heterosexual couples independently complete measures of their sexual likes and dislikes, their partner's sexual likes and dislikes, and their own sexual satisfaction. They found that, for both the men and the women, individuals who self-disclosed more about their sexual preferences had partners who had a better understanding of what pleased and displeased them sexually. In turn, the more the partner understood their sexual likes and dislikes, the more the couple engaged in mutually pleasing (and not in displeasing) sexual activities during lovemaking; the more pleasing and less displeasing the sexual script the more sexually satisfied they were.

In short, you are the leading expert in the field of what feels good to you, and your partner will never know what turns you on or what you desire at a particular moment unless you make this known, either verbally or nonverbally. But many people do not communicate their sexual desires. For example, a woman who needs a great deal of clitoral stimulation to have an orgasm may never tell her partner this; as a result, her partner provides some clitoral stimulation but not the amount of stimulation she needs. Consequently she does not orgasm.

Relationship distress; that is, disturbances in a couple's relationship, is another leading cause of sexual disorders. Frequent arguments or anger and resentment toward one's partner do not create an optimal environment for sexual enjoyment. Intimacy problems in the relationship can be a factor in sexual disorders. Poor communication, not feeling understood, a lack of common interests, and a lack of trust may interfere with the feelings of closeness and intimacy that are important to quality lovemaking and to being able to respond sexually (Basson, 2001). Sometimes individual psychological factors contribute to a lack of intimacy in the relationship. Some individuals have a fear of intimacy—that is, of deep emotional closeness to another person—often due to insecure attachment relationships with parents (Kaplan, 1979). A lack of quality time together due to an overly hectic lifestyle can also contribute to reduced feelings of intimacy and closeness and thus to relationship distress.

Predisposing Factors

The immediate or maintaining causes of sexual dysfunction are often a result of things that were learned or experienced in childhood, adolescence, or even adulthood. These early events result in negative attitudes, misinformation, cognitive interference, difficulty communicating, and so on.

In some cases of sexual disorder, the person's first sexual act was traumatic. An example would be a young man who could not get an erection the first time he attempted penetration and was laughed at by his partner. Such an experience sets the stage for future erectile disorder.

Child sexual abuse by parents or other adults is probably the more serious of the traumatic early experiences that lead to later sexual disorders. A history of sexual abuse is frequently reported by women seeking therapy for problems with sexual

desire, arousal, or aversion (Leonard & Follette, 2002). The findings are similar for men with desire or arousal problems (Loeb et al., 2002).

Growing up in a family that communicates negative messages about sex is often a predisposing factor to sexual disorders because it creates negative attitudes. The person who grew up in a very strict, religious family and was taught that sex is dirty and sinful may believe that sex is not pleasurable, that it should be gotten over with as quickly as possible, and that it is for purposes of procreation only. It is the rigid belief in sexual rights and wrongs (particularly wrongs), not religiosity per se, that likely impacts sexual functioning (Kleinplatz & Krippner, 2000). The child who is punished severely for masturbating and told never to "touch herself" again may develop negative attitudes about her genitals, and genital touching. Parents who teach their children the double standard may contribute to sexual disorders, particularly in daughters who were told that no nice lady is interested in sex or enjoys it. Growing up in a homonegative family or culture may contribute to internalizing homonegativity among gays and lesbians, which in turn may affect their sexual functioning. Such learning inhibits the enjoyment of a full sexual response.

Combined Cognitive and Physiological Factors

According to the cognitive–physiological model of sexual functioning and dysfunction, we function well sexually when we are physiologically aroused and we interpret it as sexual arousal rather than something else, like nervousness (Palace, 1995a, 1995b). As Barlow's research shows, people with sexual disorders tend to interpret their arousal as anxiety. In addition, the physiological processes and cognitive interpretations form a feedback loop (see discussion of cognitive theories in Chapter 2). That is, interpreting arousal as sexual arousal increases one's arousal further.

In a clever experiment, British Columbia women with sexual disorders were exposed, in a laboratory setting, to a frightening movie that increased their general autonomic arousal (Palace, 1995b). The women were then shown a brief erotic video and given feedback (actually false) that their genitals had shown a strong arousal response to it. This feedback created a cognitive interpretation for the way they were feeling. The combination of general auto-nomic arousal and the belief that they were responding with strong sexual arousal led these women, compared with the controls, to greater vaginal arousal responses and subjective reports of arousal in subsequent sessions. This demonstration of the effectiveness of combined physiological and cognitive factors is particularly striking because the women began with problems in sexual responding.

■ Therapies for Sexual Disorders

A variety of therapies for sexual disorders are avail-able, each relying on a different theoretical under-standing of what causes sexual disorders. Here we examine four major categories of therapies: behav-iour therapy, cognitive–behavioural therapy, couple therapy, and biomedical therapies. Effective treat-ments for sexual disorders focus on factors that are currently maintaining the sexual disorder rather than on predisposing factors.

Behaviour Therapy

Behaviour therapy has its roots in behaviourism and learning theory. The basic assumption is that sex problems are the result of prior learning (as dis-cussed above) and that they are maintained by ongoing reinforcements and punishments (imme-diate causes). It follows that these problem behav-iours can be unlearned by new conditioning. One of the key techniques is in vivo desensitization, in which the client is gradually led through exercises that reduce anxiety.

In 1970, Masters and Johnson reported on their development of a set of techniques for sex therapy with heterosexual couples and ushered in a new era of sex therapy. They operated from a behaviour ther-apy model because they saw sexual disorders as learned behaviours rather than as symptoms of psy-chiatric illness. Masters and Johnson used a rapid two-week program of intensive daily therapy that consisted mainly of discussions and specific behav-ioural exercises, or "homework assignments." They used a male–female therapy team to treat heterosex-ual couples so that each member of the couple would have a therapist of his or her own gender and would not feel outnumbered.

One of the basic goals of Masters and Johnson's therapy was to eliminate goal-oriented sexual per-formance. Many clients believe that in sex they must perform and achieve certain things. If sex is an achievement situation, it also can become the scene of failure, and perceived failures lead people to believe that they have a sexual problem. The form of cognitive interference known as *spectator-ing* (discussed earlier) contributes to this problem because it generates anxiety and other unpleasant feelings and interferes with the experience of positive sensations. The idea is to use therapy techniques to reduce anxiety.

In one technique that Masters and Johnson devised to eliminate a goal-oriented attitude toward sex, the couple is forbidden to have sexual intercourse until they are specifically permitted to by the therapists. They are assigned **sensate focus exercises** that reduce the demands on them. As the couple successfully completes each of these exer-cises, the sexual component of subsequent exer-cises is gradually increased. The couple chalk up a series of successes until eventually they are having intercourse and the disorder has disappeared.

Sensate focus exercises are based on the notion that touching and being touched are important forms of sexual expression and that touching is also an important form of communication; for example, a touch can express affection, desire, understand-ing, or a lack of caring. In the exercises, one member of the couple plays the "giving" role (touches and strokes the other), while the other person plays the "receiving" role (is touched by the other). The giving partner is instructed to massage or caress the other, while the receiving partner is instructed to commu-nicate to the giver what is most pleasurable. Thus the exercise fosters communication. The partners switch roles after a certain period of time. In the first exercises, the giver is not to stroke the genitals or breasts but may touch any other area. As the couple progress through the exercises, they are instructed to begin touching the genitals and breasts. These exercises also encourage the partners to focus their

---

Behaviour therapy: A system of therapy based on learn-ing theory, in which the focus is on the problem behav-iour and how it can be modified or changed.

Sensate focus exercise: A part of the sex therapy developed by Masters and Johnson in which one partner caresses the other, the other communicates what is pleasurable, and there are no performance demands.

attention or concentrate on the sensuous pleasures they are receiving. Many people's sexual response is dulled because they are distracted; they are thinking about how to solve a family financial problem, or are spectatoring their own performance. To use Barlow's terminology, they are victims of cognitive interference. The sensate focus exercises train people to concentrate only on their sexual experience, thereby increasing the pleasure of it.

In addition to these exercises, Masters and Johnson supplied simple education. The couple is given thorough instruction in the anatomy and physiology of the male and/or female sexual organs (depending on whether the couple are of the same sex or not). Some couples, for example, have no idea what or where the clitoris is. These instructions may also clear up myths and misinformation that either member of the couple may have had since childhood. For example, a man with an erectile disorder may have been told as a child that men can have only a fixed number of orgasms in their lifetime. As he approaches middle age, he starts to worry because his erections may come and go during lovemaking (see Chapter 12) or about whether he may have used up almost all of his orgasms, and this creates the erectile disorder. It is important for such men to learn that nature has imposed no quota on them.

Masters and Johnson collected data on the success and failure rates of their therapy. In their book *Human Sexual Inadequacy,* they reported on the treatment of 790 persons. Of these, 142 still had a disorder at the end of the two-week therapy program. This translates to a failure rate of 18 percent, or a *success rate of 82 percent.* While the failure rate ran around 18 percent for most disorders, there were two exceptions: Therapy for rapid ejaculation had a very low failure rate (2.2 percent), and therapy for lifelong erectile disorder had a high failure rate (40.6 percent). That is, rapid ejaculation was quite easy to cure, lifelong erectile disorder very difficult. Other research shows that couples' communication skills increase significantly during treatment (Tullman et al., 1981). Masters and Johnson's success rate is impressive, although their results have been called into question, as we shall see later in this chapter.

In Masters and Johnson's initial development of their therapy techniques, all the couples were heterosexual. They later used the same techniques in treating sexual disorders in gay and lesbian couples, with a comparable success rate (Masters & Johnson, 1979; see also McWhirter & Mattison, 1980).

Cognitive–Behavioural Therapy

Paralleling the increased importance of cognitive theories in psychology (see Chapter 2) is the increased importance of cognitive approaches to psychotherapy. Today, many sex therapists use a combination of the behavioural exercises pioneered by Masters and Johnson and cognitive therapy (Bancroft, 1997a; Heiman, 2002; Trudel et al., 1996, 2001). This is termed **cognitive–behavioural therapy.**

Cognitive restructuring is an important technique in a cognitive approach to sex therapy (Wincze & Carey, 1991). In cognitive restructuring, the therapist essentially helps the client restructure his or her thought patterns, helping them to become more positive (for an example, see In Focus 19.1). Cognitive restructuring is particularly useful in addressing two of the maintaining causes of sexual disorders described earlier in this chapter—negative attitudes and cognitive interference. In one form of cognitive restructuring, the therapist challenges the client's negative attitudes. These attitudes may be as general as a woman's negative, distrusting attitudes toward all men, or as specific as a man's negative attitudes toward masturbation. The client is helped to reshape these attitudes into more positive ones.

Cognitive therapists also like to address cognitive interference. The general idea is to reduce the presence of interfering thoughts during sex. First the therapist must help the client identify the presence of such thoughts. The therapist then suggests techniques for reducing these thoughts, generally by replacing them with erotic thoughts—perhaps focusing attention on a particular part of one's body and how it is responding with arousal, or perhaps having an erotic fantasy. Out go the bad thoughts, in come the good thoughts.

Couple Therapy

As we noted earlier, poor communication and relationship distress are important maintaining causes

---

Cognitive–behavioural therapy: A form of therapy that combines behaviour therapy and restructuring of negative thought patterns.

In Focus 19.1

A Case of Low Sexual Desire

Mr. and Mrs. Brown were in their early thirties, had middle-class backgrounds, and were university-educated; they had been married for four years when they entered therapy. The presenting complaint was this: Mr. Brown never initiated sexual contact and rarely appeared interested in sex. Sexual intercourse had occurred only once during the past seven months. He never experienced erectile difficulty. He professed love for his wife and denied interest in any other women.

Mrs. Brown expressed a similarly positive picture of her marriage during her separate interview. She loved her husband very much, was interested in and enjoyed sex, had no interests in other men, and could not identify any problems in their relationship other than her husband's lack of sexual interest. She felt his lack of sexual interest was the likely result of his strict religious background. Whenever she tried to act sexy, such as wearing erotic undergarments, Mr. Brown would laugh and discourage her. Currently, she said that she had just

shut down and didn't bother thinking of sex any more. She was worried about this because she wanted to become pregnant.

An assessment by a urologist revealed no medical factors that could explain Mr. Brown's low desire. The interview with him did, however, reveal some factors that might be contributors to his lack of sexual initiative and low arousal. Although Mr. Brown's religious upbringing did not affect his overall interest in sex, it did seem to dichotomize in his mind sex with "good girls" versus "bad girls." He had had some very arousing sexual experiences with a number of women before marriage. In his words, if the women were very "slutty" and sexually demanding, he became highly aroused. On the other hand, if a woman was "proper" and deserving of respect, he found it very difficult to become aroused. His wife was very attractive but very wholesome; this wholesome image seemed to contribute to a restrained approach to sex on his part.

Other possible factors emerged. Mrs. Brown

of sexual disorders. Accordingly, many sex therapists use couple therapy as part of the treatment. This approach rests on the assumption that there is a reciprocal relationship between interpersonal conflict and sex problems. Sex problems can cause conflicts, and conflicts can cause sex problems. In couple therapy, the relationship itself is treated, with the goal of reducing antagonisms and tensions between the partners. As the relationship improves, the sex problem should be reduced.

For certain disorders and certain couples, therapists may use a combination of cognitive –behavioural and couple therapy. For example, sex therapists Raymond Rosen, Sandra Leiblum, and Ilana Spector (1994) use a five-part model in treating men with erectile disorder.

1. *Sexual and performance anxiety reduction* Individuals with sexual disorders, particularly men with erectile disorder, often have a great deal of performance anxiety. This can be treated using such techniques as sensate focus exercises.

2. *Education and cognitive intervention* As noted earlier, people with sexual disorders often lack sexual information. Many also have unrealistic expectations about sexual functioning and satisfaction. For example, older men may not be aware of the natural effects of aging on male sexual response. Cognitive interventions may help men with erection problems to overcome "all or nothing" thinking—that is, the belief that if any aspect of his sexual performance is not perfect, the whole interaction is a disaster. An example is the belief "I failed sexually because my erection was not 100 percent rigid."

3. *Script assessment and modification* All couples have a sexual script that they enact together. People with sexual disorders typically have a

used to initiate sex, but during the past two years she had left the responsibility up to Mr. Brown. Furthermore, Mr. Brown never used sexual fantasies to enhance his arousal and did not expose himself to erotic materials. Finally, Mr. Brown said that he would approach his wife for sex only if he felt fully aroused. It did not occur to him that arousal would develop as a by-product of sexual activity.

All of these possible etiological (causal) factors were discussed with Mr. and Mrs. Brown. The Browns were encouraged to try sensate focus, with Mr. Brown taking the initiative. He was reminded that he did *not* have to be sexually aroused to start. He had a great deal of trouble initiating any kind of physical activity; in fact, after failing to initiate during home practice, he disclosed in therapy that he had *never* initiated contact with any female. By not initiating, he never took the chance of being rejected. He also had difficulty in expressing his emotions and found it unmanly to do so. These issues were discussed at length, with a focus on his cognitions, and he was encouraged to continue with his initiation of the sensate focus sessions.

Mrs. Brown was encouraged to be expressive of her sexual feelings in dress and in action, whereas Mr. Brown was encouraged to work on accepting her sexuality. Cognitive restructuring with Mr. Brown focused on his long-standing beliefs regarding women and sexual expression, especially as these related to Mrs. Brown's sexual behaviour.

Mr. Brown was also encouraged to practise bringing erotic thoughts into his life. He was given assignments to read erotic passages and to enjoy sexual material he viewed on TV rather than turning away from it.

Fifteen therapy sessions were held over 10 months, during which the couple experienced a very positive change in their sexual relationship. Mr. Brown became much more emotionally expressive and felt comfortable initiating sexual contacts. At the end of therapy, the couple was participating in sexual intercourse approximately once a week, and both partners were satisfied with this rate. Both took equal responsibility for initiating sex.

Source: Wincze & Carey, 2001.

restricted, repetitive, and inflexible script, using a small number of techniques that they never change. Novelty is one of the greatest turn-ons, so therapy is designed to help the couple break out of their restricted script.

4. *Conflict resolution and relationship enhancement* As we have discussed, conflicts in a couple's relationship can lead to sexual disorders. In therapy, these conflicts are identified and the couple can work to resolve them.

5. *Relapse prevention training* Sometimes a relapse—a return of the disorder—occurs following therapy. Therapists have developed techniques to help couples avoid or deal with such relapses. For example, they are told to engage in sensate focus sessions at least once a month.

Notice that part 1 represents the behaviour therapy techniques pioneered by Masters and Johnson;

parts 2 and 3 are cognitive therapy techniques; and part 4 is couple therapy. Most skilled sex therapists today use combined or integrated techniques such as these, tailored to the specific disorder and situation of the couple.

Specific Treatments for Specific Problems

Some very specific techniques have been developed for the treatment of certain sexual disorders. Of course, each of these techniques is typically only one part of a comprehensive treatment approach.

The Stop-Start Technique

The stop-start technique is used in the treatment of rapid ejaculation (see Figure 19.3). The man first learns to identify sensations prior to the point of ejaculatory inevitability (see Chapter 9). The partner manually stimulates the man to erection and then

Figure 19.3 The stop-start technique for treating rapid ejaculation and the position of the couple while using the stop-start technique.

stops the stimulation prior to this point. Gradually he loses his erection. The partner resumes stimulation, he gets another erection, the partner stops, and so on. After doing this three or four times, the man can allow himself to orgasm. The man learns that he can have an erection and be highly aroused without having an orgasm. Using this technique, the couple may extend their sex play to 15 or 20 minutes, and the man gains control over his orgasm. Another version of this method is the squeeze technique, in which the partner adds a squeeze around the coronal ridge, which also stops orgasm.

Masturbation

The most effective form of therapy for women with primary orgasmic disorder is a program of directed masturbation (LoPiccolo & Stock, 1986; Rosen & Leiblum, 1995). The data indicate that masturbation is the technique most likely to produce orgasm in women; it is therefore a logical treatment for women who have problems with having orgasms, many of whom have never masturbated. Women can use a vibrator to learn to bring themselves to orgasm. Masturbation is sometimes recommended as therapy for men as well (Zilbergeld, 1999).

Kegel Exercises

One technique that is used with women is the **Kegel exercises,** named for the physician who devised them (Kegel, 1952). They are designed to exercise and strengthen the *pubococcygeal muscle,* or PC muscle, which runs along the sides of the entrance of the vagina (refer to Figure 4.8 in Chapter 4). The exercises are particularly helpful for women who have had this muscle stretched in childbirth, who have poor muscle tone, or who have vaginismus. The woman is instructed first to find her PC muscle by sitting on a toilet with her legs spread apart, beginning to urinate, and stopping the flow of urine

Kegel (KAY-gul) exercises: A part of sex therapy for women with orgasmic disorder, in which the woman exercises the muscles surrounding the vagina; also called *pubococcygeal* or *PC muscle exercises.*

voluntarily. The muscle that stops the flow is the PC muscle. After that, the woman is told to contract the muscle 10 times during each of six sessions per day. Gradually she can work up to more.[2] The most important effect of these exercises is that they seem to increase women's sexual pleasure by increasing the sensitivity of the vaginal area (Messe & Geer, 1985). They also permit heterosexual women to stimulate her partner more because her vagina can grip his penis more tightly, and they are a cure for women who have problems with involuntarily urinating as they orgasm. Pelvic floor muscle exercises and physical therapy can also be used to treat dyspareunia (Bergeron et al., 2001; Binik et al., 2000, 2001). Kegel exercises are sometimes also used in treating men.

Bibliotherapy

Bibliotherapy refers simply to the use of a self-help book to treat a disorder. Research shows that bibliotherapy is effective for orgasmic disorders in women (van Lankveld, 1998). Julia Heiman and Joseph LoPiccolo's *Becoming Orgasmic: A Sexual Growth Program for Women* (1998) has been used extensively for this purpose. Bibliotherapy has also been shown to be effective for couples with a mixture of male and female sexual disorders (van Lankveld et al., 2001). In addition, many people describe Bernie Zilbergeld's self-help book, *The New Male Sexuality* (1999), as helpful. Other couples find sex therapy videotapes to be helpful. Interestingly, as early as 1973, Steven Neiger, a Canadian pioneer in sex therapy and sex education, developed a series of 12 audiotapes to help couples overcome sexual problems (Alexander, 1990). It may be that in the future the Internet and computer programs will replace bibliotherapy as self-help methods for treating sexual disorders (see In Focus 19.2 and In Focus 19.3 later in this chapter).

Biomedical Therapies

In the last decade, there has been increased recognition of the biological bases of some sexual disorders.

---

[2]Students should recognize the exciting possiblities for doing these exercises. For example, they are a good way to amuse yourself in the middle of a lecture, and no one will ever know you are doing them.

Consistent with this emphasis, many developments in medical and drug treatments and even surgical treatment have occurred.

Drug Treatments

Many promising advances have been made in the identification of drugs that cure sexual disorders or work well when used together with cognitive–behavioural therapy or other psychological forms of sex therapy (Rosen & Leiblum, 1995b; Rowland & Burnett, 2000). Some are drugs that have direct sexual effects, whereas others are psychotherapeutic drugs (such as antidepressants) that work by improving the person's mood.

Certainly the most widely publicized breakthrough among these treatments was the release in the United States, in 1998, of **Viagra** (sildenafil) for the treatment of erectile disorder. Viagra was approved for use in Canada by Health Canada in 1999. Earlier biomedical treatments such as intracavernosal injections were unsatisfactory for various reasons (these are discussed in the next section). Viagra is taken by mouth approximately one hour before anticipated sexual activity. It does not, by itself, produce an erection. Rather, when the man is stimulated sexually after taking Viagra, the drug facilitates the physiological processes that produce erection. Specifically, it relaxes the smooth muscles in the corpora cavernosa, allowing blood to flow in and create an erection. Averaged over 27 clinical trials, about 57 percent of men respond successfully to Viagra compared with 21 percent responding to the placebo (Fink et al., 2002, for the original clinical trial see Goldstein et al., 1998)! Men have generally been quite satisfied with Viagra. Side effects are not common; they included headache, flushing, and vision disturbances.

On balance, Viagra seems to be quite safe (Morales et al., 1998; Rosen & McKenna, 2002). It does not seem to cause priapism (an erection that just won't go away). Yet the very ease of its use may lead physicians to overprescribe it and men to demand it in inappropriate circumstances. Today it is easily available on the Internet. If the erection difficulties are due to relationship problems or individual issues, Viagra will provide at

---

Bibliotherapy: The use of a self-help book to treat a disorder.

Viagra: A drug used in the treatment of erectile disorder; sildenafil.

Figure 19.4   One of the new drugs for treating erectile disorder.

most a temporary solution. It is not helpful for sexual disorders other than erectile disorder. And there is no evidence that it enhances sexual performance in men who function sexually within the normal range. In addition, its recreational or high-performance use are causes for concern.

Viagra was such a success, financially and otherwise, that drug companies immediately sought successors—drugs that would be more convenient, or would work in cases that were not effectively treated with Viagra. One of these is Cialis, made famous by its advertising during the 2004 Superbowl. Cialis (tadalafil) is very much like Viagra in that it relaxes the smooth muscle surrounding the arteries to the penis, facilitating engorgement (Brock et al., 2002; Montorsi et al., 2004; Padma-Nathan et al., 2001). Viagra, however, lasts only a few hours. Cialis, in contrast, is effective for as long as 24 to 36 hours. Someone at the drug company apparently decided that planning to have sex, as one does with Viagra, is not a good idea. Drugs such as Cialis have been shown to have no negative effects on sperm production or sex hormone production (Hellstrom et al., 2003a).

Levitra (vardenafil) is another new drug that works much like Viagra but has a slightly different formulation and is somewhat more potent (Hatzichristou et al., 2004; Hellstrom et al., 2003b; Rosen & McKenna, 2002). A particularly important success story is that these drugs are effective in treating erectile dysfunction that results from complete surgical removal of the prostate (Brock et al., 2003).

Viagra, Cialis, and Levitra each act peripherally—that is, they act on sites in the penis. Another alternative is centrally acting drugs, meaning drugs that act on regions of the brain involved in arousal. One of these is Uprima (apomorphine SL[3]; Heaton, 2001). It acts in about 20 minutes and, like Viagra, does not produce a spontaneous erection. Rather, it has to be accompanied by sexual stimulation. Uprima acts by boosting levels of the neurotransmitter dopamine in the brain, particularly in the hypothalamus, and is effective in about 55 percent of cases (Heaton, 2001; Montorsi et al., 2003a, b).

And how about a Viagra for women? The drug company Pfizer, as well as many scientists, hoped that Viagra also would work for women—that is, it would cure their orgasm problems. The problem is that Viagra works by increasing vasocongestion, and insufficient vasocongestion is probably not what causes most women's orgasm difficulties. After many failed clinical trials, Pfizer announced in 2004 that it would give up on testing Viagra for women (Harris, 2004). For example, British Columbia researcher Rosemary Basson and her colleagues found that Viagra does not increase either arousal or orgasm in either premenopausal or postmenopausal women with sexual dysfunction (Basson & Brotto, 2003; Basson et al., 2002).

Women's sexual problems most commonly involve orgasm difficulties and low sexual desire, the latter being a problem particularly as women age and their ovaries decline in production of testosterone. The most promising lead at the moment is administration of testosterone or some other androgen (Baulieu et al., 2000). As of this writing, Procter &

---

[3]The SL means "sub-lingual" that is, you take it by putting it under your tongue and letting it dissolve, rather than by swallowing it. It gets to the brain more efficiently that way. Previously, apomorphine had been used to treat Parkinson's disease.

Gamble is in the midst of clinical trials of Intrinsa, a testosterone patch designed for postmenopausal women experiencing low sexual desire. However, initial results have not been sufficiently positive to receive approval to market the patch.

The other issue concerning women and Viagra involves the partners of men with Viagra-aided erections. Not all partners, some of whom had adjusted to a relationship without intercourse, welcome the man's new capacity, an issue that has been ignored in the medical "fix" approach (Potts et al., 2003; Rosen & McKenna, 2002). For example, for a couple with relationship problems, it may create additional problems if taking Viagra results in pressure to engage in unwanted sexual activity. Often it is important to combine couple therapy with drug therapy. Some women, of course, are absolutely delighted with the results (Montorsi & Althof, 2003).

Intravernosal Injection for Erectile Disorder

Intracavernosal injection (ICI) is a treatment for erectile disorders (Shabsigh et al., 2000). It involves injecting a drug (such as alprostadil, or Edex) into the corpora cavernosa of the penis. The drugs used are vasodilators—that is, they dilate the blood vessels in the penis so that much more blood can accumulate there, producing an erection. In one study of a sample of men treated with ICI, the erections lasted an average of 39 minutes (Levitt & Mulcahy, 1995).

Since the introduction of Viagra, ICI is now used mainly in cases in which the erection problem is organic and the man does not respond to Viagra or its successors (Shabsigh et al., 2000). It can also be used in conjunction with cognitive–behavioural therapy in cases that have combined organic and psychological causes. Like Viagra, ICI can have positive psychological effects because it restores the man's confidence in his ability to get erections. It also reduces his performance anxiety because he is able to engage in intercourse successfully. Some men experience pain from treatment and, according to research in British Columbia, about 50 percent of men who begin using ICI discontinue its use (Basson, 1998). There are also potential abuses. Men who have normal erections should not use ICI in an attempt to produce a "super erection." Alprostadil is now also available as a suppository to place inside the urethra or as a cream to rub on.

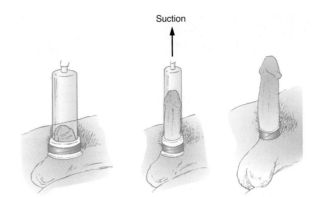

Suction

Figure 19.5 A treatment for erectile disorder. An external tube, with a rubberband around it, is placed over the lubricated penis. Suction applied to the tube produces erection, which is maintained by the constricting action of the rubberband once the plastic tube has been removed.

Vacuum Devices for Sexual Arousal Disorder

Vaccum devices are another treatment for sexual arousal disorders (Lewis & Witherington, 1997). Essentially, they pump you up! A tube is placed over the penis (see Figure 19.5). With some devices, the mouth can produce enough suction; with others, a small hand pump is used. Once a reasonably firm erection is present, the tube is removed and a rubber ring is placed around the base of the penis to maintain the penis's engorgement with blood. These devices have been used successfully with, for example, diabetic men. They can also be helpful in combination with cognitive–behavioural couple therapy for cases of erectile dysfunction that are mainly psychological in origin (Wylie et al., 2003).

There is also now a vacuum device to assist women with clitoral engorgement. However, there is little research supporting the effectiveness of this device; for most women the subjective aspects of arousal are at least equally important as is clitoral engorgement per se.

Surgical Therapy

For severe cases of erectile disorder, surgical therapy is possible. The surgery involves implanting a **prosthesis** into the penis (Hellstrom, 2003; Kabalin & Kuo, 1997). A sac or bladder of water is implanted

Penile prosthesis (prahs-THEE-sis): A surgical treatment for erectile dysfunction, in which inflatable tubes are inserted into the penis.

In Focus 19.2

How Can Computers Be Used in Sex Therapy?

Can we use the computer to help people who are too shy or too embarrassed to talk to a sex therapist about their sexual problems? There are two possibilities: sex therapy online by a live therapist, and sex therapy computer programs. Are these the wave of the future for sex therapy?

Proponents of sex therapy online argue that it is more affordable than traditional in-person therapy and that its anonymity is a major advantage. The advice columns at these sites can provide accurate, explicit, and nonjudgmental information. Interactions with a therapist online can break the wall of isolation surrounding a person with a sexual disorder. Specialized message boards and chat rooms for people who share a common interest (e.g., bisexuals, persons with disabilities) can help to create a sense of community and provide useful information, especially for those who are geographically isolated or in countries where sex therapy is unknown.

There are disadvantages, too. Currently there is no system for licensing online sex therapists, so unqualified and perhaps unethical persons could easily present themselves as therapists. In fact, it is difficult to find legitimate sex therapy Web sites because searching for terms such as "sex therapy" leads to a deluge of porn sites. Moreover, online sex therapists probably will not be able to give true intensive therapy of the kind one would get in multiple in-person sessions with a therapist. However, online therapists can provide permission and positive encouragement as well as accurate information, and that's enough to solve many people's problems.

Do people with sexual problems need a human therapist at all? In line with the emphasis on self-help in sex therapy, psychologist Yitzchak Binik and his colleagues at McGill University developed Sexpert, a computer program that interviews, assesses, counsels, and provides therapy to couples with sexual disorders. Sexpert was designed to interact with couples by asking them structured questions in much the same way a therapist would. The couple responds to the questions via the keyboard. After assessing the couple's sexual functioning, the program provides appropriate feedback to the couple and, if necessary, instructions on how to deal with the problem. Instructions are based on a cognitive–behavioural approach to sex therapy.

How effective is Sexpert? The researchers carried out four studies to evaluate its effectiveness compared to books, videotapes, and live therapists. They found that Sexpert was rated just as good or better than the other sources of self-help. Participants described Sexpert as intelligent, humanlike, and engaging. However, couples liked the therapist more than they liked Sexpert. Did Sexpert help couples solve their sexual problems? According to the diaries kept by participants, there was no change in their sexual behaviour after interacting with Sexpert. (Bibliotherapy also did not result in changes in behaviour.) However, when asked whether Sexpert had been helpful, participants retrospectively reported that their interactions with Sexpert had resulted in significant behaviour change and improved communication, relationship satisfaction, and sex knowledge. Again, live therapists did better than Sexpert.

These studies show that people are willing to use and enjoy interacting with a sex therapy computer program. For some people, the increased privacy and lack of stigma associated with interacting with a computer on sexual issues may make them more likely to seek out this type of help than help from a therapist. As a first-generation sex therapy program Sexpert shows some promise, but we're not ready to get rid of sex therapists yet.

Sources: Binik, Cantor, Oches, & Meana, 1997; Britten, 2004; Oches & Binik, 1998; Presentations by Patti Britton, Al Cooper, Sandor Gardos, and others at the 1998 meeting at the Society for the Scientific Study of Sexuality.

in the lower abdomen, connected to two inflatable tubes running the length of the corpus spongiosum, with a pump in the scrotum. Thus the man can literally pump up or inflate his penis so that he has a full erection.

The surgery takes approximately one and a half hours and requires only one incision, where the penis and scrotum meet. The cost of the procedure is usually covered by medicare.

It should be emphasized that this is a radical treatment that should be reserved only for those cases that have not been successfully treated by sex therapy or drug therapy. Typically it should be a case of erectile disorder that is the result of organic factors such as diabetes. The patient must understand that the surgery itself destroys some portions of the penis, so that a natural erection will never again be possible. Research shows that about one-fourth of men who have had this treatment are dissatisfied afterward. Reasons for dissatisfaction include the penis being smaller when erect than it was presurgery, different sensations during arousal, and different sensations during ejaculation (Steege et al., 1986). Although the treatment is radical and should be used conservatively, it is a godsend for some men who have been incapable of erection because of organic difficulties. Indeed, more than a dozen children have been born as a result of this surgery, to women whose partners were previously incapable of intercourse.

In another version of a surgical approach, a semi-rigid, siliconelike rod is implanted into the penis (Melman & Tiefer, 1992; Shandera & Thompson, 1994). This noninflatable device is less costly than the inflatable version and has a lower rate of complications (Rosen & Leiblum, 1995b).

There is also promising evidence that surgery can help women with some types of dyspareunia (Bergeron et al., 2001).

■ Critiques of Sex Therapy

One of the most basic questions we must ask about sex therapy is: Is it effective?

Psychologists Bernie Zilbergeld and Michael Evans (1980) did an extensive critique of the research methods used by Masters and Johnson in evaluating the success of their sex therapy. Zilbergeld and Evans concluded that there are a number of sub-

stantial problems. In brief, the criticisms suggest that we really do not know what the success rate of Masters and Johnson's therapy is, and it is almost surely lower than the 80 percent they claimed. A discussion of the specific criticisms follows. These points are important to bear in mind when evaluating any program of sex therapy.

First, Masters and Johnson never actually reported a *success* rate for the therapy. Instead, they reported a *failure* rate of about 20 percent. The other 80 percent apparently included a mixture of clear successes and cases that were ambiguous as to whether they were successes or failures—in short, they had 80 percent non-failures, but that does not mean 80 percent successes.

Furthermore, Masters and Johnson never defined what they meant by a "success" in therapy. This is an important issue. How improved does a person have to be to be counted as a success? Suppose a woman seeks help for anorgasmia; she has never had an orgasm. By the end of therapy, she is able to orgasm from a vibrator, but not from hand stimulation or mouth stimulation by her partner, nor by penetration. Is this case a success? How would Masters and Johnson have classified her?

Zilbergeld and Evans initiated their critical appraisal after finding that they and other sex therapists were unable to obtain success rates as dramatic as the ones Masters and Johnson reported. Other sex therapists were also not able to get Masters and Johnson's reported low relapse rate of 7 percent after five years. The obvious possibility is that other sex therapists have been using definitions of therapy success that are much stricter and more precise than the definition used by Masters and Johnson.

One recent critique pointed out that a major shortcoming of the field of sex therapy is the lack of carefully controlled studies that (1) investigate the success of various therapies compared with other therapies and with untreated controls; and (2) examine what aspect of a particular therapy or combination of therapies seems to have the beneficial effect (Rosen & Leiblum, 1995b).

Nonetheless, there is sufficient evidence evaluating certain treatments for certain disorders to reach the following conclusions (Heiman, 2002; Heiman & Meston, 1997):

■ Primary orgasmic dysfunction is successfully treated with directed masturbation, and the

In Focus 19.3

Do We Need a New View of Women's Sexual Problems?

The Working Group on a New View of Women's Sexual Problems has criticized the current way of classifying women's sexual problems as being too medical and mechanical. They argue that even if the diagnostic categories fit for men, they do not correspond to women's experience. They have proposed a new classification scheme to replace it. It is not based on the Masters and Johnson sexual response cycle, as the current classifications scheme is. Rather, it defines a sexual problem as dissatisfaction with any emotional, physical or relational aspect of sexual experience, and takes social, cultural, and relationship factors into account. They propose the following way of classifying women's sexual problems:

I.   **Sexual problems due to sociocultural, political, or economic factors:**

   A.   Ignorance and anxiety due to inadequate sex education, lack of access to health services, or other social constraints.
   B.   Sexual avoidance or distress due to perceived inability to meet cultural norms regarding correct or ideal sexuality.
   C.   Inhibition due to conflict between the sexual norms of one's subculture or culture of origin and those of the dominant culture.
   D.   Lack of interest, fatigue, or lack of time due to family and work obligations.

II.   **Sexual problems relating to partner and relationship:**

   A.   Inhibition, avoidance, or distress arising from betrayal, dislike, or fear of partner, partner's abuse or couple's unequal power, or arising from partner's negative patterns of communication.
   B.   Discrepancies in desire for sexual activity or in preferences for various sexual activities.
   C.   Ignorance or inhibition about communicating preferences or initiating, pacing, or shaping sexual activities.
   D.   Loss of sexual interest and reciprocity as a result of conflicts over commonplace issues such as money, schedules, or relatives, or resulting from traumatic experiences, e.g., infertility or the death of a child.
   E.   Inhibitions in arousal or spontaneity due to partner's health status or sexual problems.

III.   **Sexual problems due to psychological factors:**

   A.   Sexual aversion, mistrust, or inhibition of sexual pleasure due to [experience of abuse, problems with attachment depression or anxiety].
   B.   Sexual inhibition due to fear of sexual activities or of their possible consequences, e.g., pain during intercourse, pregnancy, sexually transmitted infections, loss of partner, loss of reputation.

IV.   **Sexual problems due to medical factors:**

   A.   Pain or lack of response during sexual activity despite a supportive and safe interpersonal situation, adequate sexual knowledge and positive sexual attitudes. Such problems can arise from medical conditions, pregnancy, STIs, and medication.

The Working Group on a New View of Women's Sexual Problems developed this framework to assist researchers, educators, and clinicians. They also hope that it will help the public better understand women's sexual problems. However, the proposed classification is too new for us to know whether it will change the thinking of any of these groups. Still, it challenges assumptions about the nature and causes of sexual problems. Perhaps we need a new view of men's sexual problems as well.

Source: Kaschak & Tiefer, 2001.

treatment can be enhanced with sensate focus exercises.

- Treatments for secondary orgasmic dysfunction are somewhat less successful. Therapy that combines some or all of the following components seems to be most effective: sex education, sexual skills training, communication skills training, and body image therapy. The problem here, most likely, is that there are many different patterns of secondary anorgasmia, with a need to match treatment to the pattern of the disorder, something that research has not been able to untangle.
- Vaginismus is successfully treated with progressive vaginal dilators; relaxation and Kegel exercises may also be helpful, but the evidence is not as strong.
- The squeeze technique is effective for treating premature ejaculation. Drugs, specifically some antidepressants (serotonin reuptake inhibitors), may be effective but there is less data for this.
- For some disorders—sexual desire disorders, dyspareunia, and delayed orgasm in men—research is insufficient to conclude that there is an effective treatment.

Another critique points out the *medicalization* of sexual disorders (Kleinplatz, 2003; Tiefer, 1994, 2000). Research has increasingly identified organic sources of male erectile disorder, and with these advances have come attempts to identify drugs and surgeries, rather than psychotherapies, to treat problems. In part, political issues are involved, as physicians try to seize the treatment of sexual disorders from psychologists. But there is also a cost to the patient, as the disorder may be given a quick fix with drugs while the patient's anxieties and relationship problems are ignored. That is, we treat the symptoms, not the problem (Kleinplatz, 2003). For biomedical treatments to be successful over the long term, the cognitive, affective, and interpersonal issues must also be addressed (Basson, 1998).

There also has been a move toward the medicalization of women's sexual problems, both in terms of understanding their causes and in terms of seeking drug treatments (Tiefer, 2001). The Working Group on a New View of Women's Sexual Problems (2001), a group of 12 clinicians and social scientists, has criticized the categories used to classify women's sexual problems—sexual desire disorders, arousal disorders, orgasmic disorders, and sexual pain disorders—as being too medical and mechanical, focusing too much on genital response, and thus not fitting with women's experiences. They argue that any classification scheme for women's sexual problems needs to take sociocultural and relationship factors into account. The new classification scheme that they propose is summarized in In Focus 19.3.

In contrast to these scientific criticisms, sex therapy has also been criticized on philosophical grounds. Ottawa psycholoist and sex therapist Peggy Kleinplatz (1992, 1998) has argued that the current approach to sex therapy is goal-oriented rather than pleasure-oriented. By defining problems in terms of sexual disorders, sex therapists and their clients may focus on physiological and mechanical outcomes (getting an erection, having an orgasm) rather than on clients' subjective experience of sexuality, sexual satisfaction, and eroticism (Kleinplatz, 2003). Sexual satisfaction is not just the absence of a sexual disorder (Byers, 1999). Often individuals get aroused and have orgasms but experience disappointment with the quality of their sexual encounters with their partner. Evaluation of the success of sex therapy should include more attention to whether therapy has resulted in enhanced sexual satisfaction (Handy et al., 1985). Resolving a sexual disorder often results in a decrease in sexual *dissatisfaction*, but it does not necessarily result in increased sexual satisfaction.

Psychiatrist Thomas Szasz (1980) argued that sex therapists have essentially produced a lot of illness by creating the (somewhat arbitrary) diagnostic categories of sexual disorder. This criticism may especially apply to individuals with disabilities. Ontario researcher Gina Di Giulio (2003) has argued that the diagnostic categories for sexual dysfunction do not fit for such persons. In particular, the focus on genital response may imply that persons with disabilities cannot experience a highly pleasurable and satisfying sex life. Yet, a woman with a spinal cord injury who has little genital sensation might get great pleasure from having her breasts or other parts of her body stroked, and reach orgasm from this type of pleasuring. That is, she has adapted her lovemaking to meet her own needs and situation. It is important for sex therapists to communicate to their clients with disabilities that they are fully sexual, and that there is no right way to make love.

In summary, a number of criticisms have been raised about the field of sex therapy. The research methods used by Masters and Johnson to evaluate the success of their therapy had a number of problems and, as a result, their implied success rate of 80 percent is probably unrealistically high. Despite three decades of rapid advances in both psychological and medical treatments of sexual disorders, adequate research has not yet been done on the effectiveness of many of these treatments. There is a trend to medicalize sexual disorders, particularly erectile disorder, which may lead to the neglect of patients' needs for psychological treatment. There has also been a tendency to focus on physiological outcomes such as orgasm and erection rather than on the individual's subjective experience of sexuality and sexual satisfaction. Finally, Szasz questions the whole notion of sexual disorders as such.

Where do these criticisms leave us? In our opinion, they do not invalidate the work of sex therapists. Rather, they urge us to be cautious. Most sexual disorders will not have success rates of 80 percent (but then, most therapies for other disorders don't either) but they may well turn out to have success rates of 60 percent or more, which is still pretty good. Many other clients may feel that their sexual functioning has been enhanced by sex therapy (Kaplan, 1979). A single method of therapy, such as Masters and Johnson's behaviour therapy, will not be effective with every disorder. Finally, we must be sensitive to the values expressed in labelling something as being, or someone as having, a "disorder."

■ Sex Therapy in the AIDS Era

The threat of AIDS—not to mention herpes and genital warts (HPV)—puts modern sex therapy into a new cultural context (Leiblum & Rosen, 1989). Here are a few examples of some of these factors that are changing sex therapy.

Some people who in the past may have given up on a partner and looked for a new one because sex had lost some of its excitement may now be more willing to work to maintain a long-term, monogamous relationship. Sex therapists are seeing more couples who want help in rejuvenating their sex lives.

Communication skills training (see Chapter 10), which is a standard part of sex therapy, has become increasingly important. Being able to communicate directly, openly, and effectively with a partner about condom use can literally be a matter of life or death today. The demand for communication skills training will surely increase as the AIDS epidemic continues.

Sex therapists work with people on how to have pleasurable sex using condoms. Therapists have documented case histories of men who have such negative feelings about using a condom that they literally lose their erection if they try to put one on (Leiblum & Rosen, 1989). As condoms become an increasing necessity, this might even become a sexual disorder—condom-induced erectile disorder! Sex therapists can work with such people to diminish uncomfortable feelings and substitute comfortable—perhaps even erotic—feelings about condoms.

■ Some Practical Advice

Avoiding Sexual Disorders

People can use some of the principles that emerge from sex therapists' work to avoid having sexual disorders in the first place. As the saying goes, an ounce of prevention is worth a pound of cure. The following are some principles of good sexual mental health:

1. *Communicate with your partner* Don't expect him or her to be a mind reader concerning what is pleasurable to you. One way to do this is to make it a habit to talk to your partner while you are having sex; verbal communication then does not come as a shock. Some people, though, feel uncomfortable talking at such times; nonverbal communication, such as placing your hand on top of your partner's and moving it where you want it, works well too (see Chapter 10 for more detail).
2. *Concentrate on giving and receiving sexual pleasure* Don't be a spectator, feeling as if you are putting on a sexual performance that you constantly need to evaluate. Concentrate as much as possible on the giving and receiving of sensual pleasures, not on how well you are doing.
3. *Relax and enjoy yourself* Don't set up goals for sexual performance. If you have a goal, you can fail, and failure can produce disorders. Don't set your heart on having simultaneous orgasms or, if you are a woman, on having five orgasms before your partner has one. Just relax and enjoy yourself.

4. *Be choosy about the situations in which you have sex* Don't have sex when you are in a terrific hurry or are afraid you will be disturbed. Also be choosy about who your partner is. Trusting your partner is essential to good sexual functioning; similarly, a partner who really cares for you will be understanding if things don't go well and will not laugh or be sarcastic.

5. *Accept that disappointments will occur* They do in any sexual relationship. What is important is how you interpret them. It is important that you don't see yourself as a failure and don't let them ruin the relationship. Instead, try to think, "How can we make this turn out well anyhow?"

Choosing a Sex Therapist

No provinces have licensing or certification requirements to practise sex therapy. Therefore, particularly with the popularization of Masters and Johnson's work, some quacks with no formal training in therapy or in sex therapy have hung out shingles saying "Sex Therapist."

How do you go about finding a good, qualified sex therapist? Although there are no statutory certification procedures in any province, some Ontario sex therapists choose to become certified by the Board of Examiners in Sexual Therapy and Counselling; some Québec sex therapists by L'Association des Sexalogues du Quebec. The other provinces do not have such boards. A very few Canadian sex therapists choose to get certified by a U.S. organization. However, most sex therapists in Canada operate under their discipline licences— such as psychology or psychiatry—and therefore do not seek additional certification as a sex therapist even if they have training in sex therapy. Your local medical or psychological association can provide a list of psychiatrists or psychologists and may be able to tell you which ones have special training in sex therapy. In any case, it is important to ask potential sex therapists about their specific training in sex therapy as well as about their approach to sex therapy to make sure that they are qualified to provide sex therapy. Choose a therapist or clinic that offers an *integrated approach* that recognizes the potential biological, cognitive–behavioural, and relationship influences on any sexual disorder and is prepared to address all of these and work in conjunction with professionals from other disciplines if needed.

■ ■ ■ SUMMARY

Sexual disorders fall into four categories: desire disorders (hypoactive sexual desire, discrepancy of sexual desire, sexual aversion disorder), arousal disorders (female sexual arousal disorder, erectile disorder), orgasmic disorders (rapid ejaculation, male orgasmic disorder, female orgasmic disorder), and sexual pain disorders (dyspareunia, vaginismus).

Sexual disorders may be caused by physical factors, individual psychological factors, and interpersonal factors. Organic causes include some illnesses, infections, and damage to the spinal cord. Certain drugs may also create problems with sexual functioning. Psychological causes are categorized into predisposing factors and maintaining causes including myths and misinformation, negative attitudes, anxiety, cognitive interference, psychological distress, and behavioural or lifestyle factors. Interpersonal factors include poor sexual communication and relationship distress caused by, for example, conflict in the couple's relationship or lack of intimacy.

Therapies for sexual disorders include behaviour therapy (pioneered by Masters and Johnson) based on learning theory, cognitive–behavioural therapy, couple therapy, specific treatments for specific problems (e.g., stop-start for premature ejaculation), and a variety of biomedical treatments, which include drug treatments (e.g., Viagra) and surgery.

A number of criticisms of sex therapy have been raised, including concerns about the research methods used to evaluate the success of Masters and Johnson's therapy, the lack of evaluation research on recently developed therapies, the medicalization of sexual disorders, focusing on physiological outcomes rather than on sexual pleasure and satisfaction, and the entire enterprise of identifying and labelling sexual disorders.

■ ■ ■ QUESTIONS FOR THOUGHT, DISCUSSION, AND DEBATE

1. When (or if) you engage in sexual activity with a partner, do you feel that you are under pressure to perform and that you engage in spectatoring? If so, what might you do to change this pattern?

2. Considering the predisposing causes of sexual disorders, what are the implications for parents who want to raise sexually healthy children? Could parents do certain things that would avoid or prevent sexual disorders in their children?

3. Your best friend, Steve, who is 22, discloses to you a long history of rapid ejaculation, which has been very embarrassing and frustrating for him. He has heard about Viagra and, knowing that you are taking a human sexuality course, comes to you for advice about whether he should go to a doctor to get a prescription for it. What advice would you give him?

4. Hypoactive sexual desire is a common sexual disorder in Canada today. Given what you know about this disorder and its causes, do you think it is also common in other cultures? Think about Britain, China, India, and Mexico as examples. (For further information, see Bhurga & de Silva, 1993.)

■ ■ ■ SUGGESTIONS FOR FURTHER READING

Barbach, Lonnie G. (1975). *For yourself: The fulfillment of female sexuality.* Garden City, NY: Doubleday. Provides good information for women with orgasmic disorders, based on the author's experiences as a sex therapist. Still the classic in the field.

Barbach, Lonnie G. (1983). *For each other: Sharing sexual intimacy.* Garden City, NY: Anchor Books. Barbach's sequel to *For Yourself* (see above); this volume is designed for couples.

Heiman, Julia R., & LoPiccolo, Joseph. (1988). *Becoming orgasmic: A sexual and personal growth program for women* (Revised and expanded edition). New York: Simon & Schuster.

McCarthy, Barry, & McCarthy, Emily. (2002). *Sexual awareness: Couple sexual therapy for the twenty-first century.* New York: Carroll and Graf.

Tiefer, Leonore. (2004). *Sex is not a natural act, and other essays.* 2nd ed. Boulder, CO: Westview. Tiefer is a brilliant and entertaining writer, and her criticisms of sex therapy are insightful.

Zilbergeld, Bernie. (1999). *The new male sexuality* (Revised edition). New York: Bantam.

Zoldbrod, Aline P. (1998). *Sex smart: How your childhood shaped your sexual life and what to do about it.* Oakland, CA: New Harbinger. Zoldbrod, a sex therapist, provides a detailed guide to uncovering the sources of sex problems in early childhood learning.

Online **LearningCentre**

For Review Questions, Web Resources, and other learning and study tools, visit the *Understanding Human Sexuality* Online Learning Centre at www.mcgrawhill.ca/college/hyde.

CHAPTER 20

Ethics, Religion, and Sexuality

CHAPTER HIGHLIGHTS

> A viable sexual theology for our time will affirm that sexuality is always much more than genital expression. Sexuality expresses the mystery of our creation as those who need to reach out for the physical and spiritual embrace of others. It expresses God's intention that we find our authentic humanness not in isolation but in relationship.*

A high school student is in love with her boyfriend and wonders whether they ought to begin sleeping together. A business owner hears rumours that some of his customers are taking their business elsewhere because the clerk is gay. A minister is asked to counsel a husband and wife, one of whom is involved in an affair. The leader of a political party is confronted by party members who want the party to adopt a policy supporting recriminalizing abortion. All these people are facing the need to make decisions that involve sexuality, and they find that issues of values make the decisions difficult. The two principal conceptual frameworks for dealing with questions of values are religion and ethics, which are therefore the topics of this chapter.

Two concerns give force to our consideration of the religious and ethical aspects of human sexuality. First, there is the scientific concern to explain sexual phenomena. Because religion and ethics are important influences on people's behaviours, especially in matters of sex, one cannot fully appreciate why people do what they do without looking at these influences. Second, there is also a personal side to this coin. We are all ethical decision makers; we all have a personal system of values. Each of us must make decisions with respect to our own sexuality. Therefore, we would do well to consider how such decisions are made.

Ethics refers to a system of moral principles, a way of deciding what is right and wrong. We use ethics when there is a conflict between things we prize or desire highly. Sexual pleasure may be an important value for one person but something to be avoided for another. However, regardless of the importance we attach to sex, we need a way of integrating our sexuality into our patterns of decision making. To do this we use such categories as "right

or wrong," "good or bad," "appropriate or inappropriate," and "moral or immoral." These are the kinds of distinctions made in the field of ethics; since we use them every day, we are all practical ethicists. As you read this chapter, think about how the attitudes and values you were taught growing up as well as those you have now fit with the various frameworks.

Religion enters the picture as a source of values, attitudes, and ethics. For believers, religion sets forth an ethical code and provides sanctions (rewards and punishments) that motivate them to obey the rules. When a particular religion is practised by many people in a society, it helps create culture, which then influences even those who do not accept the religion. Therefore, it is important to study the relationship of religion to sexuality for two reasons. First, it is a powerful influence on the sexual attitudes of many individuals. And second, as a creator of culture, it often forms a whole society's orientation toward human sexuality.

Let us begin by defining some terms that will be useful in discussing ethics, religion, and sexuality. **Hedonism** and **asceticism** have to do with one's approach to the physical and material aspects of life in general and to sexuality in particular. The word "hedonism" comes from the Greek word meaning "pleasure" and refers to the belief that the ultimate goal of human life is the pursuit of pleasure, the avoidance of pain, and the fulfilment of physical needs and desires: "Eat, drink, and be merry, for tomorrow we die." Asceticism, in contrast, holds that there is more to life than its mate-

*James B. Nelson (1992), *Body theology*, Louisville, KY: Westminster/John Knox Press.

Ethics: A system of moral principles; a way of determining right and wrong.
Hedonism: A moral system based on maximizing pleasure and avoiding pain.
Asceticism: An approach to life that emphasizes discipline and impulse control.

rial aspects, which must be transcended to achieve true humanity. Ascetics are likely to view sexuality as neutral at best and evil at worst; they prize self-discipline, the avoidance of physical gratification, and the cultivation of spiritual values. Orders of monks and nuns, found in Eastern religions as well as in Christianity, are good examples of institutionalized asceticism, with their affirmation of celibacy, virginity, and poverty.

Two other terms, **legalism** and **situationism,** refer to methods of ethical decision making. As an approach to ethics, legalism is concerned with following a moral law, or set of principles, which comes from a source outside the individual, such as religion. Legalistic ethics are focused on the rightness or wrongness of specific acts and set forth a series of rules—"Do this" and "Don't do that"—that persons are to follow. The term "situationism" has been used since it was coined by Joseph Fletcher in his 1966 book *Situation Ethics.* Also called contextual ethics, this approach suggests that although there may be broad general guidelines for ethical behaviour, each ethical decision should be made according to the individuals and situations involved. Situationism is based in human experience and, in matters of sexual morality, tends to focus on relationships rather than rules. Whereas legalism deals in universal laws, situationism decides matters on a case-by-case basis, informed by certain guiding principles, such as love. Traditional religious ethical systems (which we might call the Old Morality) have tended to be quite legalistic, and many continue to be so today (e.g., Orthodox Judaism, Roman Catholicism, and fundamentalist Protestantism). However, with the advent of the modern scientific world view, the situationist approach (the New Morality) has attracted many adherents (Nelson, 1978). Of course, few ethical systems are purely hedonistic or ascetic or entirely legalistic or situationist; most lie between these extremes.

■ Sexuality in Great Ethical Traditions

With these ways of looking at sexual ethics as background, let us examine certain great ethical traditions to see how they deal with norms for sexual behaviour. Although some attention will be

Table 20.1	Number and Percentage of Canadian Population Affiliated with Each of the Major Religions	
Catholic	12,936,905	44%
Protestant	8,654,805	29
Christian Orthodox	479,620	2
Other Christian	780,450	3
Muslim	579,640	2
Jewish	329,995	1
Buddhist	300,345	1
Hindu	297,200	1
Sikh	278,410	1
No religious affiliation	4,900,090	17

Source: Statistics Canada, Census of the Population, 2001.

given to non-Western sexual ethics, the focus of this section will be on ethical traditions of Western culture, primarily because this is a text for Canadian undergraduates, and Western culture is the majority culture in Canada. We are understandably interested in the world of ideals and practice in which *we* live. This culture can, at the risk of oversimplification, be seen as originating in the confrontation of Greek culture, preserved and developed by the Romans, and Jewish tradition, extended by Christianity. From that point on until rather recently, Western culture was Christian, at least officially. Even self-conscious revolts against Christian culture in the West are part of that tradition because of their roots.

It should be noted, though, that increasingly Canada is becoming a pluralistic society. Table 20.1 shows the percentages of the Canadian population who are affiliated with the major world religions according to the 2001 Census. Although the majority of Canadians still report a Christian (78 percent) or Jewish (1 percent) affiliation, substantial numbers of Canadians indicated that they

Legalism: Ethics based on the assumption that there are rules for human conduct and that morality consists of knowing the rules and obeying them.
Situationism: Ethics based on the assumption that there are no absolute rules, or at least very few, and that each situation must be judged individually.

were Muslim, Buddhist, Hindu, or Sikh. In addition, 17 percent of Canadians report no religious affiliation.

Classical Greek Philosophy

During the Golden Age of Greek culture, covering roughly the fifth and fourth centuries B.C.E.,[1] brilliant philosophers such as Socrates, Plato, and Aristotle pondered most of the great ethical questions. They regarded the beautiful and the good as the chief goal of life, and they admired the figure of the warrior-intellectual, who embodied the virtues of wisdom, courage, temperance, justice, and piety.

While nothing in Greek culture rejected sex as evil—the gods and goddesses of Greek mythology are often pictured enjoying it—the great philosophers did develop a kind of asceticism that assumed an important place in Western thought. They thought that virtue resulted from wisdom, and they believed that people would do right if they could, failing to live morally only through ignorance. To achieve wisdom and cultivate virtue, violent passions must be avoided, and these might well include sex. Plato believed that love led toward immortality and was therefore a good thing. However, since this kind of love was rather intellectual and more like friendship than vigorous sexuality, the term "platonic love" has come to mean sexless affection. There was also, especially among the warrior class, approval of **pederasty** (a sexual relationship between an older man and a younger one). The older man was to serve as the younger one's teacher and model of courage and virtue. An army of male couples was thought to be especially fierce because of the desire of each to protect his beloved (Crompton, 2003).

Later, Greek philosophy became even more ascetic than in the Golden Age. Epicurus (341–270 B.C.E.) taught that the goal of life was *ataraxia,* a tranquil state between pleasure and pain in which the mind is unaffected by emotion. He, like other Stoics of the same period, valued detachment from worldly anxieties and pleasures and, indeed, a total indifference to either life or death. Sex was seen not necessarily as evil but as less important than

[1]Before the Common Era; today it is preferred over the Christian-centred Before Christ (B.C.).

Pederasty: Sex between an older man and a younger man, or a boy; sometimes called "boy love."

Figure 20 .1   The ancient Greeks not only approved of, but idealized, pederasty.

wisdom and virtue, something to be transcended to achieve the beautiful and good.

Judaism

The basic source of the Judeo-Christian tradition, which is the religious foundation of Western culture, is the Hebrew scriptures or the Old Testament of the Bible, the basis for Judaism and a major source for Christianity as well. Written between approximately 800 and 200 B.C.E., the Old Testament has a great deal to say about the place of sexuality in human life and society, always seen in religious terms.

The view of sexuality in the Hebrew scriptures is fundamentally positive. In the Genesis myth of creation we read, "So God created man in his own image, in the image of God he created him; male and female he created them" (Genesis 1:27). Human sexual differentiation is not an afterthought or an aberration; it is part and parcel of creation, which God calls "good." Judaism sees sexuality as a gift to be used responsibly and in obedience to God's will, never as something evil in itself. The command to marry and to procreate within marriage is clear (Farley, 1994). Looking at the Hebrew scriptures as a whole, we can find three themes in this view of sexuality.

First, sex is seen not as just another biological function but as a deep and intimate part of a *relationship* between two people. The very ancient story of Adam and Eve states that "a man leaves his father and cleaves to his wife and the two become one flesh" (Genesis 2:24). Frequently, biblical Hebrew uses the verb "to know" to mean sexual intercourse (as in "Adam knew Eve and she conceived a child"). It also uses the word "knowledge," with this suggestion of deep intimacy, to describe the relationship between God and his people.[2] The use of sexual imagery in describing both marital and divine–human relationships testifies to the positive view of the Hebrew scriptures toward sex.

Second, in the Hebrew scriptures, sexuality could never be separated from its *social consequences*. Historically, Israel began as a small group of nomadic tribes fighting to stay alive in the near-desert of the Arabian peninsula. Sheer survival demanded that there be plenty of children, especially boys, so that there would be enough herdsmen and warriors.[3] Thus, non-procreative sex could not be allowed. Further, since the tribes were small and close-knit, sex had to be regulated to prevent jealousy over sexual partners, which could have divided and destroyed the group. It is not surprising, then, that so much of the Hebrew scriptures is concerned with laws regarding people living together in society and that these laws often include the regulation of sexual practices.

Finally, the Hebrew scriptures see sexual behaviour as an aspect of *national and religious loyalty*. When the Israelites settled in what is now the state of Israel, about 1200 to 1000 B.C.E., they came into contact with the original inhabitants, whom they called Canaanites. Like many agricultural peoples of the time, the Canaanites sought to encourage the growth of their crops through their religion. In this **fertility cult**, Baal, the Sky Father, was encouraged to mate with Asherah (Astarte or Ishtar), the Earth Mother, so that crops would grow. This mating was encouraged by ritual sex, and temple prostitutes (male and female) were very much a part of Canaanite religion. Hebrew religious leaders saw in the fertility cult a threat to their religion, and many sexual practices are forbidden in the Hebrew scriptures because they were found among the Canaanites and might lead to infidelity to Israel's God.

The many sexual regulations of the Hebrew scriptures should be seen both in the context of the times and against this historical background. From Israel's struggle for survival during the nomadic period came institutions such as polygamy (many wives) and concubinage (slaves kept for childbearing purposes) designed to produce children in the case of a childless marriage (Farley, 1994), and also laws against unmarried women having children and non-procreative sex. From the confrontation with the fertility cult, Israel derived prohibitions against nakedness, cultic prostitution, and other such typically Canaanite practices. Both themes are present in this passage from Leviticus 20:10–19:

> If a man commits adultery with his neighbour's wife, both adulterer and adulteress shall be put to death. The man who has intercourse with his father's wife has brought shame on his father. They shall both be put to death; their blood shall be on their own heads . . . . A man who has intercourse with any beast shall be put to death, and you shall kill the beast. . . . If a man takes his sister, his father's daughter or his mother's daughter, and they see one another naked, it is a scandalous disgrace. They shall be cut off in the presence of their people. . . . If a man lies with a woman during her monthly period and brings shame upon her, he has exposed her discharge and she has uncovered the source of her discharge; they shall both be cut off from their people.

Adultery and incest are threats to the harmony of the group. Not only is bestiality "unnatural," but it is also non-procreative and may have been a feature of Canaanite religion. The menstrual taboo is typical of many societies (see Chapter 6).

It should be noted that all societies have had laws regulating sex (Chapter 1) and that these laws,

---

[2]See, for example, Hosea, the Song of Solomon, and, in the New Testament, Revelation.

[3]Note that the heart of God's promise to the patriarch Abraham was descendants as numberless as the grains of sand or the stars in the sky (Genesis 13:14–17, among many places).

Fertility cult: A form of nature-religion in which the fertility of the soil is encouraged through various forms of ritual magic, often including ritual sexual intercourse.

however exotic they may seem to us, made sense in their historical context and were, for the most part, remarkably humane for the time. The Hebrew scriptures are characterized by a great regard for married love, affection, and sexuality; this is in marked contrast to, for example, the Greek view of marriage as an institution for breeding and housekeeping. The Judaism of the time was highly legalistic but not particularly ascetic in its high regard for responsible sexuality as a good and integral part of human life.

Christianity

As our discussion turns to Christianity, which grew in three centuries from an obscure Jewish sect to the dominant religion in the West, the complex conditions of the Mediterranean world between 100 B.C.E. and 100 C.E.[4] must be noted. The world in which Christianity developed was one of tremendous ferment in the spheres of philosophy, religion, and morals. Although Stoicism remained popular among intellectuals, ordinary folks preferred various blends of mythology, superstition, and religion. Few people were much concerned with the pursuit of wisdom and virtue. There were many strange cults, often characterized by some sort of **dualism.** This was the notion that body and spirit were unalterably separate and opposed to each other and that the goal of life was to become purely spiritual by transcending the physical and material side of life. Public morals were notably decadent, and even ethical pagans were shocked by a society in which people, at least those who could afford it, prized pleasure above all things.

VIDEO

To learn more about the role of sex in the early history of Christianity, watch the video "St. Paul's Views on Sex" in Chapter 20 of your CD.

[4]The Common Era, an alternative to Anno Domini (A.D.).

Dualism: A religious or philosophical belief that body and spirit are separate and opposed to each other and that the goal of life is to free the spirit from the bondage of the body; thus a depreciation of the material world and the physical aspect of humanity.

Figure 20.2   The Virgin Mary. During the Middle Ages, a great devotion to the mother of Jesus developed, emphasizing her perpetual virginity, purity, and freedom from all sin. That devotion lives on in most Latin American countries today.

Revulsion at the excesses of Roman life affected Judaism, which became markedly more dualistic and antisex by the time of Jesus' birth and the growth of the Christian Church. That church's ethical tradition is rooted in Old Testament Judaism and was given its direction by the teachings of Jesus, the writings of St. Paul, and the theology of the fathers of early Christianity. From these beginnings, Christian ethics has evolved and developed over 2,000 years in many and various ways. This makes oversimplification a real danger, yet it is possible to speak in general terms of a Christian tradition of sexual ethics and morality.

Christianity is distinctive among the major world religions in insisting on monogamy (Parrinder,

1996). Most other religions permit polygyny, or a man having several wives. The Christian standard of monogamy, which may seem strict by today's standards, may be viewed in another light as a major step toward equality between women and men. Men were no longer permitted to have many wives as "possessions." Similarly, Jesus opposed divorce, which again may seem strict. However, it reversed the traditional Hebrew rule—and the practice in many other cultures—that a man could divorce his wife simply at will, yet a wife had no similar power.

The New Testament

At the heart of the Christian scriptures are the Gospels, which describe the life and teachings of Jesus. Since Jesus said almost nothing on the subject of sex, it is difficult to derive a sexual ethic from the Gospels alone. Jesus' ethical teaching was based on the tradition of the Hebrew prophets, and his view of sexuality follows in that tradition. He urged his followers to strive for ethical perfection, and he spoke strongly against pride, hypocrisy, injustice, and the misuse of wealth. Toward penitent sinners, including those whose sins were sexual, the Gospels show Jesus as compassionate and forgiving (see, for example, his dealings with "fallen women" in John 4:1–30, John 8:53–9:11, and Luke 7:36–50). He did not put any particular emphasis on sexual conduct, apparently regarding it as a part of a whole moral life based on the love of God and neighbour.

The task of first applying the principles of Jesus in concrete situations fell to St. Paul, documented in his letters. Paul's view of sexuality and women was ambivalent, deriving both from the immorality of much Greco-Roman culture and from the expectation he shared with most early Christians that Jesus would return soon, bringing the world to an end (Parrinder, 1996). Paul advocated celibacy, not necessarily because he was opposed to sex but because marriage might prove a distraction from prayer, worship, and proclaiming the Gospel. As a Jew, Paul opposed all sexual expression outside marriage and judged sexual immorality harshly. However, he did not single out sexual sin. He condemned the "sins of the flesh," but by this he meant all aspects, such as "immorality, impurity, sorcery, enmity, strife, jealousy, anger, selfishness, party spirit, envy, drunkenness, carousing and the like" (Galatians 5:19–21).

Figure 20.3 The most notable of the Western Fathers was St. Augustine (354–430 C.E.), who had had a promiscuous youth and overreacted after his conversion to Christianity. For Augustine, sexuality was a consequence of the Fall, and every sexual act was tainted by concupiscence (from the Latin word concupiscentia, meaning "lust" or "evil desire of the flesh"). Even sex in marriage was sinful, and in The City of God, he wrote that "children could not have been begotten in any other way than they know them to be begotten now, i.e., by lust, at which even honorable marriage blushes" (1950 ed., Article 21). The stature of Augustine meant that his negative view of sexuality was perpetuated in subsequent Christian theology.

Later Christian theologians tended to understand the "sins of the flesh" primarily in sexual terms and thus gave Christianity a bias against sexuality beyond what Paul probably intended.

Given the times, it is not surprising that the New Testament is ambivalent about sexuality, probably more so than the Hebrew scriptures.

The Early Christian Church

The "Fathers of the Church," such as St. Augustine, wrote roughly between 150 and 600 C.E., and completed the basic theological shape of the Christian faith. During this time, Christian ethics became increasingly ascetic for several reasons: its natural tendencies, the assimilation of often dualistic Greek philosophy (especially Stoicism), the decadence of Roman society, and the conversion of the Roman Emperor Constantine in 325. As the Church became the official religion of the Roman Empire, much of its original fervour was lost and it began to grow corrupt and worldly.

Serious Christians revolted against this situation by moving to the desert to become monks and hermits, to fast, to pray, and to practise all sorts of self-denial, including **celibacy.** From this point on, monks and monasticism became a permanent reform movement within the Church, a vanguard of ascetics calling Christians to greater rigour. Their success can be seen in the twelfth-century requirement that all clergy in the West be celibate, a departure from early Church practice.[5] The Fathers of the Church, almost all of whom were celibates, allowed that marriage was good and honourable but thought virginity to be a much superior state.

The Middle Ages

During the Middle Ages, these basic principles continued to be elaborated and extended. The most important figure of the period, and even today the basic source of Catholic moral theology, was St. Thomas Aquinas (1225–1274). His great achievement was the *Summa Theologica,* a synthesis of Christian theology with Aristotelian philosophy that answered virtually any question a Christian might have on any topic. Aquinas' "natural law" approach to ethics was normative in Western Christianity for many centuries and remains so for Roman Catholicism. His argument was that whatever was natural was good, "natural" being defined by the science of 1267 C.E. Anything that was not natural was sinful.

Aquinas believed that sex was obviously intended for procreation and that, therefore, all non-procreative sex violates the natural law and is sinful, being opposed to both human nature and the will of

God. In the *Summa,* Aquinas devoted a chapter to various sorts of lust and condemned as grave sin such things as fornication (premarital intercourse), nocturnal emissions, seduction, forced intercourse, adultery, incest, and "unnatural vice," which includes masturbation, bestiality, and homosexuality.

The theology of Aquinas and other moralists was communicated to the ordinary Christian through the Church's canon law, which determined when intercourse was or was not sinful. All sex outside marriage was, by definition, a sin. Even within marriage the Church forbade intercourse during certain times in a woman's physiological cycle (during menstruation, pregnancy, and up to 40 days postpartum) as well as on certain holy days, fast days (such as Fridays), and even during whole liturgical seasons (such as Advent and Lent). These rules were "enforced" through the *Penitentials,* guidebooks for priests hearing confessions, which instructed them on how to judge certain sins and what penances to assign for them (Brundage, 1984). All of this communicated to the ordinary person that the Church regarded sex as basically evil, for procreation only, and probably not something one should enjoy!

The Protestants

The Protestant Reformation in the sixteenth century destroyed the Christian unity of Europe and shook the theological foundations of the Catholic Church. However, in matters of sexual ethics there were few changes. The Protestant churches abandoned clerical celibacy, regarding it as unnatural and the source of many abuses, and placed a higher value on marriage and family life. Reformers nonetheless feared illegitimacy and approved of sexuality only in the confines of matrimony. Even then, they were often ambivalent. For example, Martin Luther, the founder of the Reformation and happily married to a former nun, called marriage "a hospital for the sick" and saw its purpose as being to "aid human infirmity and prevent unchastity" (quoted in Thielicke, 1964, p. 136)—scarcely an enthusiastic approach.

A significant contribution of Reformation Protestantism to Christianity was a renewed emphasis on the individual conscience in matters such as the interpretation of the Bible and ethical decision making. Such an emphasis on freedom and individual responsibility has led to the serious ques-

---

[5]The First Epistle of Timothy, Chapter 3, shows the clear expectation that clergy will be married and father children.

> **Celibacy:** The practice of remaining unmarried, usually for religious reasons. Sometimes used to refer to abstaining from sexual intercourse, another term for which is "chastity."

tioning of legalistic ethics and, in part, to today's ethical debates.

The Reformation also gave rise to Puritanism. The Puritans followed Augustine in emphasizing the doctrine of "original sin" and the "total depravity" of fallen humanity. This led them to use civil law to try to regulate human behaviour in an attempt to suppress immorality. This urge to make people good by law has many sexual applications, although the Puritans were probably no more sexually repressive than other Christians of the time. The Victorian era is also known for its sexual rigidity. During the 60-year reign of Queen Victoria (1819–1901), English society held sexual expression in exaggerated disgust and probably overly emphasized its importance. While strict public standards of decency and purity were enforced, many Victorians indulged in private "vices" of pornography, prostitution, and the rest. It is against this typically Victorian combination of repressiveness and hypocrisy that many people of the twentieth century have revolted, wrongly thinking the Victorian period representative of the whole Christian ethical tradition.

Current Trends

Across Western history there has been a fairly stable consensus on the fundamentals of sexual ethics, which some call the Old Morality. Sex has been understood as a good part of divine creation but also as a source of temptation that needs to be controlled. Although at various times chastity has been exalted, marriage and the family have always been held in esteem, and sex outside marriage condemned, in theory if not always in practice. The only approved purpose for sex has been procreation, with non-procreative sex having been regarded as unnatural and sinful. However, this consensus largely broke down in the twentieth century, and sexual ethics is now a topic of heated debate. Several factors, both within the religious community and outside it, have contributed to this ferment.

The rise of historical-critical methods in biblical scholarship led to a questioning of the absoluteness of scriptural norms. Many scholars now see them as conditioned by the time and culture in which they were written and not necessarily binding today. Furthermore, traditional understandings of biblical statements about sexuality have been questioned as more is learned about the original historical con-

text. The Reformation emphasis on the Bible and individual conscience called the natural-law approach into question. The religious community has also been influenced by the behavioural sciences, which suggest that sexuality is much more complex than had been thought, and question older assumptions about what is "natural" or "normal." Technology has made it possible, for the first time in human history, to prevent conception reliably and to terminate pregnancy safely, which, among other things, blunts the force of arguments against premarital intercourse on the basis of the disapproval of illegitimacy. Indeed, technology itself has raised a host of ethical issues as humans gain more and more control over what had once been a matter of "doing what comes naturally."

All this has led religious groups into serious debate and even conflict. Within Judaism, the Orthodox who still live by the rabbinic interpretation of the Bible may be in serious conflict with the Conservative and Reformed groups. Protestants are deeply divided among conservatives who hold to the Old Morality, liberals inclined to the New Morality, and others who come out somewhere in between. Perhaps no single religious community has experienced as much tension over sexual morality as the Roman Catholic Church in North America (see In Focus 20.1).

Humanism

It would be misleading to suggest that within Western culture, at least since the Renaissance, all ethical thinking has been religious in origin. Many ethicists have quite consciously tried to find a framework for moral behaviour that does not rely on divine revelation or any direction from a source outside human intellect. Non-religious ethics covers the whole spectrum; however, we can look at a fairly broad mainstream called **humanism.**

Humanistic ethics accepts no supernatural source for direction and insists that values can be found only in human experience in this world, as observed by the philosopher or social scientist. Most humanists would hold that the basic goals of human life are happiness, self-awareness, the

> **Humanism:** A philosophical system that denies a divine origin for morality and holds that ethical judgments must be made on the basis of human experience and human reason.

In Focus 20.1

Controversies over Sexual Ethics in the Roman Catholic Church

Beginning in the 1980s, the Roman Catholic Church in Canada experienced a number of serious controversies, many of them in the area of sexual ethics. The Church's traditional teaching on sexuality was vigorously reasserted by Pope John Paul II in the face of calls for a less legalistic and strict approach. John Paul repeatedly condemned all sexual activity outside marriage and all non-procreative sex, such as masturbation. In 1983, for example, the Vatican issued *Educational Guidance in Human Love*, a pamphlet for parents and teachers. In this document procreation is seen as the essential purpose of marital sex; masturbation, extramarital sex, and homosexuality are all described as "grave moral disorders." However, such teaching has not always been welcomed either by Catholic ethicists or by ordinary Catholic laypeople. Research shows that the majority of Canadian Catholics do not agree with the Church's position on a number of sexual issues including sex before marriage, divorce, abortion, contraception, and priest celibacy (Bibby, 1993).

Contraception

Although the Vatican and the Canadian hierarchy have not moved from condemning "artificial" birth control as set forth in Pope Paul VI's encyclical *Humanae Vitae* of 1968, there is evidence that many Canadian Catholics ignore the condemnation and use contraceptives, often with the tacit approval of their priests. For example, 90 percent of Canadian Catholics are in favour of use of artificial birth control methods (Bibby, 1993). Moreover, since *Humanae Vitae* was not an infallible teaching, some Catholic ethicists still treat contraception as an open question.

Abortion

There is sharp division among Canadian Catholics on the issue of abortion. A large segment of Catholics actively or passively support the anti-abortion, or right-to-life, movement, yet there are many dissenters. For example, when asked "Do you think it should be possible for a pregnant woman to obtain a legal abortion if there is a strong chance of a serious defect to the baby?" 73 percent of Catholics outside Quebec and 90 percent in Quebec responded yes (Bibby, 1987).

Homosexuality

In 1976 Jesuit priest and psychotherapist John J. McNeill published *The Church and the Homosexual*, in which he questioned the Church's traditional teaching on homosexuality and its scriptural and theological bases. Father McNeill was forbidden to speak or write further on the subject. Similarly, the Church threatened Rev. André Guindon of St. Paul's University in Ottawa with the loss of his right to teach as a Catholic theologian and forced him to apologize publicly for the views expressed in his books (Guindon, 1977, 1986) questioning Church doctrine on homosexuality, premarital sex, and contraception (Bibby, 1993).

Reproductive Technologies

In 1987, the Congregation for the Doctrine of the Faith issued a document called "Instruction for Human Life in Its Origins and on the Dignity of Procreation," which condemned in vitro fertilization, surrogate motherhood, assisted insemination, and other new reproductive technologies. The document was severely criticized by many North American Catholic ethicists, who found it too rigid and ill-informed.

Sexual Abuse by Clergy

Perhaps the most difficult sexual issue that faces the Catholic Church today is that of sexual abuse of children by Catholic priests. Catholic priests in several provinces have been convicted of sexual abuse of children. The controversy surrounds the question

Figure 20.4   Some nuns and other Catholic wmoen challenge teachings of their church.

of whether the Roman Catholic Church responded adequantly to allegations of sexual abuse by priests.

One of the most publicized cases was that of eight Roman Catholic priests and 10 lay members of the Christian Brothers of Ireland in Canada, a celebate order, who were convicted of sexually abusing 77 boys at the Mount Cashel orphanage, a home for abandoned and abused boys in St. John's, in the 1970s. At a public inquiry into the abuse at Mount Cashel in 1990, many men testified about how they were systematically abused by members of the Roman Catholic lay order, many for years. Perhaps more upsetting to the people of Newfoundland was the finding that government, police, and church officials knew about the abuse, but did nothing to stop it. Priests in Newfoundland outports have also been convicted of sexual abuse. The revelations of sexual abuse by priests were particularly shocking to Newfoundlanders because, as one woman said, "The role of a priest in an outport was as close to being God as you could get."

This scandal and others across Canada have caused a profound shift in authority within the Catholic Church, which once dictated sexual morals for laypeople, but now finds itself defending some of its priests who committed grave sexual sins. This has led some to question the church's rule of priestly celibacy, the suggestion being that if priests were allowed to marry, these problems would not occur.

Priests in countries other than Canada have also been accused of sexual abuse. For example, as of 2004, 4 percent of Catholic priests (more than 4,000) in the United States resigned or were suspended after being accused of sexually abusing children. The scandal was intensified by the revelations that some Church officials knew about the abuse, but took no action other than to reassign the abusive priests to another parish.

Sources: Curran, 1988; Grammick, 1986; Higgins, 2002; Jenkins, 1996; McNeill, 1987; Reuther, 1985; Sipe, 1995; Reports from the *Chronicle-Herald* (2000, April 10), Newsweek, (1993, August 16), and the *Toronto Star* (1989, June 28).

avoidance of pain and suffering, and the fulfilment of human needs. Of course, the individual pursuit of these ends must be tempered by the fact that no one lives in the world alone and that some limitation of individual happiness may be required for the common good. Another important humanistic principle is that the individual must make his or her own decisions and accept responsibility for them and their consequences, without appeal to some higher authority, such as God.

In the area of human sexuality, humanism demands a realistic approach to behaviour: one that does not create arbitrary or unreasonable standards and expectations. Humanism is very distrustful of the legalistic approach. It seeks real intimacy between persons and condemns impersonal and exploitative relationships, though probably not with the vigour that marks religious ethics. It tends to be tolerant, compassionate, and skeptical of claims of absolute right or wrong.

Sexuality in Other Major Religions

The discussion so far has been mostly concerned with Western culture and the Judeo-Christian tradition. It will broaden our outlook if we consider human sexuality in religious traditions outside dominant Canadian culture. Obviously, this could be the topic for a very large book itself; we will be able to provide only a brief look at the three non-Western religions with the largest number of adherents: Islam, Hinduism, and Buddhism.

Islam

Geographically, and in terms of its roots, Islam is the closest faith to the Judeo-Christian heritage. It was founded by the Prophet Muhammad, who lived from 570 to 632 C.E. in what is now Saudi Arabia. Its followers are called *Muslims,* and its sacred scripture is the Koran. Classical Islam values sexuality very positively, and Muhammad saw intercourse in marriage as the highest good of human life. Islam sanctions both polygamy and concubinage, and the Prophet had several wives. Sex outside marriage or concubinage, however, is viewed as a sin. In reality a double standard prevails in which men's extramarital affairs are tolerated. An adulterous wife, however, may be the object of an *honour killing,* in which she is murdered for her transgression (Ilkkaracan, 2001). The prophet opposed celibacy, and Islam

has very little ascetic tradition. A male-dominated faith, Islam has a strong double standard but recognizes a number of rights and prerogatives for women as well.

Because Islam does not have a single, central source of authority like the Pope, it is not a monolithic faith, and there is great variety in the ways in which the laws of the Koran are carried out in societies throughout the Muslim world (Boonstra, 2001; Ilkkaracan, 2001). Some Arab states (e.g., Iran) are theocracies in which religious law is enacted in civil law. In these nations sexual offences are likely to be more stringently punished, and women have very little freedom, as we saw in Afghanistan under the Taliban. Other Islamic countries (such as Egypt and Syria) are secular states in which Western values have been adopted to some extent. In these, women have more rights, and sexual mores are more pluralistic. Moreover, there is considerable variation in the interpretation of the Koran, especially between Sunnis and Shi'ites, the two principal Islamic "denominations."

Although Islam accepts the Hebrew scriptures as sacred, it does not interpret the Adam and Eve story to mean that humans are tainted by original sin (Ahmadi, 2003). Striving for worldly pleasures is therefore acceptable, and sexuality is regarded primarily as a source of pleasure and only secondarily as a means of reproduction.

Contraception is not only permitted but also encouraged by Islamic law (Boonstra, 2001). Muhammad himself encouraged the practice of *al'azl* (withdrawal). Even the strict state of Iran today has an extensive family planning program, and 73 percent of married women use contraceptives.

Hinduism

"Hinduism" is a rather inclusive term that refers to a highly varied complex of mythology and religious practice founded on the Indian subcontinent. Here can be found virtually every approach to sexuality that the human species has yet invented. However, certain themes are worth mentioning. In Hinduism, four possible approaches to life are acceptable: Kama, the pursuit of pleasure; Artha, the pursuit of power and material wealth; Dharma, the pursuit of the moral life; and Moksha, the pursuit of liberation through the negation of the self in a state of being that is known as nirvana. Kama is notable because it has produced an extensive literature on

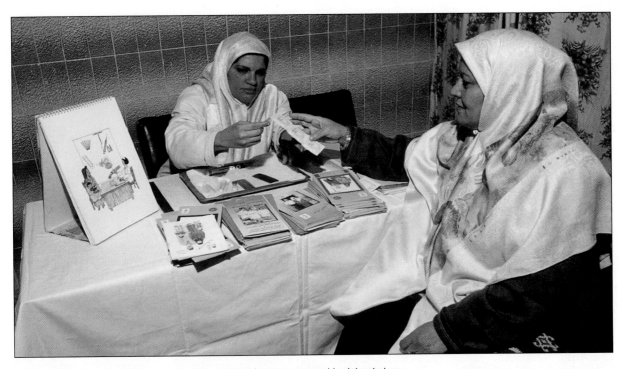

Figure 20.5   Contraception is not only permitted but encouraged by Islamic law.

the achievement of sexual pleasure, notably the *Kama Sutra* of Vatsyayana, a masterpiece of erotic hedonism. This book testifies to the highly positive view of sexuality to be found in Hinduism.

In contrast, the ways of Dharma and Moksha can be as rigorously ascetic as anything in Christianity. By avoiding all passions, including sex, the follower seeks to pass out of the cycle of continual rebirth to absorption into the godhead. Part of this is *brahmacharya*, or celibacy, which is to be cultivated at the beginning of life (for the purposes of education and discipline) and at the end of life (for the purpose of finding peace). It is interesting to note that in between it is permissible to marry and raise a family, and thus this form of Hinduism makes active sexuality and asceticism possible in the same lifetime (Noss, 1963).

Buddhism

Buddhism developed out of Hinduism; it originated in the life and thought of Gautama (560–480 B.C.E.), the Buddha, and has been elaborated in many forms since then. There is little discussion of sex in the teachings of the Buddha; his way is generally ascetic and concentrates on the achievement of enlighten-

ment and on escape from the suffering of the world. Two main traditions, Therevada and Mahayana, found in contemporary Buddhism, differ greatly. The ethics of Therevada include the strict nonindulgence of the desires that bring joy; understanding, morals, and discipline are emphasized. The ethics of Mahayana are more active and directed toward love of others. Both encourage men to live celibate lives as monks. Originally, Buddha sought a "middle way" between extreme asceticism and extreme hedonism, but today the situation is rather like that of medieval Christianity: The masses live ordinary and usually married lives, while the monks cultivate ascetic wisdom.

Tantric Buddhism, found particularly in Tibet, is a form of Buddhism that is of particular interest. There is a devotion to natural energy *(shakti)*, and followers are taught that passion can be exhausted by passion. For example, sexual desire can be overcome while engaging in intercourse, according to occult knowledge. Sexuality can therefore be used as a means of transcending the limitations of human life. This sexual mysticism is by no means common, but it is one of the various forms that Eastern religion may take (Parrinder, 1980).

Figure 20.6   Buddhism encourages men to live celibate lives as monks.

Contemporary Issues in Sexual Ethics

Human sexuality is heavily value-laden and, therefore, is likely to be the subject of strongly and emotionally held convictions. It is also likely to be the focal point of conflicts in society, if there is no broad consensus on the norms of sexual behaviour. This is clearly the case in contemporary Canadian society. The "sexual revolution" is perceived by many people as a threat to all they hold dear; not surprisingly, they respond with fear and anger. The backlash against the more liberal view of sexuality and the greater freedom of sexual behaviour that has come about in the last 40 years, accelerated by the spread of HIV and herpes, has resulted in considerable public debate. Some groups want to legislate the Old Morality back into force and reassert a highly legalistic view of the Judeo-Christian ethic. The debate promises to continue for some time and to generate much heat.

This debate over the limits, if any, of individual sexual freedom can be seen as a clash between the New Morality and the Old Morality, but let us propose a more helpful model. The Old Morality is, to a great extent, supported by people who believe that there are clearly and objectively defined standards of right and wrong and that a society has a right to insist that all its members conform to them, at least outwardly. We might call this view **moralism;** it has many proponents in the religious community who see the objective standard of morality as deriving from divine law. Opposed to this view are the proponents of **pluralism;** they see the question of public morality as being much more complex. Pluralists

Moralism: A religious or philosophical attitude that emphasizes moral behaviour, usually according to strict standards, as the highest goal of human life. Moralists tend to favour strict regulation of human conduct to help make people good.

Pluralism: A philosophical or political attitude that affirms the value of many competing opinions and believes that the truth is discovered in the clash of diverse perspectives. Pluralists, therefore, believe in the maximum human freedom possible.

deny that there are objective standards of morality, and contend that truth is to be discovered in the clash of differing opinions and convictions. According to this view, society is wise to allow many points of view to be advocated and expressed. The conscience and rights of the individual are to be stressed over society's needs for order and uniformity. Pluralists are much less likely than moralists to appeal to either law or religion for the enforcement of their views, and they are more likely to allow freedom to individuals. The debate between moralist and pluralist has been going on for a very long time and will not be settled any time soon.

An illustration of the moralist view can be found in the "profamily" position, which is rooted in religious conservatism. Profamily activists are in favour of recriminalizing abortion, against any kind of legal tolerance of the cohabitation of unmarried persons, and opposed to specifically prohibiting discrimination on the basis of sexual orientation in Canadian federal and provincial human rights codes. Although Canadians who are more committed to their religion tend to have more conservative views on many sexual issues, including premarital sex, same-gender sex, equal rights for homosexuals, and the availability of legal abortion, not all members of religiously conservative groups hold these views (Bibby, 1993). Further, even people who are highly committed to their religion do not necessarily follow the official policies of their religious leaders. For example, a study of almost 1,500 Canadians found that more than half of the highly committed approved of premarital sex (Bibby, 1993). This included 60 percent of Roman Catholics and 20 percent of evangelical Protestants. Among those with a lower level of commitment to their religion, 90 percent approved of premarital sex (90 percent of Catholics, and 83 percent of evangelical Protestants).

In the United States, the New Religious Right, a coalition of conservative religious and political groups, has been extremely vocal and politically influential. In contrast, in recent years the profamily agenda has not had much influence over federal legislation in Canada in such areas as abortion and equal rights for gay men and lesbians as most Canadians subscribe to moral pluralism and are reluctant to impose their morality on others through law (Bibby, 1987). Nonetheless, policies in some provinces have been influenced by conservative religious views. For example,

although abortion is legal in Canada, access to abortion is inadequate in many geographical areas (refer to Table 7.3).

Conflict over sexual issues can be found within most religious communities today, liberal and conservative. Here we will illustrate some of these controversies by discussing the ethical issues posed by sex outside marriage, contraception, abortion, homosexuality, HIV/AIDS, and reproductive technologies.

Sex Outside Marriage

The biblical tradition underlying Western ethics has almost always limited sexual intercourse to marriage. This is rooted in a religious understanding of marriage as God's will for most men and women, the way in which sin is avoided and children are cared for. Thus, the tradition has condemned both sex before marriage (which the Bible calls **fornication**) and sex by persons married to others (**adultery**). Today, this position continues to be held by theological conservatives among Jews, Protestants, and Roman Catholics. A Roman Catholic statement on the subject is typical of this position:

> Today there are many who vindicate the right to sexual union before marriage, at least in those cases where a firm intention to marry and an affection which is already in some way conjugal in the psychology of the subjects require this completion which they judge to be connatural. . . . This option is contrary to Christian doctrine, which states that every genital act must be within the framework of marriage. (Sacred Congregation for the Doctrine of the Faith, 1976, p. 11)

However, trends in society have caused many ethicists to reopen the question and to take less dogmatic positions. Among these are the development of safe and reliable contraception, later age at first marriage, the fact that many people experience the singleness of divorce, and empirical evidence indicating widespread sexual activity among ado-

---

Fornication: The biblical term for sex by unmarried persons and, more generally, all immoral sexual behaviour.
Adultery: Voluntary sexual intercourse by a husband or wife with someone other than one's spouse; thus, betrayal of one's marriage vows.

lescents. These ethicists are concerned that people be given more helpful guidance than "thou shalt not." For them, the quality of the relationship is more important ethically than its legal status.

Criteria for judging the morality of non-marital sexual acts could include the following (Countryman, 1994). First, is there a genuine respect for the personhood of all involved? Virtually all ethicists would agree that sexual exploitation of one person by another (whether married or not)—the use of other human beings merely for one's pleasure—is wrong. Furthermore, most would require genuine affection and serious commitment from both parties. This commitment would be manifested in responsible behaviour such as using contraceptives if the couple were not willing to or able to raise a child, and taking precautions against STIs. Finally, many ethicists would insist that moral sexual behaviour must include genuine openness and honesty between the partners. Public and private institutions, in this view, should be involved in helping people to make good ethical choices about sexual behaviour in a culture that tends to glorify and exploit sex (Lebacqz, 1987; Moore, 1987).[6]

Extramarital sex (adultery) has always been regarded as a grave matter in the Judeo-Christian tradition. In the Hebrew scriptures, the penalty for it was to be stoned to death; in the New Testament, it is the only grounds for divorce allowed by Jesus (Matthew 6:21–22). Adultery has been understood as a serious breach of trust by a spouse, as well as an act of unfaithfulness to God (a violation of religiously significant promises). Few contemporary ethicists would modify this position, but many would argue for a less judgmental, more humane approach to those involved. In this view, people in extramarital relationships should be helped to find the root causes of their infidelity and to move toward a reconciliation with their spouses based on forgiveness and love. This approach suggests that counselling is more helpful than condemnation. Above all, some argue, religious organizations need to assist people in establishing and maintaining good marriages based on mutual respect, communication, and commitment.

---

[6]A fine discussion of these issues from different perspectives (liberal Protestant and Roman Catholic, respectively) can be found in Nelson (1978) and Genovesi (1987).

Contraception

Roman Catholics and Orthodox Jews oppose any "artificial" means of contraception; other Jews and most Protestants favour responsible family planning by married couples. Moreover, most ethicists would suggest that single persons who are sexually active ought to be using birth control.

Those who oppose birth control for religious reasons see it as being contrary to the will of God, against the natural law, or both. Orthodox Judaism cites the biblical injunction to "be fruitful and multiply" (Genesis 1:26) as God's command to his people, not to be disobeyed in any way. Furthermore, some members of other Jewish communities warn that limiting family size threatens the future existence of the Jewish people, and they call for a return to the traditionally large Jewish family.

The Roman Catholic position is best articulated in Pope Paul VI's 1968 encyclical, *Humanae Vitae:*

> Marriage and conjugal love are by their nature ordained toward the begetting and educating of children. . . . In the task of transmitting life, therefore, they are not free to proceed completely at will, as if they could determine in a wholly autonomous way the honest path to follow, but they must conform their activity to the creative intention of God, expressed in the very nature of marriage and by its acts, and manifested by the constant teaching of the Church. (Pope Paul VI, 1968, p. 20)

The encyclical continued the Church's approval of "natural family planning," that is, abstinence during fertile periods, popularly known as the "rhythm method" or "Vatican roulette." *Humanae Vitae* was not enthusiastically accepted by all Catholics and the evidence indicates that many Catholic couples, often with the encouragement or tacit approval of their priest, ignore these teachings and use contraceptives anyway. Nonetheless, the teachings of *Humanae Vitae* were repeatedly and resoundingly reiterated by Pope John Paul II.

Those in the religious community who favour the use of contraceptives do so for a variety of reasons. Many express a concern that all children who are born should be "wanted," and they see family planning as a means to this end. Others, emphasizing the dangers that overpopulation poses to the quality and future of human life, the need for a more equitable distribution of natural resources,

Figure 20.7   Prolife (shown above) and prochoice advocates are both adamant about their positions regarding abortion.

and the needs of the emerging nations, call for family planning as a matter of justice. Another point of view regards the use of contraceptives as part of the responsible use of freedom. In this view, any couple that is unwilling or unready to assume the responsibility of children has a duty to use contraceptives. For these groups, the decision to use contraceptives is a highly individual one, and the government must allow each individual the free exercise of his or her conscience (Curran, 1988).

Abortion

One of the most convulsive debates of our time continues to be waged over the issue of abortion. Currently Canada has no laws related to abortion and so, legally, abortion is treated like any other medical procedure. (See Chapter 7 for a history of abortion laws in Canada.) Nonetheless, all Canadian women do not have equal access to abortion (refer to Table 7.3). Opposition to abortion comes from a coalition of antiabortion groups who call themselves "prolife." Those seeking to preserve a

woman's right to a legal abortion call themselves "prochoice." Both prolife and prochoice activists are well organized and deeply convinced of the rightness of their position. The conflict is a clash of religious belief, political conviction, and world view in the realm of public policy, one that allows for no easy solutions.[7]

Two distinctions should be made at the outset. First, there is no consensus on the relation between abortion and contraception. For the Roman Catholic Church and others within the prolife movement, the two are the same in intention; indeed, many antiabortion activists wish to ban all contraception except natural family planning. In the other camp, there are some prochoice advocates who also regard abortion as a variety of contraception—less desirable, perhaps, but better than unwanted pregnancy. However, most centrist ethicists do distinguish between abortion and contraception, typically favouring the latter while raising ethical

[7]For a thorough and careful study of what prolife and prochoice activists believe they have at stake, see Ginsburg (1989).

In Focus 20.2

Religious Position Statements on Abortion: Prolife versus Prochoice

The following statements come from a variety of major religious organizations. They reflect the nature of the arguments and the rhetoric of the abortion debate. Consider these statements in relation to the poll (Table 20.2) that shows a wide diversity of opinion among the Canadian public.

Prolife Statements

[The] Church has always rejected abortion as a grave moral evil. It has always seen that the child's helplessness, both before and after birth, far from diminishing his or her right to life, increases our moral obligation to respect and to protect that right. . . . The Church also realizes that a society which tolerates the direct destruction of innocent life, as in the current practice of abortion, is in danger of losing its respect for life in all other contexts. (National Conference of Catholic Bishops, 1985)

Orthodox Christians have always viewed the willful abortion of unborn children as a heinous act of evil. The Church's canonical tradition identifies any action intended to destroy a fetus as the crime of murder. (Orthodox Church in America, 1992)

We reaffirm our belief in the sanctity of human life, our desire to respect and protect life from conception, and to implore government leaders and legis-

Table 20.2   Canadians' Attitudes Toward Abortion

	Percentage Who Agreed		
	1975	*1991*	*2001*
Do you think abortion should be legal under any circumstance, legal only under certain circumstances, or illegal in all circumstances?			
Legal under any circumstance	23%	24%	32%
Legal only under certain circumstances	60%	60%	52%
Illegal in all circumstances	16%	14%	14%

Source: Gallup Canada, 2001.

lators to establish laws which will protect life, and to restrain those who would destroy life through abortion except in a possible situation where the mother's life may be in danger. (United Baptist Convention of the Atlantic Provinces Assembly, 1989)

The United Pentecostal Church has taken the official position of opposing abortion. We went on record with this stand at our 1974 General Confer-

questions about the former. Second, a distinction is frequently made between therapeutic abortion and elective abortion. Therapeutic abortion is a termination of pregnancy when the life or mental health of the woman is threatened or when there is trauma, such as in cases of forced intercourse or incest. Many ethical theorists are willing to endorse therapeutic abortion as the lesser of two evils but do not sanction elective abortion—that is, abortion whenever requested by a woman for any reason.

The leadership of the antiabortion movement clearly comes from the Roman Catholic Church, for which putting an end to abortion is a major policy goal. For many Catholics, opposition to abortion is seen as part of an overall commitment to respect for life, which Joseph Cardinal Bernardin called the "seamless garment" that includes opposition to capital punishment, euthanasia (mercy killing), and social injustice, and a very positive stance toward peace (Cahill, 1985). Pope John Paul ence. We are very much pro-life. (Personal communication, United Pentecostal Church International, August 24, 2000).

Prochoice Statements

We affirm the inherent value of human life, both as immature in the foetus and as expressed in the life of the mother and related persons.... Therefore, abortion is acceptable only when, after careful consideration, the medical, social and/or economic situation makes it the most responsible alternative.... All involved should earnestly consider their understanding of the particular situation while permitting the woman to bring to bear her moral and religious insights into human life in reaching a decision through a free and responsive exercise of her conscience.... We urge the Government of Canada to not use the provisions in the Criminal Code to regulate abortion. (United Church of Canada, General Council 1980, 1989)

Since 1967 the Church ... has accepted abortion, under some circumstances, as a legitimate need of pregnant women, and thus as a morally permitted choice for a woman to make and for medical personnel to carry out. It has therefore backed having abortion made legally available within these parameters. In doing so it has recognized pregnancy and childbirth as the life experience that most deeply affects a woman's being, and has shown respect for her dignity, humanity, and needs.... We

have recognized that at any stage of fetal development "abortion is the taking of a human life that otherwise, in the normal course of things, would come to be." (Anglican Church of Canada, 1989)

Abortion is an extremely difficult choice faced by a woman. In all circumstances, it should be her decision whether or not to terminate a pregnancy, backed up by those whom she trusts (physician, therapist, partner, etc.). This decision should not be taken lightly (abortion should never be used for birth control purposes) and can have life-long ramifications. However, any decision should be left up to the woman within whose body the fetus is growing. (Union for Reform Judaism, 2004)

Judaism does not believe that personhood and human rights begin with conception. The premise that personhood begins with conception is founded on a religious position that is not identical with Jewish tradition. Therefore, under special circumstances, Judaism chooses and requires abortion as an act that affirms and protects the life, well-being, and health of the mother. To deny a Jewish woman and her family the ability to obtain a safe, legal abortion when so mandated by Jewish tradition is to deprive Jews of their fundamental right of religious freedom. (United Synagogue of Conservative Judaism, 1989)

Sources: National Right to Life; Religious Coalition for Reproductive Choice, www.ncrc.org; Anglican Church of Canada; United Church of Canada.

II reaffirmed this position in his 1995 encyclical, *Evangelium Vitae* (Gospel of Life), saying "I declare that direct abortion, that is, abortion willed as an ends and a means, always constitutes a grave moral disorder, since it is the deliberate killing of an innocent human being." He went on to condemn capital punishment and euthanasia. The underlying principle of this position is that all life is a gift from God that human beings are not permitted to take. It is the position of the prolife movement that human life begins at the moment of conception and that the fetus is, from that beginning, entitled to full rights and protections. The Roman Catholic position is shared by Orthodox Jews, Eastern Orthodox Christians, and many conservative, or fundamentalist, Protestants (see In Focus 20.2). An end to legalized abortion is at the top of the political agenda of many theologically conservative groups and has been raised as a policy issue within the Canadian Alliance Party.

Nonetheless, there has been some significant dissent from this position even within the Catholic Church. Prochoice Catholics point out that for most of its history, the Church accepted Aristotle's teaching, reaffirmed by St. Thomas Aquinas, that "ensoulment," that is, the entry into the fetus of its distinctively human soul, takes place 40 days after conception for a male and 80 or 90 days after conception for a female. Theoretically, this permits abortions at least until the fortieth day. In 1869, Pope Pius IX eliminated the concept of ensoulment, holding that life begins at conception and that all abortion is therefore murder (Luker, 1984). Though regularly denounced by the Vatican and the Canadian hierarchy, some Catholic ethicists insist that the Church's position is not unchangeable and argue that the concerns and needs of women should be more carefully considered in the matter (Kolbenschlag, 1985; Maguire, 1983; Reuther, 1985).

The prochoice position takes at least two forms: absolute and modified. The absolute position argues that pregnancy is solely the concern of a woman and that she should have the absolute right to control her own body and determine whether to carry a fetus to term. Ethically, this position is based on the conviction that the individual must be free and autonomous in all personal decisions. It is also inspired by feminism, which regards such autonomy as necessary if women are to be truly equal to men. Feminists also observe that, historically, the rules about abortion were made by men, who do not become pregnant, and thus are deeply suspect. Indeed, for many feminists complete access to abortion is an absolute principle for women's liberation. Concerns for autonomy and individualism have formed a significant part of Western ethics for more than two centuries.

For those who hold the modified prochoice position—which includes most liberal Protestants and Jews—the issue is more complex and means balancing several goods against one another. They affirm that human life is good and ought to be preserved but also argue that the quality of life is important. They argue that an unborn child may have a right to life, but ask if it does not also have the right to be wanted and cared for. In high-risk situations, might not the danger to the well-being of a woman already alive take precedence over the

well-being of an unborn fetus? Few in this camp regard abortion as a good thing but suggest that there may be many situations in which it is the least bad choice. Moreover, these ethicists tend to observe that since there is no real consensus in society over the morality of abortion, the government ought to keep out and let the individual woman make up her own mind.

The "prolife" position is, as is typical with moralism, much more absolute and apparently simple, while the pluralist "prochoice" position is complex. Both positions agree on the value and dignity of human life, but are sharply divided on when life begins, how various conflicting interests are to be balanced, and how human life is best preserved and enhanced. Several factors ensure that the debate will continue for some time. Advances in neonatal medicine are pushing back the threshold of "viability" (the survival of premature infants), and this may affect the ethical acceptability of second-trimester abortions for some people (Callahan, 1986). The politicalization of the issue will keep it in the public consciousness, and pressure to recriminalize abortion will continue. Certainly, the intensity is not likely to diminish, as it is a clash about life, law, freedom, and values, and few people are neutral on these issues.

Sexual Orientation

Mirroring society as a whole, religious communities have been engaged in a vigorous debate on the subject of homosexuality. Until recently, it was assumed that persons who engaged in same-sex activity were condemned by the Judeo-Christian tradition. However, many contemporary ethicists, and some religious bodies, have started reexamining their attitudes toward homosexuality (Siker, 1994). This change has occurred in part because some recent scholarship suggests that the traditional interpretation of the Bible passages on this topic is not accurate, and in part because the impact of social science has led many ethicists to question whether homosexuality is truly abnormal and unnatural and therefore against the will of God. Paralleling these views are beliefs about ordination of gay men and lesbians as clergy. Nationally, 44 percent of Canadians are in favour of ordination of homosexuals. However, whereas 51 percent of United Church members and 53 percent of non-

Figure 20.8 In this Dürer painting, Lot and his family flee as the city of Sodom burns. In Genesis 19:4–11, God sends two angels to the city of Sodom to investigate its alleged immorality. The angels are granted hospitality by Lot, but his house is surrounded by a crowd of men demanding that he send the angels out, "that we may know them." Lot offers his virgin daughters instead, but the men of Sodom insist, the angels strike them blind, and God destroys the city. This story has been understood to condemn all same-sex sexual activity. However, some modern scholars question this interpretation, noting that at most it condemns same-sex sexual assault. Moreover, scholars point out that in other portions of the Bible and in Jewish history, the sin of Sodom is never seen as homosexuality, but rather as general immorality and lack of hospitality (a serious offence in the ancient Near East) (Helminiak, 2000).

Christians favour ordination of gay men and lesbians, this number drops to 46 percent for Anglicans, 34 percent for Roman Catholics, 32 percent for Presbyterians, 31 percent for Lutherans, and 28 percent for Baptists (Bibby, 1995). Nonetheless, the majority of people in each religious group are in favour of equal rights for gay men and lesbians (Bibby, 1987). There are three positions, broadly speaking, on the issue: rejection, modified rejection or qualified acceptance, and full acceptance (Nelson, 1978).

Rejectionism

Regarding the *rejectionist position*, it has generally been presumed that the weight of the Judeo-Christian tradition absolutely opposes any sexual acts between persons of the same sex and regards those committing such acts as dreadful sinners, utterly condemned by God. Although there are few references in the Bible, all are negative, the most famous being the passage about the destruction of Sodom (see Figure 20.8).[8]

In the Hebrew scriptures, homosexual practices are included on lists of offences against God. Jesus made no comment on the subject, but St. Paul was unambiguously against same-sex activity, seeing it as perverse behaviour by fundamentally heterosexual persons. Thus he included them in lists of sexual sins, along with adultery and fornication, that are in opposition to the will of God and symptomatic of human depravity. However, Paul did not seem to have found homosexuality any more dreadful than other sexual sins.

Homosexuality was not uncommon in the Mediterranean world of the early Church, and the Church condemned it as part of the immoral world in which it found itself. The Church saw it as a crime against nature that might bring down the wrath of God upon the whole community (Kosnick, 1977). In the Middle Ages, Thomas Aquinas stated that "unnatural vice . . . flouts nature by transgressing its basic principle of sexuality and is in this matter the gravest of sin" (1968 ed., II-II, q. 154, a. 12).

The rejectionist position continues to be held by members of the conservative religious community who condemn same-sex sexual activity and reject homosexual persons unless they repent and become heterosexual.

Modified Rejection or Qualified Acceptance

Many religious groups would modify this position somewhat, through a distinction between same-sex orientation and behaviour. In essence this stance of *modified rejection* or *qualified acceptance* regards a homosexual orientation, assuming it cannot be changed, as morally neutral, but rejects same-sex sexual activity. Thus, an ethical homosexual person may be fully obedient to the

[8]Other relevant biblical passages include Leviticus 18:22 and 20:13; Genesis 19; Romans 1:26; and I Corinthians 6:19.

will of God, as long as she or he remains abstinent. This is the official position of the Roman Catholic Church, reiterated in a Vatican directive entitled "The Pastoral Care of Homosexual Persons," which states in part:

> Although the particular inclination of the homosexual person is not a sin, it is a more or less strong tendency ordered toward an intrinsic moral evil and thus the inclination itself must be seen as an objective disorder. Therefore special concern and pastoral attention should be directed toward those who have this condition, lest they be led to believe that the living out of this orientation in homosexual activity is a morally acceptable option. It is not. (Congregation for the Doctrine of the Faith, 1986, p. 379)

Various Protestant groups have taken the same stance—that is, being gay per se may not be sinful, but same-sex activities are.

Further down the road to qualified acceptance is the 1997 statement of the Anglican Bishops of Canada:

> As Christians we believe that homosexual persons are created in the image and likeness of God and have a full and equal claim with all other persons upon the love, acceptance, concern and care of the church.... The church affirms its traditional teaching that only the sexual union of a male and female can find appropriate expression in the covenant of Holy Matrimony.

The Anglican Church is still debating whether sexuality expressed within a committed same-sex relationship is acceptable. However, it has clearly stated that while gay men or lesbians may be ordained as clergy, they must "remain chaste." Thus, rejection can be modified and acceptance qualified in a variety of ways.

After courts in several provinces ruled that restricting marriage to one man and one woman violated the Charter of Rights and Freedoms, a number of these religious groups joined together in a group called the Interfaith Coalition on Marriage and the Family to try to preserve the heterosexual definition of marriage in the federal Marriage Act on religious grounds. Most argue that they favour an alternative legal status for same-sex couples but oppose broadening the definition of marriage.

Full Acceptance

At the other end of the spectrum are those in the religious community who favour *full acceptance* of lesbian and gay persons, usually basing this on a revisionist view of the Bible and church tradition. Some scholars question whether the apparent condemnation in the scriptures is really relevant to homosexuality as it is generally understood today (Furnish, 1994). New Testament scholar Robin Scroggs, for example, says that the only form of same-sex behaviour known to the world of the New Testament involved older men and youths (often prostitutes or slaves), and he concludes that "what the New Testament was against was the image of homosexuality as pederasty and primarily here its more sordid and dehumanizing dimensions" (1983, p. 126). Yale historian John Boswell's detailed research into early and medieval Christianity led him to conclude that up until about the thirteenth century the Christian church was relatively neutral toward homosexuality and, when it did see same-sex behaviour as sinful, did not regard it as any worse than heterosexual transgressions. Boswell found a gay subculture that flourished throughout this period and argues that it was known to the church, that clergy and church officials were often part of it, that it was not infrequently tolerated by religious and civil authorities alike, and that in it same-sex marriages or "unions" occurred (Boswell, 1980, 1994). This sort of reinterpretation has led some theologians, such as Roman Catholic John McNeill and the Anglican Norman Pittenger, to question whether the tradition has been understood properly and to conclude that sexual relationships that are characterized by mutual respect, concern, and commitment— by love in its fullest sense—are to be valued and affirmed, whatever the sex of the partners (McNeill, 1987; Pittenger, 1970). The revisionist view seems to be gaining adherents over time.

Institutional expression of the position of full acceptance has been varied. In 1963 a group of English Friends challenged traditional thinking about sexuality, including homosexuality, in *Toward a Quaker View of Sex*. Since that time, the Quaker, Unitarian, and United churches have been notable for their acceptance not only of the gay or lesbian person but also of her or his sexual behaviour, as long as it is conscientious. Within virtually all the mainline churches, gay caucuses and organiza-

Figure 20.9   Darryl MacDonald was a gay minister at St. Andrew's Presbyterian Church in Lachine, Quebec. The congregation voted to leave the Presbyterian Church of Canada due to its policy against ordination of gay and lesbian ministers. In contrast, the United Church of Canada has permitted ordination of openly gay and lesbian ministers since 1988.

tions have been formed in an effort to move fellow believers toward greater understanding and tolerance. A considerable number of lesbians and gay men have simply left the established religious organizations and founded their own churches, synagogues, temples, and other groups, of which the largest is the Universal Fellowship of Metropolitan Community Churches. On the other hand, many gay men and lesbians reject all forms of religion as oppressive and invalid, making religion as controversial within the gay community as homosexuality is within religious bodies.

Two issues in particular seem to provoke the most debate: ordination and the marriage of gay men and lesbians. Beginning in the 1970s, most major Canadian Protestant denominations debated the appropriateness of ordaining lesbians and gay men to the ministry. The debates were emotional and explosive, and nearly all resulted in legislation forbidding homosexual ordination. The debate on sexual orientation leading up to the 1988 General Council of the United Church of Canada was emotional and many parts of the Church were deeply divided. However, in the end, the Council declared that all persons, regardless of their sexual orientation, are welcome to be full members of the Church and are eligible to be ordained as ministers. Although this position was seen by many members as positive and progressive, 10 congregations left the denomination as a result (Bibby, 1993). The Unitarian-Universalist Association and the Union of American Hebrew Congregations, which includes the Canadian Council for Reformed Judaism, are also willing to ordain gay and lesbian people openly. In 2003, the Episcopal Church (the name of the Anglican Church in the United States), amid much controversy, approved the consecration as bishop of an openly gay priest (Davey, 2003).

Many who favour full acceptance of gay men and lesbians argue for formal recognition of committed relationships through marriage. For many years, a number of religious denominations performed "holy unions" or "same-sex covenants," including the Metropolitan Community Church, the United Church, and rabbis who belong to the Canadian Council for Reformed Judaism. After the courts legalized same-sex marriage in 2003, clergy from these denominations began conducting same-sex marriages. However, the first same-sex marriage in Canada actually occurred in 1974 in Winnipeg. Chris Vogel and Richard North got married through the reading of the banns—an old Christian tradition of giving public notice of people's plans to marry. The marriage was performed by a Unitarian minister, but the Province of Manitoba never legally recognized this marriage. In 2002, the bishop and governing synod of the Anglican Church in New Westminster, British Columbia, authorized priests to bless same-sex unions even though the Canadian House of Bishops and the worldwide Anglican Communion has stated that the church is not "ready" for same-sex blessings.

HIV/AIDS

AIDS has raised a host of complex and difficult ethical issues for individuals, religious communities, and society as a whole. These issues are often debated in an atmosphere of fear, anger, and ignorance, which is focused on the fatality of the disease and the fact that the vast majority of sufferers in Canada are either homosexual men or injection drug users, two populations about which society has profound ambivalence. Religious groups, like the rest of society, have struggled to develop effective ways of ministering to persons with HIV infection or AIDS (Cherry & Mitulski, 1988; Jantzen, 1994). Responses have ranged from declaring AIDS to be God's punishment on sinners to actively organizing to minister to persons with AIDS and seeking to educate members of churches and synagogues about the disease and how they can respond compassionately (Countryman, 1987; Godges, 1986; Jantzen, 1994).

Broadly speaking, the major ethical conflicts centre on the dignity and autonomy of the person, on the one hand, and the welfare of society on the other. This issue has both personal and public aspects. For the person who has AIDS or who is HIV-positive, a primary issue is confidentiality. Given that disclosure can lead to the loss of friends and family, such persons may well wonder if anyone has a right to know about their condition. However, many people argue that the public, or at least certain groups within society, have a right to know who is infected in order to be protected from them. This argument is typically based on a misunderstanding of how HIV is transmitted.

Some groups in the United States have proposed that children with HIV infection should not be allowed to attend public schools and that infected persons should be registered for the protection of emergency medical personnel, health care workers, coroners, and morticians. Several large populations, including military personnel, would-be immigrants, and some prisoners, have been required to undergo mandatory testing for HIV. In Canada, the Charter of Rights and Freedoms protects persons with HIV infection from discrimination. Many of these measures, therefore, would be unconstitutional in Canada, although immigration applicants are required to have HIV testing. Most public health officials and AIDS researchers oppose these measures because they fear that persons at risk would be driven underground. They argue that public health is best protected by informed, voluntary testing, specific consent, and the fairly stringent protection of confidentiality (Jürgens, 1998; Levine & Bermel, 1985, 1986).

Ethically, a solid middle position would encourage persons engaging in risky behaviour to take responsibility for themselves by undergoing voluntary testing and practising safer sex. This position would argue that infected persons have a right to confidentiality but should voluntarily disclose their status to anyone put at risk by it—notably health care personnel and sexual partners. In fact, the courts have ruled that failing to tell a partner that you are HIV-positive can amount to a criminal assault. For health care workers, there is the personal ethical problem of whether to treat persons who are HIV-positive. The courts have ruled that there is a legal obligation to treat. Of course, there is also an obligation to take appropriate precautions (Zuger, 1987).

Public education for prevention, generally regarded as the only really effective response at present, raises some ethical problems. What kind of education is appropriate? At what age should it begin? How graphic should it be? Does government advocacy of "safer sex" mean endorsement of sexual practices that are contrary to the beliefs of some Canadians? The U.S. government has tried to fight drug abuse by restricting the availability of syringes. This policy ignores the reality that there has been a rapid spread of HIV among IV drug users through the sharing of needles. The Canadian government has endorsed needle exchange programs to prevent the spread of HIV, although clean needles are not being made available in prisons. Public health officials argue that if addicts could readily obtain clean needles, they would not have to share and risk infection.

Currently clinical trials are underway for an HIV vaccine, although it is not likely that a highly effective vaccine will be available within the next few years. This raises a number of ethical issues (Canadian HIV/AIDS Legal Network, 2002). What if individuals in HIV vaccine trials develop a false sense of security, called vaccine optimism, and thus stop engaging in safer sex? Who should be allowed to participate in vaccine trials? For example, if only gay men are permitted to participate, as is the case with the current vaccine trial, does this unfairly disadvantage other groups, such as women and IV drug users? The results of a clinical trial with men may not generalize to women. How much compensation should be offered for participation? A level of compensation to marginalized groups or people living in Third World countries that is too high might create an undue incentive to participate and undermine the ethical principal of free, informed consent. Who should have first access to a vaccine once it is developed?

One of the most contentious ethical issues stems from the high rates of HIV infection in the Third World. In Africa there are 4 million new cases each year. In sub-Saharan Africa, the worst-affected region in the world, 28.5 million adults and children are living with HIV/AIDS. However, few Africans can afford the high costs of the drugs used to treat HIV, so death usually follows soon after. Women, particularly young women, have the highest rates of infection in this region—58 percent of those infected are women. Many of these women become pregnant and pass the virus on to their babies. Treating pregnant women who are infected with HIV with the antiviral drug AZT reduces the likelihood that the baby will become infected. It is estimated that in South Africa alone, 30,000 children a year would not contract HIV from their mothers if all HIV-positive women were treated with AZT. However, the cost prevents pregnant women who are infected with HIV from getting treatment. In contrast, in the industrialized world, the number of deaths from AIDS has dropped dramatically and life expectancy has increased due to the general availability of anti-HIV drugs.

What can be done to provide access to the drugs used to treat HIV/AIDS on a worldwide basis? Some manufacturers have indicated that they may be willing to lower their prices in the Third World, yet even with these lower prices the drugs would be too costly for most individuals, and even for Third World governments. Should industrialized countries be paying for treatment of HIV-positive individuals in the Third World, a hefty price tag at current prices? Should drug companies be supplying the drugs at cost and forgoing profits? Who should pay?

Most of the choices that must be made in dealing with HIV/AIDS are unappealing, expensive, or both. Canadian society is being challenged to maintain its own values and to deal compassionately and effectively with what many have described as the greatest health crisis since the bubonic plague.

■ Technology and Sexual Ethics

A major challenge to ethicists today is the rapid development of technologies that raise new moral issues before the old ones have been resolved. We have already discussed several issues in which technology has played a major role. Although sex outside of marriage is hardly a problem unique to our time, the availability of reliable birth control techniques has probably increased the incidence of premarital and extramarital sex. The fact that millions of people can enjoy vigorous sex lives without conceiving children unless they choose to has markedly changed the basic moral climate.

The issue of abortion has also been intensified by technological advances of the past few decades and will only get more complicated in the future. The developing medical science of neonatology means that fetuses are viable outside the uterus earlier and earlier. Some late-pregnancy abortions produce a fetus that could be kept alive, confronting hospital staffs with agonizing questions about what should be done in such cases. Traditional ethics suggest that such unwanted children be kept alive, yet this can be incredibly costly and the children often have severe disabilities. Hospitals may limit, or even forbid, second-trimester abortions to deal with this issue (Callahan, 1986).

Another complex of ethical issues arises out of the host of new reproductive technologies that enable people to conceive children outside of the "normal" process of sexual intercourse in what has been called "collaborative parenting." These include assisted insemination, either by male partner or donor (AIH or AID), in vitro fertilization (IVF), embryo transfer, and surrogate motherhood.

For many ethicists, these technologies can be tentatively approved because they enable otherwise infertile people to have children with at least one partner's genes (Strong, 1997). Certainly, having children of one's own has had a very high value for most people throughout history, and infertility has been seen as a curse in most cultures.

These technologies bring with them a number of ethical problems, too, chief among which is that they involve "playing God." That is, they give human beings control over things that are, it is argued, best left up to nature and raise serious problems of who will decide how they are to be used. It is also argued that separating conception from marital intercourse may confuse the parenthood of children and have a negative effect on the family. Another concern is the possibility of exploiting others, particularly in the case of surrogacy. Some ethicists, especially those taking a feminist perspective, fear that rich couples will "rent wombs" or "buy babies" from low-income women. Many question the morality of conceiving and/or carrying a child one never intends to raise. Others wonder if AID and IVF might not be used to select the sex of a child or predetermine other characteristics, ushering in a "Brave New World" that is less than human (Boyd et al., 1986; Krimmel, 1983; McDowell, 1983; Schneider, 1985).

Now that technologies such as in vitro fertilization are commonplace, new issues are emerging. Often more than one embryo is implanted, the goal being to maximize the chances of a successful pregnancy. The result in some cases is multiple births of six or more babies, born long before nine months of gestation. One study of children born at 25 weeks of gestation or earlier—not necessarily as part of a multiple birth—found that 49 percent had a disability and 23 percent had a severe disability (Wood et al., 2000). Is it ethical to use procedures that pose such serious risks to the baby?

Two religious communities have condemned most or all of these technologies, though on somewhat different grounds. Orthodox Judaism might permit the use of techniques that would allow an otherwise infertile couple to have a child if both egg and sperm come from the couple, e.g., in AIH or IVF with implantation in the wife's uterus. Any technique involving a third party is condemned as being de facto adultery and confusing the parentage of the child (Green, 1984; Rosner, 1983). The Roman Catholic position is stated clearly in a 1987 statement issued by the Vatican, "Instruction on Respect for Human Life in Its Origin and on the Dignity of Procreation." The statement identified use of fertility techniques that remained within the woman's body using her husband's sperm not collected by masturbation as an open moral question. Otherwise all techniques such as AID, IVF, and surrogacy were unequivocally condemned as an assault on the dignity of the embryo (in Catholic theology a human person) and on the sanctity of marriage as the only licit means of procreation (Congregation for the Doctrine of the Faith, 1987).

A centrist position on new reproductive technologies might approve their use in many cases, such as AIH in which a couple use their own egg and sperm and the woman's uterus and simply accomplish fertilization and implantation by assisted means, perhaps because the wife's fallopian tubes are blocked. At the same time, this centrist position might forbid other practices, such as the buying and selling of human embryos. One question then would be whether technological conception should be regulated according to the mother's age. Rosanna Dalla Corte, a 62-year-old Italian woman, created headlines when she gave birth, having used an ovum donation because she was postmenopausal (Strong, 1997). She would be 80 at the time of her son's high school graduation.

The announcement in 1997 that Scottish scientists had successfully cloned a sheep, Dolly, confronted the public with the possibility of human cloning and its ethical issues when most had thought that cloning was at most a science-fiction fantasy. The technique itself is called **somatic cell nuclear transfer** and involves substituting the genetic material from an adult's cell for the nucleus in an egg (Shapiro, 1997). The possibility of cloning humans also raises a number of ethical issues.

In 1993, based on input from 40,000 Canadians, the Royal Commission on New Reproductive Technologies made recommendations about how new reproductive technologies should be handled in Canada. The Commission first established an ethical framework to guide its decisions. It adopted "an ethic of care" so that recommendations would foster and balance the rights and dignity of the individual and the welfare of the community. Within the ethic of care, it established principles that affirmed the importance of preserving individuals' right to make decisions about their lives, ensuring that all people are treated equally, protecting vulnerable individuals, and ensuring that reproduction does not become commercialized.

In keeping with the recommendations of the Commission, in 2002 the federal government introduced legislation to deal with some of these issues. This legislation allows most of the new reproductive technologies in use, such as assisted reproduction and IVF, to continue to be available. However, it regulates their use so that they are provided in a safe, ethical, and accountable way. For example,

Somatic cell nuclear transfer: A cloning technique that involves substituting genetic material from an adult's cell for the nucleus of an egg.

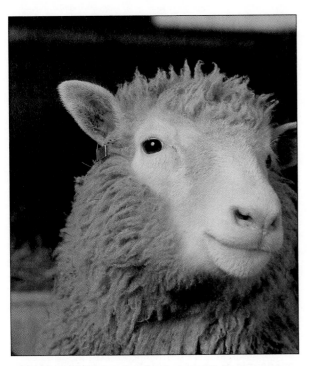

Figure 20.10   The successful cloning of Dolly, the sheep, was a technological breakthrough that raised a series of ethical questions.

the legislation prohibits identifying the sex of an embryo created for reproductive purposes except for medical reasons, paying a woman to be a surrogate mother, paying a donor for his sperm or her eggs, and buying or selling human embryos. It also created an agency to oversee clinics that provide assisted human reproduction services in Canada and to maintain a donor/offspring registry.

The newest development is **therapeutic cloning**, which refers to creating tissues or cells that are genetically identical to those of a patient who needs them to treat any of a number of diseases (Pollack, 2004). Therapeutic cloning is therefore distinct from reproductive cloning to create another individual, like Dolly. As the cloned embryo develops, *stem cells* can be extracted from it, and they hold great promise for treating various neurological diseases such as Alzheimer's. Ethicists debate the morality of stem cell research, which involves the destruction of very early embryos.

Therapeutic cloning: Creating tissues or cells that are genetically identical to those of a patient to treat disease.

There is no way to stop the development of technology, or slow its speed. Nonetheless, it is important to recognize that decisions about human life and reproduction ought not to be made on purely scientific grounds. By definition, they have the deepest moral implications, which must be adequately addressed if essential human values are to be preserved.

■ Toward an Ethics of Human Sexuality

The combined forces of the sexual revolution and the New Morality have attacked the traditional Judeo-Christian sexual ethic as narrow and repressive. This may be true, but it has not yet been proven to everyone's satisfaction that the alternatives proposed are a real improvement upon the Old Morality. Whether the debate will be resolved, and how, remains to be seen.

Whatever ethical approach toward sexuality is adopted, it is important that human rights be respected. A panel of experts convened by the World Health Organization identified a number of sexual rights for all people. They proposed that all persons have the right, free of coercion, discrimination, and violence, to:

- the highest attainable standard of health in relation to sexuality, including access to sexual and reproductive services;
- seek, receive, and impart information in relation to sexuality;
- sexuality education;
- respect for bodily integrity;
- choice of partners;
- decide to be sexual or not;
- consensual sexual relations;
- consensual marriage;
- decide whether or not, and when, to have children; and
- pursue a satisfying, safe, and pleasurable sexual life.

The responsible exercise of human rights requires that all persons respect the sexual rights of others.

■ ■ ■ SUMMARY

It is important to study religion and ethics in conjunction with human sexuality because they frequently provide the framework within which people judge the rightness or wrongness of sexual activity. They give rise to attitudes that influence the way members of a society regard sexuality, and they are therefore powerful influences on behaviour. Religion and ethics may be hedonistic (pleasure oriented) or ascetic (emphasizing self-discipline). They may be legalistic (operating by rules) or situational (making decisions in concrete situations, with few rules).

In the great ethical traditions, ancient Judaism had a positive, though legalistic, view of sexuality. Christian sources are ambivalent about sexuality, with Jesus saying little on the subject and with St. Paul, influenced by the immorality of Roman culture and his expectation of the end of the world, being somewhat negative. Later, Christianity became much more ascetic, as reflected in the writings of Augustine and Thomas Aquinas, who placed Catholic moral theology in the natural-law mould. The Protestant Reformation abolished clerical celibacy and opened the door to greater individual freedom in ethics. Today, new biblical scholarship has led to a wide variety of positions on issues of sexual ethics.

Humanistic ethics rejects external authority, replacing it with a person-centred approach to ethics. A variety of approaches to sexuality can be found in Islam, Hinduism, and Buddhism.

Six ethical issues involving human sexuality have provoked lively debate recently. Although the Western ethical tradition opposes sex outside marriage, some liberals are open to sex among the unmarried under certain conditions. Contraception is opposed by Roman Catholicism and Orthodox Judaism on scriptural and natural-law grounds, but it is positively valued by other groups. Abortion provokes a very emotional argument, with positions ranging from condemnation on the grounds that it is murder to a view that asserts the moral right of women to control their own bodies. Although the traditional view condemns homosexuality absolutely, there is some movement toward either a qualified approval of at least civil rights for gay people or a more complete acceptance of their lifestyle. The spread of AIDS poses serious ethical problems, which involve a balancing of individual needs with the welfare of society. Developments in the technology of human reproduction are creating complex ethical issues with few clear norms. The World Health Organization has proposed universal sexual rights.

■ ■ ■ QUESTIONS FOR THOUGHT, DISCUSSION, AND DEBATE

1. If you are a member of a religious group, investigate your group's beliefs on the issues discussed in this chapter (sex outside marriage, contraception, abortion, homosexuality, AIDS, and reproductive technology). Do you agree with those positions? If you are not a member of a religious group, see if you can formulate a statement of sexual ethics that is consistent with your philosophy of life.

2. Seek out a person, group, or written material that takes the opposite of your position on abortion and carefully consider those arguments. What effect does this have on your views?

3. Ruth Greenberg is the judge in a most unusual custody case. Chad and Michele are a married couple with an infertility problem. Medical testing revealed that Chad had an extremely low sperm count that was unlikely to produce successful fertilization. To make matters worse, Michele had a small, undeveloped uterus and probably would always miscarry early in a pregnancy. Yet they desperately wanted children. They contracted with a surrogate, Mary, to provide an egg and gestation, and used sperm from a sperm bank for the fertilization. The baby, a little girl, has been born, but Mary has now decided that she wants to keep her. The court battle is between Chad and Michele on the one hand and Mary on the other as to who should get the baby. What should Judge Greenberg do?

■ ■ ■ SUGGESTIONS FOR FURTHER READING

Biale, David. (1997). *Eros and the Jews.* Berkeley, CA: University of California Press. A history of sex and the Jewish people.

Boswell, John. (1980). *Christianity, social tolerance, and homosexuality.* Chicago: University of Chicago Press. A very sophisticated reassessment of Christian attitudes toward gays and their place in Western society through the Middle Ages.

Countryman, L. William. (1988). *Dirt, greed, and sex: Sexual ethics in the New Testament and their implications for today.* This seminary professor carefully examines biblical statements about sexuality to gain a better understanding of their meaning and their relevance today.

Genovesi, Vincent J. (1987). *In pursuit of love: Catholic morality and human sexuality.* Wilmington, DE: Michael Glazier. Well-written, scholarly work treating the whole field from the mainline Roman Catholic point of view.

Helminiak, Daniel A. (2000). *What the Bible really says about homosexuality.* Millennium edition. New Mexico: Alamo Square Press. The author, a Roman Catholic priest, questions traditional interpretations of biblical passages about homosexuality, arguing that they have been misinterpreted and do not in fact condemn it.

Jung, Patricia B., Hunt, Mary E., & Balakrishnan, Radhika (Eds.). (2001). *Good sex: Feminist perspectives from the world's religions.* New Brunswick, NJ: Rutgers University Press. This book examines the possibilities for women's sexuality in contemporary Islam, Buddhism, Judaism, and Christianity.

Nelson, James B. (1978). *Embodiment: An approach to sexuality and Christian theology.* Minneapolis: Augsburg. Well-written, scholarly work treating the whole field from the mainline Protestant point of view.

Nelson, James B., and Longfellow, Sandra P. (Eds.). (1994). *Sexuality and the sacred.* Louisville, KY: Westminster Press. An interesting collection of essays on a variety of topics in the realm of sexual ethics.

Parrinder, Geoffrey. (1996). *Sexual morality in the world's religions.* New York: Oxford University Press. A superb and concise treatment of the variety of religious approaches to human sexuality. The best short book in the field.

Online LearningCentre

For Review Questions, Web Resources, and other learning and study tools, visit the *Understanding Human Sexuality* Online Learning Centre at www.mcgrawhill.ca/college/hyde.

Sexuality Education

CHAPTER HIGHLIGHTS

Formal sex education in Canadian schools goes back at least to the early 1900s when Arthur W. Beall gave his "advanced purity lectures."…Those involved in public and school sex education saw themselves at the forefront of "modern thinking." Nevertheless, their message strongly reinforced conventional morality.… [T]hey appear to have been 100% successful in eliminating masturbatory insanity as a social problem. You hardly hear about that these days.*

Children are curious about sex as are most adolescents and many adults. That is perfectly good and normal, and such curiosity motivates children to learn. The only problem is that adults often do not know what to do about it. This chapter concerns **sexuality education,** the lifelong process of acquiring information about sexual behaviour and forming attitudes, beliefs, and values about identity, relationships, and intimacy (SIECUS, 1991). Sex education can occur in many settings: home, school, church or synagogue, youth programs, relationships, and via information found on the Internet.

■ Purposes of Sexuality Education

The goal of sexuality education is to promote healthy sexuality. What is healthy sexuality? In the words of Health Canada:

> Healthy sexuality is a positive and life affirming part of being human. It includes knowledge of self, opportunities for healthy sexual development and sexual experience, the capacity for intimacy, an ability to share relationships, and comfort with different expressions of sexuality including love, joy, caring, sensuality, or celibacy. Our attitudes about sexuality, our ability to understand and accept our own sexuality, to make healthy choices and respect the choices of others, are essential aspects of who we are and how we interact with the world. (Health Canada, 1999)

The Sex Education and Information Council of Canada (**SIECCAN**) is active in promoting high-quality sex education in Canada and coordinated

the development of the *Canadian Guidelines for Sexual Health Education* (Health Canada, 2003). The *Guidelines* provide a framework for sexual health education for persons of all ages that balances the well-being and desires of the individual with the rights of others and of society. There are five principles stated in the *Guidelines*: (1) Everyone should have access to effective sexual health education; (2) sexual health education should be comprehensive and address a broad range of issues relevant to diverse populations; (3) sexual health education should use methods based on the information–motivation–behavioural skills model (described in Chapter 7), as this model has been shown to be effective; (4) sexual health education teachers should be well trained and supported by their administration or organization; and (5) the impact of sexual health education should be evaluated so that programs can be updated. According to the *Guidelines*, sexuality education should help people both to achieve positive outcomes and to avoid negative ones. Positive outcomes include self-esteem, respect for self and others, non-exploitative sexual satisfaction, rewarding human relationships, and the joy of desired parenthood. Negative outcomes include unwanted pregnancy, sexually transmitted infection, sexual coercion, and sexual dysfunction. Effective sexual health education integrates four key components through a variety of sexual activities. These allow individuals:

Sexuality education: The lifelong process of acquiring information about sexual behaviour and forming attitudes, beliefs, and values about identity, relationships, and intimacy.
SIECCAN: The Sex Information and Education Council of Canada, a national resource for up-to-date information, research, and publication on human sexuality, including sexual health.

*Michael Barrett (1990), Chair, Sex Information and Education Council of Canada (SIECCAN).

1. to acquire knowledge that is relevant to their specific sexual health issues;
2. to develop the motivation and personal insight that they will need to act on that knowledge;
3. to acquire the skills necessary to enhance sexual health and avoid negative sexual health outcomes;
4. to help create an environment that is conducive to sexual health. (Health Canada, 2003, p. 12)

To achieve these goals, youth need to have an opportunity to explore attitudes, feelings, and values that may influence their decisions and behaviour. Sex education should emphasize the self-worth and dignity of the individual as well as encourage respect for diversity in values, background, and sexual orientation. The *Guidelines* recognize that students need to make their own informed and responsible choices rather than have choices imposed on them. For example, some adolescents will choose abstinence over sexual involvement; others will choose to have sexual relationships.

■ In the Home, in the School, or Somewhere Else?

When parents of children and teenagers get together to urge their school system to adopt a sex education curriculum, invariably some citizens of the community raise a protest. They might say that sex education promotes sexual intercourse, teenage pregnancy, or AIDS, and they are sure that it should take place only in the home (or possibly the church), but certainly not in the schools.

As shown in Table 21.1, school is the main source of sexual health education for grade 9 students in Canada; 41 percent of the girls and 51 percent of the boys gave this response (Council of Ministers of Education, 2003). In contrast, only 6 percent of the boys and 14 percent of the girls identified parents or other family members as their main source of sexuality information. The fact is that many children are given little or no sexuality education at home. Notice that TV, printed materials such as magazines, and the Internet are important sources of information for many youth, as are friends. In many cases the information provided on TV is sensationalized and unrealistic (refer to In Focus 11.1). Relying

Table 21.1	Main Sources of Grade 9 Students' Information about Sex	
	Boys	*Girls*
Parents or other family members	6%	14%
Friends	9	17
Internet	12	3
School	51	41
Magazines, newspapers, books	5	12
Television/movies	9	5
Physician or nurse	5	5

Source: Council of Ministers of Education (2003).

on friends for information is a classic case of the blind leading the blind. The problem with the Internet as the primary source of sexuality information for youth is that there is no quality control; there are some sites with excellent and accurate information, but others that promote misinformation. Thus, it is appropriate that school has become the main and preferred source of information (McKay & Holowaty, 1997).

Sex education in the school is not "instead of" education in the home. Most Canadian parents, teachers, and students feel that both parents and schools have a role to play in providing sex education (Byers et al., 2003a,b; Cohen et al., 2004; McKay & Holowaty, 1997; McKay et al., 1998; Weaver et al., 2002). For example, in the survey of parents in New Brunswick, 95 percent felt that responsibility for sexual health education should be shared by parents and schools (Weaver et al., 2002); somewhat fewer high school students (77 percent) and middle school students (69 percent) shared this view (Byers et al., 2003a,b). In a survey conducted in the U.S. in 2003, 88 percent of the parents of students in grades 7 and 8 and 80 percent of the parents of students in grades 9 through 12 agreed that the program in the school makes it easier to talk to their child(ren) about sexual issues (Kaiser Family Foundation, 2004a). Some sexuality education programs actively involve parents by including homework to be done jointly by parent and child. The evaluation of one program of this type found that students receiving classroom instruction plus homework felt more able to refuse high-risk behaviours, and more often intended to delay initiation of intercourse compared to students receiving only classroom instruction (Blake et al., 2003). The homework assignments appeared to reinforce the school-based program, and resulted in greater parent–child communication about sex.

How well are parents and schools doing in providing sex education? According to parents and students who participated in four New Brunswick studies described in In Focus 21.1, only between 24 percent (according to middle school students) and 38 percent (according to the parents) of children are getting excellent or very good sex education at home. According to the teachers and students, the schools are not doing much better: between 13 percent (according to high school students) and 37 percent (according to middle school students) rated the sexual health education they had received in school as very good or excellent. One research study involved interviews with 40 rural and urban youth in Nova Scotia and British Columbia about their sexual experiences, including their experiences with sexual health education (Shoveller et al., 2004). The youth indicated that neither schools nor parents promoted meaningful discussions about sex. Rather they perceived that both sexual health education and discussion with parents (if they had any) focused on prevention of pregnancy and STIs; what was missing for these respondents was discussion of issues related to sexual relationships, especially the emotional and potentially positive aspects of sexual relationships. For example, one male youth described the sexual health education he had received in school:

> It [sex] was only talked about in Sex Ed ... it was very *technical* and, of course, you couldn't ask *real* questions about your own experience. I think I understand the physical stuff but it's so emotional. And, it's the emotional stuff that you are always fucked up about when you are young. So, that's the part that was difficult. There's no question-and-answer period for that. You would never do that [emotional stuff] in a science class. (Shoveller et al., 2004, p. 480)

Similarly, youth indicated that they picked up subtle and not so subtle messages from their parents that certain kinds of questions and discussions about sex were "off limits."

The goal of this chapter is to describe effective sex education in school and at home. We will also look at

Figure 21.1 Children often have inaccurate ideas about sex. Dennis the Menace cartoon by T.M. 1983. Dennis the Menace ®: used by permission of Hank Ketcham and © North American Syndicate.

the potential of the Internet for providing sexual education. However, we first examine what research can tell us about what children should be taught about sex at different ages.

■ What to Teach at Different Ages

Sexuality education, whether at home or at school, is not something that can be carried out all at once in one week during grade 5 or by having "the talk." Like teaching math or life skills, it is a process that must begin when children are small. They should learn simple concepts first, progressing to more difficult ones as they grow older. What is taught at any particular age depends on the child's sexual behaviour (see Chapter 11), sexual knowledge, and sexual interests at that age. This section will concentrate on theories and research that provide information on the last two points.

Children's Sexual Knowledge

A few researchers have investigated what children

In Focus 21.1

Attitudes toward Sexual Health Education

A team of New Brunswick researchers collaborated with the New Brunswick Department of Education to conduct parallel surveys of New Brunswick teacher, parent, middle school student, and high school student ideas about sexual health education. They surveyed 4,206 parents, 336 teachers, 745 middle school students, and 1,666 high school students. Some of the questions they asked the four groups, such as whether they were in favour of sexual health education in the schools, were the same. Some of the questions were unique to each group. For example, they asked teachers about their comfort in teaching sexual health, and they asked students and parents about sex education in the home.

Some of the results are presented in Table 21.2. The four groups were consistent with each other in many of their views. For example, all four groups were strongly in support of sexual health education in the schools—more than 90 percent agreed that sexual health education should be provided in schools. Further, they were in favour of a comprehensive curriculum that covers a broad range of topics. This is important because the teachers reported that the greatest barrier to teaching sexual health is fear of negative reactions from parents. Although teachers are overwhelmingly in favour of sexual health education in the schools, they indicated that they felt only somewhat knowledgeable, less comfortable to teach sexual health, and, perhaps as a result, reluctant to teach it. The teachers felt particularly unknowledgeable and uncomfortable teaching about the more controversial topics, such as sexual pleasure, masturbation, and homosexuality. The authors pointed to a need for training for teachers who teach sexual health.

Parents and teachers were somewhat more positive than students were about parents and schools sharing the responsibility for sexual health education. In fact, 40 percent of the students did not wish to talk more with their parents about sexuality. Students' opinions were influenced by the quality of the sex education they had received at home. Students who rated their parents' efforts less highly were less likely to support shared responsibility between parents and schools. This may be

---

in Western countries know about sex and reproduction at various ages. Children begin to develop an understanding of gender at a very early age. They understand first, at least in North America, that sex is constant (a boy will always be a boy) and only later learn that sex is determined by whether one has a penis or a vagina (Gordon & Schroeder, 1995). There is a similar developmental process in children's understanding of pregnancy and birth. Very young children may believe that a baby has always existed, that it existed somewhere else before it got inside the mother. The following dialogue demonstrates this:

> (How did the baby happen to be in your Mommy's tummy?) It just grows inside. (How did it get there?) It's there all the time. Mommy doesn't have to do anything. She waits until she feels it. (You said that the baby wasn't in there when you were there.) Yeah, then he was in the other place . . . in America. (In America?) Yeah, in somebody else's tummy. (Bernstein & Cowan, 1975, p. 86)

As children get older, they develop—we hope—a more accurate understanding!

Children's knowledge about sex varies by social class. In one study of children 2 to 7 years of age, children from middle and upper socioeconomic families knew more about body parts and functions and pregnancy than children from lower socioeconomic families (Gordon et al., 1990). It is possible that these differences reflect parental attitudes rather than socioeconomic status; parents with lower socioeconomic status tended to have more restrictive atti-

Table 21.2 Responses of Parents, Teachers and Students

	Percentage Agreeing with Each Statement			
	Parents	Teachers	Middle School Students	High School Students
Sexual health education should be provided in the schools.	94%	93%	93%	92%
The schools and parents should share responsibility for providing children with sexual health education.	95%	95%	69%	77%
Sexual health education should start in grades K–5.	65%	78%	30%	23%

because these students do not perceive their parents to be experts in sexual health or because they perceive their parents to be uncomfortable talking about sex. Only about half of the parents indicated that they often encouraged their child to ask questions about sex.

Students were more conservative than parents or teachers about when sexual health education should start. While most parents and teachers felt that it should begin in elementary school, most students felt it should start in middle school. This may be because these students had not received sex education in elementary school and thus did not have a clear idea of how sexual health education would be taught to children younger than themselves. The results of these studies were used to revise the sexual health education curriculum in New Brunswick.

Sources: Byers et al., 2003a; Byers et al., 2003b; Cohen et al., 2004. Weaver et al., 2002.

tudes about sexuality, and reported having given their children less sex education.

By age 7 or 8, children have a more sophisticated understanding of reproduction. They may know that three things are involved in making a baby: a social relationship between two people, such as love or marriage; sexual activity; and the union of sperm and egg. However, they may not understand that the sexual activity involves intercourse. At age 12, some children can give a good physiological explanation of reproduction that includes the idea that the embryo begins its biological existence at the moment of conception and is the product of genetic material from both parents. As one preteen explained:

The sperm encounters one ovum, and one sperm breaks into the ovum which produces, the sperm makes like a cell, and the cell separates and divides. And so it's dividing, and the ovum goes through a tube and embeds itself in the wall of the, I think it's the fetus of the woman. (Bernstein & Cowan, 1975, p. 89)

Some 10- and 11-year-olds understand that one of the reasons parents want to be alone is to have sex; others are reluctant to recognize the sexual dimension of their parents' relationship (De La Vega Salas & Thériault, 2001).

As we discussed in Chapter 11, research suggests that many children engage in sexual play and exploration. How does sexual behaviour relate to sexual knowledge? One review of the literature concludes that:

sexual experience and behavior typically precede knowledge and understanding, at least among younger children. The fact that children engage in sexual behavior before they have a clear understanding of what it is all about places them at high risk for a variety of adverse experiences which can impact negatively on their development. (Gordon & Schroeder, 1995, p. 11)

These findings have important implications for sex education. Educators need to be aware of the level of the child's understanding and should not inundate him or her with information inappropriate for his or her age. Instead, the educator should attempt to clarify misunderstandings in the child's beliefs. For example, if a child believes a baby has always existed, the educator might say, "To make a baby, you need two grown-ups, a man and a woman."

Probably the most comprehensive study of children's sex knowledge was done by Ronald and Juliette Goldman in 1982. They did face-to-face interviews with 838 children aged 5 to 15 in four cultures: Australia, England, North America, and Sweden. The North American children were from New York and Ontario. A comparison of the results from the North American children with those from children in the other three cultures led the Goldmans to conclude that North American children are strikingly lacking in sexual information. For example, only 23 percent of North American 9-year-olds, but 60 percent of Australian 9-year-olds, knew the genital differences between newborn boys and girls. The Swedish children were consistently more knowledgeable than the North American children, indicating the positive effects of sex education. Sweden has compulsory sex education for all children beginning at age 8. Given that Canadian schools are increasingly offering sexual health education, it would be interesting to know whether Canadian children's knowledge about sexuality is more extensive in 2006 than it was 25 years ago.

Children's Sexual Interests

Children's knowledge of and interest in sex are reflected in the questions they ask. In a study of children's questions about sex, it was found that many questions are asked at around age 5, a time when children are generally asking questions.

(Byler, 1969). At age 5, kids may be asking where babies come from. At age 9, a boy or girl may ask about sexual behaviours: "What's oral sex?" Such questions are often stimulated by hearing the term in conversation or in the media. A 10-year-old may be interested in bodily processes and ask, "What's a period?" By age 11, many kids are asking questions related to puberty, such as "When will I get breasts?" or "When will I grow taller?" Such questions typically reflect an awareness that other youth are experiencing such growth. At age 13 or 14, many youth have specific questions about sexual activity. One young man asked, "Do girls move a lot when they have sex?" A 14-year-old girl asked her mom, "Where do people have sex?" (Blake, 2004).

It is important that sex education for a particular age group address the questions of that age group, rather than questions they haven't thought of yet or questions they thought about but answered long ago.

High school students agree that sex education should begin in early elementary school, and should progress from the simple to the complex (Byers et al., 2003a). They believe that it should cover a wide range of topics, including reproduction, pregnancy, abortion, birth control options, disease prevention, sexual violence, relationships and gender roles, sexual pleasure, homosexuality, and sexual decision making. They would like all of these topics presented by grade 8, but then revisited in high school. In particular, they want sexual health education that talks more about sex— feelings, arousal, foreplay, contraception, condoms, weighing alternatives—and is respectful of their choices (Caputo, 2000; Langille, 2000; Maticka-Tyndale, 2001).

We can also tell something about children's sexual knowledge and interest by the dirty jokes they tell. Anthropologist Rosemary Zumwalt collected dirty jokes from girls between the ages of 7 and 10 as part of her study of children's folklore (1976). The following is typical of the jokes they told her:

There's this little boy, and he wanted to take a bath with his dad. And his dad said, "If you promise not to look under the curtain." And then he took a shower, and he looked under the curtain. And he said, "Dad, what's that long hairy thing?" And the father says, "That's my banana."

Then he asks his Mom, "Can I take a shower with you, Mom?" She says, "If you promise not to look under the curtain." And they get into the shower, and he looks under the curtain. And he says, "Mom, what's that thing?" And she says, "That's my fruit bowl." And he says, "Mom, can I sleep with you and Dad?" And she says, "Yes, if you promise not to look under the covers." And he looks under the covers and says, "Mom, Dad's banana is in your fruit bowl!" (Zumwalt, 1976, p. 261)

Children's dirty jokes reflect several themes in their attitudes toward sexuality and in their interactions with their parents on the issue. First, children seem to view their parents as always trying to keep sex a secret from them. The parents consistently tell children not to look under the curtain, for example. Second, the jokes reflect children's fascination with sex, particularly with the penis, the vagina, the breasts, and intercourse. The jokes generally revolve around these topics and children's attempts to find out about them. Third, the jokes seem to satirize adults' use of euphemisms for sexual terms. The joke above hinges on a parent's using the term "banana" instead of "penis." Most frequently, the fanciful names used for the sexual organs involve food (banana, hot dog), power (light bulbs, light sockets), or animals (gorilla). Commenting on the bathtub-shower form of dirty joke, an authority said, "In all forms of the . . . joke, the wonderful humor to the child is the mocking of the parents' evasions, which are somehow so foolishly phrased" (Legman, 1968, p. 53).

Teenagers have outgrown this sort of joke, but they tell a parallel one:

This little boy walks into the bathroom, and he catches his mother naked. She was a little embarrassed. He said, "Mommy, what's that?" And she says, "Oh, that's where God hit me with an axe." And the little kid says, "Got you right in the cunt, eh?" (Zumwalt, 1976, p. 267)

Once again, this joke has the theme of a parent's embarrassment and use of evasions and euphemisms when dealing with sex. But now the child (teenager) reflects a sophistication about sex, perhaps even a greater sophistication than the parent has.

Sex educators should remember that children are aware of adults' attempts to "cover up" and of their embarrassment and their use of euphemisms, as these jokes indicate.

■ Attitudes Toward School-Based Sexuality Education

Surveys have shown repeatedly that the vast majority of parents are in favour of sex education in the schools. Research in Ontario, Nova Scotia, and New Brunswick has found very high levels of support among parents (Langille et al., 1996; McKay, 1996; McKay et al., 1998; Weaver et al., 2002). For example, a survey of 6,833 parents in rural southern Ontario found 95 percent in favour of sex education in the schools; 82 percent felt it should begin in the primary grades and continue throughout high school (McKay et al., 1998). Similarly, 94 percent of New Brunswick parents with children in grades kindergarten through 8 support sex education in schools (Weaver et al., 2002). Most parents in the U.S. are also in favour of sex education in schools. In one nationally representative sample in the U.S, 93 percent of the parents of students in grades 7 and 8 and 91 percent of parents of students in grades 9 through 12 said it is "very important" or "important" that sex education be part of the school curriculum (Kaiser Family Foundation, 2004a). The great majority of parents in both Ontario and New Brunswick favoured teaching a wide range of topics including AIDS and other STIs, sexual decision making, sexual communication, sexual assault, birth control, abortion, and homosexuality. The point is that there is strong support for detailed sex education in schools, beginning in the primary grades.

You may be surprised to learn that most adults favour sex education. The media regularly publicize controversies, cases in which parents are protesting sex education in the schools. There are three things to keep in mind about such episodes. First, they are rare. The vast majority of schools with sex education programs have not experienced such conflict. Second, the protesters are usually in a minority. Third, the controversy is often not over whether there should be a program, but over the use of a particular curriculum, book, or video.

■ The Curriculum

The term "sexuality education" has been used to refer to a wide variety of programs. All Canadian provinces and territories have, as part of their

Figure 21.2   Although some parents claim that sex education belongs in the home, it is rarely conducted there effectively. Margulies/The Record/Rothco.

health programs, province-wide, school-based sexual health curricula (Barrett, 1994; Health Canada, 2003). However, there are major differences in how fully these curricula are implemented in different communities (Barrett, 1990). The comprehensiveness of the curriculum that is taught varies considerably from school to school, from school board to school board, and from province to province. There is also considerable controversy over whether the curriculum should address homonegativity. Toronto's Human Sexuality Program was developed following the fatal beating of a gay student in Toronto in 1985 and provides classroom presentations on gay-related issues. However, there was a strong public outcry in 1997 in some parts of British Columbia when the B.C. Teachers Federation announced a decision to develop resources to help teachers address homophobia in the classroom. For example, the conservative Citizens Research Institute developed a pamphlet to help parents demand that children not "be exposed to and/or involved in any activity or program which: discusses or portrays the lifestyle of gays, lesbians, bisexual and/or transgendered individuals as one which is normal, acceptable or must be tolerated" (*Macleans*, 1997). Most Canadian parents, teachers, and students want sexual orientation included in sex education programs (Byers et al., 2003a & b; Cohen et al.,

2004; McKay et al., 1998; Weaver et al., 2002). As most classrooms will have one or two students who are not heterosexual, discussion of sexual orientation helps to meet their needs, as well as to increase acceptance of diversity among their classmates (McKay, 2000).

We will focus in the next section on the more comprehensive programs.

Early Sex Education

The first programs, developed 30 years ago, were concerned with the transmission of knowledge. The goal of these programs was to reduce the number of teen pregnancies. Accordingly, the emphasis was on teaching students about sexual intercourse, pregnancy and birth control, and the consequences of having a baby. Later programs retained the informational content of the first ones, but the emphasis was placed on values clarification and decision-making skills. Proponents of these programs believed that young people engage in sexual risk taking because they are unsure of their values and have difficulty making decisions. These programs also taught skills designed to improve communication with partners. Subsequently, evaluations

clearly demonstrated that these early sex education programs did not markedly hasten or delay onset of intercourse, reduce sexual risk-taking behavior, or reduce teen-age pregnancy. However, they may have increased slightly the use of birth control or had other positive effects that could not be measured by the evaluation methods employed. (Kirby, 1992, p. 281)

Abstinence-Only Programs

Abstinence-only programs developed out of opposition to the early curricula. Some people were opposed to any sex education in the schools; others felt that the existing programs were too liberal or permissive. The concerns led to passage by the U.S. Congress of an Act that limits the use of federal funds to abstinence-only programs that "promote sexual abstinence as the sole means of preventing pregnancy and exposure to sexually transmitted diseases" (Wilcox & Wyatt, 1997, p. 4). Millions of dollars have been spent by U.S. state and federal governments to support the development and widespread use of these programs. The two most widely known of these curricula are called *Sex Respect* and *Teen Aid*. These curricula are typically presented in four to 10 sessions, lasting one hour each, over a period of one to three months. *Sex Respect* includes catchy slogans for children to chant in class, such as "Don't be a louse, wait for your spouse!"; "Do the right thing, wait for the ring!"; and "Pet your dog, not your date!" There is a "chastity pledge" that all students take, and a chart of physical intimacy in which a prolonged kiss is characterized as the "beginning of danger." The curriculum teaches that condoms can be the road to ruin because many fail and pregnancy results.

Sex Respect throws in a lot of gender-role stereotypes as well, characterizing boys as "sexual aggressors" and girls as "virginity protectors." It presents the two-parent, heterosexual couple as "the sole model of a healthy, 'real' family."

Neither the federal nor provincial governments in Canada have supported the development or implementation of abstinence-only sexuality education in the schools. In general, school-based

sexuality education in Canada has taken the approach of not promoting a particular set of values (McKay, 1998). Nonetheless, these programs are being offered in some Canadian schools. For example, in 1992 *Teen Aid* was taught to more than 20,000 students in 203 Saskatchewan schools, even though the Department of Education in that province offers a comprehensive sexuality education curriculum (Mitchell, 1997). School boards paid $150 to $250 a day to the *Teen Aid* organization for it to offer the program. More often the programs are offered in the community, by church groups for example. Research with youth in Northern Ontario indicates that they did not believe these programs were effective (Benoit et al., 2003).

So, how effective are these curricula? Researchers who assessed the content of *Sex Respect* concluded that it omits a number of important topics, including sexual anatomy (!), sexual physiology, sexual response, contraception, and abortion (Goodson & Edmundson, 1994). We noted earlier that high school students say that all of these topics should be included in an "ideal" class. As a result of their widespread use, there have been many evaluations of these programs' effects on student attitudes and behaviour. A review of 52 evaluations concluded that for the most part the research showed these programs did not delay the onset of sexual activity or reduce the percentage of students having sex, getting pregnant, or acquiring an STI (Wilcox & Wyatt, 1997).

Therefore, it is clear that these programs are not achieving their stated goals of preventing teenagers from engaging in sexual intercourse and thereby preventing STIs and unwanted pregnancies.

HIV and AIDS Risk Education

In the 1990s, the focus of sex education shifted from pregnancy prevention to AIDS and other STIs. All provinces and territories have school-based programs that include information about HIV and AIDS (Barrett, 1994). Research has shown that more than 99 percent of Canadian parents approve of HIV/AIDS education in the schools (Weaver et al., 2002).

Programs of this type are often sharply focused on disease prevention. They have a variety of goals, including removing myths about AIDS and other STIs, encouraging delay of sexual intercourse, and supporting condom use or abstinence from

---

Abstinence-only (sex education) programs: Programs that promote sexual abstinence until marriage as the sole means of preventing pregnancy and exposure to sexually transmitted infections.

unprotected intercourse. Each curriculum relies on lectures and class discussion facilitated by a teacher, a public health nurse or, more recently, a peer educator (Dunn et al., 1998). On occasion, someone with AIDS is brought in to talk with the class. These programs were usually short, lasting as few as one or two class periods.

A review of the effectiveness of these programs found 40 published studies (Kim et al., 1997). Most of the studies reported that the educational program improved knowledge significantly. Of those that measured the impact on attitudes (12), more than half (7) found that the program increased positive attitudes toward prevention and negative attitudes about risk. Finally, six of the 10 studies reported positive changes in respondents' intention to use condoms. Interventions that addressed more topics, were based on theory, and that incorporated cultural issues were more effective.

One example of an HIV/AIDS education program in Canadian schools is the 20-hour *Skills for Healthy Relationships* program developed jointly by the federal and provincial governments. This program was designed for grade 9 students and included components aimed at delaying sexual activity, increasing condom use, creating compassion for persons living with HIV/AIDS, combatting homonegativity, and improving communications and negotiating skills. It is based on a theoretical model that includes acquiring knowledge, developing responsible attitudes, increasing motivation, and developing skills. The program uses students as peer group leaders and encourages parental involvement. The effectiveness of the program was evaluated by comparing 2,606 students who received the *Skills for Health Relationships* program from trained teachers to an equal number of students who had taken their school's regular sexuality curriculum (Boyce et al., 2000). Following the *Skills for Healthy Relationships* program, students gained significantly in knowledge, became more positive in their attitudes toward people living with HIV/AIDS, increased their intentions to communicate assertively in sexual situations, and improved their skills in being able to use condoms correctly. However, students who had taken the program did not differ from the control group in whether they were engaging in sexual intercourse or, for students who were engaging in intercourse, in condom use.

The Canada Youth Sexual Health and HIV/AIDS Study found that students in 2002 had less sexual knowledge than students who participated in the 1989 Canada Youth and AIDS Study (Council of Ministers of Education, 2003). For example, two-thirds of grade 7 students and half of grade 9 students did not know that there is no cure for HIV/AIDS. Fewer than half of the students knew that Vaseline is not a good lubricant to use with condoms. Most students knew that sharing needles and having multiple partners increases the risk of HIV infection.

On the other hand, it must be noted that HIV/AIDS risk reduction education is narrowly focused on behaviour. It does not take into account the developmental context or the broad range of social and psychological influences on one's sexual behaviour, nor does it integrate the positive aspects of sexuality (Ehrhardt, 1996). Thus, these programs are not a substitute for a comprehensive sexuality education program as described earlier in this chapter (Woloshyn & Rye, 1995).

Theoretically Based Programs

The newest programs are unique in that they are explicitly based on social science theories of health promotion, including social inoculation theory, social learning theory, and the information–motivation–behavioural skills approach (McKay, 1993). Stress inoculation theory proposes that people are better able to resist social pressure when they recognize the pressure, are motivated to resist it, and have rehearsed resisting it. The curriculum described in In Focus 21.2 on p. 610 is of this type. The best known of these curricula are called *Postponing Sexual Involvement* and *Reducing the Risk*. These programs include discussion of the social pressures to engage in sex, and ways to resist these influences (based on inoculation theory). Social learning theory emphasizes the importance of practising new skills, so these curricula include rehearsal and role-playing activities.

A large-scale evaluation of *Postponing Sexual Involvement* was carried out in California in 1992–1994. More than 10,600 seventh and eighth graders participated; each was randomly assigned to either the curriculum or a control group (Kirby et al., 1997). The *PSI* program consisted of five sessions, 45 to 60 minutes each; it included discussion, group activities, videos or slides, and role-playing. Survey data were collected before the program, 3 months after, and 17 months after the program. At 3 months, youth who participated in *PSI* showed two positive changes in attitude, endorsed more reasons for not having sex, were more likely to recognize sexual content in the media, and were more confident they could say no to sex. At 17 months, there were no differences between the groups. The program had no effect on several measures of sexual behaviour. The review concludes that the program may have been too limited in both scope and duration.

Condom Distribution

In the 1990s, the most visible conflict was over the distribution of condoms to students. Different schools and school districts in Canada have widely differing policies on making condoms available in the schools. In some schools, condoms are available through the sex education program. In other schools, clinics providing health care services to adolescents dispense condoms. In still other schools, condoms are sold in vending machines—one high school in Ottawa and two on Vancouver Island were the first to install condom machines, in 1989. Again, data indicate widespread support for the distribution of condoms in schools. A survey of Canadian adults found that 60 percent were in favour of making condoms available in schools (Ornstein, 1989). It is likely that the percentage is higher today. For example, a survey of all the students in one Denver, Colorado, high school in 1995 found that 85 percent of parents supported distribution of condoms in their school (Fanburg et al., 1995).

The most visible opposition to condom distribution programs is by the Roman Catholic Church. Others oppose such programs on the grounds that they will encourage sexual intercourse outside of marriage. As one critic put it:

> Instead of amoral, secular humanistic sex education and condom distribution in the schools, families, churches, schools, social organizations, and the business community must re-emphasize the teaching, learning, and practice of virtues like courtesy, kindness, honesty, decency, moral courage, integrity, justice, fair play, self-respect, respect for others, and the Golden Rule. (Gow, 1994, p. 184)

In one U.S. study of students in schools where condoms were available, 48 percent of students who reported having intercourse during the two years prior to the study said they had obtained condoms from school. In focus groups, students said that the availability of condoms had not led to an increase in rates of sexual activity. Students preferred that condoms be available in a private location (nurse's office) rather than public ones (vending machines). Students also wanted comprehensive sexuality education programs in conjunction with condoms.

Research indicates that condom distribution programs are associated with reductions in teenage pregnancies and abortions. For example, making condoms available through specialized health units in high schools in one county in rural Ontario resulted in a 21-percent drop in the pregnancy rate and an 11-percent drop in the number of abortions among teenagers 18 years and younger. In a study comparing students in Massachusetts at high schools that did and schools that did not have such programs, researchers found that condom distribution programs were also associated with a reduction in the incidence and frequency of sexual intercourse. Questionnaires were collected from 4,166 students, of whom 865 attended schools where condoms were available. In the analysis of the data, researchers controlled for community and district characteristics (including income, percentage minority, student achievement scores, and drop-out rates) and demographic characteristics (age, grade, ethnicity, gender). Students in schools with condoms available were less likely to report having ever had intercourse and less likely to report recent intercourse (Blake et al., 2003). Sexually active students in schools that made condoms available were twice as likely to use condoms.

■ The Teacher

Suppose you have decided to start a program of sexuality education. You have found a curriculum that is consistent with your objectives. Wherever the program is to be carried out—in the home, the school, the place of worship, or someplace else—the next resource you need is the teacher. There are two essential qualifications: the person must be educated about sexuality, and he or she must be comfortable and skillful in interacting with learners about sexual topics (Health Canada, 2003). Interviews with female high school students in

Amherst, Nova Scotia, identified teacher discomfort and lack of knowledge as important barriers in sexual health education (Langille et al., 1999). Students also see as important the ability of teachers to personalize the information; that is, to relate the material to their lives (Eisenberg et al., 1997).

Sex education teachers need to be educated about sex. Reading a comprehensive text such as this one or taking a college or university course in sexuality are good ways to acquire the information that is needed. The teacher does not have to have a graduate degree in sexology; the important qualifications are a good basic knowledge, a willingness to admit when he or she does not know the answer, and the patience to look things up. In school settings, the preparation of the teachers is an important influence on the success of the program. A survey of Canadian B.Ed. programs found that only 16 percent of them included sexuality as part of a required course (10 to 13 hours on average); about a quarter had an optional sexuality course (McKay & Barrett, 1999). In contrast, undergraduate students in the Department of Sexology at the University of Quebec in Montreal take 28 courses related to sexuality and the department offers a master's degree in sexual health education (Dupras, 2001; Gemme, 1990). A national survey found that only about half of school districts regularly offer in-service training in sexuality education and teachers do not feel comfortable or competent in teaching about sex (McCall et al., 1999). Perhaps as a result, most teachers do not cover the more sensitive issues associated with sexuality and do not use active learning strategies such as role-playing and small group discussion (Cohen et al., 2004). Clearly there is a need for more training in sexuality to prepare teachers to teach sexual health education (Barrett, 1990).

Equally important is the teacher's comfort with sexual topics. Even when parents or other adults willingly give factual information about sex to a child or adolescent, they may convey negative attitudes because they become anxious or blush or because they use euphemisms rather than explicit sexual language. According to one 16-year-old girl, "The personal development classes are a joke. Even the teacher looks uncomfortable. There is no way anybody is going to ask a serious question" (Stodghill, 1998).

Some people are relaxed and comfortable in

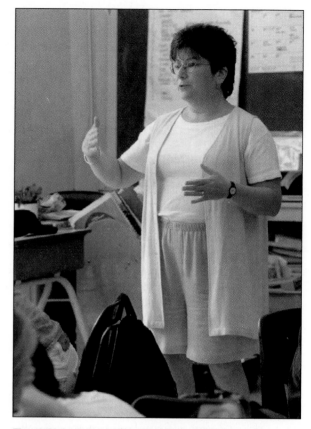

Figure 21.3 A sexual health education class for middle school students in Toronto. Questions range from "How do you know when you need a bra?" to "Can you have sex at 12?"

discussing sex. Others must work to learn this attitude. There are a number of ways to do this. For example, the teacher can role-play, with another adult, having sexual discussions with children. Some communities periodically offer programs designed to increase the comfort of the sexuality teacher or enhance awareness of his or her own sexual values and attitudes.

A good teacher is also a good listener who can assess what the learner knows from the questions asked and who can understand what a child really wants to know when she or he asks a question. As one joke had it, little Billy ran into the kitchen one day after kindergarten and asked his mother where he had come from; she gritted her teeth, realized the time had come, and proceeded with a 15-minute discussion of intercourse, conception, and birth, blushing the whole time. Billy listened, but at the end he appeared somewhat confused and walked away shaking his head, saying, "That's funny. Jimmy says he came from Winnipeg."

■ Effective School-Based Sexuality Education

In light of the continuing high levels of teenage pregnancy (about 38,000 pregnancies per year), the sharp increases in rates of STIs among persons 15 to 24 years of age, and the increasing rate of HIV infection in adolescents, it is imperative that we identify sex education programs that appear to be effective in reducing sexual risk-taking behaviour. Although most programs increase students' knowledge, many programs are not effective at changing behaviour. Unfortunately, there are few published studies evaluating school-based sex education programs in Canada (Barrett, 1990; DiCenso et al., 2002). The effectiveness of school-based programs in the United States has been reviewed, however (Kirby et al., 1994). Researchers identified six characteristics that are associated with delaying the initiation of intercourse, reducing the frequency of intercourse, reducing the number of sexual partners, and increasing the use of condoms and other contraceptives.

Effective programs focus on reducing risk-taking behaviour.   Such programs have a small number of specific goals. They do not emphasize general issues such as gender equality and dating.

Effective programs are based on theories of social learning.   Programs that utilize theory in designing the curriculum are more effective than non-theoretical programs. The theories suggest that, to be effective, the program must increase knowledge, elicit or increase motivation to protect oneself, demonstrate that specific behaviours will protect the person, and teach the person how to use those behaviours effectively.

Effective programs teach through experiential activities that personalize the messages.   Such programs avoid lectures and videos; instead they utilize small-group discussions, simulation and games, role-playing, rehearsal, and similar educational techniques. Some of these programs rely on peer educators.

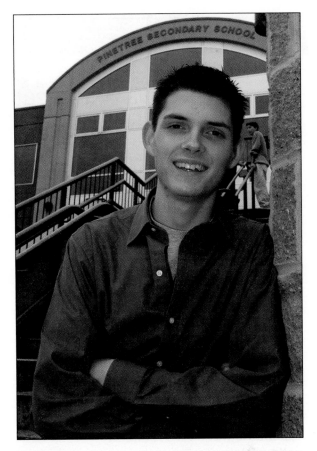

Figure 21.4   While a grade 12 student in Coquitlam, British Columbia, Brent Power formed a gay–straight alliance club to combat homophobia. Some B.C. parents strongly objected to discussion of homosexuality in the classroom.

Effective programs address media and other social influences that encourage sexual risk-taking behaviours.   Some programs look at how the media use sex to sell products. All the effective programs analyze the "lines" that young people use to try to get someone else to engage in sex, and teach ways of responding to these approaches.

Effective programs reinforce clear and appropriate values.   These programs are not value-free. They emphasize the values of postponing sex and avoiding unprotected sex and high-risk partners. The values and norms must be tailored to the target population. Different programs are needed for middle school students, for white middle-class high school students, and for ethnic minority high school students.

In Focus 21.2

A Sample Sexuality Education Curriculum

This set of curriculum guidelines for sexuality education, developed by the Sex Information and Education Council of the United States, is based on teaching about six key concepts, and teaching about each concept at each age level, with age-appropriate material. The age levels are as follows:

- Level 1: ages 5 to 8; early elementary school

- Level 2: ages 9 to 12; upper elementary school

- Level 3: ages 12 to 15; middle school or junior high

- Level 4: ages 15 to 18; high school

The guidelines recommend that the following material be taught:

Key Concept 1: Human Development

Topic 1: Reproductive Anatomy and Physiology

Level 1: Each body part has a correct name and a specific function. Boys and men have a penis, scrotum, and testicles. Girls and women have a vulva, clitoris, vagina, uterus, and ovaries. Both girls and boys have body parts that feel good when touched.

Level 2: The maturation of external and internal reproductive organs occurs during puberty. At puberty, boys begin to ejaculate and girls begin to menstruate.

Level 3: The sexual response system differs from the reproductive system. Some of the reproductive organs provide pleasure as well as reproductive capability.

Level 4: Chromosomes determine whether a developing fetus will be male or female. For both sexes, hormones influence growth and development as well as sexual and reproductive function. A woman's ability to reproduce ceases after menopause; a man can usually reproduce throughout his life. Both men and women can experience sexual pleasure throughout their life. Most people enjoy giving and receiving sexual pleasure.

Topic 2: Reproduction

Level 1: Reproduction requires both a man and a woman. Men and women have reproductive organs that enable them to have a child. Not all men and women decide to have children. When a woman is pregnant, the fetus grows inside her body in her uterus. Babies usually come out of a woman's body through an opening called a vagina. Women have breasts that can provide milk for a baby. Sexual intercourse occurs when a man and a woman place the penis inside the vagina.

Level 2: Sexual intercourse provides pleasure. Whenever genital intercourse occurs, it is possible for the woman to become pregnant. There are ways to have genital intercourse without causing pregnancy.

Effective programs enhance communication skills. Such programs provide models of good communication and opportunities for practice and skill rehearsal.

The length of the program and teacher training are also important. Effective programs are long enough to complete all these components and activities and are delivered by teachers or peers who believed in the program and had received training in how to deliver it (Kirby, 2002).

The United Nations Program on HIV/AIDS commissioned a review of the effectiveness of sexuality education programs, with data from countries as diverse as Mexico, France, Thailand, and the United States (UNAIDS, 1997). The review focused on studies that measured the impact of educational programs on behaviour. Three studies found an increase in sexual behaviour following a program. Twenty-two of 53 studies reported

Level 3: People should use contraception during sexual intercourse unless they want to have a child. Conception is most likely to occur midway between a woman's menstrual periods. Ovulation can occur any time during the month; therefore a woman may become pregnant at any time. When a girl begins to menstruate, she can become pregnant. When a boy produces sperm and can ejaculate, he can cause a pregnancy. An important first sign of pregnancy is a missed menstrual period.

Level 4: Menopause is when a woman's reproductive capacity ceases. Some people are unable to reproduce due to physiological reasons. Medical procedures can help some people with fertility problems. People who cannot reproduce can choose to adopt children. New reproductive technologies, such as artificial insemination, in vitro fertilization, and surrogate motherhood allow people with fertility problems to have children.

Topic 3: Puberty

Level 1: Bodies change as children grow older. People are able to have babies only after they have reached puberty.

Level 2: Puberty begins and ends at different ages for different people. Most changes in puberty are similar for boys and girls. Girls often begin pubertal changes before boys. Early adolescents often feel uncomfortable, clumsy, and/or self-conscious because of the rapid changes in their bodies. The sexual and reproductive systems mature during puberty. During puberty, girls begin to ovulate and menstruate, and boys begin to produce sperm and

ejaculate. During puberty, many people begin to develop sexual and romantic feelings.

Level 3: Some people will not reach full puberty until their middle or late teens.

Topic 4: Body Image

Level 1: Individual bodies are different sizes, shapes, and colours. Male and female bodies are equally special. All bodies are special, including those that are disabled. Good health habits, such as diet and exercise, can improve the way a person looks and feels. Each person can be proud of the special qualities of his or her own body.

Level 2: A person's appearance is determined by heredity, environment, and health habits. The media portray beautiful people, but most people do not fit these images. The value of a person is not determined by his or her appearance.

Level 3: The size and shape of the penis or breasts does not affect reproductive ability or the ability to be a good sexual partner. The size and shape of a person's body may affect how others feel about and behave toward that person. People with physical disabilities have the same feelings, needs, and desires as people without disabilities.

Level 4: Physical appearance is only one factor that attracts one person to another. A person who accepts and feels good about his or her body will seem more likeable and attractive to others. Physical attractiveness should not be a major factor in choosing friends or dating partners.

that the program delayed the initiation of sexual activity, led to a reduction in the number of partners, or reduced rates of unwanted pregnancy and STIs. The characteristics of the most effective programs were similar to those identified above.

Sex education programs that reduce sexual risk-taking behaviour by adolescents do exist, and the inclusion of such programs in the schools is supported by a large majority of the parents in every survey. In addition, effective sexuality education is cost-effective. A school-based program that prevents HIV infection, STIs, and unintended pregnancy among high school students can actually save money. Data from 345 sexually active high school students in California and Texas found that the program *Safer Choices* resulted in a 15-percent increase in condom use and an 11-percent increase in use of other contraceptives. Using a statistical model, researchers estimated the program prevented 0.12 cases of HIV infection, 24 cases of

In Focus 21.2   (continued)

Topic 5: Sexual Identity and Orientation

Level 1: Everyone is born a boy or a girl. Boys and girls grow up to be men and women. Most men and women are heterosexual, which means they will be attracted to and fall in love with someone of the other gender. Some men and women are homosexual, which means they will be attracted to and fall in love with someone of the same gender. Homosexuals are also known as gay men and lesbian women.

Level 2: Sexual orientation refers to whether a person is heterosexual, homosexual, or bisexual. A bisexual person is attracted to both men and women. It is not known why a person has a particular sexual orientation. Homosexual, heterosexual, and bisexual people are alike except for their sexual attraction. Homosexual and bisexual people are often mistreated, called hurtful names, or denied their rights because of their sexual orientation. Some people are afraid to admit they are homosexual because they fear they will be mistreated. Homosexual love relationships can be as fulfilling as heterosexual relationships. Gay men and lesbians can form families by adopting children or having their own children.

Level 3: Many young people have brief sexual experiences (including fantasies and dreams) with the same gender, but they mainly feel attracted to the other gender. When a homosexual person accepts his or her sexual orientation, gains strength and pride as a gay or lesbian person, and tells others, it is known as "coming out." People do not choose their sexual orientation. Sexual orientation cannot be changed by therapy or medicine.

Level 4: One's understanding and identification of one's sexual orientation may change during life. Teenagers who have questions about their sexual orientation should consult a trusted and knowledgeable adult.

The curriculum guidelines continue with equally detailed content for the remaining four key concepts:

Key Concept 2: Relationships

Key Concept 3: Personal Skills

Key Concept 4: Sexual Behaviour

Key Concept 5: Sexual Health

Space does not permit us to list all the details under each of these concepts, so interested readers may want to consult the source listed below.

Source: Condensed from SIECUS (1991), *Guidelines for comprehensive sexuality education,* New York: Sexuality Information and Education Council of the United States.

---

chlamydia, 2.8 cases of gonorrhea, 5.9 cases of pelvic inflammatory disease, and 18 pregnancies. The researchers conclude that the program saved $2.65 in medical and social costs for every dollar spent on the program (Davis et al., 2000).

We need to convince school administrators to implement such programs, to provide adequate training and support to the teachers, and to stand firm in the face of opposition from vocal opponents of these programs. We also need to make sure that our programs not only reduce negative outcomes such as unwanted teenage pregnancies, STIs, and HIV/AIDS, but also achieve positive outcomes such as self-esteem, sexual comfort, and fulfilling interpersonal relationships.

■ Home-Based Sexuality Education

Most children are given little or poor sex education at home. A New Brunswick study asked parents of elementary and middle school students about the extent to which they had discussed a number of sexual topics with their child (Weaver et al., 2002). The parents indicated that they had discussed child sexual abuse and the correct names for genitals in some detail but not in a lot of detail, on average. On average they had discussed the other topics, including puberty, STIs, birth control, and sexual decision making, in general terms or not at all. Few parents of even the middle school students had discussed these topics in a lot of detail. The results of this study also point to three major reasons why parents do not provide much explicit education to their children.

First, many people (and parents *are* people!) are embarrassed about discussing sexuality. We see few models of how to have an explicit, matter-of-fact discussion; we are much more likely to see people discussing sex indirectly, with euphemisms and innuendo, or telling dirty jokes. (As a partial corrective, we have tried to write this book in an explicit, straightforward way.)

Second, there are many things about sexuality that many adults do not know. They did not have good sexuality education themselves, and they may be painfully aware of their ignorance. Even those who received a good sex education, if they took a human sexuality course before 1980, didn't learn of the then-unheard-of disease called AIDS.

Third, parents do not know how to provide sex education to their children. They do not know at what ages they should discuss various topics. They are also not sure how to discuss various topics with their children. They do not feel that they have the resources they need to provide quality sex education to their children. Of course, whether or not sexuality is openly discussed in the home (and many of our students say that it was never talked about in their home), parents communicate to their children about sex. Thus, just as parents convey a positive attitude toward sexuality by, for example, providing children with the correct names for their genitals and comfortably answering their sexual questions, parents convey their negative attitudes toward sex by not doing these things and by not talking about sex. As such, sexual education starts at birth through the nonverbal messages we give that either lead to children feeling good about their bodies or uncomfortable with their bodies and genitals.

Many parents want to talk to their children about sex. However, they feel that they need to be more knowledgeable about sexuality and more comfortable talking about sex before they can do so. They also feel that they need guidance on how to communicate with their children about sexuality. In Focus 21.3 provides some suggestions to parents who want to communicate with their children about sexuality.

Sexuality Education in the Community

The need for accurate sexual information does not end when people graduate from school or university. People need additional information about sexuality throughout their lives, and these needs change as they reach different life stages. The pregnant woman may need to learn about pregnancy and childbirth. New parents may want to increase their understanding of sexuality in childhood or of child sexual abuse. The LGB or transgendered individual may want information about other people's coming-out process. The middle-aged woman may want to learn more about menopause. Even for children and youth, sex education can and does occur outside the home and the classroom. For example, HIV/STI prevention interventions occur in public health clinics, in community settings, or through the media. These efforts can be directed at the population at large, or at specific subgroups with specific needs—for example, men who have sex with men, or street youth, or members of specific ethnocultural minority groups. The media can also be used to increase awareness of specific sexual issues, such as prenatal nutrition, homosexuality, or sexual violence.

Physicians and other health professionals have an important role to play in educating youth about sexual health (McCall & McKay, 2004). For example, by routinely asking about sexual involvement in a nonjudgmental way, physicians make it more likely that teenagers will approach them for advice on contraception when they do begin having sexual intercourse. However, many physicians are not comfortable talking about sex with their patients, particularly their adolescent patients, and thus do not routinely ask these questions. Others do not feel knowledgeable about sexuality—many medical schools provide little education about sexuality. Perhaps as a result, a Nova Scotia study found that few high school students had ever discussed whether they were sexually active with their family doctor. Even among students who were engaging in intercourse, only 56 percent of the girls and 16 percent of the boys had discussed this with their family physician (Langille et al., 2001.)

The Internet may also be useful in providing information about sexuality. This can be as an addition to formal school-based sex education, or as a

In Focus 21.3

Talking to Your Children about Sex

Many parents want to be able to communicate with their children about sexuality but feel nervous about doing so. Here are a few guidelines for parents taken in part from the materials prepared by SIEC-CAN for the Canadian Health Network:

First, be prepared. This means that parents should educate themselves about sexuality. If they are fortunate and had a good sex education course in high school or university, they may already feel knowledgeable enough to answer their children's questions. These parents tend to talk more to their children about sexuality than do parents who did not take a human sexuality course (King et al., 1994). However, many parents do not feel that they know as much as they should and are afraid that their children will ask them questions that they can't answer. It's okay not to know everything about sex; after all, most children can get the facts from the sexual health education they receive at school. Besides, sharing the feelings and values they want their children to have, not teaching facts, is the most important contribution that parents can make to their children's sexuality education. Nonetheless, many parents will want to take steps to fill in some of the gaps they have in their knowledge about sexuality. To do this they can read books such as this textbook on human sexuality or books on talking to children about sexuality, or they can attend a workshop for parents on that subject. They can also find out what is in the sex education curriculum that their children are learning at school. Remember, parents need to talk to their children about both the positive as well as about negative aspects of sex such as sexual abuse, sexual coercion, and STIs.

Second, work to increase your comfort level. One of the most important contributions parents can make to their children's sex education is increasing their children's comfort in talking about and asking questions about sex. Children's comfort will largely reflect the parent's comfort. Parents need to acknowledge to themselves the areas and topics that make them uncomfortable and take steps to increase their comfort level. Books and workshops about talking to your children about sexuality are good ways to increase comfort level. Planning what to say and practising saying it (preferably in front of the mirror or with a partner) may also help to increase comfort.

Third, plan ahead. Most of us did not have parents who talked to us about sex, so we can't base our own approach to educating our children about sexuality on our own experiences. As a result, it is important for parents to decide how they want to approach sexuality education with their children. For example, they need to decide what they want to tell their children at various ages, how they plan to share their values with them, how they want to respond to questions about things their child hears at school, and so on. Remember that positive messages are more likely to have an influence than are lectures and threats. Also, parents need to plan for what they might say if their teenager tells them something that they find upsetting. It is important for parents to discuss these matters with teenagers

way of providing sexual information to people throughout their lives. Certainly, many Canadians already seek out sexuality information on the Internet, and Health Canada maintains a sex information Web site: www.canadian-health-network.ca. For example, in an online survey of 760 university students in British Columbia, about half (52.5 percent) had looked for sexuality information on the Internet within the past year (Boies, 2002). Further, 21 percent of the students reported that their first sexuality education material had come from the Internet. The Internet is particularly attractive because it is an affordable, available, anonymous, acceptable way to access sexuality information and people can do so without being observed (Barak & Fisher, 2001; Cooper, 1998; King, 1999). There are calmly, without yelling, or they will close the doors to further discussions. (For examples of typical questions children and adolescents have at different ages and suggestions about how to respond to these questions you can check out www.sexualityandu.ca/eng/parents/ts.)

Fourth, be proactive. Too many parents wait for their children to ask them questions. Children are naturally curious about sex, but they are unlikely to ask questions if they have been getting nonverbal messages that their parents are uncomfortable talking about sex, or if sex is never mentioned in the home. If you take the first steps, it will be easier for children to raise questions and concerns at a later date. Opening the lines of communication is as important as the information you provide.

A good way to start talking to children about sex is to use what we often call "teachable moments." For example, bath time is a good opportunity to provide children with the correct term for their genitals just as we provide them with the correct name for their other body parts—nose, knee, toes. Other teachable moments occur when someone the child knows becomes pregnant or gives birth, when something sexual is mentioned on television, or when a sexually related story is on the news. Parents can use these teachable moments to raise the topic of where babies come from, whether teenagers should be having sexual intercourse, whether a couple in a movie are engaging in safer sex, and so on.

Another way to be proactive is to provide children and youth with books and videotapes about sexuality. Parents will need to read the books or watch the videotapes with young and preadolescent children. This can lead to interesting discussions on the topics raised in the book or video. Teenagers may prefer to read books on their own, but parents should nonetheless initiate a discussion about the material in order to answer questions or concerns that the teenager has. Parents also need to initiate discussions with their teenage children on sexual decision making, and to try to ensure that their teenagers have the skills to apply their decisions in real-life situations. For example, parents can help teenagers become more comfortable talking to partners about their sexual decisions or, if they do decide to have sex, about safer sex and birth control.

Fifth, answer all questions truthfully, honestly, and accurately. For young children, this will involve providing short answers containing direct explanations. For young children, give short answers. As children grow older they will want and need more detail and will be more likely to ask questions if you've created an open environment. Parents do not need to worry about providing children with too much information too early. Children take the information they need and tend to ignore the rest. Unless you are a sex educator yourself, it is likely that your children will ask you a question and you will not know the answer. It's okay not to know everything about sex. By admitting that they don't know the answer, parents give their children permission not to know everything about sex and to ask questions. Of course, it's important for parents to then try to find the answer with their child.

several other advantages to sex education on the Internet (Barak & Fisher, 2001):

1. Materials are easily revised so all users can have access to the most up-to-date information.
2. Web sites can use multimedia communications, including text, sound, pictures, animation, and videos.
3. The material can be accessed from any computer, at any time.
4. Users can exchange information with other users.
5. The location can provide access to information and services outside the instructional site by providing links to other sites.
6. Potentially, information and programs provided can be individualized to the needs of each user

In Focus 21.4

Sexual Health Education for Persons with Developmental Disabilities

Persons with IQs below 70 are generally classified as having an intellectual or developmental disability (officially called "mental retardation"). There is a great range of capacities of individuals with developmental disabilities, from some who require institutionalization and constant care, to those who function quite well in the community, who can read and write and hold simple jobs. It is important to recognize that the great majority of persons with intellectual disabilities in the moderate range (IQs between 50 and 70) are in the category of near-normal functioning.

In the past, society has regarded persons with intellectual disabilities as asexual. Although many of these attitudes remain, society, parents, and caregivers are increasingly recognizing that persons with intellectual disabilities have normal sexual desires. However, because these children are often slower to learn the norms of society, they may express themselves sexually in ways that are not acceptable to others, such as masturbating in public. Further, persons with intellectual disabilities may be particularly vulnerable to sexual exploitation and abuse.

Unfortunately, not all intellectually disabled youth have access to adequate sexual health education; in fact, many receive little or no such education. For intellectual disabled students enrolled in regular classes, the sexual health education curriculum may not fit their learning style or level of understanding. For these reasons and others, careful sexuality education for persons with intellectual disabilities is essential. Fortunately, there are now a number of comprehensive guides and curricula that have been developed precisely to teach intellectually disabled youth about their sexuality. For example, the *Knowing Where You Stand* resource developed by Planned Parenthood Fredericton (2004) teaches intellectually disabled youth

- about their own bodies;
- to feel comfortable with their bodies;
- to make healthy informed choices for themselves;
- how to set boundaries for themselves and respect the boundaries of others;
- how to be safe whether or not they choose to engage in sexual activity; and
- about healthy and abusive relationships.

It is important that persons with intellectual dis-

based on responses to prescreening questions administered on the site.

There are also potential problems with sex education on the Internet. Anybody can establish an Internet site and nobody monitors these sites for the accuracy of their content, so the unsuspecting user may be getting incorrect information. Further, right now there are not many sex education Web sites; in contrast there are a large number of pornographic Web sites and online sex shops (Fisher & Barak, 2000). Finally, not everybody has access to the Internet; people who are socioeconomically disadvantaged and who belong to ethnocultural minorities tend to have less access. Nonetheless, the Internet certainly has the potential to enhance traditional approaches to sex education.

■ Effective Multicultural Sexuality Education

Much of the discussion in this chapter has assumed that the participants in a sexuality education pro-

Figure 21.5   There is a need to provide sex education to children with disabilities.

abilities be educated about contraception and that contraceptives be made available to them. Because persons with intellectual disabilities have normal sexual desires, they may engage in sexual activity including intercourse. In one study, 24 percent of boys and 8 percent of girls with developmental delays had engaged in intercourse by age 16 (Cheng & Udry, 2003). If these youth lack sexuality education, they may not realize that pregnancy and STIs can result. An unwanted pregnancy for a woman or couple with intellectual disabilities may be a difficult situation; they may be able to function well when taking care of themselves but not with the added burden of a baby. On the other hand, some persons with intellectual disabilities do function sufficiently well to care for a child. The important thing is that they make as educated a decision as possible and that they have access to contraceptives. Many experts recommend an IUD or other methods that do not require memory or forethought for effective use for women with intellectual disabilities.

In the 1920s, both Alberta and British Columbia passed laws allowing sterilization without their consent of people deemed to have mental retardation. While we now view this as a violation of human rights, the law was not repealed in Alberta until 1972, after 2,900 such operations had been performed. In 1996, an Alberta woman successfully sued the government for damages related to her involuntary sterilization. She had been sterilized at the age of 14 without her knowledge or consent.

In summary, persons with intellectual disabilities have sexual needs and desire. Because of their special needs, it is especially important that they receive appropriate sexual health education.

Sources: Ames, 1991; Baladerian, 1991; DiGuilio, 2003; Kempton & Kahn, 1991; Nemeth, 1995; Planned Parenthood Fredericton, 2004.

gram are homogeneous, that they are all from the same ethnocultural community. In some situations that assumption is valid; but in other settings, the learners may be from diverse ethnocultural backgrounds.

Cultures vary in a number of ways that are directly related to the success or failure of a sexuality education program (Irvine, 1995). There are cultural differences in sexual practices; some of these were discussed in Chapters 1 and 10. The acceptability of explicit sexual language or of particular types of language, such as street slang, varies from one cultural community to another. Cultures vary in the meaning they attach to sexuality. The majority cultures in Europe and North America have emphasized sex for the purpose of reproduction and thus tend to regard vaginal intercourse as the norm (see Chapter 20). Other cultures place greater emphasis on the pleasure that can be derived from sexual stimulation. Finally, cultures vary in the definition of and the roles expected within the family.

Of necessity, sexuality education programs utilize language. Street slang might enhance rapport with street youth but deeply offend recent immigrants. Curriculum developers and teachers base their programs on assumptions about the prevalence of specific sexual practices, such as vaginal and anal intercourse. They implicitly or explicitly identify some practices as desirable, for example, condom use. They reflect assumptions about the purposes of sexual intimacy; for example, abstinence-based programs assume that sexual intercourse is most or only meaningful within marriage.

If sexuality education is to be successful, it must reflect, or at least accept, the cultures of the participants. The educator must assess the audience, the intended messages, and the context, and target the program accordingly (Irvine, 1995). Educators must recognize their own sexual culture, learn about the sexual cultures of the participants, and be aware of the power differences between groups in our society. In the classroom, they should use this knowledge to enhance the effectiveness of the pre-

sentation. The use of communication styles and media common to the cultures of the participants—for example, music—can be a valuable tool. Finally, it is important that the program not advocate beliefs and practices that are incompatible with participants' cultures. Such programs are doomed to failure. This is true for school-based sexuality education as well as for workshops and outreach programs. For example, researchers in Toronto documented a need for educational outreach and services specifically for East Asian and Southeast Asian men who have sex with men. They used the results of a needs assessment to make specific recommendations about how to best provide culturally appropriate services (Poon et al., 2001).

The *First Nations HIV/TB Training Kit* is designed to train community health educators to deliver culturally based training sessions on HIV and TB (tuberculosis) (Association of Iroquois and Allied

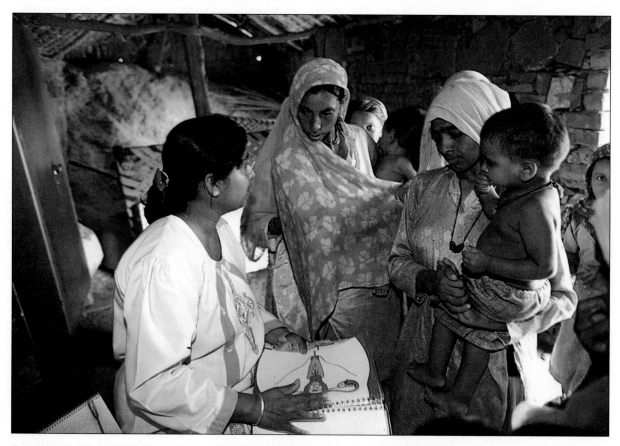

Figure 21.6   Sex education around the world. At this family planning clinic in India, an educator explains the female reproductive system to these mothers.

Indians, 1997). Training emphasizes cultural sensitivity to distinct rituals, cultural practices, and methods within each First Nation's community such as storytelling, the talking circle, traditional medicines, and the medicine wheel. Resources like this one, and the programs that result from this type of training, respond to the call for sexuality education that incorporates the family and community context in which our sexuality is grounded (Health Canada, 1994; Maddock, 1997; Young, 1996).

Another group that needs to have sexuality education tailored to its needs is those with developmental disabilities (see In Focus 21.4 on p. 616). We cannot assume that curricula designed for students in grade 6 can be presented to 12-year-olds with these disabilities (DiGiulio, 2003). Instead,

programs need to assess the cognitive and emotional abilities of each child and adolescent, then present developmentally appropriate materials. Information about forms of romantic and sexual expression may have to emphasize social norms about what is appropriate, and discourage inappropriate behaviours in public. Also, programs for persons with disabilities must recognize their vulnerability to exploitation and make special efforts to teach them self-protection skills.

An institute in Mexico had been involved in a long-term project to develop sex education programs appropriate for that culture (Pick et al., 2003). In that cultural context, programs must take into account strong, traditional gender roles. Men who have many sex partners are widely admired; women are to be modest and not display pleasure

Figure 21.7   Research indicates that sex education programs are most effective when they allow students to gain experience through role-playing and rehearsing discussions they might have with a potential partner. Here students role-play ways of resisting pressure to engage in unwanted sexual activity.

in sexuality. Decisions regarding sexuality and reproduction are made by the man, with the woman playing a passive role. Ninety-five percent of the population is Roman Catholic, and the traditions of that religion must be taken into account. Taking all of these factors into account, the educational programs that the institute developed emphasize a participatory learning style, concrete knowledge about not only sexuality but also gender roles and expectations, and communication skills, especially those for communicating with parents.

As we increasingly recognize diversity both within Canada and around the world, the development of developmentally and culturally effective sexuality educational programs will present important challenges.

■ ■ ■ SUMMARY

Many children receive their sex education from their peers or other sources, not from their parents. As a result, those who argue for sex education being taught only in the home rather than in the school are being unrealistic. Most Canadians do favour sex education in the school. Cases of opposition to sex education are rare and involve a small number of people.

The purposes of sexuality education include providing children with adequate knowledge of the physical and emotional aspects of sex, with an opportunity to develop their own values and interpersonal skills, and with the maturity to take responsibility for their sexuality.

What is taught at each age should depend on what children are thinking about at that age. Children pass through various stages in their understanding of sexuality. For example, at first they believe that a baby has always existed. Later, they realize that the parents caused the baby's creation, but they don't know exactly how. Older children acquire a more scientific understanding of reproduction. Children's sexual play seems to precede rather than follow the development of sexual knowledge. Children's dirty jokes reflect their parents' attempts to hide sex from them, their parents' use of euphemisms rather than actual terms, and their great fascination with sexual organs and intercourse.

Sexuality education curricula have evolved a great deal over the past three decades. The early programs focused on knowledge, values clarification, and decision-making skills. They did not have substantial effects. Conservative programs such as *Sex Respect* emphasize abstinence and are limited in content. Although millions of dollars are spent annually to promote these programs, the evidence indicates they are not effective. HIV education programs are required by many school boards; surveys suggest that they may lead to increased knowledge and more frequent condom use. Contemporary programs are based on social science theory and emphasize the importance of allowing children to practise new behaviours such as communication skills. An evaluation of one of these programs found some changes three months after participation. None of the changes lasted 17 months.

There is a good deal of conflict over the distribution of condoms in high schools. There is widespread support among both high school students and their parents for such programs, but the Catholic Church, among others, is a vocal opponent.

A good sexuality education instructor must have accurate knowledge about sexuality, be comfortable discussing it, and be good at listening to the questions learners ask. Students say that the instructor's ability to relate the material to their lives is also important.

Research suggests that sexuality education programs that are effective at delaying the onset of intercourse, reducing the frequency of intercourse and the number of partners, and increasing condom use share several characteristics. They focus on specific risk-taking behaviours, are based on theory, utilize experiential activities, address social influences on sexual behaviour, reinforce values, and provide opportunities to practise new skills.

To be effective, multicultural sexuality education must reflect or be consistent with the culture(s) of participants. It should present messages that are compatible with their beliefs and practices. Such programs should utilize language and styles of communication that are appropriate.

■ ■ ■ QUESTIONS FOR THOUGHT, DISCUSSION, AND DEBATE

1. Design a sample sexuality education curriculum for the schools, indicating what topics you think would be important to teach at various age levels and what your reasoning is behind your choices.

2. Debate the following topic. Resolved: A sexuality education unit, at least a week long, should be included in all grades in all schools.

3. Data from surveys indicate that the mass media are a major source of information about sexuality for children and adolescents. We saw, in Chapter 1 and In Focus 11.1, that media portrayals in North America are generally unrealistic. How would you deal with access to media portrayals of sexuality for your child at ages 5, 10, and 15? What would you do, and what would you tell your child at each age?

■ ■ ■ SUGGESTIONS FOR FURTHER READING

Gordon, Sol. (1986, Oct.). What kids need to know. *Psychology Today.* Reprinted in O. Pocs (Ed.), *Human Sexuality 88/89.* Guilford, CT: Dushkin. Sol Gordon, a leading sex educator, provides a humorous view of what sexuality education ought to be accomplishing.

Harris, Robie H. (1994). *It's perfectly normal.* Cambridge, MA: Candlewick Press. An entertaining and thorough sexuality education book for children 10 and over.

Health Canada. (2003). *Canadian guidelines for sexual health education.* Ottawa: Health Canada. The guidelines outline five principles of sexual health education as well as specific guidelines to achieve each principle. They are useful for developing sexual health education programs or in evaluating existing programs.

Mayle, P., Robins, A., and Walter, P. (1973). *Where did I come from?* Secaucus, NJ: Lyle Stuart. A delightful sexuality education book for young children. A companion volume—*What's happening to me?*—is for children approaching or experiencing puberty.

McKay, Alexander. (1998). *Sexual ideology and schooling: Towards democratic sexuality education.* Alex McKay, research coordinator at SIECCAN, describes the controversies around sexuality education. He also proposes a philosophy of sexuality education.

Planned Parenthood Federation of Canada. (2001) *Beyond the basics: A sourcebook on sexual and reproductive health education.* Ottawa: Author. This is an outstanding tool for educators who deliver sex education to 9- to 18-year-olds, based primarily on Canadian materials. It is divided into modules. Each module contains a brief primer that outlines objectives, provides background information, and highlights key issues as well as a series of participatory activities. Activities in each module are divided into elementary, middle school, and high school levels.

SIECUS. (1991). *Guidelines for comprehensive sexuality education: Kindergarten–12th grade.* New York: Sexuality Information and Education Council of the United States. The guidelines outline a comprehensive program, divided into 36 topics, and contain developmentally appropriate messages according to school level.

For Review Questions, Web Resources, and other learning and study tools, visit the *Understanding Human Sexuality* Online Learning Centre at www.mcgrawhill.ca/college/hyde.

Epilogue

In the AIDS era, the challenge for us is to create joyous, intimate, fulfilling sex. We are convinced that there are two courses of action that are absolute folly. One is to be so overwhelmed by the threat of AIDS and of abstinence-only thinking that sex becomes locked in the icy grip of anxiety. The other absolute folly is to hide our heads in the sand, ignore the threat of AIDS (and herpes and genital warts), and continue with sex as usual. The AIDS epidemic will then only intensify. All of us need to steer a middle course in which we take AIDS and other STIs seriously, while keeping sex joyful and satisfying.

We have no easy answers to these challenges. Sex education is one part of the solution, as is drug education. Continued funding for both medical and psychological research is essential. Meanwhile, we need to remember that sex can and should be joyous.

References

ABC News. (2004, May 27). American Porn: Corporate America is profiting from porn—quietly. Retrieved from Abcnews.go.com/sections/Primetime/Entertainment/porn_business.

Abbey, A. (1991). Misperception as an antecedent of acquaintance rape: A consequence of ambiguity in communication between men and women. In A. Parrott & L. Bechhofer (Eds.), *Acquaintance rape: The hidden crime.* New York: Wiley.

Abel, G. G., Becker, J. V., Mittelman, M., Cunningham-Rathner, J., Rouleau, J. L., & Murphy, W. D. (1987). Self-reported sex crimes of nonincarcerated paraphiliacs. *Journal of Interpersonal Violence, 2,* 3–25.

Abel, G. G., Osborn, C., Anthony, D., & Gardos, P. (1992). Current treatments of paraphiliacs. *Annual Review of Sex Research, 3,* 255–290.

Abel, G., & Rouleau, J.-L. (1990). The nature and extent of sexual assault. In W. L. Marshall, D. R. Laws, & H. E. Bartarce (Eds.), *Handbook of sexual assault* (pp. 9–21). New York: Plenum.

Abram, D., Viki, G., Masser, B., & Bohner, G. (2003). Perceptions of stranger and acquaintance rape: The role of benevolent and hostile sexism in victim blame and rape proclivity. *Journal of Personality and Social Psychology, 84,* 111–125.

Abramowitz, S. I. (1986). Psychosocial outcomes of sex reassignment surgery. *Journal of Consulting and Clinical Psychology, 54,* 183–189.

ACSF Investigators. (1992). AIDS and sexual behaviour in France. *Nature, 360,* 407–409.

Acker, M., & Davis, M. (1992). Intimacy, passion and commitment in adult romantic relationships: A test of the triangular theory of love. *Journal of Social and Personal Relationships, 9,* 21–50.

Adam, B. D., Sears, A., & Schellenberg, E. G. (2000). Accounting for unsafe sex: Interviews with men who have sex with men. *The Journal of Sex Research, 37,* 24–36.

Adam & Eve. (2004). *Sex Stat: Sexy Internet sites gain in popularity.* Atlanta, GA: Adam & Eve.

Adams, M.A., et al. (1997). Vascular control mechanisms in penile erection: Phylogeny and the inevitability of multiple and overlapping systems. *International Journal of Impotence Research, 9,* 85–91.

Addiego, F., Belzer, E. G., Comolli, J., Moger, W., Perry, J. D., & Whipple, B. (1981). Female ejaculation: A case study. *Journal of Sex Research, 17,* 13–21.

Adkins-Regan, E. (2002). Development of sexual partner preference in the zebra finch: A socially monogamous, pair-bonding animal. *Archives of Sexual Behavior, 31,* 27–34.

Adoya-Osiguwa, S. A., Markoulaki, S., Pocock, V., Milligan, S. R., & Fraser, L. R. (2003). 17B-estradiol and environmental estrogens significantly affect mammalian sperm function. *Human Reproduction, 18,* 101–107.

Afriat, C. (1995). Antepartum care. In D. R. Coustan, R. V. Hunning, Jr., & D. Singer (Eds.), *Human reproduction: Growth and development* (pp. 213–234). Boston: Little, Brown.

Aggarwal, A. P. (1992). *Sexual harassment: A guide for understanding and prevention.* Toronto: Butterworths.

Agnew, T. (1997). *A multicultural perspective of breastfeeding in Canada.* Ottawa: Minister of Public Works and Government Services Canada.

Ahluwalia, I. B., Merritt, R., Beck, L. E., & Rogers, M. (2001). Multiple lifestyle and psychosocial risks and delivery of small for gestational age infants. *Obstetrics and Gynecology, 97,* 649–656.

Ahmadi, N. (2003). Rocking sexualities: Iranian migrants' views on sexuality. *Archives of Sexual Behavior, 32,* 317–326.

Albin, R. S. (1977). Psychological studies of rape. *Signs, 3,* 423–435.

Alderson, K. G. (2003). The ecological model of gay male identity. *Canadian Journal of Human Sexuality, 12,* 75–85.

Alexander, E. (1990). Sexual therapy in English-speaking Canada. *SIECCAN Journal, 5*(1), 37–43.

Alexander, M. G., & Fisher, T. D. (2003). Truth and consequences: Using the bogus pipeline to examine sex differences in self-reported sexuality. *Journal of Sex Research, 40,* 27–35.

Alkhatib, G., et al. (1996). CC CKR5: A RANTES, MIP1a, MIP-Ib receptor as a fusin cofactor for macrophage-tropic HIV-1. *Science, 272,* 1955.

Allen, M., & Burrell, N. A. (2002). Sexual orientation of the parent: The impact on the child. In M. Allen & R. W. Preiss et al. (Eds.), *Interpersonal communication research: Advances through meta-analysis* (pp. 125–143). Mahwah, NJ: Erlbaum.

Allen, M., D'Alessio, D., Emmers, T., & Gebhardt, L. (1996). The role of educational briefings in mitigating effects of experimental exposure to violent sexually explicit material. *Journal of Sex Research, 33,* 135–141.

Allen, D. M. (1980). Young male prostitutes: A psychological study. *Archives of Sexual Behavior, 9,* 399–426.

Allgeier, E. R., & Wiederman, M. W. (1994). How useful is evolutionary psychology for understanding contemporary human sexual behavior? *Annual Review of Sex Research, 5,* 218–256.

Almroth, L., Almroth-Berggren, V., & Hassanein, O. M. (2001). Male complications of female genital mutilation. *Social Science & Medicine, 53,* 1455–1460.

Amara, R. R., Villinger, F., Altman, J. D., Lydy, S. L., O'Neil, S. P., Staprans, S. I., et al. (2001). Control of a mucosal challenge and prevention of AIDS by a multiprotein DNA/MVA vaccine. Science, 292, 69–74.

Ambrosone, C. B., et al. (1996). Cigarette smoking, N-Acetyltransferase 2 genetic polymorphisms, and breast cancer risk. *Journal of the American Medical Association, 276,* 1494–1501.

American Academy of Pediatrics Committee on Genetics. (2000). Evaluation of the newborn with developmental anomalies of the external genitalia. *Pediatrics, 106,* 138–142.

American Association of Retired Persons. (1999). *AARP Modern Maturity sexuality study.* Washington, D.C.: AARP.

American Psychiatric Association. (1994). *Diagnostic and statistical manual of mental disorders* (4th ed). Washington, DC: Author.

American Psychiatric Association. (2000). *Diagnostic and statistical manual of mental disorders,* 4th ed. Washington, DC: American Psychiatric Association.

American Psychiatric Association. (2000). *Diagnostic and statistical manual of mental disorders.* (4th ed., Text Revision). Washington, DC: Author.

American Psychiatric Association. (2000). Position statement on therapies focused on attempts to change sexual orientation (reparative or conversion therapies). *American Journal of Psychiatry, 157,* 1719–1721.

Ames, T.-R. (1991). Guidelines for providing sexuality-related services to severely and profoundly retarded individuals: The challenge for the 1990s. *Sexuality and Disability, 9,* 113–122.

Anderson, K., Kaplan, H., & Lancaster, J. (2001). *Men's financial expenditures on genetic children and stepchildren from current and former relationships* (Report No. 01-484). Ann Arbor, MI: Population Studies Center.

Anderson, M. C. et al. (2004). Neural systems underlying the suppression of unwanted memories. *Science, 303,* 232–235.

Anderson, M. C., Ochsner, K. N., Kuhl, B., Cooper, J., Robertson, E., Gabrieli, S. W., et al. (2004). Neural systems underlying the suppression of unwanted memories. *Science, 303,* 232–235.

Anson, R. S. (1977, October 25). *San Francisco Chronicle.*

Antle, K. (1978). Active involvement of expectant fathers in pregnancy: Some further considerations. *Journal of Obstetric, Gynecologic and Neonatal Nursing, 7*(2), 7–12.

Antoni, M. H., & Carver, C. S. (2001). Cognitive–behavioral stress management intervention decreases the prevalence of depression and enhances benefit finding among women under treatment for early-stage breast cancer. *Health Psychology, 20,* 20–32.

Apfelbaum, B. (2000). Retarded ejaculation: A much misunderstood syndrome. In S. Leiblum & R. Rosen (Eds.), *Principles and practice of sex therapy,* (3rd ed., pp. 205–241). New York: Guilford.

Appleby, B. M. (1999). *Responsible parenthood: Decriminalizing contraception in Canada.* Toronto: University of Toronto Press.

Aquinas, St. Thomas. (1968). *Summa theologica* (Vol. 43). (Thomas Gilly, Trans.). New York: McGraw-Hill.

Araujo, A. B., Durante, R., Feldman, H. A., Goldstein, I., & McKinlay, J. B. (1998). The relationship between depressive symptoms and male erectile dysfunction: Cross-sectional results from the Massachusetts Male Aging Study. *Psychosomatic Medicine, 60,* 458–465.

Araujo, A. B., Johannes, C. B., Feldman, H. A., Derby, C. A., & McKinlay, J. B. (2000). Relation between psychosocial risk factors and incident erectile dysfunction: Prospective results from the Massachusetts Male Aging Study. *American Journal of Epidemiology, 152,* 533–541.

Archibald, S. A., Lemieux, S., Byers, E. S., Tamlyn, K. & Worth, J. (in press). Chemically-induced menopause and the sexual functioning of breast cancer survivors. *Women and Therapy.*

Aries, E. (1996). *Men and women in interaction: Reconsidering the differences.* New York: Oxford University Press.

Arnold, A.P. (2003). The gender of the voice within: The neural origin of sex differences in the brain. *Current Opinion in Neurobiology, 13,* 759–764.

Arnow, B. A., Desmond, J. E., Banner, L. L., Glover, G. H., Solomon, A., Polan, M. L., et al. (2002). Brain activation and sexual arousal in healthy, heterosexual males. *Brain, 125,* 1014–1023.

Arthur, L., & Driscoll, A. (2002, May 16). Castration or life term? Judge to rule. *Miami Herald.*

Ascensio, M. (2002). *Sex and sexuality among New York's Puerto Rican youth.* Boulder, CO: Lynne Rienner.

Assalian, P., & Ravart, M. (2003). Management of professional sexual misconduct: Evaluation and recommendations. *Journal of Sexual & Reproductive Medicine, 3,* 89–92.

Associated Press. (1984, March 25). Baby girl is born from transferred embryo. *New York Times.*

Audet, M.C., et al. (2001). Evaluation of contraceptive efficacy and cycle control of a transdermal contraceptive patch vs. an oral contraceptive: A randomized controlled trial. *Journal of the American Medical Association, 285,* 2347–2354.

Augustinova, H., Hoeller, D., & Yao, F. (2004). The dominant-negative herpes simplex virus type 1 (HSV-1) recombinant CJ83193 can serve as an effective vaccine against wild-type HSV-1 infection in mice. *Journal of Virology, 78,* 5756–5765.

Auld, B. R., & Brock, G. (2002). Sexuality and erectile dysfunction: Results of a national survey. *Journal of Sexual & Reproductive Medicine, 2,* 50–54.

Autry, A. M., Hayes, E. C., Jacobson, G. F., & Kirby, R. S. (2002). A comparison of medical induction and dilation and evacuation for second-trimester abortion. *American Journal of Obstetrics and Gynecology, 187,* 393–397.

Avis, N. E., & McKinlay, S. M. (1995, March–April). The Massachusetts Women's Health Study: An epidemiological investigation of the menopause. *JAMWA, 50,* 45–63.

Bach, G., & Wyden, P. (1969). *The intimate enemy: How to fight fair in love and marriage.* New York: Morrow.

Bachmann, G. A., & Leiblum, S. R. (1991). Sexuality in sexagenarian women. *Maturitas, 13,* 43–50.

Badgley, R. (1984). *Sexual offences against children: Report of the Committee on Sexual Offences Against Children and Youths.* Ottawa: Canadian Government Publishing.

Bagemihl, B. (1999). *Biological exuberance: Animal homosexuality and natural diversity.* New York: St. Martin's Press.

Bagley, C. (1989). Prevalence and correlates of unwanted sexual acts in childhood in a national Canadian sample. *Canadian Journal of Public Health, 80,* 295–296.

Bailey, J. M., Bobrow, D., Wolfe, M., & Mikach, S. (1995). Sexual orientation of adult sons of gay fathers. *Developmental Psychology, 31,* 124–129.

Bailey, J. M., & Pillard, R. C. (1991). A genetic study of male sexual orientation. *Archives of General Psychiatry, 48,* 1089–1096.

Bailey, J. M., & Pillard, R. C. (1995). Genetics of human sexual orientation. *Annual Review of Sex Research, 6,* 126–150.

Bailey, J. M., Pillard, R. C., Neale, M. C., & Agyei, Y. (1993). Heritable factors influence sexual orientation in women. *Archives of General Psychiatry, 50,* 217–223.

Bailey, J. M., Willerman, L., & Parks, C. (1991). A test of the maternal stress theory of human male homosexuality. *Archives of Sexual Behavior, 20,* 277–294.

Bailey, J. M., & Zucker, K. J. (1995). Childhood sex-typed behavior and sexual orientation. *Developmental Psychology, 31,* 43–55.

Baker, F. C., Driver, H. S., Paiker, J., Rogers, G. G., & Mitchell, D. (2002). Acetaminophen does not affect 24-h body temperature or sleep in the luteal phase of the menstrual cycle. *Journal of Applied Physiology, 92,* 1684–1691.

Bakker, A., Vankesteren, P., Gooren, L., & Bezemer, P. (1993). The prevalence of transsexualism in the Netherlands. *Acta Psychiatrica Scandinavica, 87,* 237–238.

Baladerian, N. J. (1991). Sexual abuse of people with developmental disabilities. *Sexuality and Disability, 9,* 323–335.

Baldwin, J. D., & Baldwin, J. I. (1989). The socialization of homosexuality and heterosexuality in a non-Western society. *Archives of Sexual Behavior, 18,* 13–30.

Baldwin, J. D., & Baldwin, J. I. (1997). Gender differences in sexual interest. *Archives of Sexual Behavior, 26,* 181–210.

Ballweg, M. L. (1995). The enigma called endometriosis. In M. Ballweg and the Endometriosis Association (Eds.), *The endometriosis sourcebook* (pp.10–15). Chicago: Contemporary Books.

Balsam, K. F. (2004, August). Identity, community, and outness: Comparing bisexual and lesbian/gay adults. Paper presented at the 111th Annual Convention of the American Psychological Association, Toronto, ON.

Balter, M. (1995). Elusive HIV-suppressor factors found. *Science, 270,* 1560–1561.

Balter, M. (1996). A second coreceptor for HIV in early stages of infection. *Science, 272,* 1740.

Bancroft, J. (1978). The prevention of sexual offenses. In C. B. Qualls et al. (Eds.), *The prevention of sexual disorders* (pp. 95–116). New York: Plenum.

Bancroft, J., Herbenick, D., & Reynolds, M. (2003). Masturbation as a marker of sexual development. In John Bancroft (Ed.), *Sexual development.* Bloomington, IN: Indiana University Press.

Bancroft, J., & Gutierrez, P. (1996). Erectile dysfunction in men with and without diabetes mellitus. *Diabetic Medicine, 13,* 84–89.

Bancroft, J., Herbenick, D., & Reynolds, M. (2002). Masturbation as a marker of sexual development. In J. Bancroft (Ed.), *Sexual development.* Bloomington, IN: Indiana University Press.

Bandura, A. J. (1977). *Social learning theory.* Englewood Cliffs, NJ: Prentice-Hall.

Bandura, A. (1982). Self-efficacy mechanism in human agency. *American Psychologist, 37,* 122–147.

Bandura, A., & Walters, R. H. (1963). *Social learning and personality development.* New York: Holt.

Banks, A., & Gartrell, N. K. (1995). Hormones and sexual orientation: A questionable link. *Journal of Homosexuality, 28,* 247–268.

Barak, A., & Fisher, W. A. (2001). Toward an Internet-driven, theoretically based, innovative approach to sex education. *The Journal of Sex Research, 38,* 324–332.

Barash, D. P. (1982). *Sociobiology and behavior* (2nd ed.). New York: Elsevier.

Barbaree, H. E., & Marshall, W. L. (1991). The role of male sexual arousal in rape: Six models. *Journal of Consulting and Clinical Psychology, 59,* 621–630.

Barlow, D. H. (1986). Causes of sexual dysfunction: The role of cognitive interference. *Journal of Consulting and Clinical Psychology, 54,* 140–148.

Barlow, D. H., Leitenberg, H., & Agras, W. S. (1969). Experimental control of sexual deviation through manipulation of noxious scenes in covert sensitization. *Journal of Abnormal Psychology, 74,* 596–601.

Baron, L., & Straus, M. A. (1989). *Four theories of rape in American society.* New Haven, CT: Yale University Press.

Barouch, D. H., Santra, S., Schmitz, J. E., Kuroda, M. J., Fu, T. M., Wagner, W., et al. (2000). Control of viremia and prevention of clinical AIDS in rhesus monkeys by cytokine-augmented DNA vaccination. Science, 290, 486–492.

Barr, A., Bryan, A., & Kenrick, D. (2002). Sexual peak: Socially shared cognitions about desire, frequency, and satisfaction in men and women. *Personal Relationships, 9,* 287–299.

Barr, H. M., Streissguth, A. P., Darby, B. L., & Sampson, P. D. (1990). Prenatal exposure to alcohol, caffeine, tobacco and aspirin: Effects on fine and gross motor performance in 4-year-old children. *Developmental Psychology, 26,* 339–348.

Barrett, F. M., King, A., Levy, J., Maticka-Tyndale, E., McKay, A., & Fraser, J. (2003). Sexuality and Canada. In *Complete Encyclopedia of Human Sexuality* (pp. 126–181). London & New York: Continuum Publishing.

Barrett, M. (1990). Selected observations of sex education in Canada. *SIECCAN Journal, 5*(1), 21–30.

Barrett, M. (1994). Sexuality education in Canadian schools: An overview in 1994. *The Canadian Journal of Human Sexuality, 3,* 199–225.

Barrett, M., King, A., Levy, J., Maticka-Tyndale, E., & McKay, A. (1997). *The international encyclopedia of sexuality,* vol. 1, 221–343. New York: Continuum Publishing.

Bartell, G. D. (1970). Group sex among the mid-Americans. *Journal of Sex Research, 6,* 113–130.

Bartels, A., & Zeki, S. (2004). The neural correlates of maternal and romantic love. *Neuroimage, 21,* 1155–1166.

Bartholomew, K., & Horowitz, L. M. (1991). Attachment styles among young adults: A test of a 4-category model. *Journal of Personality and Social Psychology, 61,* 226–244.

Bartlett, N. H., Vasey, P. L., & Bukowski, W. M. (2000). Is gender identity disorder in children a mental disorder? *Sex Roles, 43,* 753–785.

Basson, R. (2000). The female sexual response: A different model. *Journal of Sex & Marital Therapy, 26,* 51–65.

Basson, R. (2001). Human sex-response cycles. *Journal of Sex & Marital Therapy, 27,* 33–43.

Basson, R. (2001). Using a different model for female sexual response to address women's problematic low sexual desire. *Journal of Sex & Marital Therapy, 27,* 395–403.

Basson, R., & Brotto, L. A. (2003). Sexual psychophysiology and effects of sildenafil citrate in oestrogenised women with acquired genital arousal disorder and impaired orgasm: A randomised controlled trial. *BJOG: International Journal of Obstetrics and Gynaecology, 110,* 1014–1024.

Basson, R., Berman, J., Burnett, A., Derogatis, L., Ferguson, D., Fourcroy, J., et al. (2001). Report of the International Consensus Development Conference on female sexual dysfunction: Definitions and classifications. *Journal of Sex & Marital Therapy, 27,* 83–94.

Basson, R., McInnes, R., Smith, M., Hodgson, G., & Koppiker, N. (2002). Efficacy and safety of sildenafil citrate in women with sexual dysfunction associated with female sexual arousal disorder. *Journal of Women's Health & Gender-Based Medicine, 11,* 367–377.

Basson, R., & VHHSC Centre for Sexuality, Gender Identity, & Reproductive Health. (1998). Integrating new biomedical treatments into the assessment and management of erectile dysfunction. *The Canadian Journal of Human Sexuality, 7,* 213–229.

Baulieu, E. E., et al. (2000). Dehydroepiandrosterone (DHEA), DHEA sulfate, and aging : Contributions of the DHEAge Study to a sociobiomedical issue. *Proceedings of the National Academy of Sciences, 97,* 4279–4284.

Baumeister, R. F. (1988a). Masochism as escape from the self. *Journal of Sex Research, 25,* 28–59.

Baumeister, R. F. (1988b). Gender differences in masochistic scripts. *Journal of Sex Research, 25,* 478–499.

Baumeister, R. F. (2000). Gender differences in erotic plasticity: The female sex drive as socially flexible and responsive. *Psychological Bulletin, 126,* 347–374.

Baumeister, R.F., Catanese, K., & Vohs, K. (2001). Is there a gender difference in strength of sex drive? Theoretical views, conceptual distinctions, and a review of relevant evidence. *Personality and Social Psychology Review, 5,* 242–273.

Baumeister, R. F. Catanese, K., & Wallace, H. (2002). Conquest by force: A narcissistic reactance theory of rape and sexual coercion. *Review of General Psychology, 6,* 92–135.

Beach, F. A. (1947). Evolutionary changes in the physiological control of mating behavior in mammals. *Psychological Review, 54,* 297–315.

Beach, F. A. (Ed.). (1976). *Human sexuality in four perspectives.* Baltimore: Johns Hopkins University Press.

Beach, F., & Merari, A. (1970). Coital behavior in dogs. V. Effects of estrogen and progesterone on mating and other forms of social behavior in the bitch. *Journal of Comparative and Physiological Psychology Monograph, 70*(1), Part 2, 1–22.

Beall, A., & Sternberg, R. (1995). The social construction of love. *Journal of Social and Personal Relationships, 12,* 417–438.

Beier, E. G., & Sternberg, D. P. (1977). Marital communication. *Journal of Communication, 27,* 92–103.

Bell, A. P. (1974a, Summer). *Childhood and adolescent sexuality.* Address delivered at the Institute for Sex Research, Indiana University.

Bell, A. P. (1974b). Homosexualities: Their range and character. In *Nebraska symposium on motivation 1973.* Lincoln, NE: University of Nebraska Press.

Bell, A. P., & Weinberg, M. S. (1978). *Homosexualities.* New York: Simon & Schuster.

Bell, A. P., Weinberg, M. S., & Hammersmith, S. K. (1981). *Sexual preference.* Bloomington, IN: Indiana University Press.

Belzer, E. G. (1981). Orgasmic expulsions of women: A review and heuristic inquiry. *Journal of Sex Research, 17,* 1–12.

Bem, D. J. (1996). Exotic becomes erotic: A developmental theory of sexual orientation. *Psychological Review, 103,* 320–335.

Bem, D. J. (1998). Is EBE theory supported by the evidence? Is it androcentric? A reply to Peplau et al. (1998). *Psychological Review, 105,* 395–398.

Bem, S. L. (1981). Gender schema theory: A cognitive account of sex typing. *Psychological Review, 88,* 354–364.

Bem, S. L. (1993). *The lenses of gender: Transforming the debate on sexual inequality.* New Haven: Yale UP.

Benedetti, J., Corey, L., & Ashley, R. (1994). Recurrence rates in genital herpes after symptomatic first-episode infection. *Annals of Internal Medicine, 121,* 847–854.

Benoit, M., Dragon, J., Boudreau, M.G., & Muhimpundu, S. (2003). La promotion de l'abstinence dans les programmes d' education en matière de santé sexuelle: Le point de vue de jeunes Franco-Ontariennes du nord. *Canadian Journal of Human Sexuality, 12,* 109–119.

Bérard, E. J. J. (1989). The sexuality of spinal cord injured women: Physiology and pathophysiology: A Review. *Paraplegia, 27,* 99–112.

Beres, M. A., Herold, E., & Maitland, S. B. (2004). Sexual consent behaviours in same-sex relationships. *Archives of Sexual Behavior, 33,* 475–486.

Beretta, G., Chelo, E., & Zanollo, A. (1989). Reproductive aspects in spinal cord injured males. *Paraplegia, 27,* 113–118.

Bergen, D. J., & Williams, J. E. (1991). Sex stereotypes in the United States revisited: 1972–1988. *Sex Roles, 24,* 413–423.

Bergeron, S., Binik, Y. M., Khalife, S., & Pagidas, K. (1997). Vulvar vestibulitis syndrome: A critical review. *The Clinical Journal of Pain, 13*(1), 27–42.

Bergeron, S., Binik, Y. M., Khalifé, S., Pagidas, K., Glazer, H. I., Meana, M., & Amsel, R. (2001). A randomized comparison of group cognitive-behavioral therapy, surface electromyographic biofeedback, and vestibulectomy in the treatment of dyspareunia resulting from vulvar vestibulitis. *Pain, 91,* 297-306.

Berkman, C., & Zinberg, G. (1997). Homophobia and heterosexism in social workers. *Journal of the National Association of Social Workers, 42,* 319–332.

Berliner, D. L., Jennings-White, C., & Lavker, R. M. (1991). The human skin: Fragrances and pheromones. *Journal of Steroid Biochemistry and Molecular Biology, 39,* 671–679.

Berman, J. R., Adhikari, S. P., & Goldstein, I. (2000). Anatomy and physiology of female sexual function and dysfunction. *European Urology, 38,* 20–29.

Bermant, G., & Davidson, J. M. (1974). *Biological bases of sexual behavior.* New York: Harper & Row.

Berne, E. (1970). *Sex in human loving.* New York: Simon & Schuster.

Bernstein, A. C., & Cowan, P. A. (1975). Children's concepts of how people get babies. *Child Development, 46,* 77–92.

Berry, L. J., Hickey, D. K., Skelding, K. A., Bao, S., Rendina, A. M., Hansbro, P.M., et al. (2004). Transcutaneous immunization with combined cholera toxin and CpG adjuvant protects against clamydia muridarum genital tract infection. *Infection and Immunity, 72,* 1019–1028.

Berscheid, E., & Walster, E. (1974a). A little bit about love. In T. L. Huston (Ed.), *Foundations of interpersonal attraction.* New York: Academic.

Berscheid, E., & Walster, E. (1974b). Physical attractiveness. *Advances in Experimental Social Psychology, 7,* 157–215.

Berscheid, E., & Hatfield, E. (1978). *Interpersonal attraction* (2nd ed.). Reading, MA: Addison-Wesley.

Berscheid, E., et al. (1971). Physical attractiveness and dating choice: A test of the matching hypothesis. *Journal of Experimental Social Psychology, 7,* 173–189.

Bibby, R. (1987). *Fragmented gods: The poverty and potential of religion in Canada.* Toronto: Irwin.

Bibby, R. (1993). *Unknown gods: The ongoing story of religion in Canada.* Toronto: Stoddart.

Bibby, R. W. (1995). *The Bibby report: Social trends Canadian style.* Toronto: Stoddart.

Bibby, R. W. (2001). *Canada's teens: Today, yesterday, and tomorrow.* Toronto: Stoddart.

Bibby, R. W., & Posterski, D. (1992). *Teen trends: A nation in motion.* Toronto: Stoddart.

Bibby, R. W., & Posterski, D. (1995). *The Bibby report: Social trends Canadian style.* Toronto: Stoddart.

Biller, H., & Meredith, D. (1975). *Father power.* New York: Anchor Books.

Billings, A. (1979). Conflict resolution in distressed and non-distressed married couples. *Journal of Consulting and Clinical Psychology, 47,* 368–376.

Binik, Y. M., Cantor, J., Ochs, E., & Meana, M. (1997). From the couch to the keyboard: Psychotherapy in cyberspace. In S. Kiesler (Ed.), *Culture on the Internet.* New Jersey: Erlbaum.

Binik, Y. M., Meana, M., Berkley, K., & Khalife, S. (2000). The sexual pain disorders: Is the pain sexual or is the sex painful? *Annual Review of Sex Research.*

Binik, Y. M., Pukall, C. F., Reissing, E. D., & Khalifé, S. (2001). The sexual pain disorders: A desexualized approach. *Journal of Sex & Marital Therapy, 27,* 113–116.

Binik, Y. M., Reissing, E., Pukall, C., Flory, N., Payne, K.A., & Khalifé, S. (2002). The female sexual pain disorders: Genital pain or sexual dysfunction? *Archives of Sexual Behavior, 31,* 425–429.

Bird, S. E. (1999). Gendered construction of the American Indian in popular media. *Journal of Communication,* 61–83.

Bissell, M. (2000). Socio-economic outcomes of teen pregnancy and parenthood: A review of the literature. *The Canadian Journal of Human Sexuality, 9,* 191–204.

Bixler, R. H. (1986). Of apes and men (including females). *Journal of Sex Research, 22,* 255–267.

Black, D., et al. (2000). Demographics of the gay and lesbian population in the United States: Evidence from available systematic data sources. *Demography, 37,* 139–154.

Blackless, M., et al. (2000). How sexually dimorphic are we? Review and synthesis. *American Journal of Human Biology, 12,* 151–166.

Blair, C. D., & Lanyon, R. I. (1981). Exhibitionism: Etiology and treatment. *Psychological Bulletin, 89,* 439–463.

Blake, J. (2004). *Words can work: When talking with kids about sexual health.* Gloucester, MA: Blake Works, Inc.

Blake, S., Ledsky, R., Goodenow, C., Sawyer, R., Lohrmann, D., & Windsor, R. (2003). Condom availability programs in Massachusetts high schools: Relationships with condom use and sexual behavior. *American Journal of Public Health, 93,* 955–962.

Blanchard, R. (1997). Birth order and sibling sex ratio in homosexual versus heterosexual males and females. *Annual Review of Sex Research, 8,* 27–67.

Blanchard, R. (2004). Quantitative and theoretical analyses of the relation between older brothers and homosexuality in men. *Journal of Theoretical Biology, 230,* 173–187.

Blanchard, R., & Bogaert, A. F. (2004). Proportion of homosexual men who owe their sexual orientation to fraternal birth order: An estimate based on two national probability samples. *American Journal of Human Biology, 16,* 151–157.

Blanchard, R., Christensen, B. K., Strong, S. M., Cantor, J. M., Kuban, M. E., Klassen, P., et al. (2002). Retrospective self-reports of childhood accidents causing unconsciousness in phallometrically diagnosed pedophiles. *Archives of Sexual Behavior, 31,* 511–526.

Blanchard, R., Clemmensen, L. H., & Steiner, B. W. (1983). Gender reorientation and psychosocial adjustment in male-to-female transsexuals. *Archives of Sexual Behavior, 12,* 503–510.

Blanchard, R., Steiner, B. W., & Clemmenson, L. H. (1985). Gender dysphoria, gender reorientation and the clinical management of transsexualism. *Journal of Consulting & Clinical Psychology, 53*(3), 295–304.

Blanchard, R., Watson, M. S., Choy, A., Dickey, R., Klassen, P., Kuban, M., et al. (1999). Pedophiles: Mental retardation, maternal age, and sexual orientation. *Archives of Sexual Behavior, 28,* 111–127.

Blumberg, E. (2003). The lives and voices of highly sexual women. *Journal of Sex Research, 40,* 146–157.

Blumstein, P. W., & Schwartz, P. (1983). *American couples.* New York: Morrow.

Boardman, J., Hummer, R., Padilla, Y., & Powers, D. (Nd). *Low birth weight, social factors, and developmental outcomes among children in the United States* (No. 01-02-05). Austin, TX: Population Research Center.

Bockting, Walter O. (1999, Oct./Nov.). From construction to context: Gender through the eyes of the transgendered. *SIECUS Report,* 3–7.

Bodlund, O., & Kullgren, G. (1996). Transsexualism-General outcome and prognostic factors: A five-year follow-up study of 19 transsexuals in the process of changing sex. *Archives of Sexual Behavior, 25,* 303–316.

Bodner, L. M., Markovic, N., Harger, G., & Roberts, J. M. (2004). Prepregnancy body mass index and the risk of preeclampsia. *Federation of American Societies for Experimental Biology Journal, 18*(5), A928.

Bogaert, A. F. (1993). *The sexual media: The role of individual differences.* Unpublished doctoral dissertation. University of Western Ontario, London, Ontario, Canada.

Bogaert, A. F. (1996). Volunteer bias in human sexuality research: Evidence for both sexuality and personality differences in males. *Archives of Sexual Behavior, 25*(2), 125–140.

Bogaert, A. F. (2001). Personality, individual differences, and preferences for the sexual media. *Archives of Sexual Behavior, 30,* 29–53.

Bogaert, A. F. (2003). Number of older brothers and sexual orientation: New tests and the attraction/behaviour distinction in two national probability samples. *Journal of Personality and Social Psychology, 84,* 644–652.

Bogaert, A. F. (2004). Asexuality: Prevalence and associated factors in a national probability sample. *Journal of Sex Research, 41,* 279–287.

Bogaert, A. F., & Sadava, S. (2002). Adult attachment and sexual behavior. *Personal Relationships, 9,* 191–204.

Bogaert, A. F., Woodard, U., & Hafer, C. L. (1999). Intellectual ability and reactions to pornography. *Journal of Sex Research, 26*(3), 283–291.

Bogren, L. Y. (1991). Changes in sexuality in women and men during pregnancy. *Archives of Sexual Behavior, 20,* 35–45.

Boies, S.C. (2002). University students uses of and reactions to online sexual information and entertainment: Links to online and offline sexual behaviour. *Canadian Journal of Human Sexuality, 11,* 77–89.

Boles, J., & Ellifson, K. (1994). *Risk factors associated with HIV seropositivity in clients of male and female prostitutes.* Presented at the Annual Meeting, Society for the Scientific Study of Sexuality, Miami, FL.

Boonstra, H. (2001). Islam, women and family planning: A primer. *The Guttmacher Report on Public Policy, 4,* 4–7.

Booth, C. L., & Meltzoff, A. N. (1984). Expected and actual experience in labour and delivery and their relationship to maternal attachment. *Journal of Reproductive and Infant Psychology, 2,* 79–91.

Bootzin, R. R., & Natsoulas, T. (1965). Evidence for perceptual defense uncontaminated by response bias. *Journal of Personality and Social Psychology, 1,* 461–468.

Bornstein, R. F. (1989). Exposure and affect: Overview and meta-analysis of research, 1968-1987. *Psychological Bulletin, 106,* 265–289.

Boroditsky, R., Fisher, W., & Sand, M. (1996, December). The 1996 Canadian contraceptive study. *Journal of the Society of Obstetricians and Gynaecologists of Canada.*

Bosch, F. X., Manos, M. M., Muñoz, N., et al. (1995). Prevalence of human papillomavirus in cervical cancer: A worldwide perspective. *Journal of the National Cancer Institute, 87,* 796–802.

Boston Women's Health Book Collective. (1992). *The new our bodies, ourselves.* New York: Simon & Schuster.

Boston Women's Health Book Collective. (1998). *Our bodies, ourselves for the new century.* New York: Simon and Schuster.

Boswell, J. (1980). *Christianity, social tolerance, and homosexuality.* Chicago: University of Chicago Press.

Boswell, J. (1994). *Same-sex unions in premodern Europe.* New York: Villard Books.

Bouyer, J., Coste, J., Shojaei, T., Pouly, J. L., Fernandez, H., Gerbaud, L., et al. (2003). Risk factors for ectopic pregnancy: a comprehensive analysis based on a large case-control, population-based study in France. *American Journal of Epidemiology, 157,* 185–194.

Bower, J. Gurevich, M., & Mathieson, C. (2002). (Con)tested identities: Bisexual women reorient sexuality. *Journal of Bisexuality, 2,* 23–52.

Boyce, W. F., King, A. J. C., & Warren, W. K. (2000). The effectiveness of a school-based HIV education program: A longitudinal comparative evaluation. *Canadian Journal of Program Evaluation, 15,* 93–116.

Boyd, K., Callaghan, B., & Shotter, E. (1986). *Life before birth.* London: SPCK.

Bradford, J. M. W. (2000). The treatment of sexual deviation using a pharmacological approach. *Journal of Sex Research, 37,* 248–257.

Bradford, J. M. W., & Greenberg, D. M. (1996). Pharmacological treatment of deviant sexual behaviour. *Annual Review of Sex Research, 7,* 283–306.

Brant, C. C. (1990). Native ethics and rules of behaviour. *The Canadian Journal of Psychiatry, 35,* 534–539.

Braun, M., Wassmer, G., Klotz, T., Reifenrath, B., Mathers, M., & Engelmann, U. (2000). Epidemiology of erectile dysfunction: Results of the 'Cologne Male Survey.' *International Journal of Impotence Research, 12,* 305–311.

Braun, V., & Kitzinger, C. (2001). "Snatch," "hole," or "honeypot"? Semantic categories and the problem of nonspecificity in female genital slang. *Journal of Sex Research, 38,* 146–158.

Brecher, E. M. (1984). *Love, sex, and aging.* Mount Vernon, NY: Consumers Union.

Brecht M. L., O'Brien, A., von Mayrhauser, C., & Anglin, M. D. (2004). Methamphetamine use behaviors and gender differences. *Addictive Behaviors, 29,* 89–106.

Breitenbecher, K. H. (2000). Sexual assault on college campuses: Is an ounce of prevention enough? *Applied and Preventive Psychology, 9,* 23–52.

Brenton, M. (1972). *Sex talk.* New York: Stein and Day.

Breslow, N., Evans, L., & Langley, J. (1985). On the prevalence and roles of females in the sadomasochistic subculture: Report of an empirical study. *Archives of Sexual Behavior, 14,* 303–318.

Breton, S., Smith, P. J. S., Lut, B., & Brown, D. (1996). Acidification of the male reproductive tract by a proton pumping (H1)-ATPase. *Nature Medicine, 2,* 470–472.

Bretschneider, J. G., & McCoy, N. L. (1988). Sexual interest and behavior in healthy 80- and 102-year-olds. *Archives of Sexual Behavior, 17,* 109–130.

Brinton, L. A., & Schairer, C. (1997). Postmenopausal hormone-replacement therapy-time for a reappraisal? *New England Journal of Medicine, 336,* 1821–1822.

Britton, P. (2004). Personal communication.

Brock, G., McMahon, C. G., Chen, K K., Costigan, T., Shen, W., Watkins, V., et al. (2002). Efficacy and safety of tadalafil in men with erectile dysfunction: An integrated analysis of registration trials. *Journal of Urology, 167,* 178.

Brock, G., Nehra, A., Lipshultz, L. I., Karlin, G. S., Gleave, M. P., Seger, M., et al. (2003). Safety and efficacy of vardenafil for the treatment of men with erectile dysfunction after radical retropubic prostatectomy. *Journal of Urology, 170,* 1278–1283.

Broderick, C. B. (1966a). Sexual behavior among preadolescents. *Journal of Social Issues, 22*(2), 6–21.

Broderick, C. B. (1966b). Socio-sexual development in a suburban community. *Journal of Sex Research, 2,* 1–24.

Broers, T., King, W. D., Arbuckle, T. E., & Liu, S. (2004). The occurrence of abruptio placentae in Canada: 1990 to 1997. *Chronic Diseases in Canada, 25,* 16–20.

Brosius, H.-B., Weaver, J. B. III, & Staab, J. (1993). Exploring the social and sexual "reality" of contemporary pornography. *Journal of Sex Research, 30,* 161–170.

Brotman, H. (1984, January 8). Human embryo transplants. *New York Times Magazine,* 42ff.

Brotto, L. A., & Gorzalka, B. B. (2002). Genital and subjective sexual arousal in postmenopausal women: Influence of laboratory-induced hyperventilation. *Journal of Sex & Marital Therapy, 28,* 39–53.

Brotto, L. A., Basson, R., & Gorzalka, B. B. (2004). Psychophysiological assessment in premenopausal sexual arousal disorder. *Journal of Sexual Medicine, 1,* 266–277.

Brotto, L. A., Chik, H. M., Ryder, A. G., Gorzalka, B. B., & Seal, B.N. (In press). Acculturation and sexual function in Asian women. *Archives of Sexual Behaviour.*

Brown, J. D. (2002). Mass media influences on sexuality. *Journal of Sex Research, 39,* 42–45.

Brown, J., & Steele, J. R. (1995). Sexuality and the mass media: An overview. *SIECUS Report, 24*(4), 3–9.

Brownmiller, S. (1975). *Against our will: Men, women, and rape.* New York: Simon & Schuster.

Bryant, J., & Rockwell, S. C. (1994). Effects of massive exposure to sexually oriented prime-time television programming on adolescents' moral judgment. In D. Zillman, J. Bryant, and A. C. Houston (Eds.), *Media, children, and the family: Social, scientific, psychodynamic, and clinical perspectives* (pp. 183–195). Hillsdale, NJ: Lawrence Erlbaum.

Brym, R. J., & Lenton, R.L. (2003). Love at first byte: Internet Dating in Canada. Retrieved June 13, 2005, from http://www.societyinquestion4e.nelson.com/article2.html.

Brzozowski, J. A. (Ed.). (2004). *Family Violence in Canada: A Statistical Profile, 2004.* (Catalogue no. 85-224-XIE). Ottawa: Canadian Centre for Justice Statistics.

Buchanan, K. M. (1986). *Apache women warriors*. El Paso, TX: Texas Western Press.

Buchbinder, S. P., et al. (1994). Long-term HIV-1 infection without immunologic progression. *AIDS, 8,* 1123–1128.

Buffet, N. Chabbert, Djakoure, C., Maitre, S., & Bouchard, P. (1998). Regulation of the human menstrual cycle. *Frontiers in Neuroendocrinology, 19,* 151–186.

Bufkin, J., & Eschholz, S. (2000). Images of sex and rape. *Violence Against Women, 6,* 1317–1344.

Bulik, C., Prescott, C., & Kendler, K. (2001). Features of childhood sexual abuse and the development of psychiatric and substance use disorders. *British Journal of Psychiatry, 179,* 444–449.

Bullivant, S. B., Sellergren, S. A., & Stern, K. (2004). Women's sexual experience during the menstrual cycle: Identification of the sexual phase by noninvasive measurement of luteinizing hormone. *Journal of Sex Research, 41,* 82–93.

Bullough, B., & Bullough, V. (1997). Are transvestites necessarily heterosexual? *Archives of Sexual Behavior, 26,* 1–12.

Bullough, V. L. (1976). *Sexual variance in society and history*. New York: Wiley.

Bullough, V. L. (1994). *Science in the bedroom: A history of sex research*. New York: Basic Books.

Burack, J. H., et al. (1993). Depressive symptoms and CD4 lymphocyte decline among HIV-infected men. *Journal of the American Medical Association, 270,* 2568–2573.

Burger, H. G. (1993). Evidence for a negative feedback role of inhibin in follicle stimulating hormone regulation in women. *Human Reproduction, 8,* Suppl. 2, 129–132.

Burgess, A. W. (1984). *Child pornography and sex rings*. Lexington, MA: Lexington Books.

Burgess, A. W., & Holmstrom, L. L. (1974a). Rape trauma syndrome. *American Journal of Psychiatry, 131,* 981–986.

Burgess, A. W., & Holmstrom, L. L. (1974b). *Rape: Victims of crisis*. Bowie, MD: Robert J. Brady.

Burleson, B., & Denton, W. (1997). The relationship between communication skill and marital satisfaction: Some moderating effects. *Journal of Marriage and the Family, 59,* 884–902.

Burt, M. R., & Estep, R. E. (1981). Apprehension and fear: Learning a sense of sexual vulnerability. *Sex Roles, 7,* 511–522.

Burton, D. L. (2000). Were adolescent sexual offenders children with sexual behavior problems? *Sex Abuse, 12,* 37–48.

Burton, F. D. (1970). Sexual climax in Macaca Mulatta. *Proceedings of the Third International Congress on Primatology, 3,* 180–191.

Busby, K. (1999). Not a victim until the conviction is entered: Sexual violence, prosecutions and legal "truth." In *Locating law: Race/class/gender connections*. Halifax: Fernwood Publishing.

Buss, A. (1966). *Psychopathology*. New York: Wiley.

Buss, D. M. (1988). The evolution of human intra-sexual competition: Tactics of mate attraction. *Journal of Personality and Social Psychology, 54,* 616–628.

Buss, D. M. (1989). Sex differences in human mate preferences: Evolutionary hypotheses tested in 37 cultures. *Behavioral and Brain Sciences, 12,* 1–49.

Buss, D. M. (1994). *The evolution of desire: Strategies of human mating*. New York: Basic Books.

Buss, D. M. (2000). *The dangerous passion: Why jealousy is as necessary as love and sex*. New York: The Free Press.

Buss, D. M., & Schmitt, D. P. (1993). Sexual strategies theory: An evolutionary perspective on human mating. *Psychological Review, 100,* 204–232.

Buss, D., & Shackelford, T. (1997a). From vigilance to violence: Mate retention tactics in married couples. *Journal of Personality and Social Psychology, 72,* 346–361.

Buss, D., & Shackelford, T. (1997b). Susceptibility to infidelity in the first year of marriage. *Journal of Research in Personality, 31,* 193–221.

Buss, D. M., Shackelford, T. K., Kirkpatrick, L. A., & Larsen, R. J. (2001). A half century of mate preferences: The cultural evolution of values. *Journal of Marriage & Family, 63,* 491–504.

Buvat, J, et al. (1990). Recent developments in the clinical assessment and diagnosis of erectile dysfunction. *Annual Review of Sex Research, 1,* 265–308.

Byard, R., Hucker, S., & Hazelwood, R. (1993). Fatal and near-fatal autoerotic asphyxial episodes in women. *The American Journal of Forensic Medicine and Pathology, 14,* 70–73.

Byers, E. S. (1988). Effects of sexual arousal on men and women's behaviour on sexual disagreement situations. *The Journal of Sex Research, 25,* 233–254.

Byers, E. S. (1989). Prevention and treatment of relationship distress. *Canadian Family Physician, 35,* 1883–1886.

Byers, E. S. (1996). How well does the traditional sexual script explain sexual coercion? Review of a program of research. *Journal of Psychology and Human Sexuality, 8,* 7–25.

Byers, E. S. (1999). The interpersonal exchange model of sexual satisfaction: Implications for sex therapy with couples. *Canadian Journal of Counselling, 33*(2), 95–111.

Byers, E. S., Crooks, R., Griffiths, B., Mackin, B., MacDonald, G., MacDonald, G., Marcoux-Galarneau, R., Renaud, C., Thomas, B., Thompson, B., & Yates, P. (1997). *The extent of sex offences and the nature of sex offenders in New Brunswick: A research project*. Submitted to the New Brunswick Department of the Solicitor General and Correctional Services Canada.

Byers, E. S., & Demmons, S. (1999). Sexual satisfaction and sexual self disclosure within dating relationships. *The Journal of Sex Research, 36,* 180–189.

Byers, E. S., Demmons, S., & Lawrance, K.-a. (1998). Sexual satisfaction within dating relationships: A test of the interpersonal exchange model of sexual satisfaction. *Journal of Social and Personal Relationships, 15*(2), 257–267.

Byers, E. S., & Eno, R. J. (1991). Predicting men's sexual coercion and aggression from attitudes, dating history, and sexual responses. *Journal of Psychology & Human Sexuality, 4*(3), 55–70.

Byers, E. S., Giles, B. L., & Price, D. L. (1987). Definiteness and effectiveness of women's responses to unwanted sexual advances: A laboratory investigation. *Basic and Applied Social Psychology, 8,* 321–338.

Byers, E. S. & Grenier, G. (2003). Premature or rapid ejaculation: Heterosexual couples' perceptions of men's ejaculatory behavior. *Archives of Sexual Behavior, 32,* 261–270.

Byers, E. S., & Heinlein, L. (1989). Predicting initiation and refusals of sexual activities in married and cohabiting heterosexual couples. *The Journal of Sex Research, 26,* 210–231.

Byers, E. S., & Lewis, K. (1988). Dating couples' disagreements over desired level of sexual activity. *The Journal of Sex Research, 24,* 15–29.

Byers, E. S., & O'Sullivan, L. F. (1998). Similar but different: Men's and women's experiences of sexual coercion. In P. B. Anderson & C. Strickman-Johnson (Eds.), *Sexually aggressive women*. New York: Guilford Press.

Byers, E. S., & O'Sullivan, L. F. (1996). How well does the traditional sexual script explain sexual coercion? Review of a program of research. In E. S. Byers (Ed.), *Sexual coercion in dating relationships*. Binghamton, NY: Hawthorn Press.

Byers, E. S., Purdon, C., & Clark, D. (1998). Sexual intrusive thoughts of college students. *The Journal of Sex Research, 35*, 359–369.

Byers, E. S., Sears, H. A., Voyer, S. D., Thurlow, J. L., Cohen, J. N., & Weaver, A. D. (2001). *New Brunswick students' ideas about sexual health education*. Report prepared for the New Brunswick Department of Education, Fredericton, NB. Retrieved November 11, 2002, from http://www.gnb.ca/0000/publications/studentsexeducation.pdf

Byers, E. S., Sears, H. A., Voyer, S. D., Thurlow, J. L., Cohen, J. N., & Weaver, A. D. (2003a). An adolescent perspective on sexual health education at school and at home: I. High school students. *Canadian Journal of Human Sexuality, 12*, 1–17.

Byers, E. S., Sears, H. A., Voyer, S. D., Thurlow, J. L., Cohen, J. N., & Weaver, A. D. (2003b). An adolescent perspective on sexual health education at school and at home: II. Middle school students. *Canadian Journal of Human Sexuality, 12*, 19–32.

Byers, E. S., & Slattery, G. (1997). Sexology in Russia and Estonia: Reflections on an exchange. *Canadian Journal of Human Sexuality, 6*, 53–64.

Byers, E. S., & Wang, A. (2004). Understanding sexuality in close relationships from the social exchange perspective. In J. H. Harvey, A. Wenzel, & S. Sprecher (Eds.), *The handbook of sexuality in close relationships* (pp. 203–234). Mahwah, NJ: Lawrence Erlbaum.

Byers, E. S., & Wilson, P. (1985). Accuracy of women's expectations regarding men's responses to refusals of sexual advances in dating situations. *International Journal of Women's Studies, 4*, 376–387.

Byers, M. E. (2001). What boys and girls should know: Youth, sexuality, and the media text. Paper presented at the meeting of the Canadian Sex Research Forum, Halifax, NS.

Byler, R. V. (1969). *Teach us what we want to know*. New York: Mental Health Materials Center (for the Connecticut State Board of Education).

Byne, W., Lasco, M. S., Kemether, E., Shinwari, A., Edgar, M. A., & Morgello, S. (2000). The interstitial nuclei of the human anterior hypothalamus: Assessment for sexual variation in volume and neuronal size, density, and number. *Brain Research, 856*, 254–258.

Byrne, D. (1971). *The attraction paradigm*. New York: Academic.

Byrne, D. (1977). Social psychology and the study of sexual behavior. *Personality and Social Psychology Bulletin, 3*, 3–30.

Byrne, D. (1983). Sex without contraception. In D. Byrne & W. A. Fisher (Eds.), *Adolescents, sex, and contraception*. Hillsdale, NJ: Lawrence Erlbaum.

Byrne, D. (1997). An overview (and underview) and research and theory within the attraction paradigm. *Journal of Social and Personal Relationships, 14*, 417–431.

Byrne, D., Ervin, C. E., & Lamberth, J. (1970). Continuity between the experimental study of attraction and real-life computer dating. *Journal of Personality and Social Psychology, 16*, 157–165.

Cado, S., & Leitenberg, H. (1990). Guilt reactions to sexual fantasies during intercourse. *Archives of Sexual Behavior, 19*, 49–64.

Cahill, L. S. (1985). The "seamless garment": Life in its beginnings. *Theological Studies, 46*, 64–80.

Cairns, K. V. (1993). Sexual entitlement and sexual accommodations: implications for female and male experience of sexual coercion. *The Canadian Journal of Human Sexuality, 2*, 203–213.

Calderwood, D. (1987, May). The male rape victim. *Medical Aspects of Human Sexuality*, 53–55.

Call, V., Sprecher, S., & Schwartz, P. (1995). The incidence and frequency of marital sex in a national sample. *Journal of Marriage and the Family, 57*, 639–652.

Callahan, D. (1986, February). How technology is reframing the abortion debate. *Hastings Center Report*, 33–42.

Calzavara, L. M., Burchell, A. N., Myers, T., Bullock, S. L., Escobar, M., & Cockerill, R. (1998). Condom use among Aboriginal people in Ontario, Canada. *International Journal of STD & AIDS, 9*, 272–279.

Canadian AIDS Society. (2004). *HIV and HCV Transmission: Guidelines for assessing risk*. Ottawa, ON: Author.

Canadian Cancer Society. (1995). *Don't play the fool: How to check for testicular cancer*. Adapted from the Imperial Cancer Research Fund, England.

Canadian Cancer Society. (2004). *Breast self-examination*. Retrieved Nov 19, 2004 from http://www.cancer.ca.

Canadian Centre for Justice Statistics. (1999). *Integration and analysis program: Sex offenders*.

Canadian HIV/AIDS Legal Network. (2000). Aboriginal people and HIV/AIDS: Immediate action required. Retrieved November 11, 2002, from http://www.aidslaw.ca/Medai/press-releases/e-releaseab.htm

Canadian HIV/AIDS Legal Network. (2002). *HIV vaccines in Canada: Legal and ethical issues: An Overview*. Retrieved November 11, 2002, from http://www.aidslaw.ca/Maincontent/issues/vaccines/overviewpaper/toc.htm

Canadian Psychological Association. (1995). *Companion manual to the Canadian Code of Ethics for Psychologists, 1991*. Ottawa: Author.

Canary, D. J., & Dindia, K. (Eds.). (1998). *Sex differences and similarities in communication*. Mahwah, NJ: Erlbaum.

Canary, D. J., & Hause, K. S. (1993). Is there any reason to research sex differences in communication? *Communication Quarterly, 41*, 129–144.

Cantor, J. M., Blanchard, P., Christensen, B. K., Dickey, R., Klassen, P. E., Beckstead, A. L., et al. (2004). Intelligence, memory, and handedness in pedophilia. *Neuropsychology, 18*, 3–14.

Cantor, J. M., Blanchard, R., Paterson, A. D., & Bogaert, A. F. (2002). How many gay men owe their sexual orientation to fraternal birth order? *Archives of Sexual Behavior, 31*, 63–71.

Caplan, P. (1995). *How do they decide who is normal?* Reading, MA: Addison-Wesley.

Cappon, P., Adrien, A., Godin, G., Mason Singer, S., Maticka-Tyndale, E., Willms, D., & Daus, T. (1996). HIV/AIDS in the context of culture: Selection of ethnocultural communities for study in Canada. *Canadian Journal of Public Health, 87*(1), S11–S25.

Caputo, T. (2000). *Hearing the voices of youth: Youth participation in selected Canadian municipalities*. Ottawa: ON: Health Canada.

Carani, C., et al. (1990). Effects of androgen treatment in impotent men with normal and low levels of free testosterone. *Archives of Sexual Behavior, 19*, 223–234.

Carnes, P. (1983). *The sexual addiction*. Minneapolis, MN: Compcare Publications.

Carpenter, L. M. (2001). The ambiguity of "having sex": The subjective experience of virginity loss in the United States. *Journal of Sex Research, 38,* 127–139.

Carroll, L., Gilroy, P. J., & Ryan, J. (2002). Counseling transgendered, transsexual, and gender-variant clients. *Journal of Counseling & Development, 80,* 131–139.

Carroll, J., Volk, K., & Hyde, J. S. (1985). Differences between males and females in motives for engaging in sexual intercourse. *Archives of Sexual Behavior, 14,* 131–139.

Carson, C. C., West, S. L., Glasser, D. B., Laumann, E. O., Flack, J. M., Rimm, E., et al. (2002). Prevalence and correlates of erectile dysfunction in a United States Nationwide population-based sample: Phase I results. *Journal of Urology, 167,* S29–30.

Carter, C. S. (1992). Hormonal influences on human sexual behavior. In J. B. Becker et al. (Eds.), *Behavioral endocrinology* (pp. 131–142). Cambridge, MA: MIT Press.

Casimiro, D. R., Tang, A., Chen, L., Fu, T. M., Evans, R. K., Davies, M. E., et al. (2003). Vaccine-induced immunity in baboons by using DNA and replication-incompetent adenovirus type 5 vectors expressing a human immunodeficiency virus type 1 gag gene. *Journal of Virology, 77,* 7663–7668.

Cass, V. C. (1979). Homosexual identity formation: A theoretical model. *Journal of Homosexuality, 4,* 219–235.

Catania, J. A., Binson, D., Van Der Straten, A., & Stone, V. (1995). Methodological research on sexual behavior in the AIDS era. *Annual Review of Sex Research, 6,* 77–125.

Catania, J. A., Gibson, D., Marin, B., Coates, T., & Greenblatt, R. (1990a). Response bias in assessing sexual behaviors relevant to HIV transmission. *Evaluation and Program Planning, 13,* 19–29.

Catellsagué, X., Bosch, F. X., Muñoz, N., Meijer, C. J. L. M.., Shah, K V., de Sanjosé, S., et al. (2002). Male circumcision, penile human papillomavirus infection, and cervical cancer in female partners. *New England Journal of Medicine, 346,* 1105–1112.

Cates, W. (2001). The NIH condom report: The glass is 90% full. *Family Planning Perspectives, 33,* 231–233.

CDC. (2004). *Intimate partner violence: Fact sheet.* Retrieved June 1, 2004 from www.cdc.gov/ncipc/factsheets/ipvfacts.htm.

Centers for Disease Control and Prevention. (2002). Alcohol use and pregnancy: Fact sheet. www.cdc.gov/ncbddd/factsheets/alcoholuse.pdf.

Chan, Connie S. (1995). Issues of sexual identity in an ethnic minority: The case of Chinese American lesbians, gay men, and bisexual people. In A. R. D'Augelli & C. J. Patterson (Eds.), *Lesbian, gay, and bisexual identities over the lifespan* (pp. 87–101). New York: Oxford University Press.

Chapman, H., Hobfoll, S., & Ritter, C. (1997). Partners' stress underestimations lead to women's distress: A study of pregnant inner-city women. *Journal of Personality and Social Psychology, 73,* 418–425.

Charon, J. (1995). *Symbolic interactionism: An introduction, interpretation, and integration* (5th ed). Englewood Cliffs, NJ: Prentice Hall.

Chen, C. L., Weiss, N. S., Newcomb, P., Barlow, W., & White, E. (2002). Hormone replacement therapy in relation to breast cancer. *Journal of the American Medical Association, 287,* 734–741.

Cheng, J., Elam-Evans, L. D., Berg, C. J., Herndon, J., Flowers, L., Seed, K.A., et al. (2003, February 21). Pregnancy-related mortality surveillance: United States, 1991–1999. *Morbidity & Mortality Weekly Report, 52,* 1–8.

Cheng, Mariah M., & Udry, J. Richard. (2003). How much do mentally disabled adolescents know about sex and birth control? *Adolescent & Family Health, 3,* 28–38.

Cherry, K., & Mitulski, J. (1988). We are the church alive, the Church with AIDS. *Christian Century, 105,* 85–88.

Chesler, E. (1992). *Woman of valor: Margaret Sanger and the birth control movement.* New York: Simon & Schuster.

Chivers, M., & Blanchard, R. (1996). Prostitution advertisements suggest association of transvestism and masochism. *Journal of Sex & Marital Therapy, 22*(2), 97–102.

Choi, E. J, Ha, C. M, Choi, J., Kang, S. S., Choi, W. S., Park, S. K., et al. (2001). Low-density DNA array-coupled to PCR differential display identifies new estrogen-responsive genes during the postnatal differentiation of the rat hypothalamus. *Molecular Brain Research, 97,* 115–128.

Chow, J. M., et al. (1990). The association between chlamydia trachomatis and ectopic pregnancy: A matched-pair, case-control study. *Journal of the American Medical Association, 263,* 3164.

Chow, Y.-K., et al. (1993). Use of evolutionary limitations of HIV-1 multidrug resistance to optimize therapy. *Nature, 361,* 650–654.

Christensen, C. V. (1971). *Kinsey: A biography.* Bloomington, IN: Indiana University Press.

Christopher, F. S., & Sprecher, S. (2000). Sexuality in marriage, dating, and other relationships: A decade review. *Journal of Marriage and the Family, 62,* 999–1017.

Chu, J. A., Frey, L. M., Ganzel, B., & Mattews, J. (1999). Memories of childhood abuse: Dissociation amnesia, and corroboration. *American Journal of Psychiatry, 156,* 749–755.

Church, S., Henderson, M., Barnard, M., & Hart, G. (2001). Violence by clients towards female prostitutes in different work settings: Questionnaire survey. *British Medical Journal, 322,* 524–525.

Cimbalo, R. S., Faling, B., & Mousaw, P. (1976). The course of love: A cross-sectional design. *Psychological Reports, 38,* 1292–1294.

Clark, L., & Lewis, D. (1977). *Rape: The price of coercive sexuality.* Toronto: Women's Educational Press.

Clements-Schreiber, M. E., Rempel, J. K., & Desmarais, S. (1998). Women's sexual pressure tactics and adherence to related attitudes: A step towards prediction. *The Journal of Sex Research, 35*(2), 197–205.

Cocchi, F., et al. (1995). Identification of RANTES, MIP-1a, and MIP-1b as the major HIV-suppressive factors produced by CD81 T cells. *Science, 270,* 1811–1815.

Cochran, S. D., & Peplau, L. A. (1985). Value orientations in heterosexual relationships. *Psychology of Women Quarterly, 9,* 477–488.

Cochran, S., Sullivan, J. G., & Mays, V. (2003). Prevalence of mental disorders, psychological distress, and mental health services use among lesbian, gay, and bisexual adults in the United States. *Journal of Consulting and Clinical Psychology, 71,* 53–61.

Cochran, W. G., Mosteller, F., & Tukey, J. W. (1953). Statistical problems of the Kinsey report. *Journal of the American Statistical Association, 48,* 673–716.

Cohen, D. J., & Bruce, K. E. (1997). Sex and mortality: Real risk and perceived vulnerability. *Journal of Sex Research, 34,* 279–291.

Cohen, I., et al. (1990). Improved pregnancy outcome following successful treatment of chlamydial infection. *Journal of the American Medical Association, 263,* 3160.

Cohen, J. (1997). Exploiting the HIV-chemokine nexus. *Science, 275,* 1261–1264.

Cohen, J. (1998). Exploring how to get at-and eradicate-hidden HIV. *Science, 279,* 1854–1855.

Cohen, J. (2001). AIDS vaccines show promise after years of frustration. *Science, 291,* 1686–1688.

Cohen, J. (2002). Confronting the limits of success. *Science, 296,* 2320–2326.

Cohen, J. (2003). Thailand and Cambodia: Two hard-hit countries offer rare success stories. *Science, 301,* 1658–1663.

Cohen, J. N., Byers, E. S., Sears, H. A., & Weaver, A. D. (2004). Sexual health education: Attitudes, knowledge, and comfort of teachers in New Brunswick schools. *Canadian Journal of Human Sexuality, 13,* 1–15.

Cohen, K. M. (2002). Relationships among childhood sex-atypical behavior, spatial ability, handedness, and sexual orientation in men. *Archives of Sexual Behavior, 31,* 129–144.

Cohen, J. N., Byers, E. S., Sears, H. A., & Weaver, A. D. (2001). *New Brunswick teachers' ideas about sexual health education.* Report prepared for the New Brunswick Department of Education, Fredericton, NB. Retrieved November 11, 2002, from http://www.gnb.ca/0000/publications/ss/nbteachersidea/pdf

Cohn, L. (1983, November 16). Pix less able but porn is stable. *Variety, 313*(3), 1–2.

Cole, S. W., Kemeny, M. E., Taylor, S. E., & Visscher, B. R. (1996). Elevated physical health risk among gay men who conceal their homosexual identity. *Health Psychology, 15,* 243–251.

Cole, T. M., & Cole, S. (1978). The handicapped and sexual health. In A. Comfort (Ed.), *Sexual consequences of disability.* Philadelphia, PA: G. F. Stickley.

Coleman, E. (1982). Developmental stages of the coming-out process. In W. Paul et al. (Eds.), *Homosexuality: Social, psychological, and biological issues.* Beverly Hills, CA: Sage.

Coleman, E. (1991). Compulsive sexual behavior: New concepts and treatments. *Journal of Psychology and Human Sexuality, 4*(2), 37–51.

Coleman, E., Miner, M., Ohlerking, F., & Raymond, N. (2001). Compulsive Sexual Behavior inventory: A preliminary study of reliability and validity. *Journal of Sex and Marital Therapy, 27,* 325–332.

Coleman, E., Raymond, N., & McBean, A. (2003, July 2003). Assessment and treatment of compulsive sexual behaviour. *Minnesota Medicine, 86,* 42–47.

Collaborative Group on Hormonal Factors in Breast Cancer. (2002). Breast cancer and breast-feeding. *Lancet, 360,* 187–195.

Collaer, M. L., & Hines, M. (1995). Human behavioral sex differences: A role for gonadal hormones during early development? *Psychological Bulletin, 118,* 55–107.

Collins, N. L., & Miller, L. C. (1994). Self-disclosure and liking: A meta-analytic review. *Psychological Bulletin, 116,* 457–475.

Collins, R. L., Elliott, M. N., Berry, S. H., Kanouse, D. E., Kunkel, D., & Hunter, S. B. (2004). Watching sex on television predicts adolescent initiation of sexual behavior. *Pediatrics, 114,* 280–289.

Collin-Vézina, D., & Hébert, M. (2005). Comparing dissociation and PTSD in sexually abused school-aged girls. *Journal of Mental & Nervous Disease, 193,* 47–52.

Comet (Comparative Obstetric Mobile Epidural Trial) Study Group. (2001). Effect of low-dose mobile versus traditional epidural techniques on mode of delivery: A randomised controlled trial. *Lancet, 358,* 19–23.

Comfort, A. (1991). *The new joy of sex: A gourmet guide to lovemaking for the nineties.* New York: Crown.

Committee on Lesbian and Gay Concerns, American Psychological Association. (1991). Avoiding heterosexual bias in language. *American Psychologist, 46,* 973–974.

Compas Inc. (2001). Valentine's Day Poll. Toronto, ON: Author.

Compas, B. E., & Luecken, L. (2002). Psychological adjustment to breast cancer. *Current Directions in Psychological Science, 11,* 111–114.

Comstock, G. D. (1991). *Violence against lesbians and gay men.* New York: Columbia University.

Congregation for the Doctrine of the Faith. (1986). The pastoral care of homosexual persons. *Origins, 26,* 378–382.

Congregation for the Doctrine of the Faith. (1987). Instruction on respect for human life in its origin and on the dignity of procreation. *Origins, 16,* 198–211.

Connolly, J., Craig, W., Goldberg, A., & Pepler, D. (2004). Mixed-gender groups, dating, and romantic relationships in early adolescence. *Journal of Research on Adolescence, 14,* 185–207.

Contessini, C. (2003). Personal communication.

Cook, K., & Rice, E. (2004). Social exchange theory. In J. DeLamater (Ed.), *The handbook of social psychology.* New York: Kluwer-Plenum.

Cooper, A. (1998). Sexuality and the Internet: Surfing into the new millennium. *CyberPsychology & Behavior, 1,* 187–193.

Cooper, A., Delmonico, D., & Burg, R. (2000). Cybersex users, abusers, and compulsives: New findings and implications. In A. Cooper (Ed.), *Cybersex: The dark side of the force* (pp. 5–29). Philadelphia: Brunner Routledge.

Cooper, A., Putnam, D., Planchon, L., & Boies, S. (1999). Sexuality on the Internet: from sexual exploration to pathological expression. *Professional Psychology Research and Practice, 30,* 154–164.

Cooper, A., Putnam, D. E., Planchon, L. A., & Boies, S. C. (1999a). Online sexual compulsivity: Getting tangled in the Net. *Sexual Addiction & Compulsivity: The Journal of Treatment and Prevention, 6,* 79–104.

Cooper, A., Scherer, C. R., Gordon, B. L., & Boies, S. C. (1999b). Sexuality on the Internet: From sexual exploration to pathological expression. *Professional Psychology: Research & Practice, 30*(2), 154–164.

Cordova, M. J., Cunningham, L., Carlson, C., & Andrykowski, M. (2001). Posttraumatic growth following breast cancer: A controlled comparison study. *Health Psychology, 20,* 176–185.

Corey, L. (1990). Genital herpes. In K. Holmes et al. (Eds.), *Sexually transmitted diseases* (pp. 391–414). New York: McGraw-Hill.

Corey, L., Wald, A., Patel, R., Sacks, S. L., Tyring, S. K., Warren, T., et al. (2004). Once-daily valacyclovir to reduce the risk of transmission of genital herpes. *New England Journal of Medicine, 350,* 11–20.

Council of Ministers of Education, Canada. (2003). *Canadian youth, sexual health and HIV/AIDS Study: Factors influencing knowledge, attitudes and behaviours.* Ottawa: Health Canada.

Council on Scientific Affairs. (1995). Female genital mutilation. *Journal of the American Medical Association, 274,* 1714–1716.

Countryman, L. W. (1994). New Testament sexual ethics and today's world. In J. B. Nelson & S. P. Longfellow (Eds.), *Sexuality and the sacred* (pp. 28–53). Louisville, KY: Westminster/John Knox Press.

Coustan, D. (1995a). Obstetric analgesia and anesthesia. In D. R. Coustan, R. V. Hunning, Jr., & D. Singer (Eds.), *Human reproduction: Growth and development* (pp. 327–340). Boston: Little, Brown.

Coustan, Donald, & Angelini, Diane. (1995). The puerperium. In Donald R. Coustan, Ray V. Hunning, Jr., & Don Singer (Eds.), *Human reproduction: Growth and development* (pp. 341–358). Boston: Little, Brown & Co.

Couzin, J. (2003). The twists and turns in BRCA's path. *Science, 302,* 591–593.

Couzinet, B., et al. (1986). Termination of early pregnancy by the progesterone antagonist RU486 (mifepristone). *New England Journal of Medicine, 315,* 1565–1569.

Cowley, J. J., & Brooksbank, B. W. L. (1991). Human exposure to putative pheromones and changes in aspects of social behavior. *Journal of Steroid Biochemistry and Molecular Biology, 39,* 647–659.

Cox, D. J. (1988). Incidence and nature of male genital exposure behavior as reported by college women. *Journal of Sex Research, 24,* 227–234.

Coyne, J. A., & Berry, A. (2000). Rape as an adaptation. *Nature, 404,* 121–122.

Crawford, J., Kippax, S., & Waldby, C. (1994). Women's sex talk and men's sex talk: Different worlds. *Feminism and Psychology,* 571–587.

Crawford, M., & Popp, D. (2003). Sexual double standards: A review and methodological critique of two decades of research. *Journal of Sex Research, 40,* 13–26.

Craze, R. (2003). *Teach yourself tantric sex.* McGraw-Hill, Whitby, ON.

Creighton, J. (1992). *Don't go away mad.* New York: Doubleday.

Creighton, S. M., & Minto, C. (2001). Managing intersex: Most vaginal surgery in childhood should be deferred. *British Medical Journal, 323,* 1264–1265.

Creighton, S. M., Minto, C., & Steele, S. (2001). Objective cosmetic and anatomical outcomes at adolescence of feminising surgery for ambiguous genitalia done in childhood. *Lancet, 358,* 124–125.

Crenshaw, T L., & Goldberg, J P. (1996). *Sexual pharmacology: Drugs that affect sexual function.* New York: Norton.

Creti, L., & Libman, E. (1989). Cognitions and sexual expression in the aging. *Journal of Sex & Marital Therapy, 15*(2), 83–101.

Crocker, D., & Kalemba, V. (1999). The incidence and impact of women's experiences of sexual harassment in Canadian workplaces. *Canadian Review of Sociology and Anthropology, 36,* 541–558.

Crompton, L. (2003). *Homosexuality and civilization.* Cambridge, MA: Harvard University Press.

Cruess, S., Antoni, M. H., Hayes, A., Penedo, F. J., Ironson, G. H, Fletcher, M. A., et al. (2002). Changes in mood and depressive symptoms and related change processes during cognitive-behavioral stress management in HIV-infected men. *Cognitive Therapy & Research, 26,* 373–392.

Cunningham, F. G., MacDonald, P. C., Gant, N. F., Leveno, K. J., & Gilstrap, L. C., III. (1993). *Williams obstetrics* (19th ed.). Norwalk, CT: Appleton and Lange.

Cunningham, M., Roberts, A., Wu, C.-H., Burbee, A., & Druen, P. (1995). "Their ideas of beauty are, on the whole, the same as ours": Consistency and variability in the cross-cultural perception of female physical attractiveness. *Journal of Personality and Social Psychology, 68,* 261–279.

Cunningham, M. R., Barbee, A. P., & Druen, P. B. (1996). Social allergens and the reactions that they produce: Escalation of annoyance and disgust in love and work. In R.M. Kowalski (Ed.), *Aversive interpersonal behaviors* (pp. 189–214). New York: Plenum.

Curran, C. E. (1988). Roman Catholic sexual ethics: A dissenting view. *Christian Century, 105,* 1139–1142.

Curtis, J. T., & Wang, Z. X. (2003). The neurochemistry of pair bonding. *Current Directions in Psychological Science, 12,* 49–53.

Cutler, W. B. (1999). Human sex-attractant hormones. *Psychiatric Annals, 29,* 54–59.

Cyberatlas. (2004). *Top searches of 2003.* Retrieved January 25, 2004 from http://cyberatlas.internet.com.

Daignault, I. V., & Hébert, M. (In press). L'adaptation scolaire des enfants ayant dévoilé une aggression sexuelle. *Psychologie Canadienne.*

Daniluk, J. C. (1999). When biology isn't destiny: Implications for the sexuality of women without children. *Canadian Journal of Counselling, 33,* 79–94.

Daniluk, J. C. (2001a). "If we had it to do over again…": Couples' reflections on their experiences of infertility treatments. *The Family Journal: Counseling and Therapy for Couples and Families, 9,* 122–133.

Daniluk, J. C. (2001b). Reconstructing their lives: A longitudinal, qualitative analysis of the transition to biological childlessness for infertile couples. *Journal of Counseling & Development, 79,* 439–449.

Darling, C. A., Davidson, J. K., & Conway-Welch, C. (1990). Female ejaculation: Perceived origins, the Gräfenberg spot/ area, and sexual responsiveness. *Archives of Sexual Behavior, 19,* 29–48.

Darling, C. A., Davidson, J. K., & Jennings, D. A. (1991). The female sexual response revisited: Understanding the multi-orgasmic experience in women. *Archives of Sexual Behavior, 20,* 527–540.

Darroch, J. E., Frost, J. J., Singh, S., and the Study Team. (2001). *Teenage sexual and reproductive behavior in developed countries: Can more progress be made?* New York: Alan Guttmacher Institute.

Darroch, J. E., Singh, S., Frost, J. J., & the Study Team. (2001). Differences in teenage pregnancy rates among five developed countries: The roles of sexual activity and contraceptive use. *Family Planning Perspectives, 33,* 244–250.

D'Augelli, A. R. (1992). Lesbian and gay male undergraduates' experiences of harassment and fear on campus. *Journal of Interpersonal Violence, 7,* 383–395.

Davey, M. (2003, August 4). Episcopalians give first nod for gay bishop. *New York Times.*

David, H. P., Dytrych, Z., & Matejcek, Z. (2003). Born unwanted: Observations from the Prague study. *American Psychologist, 58,* 224–229.

Davidson, J. K., & Darling, C. A. (1988). The stereotype of single women revisited: Sexual practices and sexual satisfaction among professional women. *Health Care for Women International, 9,* 317–336.

Davidson-Harden, J., Fisher, W. A., & Davidson, P. R. (2000). Attitudes toward people in exclusive dating relationships who initiate condom use. *Canadian Journal of Human Sexuality, 9,* 1–14.

Davis, C. M., & Bauserman, R. (1993). Exposure to sexually explicit materials: An attitude change perspective. *Annual Review of Sex Research, 4,* 121–210.

Davis, K. R., & Weller, S. C. (1999). The effectiveness of condoms in reducing heterosexual transmission of HIV. *Family Planning Perspectives, 31,* 272–279.

Day, R. (1992). The transition to first intercourse among racially and culturally diverse youth. *Journal of Marriage and the Family, 54,* 749–762.

Dean, K. E., & Malamuth, N. M. (1997). Characteristics of men who aggress sexually and of men who imagine aggressing: Risk and moderating variables. *Journal of Personality and Social Psychology, 72,* 449–455.

DeKeseredy, W. S., & Kelly, K. (1993). Woman abuse in university and college dating relationships: The contribution of the ideology of familial patriarchy. *The Journal of Human Justice, 4*(2), 25–52.

DeKeseredy, W. S., & Schwartz, M. D. (1998). *Women abuse on campus: Results from the Canadian national survey.* Thousand Oaks: Sage Publications.

DeLamater, J. (1981). The social control of sexuality. *Annual Review of Sociology, 7,* 263–290.

DeLamater, J. (1982). Response effects of question content. In W. Dijkstra & J. Van derZouwen (Eds.), *Response behavior in the survey-interview.* London, England: Academic.

DeLamater, J. (1987). A sociological perspective. In J. H. Geer & W. T. O'Donohue (Eds.), *Theories of human sexuality* (pp. 237–256). New York: Plenum.

DeLamater, J. (2003). Discussion paper. In John Bancroft (Ed.), *Sexual development* (pp. 186–191). Bloomington, IN: Indiana University Press.

DeLamater, J., & MacCorquodale, P. (1979). *Premarital sexuality: Attitudes, relationships, behavior.* Madison: University of Wisconsin Press.

DeLamater, J., & Sill, M. (2003). *Sexual behavior in later life.* Presented at the Annual Meeting of the Society for the Scientific Study of Sexuality, San Antonio, TX, November 7.

DeLamater, J., Wagstaff, D., & Havens, K. K. (1994). *The impact of a health-promotion intervention on condom use by Black male adolescents.* Madison, WI: Center for Demography and Ecology, Working Paper 94–26.

DeLamater, J., Wagstaff, D. A., & Havens, K. K. (2000). The impact of a culturally appropriate STD/AIDS education intervention on Black male adolescents' sexual and condom use behavior. *Health Education and Behavior, 27,* 454–470.

De La Vega Salas, M. L., & Thériault, J. (2001). Sexualité parental et relation intime du couple parental: Conceptualisations des enfants âgés de dix et 11 ans. *Gynécologie, obstétrique, & fertilité, 29,* 226–233.

Deligeor-Oglov, E. (2000). Dysmenorrhea. *Annals of the New York Academy of Sciences, 900,* 237–244.

Delmas, P. D., et al. (1997). Effects of raloxifene on bone mineral density, serum cholesterol concentrations, and uterine endometrium in postmenopausal women. *New England Journal of Medicine, 337,* 1641–1647.

Denizet-Lewis, B. (2004, May 30). Friends, friends with benefits, and the benefits of the local mall. *The New York Times Magazine,* 30–35ff.

Denov, M. S. (2003). The myth of innocence: Sexual scripts and the recognition of child sexual abuse by female perpetrators. *Journal of Sex Research, 40,* 303–314.

Denton, A. B., & Scott, K. E. (1994). Unintended and unwanted pregnancy in Halifax: The rate and associated factors. *Canadian Journal of Public Health, 85,* 234–238.

Denzin, N. K., & Lincoln, Y. S. (1994). Introduction: Entering the field of qualitative research. In N. K. Denzin, & Y. S. Lincoln (Eds.), *Handbook of qualitative research* (pp.1–17). Thousand Oaks, CA: Sage.

Derby, C. A., Mohr, B. A., Goldstein, I., Feldman, H. A., Johannes, C. B., & McKinlay, J. B. (2000). Modifiable risk factors and erectile dysfunction: Can lifestyle changes modify risk? *Urology, 56,* 302–306.

Deren, S., Tortu, S., & Davis, W. R. (1993). An AIDS risk reduction project with inner-city women. In C. Squire (Ed.), *Women and AIDS: Psychological perspectives* (pp. 73–89). London: Sage.

Derlega, V. J. (Ed.). (1984). *Communication, intimacy, and close relationships.* New York: Academic.

Derlega, V. J., Metts, S., & Margulis, S. T. (1993). *Self-disclosure.* Newbury Park, CA: Sage.

Devor, A. H. (1989). *Gender blending: Confronting the limits of duality.* Bloomington, IN: Indiana University Press.

Devor, A. H. (2004). Witnessing and mirroring. A fourteen stage model of transsexual identity formation. *Journal of Gay and Lesbian Psychotherapy, 8,* 41–67.

Devor, H. (1996). Female gender dysphoria in context: Social problem or personal problem? *Annual Review of Sex Research: An Integrative & Interdisciplinary Review, 7,* 44–89.

Devor, H. (1997). *FTM: Female-to-male transsexuals in society.* Bloomington, IN: Indiana University Press.

Devor, H. (1997). More than manly women: How female to male transsexuals reject lesbian identities. In B. Bullough, V. Bullough, & J. Elias (Eds.), *Gender blending.* Amherst, NJ: Prometheus.

De Waal, F. B. M. (1995). The behavior of a close relative challenges assumptions about male supremacy in human evolution. *Scientific American,* 82–88.

De Waal, F. (2002). Evolutionary psychology: The wheat and the chaff. *Current Directions in Psychological Science, 11,* 187–191.

Diamond, L. M. (1998). Development of sexual orientation among adolescents and young women. *Developmental Psychology, 34,* 1085–1095.

Diamond, L. M. (2000). Sexual identities, attractions, and behavior among young sexual-minority women over a two-year period. *Developmental Psychology, 36,* 241–250.

Diamond, L.M. (2003). Was it a phase? Young women's relinquishment of lesbian/bisexual identities over a 5-year period. *Journal of Personality and Social Psychology, 84,* 352–364.

Diamond, M. (1996). Prenatal predisposition and the clinical management of some pediatric conditions. *Journal of Sex and Marital Therapy, 22,* 139–147.

Diamond, M. (1999). Pediatric management of ambiguous and traumatized genitalia. *Journal of Urology, 162,* 1021–1028.

Diamond, M., & Sigmundson, H. K. (1997). Sex reassignment at birth: Long-term review and clinical implications. *Archives of Pediatric and Adolescent Medicine, 151,* 298–304.

DiCenso, A., Gyatt, G., Willan, A., & Griffith, L. (2002). Interventions to reduce unintended pregnancies among adolescents: Systematic review of randomized controlled trials. *British Medical Journal, 324,* 1426.

Dickey, R. P. (2000). *Managing contraceptive pill patients* (10th ed.). Dallas, TX: EMIS.

Dickinson, R. L. (1949). *Atlas of human sex anatomy.* Baltimore: Williams & Wilkins.

Di Giulio, G. (2003). Sexuality and people living with physical or developmental disabilities: A review of key issues. *Canadian Journal of Human Sexuality, 12,* 53–68.

Dieben, T., Roumen, F., & Apter, D. (2002). Efficacy, cycle control, and user acceptability of a novel combined contraceptive vaginal ring. *Obstetrics and Gynecology, 100,* 585–593.

Dindia, K., & Allen, M. (1992). Sex differences in self-disclosure: A meta-analysis. *Psychological Bulletin, 112,* 106–124.

Dion, K. K., & Dion, K. L. (1993b). Individualistic and collectivistic perspectives on gender and the cultural content of love and intimacy. *Journal of Social Issues, 49,* 53–69.

Dion, K. L. (1977). The incentive value of physical attractiveness for young children. *Personality and Social Psychology Bulletin, 3,* 67–70.

Dion, K. L., & Dion, K. K. (1993a). Gender and ethnocultural comparisons in styles of love. *Psychology of Women Quarterly, 17,* 463–474.

DND/CF Human Resources (1999). Harassment in the Canadian Forces: Results of the 1998 survey sponsor research report 99-11. Retrieved June 27, 2005 from www.forces.gc.ca

Docter, R. F., & Prince, V. (1997). Transvestism: A survey of 1032 cross-dressers. *Archives of Sexual Behavior, 26,* 589–606.

Donahey, K. M., & Carroll, R. A. (1993). Gender differences in factors associated with hypoactive sexual desire. *Journal of Sex & Marital Therapy, 19,* 25–40.

Donahue, J. E., Stopa, E. G, & Chorsky, R. L. (2000). Cells containing immunoreactive estrogen receptor-α in the human basal forebrain. Brain Research, 856, 142–151.

Donnelly, D. A. (1993). Sexually inactive marriages. *Journal of Sex Research, 30,* 171–179.

Donnelly, D., Burgess, E., Anderson, S., Davis, R., & Dillard, J. (2001). Involuntary celibacy: A life course analysis. *Journal of Sex Research, 38,* 159–169.

Donnerstein, E., Linz, D., & Penrod, S. (1987). *The question of pornography: Research findings and policy implications.* New York: Free Press.

Donovan, B., Bassett, I., & Bodsworth, N. J. (1994). Male circumcision and common sexually transmissible diseases in a developed nation setting. *Genitourinary Medicine, 70,* 317–320.

Doran, T. A. (1990). Chorionic villus sampling as the primary diagnostic tool in prenatal diagnosis. *Journal of Reproductive Medicine, 35,* 935–940.

Doshi, M. L. (1986). Accuracy of consumer performed in-home tests for early pregnancy detection. *American Journal of Public Health, 76,* 512–514.

Douglas, M. (1970). *Purity and danger: An analysis of concepts of pollution and taboo.* Baltimore: Penguin.

Downs, B. (2003). *Fertility of American women: June 2002. Current Population Reports* (P20-548). Washington, DC: U.S. Census Bureau.

Drea, C., & Wallen, K. (2003). Female sexuality and the myth of male control. In C. Travis (Ed.), *Evolution, gender, and rape* (pp. 29–60). Cambridge, MA: MIT Press.

Dreznick, M. T. (2003). Heterosocial competence of rapists and child molesters: A meta- analysis. *Journal of Sex Research, 40,* 170–178.

Driscoll, R., Davis, K. E., & Lipetz, M. E. (1972). Parental interference and romantic love: The Romeo and Juliet effect. *Journal of Personality and Social Psychology, 24,* 1–10.

Dryburgh, H. (2000). Teenage pregnancy. *Health Reports* (Statistics Canada, Catalogue 82-003), *12,* 9–19.

Dryer, P. C., & Horowitz, L. (1997). When do opposites attract? Interpersonal complementarity vs. similarity. *Journal of Personality and Social Psychology, 72,* 592–603.

Duchesne, D. (1999). Street prostitution in Canada. In *The Juristat reader: A statistical overview of the Canadian justice system.* Toronto: Thomson Educational Publishing.

Duff, S. J. and Hampson, E. (2000). A beneficial effect of estrogen on working memory in postmenopausal women taking hormone replacement therapy. *Hormones and Behavior, 38,* 262–276.

Dumas, J., & Peron, Y. (1992). *Marriage and conjugal life in Canada: Current demographic analysis.* Ottawa: Statistics Canada, Cat. No. 3-91-534E.

Dunn, L., Ross, B., Caines, T., & Howorth, P. (1998). A school-based HIV/AIDS prevention education program: Outcomes of peer-led versus community health nurse-led interventions. *Canadian Journal of Human Sexuality, 7,* 339–345.

Dunn, M. E., & Trost, J. E. (1989). Male multiple orgasms: A descriptive study. *Archives of Sexual Behavior, 18,* 377–388.

Dupras, A. (2001). Sexology as innovation. *Scandinavian Journal of Sexology, 4,* 139–148.

Du Toit, B. M. (1994). Menstruation: Attitudes and experience of Indian South Africans. In B. M. du Toit (Ed.), *Human sexuality: Cross-cultural readings,* 3rd ed. (pp. 11–25). New York: McGraw.

Dutton, D. G., & Aron, A. P. (1974). Some evidence for heightened sexual attraction under conditions of high anxiety. *Journal of Personality and Social Psychology, 30,* 470–517.

Earls, C. M., & David, H. (1989). A psychosocial study of male prostitution. *Archives of Sexual Behavior, 18,* 401–420.

Earls, C. M., & Lalumière, M. L. (2002). A case study of preferential bestiality (zoophilia). *Sexual Abuse: A Journal of Research and Treatment, 14,* 83–88.

Ebel, C. (1994). *Managing herpes: How to live and love with a chronic STD.* Research Triangle Park, NC: American Social Health Association.

Egan, J. (2000, December 10). Lonely gay teen seeking same. *The New York Times Magazine,* p. 110.

Ehrhardt, A. (1996). Sexual behavior among heterosexuals. In J. Mann & D. Tarantola (Eds.), *AIDS in the world II* (pp. 259–263). New York: Oxford University Press.

Ehrhardt, A. A., Yingling, S., & Warne, P. A. (1991). Sexual behavior in the era of AIDS: What has changed in the United States? *Annual Review of Sex Research, 2,* 25–48.

Eisenberg, M. E., Wagenaar, A., Neumark-Sztainer, D. (1997). Viewpoints of Minnesota students on school-based sexuality education. *Journal of School Health, 67,* 322–326.

EKOS Research Associates Inc. (2003). HIV/AIDS—An attitudinal survey: Final Report. Ottawa: Health Canada.

Elder, G. (1969). Appearance and education in marriage mobility. *American Sociological Review, 34,* 519–533.

Elias, J., & Gebhard, P. (1969). Sexuality and sexual learning in childhood. *Phi Delta Kappan, 50,* 401–405.

Elias, M. (1997, August 14). Modern matchmaking. *USA Today,* D1–D2.

Elliott, A. N., & O'Donohue, W. T. (1997). The effects of anxiety and distraction on sexual arousal in a nonclinical sample of heterosexual women. *Archives of Sexual Behavior, 26,* 607–624.

Ellis, H. H. (1939). *My life.* Boston: Houghton Mifflin.

Ellis, L. (1996). The role of perinatal factors in determining sexual orientation. In R. C. Savin-Williams & K. M. Cohen (Eds.), *The lives of lesbians, gays, and bisexuals* (pp. 35–70). Fort Worth, TX: Harcourt Brace.

Ellis, L., & Cole-Harding, S. (2001). The effects of prenatal stress, and of prenatal alcohol and nicotine exposure, on human sexual orientation. *Physiology & Behavior, 74,* 213–226.

Emmers-Sommer, T., Allen, M., Bourhis, J., Sahlstein, E., Laskowski, K., Falato, W., et al. (2004). A meta-analysis of the relationship between social skills and sexual offenders. *Communication Reports, 17,* 1–10.

Epting, L. K. & Overman, W. H. (1998). Sex-sensitive tasks in men and women: A search for performance fluctuations across the menstrual cycle. *Behavioral Neuroscience, 112,* 1304–1317.

Erikson, E. H. (1950). *Childhood and society.* New York: Norton.

Ernulf, K. E., & Innala, S. M. (1995). Sexual bondage: A review and ubobtrusive investigation. *Archives of Sexual Behavior, 24,* 631–654.

Eskenazi, B., Wyrobek, A. J., Sloter, E., Kidd, S. A., Moore, L., Young, S., Moore, D. (2003). The association of age and semen quality in healthy men. *Human Reproduction, 18,* 447–454.

Espin, O. (1987). Issues of identity in the psychology of Latina lesbians. In Boston Lesbian Psychologies Collective, *Lesbian psychologies.* Urbana, IL: University of Illinois Press.

Esterberg, K. G. (1996). Gay cultures, gay communities: The social organization of lesbians, gay men, and bisexuals. In R. C. Savin-Williams & K. M. Cohen (Eds.), *The lives of lesbians, gays, and bisexuals* (pp. 377–392). Fort Worth, TX: Harcourt Brace.

Everett, G. M. (1975). Amyl nitrate ("poppers") as an aphrodisiac. In M. Sandler and G. L. Gessa (Eds.), *Sexual behavior: Pharmacology and biochemistry.* New York: Raven.

Everitt, B. J., & Bancroft, J. (1991). Of rats and men: The comparative approach to male sexuality. *Annual Review of Sex Research, 2,* 77–118.

Exton, M. S., Bindert, A., Kruger, T., Scheller, F., Hartmann, U., & Schedlowski, M. (1999). Cardiovascular and endocrine alterations after masturbation-induced orgasm in women. *Psychosomatic Medicine, 61,* 280–289.

Eyler, A. E., & Wright, K. (1997, July–September). Gender identification and sexual orientation among genetic females with gender-blended self-perception in childhood and adolescence [Electronic version]. *The International Journal of Transgenderism, 1.* Retrieved May 20, 2001, from http://www.symposium.com

Ezzell, C. (1996, January). Emergence of the protease inhibitors: A better class of AIDS drugs? *Journal of NIH Research, 8,* 41–43.

Ezzell, C. (1996, May). Gene-therapy trial using BRCA1 to begin with ovarian cancer. *Journal of NIH Research, 8,* 24–25.

Fanburg, J. T., Kaplan, D., & Naylor, K. (1995). Student opinion of condom distribution at a Denver, Colorado high school. *Journal of School Health, 65,* 181–185.

Farkas, G. M., Sine, L. G., & Evans, I. M. (1978). Personality, sexuality, and demographic differences between volunteers and nonvolunteers for a laboratory study of male sexual behavior. *Archives of Sexual Behavior, 7,* 513–520.

Farley, M. A. (1994). Sexual ethics. In J. B. Nelson & S. P. Longfellow (Eds.), *Sexuality and the sacred* (pp. 54–67). Louisville, KY: Westminster/John Knox Press.

Fasteau, M. F. (1974). *The male machine.* New York: McGraw-Hill.

Fazekas, A., Senn, C. Y., & Ledgerwood, D. M. (2001). Predictors of intention to use condoms among university women: An application and extension of the theory of planned behaviour. *Canadian Journal of Behavioural Science, 33,* 103–117.

Feder, H. H. (1984). Hormones and sexual behavior. *Annual Review of Psychology, 35,* 165–200.

Federoff, J. P. (1995). Antiandrogens vs. serotonergic medications in the treatment of sex offenders: A preliminary compliance study. *Canadian Journal of Human Sexuality, 4,* 111–122.

Federoff, J. P., & Moran, B. (1997). Myths and misconceptions about sex offenders. *Canadian Journal of Human Sexuality, 6,* 263–276.

Feingold, A. (1988). Matching for attractiveness in romantic partners and same-sex friends: A meta-analysis and theoretical critique. *Psychological Bulletin, 104,* 226–235.

Feingold, A. (1990). Gender differences in effects of physical attractiveness on romantic attraction. *Journal of Personality and Social Psychology, 59,* 981–993.

Feinleib, J. A., & Michael, R. T. (2001). Reported changes in sexual behavior in response to AIDS in the United States. In E.O. Laumann & R.T. Michael (Eds.), *Sex, love, and health in America* (pp. 302–326). Chicago: University of Chicago Press.

Feldman-Summers, S., & Pope, K. S. (1994). The experience of "forgetting" childhood abuse: A national survey of psychologists. *Journal of Consulting and Clinical Psychology, 62,* 636–639.

Felton, G., & Segelman, F. (1978). Lamaze childbirth training and changes in belief about person control. *Birth and the Family Journal, 5,* 141–150.

Feng, Y., Broder, C. C., Kennedy, P. E., & Berger, E. A. (1996). HIV-1 entry cofactor: Functional cDNA cloning of a seven-trans membrane G protein-coupled reception. *Science, 272,* 872.

Field, D., & Rabinovitch, J. (Eds.) (2003). *Stories from the margins: Writing by sex trade workers past and present.* Retrieved from http://www.peers.bc.ca/images/StoriesBookletWeb.pdf.

Figueira, I., Possidente, E., Marques, C., & Hayes, K. (2001). Sexual dysfunction: A neglected complication of panic disorder and social phobia. *Archives of Sexual Behavior, 30,* 369–377.

Filipp, D., et al. (2001). Soluble CD14 enriched in colostrums and milk induces B cell growth and differentiation. *Proceedings of the National Academy of Sciences, 98,* 603–608.

Finkelhor, D., & Daro, D. (1997). Prevention of child sexual abuse. In M. E. Helfer & R. S. Kempe (Eds.), *The battered child,* 5th edition (pp. 615–626). Chicago: University of Chicago Press.

Finkelhor, D., & Russell, D. (1984). Women as perpetrators: Review of the evidence. In D. Finkelhor (Ed.), *Child sexual abuse: New theory and research.* New York: The Free Press.

Finkelhor, D., Mitchell, K., & Wolak, J. (2000). *Online victimization: A report on the nation's youth.* Washington, DC: National Center for Missing & Exploited Children.

Finzi, Diana, et al. (1997). Identification of a reservoir for HIV-1 in patients on highly active antiretroviral therapy. *Science, 278,* 1295–1300.

Firestone, P., Bradford, J. M., McCoy, M., Greenberg, D. M., Curry, S., & Larose, M. R. (2000). Prediction of recidivism in extrafamilial child molesters based on court-related assessments. *Sexual Abuse: A Journal of Research and Treatment, 12,* 203–221.

Firestone, P., Bradford, J. M., McCoy, M., Greenberg, D. M, Larose, M. R., & Curry, S. (1999). Prediction of recidivism in incest offenders. *Journal of Interpersonal Violence, 14,* 511–532.

Fisher, D., Hill, D., Grube, J., & Grube, E. (2004). *Youth and television: Examining sexual content across program genres.* Presented at Society for Research on Adolescence, Baltimore, MD, March 2004.

Fisher, H. (1992). *Anatomy of love: The mysteries of mating, marriage and why we stray.* New York: Ballantine Books.

Fisher, W. A., & Barak, A. (2000). Online sex shops: Phenomenological, psychological, and ideological perspectives on Internet sexuality. *Cyberpsychology & Behavior, 3,* 575–589.

Fisher, W. A., & Boroditsky, R. (2000). Sexual activity, contraceptive choice, and sexual and reproductive health indicators among single Canadian women aged 15-29: Additional findings from the Canadian contraception study. *The Canadian Journal of Human Sexuality, 9,* 79–93.

Fisher, W. A., Boroditsky, R., & Bridges, M. L. (1999). Familiarity with opinions about and use of contraceptive methods among Canadian women. *Canadian Journal of Human Sexuality, 18,* 167–174.

Fisher, W. A., Boroditsky, R., & Bridges, M. L. (1999). The 1998 contraception study. *Canadian Journal of Human Sexuality, 8,* 161–216.

Fisher, W. A., Byrne, D., & White, L. A. (1983). Emotional barriers to contraception. In D. Byrne and W. A. Fisher (Eds.), *Adolescents, sex, and contraception.* Hillsdale, NJ: Lawrence Erlbaum.

Fisher, W. A., Byrne, D., White, L. A., & Kelley, K. (1988). Erotophobia-erotophilia as a dimension of personality. *Journal of Sex Research, 25,* 123–151.

Fisher, W. A., Sukhbir, S. S., Shuper, P. A., Carey, M., Otchet, F., MacLean-Brine, D., Dal Bello, D., & Gunter, J. (2005). Characteristics of women undergoing repeat induced abortion. *Canadian Medical Association Journal, 172,* 637–641.

Fisher, W., Boroditsky, R., & Morris, B. (2004a). The 2002 Canadian contraception study: Part 1. *Journal of Obstetrics and Gynaecology Canada, 26,* 580–590.

Fisher, W., Boroditsky, R., & Morris, B. (2004b). The 2002 Canadian contraception study: Part 2. *Journal of Obstetrics and Gynaecology Canada, 26*, 646–656.

Fisher, W. A., & Fisher, J. D. (1992). Understanding and promoting AIDS preventive behaviour: A conceptual model of educational tools. *Canadian Journal of Human Sexuality, 1*, 99–106.

Fisher, W. A., & Fisher, J. D. (1998). Understanding and promoting sexual and reproductive health behaviour: Theory and method. *Annual Review of Sex Research, 9*, 39–76.

Fisher, W. A., & Grenier, G. (1994). Violent pornography, anti-woman thoughts, and antiwoman acts: In search of reliable effects. *Journal of Sex Research, 31*, 23–38.

Fiske, S. T., & Glick, P. (1995). Ambivalence and stereotypes cause sexual harassment: A theory with implications for organizational change. *Journal of Social Issues, 51*(1), 97–115.

Fitch, R. H., & Bimonte, H. A. (2002). Hormones, brain, and behavior: Putative biological contributions to cognitive sex differences. In A. McGillicuddy-DeLisi & R. DeLisi (Eds.), *Biology, society, and behavior: The development of sex differences in cognition* (pp. 55–92). Westport, CT: Ablex.

Fitzgerald, L. F. (1993). Sexual harassment. *American Psychologist, 48*, 1070–1076.

Fleming, A., Ruble, D., Krieger, H., & Wong, P. Y. (1997). Hormonal and experiential correlates of internal responsiveness during pregnancy and the puerperium in human mothers. *Hormones and Behavior, 31*, 145–158.

Fleming, C., & Ingrassia, M. (1993, Aug. 16). "The Heidi Chronicles." *Newsweek,* 50ff.

Fleming, M., Steinman, C., & Boeknok, G. (1980). Methodological problems in assessing sex reassignment surgery: A reply to Meyer and Reter. *Archives of Sexual Behavior, 9*, 451–456.

Foa, E. B., Steketee, G., & Olasov, B. (1989). Behavioral/cognitive conceptualization of post-traumatic stress disorder. *Behavior Therapy, 20*, 155–176.

Forbes. (2001, May 25). How big is porn?

Ford, C. S., & Beach, F. A. (1951). *Patterns of sexual behavior.* New York: Harper & Row.

Ford, J. G. (2001). Healing homosexuals: A psychologist's journey through the ex-gay movement and the pseudo-science of reparative therapy. In A. Shidlo, M. Schroeder, & J. Drescher (Eds.), *Sexual conversion therapy: Ethical, clinical, and research perspectives* (pp. 69–86). New York: Haworth.

Ford, K., & Norris, A. (1991). Methodological considerations for survey research on sexual behavior: Urban African American and Hispanic youth. *Journal of Sex Research, 28*, 539–555.

Ford, N., & Koetsawang, S. (1991). The socio-cultural context of the transmission of HIV in Thailand. *Social Science and Medicine, 33*, 405–414.

Fortenberry, J. D. (2002). Clinic-based service programs for increasing responsible sexual behavior. *Journal of Sex Research, 39*, 63–66.

Foster, C. A., Witcher, B. S., Campbell, W. K., & Green, J. D. (1998). Arousal and attraction: Evidence for automatic and controlled processes. *Journal of Personality and Social Psychology, 74*, 86–101.

Fox, D. (2002). Gentle persuasion. *New Scientist, 173*, 32.

Fox, R. C. (1995). Bisexual identities. In A. R. D'Augelli & C. J. Patterson (Eds.), *Lesbian, gay, and bisexual identities over the lifespan.* New York: Oxford University Press.

Frank, L. K. (1961). *The conduct of sex.* New York: Morrow.

Frank, K. (2003). "Just trying to relax": Masculinity, masculinizing practices, and strip club regulars. *Journal of Sex Research, 40*, 61–75.

Fraser, P., et al. (1985). *Pornography and prostitution in Canada: Report of the Special Committee on Pornography and Prostitution.* Ottawa: Minister of Supply and Services Canada.

Frayser, S. (2004). Personal communication.

Frayser, S. G. (1985). *Varieties of sexual experience: An anthropological perspective on human sexuality.* New Haven, CT: Human Relations Area Files Press.

Frayser, S. G. (1994). Defining normal childhood sexuality: An anthropological approach. *Annual Review of Sex Research, 5*, 173–217.

Frazier, P., Tashiro, T., Berman, M., Steger, M., & Long, J. (2004). Correlates of levels and patterns of positive life changes following sexual assault. *Journal of Consulting and Clinical Psychology, 72*, 19–30.

Freese, J., & Meland, S. (2002). Seven tenths incorrect: Heterogeneity and change in the waist-to-hip ratios of Playboy centerfold models and Miss America pageant winners. *Journal of Sex Research, 39*, 133–138.

Fried, P. A. (2002). Conceptual issues in behavioral teratology and their application in determining long-term sequelae of prenatal marihuana exposure. *Journal of Child Psychology and Psychiatry, 43*, 81–102.

Fried, P. A., & Smith, A. M. (2001). A literature review of the consequences of prenatal marihuana exposure: An emerging theme of a deficiency in aspects of executive function. *Neurotoxicology and Teratology, 23*, 1–11.

Friedrich, W. N., Fisher, J., Broughton, D., Houston, M., & Shafran, M. (1998). Normative sexual behavior in children: A contemporary sample. *Pediatrics, 101*, 9.

Freud, S. (1924). A general introduction to psychoanalysis. New York: Permabooks, 1953. (Boni & Liveright edition, 1924).

Freud, S. (1948). The psychogenesis of a case of homosexuality in a woman (1920). In *The collected papers* (Vol. II, pp. 202–231). London: Hogarth.

Freund, M., Lee, N., & Leonard, T. (1991). Sexual behavior of clients with street prostitutes in Camden, NJ. *Journal of Sex Research, 28*, 579–591.

Freyd, J. J. (1996). *Betrayal trauma theory.* Cambridge, MA: Harvard University Press.

Friday, N. (1973). *My secret garden: Women's sexual fantasies.* New York: Simon & Schuster.

Friday, N. (1975). *Forbidden flowers: More women's sexual fantasies.* New York: Simon & Schuster.

Friedrich, W. N., Beilke, R. L., & Urquiza, A. J. (1988). Behavior problems in young sexually abused boys. *Journal of Interpersonal Violence, 3*, 1–12.

Frisch, R. E., & McArthur, J. W. (1974). Menstrual cycles: Fatness as a determinant of minimum weight for height necessary for their maintenance or onset. *Science, 185*, 949–951.

Frohlich, P., & Meston, C. (2002). Sexual functioning and self-reported depressive symptoms among college women. *Journal of Sex Research, 39*, 321–325.

Fromm, E. (1956). *The art of loving.* New York: Harper & Row.

Fuleihan, G. (1997). Tissue-specific estrogens–The promise for the future. *New England Journal of Medicine, 337*, 1686–1687.

Fung, S., & Lok, A. (2004). Viral hepatitis in 2003. *Current Opinion in Gastroenterology, 20*, 241–247.

Furmanan, W. (2002). The emerging field of adolescent romantic relationships. *Current Directions in Psychological Science, 11*, 177–180.

Furnish, V. P. (1994). The Bible and homosexuality: Reading the texts in context. In J. S. Siker (Ed.), *Homosexuality in the church* (pp. 18–35). Louisville, KY: Westminster/John Knox Press.

Furstenberg, F. F., Brooks-Gunn, J., & Morgan, S. P. (1987). *Adolescent mothers in later life.* New York: Cambridge University Press.

Gabelnick, H. L. (1998). Future methods. In R. Hatcher et al. (Eds.), *Contraceptive technology,* 17th ed., (pp. 615–622). New York: Ardent Media.

Gagnon, J. H. (1977). *Human sexualities.* Glenview, IL: Scott, Foresman.

Gagnon, J. H. (1990). The explicit and implicit use of the scripting perspective in sex research. *Annual Review of Sex Research, 1,* 1–44.

Gagnon, J. H., & Simon, W. (1973). *Sexual conduct: The social origins of human sexuality.* Chicago: Aldine.

Gagnon, M. D., Husen, M., Kabacoff, R. I., & Van Hasselt, V. B. (1999). Interpersonal and psychological correlates of marital dissatisfaction in late life: A review. *Clinical Psychology Review, 19*(3), 359–378.

Gajewskji, J. B. (1998). Sexual effects of medications and their interactions: Implications for men with physical disabilities or chronic illness. *Canadian Journal of Human Sexuality, 7,* 287–294.

Galbreath, N., Berlin, F., & Sawyer, D. (2002). Paraphilias and the Internet. In A. Cooper (Ed.), *Sex and the Internet: A guidebook for clinicians* (pp. 187–205). New York: Brunner-Routledge.

Gallant, S. J, Popiel, D. A., Hoffman, D. M., Chakraborty, P. K., & Hamilton, J. A. (1992). Using daily ratings to confirm premenstrual syndrome/late luteal phase dysphoric disorder: What makes a real difference? *Psychosomatic Medicine, 54,* 167–181.

Gangestad, S. W., & Buss, D. M. (1993). Pathogen prevalence and human mate preferences. *Ethology and Sociobiology, 14,* 89–96.

Gangestad, S. W., & Thornhill, R. (1997). Human sexual selection and developmental stability. In J. A. Simpson & D. T. Kenrick (Eds.), *Evolutionary social psychology* (pp. 169–195). Mahwah, NJ: Lawrence Erlbaum Associates.

Ganz, T. (2002). Versatile defensins. *Science, 298,* 977–979.

Gao, F., et al. (1992). Human infection by genetically diverse SIV-SM-related HIV-2 in West Africa. 495–499. *Nature, 358,* 495.

Garcia-Velasco, J., & Mondragon, M. (1991). The incidence of the vomeronasal organ in 1000 human subjects and its possible clinical significance. *Journal of Steroid Biochemistry and Molecular Biology, 39,* 561–563.

Garnets, L. D. & Peplau, L. A. (2001). A new paradigm for women's sexual orientation: Implications for therapy. In Ellyn Kaschak & Leonore Tiefer (Eds.), *A new view of women's sexual problems.* New York: Haworth.

Gatali, M., & Archibald, C. (2004). Women and HIV. *BMC Women's Health, 4 (Suppl 1),* S27.

Gay, P. (1984). *The bourgeois experience: Victoria to Freud.* New York: Oxford University Press.

Gebhard, P. H. (1976). The Institute. In M. S. Weinberg (Ed.), *Sex research: Studies from the Kinsey Institute.* New York: Oxford University Press.

Gebhard, P. H., Gagnon, J. H., Pomeroy, W. B., & Christenson, C. V. (1965). *Sex offenders: An analysis of types.* New York: Harper & Row.

Gemme, R. (1990). Sexology in Quebec. *SIECCAN Journal, 5*(1), 3–10.

Gemme, R. (1998). Legal and sexological aspects of adult street prostitution: A case for sexual pluralism. In James Elias, Vern J. Bullough, Veronica Elias, & Gwen Brewer (Eds.), *Prostitution: On whores, hustlers & johns.* Amherst, NY: Prometheus Books.

Gemme, R., & Payment, N. (1993). Evaluation de la repression de la prostitution de rue à Montréal de 1970 à 1991. *Revue Sexologique, 1*(2), 161–192.

Genel, M. (2000). Gender verification no more? *Medscape Women's Health, 5(3).*

Genovesi, V. J. (1987). *In pursuit of love: Catholic morality and human sexuality.* Wilmington, DE: Michael Glazier.

George, W. H., & Stoner, S. A. (2000). Understanding acute alcohol effects on sexual behavior. *Annual Review of Sex Research, 11,* 92-124.

Georges, E. (1996). Abortion policy and practice in Greece. *Social Science & Medicine, 42,* 509–519.

Gerbner, G., Gross, L., & Morgan, M. (2002). Growing up with television: Cultivation processes. In J. Bryant & D. Zillman (Eds.), *Media effects: Advances in theory and research.* (2nd ed., pp. 43–67). Mahwah, NJ: Erlbaum.

Gilbert, L. (2000, August). Cosmo's hugest sex survey ever. *Cosmopolitan,* 186–189.

Gilligan, C. (1982). *In a different voice: Psychological theory and women's development.* Cambridge, MA: Harvard University Press.

Gilmartin, B. G. (1975). The swinging couple down the block. *Psychology Today, 8*(9), 54.

Giuliano, F., Chevret-Measson, M., Tsatsaris, A., Reitz, C., Murino, M., & Thonneau, P. (2002). Prevalence of erectile dysfunction in France: Results of an epidemiological survey of a representative sample of 1004 men. *European Urology, 42,* 382–389.

Gjerdingen, D. (2003). The effectiveness of various postpartum depression treatments and the impact of antidepressant drugs on nursing infants. *Journal of the American Board of Family Practice 16,* 372–382.

Glascock, J., & LaRose, R. (1993). Dial-a-porn recordings: The role of the female participant in male sexual fantasies. *Journal of Broadcasting & Electronic Media,* 313–324.

Glass, S. J., & Johnson, R. W. (1944). Limitations and complications of organotherapy in male homosexuality. *Journal of Clinical Endocrinology, 4,* 540–544.

Gold, E. R. (1986). Long-term effects of sexual victimization in childhood: An attributional approach. *Journal of Consulting and Clinical Psychology, 54*(4), 471–475.

Gold, S. N., Hughes, D., & Hohnecker, L. (1994). Degrees of repression of sexual abuse memories. *American Psychologist, 49,* 441–442.

Goldberg, M. (1987). Understanding hypersexuality in men and women. In G. R. Weeks & L. Hof (Eds.), *Integrating sex and marital therapy.* New York: Brunner-Mazel.

Goldberg, S. (1983). Parent-infant bonding: Another look. *Child Development, 54,* 1355–1382.

Goldfoot, D. A., Westerberg-van Loon, W., Groeneveld, W., & Koos Slob, A. (1980). Behavioral and physiological evidence of sexual climax in the female stump-tailed macaque (Macaca arctoides). *Science, 208,* 1477–1478.

Goldman, R. J., & Goldman, J. D. G. (1982). *Children's sexual thinking.* London: Routledge & Kegan Paul.

Goldstein, I., et al. (1998). Oral sildenafil in the treatment of erectile dysfunction. *New England Journal of Medicine, 338,* 1397–1404.

Goldstein, J. M, Seidman, L. J., Horton, N. J., Makris, N., Kennedy, D. N., Caviness, V., et al. (2001). Normal sexual dimorphism of the adult human brain assessed by in vivo magnetic resonance imaging. *Cerebral Cortex, 11,* 490–497.

Golombok, S., Perry, B., Burston, A., Murray, C., Mooney-Somers, J., Stevens, M., et al. (2003). Children with lesbian parents: A community study. *Developmental Psychology, 39,* 20–33.

Golombok, S., & Tasker, F. (1996). Do parents influence the sexual orientation of their children? Findings from a longitudinal study of lesbian families. *Developmental Psychology, 32,* 3–11.

Golub, S. (1992). *Periods: From menarche to menopause.* Newbury Park, CA: Sage.

Gonsiorek, J. C. (1996). Mental health and sexual orientation. In R. C. Savin-Williams & K. M. Cohen (Eds.), *The lives of lesbians, gays, and bisexuals* (pp. 462–478). Fort Worth, TX: Harcourt Brace.

Gonzalez, F., & Espin, O. (1996). Latino men, Latina women, and homosexuality. In R. Cabaj & T. Stein (Eds.), *Textbook of homosexuality and mental health* (pp. 583–601). Washington, DC: American Psychiatric Association.

Gooren, L., Fliers, E., & Courtney, K. (1990). Biological determinants of sexual behavior. *Annual Review of Sex Research, 1,* 175–196.

Gordon, B. N., Schroeder, C. S., & Abrams, J. M. (1990). Age and social-class differences in children's knowledge of sexuality. *Journal of Clinical Child Psychology, 19,* 33–43.

Gordon, B., & Schroeder, C. (1995). *Sexuality: A developmental approach to problems.* New York: Plenum Press.

Gosling, S. D., Vazire, S., Srivastava, S., & John, O. P. (2004). Should we trust web-based studies? A comparative analysis of six preconceptions about internet questionnaires. *American Psychologist, 59,* 93–104.

Gosselin, C., & Wilson, G. (1980). *Sexual variations: Fetishism, sadomasochism, transvestism.* New York: Simon & Schuster.

Gottheil, M., Sternberg, R., & Granger, L. (1999). An exploration of clinicians' diagnostic approaches to premenstrual symptomatology. *Canadian Journal of Behavioural Science, 31*(4), 254–260.

Gottman, J., Conn, J., Carrere, S., & Swanson, C. (1998). Predicting marital happiness and stability from newlywed interactions. *Journal of Marriage and the Family, 60,* 5–22.

Gottman, J., Markman, H., & Notarius, C. (1977). The topography of marital conflict: A sequential analysis of verbal and nonverbal behavior. *Journal of Marriage and the Family, 39,* 461–478.

Gottman, J., Notarius, C., Gonso, J., & Markman, H. (1976). *A couple's guide to communication.* Champaign, IL: Research Press.

Gottman, J. M. (1994). Why marriages succeed or fail. New York: Simon & Schuster.

Gottman, J. M., & Notarius, C. I. (2002). Marital research in the 20th century and a research agenda for the 21st century. *Family Process, 41,* 159–197.

Gottman, J. M., Levenson, R. W., Swanson, C., Swanson, K., Tyson, R., & Yoshimoto, D. (2003a). Observing gay, lesbian and heterosexual couples' relationships: Mathematical modeling of conflict interaction. *Journal of Homosexuality, 45,* 65–91.

Gottman, J. M., Levenson, R. W., Gross, J., Frederickson, B. L., McCoy, K., Rosenthal, L., et al. (2003b). Correlates of gay and lesbian couples' relationship satisfaction and relationship dissolution. *Journal of Homosexuality, 45,* 23–43.

Gottman, J. M., & Porterfield, A. L. (1981). Communicative competence in the nonverbal behavior of married couples. *Journal of Marriage and the Family, 43,* 817–824.

Gould, S. J. (1987). *An urchin in the storm.* New York: Norton.

Gouliquer, L. (2000). Negotiation sexuality: Lesbians in the Canadian military. In B. Miedema, Janet Stoppard, & V. Anderson (Eds.). Toronto: Second Story Press.

Gow, H. B. (1994). Condom distribution in high school. *The Clearing House, 67,* 183–184.

Gower, D. B., & Ruparelia, B. A. (1993). Olfaction in humans with special reference to odorous 16-androstenes: Their occurrence, perception and possible social, psychological and sexual impact. *Journal of Endocrinology, 137,* 167–187.

Graham, C. A., et al. (1995). The effects of steroidal contraceptives on the well-being and sexuality of women. *Contraception, 52,* 363–369.

Graham, C. A., Sanders, S. A., Milhausen, R. R., & McBride, K. R. (2004). Turning on and turning off: A focus group study of the factors that affect women's sexual arousal. *Archives of Sexual Behavior, 33,* 527–538.

Grammick, J. (1986). The Vatican's battered wives. *Christian Century, 103,* 17–20.

Grau, I., & Kimpf, M. (1993). Love, sexuality, and satisfaction: Interventions of men and women. *Zeitschrift fur Sozial Psychologie, 24,* 83–93.

Greeley, A. (1994). Review of the Janus Report on Sexual Behavior. *Contemporary Sociology, 23,* 221–223.

Green, R. (1975). Adults who want to change sex; adolescents who cross-dress; and children called "sissy" and "tomboy." In R. Green (Ed.), *Human sexuality: A health practitioner's text.* Baltimore, MD: Williams & Wilkins.

Green, R. (1987). *The Sissy Boy Syndrome and the development of homosexuality.* New Haven: Yale University Press.

Green, R., & Fleming, D. T. (1990). Transsexual surgery follow-up: Status in the 1990s. *Annual Review of Sex Research, 1,* 163–174.

Green, R. M. (1984). Genetic medicine in Jewish legal perspective. *The Annual of the Society of Christian Ethics,* 249–272.

Greenberg, B. S., & Busselle, R. (1996). What's old, what's new: Sexuality on the soaps. *SIECUS Report, 24*(5), 14–16.

Greenberg, D. M., Bradford, J., Firestone, P., & Curry, S. (2000). Relationships of child molesters: A study of victim relationship with the perpetrator. *Child Abuse and Neglect, 24,* 1485–1494.

Greenberg, S., Rabinowitz, R., Firestone, P., Bradford, J. M., & Greenberg, D. M. (2002). Prediction of recidivism in exhibitionists: Psychological, phallometric, and offence factors. *Sexual Abuse: A Journal of Research and Treatment* (pp.329–347).

Greenspan, E. L., & Rosenberg, M. (2005). *Martin's annual criminal code 2005.* Aurora, ON: Canada Law Book Inc.

Greer, A., Barbaree, H., & Brown, C. (1997). Canada. In Donald J. West & Richard Green (Eds.), *Sociolegal control of homosexuality: A multi-nation comparison.* New York: Plenum Press.

Gregersen, E. (1996). *The world of human sexuality: Behaviors, customs, and beliefs.* New York: Irvington.

Gregor, T. (1985). *Anxious pleasures: The sexual lives of an Amazonian people.* Chicago: University of Chicago Press.

Grenier, G., & Byers, E. S. (1995). Rapid ejaculation: A review of conceptual, etiological, and treatment issues. *Archives of Sexual Behavior, 24,* 447–474.

Grenier, G., & Byers, E. S. (1997). The relationships among ejaculatory control, ejaculatory latency, and attempts to prolong heterosexual intercourse. *Archives of Sexual Behavior, 26,* 27–48.

Grenier, G., & Byers, E. S. (2001). Operationalizing premature or rapid ejaculation. *The Journal of Sex Research, 38,* 369–378.

Griffin, K. (1995). One-third of homosexuals face threats of violence, study finds. *Vancouver Sun:* Final Edition, August 1.

Griffin, S. (1981). *Pornography and silence.* New York: Harper & Row.

Griffith, M. (2000). Excessive Internet use: Implications for sexual behavior. *CyberPsychology and Behavior, 3,* 537–552.

Griffith, M. (2001). Sex on the Internet: Observations and implications for Internet sex addiction. *The Journal of Sex Research, 38,* 333–342.

Grindstaff, C. (1988). Adolescent marriage and childbearing: The long-term economic outcome, Canada in the 1980s. *Adolescence, 23,* 45–58.

Grodstein, F., et al. (1997). Postmenopausal hormone therapy and mortality. *New England Journal of Medicine, 336,* 1769–1775.

Gruenbaum, E. (2000). *The female circumcision controversy: An anthropological perspective.* Philadelphia: University of Pennsylvania Press.

Grumbach, M. M., & Styne, D. M. (1998). Puberty: Ontogeny, neuroendocrinology, physiology, and disorders. In J.D. Wilson et al. (Eds.), *Williams Textbook of Endocrinology,* 9th ed. (pp. 1509-1625). Philadelphia: Saunders.

Guay, J.-P., Proulx, J., Cusson, M., & Ouimet, M. (2001). Victim-choice polymorphia among serious sex offenders. *Archives of Sexual Behavior, 30,* 521–534.

Guerrero, L., Spitzberg, B., & Yoshimura, S. (2004). Sexual and emotional jealousy. In J.H. Harvey, A. Wenzel, & S. Sprecher (Eds.), *The handbook of sexuality in close relationships* (pp. 311–345). Mahwah, NJ: Lawrence Erlbaum.

Guindon, A. (1977). *The sexual language: An essay in moral theology.* Ottawa: University of Ottawa Press.

Guindon, A. (1986). *The sexual creators: An ethical proposal for concerned Christians.* Lanham, MD: University Press of America.

Guise, J.-M., Palda, V., Westhoff, C., Chan, B. K. S., Helfand, K., & Lieu, T. A. (2003). The effectiveness of primary care-based interventions to promote breastfeeding: Systematic evidence review and meta-analysis for the US Preventive Services Task Force. *Annals of Family Medicine, 1,* 70–78.

Gunderson, B. H., et al. (1981). Sexual behavior of preschool children. In L. L. Constantine & F. M. Martinson (Eds.), *Children and sex* (pp. 45–62). Boston: Little, Brown.

Gursoy, A. (1996). Abortion in Turkey: A matter of state, family, or individual decision. *Social Science & Medicine, 42,* 531–542.

Gutek, B. A. (1985). *Sex and the workplace.* San Francisco: Jossey-Bass.

Haddock, Geoffrey, Zanna, Mark P., & Esses, Victoria M. (1993). Assessing the structure of prejudicial attitudes: The case of attitudes toward homosexuals. *Journal of Personality and Social Psychology, 65,* 1105–1118.

Hahn, S. R., & Paige, K. E. (1980). American birth practices: A critical review. In J. E. Parsons (Ed.), *The psychobiology of sex differences and sex roles.* New York: McGraw-Hill, Hemisphere.

Halbreich, U. (1996). Reflections on the cause of premenstrual syndrome. *Psychiatric Annals, 26,* 581–585.

Haldeman, D. C. (1994). The practice and ethics of sexual orientation conversion therapy. *Journal of Consulting and Clinical Psychology, 62,* 221–227.

Haldeman, D. C. (2001). Therapeutic antidotes: Helping gay and bisexual men recover from conversion therapies. In A. Shidlo, M. Schroeder, & J. Drescher (Eds.), *Sexual conversion therapy: Ethical, clinical, and research perspectives* (pp. 117–130). New York: Haworth.

Hall, G. C. N. (1995). Sexual offender recidivism revisited: A meta-analysis of recent treatment studies. *Journal of Consulting and Clinical Psychology, 63,* 802–809.

Hall, G. C. N., & Barongan, C. (1997). Prevention of sexual aggression. *American Psychologist, 52,* 5–14.

Hall, J. A. (1998). How big are nonverbal sex differences? The case of smiling and sensitivity to nonverbal cues. In D. Canary & K. Dindia (Eds.), *Sex differences and similarities in communication* (pp. 155–178). Mahwah, NJ: Erlbaum.

Halpern, C., Joyner, K., Udry, J. R., & Suchindran, C. (2000). Smart teens don't have sex (or kiss much either). *Journal of Adolescent Health, 26,* 213–225.

Hamer, D., Hu, S., Magnuson, V. L., Hu, N., & Pattatucci, A. M. L. (1993). A linkage between DNA markers on the X chromosome and male sexual orientation. *Science, 261,* 321–327.

Hampton, M. R., McWatters, B., & Jeffery, B. (2000). Method-related experiences of Canadian women using Depo-Provera for contraception. *The Canadian Journal of Human Sexuality, 9,* 247–257.

Handy, L. C., Valentich, M., Cammaert, L. P., & Gripton, J. (1985). Feminist issues in sex therapy. In M. Valentich & J. Gripton (Eds.), *Feminist perspectives on social work and human sexuality.* Hawthorne Press.

Hanson, R. K. (2000). Will they do it again? Predicting sex-offense recidivism. *Current Directions in Psychological Science, 9,* 106–109.

Hanson, R. K., & Bussière, M. T. (1998). Predicting relapse: A meta-analysis of sexual offender recidivism studies. *Journal of Consulting and Clinical Psychology, 66,* 348–362.

Hanson, R. K., Gordon, A., Harris, A. J. R., Marques, J. K., Murphy, W., Quinsey, V. L., & Seto, M. C. (2002). First report of the collaborative outcome data project on the effectiveness of psychological treatment for sex offenders. *Sexual Abuse: A Journal of Research and Treatment, 14,* 169–194.

Hardwick, D., & Patychuk, D. (1999). Geographic mapping demonstrates the association between social inequality, teen births and STDs among youth. *The Canadian Journal of Human Sexuality, 8,* 77–90.

Harlow, H. F., Harlow, M. K., & Hause, F. W. (1963). The maternal affectional system of rhesus monkeys. In H. L. Rheingold (Ed.), *Maternal behavior in mammals.* New York: Wiley.

Harper, D. M., Franco, E. L., Wheeler, C., Ferris, D. G., Jenkins, D., & Schuind, A. (2004). Efficacy of a bivalent L1 virus-like particle vaccine in prevention of infection with human papillomavirus types 16 and 18 in young women: A randomised controlled trial. *Lancet, 364,* 1757–1765.

Harris, C. (2002). Sexual and romantic jealousy in heterosexual and homosexual adults. *Psychological Science, 13,* 7–12.

Harris, C. (2003). A review of sex differences in sexual jealousy, including self-report data, psychophysiological responses, interpersonal violence, and morbid jealousy. *Personality and Social Psychology Review, 7,* 102–128.

Harris, G. (2004, February 28). Pfizer gives up testing Viagra on women. *New York Times,* pp. C1.

Harris, G. W., & Levine, S. (1965). Sexual differentiation of the brain and its experimental control. *Journal of Physiology, 181,* 379–400.

Harris, N. S., Thompson, S. J., Ball, R., Hussey, J., & Sy, F. (2002). Zidovudine and perinatal Human Immunodeficiency Virus type 1 transmission: A population-based approach. *Pediatrics, 109,* e60.

Harrison, Albert. (1977). Mere exposure. In L. Berkowitz (Ed.), *Advances in experimental social psychology* (Vol. 10). New York: Academic.

Harrison, D. (2000). Violence in the military community. In L. Beaman (Ed.), *New perspectives on deviance: The construction of deviance in everyday life.* Scarborough: Prentice Hall.

Hart, L. L. (1990). Accuracy of home pregnancy tests. *Annals of Pharmacotherapy, 24,* 712–713.

Hartlage, S., & Gehlert, S. (2001). Differentiating premenstrual dysphoric disorder from premenstrual exacerbations of other disorders: A methods dilemma. *Clinical Psychology: Science and Practice, 8,* 242–253.

Hartman, W., & Fithian, M. (1984). *Any man can: The multiple orgasmic technique for every loving man.* New York: St. Martin's Press.

Harvey, J., Poulin, C., & Gouliquer, L. (2001). *Developing a positive sexual identity as a gay woman in the Canadian military: An oxymoron?* Paper presented at the Canadian Lesbian and Gay Studies Association Meeting, Social Sciences and Humanities Congress, Laval, Quebec.

Hass, A. (1979). *Teenage sexuality.* New York: Macmillan.

Hatcher, R. A., et al. (1994). *Contraceptive technology* (16th ed.). New York: Irvington.

Hatcher, R. A., et al. (1998). *Contraceptive technology* (17th ed.). New York: Ardent Media.

Hatcher, R. A., Trussell, J., Stewart, F., Nelson, A., Cates, W., Guest, F., & Kowal, D. (2004). *Contraceptive technology* (18th ed.). New York: Ardent Media.

Hatfield, E. (1978). Equity and extramarital sexuality. *Archives of Sexual Behavior, 7,* 127–141.

Hatfield, E., & Rapson, R. (1993a). Historical and cross-cultural perspectives on passionate love and sexual desire. *Annual Review of Sex Research, 4,* 67–97.

Hatfield, E., & Rapson, R. (1993b). *Love, sex, and intimacy.* New York: HarperCollins.

Hatfield, E., & Sprecher, S. (1986a). Measuring passionate love in intimate relations. *Journal of Adolescence, 9,* 383–410.

Hatfield, E., & Sprecher, S. (1986b). *Mirror, mirror . . . : The importance of looks in everyday life.* Albany: State University of New York Press.

Hatfield, E., & Walster, G. W. (1978). *A new look at love.* Reading, MA: Addison-Wesley.

Hatfield, E., Walster, G. W., & Berscheid, E. (1978). *Equity theory and research.* Boston: Allyn & Bacon.

Hatzichristou, D., Montorsi, F., Buvat, J., Laferriere, N., Bandel, T. J., & Porst, H. (2004). The efficacy and safety of flexible-dose vardenafil (Levitra) in a broad population of European men. *European Urology, 45,* 634–641.

Hausknecht, R. U. (1995). Methotrexate and misoprostol to terminate early pregnancy. *New England Journal of Medicine, 333,* 537–540.

Haynes, B. F., Pantaleo, G., & Fauci, A. S. (1996). Toward an understanding of the correlates of protective immunity to HIV infection. *Science, 271,* 324–328.

Hazan, C., & Shaver, P. (1987). Love conceptualized as an attachment process. *Journal of Personality and Social Psychology, 52,* 511–524.

Health Canada. (1996a). *Breastfeeding.* Canadian Perinatal Surveillance System – Fact Sheets, 1–6.

Health Canada. (1996b). *HIV/AIDS and Aboriginal people in Canada.* Ottawa: Author.

Health Canada, Laboratory Centre for Disease Control. (1996c). *HIV/AIDS Epidemiology among Aboriginal peoples in Canada. Epi Update.* Ottawa: Author.

Health Canada. (1998c, March). Cervical cancer in Canada – cancer updates. Laboratory Centre for Disease Control, 1–8.

Health Canada. (1998). *Canadian STD guidelines: 1998 edition.* Division of STD Prevention and Control. Bureau of HIV/AIDS, STD, and TB. Laboratory Centre for Disease Control, Health Protection Branch. Ottawa: Author.

Health Canada. (1998). HIV/AIDS and Aboriginal people in Canada. www.hc-sc.gc.ca/hppb/hiv_aids/programs/aboriginal.html.

Health Canada. (1998). *Cancer in Canada – Estimated number of deaths.* Health Protection Branch – Laboratory Centre for Disease Control – Cancer Bureau. www.hc-sc.gc.ca/hpb/lcdc/bc/canadadeaths/index.html.

Health Canada: Health Protection Branch, Laboratory Centre for Disease Control. (1998). *Sexual risk behaviours of Canadians. Bureau of HIV/AIDS, STD & TB Update Series: HIV/AIDS Epi Update.*

Health Canada. (1999, April). Breast cancer in Canada – cancer updates. Laboratory Centre for Disease Control, 1–10.

Health Canada. (1999). *Report from consultations on a framework for sexual and reproductive health.*

Health Canada. (1999). Sequelae of STD: Pelvic inflammatory disease and ectopic pregnancy. Ectopic pregnancies in Canada, 1986–1994. Canada Communicable Disease Report, 25S1.

Health Canada. (1999). Sexually transmitted diseases in Canada: 1996 surveillance report. Canada Communicable Disease Report. Ottawa: Author.

Health Canada. (1999). Teen pregnancy and underweight birth. Statistical report on the health of Canadians, 64, 255–257.

Health Canada. (2000). What everyone should know about human papillomavirus (HPV): Questions and Answers. *Bureau of HIV/AIDS, STD and TB Update Series: Population and Public Health Branch, STD Epi Update.* Ottawa: Health Canada.

Health Canada. (2001). *HIV and AIDS in Canada. Surveillance Report to December 31, 2000.* Division of HIV/AIDS Epidemiology and Surveillance, Bureau of HIV/AIDS, STD and TB, Centre for Infectious Disease Prevention and Control. Ottawa: Health Canada.

Health Canada (2002). Perinatal Transmission of HIV. *Bureau of HIV/AIDS, STD and TB Update Series: Population and Public Health Branch, STD Epi Update.* Ottawa: Health Canada.

Health Canada. (2003). *HIV and AIDS in Canada. Surveillance Report to December 31, 2003.* Surveillance and Risk Assessment Division, Centre for Infectious Disease Prevention and Control, Health Canada.

Health Canada. (2003). *Canadian guidelines for sexual health education.* Ottawa: Health Canada.

Health Canada. (2003). *Canadian Perinatal Health Report, 2003.* Ottawa: Minister of Public Works and Government Services Canada.

Health Canada. (2003). *Introduction to assisted human reproduction.* Retrieved December 8, 2004 from http://www.hc-sc.gc.ca.

Health Canada. (2004). *Health Canada advises of potential adverse effects of SSRIs and other anti-depressants on newborns.* [Advisory 2004-44]. Retrieved October 12, 2004 from http://www.hcsc.gc.ca

Health Canada. (2005). *Canadian Tobacco Use Monitoring Survey (CTUMS).* Retrieved May 25, 2005, from http://www.gosmokefree.ca

Hearn, K. D., O'Sullivan, L. F., & Dudley, C. D. (2003). Assessing reliability of early adolescent girls' reports of romantic and sexual behavior. *Archives of Sexual Behavior, 32,* 513–522.

Heath, R. C. (1972). Pleasure and brain activity in man. *Journal of Nervous and Mental Disease, 154,* 3–18.

Heaton, J. P. W. (2000). Central neuropharmacological agents and mechanisms in erectile dysfunction: The role of dopamine. *Neuroscience and Biobehavioral Reviews, 24,* 561–569.

Heaton, J. P. W. (2001). Key issues from the clinical trials of apomorphine SL. *World Journal of Urology, 19,* 25–31.

Hébert, M., Lavoie, F., Piché, C., & Poitras, M. (2001). Proximate effects of a child sexual abuse prevention program in elementary school children. *Child Abuse & Neglect, 25,* 505–522.

Hébert, M., & Tourigny, M. (2004). Child sexual abuse prevention: A review of evaluative studies and recommendations for program development. *Advances in Psychology Research, 32,* 109–142.

Hébert, M., Lavoie, F., & Parent, N. (2002). An assessment of outcomes following parents' participation in a child abuse prevention program. *Victims and Violence, 17,* 355–372.

Hébert, M., & Tremblay, C. (2000). La prévention de l'agression sexuelle à l'égard des enfants. In F. Vitaro & C. Gagnon (Eds.), *Prévention des problèmes d'adaptation chez les enfants et les adolescents*-Tome 1 *Les problèmes internalisès* (pp. 429–503). Ste-Foy: Presses de l'Université du Québec.

Heilman, C. A., & Baltimore, D. (1998). HIV-vaccines–where are they going? *Nature Medicine Vaccine Supplement, 4,* 532–534.

Heiman, J. R. (1975). The physiology of erotica: Women's sexual arousal. *Psychology Today, 8*(11), 90–94.

Heiman, J. R. (2002a). Sexual dysfunction: Overview of prevalence, etiological factors, and treatment. *Journal of Sex Research, 39,* 73–78.

Heiman, J. R. (2002b). Psychologic treatments for female sexual dysfunction: Are they effective and do we need them? *Archives of Sexual Behavior, 31,* 445–450.

Heiman, J. R., & Meston, C. M. (1997). Empirically validated treatment for sexual dysfunction. *Annual Review of Sex Research, 8,* 148–194.

Heise, Lori. (1993). Violence against women: The hidden health burden. *World Health Statistics Quarterly, 46,* 78–85.

Helgeson, V., Cohen, S., Schulz, R., & Yasko, J. (2001). Long-term effects of educational and peer discussion group interventions on adjustment to breast cancer. *Health Psychology, 20,* 387–392.

Hellerstein, H. K., & Friedman, E. H. (1969, March). Sexual activity and the post-coronary patient. *Medical Aspects of Human Sexuality, 3,* 70–74.

Hellstrom, W. (2003). Three-piece inflatable penile prosthesis components (surgical pearls on reservoirs, pumps, and rear-tip extenders). *International Journal of Impotence Research, 15,* S136–S138.

Hellstrom, W. J., Gittelman, M., Karlin, G., Segerson, T., Thibonnier, M., & Taylor, T., (2003b). Sustained efficacy and tolerability of vardenafil, a highly potent selective phosphodiesterase type 5 inhibitor, in men with erectile dysfunction: results of a randomized, double-blind, 26-week placebo-controlled pivotal trial. *Urology, 61,* 8–14.

Hellstrom, W., Overstreet, J. W., Yu, A. S., Saikali, K., Shen, W., Beasley, C. M., et al. (2003a). Tadalafil has no detrimental effect on human spermatogenesis or reproductive hormones. *Journal of Urology, 170,* 887–891.

Helminiak, D. A. (2000). *What the Bible really says about homosexuality.* Sacramento, CA: Alamo Square Press.

Henahan, J. (1984). Honing the treatment of early breast cancer. *Journal of the American Medical Association, 251,* 309–310.

Hendrick, C., & Hendrick, S. S. (1986). A theory and method of love. *Journal of Personality and Social Psychology, 50,* 392–402.

Hendrick, C., & Hendrick, S. (2004). Sex and romantic love: Connects and disconnects. In J. H. Harvey, A. Wenzel, & S. Sprecher (Eds.), *The handbook of sexuality in close relationships* (pp. 159–182). Mahwah, NJ: Lawrence Erlbaum.

Hendrick, S., & Hendrick, C. (1992). *Liking, loving, and relating* (2nd ed.). Pacific Grove, CA: Brooks/Cole.

Herdt, G. H. (1984). *Ritualized homosexuality in Melanesia.* Berkeley, CA: University of California Press.

Herdt, G. (1990). Mistaken gender: 5-alpha reductase hermaphroditism and biological reductionism in sexual identity reconsidered. *American Anthropologist, 92,* 433–446.

Herek, G. M. (2000). The psychology of sexual prejudice. *Current Directions In Psychological Science, 9,* 19–22.

Herek, G. M. (2002). Heterosexuals' attitudes toward bisexual men and women in the United States. *Journal of Sex Research, 39,* 264–274.

Hergenhahn, B. R. (2001). *An introduction to the history of psychology* (4th ed.). Toronto: Wadsworth/Thomas Learning.

Herman, J. L. (1981). *Father-daughter incest.* Cambridge, MA: Harvard University Press.

Herman-Gibbens, M. E., et al. (1997). Secondary sexual characteristics and menses in young girls seen in office practice. *Pediatrics, 99,* 505–512.

Herold, E. (1981). Contraceptive embarrassment and contraceptive behaviour among young single women. *Journal of Youth & Adolescence, 10*(3), 233–242.

Herold, E. S., & Milhausen, R. R. (1999). Dating preferences of university women: An analysis of the nice guy stereotype. *Journal of Sex & Marital Therapy, 25,* 333–343.

Herold, E. S., & Way, L. (1988). Sexual self disclosure among university women. *Journal of Sex Research, 24,* 1–14.

Herrero, R., Castellsague, X., Pawlita, M., Lissowska, J., Kee, F., Balaram, P., et al. (2003). Human papillomavirus and oral cancer: The International Agency for Research on Cancer multicenter study. *Journal of the National Cancer Institute, 95,* 1772–1783.

Heyl, B. S. (1979). *The madam as entrepreneur.* New Brunswick, NJ: Transaction Books.

Higgins, M. (2002, May 13). The church must change. *Maclean's.*

Hill, D. B. (2000). Categories of sex and gender: Either/or, both/and, and neither/nor. *History and Philosophy of Psychology Bulletin, 12,* 25–33.

Hill, M. (2002). Skin color and the perception of attractiveness among African Americans: Does gender make a difference? *Social Psychology Quarterly, 65,* 77–91.

Hite, S. (1976). *The Hite report.* New York: Macmillan.

Hite, S. (1981). *The Hite report on male sexuality.* New York: Alfred Knopf.

Ho, G. Y. F., et al. (1998). Natural history of cervicovaginal papillomavirus infection in young women. *New England Journal of Medicine, 338,* 423–428.

Hobfoll, S., Ritter, C., Lavin, J., Hulsizer, M., et al. (1995). Depression prevalence and incidence among inner-city pregnant and postpartum women. *Journal of Consulting and Clinical Psychology, 63,* 445–453.

Hoff, G. A., & Schneiderman, L. J. (1985, December). Having babies at home: Is it safe? Is it ethical? *Hastings Center Report,* 19–27.

Hofferth, S. L. (1990). Trends in adolescent sexual activity, contraception, and pregnancy in the United States. In J. Bancroft & J. Reinisch (Eds.), *Adolescence and puberty* (pp. 217–233). New York: Oxford University Press.

Hoffmann, H., Janssen, E., & Turner, S. L. (2004). Classical conditioning of sexual arousal in women and men: Effects of varying awareness and biological relevance of the conditioned stimulus. *Archives of Sexual Behavior, 33,* 43–54.

Hogben, M., & Byrne, D. (1998). Using social learning theory to explain individual differences in human sexuality. *Journal of Sex Research, 35,* 58–71.

Hollander, D. (1996). Programs to bring down cesarean section rate prove to be successful. *Family Planning Perspectives, 28,* 182–185.

Holmes, M. (2002). Rethinking the meaning and management of intersexuality. *Sexualities, 5,* 159–180.

Holmstrom, L. L., & Burgess, A. W. (1980). Sexual behavior of assailants during reported rapes. *Archives of Sexual Behavior, 9,* 427–440.

Holroyd, J. C., & Brodsky, A. M. (1977). Psychologists' attitudes and practices regarding erotic and nonerotic physical contact with patients. *American Psychologist, 34,* 843–849.

Holstege, G., Georgiadis, J. R., Paans, A. M., Meiners, L. C., van der Graaf, F. H., & Reinders, A. A. (2003). Brain activation during human male ejaculation. *Journal of Neuroscience, 23,* 9185–9193.

Hom, X., Little, N. R., Gardner, S. D., & Jonas, M. M. (2004). Predictors of virologic response to lamivudine treatment in children with chronic hepatitis B infection. *Pediatric Infectious Disease Journal, 23,* 441–445.

Hong, L. K. (1984). Survival of the fastest: On the origin of premature ejaculation. *Journal of Sex Research, 20,* 109–122.

Hook, E. W., & Handsfield, H. H. (1990). Gonococcal infections in adults. In K. Holmes et al. (Eds.), *Sexually transmitted diseases* (pp. 149–160). New York: McGraw-Hill.

Hopwood, N. J., et al. (1990). The onset of human puberty: Biological and environmental factors. In J. Bancroft & J. M. Reinisch (Eds.), *Adolescence and puberty.* New York: Oxford University Press.

Horney, K. (1973). The flight from womanhood (1926). In K. Horney, *Feminine psychology.* New York: Norton.

Horowitz, C. R., & Jackson, T. C. (1997). Female "circumcision": African women confront American medicine. *Journal of General Internal Medicine, 12,* 491–499.

Horrocks, R. (1997). *An introduction to the study of sexuality.* New York: St. Martin's Press.

House, C. (1997). Navajo warrior women: An ancient tradition in a modern world. In S. Jacobs, et al. (Eds.), *Two-spirit people* (pp. 223–227). Urbana, IL: University of Illinois Press.

Houston, L. N. (1981). Romanticism and eroticism among black and white college students. *Adolescence, 16,* 263–272.

Hubacher, D. (2002). The checkered history and bright future of intrauterine contraception in the United States. *Perspectives on Sexual and Reproductive Health, 34,* 98–103.

Huber, J. D., & Kleinplatz, P. J. (2002). Sexual orientation identification of men who have sex with men in public settings in Canada. *Journal of Homosexuality, 42,* 1–16.

Hucker, S., & Blanchard, R. (1992). Death scene characteristics in 118 fatal cases of autoerotic asphyxia compared with suicidal asphyxia. *Behavioural Sciences and the Law, 10,* 509–523.

Huffstutter, P.J., & Frammolino, R. (2001). Lights, camera, Viagra: When the show must go on, sometimes a little chemistry helps. *Los Angeles Times,* July 6, A1.

Hughes, J. O., & Sandler, B. R. (1987). *"Friends" raping friends: Could it happen to you?* Washington, DC: Association of American Colleges.

Human Rights Watch. (2001). *Hatred in the hallways: Violence and discrimination against lesbian, gay, bisexual, and transgender students in U. S. schools.* New York: Author.

Humphreys, L. (1970). *Tearoom trade: Impersonal sex in public places.* Chicago: Aldine.

Hunt, M. (1974). *Sexual behavior in the 1970s.* Chicago: Playboy Press.

Huston, T. L., & Levinger, G. (1978). Interpersonal attraction and relationships. In M. R. Rosenzweig & L. W. Porter (Eds.), *Annual Review of Psychology* (Vol. 29). Palo Alto, CA: Annual Reviews.

Hutchins, L., & Kaahumanu, L. (Eds.). (1991). *Bi any other name: Bisexual people speak out.* Boston: Alyson.

Hutchinson, K. A. (1995). Androgens and sexuality. *American Journal of Medicine, 98* (Suppl. 1A), 1A111S–1A115S.

Hyde, J. S. (1984). How large are gender differences in aggression? A developmental meta-analysis. *Developmental Psychology, 20,* 722–736.

Hyde, J. S. (1996). *Half the human experience: The psychology of women* (5th ed.). Boston: Houghton-Mifflin.

Hyde, J. S., & Jaffee, S. R. (2000). Becoming a heterosexual adult: The experiences of young women. *Journal of Social Issues, 56,* 283–296.

Hyde, J. S., DeLamater, J., & Hewitt, E. (1998). Sexuality and the dual-earner couple: Multiple rules and sexual functioning. *Journal of Family Psychology, 12,* 354–368.

Hyde, J. S., DeLamater, J., Plant, E. A., & Byrd, J. M. (1996). Sexuality during pregnancy and the year postpartum. *Journal of Sex Research, 33,* 143–151.

Hynes, H. P., & Raymond, J. G. (2002). Put in harm's way: The neglected health consequences of sex trafficking in the United States. In J. Silliman, & A. Bhattacharjee (Eds.), *Policing the national body: Sex, race, and criminalization* (pp. 197–229). Cambridge, MA: South End Press.

Hynie, M., & Lydon, J. E. (1995). Women's perceptions of female contraceptive behaviour: Experimental evidence of the social double standard. *Psychology of Women Quarterly, 19,* 563–581.

Hynie, M., & Lydon, J. E. (1996). Sexual attitudes and contraceptive behavior revisited: Can there be too much of a good thing? *The Journal of Sex Research, 33,* 127–134.

Hynie, M., Lydon, J. E., Cote, S., & Weiner, S. (1998). Relational sexual scripts and women's condom use: The importance of internalized norms. *Journal of Sex Research, 35*(4), 370–380.

Hynie, M., Lydon, J. E., & Taradash, A. (1997). Commitment, intimacy, and women's perceptions of premarital sex and contraceptive readiness. *Psychology of Women Quarterly, 21,* 447–464.

Ilkkaracan, P. (2001). Islam and women's sexuality. In P. B. Jung, M. E. Hunt, & R. Balakrishnan (Eds.) (2001). *Good sex: Feminist perspectives from the world's religions* (pp. 61–76). New Brunswick, NJ: Rutgers University Press.

Imperato-McGinley, J., et al. (1974). Steroid 5 reductase deficiency in man: An inherited form of male pseudohermaphroditism. *Science, 186,* 1213–1215.

Institute of Medicine. (2004). *New frontiers in contraceptive research.* Washington, DC: National Academies Press.

Iqbal, M. M., Gundlapalli, S. P., Ryan, W. G., Ryals, T., & Passman, T. E. (2001). Effects of antimanic mood-stabilizing drugs on fetuses, neonates, and nursing infants. *Southern Medical Journal, 94,* 305–322.

Irvine, J. M. (1995). *Sexuality education across cultures: Working with differences.* San Francisco: Jossey-Bass.

Jaakkola, J., & Gissler, M. (2004). Maternal smoking in pregnancy, fetal development and childhood asthma. *American Journal of Public Health, 94,* 136–141.

Jacobs, S.-E., Thomas, W., & Lang, S. (Eds.). (1997). *Two-spirit people.* Urbana, IL: University of Illinois Press.

Jacobson, S. W., Jacobson, J. L., & Sokol, R. J. (1994). Effects of fetal alcohol exposure on infant reaction time. *Alcoholism: Clinical and Experimental Research, 18,* 1125–1132.

Jacobson, S. W., Jacobson, J. L., Sokol, R. J., Martier, S. S., & Ager, J. W. (1993). Prenatal alcohol exposure and infant information processing ability. *Child Development, 64,* 1706–1721.

Jadack, R. A., Keller, M. L., & Hyde, J. S. (1990). Genital herpes: Gender comparisons and the disease experience. *Psychology of Women Quarterly, 14,* 419–434.

Jamieson, D. J., Kaufman, S. C., Costello, C., Hillis, S. D., Marchbanks, P.A., & Peterson, H. B. (2002). A comparison of women's regret after vasectomy versus tubal sterilization. *Obstetrics and Gynecology, 99,* 1073–1079.

Janicek, M. F., & Averette, H. E. (2001). Cervical cancer: Prevention, diagnosis, and therapeutics. *CA: Cancer Journal for Clinicians, 51,* 92–114.

Janowsky, J.S., Chavez, B. Zamboni, B., & Orwoll, E. (1998). The cognitive neuropsychology of sex hormones in men and women. *Developmental Neuropsychology, 14,* 421–440.

Jantzen, G. (1994). AIDS, shame, and suffering. In J. B. Nelson & S. P. Longfellow (Eds.), *Sexuality and the sacred* (pp. 305–313). Louisville, KY: Westminster/John Knox Press.

Janus, S. S., & Janus, C. L. (1993). *The Janus report on sexual behavior.* New York: Wiley.

Jay, K., & Young, A. (1979). *The gay report.* New York: Summit Books.

Jemail, J. A., & Geer, J. (1977). Sexual scripts. In R. Gemme & C. C. Wheeler (Eds.), *Progress in sexology.* New York: Plenum.

Jenkins, J. S., & Nussey, S. S. (1991). The role of oxytocin: Present concepts. *Clinical Endocrinology, 34,* 515–525.

Jenks, R. J. (1985). Swinging: A replication and test of a theory. *Journal of Sex Research, 21,* 199–210.

Jenks, R. (1998). Swinging: A review of the literature. *Archives of Sexual Behavior, 27,* 507–521.

Jenny, C., Roesler, T. A., & Poyer, K. A. (1994). Are children at risk for sexual abuse by homosexuals? *Pediatrics, 94,* 41–44.

Jensen, G. D. (1976a). Adolescent sexuality. In B. J. Sadock et al. (Eds.), *The sexual experience.* Baltimore: Williams & Wilkins.

John, E. M., Savitz, D. A., & Sandler, D. P. (1991). Prenatal exposure to parents' smoking and childhood cancer. *American Journal of Epidemiology, 133,* 123–132.

Johnson, A. M., Mercer, C. H., Erens, B., Copas, A. J., McManus, S., Wellings, K., et al. (2001). *Sexual behaviour in Britain: Partnerships, practices, and HIV risk behaviours. Lancet, 358,* 1835–1842.

Johnson, A. M., Wadsworth, J., Wellings, K., Bradshaw, S., & Field, J. (1992). Sexual lifestyles and HIV risk. Nature, 360, 410–412.

Johnson, B. R., Horga, M., & Andronache, L. (1996). Women's perspectives on abortion in Romania. *Social Science & Medicine, 42,* 521–530.

Johnson, S. D., Phelps, D., & Cottier, L. (2004). The association of sexual dysfunction and substance use among a community epidemiological sample. *Archives of Sexual Behavior, 33,* 55–64.

Johri, A., Heaton, J., & Morales, A. (2001). Severe erectile dysfunction is a marker for hyperprolactinemia. *International Journal of Impotence Research, 13,* 176–182.

Jones, J. H. (1997). *Alfred C. Kinsey: A public/private life.* New York: Norton.

Jones, R. K., Darroch, J. & Henshaw, S. (2002). Contraceptive use among U.S. women having abortions in 2000-2001. *Perspectives on Sexual and Reproductive Health, 34,* 294–303.

Jorgensen, S. R. (1980). Contraceptive attitude-behavior consistency in adolescence. *Population and Environment, 3,* 174–194.

Jürgens, R. (1998). *HIV testing and confidentiality.* Final Report HIV/AIDS Legal Network & Canadian AIDS Society.

Julien, D., Chartrand, E., Simard, M. C., Bouthillier, D., & Begin, J. (2003). Conflict, social support, and relationship quality: An observational study of heterosexual, gay male, and lesbian couples' communication. *Journal of Family Psychology, 17,* 419–428.

Kabalin, J. N., & Kuo, J. C. (1997). Long-term follow-up of and patient satisfaction with the Dynaflex self-contained inflatable penile prosthesis. *Journal of Urology, 158,* 456–469.

Kafka, M. P. (1997). Hypersexual desire in males: An operational definition and clinical implications for males with paraphilias and paraphilia-related disorders. *Archives of Sexual Behavior, 26,* 505–526.

Kai, L., & Pourier, D. J. (2001). Using the National Longitudinal Study of Youth in the U.S. to study the birth process: A Bayesian approach. *Research in Official Statistics, 4,* 127–150.

Kaiser Family Foundation. (1998). *Sex in the 90s: 1998 national survey of Americans on sex and sexual health* (Publication No. 1430). Menlo Park, CA: Author.

Kaiser Family Foundation. (2001). *Biennial report on sex in the media: Executive summary.* Menlo Park, CA: Kaiser Family Foundation.

Kaiser Family Foundation. (2000). Sex smarts: Decision-making (Publication No. 3064). Menlo Park, CA: Author.

Kaiser Family Foundation. (2003). A biennial report of the Kaiser Family Foundation on Sex on TV3: Executive summary. Menlo Park, CA: Author.

Kaiser Family Foundation. (2003). *A biennial report of the Kaiser Family Foundation on Sex on TV3: Executive summary.* Menlo Park, CA: Author.

Kaiser Family Foundation. (2004). *Sex education in America: General public/parents survey.* Menlo Park, CA: Kaiser Family Foundation.

Kalick, S. M., Zebowitz, L., Langlois, J., & Johnson, R. (1998). Does human facial attractiveness honestly advertise health? Longitudinal data on an evolutionary question. *Psychological Science, 9,* 8–13.

Kalil, K., Gruber, J., Conley, J., & Sytniac, M. (1993). Social and family pressures on anxiety and stress during pregnancy. *Pre- and Perinatal Psychology Journal, 8,* 113–118.

Kambic, R. T. (1999). The effectiveness of natural family planning methods for birth spacing: A comprehensive review. Hopkins Population Center Papers on Population, WP 99-07. Retrieved November 30, 2002, from http://popctr.jhsph.edu/publications/wp/papers/wp9907/fulltext.html.

Kamel, H. K., Perry, H. M., & Morley, J. E. (2001). Hormone replacement therapy and fractures in older adults. *Journal of the American Geriatrics Society, 49,* 179–187.

Kantner, J. F., & Zelnik, M. (1972). Sexual experience of young unmarried women in the United States. *Family Planning Perspectives, 4*(4), 9–18.

Kantner, J. F., & Zelnik, M. (1973). Contraception and pregnancy: Experience of young unmarried women in the United States. *Family Planning Perspectives, 5*(1), 21–35.

Kaplan, H. S. (1974). *The new sex therapy.* New York: Brunner/Mazel.

Kaplan, H. S. (1979). *Disorders of sexual desire.* New York: Simon & Schuster.

Kaplan, H. S. (1994). A neglected issue: The sexual side-effects of current treatments for breast cancer. *Canadian Journal of Human Sexuality, 3,* 151–163.

Kaplan, H. S. (1995). *The sexual desire disorders: Dysfunctional regulation of sexual motivation.* New York: Brunner/Mazel.

Kaplan, H. S., & Owett, T. (1993). The female androgen deficiency syndrome. *Journal of Sex and Marital Therapy, 19,* 3–25.

Kaplan, H. S., & Sager, C. J. (1971, June). Sexual patterns at different ages. *Medical Aspects of Human Sexuality,* 10–23.

Karama, S., Lecours, A. R., Leroux, J. M., Bourgouin, P., Beaudoin, G., Joubert, S., et al. (2002). Areas of brain activation in males and females during viewing of erotic film excerpts. *Human Brain Mapping, 16,* 1–13.

Karr, R. K. (1978). Homosexual labeling and the male role. *Journal of Social Issues, 34*(3), 73–83.

Kaschak, E. & Tiefer, L. (2001). *A new view of women's sexual problems.* New York: Haworth.

Kaufman, M., Silverberg, C., & Odette, F. (2003). *The ultimate guide to sex and disability.* San Francisco: Cleis Press.

Keefe, D. L. (2002). Sex hormones and neural mechanisms. *Archives of Sexual Behavior, 31,* 401–404.

Keelan, P. R., Dion, K. L., & Dion, K. K. (1994). Attachment style and heterosexual relationships among young adults: A short-term panel study. *Journal of Social and Personal Relationships, 11,* 201–214.

Keenan, T., & Ward, T. (2000). A theory of mind perspective on cognitive, affective, and intimacy deficits in child sex offenders. *Sex Abuse, 12,* 49–60.

Kegel, A. H. (1952). Sexual functions of the pubococcygeus muscle. *Western Journal of Surgery, 60,* 521–524.

Kempf, D. J., et al. (1995). ABT-538 is a potent inhibitor of human immunodeficiency virus protease. *Proceedings of the National Academy of Sciences, 92,* 2484.

Kempton, W., & Kahn, E. (1991). Sexuality and people with intellectual disabilities: A historical perspective. *Sexuality and Disability, 9,* 93–111.

Kendall-Tackett, K., Williams, L., & Finkelhor, D. (1993). Impact of sexual abuse on children: A review and synthesis of recent empirical studies. *Psychological Bulletin, 113,* 164–180.

Kendler, K. S., Bulik, C. M., Silberg, J., Hettema, J. M., Myers, J., Prescott, C. A., et al. (2000). Childhood sexual abuse and adult psychiatric and substance use disorders in women: An epidemiological and cotwin control analysis. *Archives of General Psychiatry, 57,* 953–959.

Kendler, K. S., Thornton, L., Gilman, S., & Kessler, R. (2000). Sexual orientation in a US national sample of twin and nontwin sibling pairs. *American Journal of Psychiatry, 157,* 1843–1846.

Kennedy, R., & Suttenfield, K. (2001). Postpartum depression. *Medscape Mental Health 6,* No. 4.

Kenrick, D., et al. (1980). Sex differences, androgyny and approach responses to erotica: A new variation on an old volunteer problem. *Journal of Personality and Social Psychology, 38,* 517–524.

Kero, A., Lalos, A., Högberg, U., & Jacobssen, L. (1999). The male partner involved in legal abortion. *Human Reproduction, 14,* 2669–2675.

Keverne, E. B. (1999). The vomeronasal organ. *Science, 286,* 716–720.

Kiernan, K. (1988). Who remains celibate? *Journal of Biosocial Science, 20,* 253–263.

Kikuras, A. (2004). An interview with Dave Cummings, Unchain the underground. www.unchain.com.

Kim, N., Stanton, B., Li, X., Dickersin, K., & Galbraith, J. (1997). Effectiveness of the 40 adolescent AIDS-risk reduction interventions: A quantitative review. *Journal of Adolescent Health, 20,* 204–215.

King, A. J. C., Beazley, R. P., Warren, W. K., Hankins, C. A., Robertson, A. S., & Radford, J. L. (1988). *Canada youth and AIDS study.* Kingston, ON: Social Program Evaluation Group, Queen's University.

King, M., & Woollett, E. (1997). Sexually assaulted males: 115 men consulting a counseling service. *Archives of Social Behavior, 26,* 579–588.

King, M., Marks, J., & Mandell, J. (2003). Breast and ovarian cancer risks due to inherited mutations in BRCA1 and BRCA2. *Science, 302,* 643–646.

King, S. A. (1999). Internet gambling and pornography: Illustrative examples of the psychological consequences of communication anarchy. *CyberPsychology & Behavior, 2,* 175–193.

Kinsey, A. C., Pomeroy, W. B., & Martin, C. E. (1948). *Sexual behavior in the human male.* Philadelphia: Saunders.

Kinsey, A. C., Pomeroy, W. B., Martin, C. E., & Gebhard, P. H. (1953). *Sexual behavior in the human female.* Philadelphia: Saunders.

Kinsman, G. (1996). *The regulation of desire: Sexuality in Canada.* Montreal: Black Rose Books.

Kippin, T. E., Talianakis, S., Schattmann, L., Bartholomew, S., & Pfaus, J. G. (1998). Olfactory conditioning of sexual behavior in the male rat *(Rattus norvegicus). Journal of Comparative Psychology, 112,* 389–399.

Kiragu, K. (1995, October). Female genital mutilation: A reproductive health concern. *Population Reports* (Supplement), Series J, No. 41, Vol. 23.

Kiragu, K., et al. (2001). Can we avoid catastrophe? Youth and HIV/AIDS. *Population Reports, Series L, No. 12.* Johns Hopkins University School of Public Health.

Kirby, D. (2002). Effective approaches to reducing adolescent unprotected sex, pregnancy, and childbearing. *The Journal of Sex Research, 39,* 51–57.

Kirby, D., Koupi, M., Barth, R. P., & Cagampang, H. H. (1997). The impact of the Postponing Sexual Involvement curriculum among youths in California. *Family Planning Perspectives, 29,* 100–108.

Kirby, D., Short, L., Collins, J., Rugg, D., Kolbe, L., Howard, et al. (1994). School-based programs to reduce sexual risk behaviors: A review of effectiveness. *Public Health Reports, 109,* 339–360.

Kirk, K., Bailey, J., Dunne, M., & Martin, N. (2000). Measurement models for sexual orientation in a community twin sample. *Behavior Genetics, 30,* 345–356.

Kiselica, M., & Scheckel, S. (1995). The couvade syndrome (sympathetic pregnancy) and teenage fathers: A brief primer for counselors. *School Counselor, 43,* 42–51.

Klaus, M., & Kennell, J., (1976). Human maternal and paternal behavior. In M. Klaus & J. Kennell (Eds.), *Maternal infant bonding.* St. Louis, MO: Mosby.

Klebanov, P. K., & Jemmott, J. B. (1992). Effects of expectations and bodily sensations on self-reports of premenstrual symptoms. *Psychology of Women Quarterly, 16,* 289–310.

Klein, R., & Knäuper, B. (2003). The role of cognitive avoidance of STIs for discussing safer sex practices and for condom use consistency. *Canadian Journal of Human Sexuality, 12,* 137–149.

Kleinpatz, P. J. (2003b). What's new in sex therapy? From stagnation to fragmentation. *Sexual & Relationship Therapy, 18,* 95–106.

Kleinplatz, P. J. (2003a). Beyond sexual mechanics and hydraulics: Humanizing the discourse surrounding erectile dysfunction. *Journal of Humanistic Psychology, 43,* 1–29.

Kleinplatz, P .J., & Krippner, S. (2005). Spirituality and sexuality: Celebrating erotic transcendence and spiritual embodiment. In S. G. Mijares, & G. S. Khalsa (Eds.), *The psychospiritual clinician's handbook: Alternative methods for understanding and treating mental disorders.* Binghamton, NY: Haworth Press, Inc.

Knauper, B., & Kornik, R. (2004). Perceived transmissibility of STIs: Lack of differentiation between HIV and chlamydia. *Sexually Transmitted Infections, 80,* 74–78.

Koelman, C. A., Coumans, A. B., Nijman, H. W., Doxiadis, I. I., Dekker, G. A., & Claas, F. H. (2000). Correlation between oral sex and a low incidence of preeclampsia: A role for soluble HLA in seminal fluid? *Journal of Reproductive Immunology, 46,* 155–166.

Kolata, G. (2001, March 25). Researchers find grave defect risk in cloning animals. *New York Times,* p. 1ff.

Kolbenschlag, M. (1985). Abortion and moral consensus: Beyond Solomon's choice. *Christian Century, 102,* 179–183.

Kolker, A. (1989). Advances in prenatal diagnosis. *International Journal of Technology Assessment in Health Care, 5,* 601–617.

Kolodny, R. C., Masters, W. H., Kolodny, R. M., & Toro, G. (1974). Depression of plasma testosterone levels after chronic intensive marihuana use. *New England Journal of Medicine, 290,* 872–874.

Komisaruk, B. R., Gerdes, C. A., & Whipple, B. (1997). 'Complete' spinal cord injury does not block perceptual responses to genital self-stimulation in women. *Archives of Neurology, 54,* 1513–1520.

Korff, J., & Geer, J. H. (1983). The relationship between sexual arousal experience and genital response. *Psychophysiology, 20,* 121–127.

Kosnick, A., et al. (1977). *Human sexuality: New directions in American Catholic thought.* New York: Paulist Press.

Koss, M. P. (1993). Rape: Scope, impact, interventions, and public policy response. *American Psychologist, 48,* 1062–1063.

Koss, M. P., Goodman, L. A., Browne, A., Fitzgerald, L. F., Russo, N. F., & Keita, G. P. (1994). *No safe haven: Male violence against women at home, at work, and in the community.* Washington, DC: American Psychological Association.

Koss, M P., & Heslet, L. (1992). Somatic consequences of violence against women. *Archives of Family Medicine, 1,* 53–59.

Koss, M. P., Koss, P. G., & Woodruff, W. J. (1991). Deleterious effects of criminal victimization on women's health and medical utilization. *Archives of Internal Medicine, 151,* 342–347.

Kothari, P. (1984). For discussion: Ejaculatory disorders–a new dimension. *British Journal of Sexual Medicine, 11,* 205–209.

Kovacs, P. (2002a). Congenital anomalies and low birth weight associated with assisted reproductive technologies (Article 435963). *Medscape Women's Health 7,* No. 3.

Kovacs, P. (2002b). Preconception sex selection. *Medscape Ob/Gyn & Women's Health, 7,* No 2. Retrieved from www.medscape.com/viewarticle/441313

Kraut, R., Olson, J., Banaji, M., Bruckman, A., Cohen, J., & Couper, M. (2004). Psychological research online: Report of the Board of Scientific Affairs' Advisory Group on the Conduct of Research on the Internet. *American Psychologist, 59,* 105–117.

Kreimer, A. R., Alberg, A. J., Daniel, R., Gravitt, P. E., Viscidi, R., Garrett, E. S., et al. (2004). Oral human papillomavirus infection in adults is associated with sexual behavior and HIV serostatus. *Journal of Infectious Diseases, 189,* 686–698.

Krieger, J. N., & Alderete, J. F. (1999). Trichomonas vaginalis and trichomoniasis. In K. Holmes et al. (Eds.), *Sexually transmitted diseases,* 3rd ed. (pp. 587–604). New York: McGraw-Hill.

Kowser, O. H., & Entwistle, M. (1995). Female genital mutilation: Cultural and health issues and their implications for sexuality counselling in Canada. *Canadian Journal of Human Sexuality, 4,* 137–148.

Krimmel, H. T. (1983, Oct.). The case against surrogate parenting. *Hastings Center Report,* 35–39.

Kroeber, A. L., & Kluckhohn, C. (1963). *Culture: A critical review of concepts and definitions.* New York: Vintage Books.

Kruger, T. H., Haake, P., Hartmann, U., Schedlowski, M., & Exton, M. S. (2002). Orgasm-induced prolactin secretion: Feedback control of sexual drive? *Neuroscience and Biobehavioral Reviews, 26,* 31–44.

Kruijver, F., et al. (2000). Male-to-female transsexuals have female neuron numbers in a limbic nucleus. *Journal of Clinical Endocrinology and Metabolism, 85,* 2034–2041.

Kunkel, D., Biely, E., Eyal, K., Cope-Farrar, K., & Donnerstein, E. (2003). *Sex on TV 2003.* Menlo Park, CA: Kaiser Family Foundation.

Kunkel, D., Cope, K. M., & Colvin, C. (1996). *Sexual messages on family hour television: Content and context.* Menlo Park, CA: Kaiser Family Foundation.

Kunkel, D., Cope, K., Farinola, W. J. M., Biely, E., Rollin, E., & Donnerstein, E. (1999). *Sex on TV: A biennial report to the Kaiser Family Foundation.* Menlo Park, CA: Kaiser Family Foundation.

Kurdek, L. A. (1995a). Developmental changes in relationship quality in gay and lesbian cohabiting couples. *Developmental Psychology, 31,* 86–94.

Kurdek, L. A. (1995b). Lesbian and gay couples. In A. R. D'Augelli & C. J. Patterson (Eds.), *Lesbian, gay, and bisexual identities over the lifespan* (pp. 243–261). New York: Oxford.

Laan, E., & Everaerd, W. (1995). Determinants of female sexual arousal: Psychophysiological theory and data. *Annual Review of Sex Research, 6,* 32–76.

Laan, E., Everaerd, W., van Bellen, G., & Hanewald, G. (1994). Women's sexual and emotional responses to male- and female-produced erotica. *Archives of Sexual Behavior, 23,* 153–170.

Lacroix, N. (2003). *Kama Sutra: A modern guide to the ancient art of sex.* Hylas Publishing: New York.

LaFromboise, T. D., Heyle, A. M., & Ozer, E. J. (1990). Changing and diverse roles of women in American Indian cultures. *Sex Roles,* 455–476.

Lahey, K. A. (1999). *Are we "persons" yet? Law and sexuality in Canada.* Toronto: University of Toronto Press.

Lalumière, M., Blanchard, R., & Zucker, K. (2000). Sexual orientation and handedness in men and women: A meta-analysis. *Psychological Bulletin, 126,* 575–592.

Lalumière, M. L., Blanchard, R., & Zucker, K. J. (2000). Sexual orientation and handedness in men and women: A meta-analysis. *Psychological Bulletin, 126,* 575–592.

Lalumière, M. L., Chalmers, L. J., Quinsey, V. L., & Seto, M. C. (1996). A test of mate deprivation hypothesis of sexual coercion. *Ethology & Sociobiology, 17,* 299–318.

Lalumière, M. L., Quinsey, V. L., Harris, G. T., Rice, M. E., & Trautrimas, C. (2003). Are rapists differentially aroused by coercive sex in phallometric assessments? *Annals of the New York Academy of Sciences, 989,* 211–224.

Lalumière, M. L., & Quinsey, V. L. (1996). Sexual deviance, antisociality, mating effort, and the use of sexually coercive behaviors. *Personality and Individual Differences, 21,* 33–48.

Lalumière, M. L., & Quinsey, V. L. (1998). Pavlovian conditioning of sexual interests in human males. *Archives of Sexual Behavior, 27,* 241–252.

Lamb, M. (1982, April). Second thoughts on first touch. *Psychology Today*, 9–10.

Lamb, M. E., & Hwang, C. (1982). Maternal attachment and mother-neonate bonding: A critical review. In M. E. Lamb & A. L. Brown (Eds.), *Advances in developmental psychology* (Vol. 2). Hillsdale, NJ: Lawrence Erlbaum.

Lamberts, S. W. J., et al. (1997). The endocrinology of aging. *Science, 278*, 419–424.

Lande, R. E. (1995). New era for injectables. *Population Reports,* Series K, No. 5.

Langer, E. J., & Dweck, C. S. (1973). *Personal politics: The psychology of making it.* Englewood Cliffs, NJ: Prentice-Hall.

Langille, D. (2000). *Adolescent sexual health services and education: Options for Nova Scotia.* Maritime Centre of Excellence for Women's Health. Policy discussion Series Paper #8. Halifax, NS: Maritime Centre of Excellence for Women's Health.

Langille, D., Beazley, R., & Doncaster, H. (1996). *Amherst parents' attitudes towards school-based sexual health education.* Amherst, NS: Amherst Initiative for Healthy Adolescent Sexuality.

Langille, D. B., Beazley, R., Shoveller, J., & Johnston, G. (1994). Prevalence of high risk sexual behaviour in adolescents attending school in a county in Nova Scotia. *Canadian Journal of Public Health, 85*(4), 227–230.

Langille, D., Graham, J., Marshall, E., Blake, M., Chittey, C., & Doncaster-Scott, H. (1999). *Developing understanding from young women's experiences in obtaining sexual health services and education in a Nova Scotia community.* Maritime Centre of Excellence for Women's Health.

Langille, D. B., Murphy, G. T., Hughes, J., & Rigby, J. A. (2001). Nova Scotia high school students' interactions with physicians for sexual health information and services. *Canadian Journal of Public Health, 92*, 219–222.

Langfeldt, T. (1981). Childhood masturbation. In L. L. Constantine & F. M. Martinson (Eds.), *Children and sex* (pp. 63–74). Boston: Little Brown.

LaMarre, A. K., Paterson, L. Q., & Gorzalka B. B. (2003). Breastfeeding and postpartum maternal sexual functioning: A review. *Canadian Journal of Human Sexuality, 12*, 151–168.

Lambert, T. A., Kahn, A., & Apple, K. (2003). Pluralistic ignorance and hooking up. *Journal of Sex Research, 40*, 129–133.

Landott, M. A., Bartholomew, K., Saffrey, C., Oram, D., & Perlman, D. (2004). Gender nonconformity, childhood rejection, and adult attachment: A study of Gay men. *Archives of Sexual Behavior, 33*, 117–128.

Langille, D. B., Flowerdew, G., & Andreou, P. (In press). Teenage pregnancy in Nova Scotia communities: Associations with contextual factors. *Canadian Journal of Human Sexuality.*

Langille, D. B., Hughes, J., Tomblin Murphy, G., & Rigby, J. A. (2002). Contraception among young women attending high school in rural Nova Scotia. *Canadian Journal of Public Health, 93*, 461–464.

Larsen, S. A., et al. (1996). Syphilis. In S. Morse et al. (Eds.), *Atlas of sexually transmitted diseases and AIDS* (pp. 21–46). London: Mosby-Wolfe.

Larson, I., & Svedin, C. G. (2002a). Teachers' and parents' reports on 3- to 6-year-old children's sexual behaviour: A comparison. *Child Abuse & Neglect, 26*, 247–266.

Larsson, I., & Svedin, C. G. (2002b). Sexual experiences in childhood: Young adults' recollections. *Archives of Sexual Behavior, 31*, 263–274.

Latty-Mann, H., & Davis, K. (1996). Attachment theory and partner choice: Preference and actuality. *Journal of Social and Personal Relationships, 13*, 5–23.

Laumann, E. O., Gagnon, J. H., Michael, R. T., & Michaels, S. (1994). *The social organization of sexuality: Sexual practices in the United States.* Chicago: University of Chicago Press.

Laumann, E. O., & Parish, W. (in press). Chinese Family Health Survey (CFHS). In E. Laumann (Ed.).

Laumann, E. O., Masi, C., & Zuckerman, E. (1997). Circumcision in the United States: Prevalence, prophylactic effects, and sexual practice. *JAMA, 277*, 1052–1057.

Laumann, E. O., Paik, A., & Rosen, R. (1999). Sexual dysfunction in the United States: Prevalence and predictors. *Journal of the American Medical Association, 281*, 537–544.

Laurenceau, J.-P., Feldman, B., & Pietromonaco, P. R. (1998). Intimacy as an interpersonal process: The importance of self-disclosure, partner disclosure, and perceived partner responsiveness in interpersonal exchanges. *Journal of Personality and Social Psychology, 74*, 1238–1251.

Lavine, H., Sweeney, D., & Wagner, S. (1999). Depicting women as sex objects in television advertising: Effects on body dissatisfaction. *Personality and Social Psychology Bulletin, 25*, 1049–1058.

Lawrance, K.-A., & Byers, E. S. (1995). Sexual satisfaction in long-term heterosexual relationships: The interpersonal exchange model of sexual satisfaction. *Personal Relationships, 2*, 267–285.

Lawrance, K.-A., & Herold, E. S. (1988). Women's attitudes toward and experience with sexually explicit materials. *Journal of Sex Research, 24*, 161–169.

Lawrance, K.-A., Taylor, D., & Byers, E. S. (1996). Differences in men's and women's global, sexual and ideal-sexual expressiveness and instrumentality. *Sex Roles, 34*(5 & 6), 337–357.

Lawrence, A. A. (2003). Factors associated with satisfaction or regret following male-to-female sex reassignment surgery. *Archives of Sexual Behavior, 32*, 299–316.

Law Reform Commission of Canada. (1992). *Medically assisted procreation working paper 65.* Ottawa: Canada Communication Group-Publishing, cat. #J32-1/65-1992.

Leader, A. (1999). New reproductive technologies: Why are we limiting choices for infertile couples? *Canadian Medical Association Journal, 161*, 1411–1412.

Leavitt, F. (1974). *Drugs and behavior.* Philadelphia: Saunders.

Lebacqz, K. (1987). Appropriate vulnerability: A sexual ethic for singles. *Christian Century, 104*, 435–438.

Lebeque, B. (1991). Paraphilias in U.S. pornography titles: "Pornography made me do it" (Ted Bundy). *Bulletin of the American Academy of Psychiatry and Law, 19*, 43–48.

Lechner, S. C., Antoni, M. H., Lydston, D., LaPerriere, A., Ishii, M., Devieux, J., et al. (2003). Cognitive-behavioral interventions improve quality of life in women with AIDS. *Journal of Psychosomatic Research, 54*, 253–261.

Lederer, L. (Ed.). (1980). *Take back the night: Women on pornography.* New York: Morrow.

Lee, J. A. (1973). *The colors of love: An exploration of the ways of loving.* Don Mills, ON: New Press.

Lee, J. A. (1979). The social organization of sexual risk. *Alternative Lifestyles, 2*, 69–100.

Leger Marketing. (2004). *Canadians and their tolerance towards homosexuality.* Retrieved November 25, 2004 from http://www.legermarketing.com.

Leger Marketing. (2004). *The lifestyles of Canadians.* Retrieved November 25, 2004 from http://www.legermarketing.com.

Legman, G. (1968). *Rationale of the dirty joke.* New York: Grove.

Leiblum, S. R. (2000). Vaginismus: A most perplexing problem. In S. R. Leiblum & R. C. Rosen (Eds.), *Principles and practice of sex therapy*, 3rd ed., New York: Guilford.

Leifer, M. (1980). *Psychological effects of motherhood: A study of first pregnancy.* New York: Praeger.

Leitenberg, H., & Henning, K. (1995). Sexual fantasy. *Psychological Bulletin, 117,* 469–496.

LeMagnen, J. (1952). Les pheromones olfactosexuals chez le rat blanc. *Archives des Sciences Physiologiques, 6,* 295–332.

Lemieux, S., & Byers, E. S. (1996). *The relationship between child sexual abuse, adult attachment & adult adjustment.* Paper presented at the meeting of the Canadian Sex Research Forum, Montreal.

Leonard, L. (2000). Interpreting female genital cutting: Moving beyond the impasse. *Annual Review of Sex Research, 11,* 158–190.

Leonard, L. M., & Follette, V. M. (2002). Sex functioning in women reporting a history of child sexual abuse: Clinical and empirical considerations. *Annual Review of Sex Research, 13,* 346–388.

Lerman, H. (1986). From Freud to feminist personality theory. *Psychology of Women Quarterly, 10,* 1–18.

LeVay, S. (1991). A difference in hypothalamic structure between heterosexual and homosexual men. *Science, 253,* 1034–1037.

LeVay, S. (1996). *Queer science: The use and abuse of research into homosexuality.* Cambridge, MA: MIT Press.

Lever, J. (1994, August). Sexual revelations. The 1994 Advocate Survey of Sexuality and Relationships: The Men. *The Advocate,* 17–24.

Lever, J. (1995, August). Lesbian sex survey. The 1995 Advocate Survey of Sexuality and Relationships: The Women. *The Advocate,* 22–30.

Levin, R. J. (2003). Is prolactin the biological 'off switch' for human sexual arousal? *Sexual and Relationship Therapy, 18,* 237–243.

Levine, C., & Bermel, J. (Eds.). (1985, Aug.). *AIDS: The emerging ethical dilemmas.* Hastings Center Report Special Supplement, 1–31.

Levine, C., & Bermel, J. (Eds.). (1986, Dec.). *AIDS: Public health and civil liberties.* Hastings Center Report Special Supplement, 1–36.

Levine, R., Sato, S., Hashimoto, T., & Verma, J. (1995). Love and marriage in eleven cultures. *Journal of Cross-Cultural Psychology, 26,* 554–571.

Levitas, E. et al. (2003). Are semen parameters related to abstinence? Analysis of 7233 semen samples. Presented at European Society for Human Reproduction and Embryology, Madrid.

Levitt, E., Moser, C., & Jamison, K. (1994). The prevalence and some attributes of females in the sadomasochistic subculture: A second report. *Archives of Sexual Behavior, 23,* 465–473.

Levitt, E. E., & Mulcahy, J. J. (1995). The effect of intracavernosal injection of papaverine hydrochloride on orgasm latency. *Journal of Sex & Marital Therapy, 21,* 39–41.

Levy, J. J., Maticka-Tyndale, E., & Lew, V. A. (1992). Pratique contraceptives et preventive face au sida parmi un groupe de cegepiens de Montreal: Variations interethniques. *Novelles Pratique Sociale, 5*(2), 25–36.

Lewis, J., & Maticka-Tyndale, E. (1998). *Final report: Erotic/exotic dancing: HIV-related risk factors.* Ottawa: Health Canada.

Lewis, J., Maticka-Tyndale, E., Shaver, F., & Schramm, H. (In press). Managing risk and safety on the job: The experiences of Canadian sex workers. *Journal of Psychology and Human Sexuality.*

Lewis, R. W., & Witherington, R. (1997). External vacuum therapy for erectile dysfunction: Use and results. *World Journal of Urology, 15,* 78–82.

Lewis, W. J. (1997). Factors associated with post-abortion adjustment problems: Implications for triage. *Canadian Journal of Human Sexuality, 6,* 9–16.

Libman, E. (1989). Sociocultural and cognitive factors in aging and sexual expression: Conceptual and research issues. *Canadian Psychology, 3*(3), 560–567.

Libman, E., & Fichten, C. S. (1987). Prostatectomy and sexual function. *Urology, 24*(5), 467–478.

Libman, E., Fichten, C. S., Creti, L., Weinstein, N., Amsel, R., & Brender, W. (1989). Transurethral prostatectomy: Differential effects of age category and presurgery sexual functioning on postprostatectomy sexual adjustment. *Journal of Behavioural Medicine, 12*(5), 469–485.

Liebmann-Smith, J. (1987). *In pursuit of pregnancy: How couples discover, cope with, and resolve their fertility problems.* New York: Newmarket Press.

Lief, H. I., & Hubschman, L. (1993). Orgasm in the postoperative transsexual. *Archives of Sexual Behavior, 22,* 145–156.

Lightfoot-Klein, H. (1993). *Prisoners of ritual: An odyssey into female genital circumcision in Africa.* New York: Haworth.

Liljeros, F., Edling, C. R., Amaral, L. A., Stanley, H. E., & Aberg, Y. (2001). The web of human sexual contacts. *Nature, 411,* 907–908.

Linz, D. (1989). Exposure to sexually explicit materials and attitudes toward rape: A comparison of study results. *Journal of Sex Research, 26,* 50–84.

Linz, D., Donnerstein, E., & Penrod, S. (1987). The findings and recommendations of the Attorney General's Commission on pornography: Do the psychological "facts" fit the political fury? *American Psychologist, 42,* 946–953.

Lippa, R. A. (2003). Are 2D:4D finger-length ratios related to sexual orientation? Yes for men, no for women. *Journal of Personality and Social Psychology, 85,* 179–188.

Lisak, D., & Miller, P. M. (2002). Repeat rape and multiple offending among undetected rapists. *Violence & Victims, 17,* 73–84.

Liskin,. (1985, November–December). Youth in the 1980s: Social and health concerns. *Population Reports, XIII,* No. 5, M350–M388.

Liu, C. (2003). Does quality of marital sex decline with duration? *Archives of Sexual Behavior, 32,* 55–60.

Loeb, T. B., Williams, J. K., Carmona, J. V., Rivkin, I., Wyatt, G. E., Chin, D., et al. (2002). Child sexual abuse: Associations with the sexual functioning of adolescents and adults. *Annual Review of Sex Research, 13,* 307–345.

Loeb, T.B. et al. (2002). Child sexual abuse: Associations with the sexual functioning of adolescents and adults. *Annual Review of Sex Research, 13,* 307–345.

Loffreda, B. (2000). *Losing Matt Shepard: Life and politics in the aftermath of anti-gay murder.* New York: Columbia University Press.

Loftus, E. F. (1993). The reality of repressed memories. *American Psychologist, 48,* 518–537.

Loftus, E. F., Polonsky, S., & Fullilove, M. T. (1994). Memories of childhood sexual abuse: Remembering and repressing. *Psychology of Women Quarterly, 18,* 67–84.

Lombardi, E. L., Wilchins, R., Priesing, D., & Malouf, D. (2001). Gender violence: Transgender experiences with violence and discrimination. *Journal of Homosexuality, 42,* 89–101.

Longo, D. J., Clum, G. A., & Yaeger, N. J. (1988). Psychosocial treatment for recurrent genital herpes. *Journal of Consulting and Clinical Psychology, 56,* 61–66.

Lonsway, K. A. & Kothari, C. (2000). First-year campus acquaintance rape education: Evaluating the impact of a mandatory intervention. *Psychology of Women Quarterly, 24,* 220–232.

LoPiccolo, J., & Stock, W. E. (1986). Treatment of sexual dysfunction. *Journal of Consulting and Clinical Psychology, 54,* 158–167.

LoPiccolo, L. (1980). Low sexual desire. In S. R. Leiblum & L. A. Pervin (Eds.), *Principles and practice of sex therapy.* New York: Guilford Press.

Los, M. (1994). The struggle to redefine rape in the early 1980s. In J. V. Roberts & R. M. Mohr (Eds.), *Confronting sexual assault: A decade of legal change.* Toronto: University of Toronto Press.

Louv, W. C., et al. (1989). Oral contraceptive use and risk of chlamydial and gonococcal infections. *American Journal of Obstetrics and Gynecology, 160,* 396.

Lowman, J. (1995). Prostitution in Canada. In M. A. Jackson & C. T. Griffiths (Eds.), *Canadian criminology: Perspectives on crime and criminality.* Toronto: Harcourt Brace.

Luby, E. C., & Klinge, V. (1985). Genital herpes: A pervasive psychosocial disorder. *Archives of Dermatology, 121,* 494–497.

Luke, B. (1994). Nutritional influences on fetal growth. *Clinical Obstetrics and Gynecology, 37,* 538–549.

Luker, K. (1975). *Taking chances: Abortion and the decision not to contracept.* Berkeley: University of California Press.

Luker, K. (1984). *Abortion and the politics of motherhood.* Berkeley: University of California Press.

Luo, M., Fee, M., & Katz, L. (2003). Encoding pheromonal signals in the accessory olfactory bulb in behaving mice. *Science, 299,* 1196–1201.

Lydon-Rochelle, M., Holt, V., Easterling, T., & Martin, D. (2001). Risk of uterine rupture during labor among women with a prior cesarean delivery. *New England Journal of Medicine, 345,* 3–8.

Lytton, H., & Romney, D. M. (1991). Parents' differential socialization of boys and girls: A meta-analysis. *Psychological Bulletin, 109,* 267–296.

Maass, A., Cadinu, M., Guarnieri, G., & Grasselli, A. (2003). Sexual harassment under social identity threat: The computer harassment paradigm. *Journal of Personality and Social Psychology, 85,* 853–870.

Maccoby, E. (1998). *The two sexes: Growing up apart, coming together.* Cambridge, MA: Harvard University Press.

MacDonald, G., & Jeffrey, L. (2000). The ethics of social control in researching the sex trade: Prostitutes and professors. Prepared for Gendering Ethics/Ethics of Gender Conference at the Centre for Interdisciplinary Gender Studies on June 21, 2000, at the University of Leeds, UK.

MacDonald, T. K., & Ross, M. (1999). Assessing the accuracy of predictions about dating relationships: How and why do lovers' predictions differ from those made by observers? *Personality and Social Psychology Bulletin, 25,* 1417–1429.

MacFarlane, J. A., et al. (1978). The relationship between mother and neonate. In S. Kitzinger & J. A. Davis (Eds.), *The place of birth.* Oxford: Oxford University Press.

Mackie, M. (1991). *Gender relations in Canada: Further explorations.* Toronto: Harcourt Brace Canada.

MacLean, Paul. (1962). New findings relevant to the evolution of psychosexual functions of the brain. Journal of Nervous and Mental Disease, 135, 289–301.

Maclean's. (2003, October 6). Internet sex unzipped.

*Maclean's/*CTV Poll. (1994, January 3). Canada under the covers." *Maclean's, 107*(1).

*Maclean's/*CTV Poll. (1995, January 2). Looking inward. *Maclean's.*

*Maclean's/*Global Poll. (2000, December 25). Sexual attitudes. *Maclean's.*

MacMillan, H. L., Fleming, J. E., Trocmé, N., Boyle, M. H., Wong, M., Racine, et al. (1997). Prevalence of child physical and sexual abuse in the community: Results from the Ontario Health Supplement. *Journal of the American Medical Association, 278,* 131–135.

MacNeil, S., & Byers, E. S. (1997). The relationship between sexual problems, communication and sexual satisfaction. *Canadian Journal of Human Sexuality, 6,* 277–283.

MacNeil, S., & Byers, E. S. (2005). Dyadic assessment of sexual self-disclosure and sexual satisfaction in heterosexual dating couples. *Journal of Social and Personal Relationships, 22,* 169–181.

Maddock, J. W. (1997). Sexuality education: A history lesson. In J. W. Maddock (Ed.), *Sexuality education in post-secondary and professional training settings* (pp. 1–22). Binghamton, NY: The Haworth Press.

Magana, J. R., & Carrier, J. M. (1991). Mexican and Mexican American male sexual behavior and spread of AIDS in California. *Journal of Sex Research, 28,* 425–441.

Maguire, D. C. (1983). Abortion: A question of Catholic honesty. *Christian Century, 100,* 803–807.

Mah, K., & Binik, Y. M. (2001). The nature of human orgasm: A critical review of major trends. *Clinical Psychology Review, 21,* 823–856.

Mah, K., & Binik, Y. M. (2002). Do all orgasms feel alike? Evaluating a two-dimensional model of the orgasm experience across gender and sexual context. *Journal of Sex Research, 39,* 104–113.

Mahoney, E. R. (1983). *Human sexuality.* New York: McGraw-Hill.

Maines, R. P. (1999). *The technology of orgasm: "Hysteria," the vibrator, and women's sexual satisfaction.* Baltimore: Johns Hopkins University Press.

Major, B., Cozzarelli, C., Cooper, M. L., Zubek, J., Richards, C., Wilhite, M., et al. (2000). Psychological responses of women after first-trimester abortion. *Archives of General Psychiatry, 57,* 777–784.

Malamuth, N. M. (1998). The confluence model as an organizing framework for research on sexually aggressive men: Risk moderators, imagined aggression and pornography consumption. In R. Geen & E. Donnerstein (Eds.), *Aggression: Theoretical and empirical reviews.* New York: Academic Press.

Malamuth, N. M., & Brown, L. M. (1994). Sexually aggressive men's perceptions of women's communications. *Journal of Personality and Social Psychology, 67,* 699–712.

Malamuth, N. M., Sockloskie, R. J., Koss, M. P., & Tanaka, J. S. (1991). Characteristics of aggressors against women: Testing a model using a national sample of college students. *Journal of Consulting and Clinical Psychology, 59,* 670–781.

Maletzky, B. M. (1997). Exhibitionism: Assessment and treatment. In D. R. Laws & w. O'Donohue (Eds). *Sexual deviance: Theory, assessment, and treatment.* New York: Guilford.

Maltz, W., & Boss, S. (1997). *In the garden of desire. The intimate world of women's sexual fantasies.* New York: Broadway Books.

Markman, H. J. (1979). Application of a behavioral model of marriage in predicting relationship satisfaction of couples planning marriage. *Journal of Consulting and Clinical Psychology, 47,* 743–749.

Markman, H. J. (1981). Prediction of marital distress: A 5-year follow-up. *Journal of Consulting and Clinical Psychology, 49,* 760–762.

Markman, H., & Kadushin, F. (1986). Preventive effects of human training for first-time parents: A short-term longitudinal study. *Journal of Consulting and Clinical Psychology, 54,* 872–874.

Marquis, J. N. (1970). Orgasmic reconditioning: Changing sexual object choice through controlling masturbation fantasies. *Journal of Behavior Therapy and Experimental Psychiatry, 1,* 263–272.

Marshall, D. C. (1971). Sexual behavior on Mangaia. In D. S. Marshall & R. C. Suggs (Eds.), *Human sexual behavior.* New York: Basic Books.

Marshall, E. (1995). NIH's "Gay Gene" study questioned. *Science, 268,* 1841.

Marshall, W. L. (1992). The social values of treatment for sexual offenders. *Canadian Journal of Human Sexuality, 1,* 109–114.

Marshall, W. L. (1993). A revised approach to the treatment of men who sexually assault adult females. In G. N. Hall et al. (Eds.), *Sexual aggression* (pp. 143–165). Washington, DC: Taylor & Francis.

Marshall, W. L., & Barbaree, H. E. (1990). Outcome of comprehensive cognitive-behavioural treatment programs. In W. L. Marshall, D. R. Laws, & H. E. Barbaree (Eds.), *Handbook of sexual assault: Issues, theories, and treatment of the offender.* New York: Plenum Press.

Marshall, W. L., & Eccles, A. (2000). Issues in clinical practice with sex offenders. *Journal of Interpersonal Violence, 16,* 68–93.

Marshall, W. L., Eccles, A., & Barbaree, H. E. (1991). The treatment of exhibitionists: A focus on sexual deviance versus cognitive and relationship features. *Behavioural Research and Therapy, 20,* 120–135.

Marshall, W. L., Jones, R., Ward, T., Johnson, P., & Barbaree, H. E. (1991). Treatment outcome with sex offenders. *Clinical Psychology Review, 11,* 465–485.

Marshall, W. L., Payne, K., Barbaree, H. E., & Eccles, A. (1991). Exhibitionists: Sexual preferences for exposing. *Behavioural Research Therapy, 20*(1), 37–40.

Marshall, W. L., & Pithers, W. D. (1994). A reconsideration of treatment outcome with sex offenders. *Criminal Justice and Behavior, 21,* 10–27.

Martin, C. L., & Halverson, C. F. (1983). The effects of sex-typing schemas on young children's memory. *Child Development, 54,* 563–574.

Martin, C. L., Ruble, D., & Szkrybalo, J. (2002). Cognitive theories of early gender development. *Psychological Bulletin, 128,* 903–933.

Martin, C., & Ruble, D. (2004). Children's search for gender cues: Cognitive perspectives on gender development. *Current Directions in Psychological Science, 13,* 67–70.

Martinson, F. M. (1994). *The sexual life of children.* Westport, CT: Bergin & Garvey.

Marx, J. (1995b). Sharing the genes that divide the sexes for mammals. *Science, 269,* 1824–1827.

Masters, W. H., & Johnson, V. (1966). *Human sexual response.* Boston: Little, Brown.

Masters, W. H., & Johnson, V. (1970). *Human sexual inadequacy.* Boston: Little, Brown.

Masters, W. H., & Johnson, V. (1979). *Homosexuality in perspective.* Boston: Little, Brown.

Masters, W. H., Johnson, V. E., & Kolodny, R. C. (1982). *Human sexuality.* Boston: Little, Brown.

Masterton, G. (1993). *Drive him wild: A hands-on guide to pleasuring your man in bed.* New York: Signet Books.

Mathy, R., & Cooper, A. (2003). The duration and frequency of Internet use in a nonclinical sample: Suicidality, behavioral problems, and treatment history. *Psychotherapy: Theory, Research, Practice, Training, 40,* 125–135.

Maticka-Tyndale, E. (1992). Social construction of HIV transmission and prevention among heterosexual young adults. *Social Problems, 39*(93), 238–252.

Maticka-Tyndale, E. (1997). Reducing the incidence of sexually transmitted disease through behavioural and social change. *Canadian Journal of Human Sexuality, 6,* 89–104.

Maticka-Tyndale, E. (2001). Sexual health and Canadian youth: How do we measure up? *The Canadian Journal of Human Sexuality, 10,* 1–17.

Maticka-Tyndale, E., Barrett, M., & McKay, A. (2000a). Adolescent sexual and reproductive health in Canada: A review of national data sources and their limitations. *The Canadian Journal of Human Sexuality, 9,* 41–65.

Maticka-Tyndale, E., & Bicher, M. (1996). The impact of medicalization on women. In Bernard Schissel & Linda Mahood (Eds.), *Social control in Canada: A reader on the social construction of deviance.* Toronto: Oxford University Press.

Maticka-Tyndale, E., Adams, B.D., & Cohen, J. (2002). Sexual desire and practice among people living with HIV and using combination anti-retroviral therapies. *Canadian Journal of Human Sexuality, 11,* 33–40.

Maticka-Tyndale, E., Godin, G., LeMay, G., Adrien, A., Manson-Singer, S., Willms, D., et al. (1996). Canadian ethnocultural communities facing AIDS: Overview and summary of survey results from phase III. *Canadian Journal of Public Health, 87* (supp. 1), S38–S43.

Maticka-Tyndale, E., & Herold, E. S. (1997). The scripting of sexual behaviour: Canadian university students on spring break in Florida. *Canadian Journal of Human Sexuality, 6,* 317–328.

Maticka-Tyndale, E., & Herold, E. S. (1999). Condom use on spring break vacation: The influence of intention, prior use & context. *Journal of Applied Psychology, 29,* 1010–1027.

Maticka-Tyndale, E., Herold, E. S., & Mewhinney, D. (1998). Casual sex on spring break: Intentions and behaviours of Canadian students. *Journal of Sex Research, 35,* 254–264.

Maticka-Tyndale, E., Herold, E., & Oppermann, M. (2003). Casual sex among Australian schoolies. *Journal of Sex Research, 40,* 158–169.

Maticka-Tyndale, E., Lewis, J., & Street, M. (In press). Making a place for escort work: A case study. *Journal of Sex Research.*

Maticka-Tyndale, E., Lewis, J., Clark, J. P., Zubick, J., & Young, S. (1999). Social and cultural vulnerability to sexually transmitted infection: The work of exotic dancers. *Canadian Journal of Public Health, 90,* 19–22.

Maticka-Tyndale, E., Lewis, J., Clark, J. P., Zubrick, J., & Young, S. (2000b). Exotic dancing and health. *Women & Health, 31,* 87–108.

Matteson, D. R. (1985). Bisexual men in marriage: Is a positive homosexual identity and stable marriage possible? In F. Klein & T. J. Wolf (Eds.), *Bisexualities: Theory and research.* New York: Haworth.

Mattson, S., & Riley, E. (1998). A review of the neurobehavioral deficits in children with fetal alcohol syndrome or prenatal exposure to alcohol. *Alcoholism: Clinical and Experimental Research, 22,* 279–294.

Mauck, C., Rosenberg, Z., & Van Damme, L. (2001). Recommendations for the clinical development of topical microbicides. *AIDS, 15,* 857–868.

Maurer, H. (1994). *Sex: Real people talk about what they really do.* New York: Penguin Books.

May, R. (1974). *Love and will.* New York: Dell Books.

Mazer, D. B., & Percival, E. F. (1989). Students' experiences of sexual harassment at a small university. *Sex Roles, 20*(1&2), 1–22.

Mazur, A. (1986). U.S. trends in feminine beauty and overadaptation. *Journal of Sex Research, 22*, 281–303.

Mazzuca, J. (2004, November 2). Origin of homosexuality? Britons, Canadians say "nature." *Gallup News Service*. Washington DC: The Gallup Organization.

McCabe, M. P. (2002). Relationship functioning and sexuality among people with multiple sclerosis. *Journal of Sex Research, 39*, 302–309.

McCabe, M. P., & Taleporos, G. (2003). Sexual esteem, sexual satisfaction, and sexual behavior among people with physical disability. *Archives of Sexual Behavior, 32*, 359–370.

McCall, D., & McKay, A. (2004). SOGC policy statement: School-based and school-linked sexual health education and promotion in Canada. *Journal of Obstetrics and Gynaecology Canada, 146*, 596–600.

McBride, A. F., & Hebb, D. O. (1948). Behavior of the captive bottlenose dolphin, Tursiops truncatus. *Journal of Comparative and Physiological Psychology, 41*, 111–123.

McCall, D., Beazley, R., Doherty-Poirier, M., Lovato, C., MacKinnon, D., Otis, J., & Shannon, M. (1999). *Schools, public health, sexuality and HIV: A status report*. Toronto: Council of Ministers of Education.

McCarthy, B. W. (1989). Cognitive-behavioral strategies and techniques in the treatment of early ejaculation. In S. R. Leiblum & R. C. Rosen (Eds.), *Principles and practice of sex therapy* (2nd ed.). New York: Guilford.

McClelland, S. (1999, July 26). The bedroom and the new era of swing. *Maclean's*.

McClelland, S. (2001, December 3). Inside the sex trade. *Maclean's*.

McClintock, M. K. (1971). Menstrual synchrony and suppression. *Nature, 229*, 244–245.

McClintock, M. K. (1998). Whither menstrual synchrony? *Annual Review of Sex Research, 9*, 77–95.

McClintock, M. K. (2000). Human pheromones: Primers, releasers, signalers, or modulators? In K. Wallen & J. Schneider (Eds.), *Reproduction in context* (pp. 355–420). Cambridge, MA: MIT Press.

McClintock, M., & Herdt, G. (1996). Rethinking puberty: The development of sexual attraction. *Current Directions in Psychological Science, 5*, 178–183.

McClure, R., & Brewer, R. T. (1980). Attitudes of new parents towards child and spouse with Lamaze or non-Lamaze methods of childbirth. *Journal of Human Behavior, 17*, 45–48.

McCormick, N. B. (1993). Cultural diversity and women's sexuality. *Canadian Journal of Human Sexuality, 2*, 193–201.

McCoy, N. L., & Matyas, J. R. (1996). Oral contraceptives and sexuality in university women. *Archives of Sexual Behavior, 25*, 73–90.

McCoy, N. L., & Pitino, L. (2002). Pheromonal influences on sociosexual behavior in young women. *Physiology & Behavior, 75*, 367–375.

McDermid, S. A., Zucker, K. J., Bradley, S. J., & Maing, D. M. (1998). Effects of physical appearance on masculine trait ratings of boys and girls with gender identity disorder. *Archives of Sexual Behavior, 27*(3), 253–267.

McDonald, J., & Bradford, W. (2000). The treatment of sexual deviation using a pharmacological approach. *The Journal of Sex Research, 37*, 248–257.

McDowell, J. D. (1983). Ethical implications of in vitro fertilization. *The Christian Century, 100*, 936–938.

McEwen, B. S. (1997). Meeting report–Is there a neurobiology of love? *Molecular Psychiatry, 2*, 15–16.

McEwen, B. S. (2001). Estrogen effects on the brain: Multiple sites and molecular mechanisms. *Journal of Applied Physiology, 91*, 2785–2801.

McFarland, W. P. (2001). The legal duty to protect gay and lesbian students from violence in school. *Professional School Counseling, 4*, 171–180.

McFarlane, J., Martin, C. L., & Williams, T. M. (1988). Mood fluctuations: Women versus men and menstrual versus other cycles. *Psychology of Women Quarterly, 12*, 201–224.

McFarlane, J. A., & Williams, T. M. (1990). The enigma of premenstrual syndrome. *Canadian Psychology, 31*(2), 95–108.

McFarlane, J. M., & Williams, T. M. (1994). Placing premenstrual syndrome in perspective. *Psychology of Women Quarterly, 18*, 339–374.

McGuire, R. J., Carlisle, J. M., & Young, B. G. (1965). Sexual deviations as conditioned behavior: A hypothesis. *Behavioral Research and Therapy, 2*, 185–190.

McKay, A. (1993). Research supports broadly-based sex education. *Canadian Journal of Human Sexuality, 2*, 89–98.

McKay, A. (1996). Rural parents' attitudes toward school-based sexual health education. *Canadian Journal of Human Sexuality, 5*, 15–29.

McKay, A. (2000). Common questions about sexual health education. *SIECCAN Newsletter, 35*, 129–137.

McKay, A., & Barrett, M. (1999). Pre-service sexual health education training of elementary, secondary, and physical health education teachers in Canadian faculties of education. *Canadian Journal of Human Sexuality, 8*, 91–101.

McKay, A., & Holowaty, P. (1997). Sexual health education: A study of adolescents' opinions, self-perceived needs, and current and preferred sources of information. *Canadian Journal of Human Sexuality, 6*, 29–38.

McKay, A., Pietrusiak, M.-A., & Holowaty, P. (1998). Parents' opinions and attitudes towards sexuality education in schools. *Canadian Journal of Human Sexuality, 7*, 139–145.

McKeganey, N. (1994). Why do men buy sex and what are their assessments of the HIV-related risks when they do? *AIDS Care, 6*, 289–301.

McKenna, K. E. (2000). Some proposals regarding the organization of the central nervous system control of penile erection. *Neuroscience and Biobehavioral Reviews, 24*, 535–540.

McKenna, K. Y. A., Green, A. S., & Smith, P. K. (2001). Demarginalizing the sexual self. *Journal of Sex Research, 38*, 302–311.

McKenna, K., & Bargh, J. (1998). Coming out in the age of the Internet: Identity "demarginalization" through virtual group participation. *Journal of Personality and Social Psychology, 75*, 681–694.

McKenzie-Mohr, D., & Zanna, M. P. (1990). Treating women as sexual objects: Look to the (gender schematic) male who has viewed pornography. *Personality and Social Psychology Bulletin, 16*(2), 296–308.

McKinlay, S. M., Brambilla, D. J., & Posner, J. G. (1992). The normal menopause transition. *American Journal of Human Biology, 4*, 37–46.

McMahon, S., Hansen, L., Mann, J., Sevigny, C., Wong, T., & Roache, M. (2004). Contraception. *BMC Women's Health, 4 (Suppl 1)*, S25.

McMaster, L. E., Connolly, J., Pepler, D., & Craig, W. M. (2002). Peer to peer sexual harassment in early adolescence: A developmental perspective. *Development and Psychopathology, 14*, 91–105.

McMillen, C., Zuravin, S., & Rideout, G. (1995). Perceived benefit from child sexual abuse. *Journal of Consulting and Clinical Psychology, 63*, 1037–1043.

McNeill, J. J. (1987). Homosexuality: Challenging the Church to grow. *Christian Century, 104*, 242–246.

McWhirter, D. P., & Mattison, A. M. (1980). Treatment of sexual dysfunction in homosexual male couples. In S. R. Leiblum & L. A. Pervin (Eds.), *Principles and practice of sex therapy*. New York: Guilford.

Meana, M., Binik, Y. M., Khalife, S., & Cohen, D. R. (1997). Biopsychosocial profile of women with dyspareunia. *Obstetrics & Gynecology, 90*, 583–589.

Medical Research Council of Canada. (1998). *Tri-council policy statement: Ethical conduct for research involving humans*. Ottawa: Public Works and Government Services Canada.

Meischke, H. (1995). Implicit sexual portrayals in the movies: Interpretations of young women. *Journal of Sex Research, 32*, 29–36.

Melman, A., & Tiefer, L. (1992). Surgery for erectile disorders: Operative procedures and psychological issues. In R. C. Rosen & S. R. Leiblum (Eds.), *Erectile disorders* (pp. 255–282). New York: Guilford.

Mertz, G. J. (1993). Epidemiology of genital herpes infection. In M. Cohen, E. W. Hook, & P. J. Hitchcock (Eds.), *Infectious disease clinics of North America* (Vol. 7, pp. 825–840). Philadelphia: Harcourt, Brace, Jovanovich.

Meseda, C. A., Schmeisser, F., Pedersen, R., Woerner, A., & Weir, J. P. (2004). DNA immunization with a herpes simplex virus 2 bacterial artificial chromosome. *Virology, 318*, 420–428.

Messe, M. R., & Geer, J. H. (1985). Voluntary vaginal musculature contractions as an enhancer of sexual arousal. *Archives of Sexual Behavior, 14*, 13–28.

Messenger, J. C. (1993). Sex and repression in an Irish folk community. In D. N. Suggs & A. W. Miracle (Eds.), *Culture and human sexuality*. Pacific Grove, CA: Brooks/Cole.

Meston, C. M., Trapnell, P. D., & Gorzalka, B. B. (1996). Ethnic and gender differences in sexuality: Variations in sexual behavior between Asian and non-Asian university students. *Archives of Sexual Behavior, 25*, 33–72.

Meston, C., Trapnell, P., & Gorzalka, B. (1998). Ethnic, gender, and length-of-residency influences on sexual knowledge and attitudes. *The Journal of Sex Research, 35*, 176–188.

Metcalf, M. G., Skidmore, D. S. Lowry, G. F., & Mackenzie, J. A. (1983). Incidence of ovulation in the years after the menarche. *Journal of Endocrinology, 97*, 213–219.

Metz, M. E., et al. (1997). Premature ejaculation: A psychophysiological review. *Journal of Sex & Marital Therapy, 23*, 3–23.

Mewhinney, D., Maticka-Tyndale, E., & Herold, E. (1995). Sexual scripts and risk taking of Canadian university students on spring break in Daytona Beach, Florida. *Canadian Journal of Human Sexuality, 4*, 273–288.

Meyer, I. H. (2003). Prejudice, social stress, and mental health in lesbian, gay, and bisexual populations: Conceptual issues and research evidence. *Psychological Bulletin, 129*, 674–697.

Meyer, J. K. (1979). Sex reassignment. *Archives of General Psychiatry, 36*, 1010–1015.

Meyer-Bahlburg, H. F. L. (1997). The role of prenatal estrogens in sexual orientation. In L. Ellis & L. Ebertz (Eds.), *Sexual orientation: Toward biological understanding*. Westport, CT: Praeger.

Meyer-Bahlburg, H. F. L., et al. (1995). Prenatal estrogens and the development of homosexual orientation. *Developmental Psychology, 31*, 12–21.

Meyerowitz, B. E. (1980). Psychosocial correlates of breast cancer and its treatments. *Psychological Bulletin, 87*, 108–131.

Mezzacappa, E., & Katkin, E. (2002). Breast-feeding is associated with reduced perceived stress and negative mood in mothers. *Health Psychology, 21*, 187–193.

Michael, R. T., Gagnon, J. H., Laumann, E. O., & Kolata, G. (1994). *Sex in America: A definitive survey*. Boston: Little, Brown.

Milan, R. J., & Kilmann, P. R. (1987). Interpersonal factors in premarital contraception. *Journal of Sex Research, 23*, 289–321.

Miller, D., & Kernes, M. (2004). HIV outbreak has adult industry facing spectre of government regulation. *AVN: Adult Video News*. www.adultvidoenews.com/cover0604.02.html.

Miller, E. M. (1986). *Street woman*. Philadelphia: Temple University Press.

Miller, J., & Schwartz, M. (1995). Rape myths and violence against street prostitutes. *Deviant Behavior, 76*, 1–23.

Miller, L. C., & Fishkin, S. A. (1997). On the dynamics of human bonding and reproductive success: Seeking windows on the adapted-for-human-environmental interface. In J. A. Simpson & D. T. Kenrick (Eds.), *Evolutionary social psychology* (pp. 197–235). Mahwah, NJ: Lawrence Erlbaum.

Miller, N. (1992). *Out in the world: Gay and lesbian life from Buenos Aires to Bangkok*. New York: Random House.

Miller, S. A. & Byers, E. S. (2004). Actual and desired duration of foreplay and intercourse: Discordance and misperceptions within heterosexual couples. *Journal of Sex Research, 41*, 301–309.

Miller, S. A., & Byers, E. S. (2004). Actual and desired duration of foreplay and intercourse: Discordance and misperceptions within heterosexual couples. *The Journal of Sex Research, 41*, 301–309.

Miller, S., Corrales, R., & Wachman, D. B. (1975). Recent progress in understanding and facilitating marital communication. *The Family Coordinator, 24*, 143–152.

Millett, K. (1969). *Sexual politics*. New York: Doubleday.

Milligan, G. N., Dudley-McClain, K. L., Chu, C. F., & Young, C. G. (2004). Efficacy of genital T cell responses to herpes simplex virus type 2 resulting from immunization of the nasal mucosa. *Virology, 318*, 507–515.

Miner, M., & Coleman, E. (2001). Advances in sex offender treatment and challenges for the future. *Journal of Psychology and Human Sexuality, 13*, 5–24.

Minto, C. L., Liao, L. M., Woodhouse, C. R. J., Ransley, P. G., & Creighton, S. M. (2003). The effect of clitoral surgery on sexual outcome in individuals who have intersex conditions with ambiguous genitalia: A cross-sectional study. *Lancet, 361*, 1252–1257.

Monro, S. (2000). Theorizing transgender diversity: Towards a social model of health. *Sexual and Relationship Therapy, 15*, 33–45.

Moffatt, M. (1989). *Coming of age in New Jersey*. New Brunswick, NJ: Rutgers University Press.

Mohr, R. M., & Roberts, J. V. (1994). Sexual assault in Canada: Recent developments. In J. V. Roberts & R. M. Mohr (Eds.), *Confronting sexual assault: A decade of legal social change*. Toronto: University of Toronto Press.

Molitch, M. E. (1995). Neuroendocrinology. In P. Felig et al. (Eds.), *Endocrinology and metabolism*. New York: McGraw-Hill.

Money, J. (1987). Sin, sickness, or status: Homosexual gender identity and psychoneuroendocrinology. *American Psychologist, 42*, 384–399.

Money, J., & Ehrhardt, A. (1972). *Man and woman, boy and girl*. Baltimore: Johns Hopkins. Reissued in a facsimile edition by Jason Aronson, Northvale, NJ, 1996.

Montorsi, F., & Althof, S. (2004). Partner responses to sildenafil citrate (Viagra) treatment of erectile dysfunction. *Urology, 63*, 762–767,

Montorsi, F., Perani, D., Anchisi, D., Salonia, A., Scifo, P., Rigiroli, P., et al. (2003a). Apomorphine-induced brain modulation during sexual stimulation: A new look at central phenomena related to erectile dysfunction. *International Journal of Impotence Research, 15,* 203–209.

Montorsi, F., Perani, D., Anchisi, D., Salonia, A., Scifo, P., Rigiroli, P., et al. (2003b). Brain activation patterns during video sexual stimulation following the administration of apomorphine. *European Urology, 43,* 405–411.

Montorsi, F., Verheyden, B., Meuleman, E., Junemann, K. P., Moncada, I., Valiquette, L., et al. (2004). Long-term safety and tolerability of tadalafil in the treatment of erectile dysfunction. *European Urology, 45,* 339–345.

Moore, A. J. (1987). Teenage sexuality and public morality. *Christian Century, 104,* 747–750.

Morales, A., et al. (1998). Clinical safety of oral sildenafil (Viagra) in the treatment of erectile dysfunction. *International Journal of Impotence Research, 10,* 69–74.

Morales, A. & Heaton, J. (2001). Hormonal erectile dysfunction: Evaluation and management. *Urologic Clinics of North America, 28,* 279.

Moreland, A. A., Majmudar, B., & Vernon, S. D. (1996). Genital human papilloma-virus infections. In S. A. Morese et al. (Eds.), *Atlas of sexually transmitted diseases and AIDS* (pp. 225–240). London: Mosby-Wolfe.

Moreland, A. A., Shafran, S. D., Bryan, J., & Pellett, P. (1996). Genital herpes. In S. A Morese et al. (Eds.), *Atlas of sexually transmitted diseases and AIDS* (pp. 207–224). London: Mosby-Wolfe.

Morell, V. (1998). A new look at monogamy. *Science, 281,* 1982–1983.

Morgan, R. (1978, November). How to run the pornographers out of town (and preserve the first amendment). *Ms. 55,* 78–80.

Morgan, R. (1980). Theory and practice: Pornography and rape. In L. Lederer (Ed.), *Take back the night: Women on pornography.* New York: Morrow.

Morin, J. (1981). *Anal pleasure and health.* Burlingame, CA: Down There Press.

Morison, L., Scherf, C., Ekpo, G., Paine, K., West, B., Coleman, R., & Walraven, G. (2001). The long-term reproductive health consequences of female genital cutting in rural Gambia: A community-based survey. *Tropical Medicine & International Health, 6,* 643–653.

Morokoff, P. J. (1986). Volunteer bias in the psychophysiological study of female sexuality. *Journal of Sex Research, 22,* 35–51.

Morris-Rush, J., & Bernstein, P. (2002). Postpartum depression. *Medscape Women's Health, 7.*

Morrison, D. M. (1985). Adolescent contraceptive behavior: A review. *Psychological Bulletin, 98,* 538–568.

Morrison, M. A., & Morrison, T. G. (1999). *Development and validation of a scale measuring modern prejudice toward gay men and lesbians.* Presented at the 26th Annual Convention of the Canadian Sex Research Forum, September.

Morrow, K., Rosen, R., Richter, L., Emans, A., Forbes, A., Day, J., et al. (2003). The acceptability of an investigational vaginal microbicide, PRO 2000 gel, among women in a Phase I clinical trial. *Journal of Women's Health, 12,* 655–666.

Mortola, J. F. (1998). Premenstrual syndrome-pathophysiologic considerations. *New England Journal of Medicine, 338,* 256–257.

Moser, C. (1998). S/M (Sadomasochistic) interactions in semipublic settings. *Journal of Homosexuality, 36,* 19–29.

Moser, C. (2001). Paraphilia: Another confused sexological concept. In P.J. Kleinpatz (Ed.), *New directions in sex therapy: Innovations and alternatives* (pp. 91–108.), Philadelphia, PA: W.B. Saunders Company.

Moser, C., & Kleinpatz, P. J. (2002). Transvestic fetishism: Psychopathology or iatrogenic artifact? *New Jersey Psychologist, 52,* 16–17.

Moser, C., & Kleinpatz, P. J. (In press). DSM-IV-TR and the paraphilias: An argument for removal. *Journal of Psychology and Human Sexuality.*

Moser, C., Kleinplatz, P. J., & Zuccarini, D. (2004). Situating unusual child and adolescent sexual behavior in context. *Child & Adolescent Psychiatric Clinics of North America, 13,* 569–589.

Moser, C., & Levitt, E. E. (1987). An exploratory-descriptive study of a sadomasochistically oriented sample. *Journal of Sex Research, 23,* 322–337.

Moses, S., et al. (1990). Geographical patterns of male circumcision practices in Africa: Association with HIV seroprevalence. *International Journal of Epidemiology, 19,* 693–697.

Mosher, D., & MacIan, P. (1994). College men and women respond to X-rated videos intended for male or female audiences: Gender and sexual scripts. *Journal of Sex Research, 31,* 99–113.

Moss, B. F., & Schwebel, A. I. (1993). Marriage and romantic relationships: Defining intimacy in romantic relationships. *Family Relations, 42,* 31–37.

Mulders, T., & Dieben, T. (2001). Use of the novel combined contraceptive vaginal ring NuvaRing for ovulation inhibition. *Fertility and Sterility, 75,* 865–870.

Muller, J., Mittleman, M., Maclure, M., Sherwood, J., & Tofler, G. (1996). Triggering myocardial infarction by sexual activity. *Journal of the American Medical Association, 275,* 1405–1409.

Murnen, S. K., & Stockton, M. (1997). Gender and self-reported sexual arousal in response to sexual stimuli: A meta-analytic review. *Sex Roles, 37,* 135–154.

Murnen, S. K., Wright, C., & Kaluzny, G. (2002). If "boys will be boys," then girls will be victims? A meta-analytic review of the research that relates masculine ideology to sexual aggression. *Sex Roles, 46,* 359–376.

Murray, S. L. & Holmes, J. G. (1997). A leap of faith? Positive illusions in romantic relationships. *Personality and Social Psychology Bulletin, 23,* 586–604.

Murray, S. L., Holmes, J. G., & Griffin, D. W. (1996). The benefits of positive illusions: Idealization and the construction of satisfaction in close relationships. *Journal of Personality and Social Psychology, 70*(1), 79–98.

Murray, S. O. (2000). Homosexualities. Chicago: University of Chicago Press.

Mustanski, B. S. (2001). Getting wired: Exploiting the Internet for the collection of valid sexuality data. *Journal of Sex Research, 38,* 292–301.

Myers, B. J. (1984). Mother-infant bonding: The status of this critical-period hypothesis. *Developmental Review, 4,* 240–274.

Myers, P. N., & Biocca, F. A. (1992). The elastic body image: The effect of television advertising and programming on body image distortions in young women. *Journal of Communication, 42,* 108–133.

Myers, T., Bullock, S. L., Calzavara, L. M., Cockerill, R., Marshall, V. W., & George-Mandoka, C. (1999). Culture and sexual practices in response to HIV among Aboriginal people living on reserve in Ontario. *Culture, Health & Sexuality, 1*(1).

Myers, T., Calzavara, L. M., Bullock, S., Cockerill, R., & Marshall, V. (1994). The Ontario First Nations aids and healthy lifestyle survey: A model for community-based research in diverse reserve communities. *Arctic Medical Research, 53* (suppl. 2), 726–731.

Myers, T., Godin, G., Calzavara, L., Lambert, J., & Locker, D. (1993). *The Canadian survey of gay and bisexual men and HIV infection: Men's survey.* Ottawa: Canadian Aids Society.

Nanda, S. (1997). The Hijras of India. In M. Duberman (Ed.), *A queer world* (pp. 82–86). New York: New York University Press.

Narod, S A., et al. (1988). Human mutagens: Evidence from paternal exposure? *Environmental and Molecular Mutagenesis, 11,* 401–415.

National Cancer Institute of Canada. (2004). *Canadian Cancer Statistics 2004.*

Nelson, J. B. (1978). *Embodiment: An approach to sexuality and Christian theology.* Minneapolis, MN: Augsburg.

Nemeth, M. (1995, June 26). Nobody has the right to play God. *Maclean's.*

Neville, V. A., & Heppner, M. S. (1999). Contextualizing rape: Reviewing sequelae and proposing a culturally inclusive ecological model of sexual assault recovery. *Applied and Preventive Psychology, 8,* 41–62.

Newhouse, D. (1998). Magic & joy: Traditional aboriginal views of human sexuality. *Canadian Journal of Sexuality, 7,* 183–187.

Newton, N. A. (1972). Childbearing in broad perspective. In Boston Children's Medical Center, *Pregnancy, birth and the newborn baby.* New York: Delacorte Press.

Noll, J., Trickett, P., & Putnam, F. (2003). A prospective investigation of the impact of childhood sexual abuse on the development of sexuality. *Journal of Consulting and Clinical Psychology, 71,* 575–586.

Norton, A. J. (1987, July–August). Families and children in the year 2000. *Children Today,* 6–9.

Noss, J. B. (1963). *Man's religions* (3rd ed.). New York: Macmillan.

Notzon, F. C. (1990). International differences in the use of obstetric interventions. *Journal of the American Medical Association, 263,* 3286–3291.

Novak, E., & Novak, E. R. (1952). *Textbook of gynecology.* Baltimore: Williams & Wilkins.

Nova Scotia Department of Community Services. (1991). *Mothers and children: One decade later.* Halifax, NS: Author.

Ochs, E., & Binik, Y. M. (1999). The use of couple data to determine the reliability of self-reported sexual behaviour. *Journal of Sex Research, 36,* 374–384.

Ochs, E. P., Mah, K., & Binik, Y. (2002). Obtaining data about human sexual functioning from the Internet. In A. Cooper (Ed.), *Sex and the Internet: A guidebook for clinicians* (pp. 245–262). New York: Routledge.

O'Connell, H. E., et al. (1998). Anatomical relationship between urethra and clitoris. *Journal of Urology, 159,* 1982–1897.

O'Connor, A. (1987). Female sex offenders. *British Journal of Psychiatry, 150,* 615–620.

Oesterling, J. E. (1995). Benign prostatic hyperplasia. *New England Journal of Medicine, 332,* 99–109.

Offman, A. & Matheson, K. (2004). The sexual self-perceptions of young women experiencing abuse in dating relationships. *Sex Roles, 51,* 551–560.

Offman, A., & Kleinplatz, P. J. (2004). Does PMDD belong in the DSM? Challenging the medicalization of women's bodies. *Canadian Journal of Human Sexuality, 13,* 17–27.

Ogletree, S. M., & Ginsburg, H. J. (2000). Kept under the hood: Neglect of the clitoris in common vernacular. *Sex Roles, 43,* 917–926.

O'Hara, M. W., & Swain, A. M. (1996). Rates and risk of postpartum depression: A meta-analysis. *International Review of Psychiatry, 8,* 37–54.

Okami, P. (1995). Childhood exposure to parental nudity, parent-child co-sleeping, and "primal scenes": A review of clinical opinion and empirical evidence. *Journal of Sex Research, 32,* 51–64.

Oliver, M. B., & Hyde, J. S. (1993). Gender differences in sexuality: A meta-analysis. *Psychological Bulletin, 114,* 29–51.

Olson, B., & Douglas, W. (1997). The family on television: Evaluation of gender roles in situation comedy. *Sex Roles, 36,* 409–427.

Olsson, S., & Möller, A.R. (2003). On the incidence and sex ratio of transsexualism in Sweden, 1972–2002. *Archives of Sexual Behavior, 32,* 381–386.

Ontario College of Physicians & Surgeons. (1991). *The Final Report of the Task Force on Sexual Abuse.*

Ornstein, M. (1989). *AIDS in Canada: Knowledge, behaviour, and attitudes of adults.* Toronto: Institute for Social Research, York University.

Oosterhuis, H. (2000). *Step children of nature: Krafft-Ebing, psychiatry, and the making of sexual identity.* Chicago: University of Chicago Press.

O'Shea, P. A. (1995). Congenital defects and their causes. In D. R. Constan, R. V. Haning, Jr., & D. B. Singer (Eds.), *Human reproduction: Growth and development.* Boston: Little, Brown.

Osman, S. L. (2003). Predicting men's rape perceptions based on the belief that "no" really means "Yes." *Journal of Applied Social Psychology, 33,* 683–692.

Østensten, M. (1994). Optimisation of antirheumatic drug treatment in pregnancy. *Clinical Pharmacokinetics, 27,* 486–503.

O'Sullivan, L. (1995). Less is more: The effects of sexual experience on judgments of men's and women's personality characteristics and relationship desirability. *Sex Roles, 33,* 159–181.

O'Sullivan, L., & Byers, E. S. (1992). College students' incorporation of initiator and restrictor role in sexual dating interactions. *Journal of Sex Research, 29,* 435–446.

O'Sullivan, L., & Meyer-Bahlburg, H. (2003). African-American and Latina inner-city girls' reports of romantic and sexual development. *Journal of Social and Personal Relationships, 20,* 221–238.

O'Sullivan, L. F., & Byers, E. Sandra. (1993). Eroding stereotypes: College women's attempts to influence reluctant sexual partners. *Journal of Sex Research, 30,* 270–282.

O'Sullivan, L. F., & Byers, E. S. (1996). Gender differences in responses to discrepancies in desired level of sexual intimacy. *Journal of Psychology & Human Sexuality, 8*(1&2), 49–67.

O'Sullivan, L. F., Byers, E. S., & Finkelman, L. (1998). A comparison of male and female college students' experiences of sexual coercion. *Psychology of Women Quarterly, 22,* 177–195.

Otis, J., Levy, J., Samson, J.-M., Pilote, F., & Fugere, A. (1997). Gender differences in sexuality and interpersonal power relations among French-speaking young adults from Quebec: A province-wide study. *Canadian Journal of Human Sexuality, 6,* 17–28.

Padma-Nathan, H., McMurray, J. G., Pullman, W. E., Whitaker, J. S., Saoud, J. B., Ferguson, K. M., et al. (2001). On-demand IC351 (Cialistrade mark) enhances erectile function in patients with erectile dysfunction. *International Journal of Impotence Research, 13,* 2–9.

Page, D. C., et al. (1987). The sex-determining region of the human Y chromosome encodes a finger protein. *Cell, 51,* 1091–1104.

Paige, K. E. (1971). Effects of oral contraceptives on affective fluctuations associated with the menstrual cycle. *Psychosomatic Medicine, 33,* 515–537.

Pakenham, K. I., Dadds, M. R., & Terry, D. J. (1994). Relationships between adjustment to HIV and both social support and coping. *Journal of Consulting and Clinical Psychology, 62,* 1194–1203.

Palace, E. M. (1995a). A cognitive-physiological process model of sexual arousal and response. *Clinical Psychology: Science and Practice, 2,* 370–384.

Palace, E. M. (1995b). Modification of dysfunctional patterns of sexual response through autonomic arousal and false physiological feedback. *Journal of Consulting and Clinical Psychology, 63,* 604–615.

Palace, E. M., & Gorzalka, B. B. (1992). Differential patterns of arousal in sexually functional and dysfunctional women: Physiological and subjective components of sexual response. *Archives of Sexual Behavior, 21*(2), 135–159.

Paredes, R. G., & Baum, M. J. (1997). Role of the medial preoptic area/anterior hypothalamus in the control of masculine sexual behavior. *Annual Review of Sex Research, 8,* 68–101.

Parents Television Council. (2000). What a difference a decade makes: A comparison of prime time sex, language, and violence in 1989 and '99. *Special Report.* Retrieved from www.parentstv.org/publications/reports/Decadestudy/decadestudy.html.

Park, K., et al. (2001). A new potential of blood oxygenation level dependent (BOLD) functional MRI for evaluating cerebral centers of penile erection. *International Journal of Impotence Research, 13,* 73–81.

Parker, G. (1983). The legal regulation of sexual activity and the protection of females. *Osgoode Hall Law Journal, 21,* 187–244.

Parrinder, G. (1980). *Sex in the world's religions.* New York: Oxford University Press.

Parrinder, G. (1996). *Sexual morality in the world's religions.* Oxford: Oneworld.

Pasacreta, J. V., & McCorkle, R. (1998). Providing accurate information to women about tamoxifen therapy for breast cancer: Current indications, effects, and controversies. *Oncology Nursing Forum, 9,* 1577–1583.

Patrick, D. M., Wong, T., & Jordan, R. A. (2000). Sexually transmitted infections in Canada: Recent resurgence threatens national goals. *The Canadian Journal of Human Sexuality, 9,* 149–165.

Patterson, C. (1992). Children of lesbian and gay parents. *Child Development, 63,* 1025–1042.

Patterson, C. J. (1995). Families of the lesbian baby boom: Parents' division of labor and children's adjustment. *Developmental Psychology, 31,* 115–123.

Paul, E., McManus, B., & Hayes, A. (2000). "Hookups": Characteristics and correlates of college students' spontaneous and anonymous sexual experiences. *Journal of Sex Research, 37,* 76–88.

Paulson, R. J., Milligan, R. C., & Sokol, R. Z. (2001). The lack of influence of age on male fertility. *American Journal of Obstetrics and Gynecology, 184,* 818–824.

Payne, J. (2004). The impact of a reduced fertility rate on women's health. *BMC Womens's Health, 4(Suppl 1),* S11.

Peat, Marwick & Partners. (1984). Canadians' attitudes toward and perceptions of pornography and prostitution. *Working Papers on Pornography and Prostitution, Report #6.* Ottawa: Department of Justice.

Pedersen, W., Miller, L. C., Putcha-Bhagavatula, A., & Yang, Y. (2002). Evolved sex differences in the number of partners desired? The long and short of it. *Psychological Science, 13,* 157–159.

Pennisi, E. (1996). Homing in on a prostate cancer gene. *Science, 274,* 1301.

Peplau, L. A. (2003). Human sexuality: How do men and women differ? *Current Directions in Psychological Science, 12,* 37–40.

Peplau, L. A., Garnets, L. D., Spalding, L. R., Conley, T. D., & Veniegas, R. C. (1998). A critique of Bem's "Exotic becomes erotic" theory of sexual orientation. *Psychological Review, 105,* 387–394.

Peplau, L. A., Veniegas, R. C., & Campbell, S. M. (1996). Gay and lesbian relationships. In R. C. Savin-Williams & K. M. Cohen (Eds.), *The lives of lesbians, gays, and bisexuals* (pp. 250–273). Fort Worth, TX: Harcourt Brace.

Perez, M. A., Skinner, E. C., & Meyerowitz, B. E. (2002). Sexuality and intimacy following radical prostatectomy: Patient and partner perspectives. *Health Psychology, 21,* 288–293.

Perkins, R., & Bennett, G. (1985). *Being a prostitute: Prostitute women and prostitute men.* London: Allen & Unwin.

Perlman, D., & Fehr, B. (1987). The development of intimate relationships. In D. Perlman & S. Duck (Eds.), *Intimate relationships: Development, dynamics, and deterioration.* Newbury Park, CA: Sage.

Perry, J. D., & Whipple, B. (1981). Pelvic muscle strength of female ejaculators: Evidence in support of a new theory of orgasm. *Journal of Sex Research, 17,* 22–39.

Petersen, M. E., & Dickey, R. (1995). Surgical sex reassignment: A comparative survey of international centers. *Archives of Sexual Behavior, 24,* 135–156.

Petkovich, A. (2004). From gonzo porn to mainstream? Porn starlet Sienna. *Spectator,* www.spectator.net.

Pfaus, J. G., Kippin, T. E., & Coria-Avila, G. (2003). What can animal models tell us about human sexual response? *Annual Review of Sex Research, 14,* 1–63.

Pfeiffer, E., Verwoerdt, A., & Wang, H. S. (1968). Sexual behavior in aged men and women. *Archives of General Psychiatry, 19,* 753–758.

Phelps, J., Albo, M., Dunn, K., & Joseph, A. (2001). Spinal cord injury and sexuality in married or partnered men: Activities, function, needs, and predictors of sexual adjustment. *Archives of Sexual Behavior, 30,* 591–602.

Phoenix, C. H., Goy, R. W., Gerall, A. A., & Young, W. C. (1959). Organizing action of prenatally administered testosterone propionate on the tissues mediating mating behavior in the female guinea pig. *Endocrinology, 65,* 369–382.

Phoolcharoen, W. (1998). HIV/AIDS prevention in Thailand: Success and challenges. *Science, 280,* 1873–1874.

Pick, S. Givaudan, M., & Poortinga, Y. (2003). Sexuality and life skills education: A multistrategy intervention in Mexico. *American Psychologist, 58,* 230–234.

Pilkington, N. W., & Lydon, J. E. (1997). The relative effect of attitude similarity and attitude dissimilarity and interpersonal attraction: Investigating the moderating roles of prejudice and group membership. *Journal of Personality and Social Psychology Bulletin, 23*(2), 107–122.

Pillard, R. C., & Weinrich, J. D. (1987). Periodic table model of transpositions. *Journal of Sex Research, 23,* 425–454.

Pinheiro, R. C., Lambert, J., Benard, F., Mauffette, F., & Miron, P. (1999). Effectiveness of in vitro fertilization with intracytoplasmic sperm injection for severe male infertility. *Canadian Medical Association Journal, 161,* 1397–1442.

Pithers, W. D. (1993). Treatment of rapists. In G. N. Hall et al. (Eds.), *Sexual aggression* (pp. 167–196). Washington, D.C.: Taylor & Francis.

Pittenger, W. Norman. (1970). *Making sexuality human.* Philadelphia: Pilgrim Press.

Pittman, F., III. (1993, May–June). Beyond betrayal: Life after infidelity. *Psychology Today,* 32–38, ff.

Planned Parenthood Federation of America (2002). *White Paper: Masturbation-from stigma to sexual health.* Washington, DC: Katharine Dexter McCormick Library.

Planned Parenthood Fredericton. (2004). *Knowing where you stand: A resource for providing sexuality education to individuals with intellectual disabilities.* Fredericton, NB: Planned Parenthood Fredericton.

Plant, T. M., Winters, S. J., Attardi, B. J., & Majumdar, S. S. (1993). The follicle stimulating hormone-inhibin feedback loop in male primates. *Human Reproduction, 8,* Suppl. 2, 41–44.

Ploem, C., & Byers, E. S. (1997). The effects of two AIDS risk-reduction interventions on heterosexual college women's AIDS-related knowledge and condom use. *Journal of Psychology & Human Sexuality, 9*(1), 1–24.

Plummer, K. (1975). *Sexual stigma: An interactionist account.* London: Routledge & Kegan Paul.

Pollack, A., Dean, C., & Dreifus, C. (2004, February 13). Medical and ethical issues cloud plans to clone for therapy. *New York Times.*

Pomeroy, W. B. (1975). The diagnosis and treatment of transvestites and transsexuals. *Journal of Sex and Marital Therapy, 1,* 215–224.

Pomeroy, W. B. (1972). *Dr. Kinsey and the Institute for Sex Research.* New York: Harper & Row.

Poon, M. K-L., Ho, Peter T-T, & Wong, J. P-H. (2001). Developing a comprehensive AIDS prevention outreach program: A needs assessment survey of MSM of East and Southeast Asian descent who visit bars and/or bath houses in Toronto. *The Canadian Journal of Human Sexuality, 10,* 25–37.

Pope, K. (2001). Sex between therapists and clients. In J. Worell (Ed.), *Encyclopedia of women and gender* (pp. 955–862). New York: Academic Press.

Pope Paul VI. (1968, July 30). Humanae vitae. (English text in the *New York Times,* p. 20.)

Population Information Program. (1983). Vasectomy–Safe and simple. *Population Reports,* Series D, No. 4, D61–D100.

Posner, R. (1992). *Sex and reason.* Cambridge, MA: Harvard University Press.

Potts, A., Gavey, N., Grace, V. M., & Vares, T. (2003). The downside of Viagra: Women's experiences and concerns. *Sociology of Health & Illness, 25,* 697–719.

Poulin, C., & Gouliquer, L. (2003). Part-time disabled lesbian passing on roller blades, or PMS, Prozac, and essentializing women's ailments. *Women & Therapy: A Feminist Quarterly, 26,* 95–108.

Powdermaker, H. (1933). *Life in Lesu.* New York: Norton.

Prather, R. S. (2000). Pigs is pigs. *Science, 289,* 1886–1887

Price, E. L., Byers, E. S., & The Dating Violence Research Team. (1999). Attitudes towards dating violence scales: Development and initial validation. *Journal of Family Violence, 14,* 351–375.

Price, E. L., Byers, E. S., Sears, H., Whelan, J., & Saint-Pierre, M. (2000, January). Dating violence amongst New Brunswick adolescents: A summary of two studies. *Research Paper Series,* #2. Muriel McQueen Fergusson Centre for Family Violence Research.

Price, J., Allensworth, D., & Hillman, K. (1985). Comparison of sexual fantasies of homosexuals and heterosexuals. *Psychological Reports, 57,* 871–877.

Price, J. H. (1981). Toxic shock syndrome–An update. *Journal of School Health, 51,* 143–145.

Proulx, J., Pellerin, B., Paradis, Y., McKibben, A., Aubut, J., & Ouimet, M. (1997). Static and dynamic predictors of recidivism in sexual aggressors. *Sexual Abuse: A Journal of Research and Treatment, 9,* 7–27.

Puar, J. K. (2001). Global circuits: Transnational sexualities and Trinidad. *Signs: Journal of Women in Culture and Society, 26,* 1039–1065.

Pukall, C. F., Payne, K. A., Binik, Y. M., & Khalifé, S. (2003). Pain measurement in vulvodynia. *Journal of Sex & Marital Therapy, 29(s),* 111–120.

Pukall, C. F., Reissing, E. D., Binik, Y. M., Khalifé, S., & Abbott, F. V. (2000). New clinical and research perspectives on the sexual pain disorders. *Journal of Sex Education and Therapy, 25,* 36–44.

Purnine, D., & Carey, M. (1997). Interpersonal communication and sexual adjustment: The roles of understanding and agreement. *Journal of Consulting & Clinical Psychology, 65,* 1017–1025.

Pyke, S. (1996). Sexual harassment and sexual intimacy in learning environments. *Canadian Psychology, 37*(1),13–22.

Quadagno, D., et al. (1991). The menstrual cycle: Does it affect athletic performance? *Physician & Sports Medicine, 19,* 121–124.

Quadagno, D., Nation, A. J., et al. (1995). Cardiovascular disease and sexual functioning. *Applied Nursing Research, 8,* 143–146.

Qualls, C. B., Wincze, J. P., & Barlow, D. H. (1978). *The prevention of sexual disorders.* New York: Plenum.

Quinn, T. C., et al. (2000). Viral load and heterosexual transmission of human immunodeficiency virus type 1. *The New England Journal of Medicine, 342,* 921–929.

Quittner, J. (1997, April 14). Divorce, Internet style. *Time,* 72.

Rachman, S. (1966). Sexual fetishism: An experimental analogue. *Psychological Record, 16,* 293–296.

Randall, H. E. & Byers, E. S. (2003). What is sex?: Students' definitions of having sex, sexual partner, and unfaithful sexual behaviour. *Canadian Journal of Human Sexuality, 12,* 87–96.

Rasmussen, S. J. (1998). Chlamydia immunology. *Current Opinion in Infectious Diseases, 11,* 37–41.

Ratnam, S., Franco, E., & Ferenczy, A. (2000). Human papillomavirus testing for primary screening of cervical cancer precursors. *Cancer Epidemiology Biomarkers & Prevention, 9,* 945–951.

Rawicki, H. B., & Hill, S. (1991). Semen retrieval in spinal cord injured men. *Paraplegia, 29,* 443–446.

Raymond, E., Chen, P, & Luoto, J. (2004). Contraceptive effectiveness and safety of five nonoxynol-9 spermicides: A randomized trial. *Obstetrics and Gynecology, 103,* 430–439.

Raymond, N. C., Grant, J. E., Kim, S. W., & Coleman, E. (2002). Treatment of compulsive sexual behaviour with naltrexone and serotonin reuptake inhibitors: Two case studies. *International Clinical Psychopharmacology 127,* 201–205.

Reamy, K. J., & White, S. E. (1987). Sexuality in the puerperium: A review. *Archives of Sexual Behavior, 16,* 165–186.

Reddy, K. J., Banapour, B., Anderson, D. E., Lee, S. H., Marquez, J. P., Carlos, M. P., et al. (2004). Induction of immune responses against human papillomaviruses by hypervariable epitope constructs. *Immunology, 112,* 321–327.

Regan, P. (2004). Sex and the attraction process: Lessons from science (and Shakespeare) on lust, love, chastity, and fidelity. In J.H. Harvey, A. Wenzel, & S. Sprecher (Eds.), *The handbook of sexuality in close relationships* (pp. 159–182). Mahwah, NJ: Lawrence Erlbaum.

Reichert, T. (2002). Sex in advertising research: A review of content, effects, and functions of sexual information in consumer advertising. *Annual Review of Sex Research, 13,* 241–273.

Reinharz, S. (1992). *Feminist methods in social research.* New York: Oxford University Press.

Reisenzein, R. (1983). The Schachter theory of emotion: Two decades later. *Psychological Bulletin, 94,* 239–264.

Reiss, I. L. (1960). *Premarital sexual standards in America.* New York: Free Press.

Reiss, I. L. (1986). *Journey into sexuality: An exploratory voyage.* Englewood Cliffs, NJ: Prentice-Hall.

Reissing, E. D., Binik, Y. M., & Khalife, S. (1999). Does vaginismus exist? A critical review of the literature. *Journal of Nervous and Mental Disease, 187,* 261–274.

Reissing, E. D., Binik, Y., Khalife, S., Cohen, D., & Arose, R. (2004). Vaginal spasm, pain, and behavior: An empirical investigation of the diagnosis of vaginismus. *Archives of Sexual Behavior, 33,* 5–18.

Rempel, J. K., & Baumgartner, B. (2003). The relationship between attitudes towards menstruation and sexual attitudes, desires, and behavior in women. *Archives of Sexual Behavior, 32,* 155–163.

Rempel, J. K., Holmes, J. G., & Zanna, M. P. (1985). Trust in close relationships. *Journal of Personality and Social Psychology, 49,* 93–112.

Rempel, L. A., & Rempel, J. K. (2004). Partner influence on health behavior decision-making: Increasing breastfeeding duration. *Journal of Social and Personal Relationships, 21,* 92–111.

Renaud, C. A. & Byers, E. S. (2001). Positive and negative sexual cognitions: Subjective experience and relationships to sexual adjustment. *The Journal of Sex Research, 38,* 252–262.

Renaud, C. A., & Byers, E. S. (1999). Exploring the frequency, diversity, and content of university students' positive and negative sexual cognitions. *Canadian Journal of Human Sexuality, 8,* 17–30.

Renaud, C., & Byers, E. S. (2001). Positive and negative sexual cognitions: Subjective experience and relationships to sexual adjustment. *The Journal of Sex Research, 38,* 252–262.

Renaud, C., Byers, E. S., & Pan, S. (1997). Sexual and relationship satisfaction in mainland China. *Journal of Sex Research, 34,* 399–410.

Renne, E. P. (1996). The pregnancy that doesn't stay: The practice and perception of abortion by Ekiti Yoruba women. *Social Science & Medicine, 42,* 483–494.

Renner, K. E., & Wackett, C. (1987). Sexual assault: Social and stranger rape. *Canadian Journal of Community Mental Health, 6*(1), 49–57.

Repke, J. T. (1994). Calcium and vitamin D. *Clinical Obstetrics and Gynecology, 37,* 550–557.

Reppucci, N. D., Land, D., & Haugaard, J. J. (1999). Child sexual abuse prevention programs that target young children. In P. K. Trickett, and C. J. Schellenbach (Eds.), *Violence against children in the family and the community.* Washington, DC: American Psychological Association.

Reuther, R. R. (1985). Catholics and abortion: Authority vs. dissent. *Christian Century, 102,* 859–862.

Reynolds, M. A., Herbenick, D., & Bancroft, J. (2003). The nature of childhood sexual experiences: Two studies 50 years apart. In J. Bancroft (Ed.), *Sexual development in childhood* (pp. 134–155). Bloomington, IN: Indiana University Press.

Rice, G., Anderson, C., Risch, N., & Ebers, G. (1999). Male homosexuality: Absence of linkage to microsatellite markers at Xq28. *Science, 284,* 665–667.

Rice, M. E., Quinsey, V. L., & Harris, G. T. (1991). Sexual recidivism among child molesters released from a maximum security psychiatric institution. *Journal of Consulting and Clinical Psychology, 59,* 381–386.

Richardson, H. R. L., & Beazley, R. P. (1997). Factors influencing condom use among students attending high school in Nova Scotia. *Canadian Journal of Human Sexuality, 6,* 185–196.

Richardson, J. D. (1991). I. Medical causes of male sexual dysfunction. *Medical Journal of Australia, 155,* 29–33.

Rigdon, S. M. (1996). Abortion law and practice in China: An overview with comparisons to the United States. *Social Science & Medicine, 42,* 543–560.

Rimm, M. (1995). Marketing pornography on the information superhighway: A survey of 917,410 images. *Georgetown Law Journal, 83,* 1849–1925.

Rind, B., Tromovitch, P., & Bauserman, R. (1998). A meta-analytic examination of assumed properties of child sexual abuse using college samples. *Psychological Bulletin, 124,* 22–53.

Riportella-Muller, R. (1989). Sexuality in the elderly: A review. In K. McKinney & S. Sprecher (Eds.), *Human sexuality: The societal and interpersonal context* (pp. 210–236). New York: Ablex.

Roach, K. (2000). *Criminal law* (2nd ed.). Toronto: Irwin.

Roberson, B., & Wright, R. (1994). Difficulty as a determinant of interpersonal appeal: A social-motivational application of energization theory. *Basic and Applied Social Psychology, 15,* 373–388.

Roberts, C. M., Pfister, J. R., & Spear, S. J. (2003). Increasing proportion of herpes simplex virus type I as a cause of genital herpes infection in college students. *Sexually Transmitted Diseases, 30,* 797–800.

Robertson, D. L., Hahn, B., & Sharp, P. M. (1995). Recombination in AIDS viruses. *Molecular Evolution, 40,* 249–259.

Robertson, S., & Sharkey, D. (2001). The role of semen in induction of maternal immune tolerance to pregnancy. *Seminars in Immunology, 13,* 243.

Robinson, D., & Rock, J. (1967). Intrascrotal hyperthermia induced by scrotal insulation: Effect on spermatogenesis. *Obstetrics and Gynecology, 29,* 217.

Rodriguez, I., Greer, C. A., Mok, M. Y., & Mombaerts, P. (2000). A putative pheromone receptor gene expressed in human olfactory mucosa. *Nature Genetics, 26,* 18–19.

Roisman, G., Masten, A., Coatsworth, J. D., & Tellegen, A. (2004). Salient and emerging developmental tasks in the transition to adulthood. *Child Development, 75,* 123–133.

Romer, D. et al. (1997). "Talking computers": A reliable and private method to conduct interviews on sensitive topics with children. *Journal of Sex Research, 34,* 3–9.

Rosaldo, M. A. (1974). Woman, culture, and society: A theoretical overview. In M. S. Rosaldo & L. Lamphere (Eds.), *Woman, culture, and society.* Stanford, CA: Stanford University Press.

Rosario, M., Meyer-Bahlburg, H., Hunter, J., Exner, T., Swadz, M., & Keller, A. (1996). The psychosexual development of urban lesbian, gay and bisexual youths. *Journal of Sex Research, 33,* 113–126.

Roscoe, B., Cavanaugh, L., & Kennedy, D. (1988). Dating infidelity: Behaviors, reasons, and consequences. *Adolescence, 89,* 36–43.

Roscoe, B., Kennedy, D., & Pope, T. (1987). Adolescents' views of intimacy: Distinguishing intimate from nonintimate relationships. *Adolescence, 22,* 511–516.

Rose, S., & Frieze, I. H. (1993). Young singles' contemporary dating scripts. *Sex Roles, 28,* 499–509.

Roselli, C. E., Resko, J. A., & Stormshak, F. (2002). Hormonal influences on sexual partner preference in rams. *Archives of Sexual Behavior, 31,* 43–49.

Rosen, D. H. (1974). *Lesbianism: A study of female homosexuality.* Springfield, IL: Charles C. Thomas.

Rosen, R. C. (1991). Alcohol and drug effects on sexual response: Human experimental and clinical studies. Annual *Review of Sex Research, 2,* 119–180.

Rosen, R. C. & McKenna, K. E. (2002). PDE-5 inhibition and sexual response: Pharmacological mechanisms and clinical outcomes. *Annual Review of Sex Research, 13,* 36–88.

Rosen, R. C., & Leiblum, S. R. (1995). Hypoactive sexual desire. *Psychiatric Clinics of North America, 18,* 107–121.

Rosen, R. C., Leiblum, S. R., & Spector, I. P. (1994). Psychologically-based treatment for male erectile disorder: A cognitive-interpersonal model. *Journal of Sex & Marital Therapy, 20,* 67–85.

Rosenberg, E. S., Altfeld, M., Poon, S. H., Phillips, M. N., Wilkes, B. M., Eldridge, R. L., et al. (2000). Immune control of HIV-1 after early treatment of acute infection. *Nature, 407,* 523–526.

Rosenberg, L. (1993). Hormone replacement therapy: The need for reconsideration. *American Journal of Public Health, 83,* 1670–1673.

Rosenblatt, K. A., Wicklund, K., & Stanford, J. (2001). Sexual factors and the risk of prostate cancer. *American Journal of Epidemiology, 153,* 1152–1158.

Rosler, A., & Witztum, E. (1998). Treatment of men with paraphilia with a long-lasting analogue of gonadotropin-releasing hormone. *New England Journal of Medicine, 338,* 416–422.

Rosner, F. (1983). In vitro fertilization and surrogate motherhood: The Jewish view. *Journal of Religion and Health, 22,* 139–160.

Ross, L. R., & Spinner, B. (2001). General and specific attachment representations in adulthood: Is there a relationship? *Journal of Social and Personal Relationships, 18,* 747–766.

Ross, M., & Williams, M. (2002). Effective targeted and community HIV/STD prevention programs. *Journal of Sex Research, 39,* 58–62.

Ross, M. N., Paulsen, J. A., & Stalstrom, O. W. (1988). Homosexuality and mental health: A cross-cultural review. *Journal of Homosexuality, 15,* 131–152.

Rotello, G. (1997). *Sexual ecology: AIDS and the destiny of gay men.* New York: Dutton.

Rothbaum, B. O., Foa, E. B., Riggs, D. S., Murdock, T., & Walsh, W. (1992). A prospective examination of post-traumatic stress disorder in rape victims. *Journal of Traumatic Stress, 5,* 455–475.

Rothblum, E. D. (1994). "I only read about myself on bathroom walls": The need for research on the mental health of lesbians and gay men. *Journal of Consulting and Clinical Psychology, 62,* 213–220.

Rothblum, E. D., & Bond, L. A. (Eds.). (1996). *Preventing heterosexism and homophobia.* Thousand Oaks, CA: Sage.

Rousseau, S., et al. (1983). The expectancy of pregnancy for "normal" infertile couples. *Fertility & Sterility, 40,* 768–772.

Rowland, D. A., & Slob, A. K. (1997). Premature ejaculation: Psychophysiological considerations in theory, research, and treatment. *Annual Review of Sex Research, 8,* 224–253.

Rowland, D. L., & Burnett, A. L. (2000). Pharmacotherapy in treatment of male sexual dysfunction. *Journal of Sex Research, 37,* 226–243.

Royal Commission on New Reproductive Technologies. (1993). *Proceed with care: Final report of the Royal Commission on New Reproductive Technologies.* Ottawa: Minister of Government Services Canada.

Rozée, P. D., & Koss, M. P. (2001). Rape: A century of resistance. *Psychology of Women Quarterly, 25,* 295–311.

Ruan, F. F., & Lau, M. P. (1998). China. In R. Francoeur (Ed.), *The international encyclopedia of sexuality* (Vol. 1, pp. 344–399). New York: Continuum.

Rubin, I. (1966). Sex after forty—and after seventy. In R. Brecher & E. Brecher (Eds.), *An analysis of human sexual response.* New York: Signet Books, New American Library.

Rubin, R. T., Reinisch, J. M., & Haskett, R. F. (1981). Postnatal gonadal steroid effects on human behavior. *Science, 211,* 1318–1324.

Rubin, Z. (1973). *Liking and loving: An invitation to social psychology.* New York: Holt.

Rubin, Z., et al. (1980). Self-disclosure in dating couples: Sex roles and the ethic of openness. *Journal of Marriage and the Family, 42,* 305–317.

Ruble, D. N. (1977). Premenstrual symptoms: A reinterpretation. *Science, 197,* 291–292.

Ruble, D. N., & Stangor, C. (1986). Stalking the elusive schema: Insights from developmental and social-psychological analyses of gender schemas. *Social Cognition, 4,* 227–261.

Runtz, M. G., & Roche, D. N. (1999). Validation of the trauma symptom inventory in a Canadian sample of university women. *Child Maltreatment, 4*(1), 69–80.

Runtz, M. G., & Schallow, J. R. (1997). Social support and coping strategies as mediators of adult adjustment following childhood maltreatment. *Child Abuse & Neglect, 21,* 211–226.

Rusbult, C. (1983). A longitudinal test of the investment model: The development (and deterioration) of satisfaction and commitment in heterosexual involvements. *Journal of Personality and Social Psychology, 45,* 101–117.

Rusbult, C., Johnson, D. J., & Morrow, G. D. (1986). Predicting satisfaction and commitment in adult romantic involvements: An assessment of the generalizability of the investment model. *Social Psychology Quarterly, 49,* 81–89.

Russell, D. E. H. (1980). Pornography and violence: What does the new research say? In L. Lederer (Ed.), *Take back the night: Women on pornography.* New York: Morrow.

Russell, D. E. H. (1990). *Rape in marriage.* (Rev. ed.). Bloomington, IN: Indiana University Press.

Rust, P. C. (2000a). Bisexuality: A contemporary paradox for women. *Journal of Social Issues, 56,* 205–221.

Rust, P. C. (2000b). *Bisexuality in the United States: A social science reader.* New York: Columbia University Press.

Rust, P. C. (2001). Two many and not enough: The meaning of bisexual identities. *Journal of Bisexuality, 1,* 31–68.

Rust, P. C. (2002). Bisexuality: The state of the union. *Annual Review of Sex Research, 13,* 180–240.

Rylko-Bauer, B. (1996). Abortion from a cross-cultural perspective. *Social Science & Medicine, 42,* 479–482.

Sacks, S. L. (2004). Famciclovir suppression of asymptomatic and symptomatic recurrent anogenital herpes simplex virus shedding in women. *Journal of Infectious Diseases, 189,* 1341–1347.

Sacred Congregation for the Doctrine of the Faith (1976, January 16). Declaration on certain questions concerning sexual ethics. (English text in the *New York Times*, p. 2).

Sadock, B. J., & Sadock, V. A. (1976). Techniques of coitus. In B. J. Sadock et al. (Eds.), *The sexual experience*. Baltimore, MD: Williams & Wilkins.

Saegert, S., Swap, W., & Zajonc, R. B. (1973). Exposure, context, and interpersonal attraction. *Journal of Personality and Social Psychology, 25*, 234–242.

Sagarin, E. (1973). Power to the peephole. *Sexual Behavior, 3*, 2–7.

St. Augustine. (1950). *The city of God.* (Marcus Dods, Trans.). New York: Modern Library.

Salamon, E. (1989). The homosexual escort agency: Deviance disavowal. *British Journal of Sociology, 40*, 1–21.

Saltik-Temizel, I., Kocak, N., & Demit, H. (2004). Interferon-alpha and lamivudine combination therapy of children with chronic hepatitis B infection who were interferon-alpha non-responders. *Pediatric Infectious Disease Journal, 23*, 466–468.

Samson, J.-M., Levy, J. J., Dupras, A., & Tessier, D. (1991). Coitus frequency among married or cohabiting heterosexual adults: A survey in French Canada. *Australian Journal of Marriage & Family, 12*, 103–109.

Samson, J.-M., Levy, J. J., Dupras, A., & Tessier, D. (1993). Active oral-genital sex among married and cohabiting heterosexual adults. *Sexological Review, 1*, 143–156.

Sanday, P. R. (1981). The socio-cultural context of rape: A cross-cultural study. *Journal of Social Issues, 37*(4), 5–27.

Santen, R. J. (1995). The testis. In P. Felig, J. D. Baxter, & L. A. Frohman (Eds.), *Endocrinology and metabolism* (3rd ed.). New York: McGraw-Hill.

Santilla, P., Sandnabba, N., K., Laurence, A., & Nordling, N. (2002). Investigating the underlying structure in sadomasochistically oriented behavior. *Archives of Sexual Behavior, 31*, 185–196.

Sarrel, L., & Sarrel, P. (1984). *Sexual turning points: The seven stages of adult sexuality.* New York: Macmillan.

Sarrell, P., & Masters, W. (1982). Sexual molestation of men by women. *Archives of Sexual Behavior, 11*, 117–132.

Savin-Williams, R. (1995). An exploratory study of pubertal maturation timing and self-esteem among gay and bisexual male youths. *Developmental Psychology, 31*, 56–64.

Savin-Williams, R. (2001). Suicide attempts among sexual-minority youths: Population and measurement issues. *Journal of Consulting and Clinical Psychology, 69*, 983–991.

Sayle, A. E., Savitz, D. A., Thorpe, J. M., Jr., Hertz-Picciotto, L., & Wilcox, A. J. (2001). Sexual activity during late pregnancy and risk of preterm delivery. *Obstetrics and Gynecology, 97*, 283–289.

Schachter, S. (1964). The interaction of cognitive and physiological determinants of emotional state. In L. Berkowitz (Ed.), *Advances in experimental social psychology* (Vol. I). New York: Academic.

Schaefer, M. T., & Olson, D. H. (1981). Assessing intimacy: The PAIR Inventory. *Journal of Marital and Family Therapy*, 47–60.

Schaffer, H. R., & Emerson, Peggy E. (1964). Patterns of response to physical contact in early human development. *Journal of Child Psychology and Psychiatry, 5*, 1–13.

Scharfe, E., & Bartholomew, K. (1995). Accommodation and attachment representations in young couples. *Journal of Social and Personal Relationships, 12*, 389–401.

Schenker, J. G., & Evron, S. (1983). New concepts in the surgical management of tubal pregnancy and the consequent postoperative results. *Fertility and Sterility, 40*, 709–723.

Schiavi, R. C. (1990). Sexuality in aging men. *Annual Review of Sex Research, 1*, 227–250.

Schiavi, R. C., Mandeli, J., & Schreiner-Engel. (1994). Sexual satisfaction in healthy aging men. *Journal of Sex and Marital Therapy, 20*, 3–13.

Schieffelin, E. L. (1976). *The sorrow of the lonely and the burning of the dancers.* New York: St. Martin's Press.

Schlenker, J. A., Caron, S. L., & Halteman, W. A. (1998). A feminist analysis of *Seventeen* magazine: Content analysis from 1945 to 1995. *Sex Roles, 38*, 135–150.

Schmitt, D., & Buss, D. (1996). Strategic self-promotion and competitor derogation: Sex and content effects on the perceived effectiveness of mate attraction tactics. *Journal of Personality and Social Psychology, 70*, 1185–1204.

Schmitt, D. P. (2003). Universal sex differences in the desire for sexual variety: Tests from 52 nations, 6 continents, and 13 islands. *Journal of Personality and Social Psychology, 85*, 85–104.

Schneider, E. D. (Ed.). (1985). *Questions about the beginning of life.* Minneapolis, MN: Augsburg.

Schneider, M. (1991). Developing service for lesbian and gay adolescents. *Canadian Journal of Community Mental Health, 10*, 133–151.

Schofield, A. T., & Vaughan-Jackson, P. (1913). *What a boy should know.* New York: Cassell.

Schooley, R. T., Spino, C., Kuritzkes, D., Walker, B. D., Valentine, F. A., Hirsch, M. S., et al. (2000). Two double-blinded, randomized, comparative trials of 4 human immunodeficiency virus type 1 (HIV-1) envelope vaccines in HIV-1-infected individuals across a spectrum of disease severity. *Journal of Infectious Diseases, 182*, 1357–1364.

Schroeder, A. (2000, January 28). The money was great, risks were real. Student reflects on her year as a phone sex operator. *The Brunswickan.*

Schroeder, P. (1994). Female genital mutilation–a form of child abuse. *New England Journal of Medicine, 331*, 739–740.

Schubach, G. (2002). The G-spot is the female prostate. *American Journal of Obstetrics and Gynecology, 186*, 850.

Schultz, W. C. M., et al. (1989). Vaginal sensitivity to electric stimuli: Theoretical and practical implications. *Archives of Sexual Behavior, 18*, 87–96.

Schultz, W. W., van Andel, P., Sabelis, I., & Mooyaart, E. (1999). Magnetic resonance imaging of male and female genitals during coitus and female sexual arousal. *British Medical Journal, 319*, 1596–1600.

Schwartz, L. B. (1997, December 20/27). Understanding human parturition. *The Lancet, 350*, 1792–1793.

Scott, J. P. (1964). The effects of early experience on social behavior and organization. In W. Etkin (Ed.), *Social behavior and organization among vertebrates*. Chicago: University of Chicago Press.

Segraves, R. T. & Balon, R. (2003). *Sexual pharmacology: Fast facts.* New York: Norton.

Sell, R. L. (1997). Defining and measuring sexual orientation: A review. *Archives of Sexual Behavior, 26*, 643–658.

Sell, R. L., Wells, J. A., & Wypij, D. (1995). The prevalence of homosexual behavior and attraction in the United States, the United Kingdom and France. *Archives of Sexual Behavior, 24*, 235–248.

Sellors, J. W., Mahoney, J. B., Kczorowski, J., Lytwyn, A., Bangura, H., Chong, S., et al. (2000). Prevalence and predictors of human papillomavirus infection in women in Ontario, Canada. *Canadian Medical Association Journal, 163*, 503–509.

Semple, S. J., Patterson, T. L., & Grant, I. (2004). The context of sexual risk behavior among heterosexual methamphetamine users. *Addictive Behaviors, 29,* 807–810.

Senn, C. Y., & Desmarais, S. (2001). Are our recruitment practices for sex studies working across gender? The effect of topic and gender of recruiter on participation rates of university men and women. *The Journal of Sex Research, 38,* 111–117.

Senn, C. Y., Desmarais, S., Verberg, N., & Wood, E. (2000). Predicting coercive sexual behaviour across the lifespan in a random sample of Canadian men. *Journal of Social and Personal Relationships, 17,* 95–113.

Senn, C. Y., & Dzinas, K. (1996). Measuring fear of rape: A new scale. *Canadian Journal of Behavioural Science, 28,* 141–144.

Senn, C. Y., & Radtke, H. L. (1990). Women's evaluations of and affective reactions to mainstream violent pornography, nonviolent pornography and erotica. *Violence and Victims, 5,* 143–155.

Seto, M. C., Lalumière, M. L., & Blanchard, R. (2000). The discriminative validity of a phallometric test for pedophilic interests among adolescent sex offenders against children. *Psychological Assessment, 12,* 319–327.

Seto, M. C., Maric, A., & Barbaree, H. E. (2001). The role of pornography in the etiology of sexual aggression. *Aggression and Violent Behavior, 6,* 35–53.

Seto, M. C., Murphy, W. D., Page, J., & Ennis, L. (2003). Detecting anomalous sexual interests in juvenile sex offenders. *Annals of the New York Academy of Sciences, 898,* 118–130.

Setty-Venugopal, V., & Upadhyay, U. D. (2002). Three to five saves lives. Population Reports, Series L, Number 13. Baltimore: Johns Hopkins University School of Public Health.

Sex Industry, The. (1998, February 14). *The Economist,* 21–23.

Shackelford, T., & Buss, D. (1997). Cues to infidelity. *Personality and Social Psychology Bulletin, 23,* 1034–1045.

Shabsigh, R., et al. (2000). Intracavernous alprostadil alfadex (Edex/viridal) is effective and safe in patients with erectile dysfunction after failing sildenafil (Viagra). *Urology, 55,* 477–480.

Shandera, K. C., & Thompson, I. M. (1994). Urologic prostheses. *Emergency Medicine Clinics of North America, 12,* 729–748.

Shapiro, C. N., & Alter, M. J. (1996). Syphilis. In S. A. Morse et al. (Eds.), *Atlas of sexually transmitted diseases* (pp. 241–268). London: Mosby-Wolfe.

Shapiro, E. D. (1986). New innovations in conception and their effects upon our law and morality. *New York Law Review, 21,* 37–59.

Sharpstein, D. J., & Kirkpatrick, L. (1997). Romantic jealousy and adult romantic attachment. *Journal of Personality and Social Psychology, 72,* 627–640.

Shaver, F. (1996). Prostitution: On the dark side of the service industry. In Tom Fleming (Ed.), *Post critical criminology.* Scarborough: Prentice Hall.

Shaver, F. (1996). Regulation of prostitution: Setting the morality trap. In B. Schissel & L. Mahood (Eds.), *Social control in Canada.* Toronto: Oxford University Press.

Shaver, F. M. (1994). The regulation of prostitution: Avoiding morality traps. *CHS/RCDS, 9*(1), 123–145.

Shaver, F. M. (In press). Sex work research: Methodological and ethical challenges. *Journal of Interpersonal Violence.*

Shaver, F. M., & Newmeyer, T. (1996). Men who have sex with men: A comparison of the sexual practices and risk taking behaviour of gay and bisexual men and male prostitutes. Presented at *Sida, Jeunesse et Prevention au dela du Discours, des Actions.*

Sherrard, J., & Barlow, D. (1996). Gonorrhoea in men: Clinical and diagnostic aspects. *Genitourinary Medicine, 72,* 422–426.

Sherwin, B. B. (1991). The psychoendocrinology of aging and female sexuality. *Annual Review of Sex Research, 2,* 181–198.

Shidlo, A., Schroeder, M., & Drescher, J. (Eds.) (2002). *Sexual conversion therapy: Ethical, clinical, and research perspectives.* New York: Haworth.

Shifren, J. L., Braunstein, G. D., Simon, J. A., Casson, P. R., Buster, J. E., & Redmond, G. P. (2000). Transdermal testosterone treatment in women with impaired sexual function after oophorectomy. *New England Journal of Medicine, 343,* 682–688.

Shifren, J. L., Nahum, R., & Mazer, N. A. (1998). Incidence of sexual dysfunction in surgically menopausal women. *Menopause, 5,* 189–190.

Shoveller, J. A., Johnson, J. L., Langille, D. B., & Mitchell, T. (2004). Socio-cultural influences on young people's sexual development. *Social Sciences & Medicine, 59,* 473–487.

SIECUS. (1991). *Guidelines for comprehensive sexuality education.* New York: Sexuality Information and Education Council of the United States.

Siegel, K., & Scrimshaw, E. (2003). Reasons for the adoption of celibacy among older men and women living with HIV/AIDS. *Journal of Sex Research, 40,* 189–200.

Siegel, K., Krauss, B. J., & Karus, D. (1994). Reporting recent sexual practices: Gay men's disclosure of HIV risk by questionnaire and interview. *Archives of Sexual Behavior, 23,* 217–230.

Siegel, L. J., & McCormick, C. (1999). *Criminology in Canada: Theories, patterns and typologies.* Scarborough: ITP Nelson.

Signorielli, N. (1990). Children, television, and gender roles. *Journal of Adolescent Health Care, 11,* 50–58.

Signorile, M. (1997). *Life on the outside: The Signorile report on gay men.* New York: HarperCollins.

Siker, J. S. (Ed.). (1994). *Homosexuality in the church: Both sides of the debate.* Louisville, KY: Westminster/John Knox Press.

Silvera, M. (1990). Man royal and sodomites: Some thought on the invisibility of Afro-Caribbean lesbians. In Sharon Dale Stone (Ed.), *Lesbians in Canada.* Toronto: Between the Lines.

Silvestre, L., et al. (1990). Voluntary interruption of pregnancy with mifepristone (RU-486) and a prostaglandin analogue: A large-scale French experience. *New England Journal of Medicine, 322,* 645.

Simpson, J. A. (1990). Influence of attachment styles on romantic relationships. *Journal of Personality and Social Psychology, 59,* 971–980.

Singer, D. B. (1995). Human embryogenesis. In D. R. Coustan, R. V. Haning, Jr., & D. B. Singer (Eds.), *Human reproduction: Growth and development.* Boston: Little, Brown.

Singh, D. (1993). Adaptive significance of female physical attractiveness: Role of waist-to-hip ratio. *Journal of Personality and Social Psychology, 65,* 293–307.

Singh, D., & Bronstad, P. (2001). Female body odour is a potential cue to ovulation. *Proceedings of the Royal Society London B Biology, 268,* 797–801.

Singh, S., & Darroch, J. E. (2000). Adolescent pregnancy and childbearing: Levels and trends in developed countries. *Family Planning Perspectives, 32,* 14–23.

Singh, S., Darroch, J. E., Frost, J. J., & the Study Team. (2001). Socioeconomic disadvantage and adolescent women's sexual and reproductive behavior: The case of five developed countries. *Family Planning Perspectives, 33,* 251–258, 289.

Siosteen, A., et al. (1990). Sexual ability, activity, attitudes and satisfaction as part of adjustment in spinal cord–injured subjects. *Paraplegia, 28,* 285–295.

Sipe, A. W. Richard. (1995). *Sex priests, and power: Anatomy of a crisis.* New York: Brunner/Mazel.

Sipski, M. L. (2002). Central nervous system based neurogenic female sexual dysfunction: Current status and future trends. *Archives of Sexual Behavior, 31,* 421–424.

Sipski, M. L., Alexander, C., & Rosen, R. (2001). Sexual arousal and orgasm in women: Effects of spinal cord injury. *Annals of Neurology, 49,* 35–44.

Sipski, M. L., & Alexander, C. J. (1995). Spinal cord injury and female sexuality. *Annual Review of Sex Research, 6,* 224–244.

Sipski, M. L., & Alexander, C. J. (Eds.). (1997). *Sexual function in people with disability and chronic illness.* Gaithersburg, MD: Aspen.

Siushansian, J. A., Nguyen, M., & Archibald, C. P. (2000). HIV and men who have sex with men: Where is the Canadian epidemic headed? *The Canadian Journal of Human Sexuality, 9,* 219–237.

Skaletsky, H., Kuroda-Kawaguchi, T., Minx, P. J., Cordum, H. S., Hillier, L., Brown, L. G., et al. (2003). The male-specific region of the human Y chromosome is a mosaic of discrete sequence classes. *Nature, 423,* 825–837.

Slob, A. K., et al. (1991). Menstrual cycle phase and sexual arousability in women. *Archives of Sexual Behavior, 20,* 567–578.

Small, M. F. (1993). *Female choices: Sexual behavior of female primates.* Ithaca, NY: Cornell University Press.

Smallwood, G. H., Meador, M. L., Lenihan, J. P., Shangold, G. A., Fisher, A. C., & Creasy, G. W. (2001). Efficacy and safety of a transdermal contraceptive system. *Obstetrics and Gynecology, 98,* 799–805.

Smith, D. (2002, October). Canceled trial is yielding useful data. *Monitor on Psychology, 33,* 52.

Smith, G., Frankel, S., & Yarnell, J. (1997). Sex and death: Are they related? Findings from the Caerphilly cohort study. *British Medical Journal, 315,* 1641–1645.

Smith, J. R., et al. (1996). Major susceptibility locus for prostate cancer on chromosome 1 suggested by a genome-wide search. *Science, 274,* 1371–1373.

Smith, M. (1999). *Lesbian and gay rights in Canada: Social movements and equality seeking, 1971–1995.* Toronto: University of Toronto Press.

Smyth, L. J. C. et al. (2004). Immunological responses in women with human papillomavirus type 16 (HPV-16) associated anogenital intraepithelial neoplasia induced by heterologous prime-boost HYP-16 oncogene vaccination. *Clinical Cancer Research, 10,* 2954–2961.

Society of Obstetricians and Gynaecologists of Canada. (2000). *Sex sense: Canadian contraception guide.* Ottawa: Author.

Soley, L. C., & Kurzbard, G. (1986). Sex in advertising: A comparison of 1964 and 1984 magazine advertisements. *Journal of Advertising, 15*(3), 46–54.

Solms, M. (1997). *The neuropsychology of dreams: A clinico-anatomical study.* Mahwah, NJ: Erlbaum.

Sommers-Flanagan, R., Sommers-Flanagan, J., & Davis, B. (1993). What's happening on music television? A gender role content analysis. *Sex Roles, 28,* 745–753.

Song, Y. I. (1991). Single Asian women as a result of divorce: Depressive affect and changes in social support. *Journal of Divorce and Remarriage, 14,* 219–230.

Soon, J. A., Levine, M., Osmond, B. L., Ensom, M. H. H., & Fielding, D. W. (2005). Effects of making emergency contraception available without a physician's prescription: A population-based study. *Canadian Medical Association Journal, 172,* 878–883.

Sorensen, R. C. (1973). *Adolescent sexuality in contemporary America.* New York: World.

Spalding, L. R., & Peplau, L. A. (1997). The unfaithful lover: Heterosexuals' perceptions of bisexuals and their relationships. *Psychology of Women Quarterly, 21,* 611–625.

Spector, I. P., & Carey, M. P. (1990). Incidence and prevalence of the sexual dysfunctions: A critical review of the empirical literature. *Archives of Sexual Behavior, 19,* 389–408.

Spehr, M., Gisselmann, G., Poplawski, A., Riffell, J. A., Wetzel, C. H., Zimmer, R. K., & Hatt, H. (2003). Identification of a testicular odorant receptor mediating human sperm chemotaxis. *Science, 299,* 2054–2058.

Spitz, I. M., et al. (1998). Early pregnancy termination with mifepristone and misoprostol in the United States. *New England Journal of Medicine, 338,* 1241–1247.

Spitz, R. A. (1949). Autoeroticism: Some empirical findings and hypotheses on three of its manifestations in the first year of life. *The Psychoanalytic Study of the Child* (Vols. III–IV, pp. 85–120). New York: International Universities Press.

Spourk, R. F. (2002). Dehydroepiandrosterone: A springboard hormone for female sexuality. *Fertility and Sterility, 77,* S19–S25.

Sprecher, S., Barbee, A., & Schwartz, P. (1995). "Was it good for you, too?": Gender differences in first sexual intercourse experiences. *Journal of Sex Research, 32,* 3–15.

Sprecher, S., & McKinney, K. (1993). *Sexuality.* Newbury Park, CA: Sage.

Sprecher, S., Sullivan, Q., & Hatfield, E. (1994). Mate selection preferences: Gender differences examined in a national sample. *Journal of Personality and Social Psychology, 66,* 1074–1080.

Springen, K., & Noonan, D. (2002). Sperm banks go online. MSNBC News 899016.

Stack, S., & Gundlach, J. H. (1992). Divorce and sex. *Archives of Sexual Behavior, 21,* 359–368.

Stanton, A. L., Lobel, M., Sears, S., & DeLuca, R. (2002). Psychosocial aspects of selected issues in women's reproductive health: Current status and future directions. *Journal of Consulting and Clinical Psychology, 70,* 751–770.

Starks, K. J., & Morrison, E. S. (1996). *Growing up sexual* (2nd ed.). New York: HarperCollins.

Statistics Canada. (1993). The violence against women survey. *The Daily.* Catalogue no. 11-001E.

Statistics Canada. (1995). Therapeutic abortions. *Statistical report on the health of Canadians: Conditions and diseases.* Statistics Canada. Catalogue no. 82-219-XPB.

Statistics Canada. (1997). 1996 census: Marital status, common-law unions and families. *The Daily.* Catalogue no. 93F0022XDB9.

Statistics Canada. (1997). Population in private households by age group (17a) and sex showing living arrangements for Canada, provinces, territories and census metropolitan areas, 1996 census (93F0022XDB96010). In *Census of Population 1996: Nation Series* [computer file].

Statistics Canada. (1998a, February 17). 1996 census: Ethnic origin, visible minorities. *The Daily.*

Statistics Canada. (1998b). *National population health survey, 1996–1997* [computer file]. Ottawa: Author.

Statistics Canada. (2000, March 16). Canadian social trends: The changing face of conjugal relationships. *The Daily.*

Statistics Canada. (2000, July 25). Family violence. *The Daily.*

Statistics Canada. (2001, November 15). Marriages. *The Daily.*

Statistics Canada. (2002, January 18). Therapeutic abortions. *The Daily.*

Statistics Canada. (2002). *Canadian community health survey* (Cycle 1) [data file]. Ottawa: Statistics Canada.

Statistics Canada. (2004). First information on sexual orientation. *Canadian Community Health Survey.* Ottawa: Author.

Steben, M., & Sacks, Sn. (1997). Genital herpes: The epidemiology and control of a common sexually transmitted disease. *Canadian Journal of Human Sexuality, 6,* 127–134.

Steege, J. F., Stout, A. L., & Carson, Culley C. (1986). Patient satisfaction in Scott and Small-Carrion penile implant recipients. *Archives of Sexual Behavior, 15,* 393–400.

Steinberg, K. K., et al. (1991). A meta-analysis of the effect of estrogen replacement therapy on the risk of breast cancer. *Journal of the American Medical Association, 265,* 1985–1990.

Steinberg, L. (2002). *Adolescence* (6th ed). New York: McGraw-Hill.

Steiner, B. (1990). Intake assessment of gender-dysphoric patients. In R. Blanchard & B. W. Steiner (Eds.), *Clinical management of gender identity disorders in children & adults.* Washington: American Psychiatric Press.

Steinman, D. L., et al. (1981). A comparison of male and female patterns of sexual arousal. *Archives of Sexual Behavior, 10,* 529–548.

Stephens, T. (1991, February). AIDS in women reveals health-care deficiencies. *The Journal of NIH Research, 3,* 27–30.

Stern, K., & McClintock, M. K. (1998). Regulation of ovulation by human pheromones. *Nature, 392,* 177–179.

Sternberg, R. J. (1986). A triangular theory of love. *Psychological Review, 93,* 119–135.

Sternberg, R. J. (1987). Liking versus loving: A comparative evaluation of theories. *Psychological Bulletin, 102,* 331–345.

Sternberg, R. (1996). Love stories. *Personal Relationships, 3,* 59–79.

Sternberg, R. (1997). Construct validation of a triangular love scale. *European Journal of Social Psychology, 27,* 313–335.

Sternberg, R. (1998). *Love is a story: A new theory of relationships.* New York: Oxford University Press.

Stevenson, M. R. (1995). Searching for a gay identity in Indonesia. *Journal of Men's Studies, 4,* 93–108.

Stewart, S., Stinnett, H., & Rosenfeld, L. B. (2000). Sex differences in desired characteristics of short-term and long-term relationship partners. *Journal of Social and Personal Relationships, 17,* 843–853.

Stiles, W. B., Walz, N., Schroeder, M., Williams, L., & Ickes, W. (1996). Attractiveness and disclosure in initial encounters of mixed-sex dyads. *Journal of Social and Personal Relationships, 13,* 303–312.

Stobert, S. & Kemeny, A. (2003, Summer). *Childfree by choice* (Catalogue No. 11-008). Ottawa, ON: Statistics Canada.

Stodghill, R., II. (1998, June 15). Where'd you learn that? *Time 151,* 52–59.

Stoneburner, R. L., & Low-Beer, D. (2004). Population-level HIV declines and behavioral risk avoidance in Uganda. *Science, 304,* 714–718.

Stoneburner, R. L., Sato, P., Burton, A., & Mertens, T. (1994). The global HIV pandemic. *Acta Paediatrica,* Suppl. 400, 1–4.

Storey, A. E., Walsh, C. J., Quinton, R. L., & Wynne-Edwards, K. E. (2000). Hormonal correlates of paternal responsiveness in new and expectant fathers. *Evolution and Human Behavior, 21,* 79–95.

Storms, M. D. (1980). Theories of sexual orientation. *Journal of Personality and Social Psychology, 38,* 783–792.

Strassberg, D. S., & Lowe, K. (1995). Volunteer bias in sex research. *Archives of Sexual Behavior, 24,* 369–382.

Streissguth, A. P., Barr, H. M., Bookstein, F. L., Sampson, P. D., & Olson, H. C. (1999). The long-term neurocognitive consequences of prenatal alcohol exposure: A 14-year study. *Psychological Science, 10,* 186–190.

Strickland, B. R. (1995). Research on sexual orientation and human development. *Developmental Psychology, 31,* 137–140.

Striegel-Moore, R., Goldman, S., Garvin, V., & Rodin, J. (1996). A prospective study of somatic and emotional symptoms of pregnancy. *Psychology of Women Quarterly, 20,* 393–408.

Strong, C. (1997). *Ethics in reproductive and perinatal medicine.* New Haven: Yale University Press.

Struckman-Johnson, C. (1988). Forced sex on dates: It happens to men, too. *Journal of Sex Research, 24,* 234–241.

Struckman-Johnson, C., et al. (1996). Sexual coercion reported by men and women in prison. *Journal of Sex Research, 33,* 67–76.

Struckman-Johnson, C., Struckman-Johnson, D., & Anderson, P. B. (2003). Tactics of sexual coercion: When men and women won't take no for an answer. *Journal of Sex Research, 40,* 76–86.

Stryker, S. (1987). The vitalization of symbolic interactionism. Social Psychology *Quarterly, 50,* 83–94.

Swaab, D. F. (2005). The role of the hypothalamus and endocrine system in sexuality. In J. Hyde (Ed.), *Biological substrates of human sexuality.* Washington, DC: American Psychological Association.

Swaab, D. F., Gooren, L. J. G., & Hofman, M. A. (1995). Brain research, gender, and sexual orientation. *Journal of Homosexuality, 28,* 283–301.

Swerdloff, R. S., & Wang, C. (2000). Causes of male infertility. *Up to Date: Electronic Clinical Reference Library,* Medscape. (*www.medscape.com*).

Swygard, H., Sena, A. C., Hobbs, M. M., & Cohen, M. S. (2004). Trichomoniasis: Clinical manifestations, diagnosis, and management. *Sexually Transmitted Infections, 80,* 91–95.

Symbalauk, D. G., & Jones, K. M. (1999). Prostitution offender programs: An educational alternative to sentencing. *Law Now, 23,* 38.

Symons, D. (1979). *The evolution of human sexuality.* New York: Oxford University Press.

Symons, D. (1987). An evolutionary approach: Can Darwin's view of life shed light on human sexuality? In J. H. Geer & W. T. O'Donohue (Eds.), *Theories of human sexuality* (pp. 91–126). New York: Plenum.

Szabo, R. (2000). How does male circumcision protect against HIV infection? *British Medical Journal, 320,* 1592.

Szasz, T. S. (1965). Legal and moral aspects of homosexuality. In J. Marmor (Ed.), *Sexual inversion: The multiple roots of homosexuality.* New York: Basic Books.

Szasz, T. S. (1980). *Sex by prescription.* Garden City, NY: Anchor Press/Doubleday.

Taberner, P. V. (1985). *Aphrodisiacs: The science and the myth.* Philadelphia: University of Pennsylvania Press.

Tabet, S. R, Callahan, M. M., Mauck, C. K., Gai, F., Coletti, A. S., Profy, A. T., et al. (2003). Safety and acceptability of penile application of 2 candidate topic microbicides: BufferGel and PRO 2000 Gel. *JAIDS: Journal of Acquired Immune Deficiency Syndromes, 33,* 476–483.

Tafoya, T., & Wirth, D. A. (1996). Native American two-spirit men. In J. F. Longres (Ed.), *Men of color* (pp. 51–67). New York: Haworth.

Talamini, J. T. (1982). *Boys will be girls: The hidden world of the heterosexual male transvestite.* Washington, DC: University Press of America.

Tamir, L. M. (1982). *Men in their forties: The transition to middle age.* New York: Springer.

Tangri, S., Burt, M. R., & Johnson, L. B. (1982). Sexual harassment at work: Three explanatory models. *Journal of Social Issues, 38*(4), 33–54.

Tannahill, Reay (1980). *Sex in history.* Stein & Day: New York

Tannen, D. (1991). *You just don't understand: Women and men in conversation.* New York: William Morrow.

Tanner, J. M. (1967). Puberty. In A. McLaren (Ed.), *Advances in reproductive physiology* (Vol. II). New York: Academic.

Taylor, Robert. (1994, Apr.). Quiet clues to HIV-1 immunity: Do some people resist infection? *Journal of NIH Research, 6,* 29–31.

Templeman, T. L., & Stinnett, R. D. (1991). Patterns of sexual arousal and history in a "normal" sample of young men. *Archives of Sexual Behavior, 20,* 137–150.

Tepper, M. L., & Gully, P. R. (1997). Lovers & livers: Hepatitis B as an STD. *Canadian Journal of Human Sexuality, 6,* 135–142.

Terman, L., et al. (1938). *Psychological factors in marital happiness.* New York: McGraw-Hill.

Terman, L. M. (1948). Kinsey's *Sexual Behavior in the Human Male*: Some comments and criticisms. *Psychological Bulletin, 45,* 443–459.

Thielicke, H. (1964). *The ethics of sex.* New York: Harper & Row.

Thompson, Anthony P. (1983). Extramarital sex: A review of the research literature. *Journal of Sex Research, 19,* 1–22.

Thorne, B. (1993). *Gender play: Girls and boys in school.* New Brunswick, NJ: Rutgers University Press.

Thorne, N., & Amrein, H. (2003). Vomeronasal organ: Pheromone recognition with a twist. *Current Biology, 13,* R220–R222.

Thornhill, R., & Palmer, C. T. (2000). *A natural history of rape: Biological bases of sexual coercion.* Cambridge, MA: MIT Press.

Thorpe, L. P., Katz, B., & Lewis, R. T. (1961). *The psychology of abnormal behavior.* New York: Ronald Press.

Tiefer, L. (1991a). Historical, scientific, clinical, and feminist criticisms of "The Human Sexual Response Cycle" model. *Annual Review of Sex Research, 2,* 1–24.

Tiefer, L. (1991b). New perspectives in sexology: From rigor (mortis) to richness. *Journal of Sex Research, 28,* 593–602.

Tiefer, L. (1994). Three crises facing sexology. *Archives of Sexual Behavior, 23,* 361–374.

Tiefer, L. (1995). *Sex is not a natural act, and other essays.* Boulder, CO: Westview.

Tiefer, L. (2000). Sexology and the pharmaceutical industry: The threat of co-optation. *Journal of Sex Research, 37,* 273–283.

Tiefer, L. (2001). Arriving at a "new view" of women's sexual problems: Background, theory, and activism. In E. Kachak & L. Tiefer (Eds.), *A new view of women's sexual problems* (pp. 63–98). New York: Haworth Press.

Tiefer, L. (2004). *Sex is not a natural act and other essays* (2nd ed.). Boulder, CO: Westview Press.

Timmerman, G. (2003). Sexual harassment of adolescents perpetrated by teachers and by peers; An exploration of the dynamics of power, culture, and gender in secondary schools. *Sex Roles, 48,* 231–244.

Toubia, N. (1994). Female circumcision as a public health issue. *New England Journal of Medicine, 331,* 712–716.

Toubia, N. (1995). *Female genital mutilation: A call for global action.* New York: Women Ink.

Townsend, J.W. (2003). Reproductive behavior in the context of global population. *American Psychologist, 58,* 197–2004.

Traish, A. M., Kim, N. N., Munarriz, R., Moreland, R., & Goldstein, I. (2002). Biochemical and physiological mechanisms of female genital sexual arousal. *Archives of Sexual Behavior, 31,* 393–400.

Traven, S., Cuyllen, K., & Protter, B. (1990). Female sexual offenders: Severe victims and victimizers. *Journal of Forensic Sciences, 35,* 140–150.

Treiman, K., et al. (1995). IUDs–An update. *Population Reports,* Series B, No. 6. Baltimore, MD: Johns Hopkins School of Public Health.

Tremblay, C., Hébert, M., & Piché, C. (1999). Coping strategies and social support as mediators of consequences in child sexual abuse victims. *Child Abuse & Neglect, 23,* 929–945.

Tremblay, C., Hébert, M., & Piché, C. (2000). Type I and type II posttraumatic stress disorder in sexually abused children. *Journal of Child Sexual Abuse, 9,* 65–90.

Tremblay, L., & Frignon J. (2004). Biobehavioural and cognitive determinants of adolescent girls' involvement in sexual risk behaviours: A test of three theoretical models. *Canadian Journal of Human Sexuality, 13,* 29–43.

Triandis, H. C., McCusker, C., & Hui, C. H. (1990). Multimethod probes of individualism and collectivism. *Journal of Personality and Social Psychology, 59,* 1006–1020.

Trocmé, N., MacLaurin, B., Fallon, B., Daciuk, J., Billingsley, D., Tourigny, M., et al. (2001). *Canadian Incidence Study of Reported Child Abuse and Neglect: Final Report.* Ottawa, Ontario: Minister of Public Works and Government Services Canada.

Trudel, G. (2002). Sexuality and marital life: Results of a survey. *Journal of Sex & Marital Therapy, 28,* 241–261.

Trudel, G., Marchand, A., Ravart, M., Aubin, S., Turgeon, L., & Fortier, P. (2001). The effect of a cognitive-behavioral group treatment program on hypoactive sexual desire in women. *Sexual and Relationship Therapy, 16,* 145–164.

Trudel, G., Ravart, M., & Aubin, S.. (1996). Hypoactive sexual desire in couples: A cognitive-behavioral perspective. In J. Lonsdale, S. Powell, & L. Solomon (Eds), *The Hatherleigh guide to marriage and family therapy.* New York: Hatherleigh Press.

Trussell, J., et al. (2000). Emergency contraception: A cost-effective approach to preventing unintended pregnancy. *Women's Health, 5.*

Trynka, S., & Tucker, N. (1995). Overview. In Tucker, N. (Ed.), *Bisexual politics: Theories, queries, and visions.* New York: Harrington Park Press.

Tullman, G. M., et al. (1981). The pre- and post-therapy measurement of communication skills of couples undergoing sex therapy at the Masters & Johnson Institute. *Archives of Sexual Behavior, 10,* 95–109.

Turkle, S. (1995). *Life on the screen: Identity in the age of the Internet.* New York: Simon & Schuster.

Turner, P. K., Runtz, M. G., & Galambos, N. L. (1999). Sexual abuse, pubertal timing, and subjective age in adolescent girls: A research note. *Journal of Reproductive and Infant Psychology, 17*(2), 111–118.

Tutin, C. E. G., & McGinnis, P. R. (1981). Chimpanzee reproduction in the wild. In C. E. Graham (Ed.), *Reproductive biology of the great apes* (pp. 239–264). New York: Academic Press.

Tutty, L. M. (1997). Child sexual abuse prevention programs: Evaluating who do you tell. *Child Abuse & Neglect, 21,* 869–881.

Tutuer, W. (1984). Dangerousness of peeping toms. *Medical Aspects of Human Sexuality, 18,* 97.

Udry, J. R. (1988). Biological predispositions and social control in adolescent sexual behavior. *American Sociological Review, 53,* 709–722.

Udry, J. R., et al. (1985). Serum androgenic hormones motivate sexual behavior in adolescent boys. *Fertility and Sterility, 43,* 90–94.

Udry, J. R., & Eckland, B. K. (1984). Benefits of being attractive: Differential payoffs for men and women. *Psychological Reports, 54,* 47–56.

Ullman, S. E., & Knight, R. A. (1993). The efficacy of women's resistance strategies in rape situations. *Psychology of Women Quarterly, 17,* 23–38.

Ulmann, A., Teutsch, G., & Philibert, D. (1990, June). RU-486. *Scientific American, 262,* 42–48.

UNAIDS–United Nations Program on HIV/AIDS. (1997). *Impact of HIV and sexual health education on the sexual behavior of young people.* Geneva, SU.

Union for Reform Judaism. (2004). What is the Reform perspective on abortion? Retrieved from http://uahc.org.

United Synagogue of Conservative Judaism. (1989). Retrieved from www.ncrc.org.

UPI (1981, November 5). Toxicologist warns against butyl nitrite. *Delaware Gazette,* p. 3.

Upadhyay, U. D., & Robey, B. (1999). Why family planning matters. *Population Reports,* Series J, No. 49. Baltimore, Johns Hopkins University School of Public Health, Population Information Program.

Urban, J. R. (1992). Neuroendocrinology of aging in the male and female. *Endocrinology and Metabolism Clinics of North America, 21,* 921–931.

Urbina, A., & Jones, K. (2004). Crystal methamphetamine, its analogues, and HIV infection; Medical and psychiatric aspects of a new epidemic. *Clinical Infectious Diseases, 38,* 890–894.

Vacca, J. P., et al. (1994). L-735, 524: An orally bioavailable human immunodeficiency virus Type I protease inhibitor. *Proceedings of the National Academy of Sciences USA, 91,* 4096.

Valentich, M. (1994). Rape revisited: Sexual violence against women in the former Yugoslavia. *Canadian Journal of Human Sexuality, 3,* 53–64.

Vance, E. B., & Wagner, N. N. (1976). Written descriptions of orgasm: A study of sex differences. *Archives of Sexual Behavior, 5,* 87–98.

Van Damme, L., Jespers, V., Van Dyck, E., & Chapman, A. (2002b). Penile application of dextrin sulphate gel (Emmelle). *Contraception, 66,* 133–136.

Van Damme, L., Ramjee, G., Alary, M., Vuylsteke, B., Chandeying, V., Rees, H., et al. (2002a). Effectiveness of COL-1492, a nonxynol-9 vaginal gel, on HIV-1 transmission in female sex workers: A randomised controlled trial. *Lancet, 360,* 971–977.

Van Dis, H., & Larsson, K. (1971). Induction of sexual arousal in the castrated male rat by intracranial stimulation. *Physiology & Behavior, 6,* 85–86.

Van Goozen, S. H. M., et al. (1997). Psychoendocrinological assessment of the menstrual cycle: The relationship between hormones, sexuality, and mood. *Archives of Sexual Behavior, 26,* 359–382.

Van Lankveld, J. (1998). Bibliotherapy in the treatment of sexual dysfunctions: A meta-analysis. *Journal of Consulting and Clinical Psychology, 66,* 702–708.

Van Lent, P. (1996). Her beautiful savage: The current sexual image of the Native American male. In S. E. Bird (Ed.), *Dressing in feathers: The construction of the Indian in American popular culture* (pp. 211–228). Boulder, CO: Westview.

Vanwesenbeeck, I. (1994). *Prostitutes' well-being and risk.* Amsterdam: VU University Press.

Vanwesenbeeck, I. (2004). Another decade of social scientific work on sex work: A review of research 1990–2000. *Annual Review of Sex Research, 12,* 242–289.

Varghese, B., Maher, J. E., Peterman, T. A., Branson, B. M., & Steketee, R. W. (2002). Reducing the risk of sexual HIV transmission: quantifying the per-act risk for HIV on the basis of choice of partner, sex act, and condom use. *Sexually Transmitted Diseases, 29,* 38–43.

Vasey, P. L. (2002). Same-sex sexual partner preference in hormonally and neurologically unmanipulated animals. *Annual Review of Sex Research, 13,* 141–179.

Ve Ard, C., & Veaux, F. (2003). Polyamory 101. Retrieved from http://www.xeromag.com/poly101.pdf

Venicz, L., & Vanwesenbeeck, I. (2000). *Something is going to change in prostitution: Social position and the psychological well being of indoor prostitutes before the law reform.* Utrecht/The Hague, The Netherlands: NISSO/Ministry of Justice.

Vasey, P. L. (2002). Sexual partner preference in female Japanese macaques. *Archives of Sexual Behavior, 31,* 51–62.

Veronesi, U., et al. (1981). Comparing radical mastectomy with quadrantectomy, axillary dissection, and radiotherapy in patients with small cancers of the breast. *New England Journal of Medicine, 305,* 6–11.

Vilain, E. (2000). The genetics of sexual development. *Annual Review of Sex Research, 11,* 1–25.

Vincent, J. P., Friedman, L. C., Nugent, J., & Messerly, L. (1979). Demand characteristics in observations of marital interaction. *Journal of Consulting and Clinical Psychology, 47,* 557–566.

Von Hertzen, H., Piaggio, G., Ding, J., Chen, J., Song, S., & Bartfai, G. (2002). Low dose mifepristone and two regimens of levonorgestrel for emergency contraception: A WHO multicentre randomised trial. *Lancet, 360,* 1803–1810.

Von Hertzen, H., & Van Look, P. (1996). Research on new methods of emergency contraception. *Family Planning Perspectives, 28,* 52–57.

Von Krafft-Ebing, R. (1886). *Psychopathia sexualis.* (Reprinted by Putnam, New York, 1965).

Von Kries, R., Koletzko, B., Sauerwald, T., von Mutius, E., Barnert, D., Grunert, V., von Voss, H. (1999). Breast feeding and obesity: Cross sectional study. *British Medical Journal, 319,* 147–150.

Von Sydow, K. (1999). Sexuality during pregnancy and after childbirth: A metacontent analysis of 59 studies. *Journal of Psychosomatic Research, 47,* 27–49.

Wabrek, A. J., & Burchell, R. C. (1980). Male sexual dysfunction associated with coronary heart disease. *Archives of Sexual Behavior, 9,* 69–75.

Wade, L., & DeLamater, J. (2002). Relationship dissolution as a life stage transition: Effects on sexual attitudes and behaviors. *Journal of Marriage and the Family, 64,* 898–914.

Walen, S. R., & Roth, D. (1987). A cognitive approach in J. H. Geer & W. T. O'Donohue (Eds.), *Theories of human sexuality.* New York: Plenum.

Wallen, K. (2001). Sex and context: Hormones and primate sexual motivation. *Hormones and Behavior, 40,* 339–357.

Wallen, K., & Parsons, W. A. (1997). Sexual behavior in same-sexed nonhuman primates: Is it relevant to understanding human homosexuality? *Annual Review of Sex Research, 8,* 195–223.

Wallen, K., & Zehr, J. L. (2004). Hormones and history: The evolution and development of primate female sexuality. *Journal of Sex Research, 41,* 101–112.

Wallerstein, E. (1980). *Circumcision: An American health fallacy.* New York: Springer.

Wallin, P. (1949). An appraisal of some methodological aspects of the Kinsey report. *American Sociological Review, 14,* 197–210.

Walsh, T. L., Frezieres, R. G., Peacock, K., Nelson, A. L., Clark, V. A., & Bernstein, L. (2003). Evaluation of the efficacy of a non-latex condom: Results from a randomized, controlled clinical trial. *Perspectives on Sexual and Reproductive Health, 35,* 79–86.

Walster, E., et al. (1973). "Playing hard-to-get": Understanding an elusive phenomenon. *Journal of Personality and Social Psychology, 26,* 113–121.

Walster, E., Walster, W., & Berscheid, E. (1978). *Equity: Theory and research.* Boston, MA: Allyn and Bacon.

Wang, P. J., McCarrey, J., Yang, F., & Page, D. (2001). An abundance of X-linked genes expressed in spermatogonia. *Nature Genetics, 27,* 422–426.

Ward, L. M. (2002). Does television exposure affect emerging adults' attitudes and assumptions about sexual relationships? Correlational and experimental confirmation. *Journal of Youth and Adolescence, 31,* 1–15.

Ward, O. B., Ward, I. L., Denning, J. H., Hendricks, S. E., & French, J. A. (2002). Hormonal mechanisms underlying aberrant sexual differentiation in male rats prenatally exposed to alcohol, stress, or both. *Archives of Sexual Behavior, 31,* 9–16.

Weaver, A. D., Byers, E. S., Sears, H. A., Cohen, J. N., & Randall, H. E. S. (2001). *New Brunswick parents' ideas about sexual health education.* Report prepared for the New Brunswick Department of Education, Fredericton, NB. Retrieved November 11, 2002, from http://www.gnb.ca/0000/publications/ss/nbparentidea.pdf.

Weaver, A. D., Byers, E. S., Sears, H. A, Cohen, J. N., & Randall, H. E. S. (2002). New Brunswick parents' attitudes towards sexual health education at school and at home. *Canadian Journal of Human Sexuality, 11,* 19–31.

Weber, R. P. (1990). *Basic content analysis* (2nd ed.). Newbury Park, CA: Sage.

Weideger, P. (1976). *Menstruation and menopause.* New York: Knopf.

Weight gain during pregnancy. (2003). *The Journal of Midwifery and Women's Health, 48,* 229–230.

Weinberg, M., Williams, C., & Calhan, C. (1995). "If the shoe fits . . .": Exploring male homosexual foot fetishism. *Journal of Sex Research, 32,* 17–27.

Weinberg, M. S., Shaver, F. S., & Williams, C. J. (1999). Gendered sex work in the San Francisco tenderloin. *Archives of Sexual Behavior, 28,* 503–521.

Weinberg, M. S., Williams, C. J., & Pryor, D. W. (1994). *Dual attraction: Understanding bisexuality.* New York: Oxford University Press.

Weinberg, M. S., Williams, C., & Pryor, D. (2001). Bisexuals at midlife: Commitment, salience, and identity. *Journal of Contemporary Ethnography, 30,* 180–208.

Weinberg, T. S. (1994). Research in sadomasochism: A review of sociological and social psychological literature. *Annual Review of Sex Research, 5,* 257–279.

Weinberg, T. S. (1987). Sadomasochism in the United States: A review of recent sociological literature. *Journal of Sex Research, 23,* 50–69.

Weinhardt, L. S., & Carey, M. P. (1996). Prevalence of erectile disorder among men with diabetes mellitus. *Journal of Sex Research, 33,* 205–214.

Wellings, K., Nanchahal, K., Macdowall, W., McManus, S., Erens, B., Mercer, C. H., et al. (2001). Sexual behaviour in Britain: Early heterosexual experience. *The Lancet, 358,* 1843–1850.

Wheeler, G. D., et al. (1984). Reduced serum testosterone and prolactin levels in male distance runners. *Journal of the American Medical Association, 252,* 514–516.

Whipple, B., Ogden, G., & Komisanak, B. (1992). Physiological correlates of imagery-induced orgasm in women. *Archives of Sexual Behavior, 21,* 121–133.

Whitam, F. L. (1983). Culturally invariable properties of male homosexuality: Tentative conclusions from cross-cultural research. *Archives of Sexual Behavior, 12,* 207–226.

Whitam, F. L., & Mathy, R. M. (1991). Childhood cross-gender behavior of homosexual females in Brazil, Peru, the Philippines, and the United States. *Archives of Sexual Behavior, 20,* 151–170.

White, G. L., Fishbein, S., & Rutstein, J. (1981). Passionate love and the misattribution of arousal. *Journal of Personality and Social Psychology, 41,* 56–62.

White, G. L., & Mullen, P. E. (1989). *Jealousy: Theory, research, and clinical strategies.* New York: Guilford.

Whitley, B., Jr. (1993). Reliability and aspects of the construct validity of Sternberg's Triangular Love Scale. *Journal of Social and Personal Relationships, 10,* 475–480.

Wickham, D. (2001, September 3). Castration often fails to halt offenders. *USA Today.*

Wickler, W. (1973). *The sexual code.* New York: Anchor Books. (Original in German, 1969).

Widmer, E. D., Tread, J., & Newcomb, R. (1998). Attitudes toward non-marital sex in 24 countries. *Journal of Sex Research, 35,* 349–358.

Wiederman, M. W., & Hurd, C. (1999). Extradyadic involvement during dating. *Journal of Social and Personal Relationships, 16,* 265–274.

Wiederman, M. W., Weis, D. L., & Allgeier, E. R. (1994). The effect of question preface on response rates to a telephone survey of sexual experience. *Archives of Sexual Behavior, 23,* 203–216.

Wiesenfeld, H. C., Lowry, D. L., Heine, R. P., Krohn, M. A., Bittner, H., Kellinger, K., et al. (2001). Self-collection of vaginal swabs for the detection of Chlamydia, gonorrhea, and trichomoniasis: Opportunity to encourage sexually transmitted disease testing among adolescents. *Sexually Transmitted Diseases, 28,* 321–325.

Wilcox, A. J., Weinberg, C. R., & Baird, D. D. (1995). Timing of sexual intercourse in relation to ovulation. *New England Journal of Medicine, 333,* 1517–1521.

Wilcox, B. L., & Wyatt, J. (1997). *Adolescent abstinence education programs: A meta-analysis.* Presented at the annual meeting, Society for the Scientific Study of Sexuality, Arlington, VA.

Wilkinson, Ross. (1995). Changes in psychological health and the marital relationship through child bearing: Transition or process as stressor. *Australian Journal of Psychology, 47,* 86–92.

Willetts, M., Sprecher, S., & Beck, F. (2004). Overview of sexual practices and attitudes within relational contexts. In J. H. Harvey, A. Wenzel, & S. Sprecher (Eds.), *The handbook of sexuality in close relationships* (pp. 57–85). Mahwah, NJ: Lawrence Erlbaum.

Williams, C., & Weinberg, M. (2003). Zoophilia in men: A study of sexual interest in animals. *Archives of Sexual Behavior, 32,* 523–535.

Williams, L., & Sobieszczyk, T. (1997). Attitudes surrounding the continuation of female circumcision in the Sudan: Passing tradition to the next generation. *Journal of Marriage and the Family, 59,* 966–981.

Williams, L. M. (1994). Recall of childhood trauma: A prospective study of women's memories of child sexual abuse. *Journal of Consulting and Clinical Psychology, 62,* 1167–1176.

Williams, T., Taradash, A., & Connolly, J. (2004). *Sexual behavior and dating activities among young Canadian adolescents: Normative patterns and biosocial links.* Presented at Society for Research on Adolescence, Baltimore, MD.

Wilson, E. O. (1975). *Sociobiology: The new synthesis.* Cambridge, MA: Harvard University Press.

Wilson, G. (1997). Gender differences in sexual fantasy: An evolutionary analysis. *Personality and Individual Differences, 22,* 27–31.

Wilt, T. J., Fink, H. A., MacDonald, R., & Rutks, I. R. (2002). Sildenafil for male erectile dysfunction: A systematic review and meta-analysis. *Archives of Internal Medicine, 162,* 1349–1360.

Wincze, J. P., & Carey, M. P. (1991). *Sexual dysfunction: A guide for assessment and treatment.* New York: Guilford.

Wincze, J.P., & Carey, M.P. (2001). *Sexual dysfunction: A guide for assessment and treatment* (2nd ed.). New York: The Guilford Press.

Winn, R. L., & Newton, N. (1982). Sexuality in aging: A study of 106 cultures. *Archives of Sexual Behavior, 11,* 283–298.

Winter, J. S. D., & Couch, R. M. (1995). Sexual differentiation. In P. Felig, J. D. Baxter, & L. A. Frohman (Eds.), *Endocrinology and metabolism* (3rd ed., pp. 1053–1104). New York: McGraw-Hill.

Wise, P. M., Krajnak, K. M., & Kashon, M. L. (1996). Menopause: The aging of multiple pacemakers. *Science, 273,* 67–70.

Wisniewski, A.B., et al. (2000). Complete androgen insensitivity syndrome: Long-term medical, surgical, and psychosexual outcome. *Journal of Clinical Endocrinology & Metabolism, 85,* 2664–2669.

Wisniewski, A. B., Migeon, C. J., Gearhart, J. P., Rock, J. A., Berkovitz, G. D., Plotnick, L. P., et al. (2001). Congenital micropenis: Long-term medical, surgical, and psychosexual follow-up of individuals raised male or female. *Hormone Research, 56,* 3–11.

Wiswell, T. E., Enzenauer, R. W., Cornish, J. D., & Hawkins, C. T. (1987). Declining frequency of circumcision: Implications for changes in the absolute incidence and male to female sex ratio of urinary tract infections in early infancy. *Pediatrics, 79,* 338–342.

Wohl, A. R., Johnson, D. F., Lu, S., Jordan, W., Beall, G., Currier, J., et al. (2002). HIV risk behaviors among African American men in Los Angeles County who self-identify as heterosexual. *Journal of Acquired Immune Deficiency Syndromes, 31,* 354–360.

Wolchik, S. A., Spencer, S. L., & Lisi, I. S. (1983). Volunteer bias in research employing vaginal measures of sexual arousal. *Archives of Sexual Behavior, 12,* 399–408.

Wolf, T. J. (1985). Marriages of bisexual men. In F. Klein & T. J. Wolf (Eds.), *Bisexualities: Theory and research.* New York: Haworth.

Wolff, L., & Geissel, D. (1994). Street prostitution in Canada. *Canadian Social Trends.* Statistics Canada, Catalogue no. 11-008E.

Woloshy, V., & Rye, B. J. (1995). Using Bloom's taxonomies to conceptualize effective sexuality education for adolescents. *Canadian Journal of Human Sexuality, 4,* 155–166.

Wonders, N.A., & Michalowski, R. (2001). Bodies, borders, and sex tourism in a globalized world: A tale of two cities-Amsterdam and Havana. *Social Problems, 48,* 645–571.

Wong, J. K., et al. (1997). Recovery of replication-competent HIV despite prolonged suppression of plasma viremia. *Science, 278,* 1291–1295.

Wong, T., & Jordan, R. A. (2000). Commentary: Syphilis elimination in Canada: If not now, when? *The Canadian Journal of Human Sexuality, 9,* 205–209.

Wood, N.S., et al. (2000). Neurologic and developmental disability after extreme preterm birth. *New England Journal of Medicine, 343,* 378–384.

Woods, S., & Raju, U. (2001). Maternal smoking and the risk of congenital birth defects: A cohort study. *Journal of the American Board of Family Practice, 14,* 330–334.

Woollett, A., Dosaujh, N., et al. (1995). The ideas and experiences of pregnancy and childbirth of Asian and non-Asian women in East London. *British Journal of Medical Psychology, 68,* 65–84.

Working Group for a New View of Women's Sexual Problems. (2001). Part I: A new view of women's sexual problems. In E. Kachak & L. Tiefer (Eds.), *A new view of women's sexual problems* (pp. 1–8). New York: Haworth Press.

World Health Organization. (2004). Gender and reproductive rights. Retrieved November 16, 2004, from http://www.who.int

Worthington, E., Martin, G., Shumate, M., & Carpenter, J. (1983). The effect of brief Lamaze training and social encouragement on pain endurance in a cold pressor task. *Journal of Applied Social Psychology, 13,* 223–233.

Writing Group for the Women's Health Initiative Investigators. (2002). Risks and benefits of estrogen plus progestin in healthy postmenopausal women. *Journal of the American Medical Association, 288,* 321–333.

Wyatt, G. E. (1991). Child sexual abuse and its effects on sexual functioning. *Annual Review of Sex Research, 2,* 249–266.

Wyatt, G. E., Peters, S. D., & Guthrie, D. (1988). Kinsey revisited, Part I: Comparisons of the sexual socialization and sexual behavior of white women over 33 years. *Archives of Sexual Behavior, 17,* 201–240.

Wyatt, G. E. (1997). *Stolen women: Reclaiming our sexuality, taking back our lives.* New York: Wiley.

Wyatt, T. D. (2003). *Pheromones and animal behaviour.* New York: Cambridge University Press.

Wylie, K. R., Jones, R., & Walters, S. (2003). The potential benefit of vacuum devices augmenting psychosexual therapy for erectile dysfunction: A randomized controlled trial. *Journal of Sex & Marital Therapy, 29,* 227–236.

Wysocki, C. J., & Lepri, J. J. (1991). Consequences of removing the vomeronasal organ. *Journal of Steroid Biochemistry and Molecular Biology, 39,* 661–669.

Yalom, I. D. (1960). Aggression and forbiddenness in voyeurism. *Archives of General Psychiatry, 3,* 317.

Yost, L. (1991). Bisexual tendencies. In L. Hutchins & L. Kaahumanu (Eds.), *Bi any other name: Bisexual people speak out.* Boston: Alyson.

Young, I. (1996). Education for sexuality—the role of the school. *Journal of Biological Education, 30,* 250–255.

Young, K., Griffin-Shelley, E., Cooper, A., O'mam, J., & Buchananan, J. (2000). Online infidelity: A new dimension in couple relationships with implications for evaluation and treatment. *Sexual Addiction and Compulsivity, 7,* 59–74.

Yuan, L., & Robinson, G. (1994). Hepatitis B vaccination and screening for markers at a sexually transmitted disease clinic for men. *Canadian Journal of Public Health, 85,* 338–341.

Zabin, L. S., Hirsch, M. B., Smith, E. A., & Hardy, J. B. (1984). Adolescent sexual attitudes and behaviors: Are they consistent? *Family Planning Perspectives, 4,* 181–185.

Zak, P. J., Kursban, R. O., & Matzner, W. L. (2004). The neurobiology of trust. *Annals of the New York Academy of Science, 1032,* 224–227.

Zaslow, M. J., et al. (1985). Depressed mood in new fathers: Association with parent-infant interaction. *Genetic, Social, and General Psychology Monographs, 111*(2), 133–150.

Zaviačič, M. (1994). Sexual asphyxiophilia (Koczwarism) in women and the biological phenomenon of female ejaculation. *Medical Hypotheses, 42,* 318–322.

Zaviacic, M. et al. (2000). Immunohistochemical study of prostate-specific antigen in normal and pathological human tissues: Special reference to the male and female prostate and breast. *Journal of Histotechnology, 23,* 105–111.

Zaviacic, M., Ablin, R. J., Zaviacic, T., Kopani, M., Stvrtina, S., Holoman, K., et al. (2000). Weight, size, macroanatomy, and histology of the normal prostate in the adult human female: A minireview. *Journal of Histotechnology, 23,* 61–69.

Zax, M., Sameroff, A., & Farnum, J. (1975). Childbirth education, maternal attitude and delivery. *American Journal of Obstetrics and Gynecology, 123,* 185–190.

Zelnik, M., & Kantner, J. F. (1980). Sexual activity, contraceptive use and pregnancy among metropolitan-area teenagers: 1971–1979. *Family Planning Perspectives, 12*(5), 230–237.

Zemishlany, Z., Aizenberg, D., & Weizman, A. (2001). Subjective effects of MDMA ('Ecstasy') on human sexual function. *European Journal of Psychiatry, 16,* 127–130.

Zhang, J., Zou, S., & Giulivi, A. (2001). *Hepatitis B in Canada: Viral hepatitis and emerging bloodborne pathogens in Canada.* Canada Communicable Disease Report, 27S3.

Zhou, J., Hogman, M., Gooren, L., & Swaab, D. (1995). A sex difference in the human brain and its relation to transsexuality. *Nature, 378,* 68–70.

Zilbergeld, B. (1978). *Male sexuality.* Boston: Little, Brown.

Zilbergeld, B. (1992). *The new male sexuality.* New York: Bantam Books.

Zilbergeld, B. (1999). The truth about men, sex, and pleasure. In *The new male sexuality* (Rev. ed.). New York: Bantam.

Zilbergeld, B., & Ellison, C. R. (1980). Desire discrepancies and arousal problems in sex therapy. In S. R. Leiblum & L. A. Pervin (Eds.), *Principles and practice of sex therapy* (pp. 65–104). New York: Guilford.

Zilbergeld, B., & Evans, M. (1980, August). The inadequacy of Masters and Johnson. *Psychology Today, 14,* 28–43.

Zillmann, D., Schweitzer, K. J., & Mundorf, N. (1994). Menstrual cycle variations of women's interest in erotica. *Archives of Sexual Behavior, 23,* 579–598.

Zimmer, D. (1983). Interaction patterns and communication skills in sexually distressed and normal couples: Two experimental studies. *Journal of Sex and Marital Therapy, 9,* 251–265.

Zimmerman-Tansella, C., Bertagni, P., Siani, R., & Micciolo, R. (1994). Marital relationships and somatic and psychological symptoms in pregnancy. *Social Science and Medicine, 38,* 559–564.

Zoldbrod, A. P. (1993). *Men, women, and infertility: Intervention and treatment strategies.* New York: Lexington Books.

Zoucha-Jensen, J. M., & Coyne, A. (1993). The effects of resistance strategies on rape. *American Journal of Public Health, 83,* 1633–1634.

Zucker, K. J. (2000). Gender identity disorder. In A. J. Sameroff et al. (Eds.), *Handbook of developmental psychopathology,* (2nd ed., pp. 671–686).

Zucker, K. J., & Green, R. (1993). Psychological and familial aspects of gender identity disorder. *Sexual and Gender Identity Disorders, 2,* 513–542.

Zucker, K. J., Wilson-Smith, D. N., Kurita, J. A., & Stern, A. (1995). Children's appraisals of sex-typed behaviour in their peers. *Sex Roles, 33,* 703–725.

Zuger, A. (1987, June). AIDS on the wards: A residency in medical ethics. *Hastings Center Report,* 16–20.

Zuk, M. (2002). *Sexual selections: What we can and can't learn about sex from animals.* Berkeley: University of California Press.

Zumpe, D., & Michael, R. P. (1968). The clutching reaction and orgasm in the female rhesus monkey (Macaca mulatta). *Journal of Endocrinology, 40,* 117–123.

Zumwalt, R. (1976). Plain and fancy: A content analysis of children's jokes dealing with adult sexuality. *Western Folklore, 35,* 258–267.

Zussman, L., Zussman, S., Sunley, R., & Bjornson, E. (1981). Sexual response after hysterectomy-oophorectomy. *American Journal of Obstetrics and Gynecology, 140,* 725–729.

Glossary

Abortion   The termination of a pregnancy.

Abstinence-only (sex education) programs   Programs that promote sexual abstinence until marriage as the sole means of preventing pregnancy and exposure to sexually transmitted infections.

Abstinence (sexual)   A standard in which premarital intercourse is considered wrong, regardless of the circumstances.

Acquired immune deficiency syndrome (AIDS)   A sexually transmitted disease that destroys the body's natural immunity to infection so that the person is susceptible to and may die from a disease such as pneumonia or cancer.

Acquired sexual disorder   A sexual disorder that develops after a period of normal functioning.

Activating effects of hormones   Effects of sex hormones in adulthood, resulting in the activation of behaviours, especially sexual behaviours and aggressive behaviours.

Adrenal glands   Endocrine glands located just above the kidneys; in the female they are the major producers of androgens.

Adrenarche   A time of increased secretion of adrenal androgens, usually just before age 8.

Adrenogenital syndrome   See *congenital adrenal hyperplasia.*

Adultery   Voluntary sexual intercourse by a husband or wife with someone other than one's spouse; thus betrayal of one's marriage vows.

Agenda-setting   In communications theory, the idea that the media define what is important and what is not by which stories they cover.

AIDS   See *Acquired Immune Deficiency Syndrome.*

Amenorrhea   The absence of menstruation.

Amniocentesis   A test to determine whether a fetus has birth defects; done by inserting a fine tube into the woman's abdomen in order to obtain a sample of amniotic fluid.

Amniotic fluid   The watery fluid surrounding a developing fetus in the uterus.

Anal intercourse   Insertion of the penis into the partner's rectum.

Analogous organs   Organs in the male and female that have similar functions.

Anaphrodisiac   A substance that decreases sexual desire.

Androgen-insensitivity syndrome (AIS)   A genetic condition in which the body is unresponsive to androgens so that a genetic male may be born with a female-appearing body.

Androgens   The group of "male" sex hormones, one of which is testosterone.

Andropause   The time of declining androgen levels in middle-aged men. The male version of menopause. Also called ADAM (androgen decline in the aging male).

Anilingus   Mouth stimulation of the partner's anus.

Aphrodisiac   A substance that increases sexual desire.

Asceticism   An approach to life that emphasizes discipline and impulse control.

Asphyxiophilia   The desire to induce in oneself a state of oxygen deficiency in order to create sexual arousal or to enhance excitement and orgasm.

Assisted insemination   Procedure in which sperm are placed into the vagina by means other than sexual intercourse.

Asymptomatic   Having no symptoms.

Attachment   A psychological bond that forms between an infant and the mother, father, or other caregiver.

Autoeroticism   Sexual self-stimulation; for example, masturbation.

AZT   A drug used to treat HIV-infected persons; also called ZDV.

Bartholin glands   Two tiny glands located on either side of the vaginal entrance.

Basal body temperature method   A type of fertility awareness method of birth control in which the woman determines when she ovulates by keeping track of her temperature.

Behaviour modification   A set of operant conditioning techniques used to modify human behaviour.

Behaviour therapy   A system of therapy based on learning theory, in which the focus is on the problem behaviour and how it can be modified or changed.

Bibliotherapy   The use of a self-help book to treat a disorder.

Bisexual   A person whose sexual orientation is toward both men and women.

Body-centred sex   Sexual expression in which the emphasis is on the body and physical pleasure.

Bondage and discipline   The use of physical or psychological restraint to enforce servitude, from which both participants derive sensual pleasure.

Braxton-Hicks contractions   Contractions of the uterus during pregnancy that are not part of actual labour.

Brothel   A house of prostitution where prostitutes and customers meet for sexual activity.

Buccal smear   A test of genetic sex, in which a small scraping of cells is taken from the inside of the mouth, stained, and examined under a microscope.

Bulbourethral glands   See *Cowper's glands.*

Caesarean section   A method of delivering a baby surgically, by an incision in the abdomen.

CAH   See *congenital adrenal hyperplasia.*

Calendar method   A type of fertility awareness method of birth control in which the woman determines when she ovulates by keeping a calendar record of the length of her menstrual cycles.

Call girl   The most expensive and exclusive category of prostitutes.

Celibacy   The practice of remaining unmarried, usually for religious reasons. Sometimes used to refer to abstaining from sexual intercourse, another term for which is "chastity."

Cervical cap   A method of birth control involving a rubber cap that fits snugly over the cervix.

Cervical mucus method   A type of fertility awareness method of birth control in which the woman determines when she ovulates by checking her cervical mucus.

Chancre   A painless, ulcerative lesion with a hard, raised edge that is a symptom of syphilis.

Chaste   Abstaining from sexual intercourse; sexually celibate.

Child pornography   Pictures or films of sexual acts involving children.

Chlamydia   An organism causing a sexually transmitted infection; the symptoms in males are a thin, clear discharge and mild pain on urination; females are frequently asymptomatic.

Chorionic villus sampling (CVS)   A technique for prenatal diagnosis of birth defects involving taking a sample of cells from the chorionic villus and analyzing them.

Circumcision   Surgical removal of the foreskin of the penis.

Classical conditioning   The learning process in which a previously neutral stimulus (conditioned stimulus) is repeatedly paired with an unconditioned stimulus that reflexively elicits an unconditioned response. Eventually the conditioned stimulus itself will evoke the response.

Climacteric   See *menopause.*

Clitoral orgasm   Freud's term for orgasm in the female resulting from stimulation of the clitoris.

Clitoris   A small, highly sensitive sexual organ in the female, found in front of the vaginal entrance.

Cognitive-behavioural therapy   A form of therapy that combines behaviour therapy and restructuring of negative thought patterns.

Cognitive interference   Negative thoughts that distract a person from focusing on the erotic experience.

Coitus   Sexual intercourse, insertion of the penis into the vagina.

Coitus interruptus   See *withdrawal.*

Colostrum   A watery substance that is secreted from the breast at the end of pregnancy and during the first few days after delivery.

Combination birth control pills   Birth control pills that contain a combination of estrogen and progestin (progesterone).

Coming out   The process of acknowledging to oneself, and then to others, that one is gay or lesbian.

Common bawdy-house   A place kept, occupied, or used by one or more persons to engage in prostitution or indecency.

Common-law relationship   Two people of the opposite or the same gender who live together as a couple but who are not married to each other.

Community standards of tolerance test   The test used by courts to determine whether something is obscene based on what Canadians would accept other Canadians being exposed to.

Companionate love   A feeling of deep attachment and commitment to a person with whom one has an intimate relationship.

Compulsive sexual behaviour   A disorder in which the person experiences intense sexually arousing fantasies, urges, and associated sexual behaviour.

Computer-assisted self-interview method (CASI)   A method of data collection in which the respondent fills out questionnaires on a computer. Headphones and a soundtrack reading the questions can be added for young children or poor readers.

Congenital adrenal hyperplasia (CAH)   A condition in which a genetic female has abnormal levels of testosterone prenatally and therefore has male-appearing genitals at birth. Also called adrenogenital syndrome.

Congenital (kun-JEN-ih-tul) syphilis   A syphilis infection in a newborn baby resulting from transmission from an infected mother.

Content analysis   A set of procedures used to make valid inferences about text.

Contraceptive sponge   A round, polyurethane foam contraceptive device containing a combination of spermicides that fits over the cervix.

Conversion therapy   Any one of a number of treatments designed to turn LGBs into heterosexuals.

Coprophilia   Deriving sexual satisfaction from contact with feces.

Corpora cavernosa   Spongy bodies running the length of the top of the penis.

Corpus spongiosum   A spongy body running the length of the underside of the penis.

Correlation   A number that measures the relationship between two variables.

Correlational study   A study in which the researcher does not manipulate variables but rather studies naturally occurring relationships (correlations) among variables.

Covert homosexual   A homosexual who is "in the closet," who keeps his or her sexual orientation a secret.

Cowper's glands   Glands that secrete a clear alkaline fluid into the male's urethra.

Cross-dressing   Dressing in the stereotypic clothing of the other gender.

Cryptorchidism   Undescended testes; the condition in which the testes do not descend to the scrotum as they should during prenatal development.

Cultivation   In communications theory, the view that exposure to the mass media makes people think that what they see there represents the mainstream of what really occurs.

Culture   Traditional ideas and values passed down from generation to generation within a group and transmitted to members of the group by symbols (such as language).

Cunnilingus   Mouth stimulation of the female genitals.

Cyberaffair   A romantic or sexual relationship initiated by online contact and maintained primarily via online communication.

Cybersex   The practice of engaging in sexual talk online.

Cystitis   An infection of the urinary bladder in women, causing painful, burning urination.

Deprivation homosexuality   Homosexual activity that occurs in certain situations, such as prisons, when people are deprived of their regular heterosexual activity.

Diaphragm   A cap-shaped rubber contraceptive device that fits inside a woman's vagina over the cervix.

Dilation   An opening up of the cervix during labour; also called dilatation.

Dildo   A rubber or plastic cylinder, often shaped like a penis.

Discrepancy of sexual desire   A sexual problem in which the partners have considerably different levels of sexual desire.

Documenting   Giving specific examples of the issue being discussed.

Dominance and submission   The use of power consensually given to control the sexual stimulation and behaviour of the other person.

Double standard   A standard in which premarital intercourse is considered acceptable for males but not for females.

Douching (DOOSH-ing)   Flushing out the inside of the vagina with a liquid.

Drag queen   A male homosexual who dresses in women's clothing.

Dualism   A religious or philosophical belief that body and spirit are separate and opposed to each other and that the goal of life is to free the spirit from the bondage of the body; thus a depreciation of the material world and the physical aspect of humanity.

Ductus deferens   See *vas deferens*.

Dysmenorrhea   Painful menstruation.

Dyspareunia   Painful intercourse.

Ectopic pregnancy   A pregnancy in which the fertilized egg implants somewhere other than the uterus.

Editing   Censoring or not saying things that would be deliberately hurtful to your partner or that are irrelevant.

Effacement   A thinning out of the cervix during labour.

Effective communicator   A communicator whose impact matches his or her intent.

Ego   According to Freud, the part of the personality that helps the person have realistic, rational interactions.

Embryo transfer   Procedure in which an embryo is transferred from the uterus of one woman into the uterus of another.

Endometriosis   A condition in which the endometrium grows abnormally outside the uterus; the symptom is unusually painful periods with excessive bleeding.

Epididymis   Highly coiled tubes located on the edge of the testies, where sperm mature.

Episiotomy (ih-pee-see-ah-tuh-mee)   An incision made in the skin just behind the vagina, allowing the baby to be delivered more easily.

Equity theory   A social exchange theory that states that people mentally calculate the benefits and costs for them in a relationship; their behaviour is then affected by whether they feel there is equity or inequity, and they will act to restore equity if there is inequity.

Erectile disorder   The inability to have or maintain an erection.

Erogenous zones   Areas of the body that are particularly sensitive to sexual stimulation.

Erotica   Sexually arousing material that is not degrading or demeaning to women, men, or children.

Erotophilia   Positive orientation toward sexuality; feeling comfortable with and positive toward sex.

Erotophobia   Negative orientation toward sexuality; feeling guilty and fearful about sex.

Estrogens   The group of "female" sex hormones.

Ethics   A system of moral principles; a way of determining right and wrong.

Ethnocentrism   The tendency to regard one's own ethnic group and culture as superior to others and to believe that its customs and way of life are the standards by which other cultures should be judged.

Evolution   A theory that all living things have acquired their present forms through gradual changes in their genetic endowment over successive generations.

Evolutionary psychology   The study of psychological mechanisms that have been shaped by natural selection.

Excitement   The first stage of sexual response, during which erection in the male and vaginal lubrication in the female occur.

Exhibitionist   A person who derives sexual gratification from exposing his genitals to others in situations in which this is inappropriate.

Experiment   A type of research study in which one variable (the independent variable) is manipulated by the experimenter while all other factors are held constant; the researcher can then study the effects of the independent variable on some measured variable (the dependent variable); the researcher is permitted to make causal inferences about the effects of the independent variable on the dependent variable.

Extradyadic sex   Sexual activity between a person in a serious or exclusive relationship and someone other than their steady partner.

Extramarital sex   Sexual activity between a married person and someone other than that person's spouse; adultery.

Failure rate   The pregnancy rate occurring using a particular contraceptive method; the percentage of women who will be pregnant after a year of use of the method.

Fallopian tube   The tube extending from the uterus to the ovary; also called the oviduct.

Fellatio   Mouth stimulation of the male genitals.

Female impersonator   A man who dresses up as a woman as part of a job in entertainment.

Female Oedipus complex   According to Freud the sexual attraction of a little girl for her father. Sometimes called the Electra complex.

Female orgasmic disorder   A sexual disorder in which the woman is unable to have an orgasm.

Female sexual arousal disorder   A sexual disorder in which there is a lack of response to sexual stimulation.

Female-to-male transsexual (FtM)   A person born with a female body whose gender identity is male and who wishes to undergo gender reassignment.

Fertility awareness (rhythm) method   A method of birth control that involves abstaining from intercourse around the time the woman ovulates.

Fertility cult   A form of nature-religion in which the fertility of the soil is encouraged through various forms of ritual magic, often including ritual sexual intercourse.

Fetal alcohol syndrome (FAS)   Serious growth deficiency and malformations in the child of a mother who abuses alcohol during pregnancy.

Fetishism   A person's sexual fixation on some object other than another human being and attachment of great erotic significance to that object.

Fighting fair   A set of rules designed to make arguments constructive rather than destructive.

First-stage labour   The beginning of labour, during which there are regular contractions of the uterus; the stage lasts until the cervix is dilated 8 centimetres (3 inches).

Follicle-stimulating hormone (FSH)   A hormone secreted by the pituitary; it stimulates follicle development in females and sperm production in males.

Foreskin   A layer of skin covering the glans or tip of the penis in an uncircumcised male; also called prepuce.

Form fetish   A fetish whose object is a particular shape, such as high-heeled shoes.

Fornication   The biblical term for sex by unmarried persons and, more generally, all immoral sexual behaviour.

Free and informed consent   An ethical principle in research, in which people have a right to be informed, before participating, of what they will be asked to do in the research.

Frequency   How often a person does something.

Frotteurism Rubbing one's genitals against the body of a nonconsenting person.

Gay bar A gay-friendly bar or club frequented by lesbians and gays.

Gay baths Clubs where gay men can socialize; features include a swimming pool or whirlpool and access to casual sex.

Gender The state of being male or female.

Gender dysphoria (dis-FOR-ee-uh) Unhappiness with one's gender.

Gender identity disorder (GID) A strong and persistent cross-gender identification.

Gender-reassignment The surgery done on transsexuals to change their anatomy to match their gender identity.

Gender role A set of norms, or culturally defined expectations, that define how people of one gender ought to behave.

Gender-segregated social organization A general form of social grouping in which males play and associate with other males, and females play and associate with other females; that is, the genders are separate from each other.

Genitals The sexual or reproductive organs.

Genital herpes (HER-pees) A sexually transmitted infection, the symptoms of which are small, painful bumps or blisters on the genitals.

Genital warts A sexually transmitted infection causing warts on the genitals.

GIFT Gamete intra-fallopian transfer, a procedure in which sperm and eggs are collected and then inserted together into the fallopian tube.

Gigolo (JIG-uh-loh) A male who provides companionship and sexual gratification on a continuing basis to a woman in exchange for money.

Gonadotropin-releasing hormone (GnRH) A hormone secreted by the hypothalamus that regulates the pituitary's secretion of gonad-stimulating hormones.

Gonorrhea (gon-uh-REE-uh) A sexually transmitted infection that usually causes symptoms of a puslike discharge and painful, burning urination in the male but is frequently asymptomatic in the female.

Gräfenberg spot (G-spot) A hypothesized small region on the front wall of the vagina, emptying into the urethra, and responsible for female ejaculation. Also called the female prostate or the Skene's gland.

Harms-benefit analysis An approach to analyzing the ethics of a research study, based on weighing the harms of the research (such as, stress to subjects) against the benefits of the research (gaining knowledge about human sexuality).

Hedonism A moral system based on maximizing pleasure and avoiding pain.

Heterosexism Belief that heterosexuality is the best and expected way of living.

Heterosexual A person who is sexually attracted to members of the other gender.

HIV Human immune deficiency virus, the virus that causes AIDS.

Homologous organs Organs in the male and female that develop from the same embryonic tissue.

Homonegativity Negative attitudes and behaviours toward gays and lesbians. Sometimes called antigay prejudice or sexual prejudice.

Homophily The tendency to have contact with people who are equal in social status.

Homophobia A strong, irrational fear of homosexuals; negative attitudes and reactions to homosexuals.

Homosexual A person whose sexual orientation is toward members of the same gender.

Hooking up A sexual encounter that usually occurs on one occasion involving people who are strangers or acquaintances.

Hormones Chemical substances secreted by the endocrine glands into the bloodstream.

HPG axis Hypothalamus–pituitary–gonad axis, the negative feedback loop that regulates sex-hormone production.

HPV Human papillomavirus, the organism that causes genital warts.

HSV The herpes simplex virus.

Humanism A philosophical system that denies a divine origin for morality and holds that ethical judgments must be made on the basis of human experience and human reason.

Human chorionic gonadotropin (hCG) A hormone secreted by the placenta; it is the substance detected in pregnancy tests.

Hustler A male prostitute who sells his services to men.

Hyaluronidase An enzyme secreted by the sperm that allows one sperm to penetrate the egg.

Hymen A thin membrane that may partially cover the vaginal entrance.

Hypersexuality An excessive, insatiable sex drive in either men or women.

Hypoactive sexual desire (HSD) A sexual disorder in which there is a lack of interest in sexual activity; also termed "inhibited sexual desire" or "low sexual desire."

Hypothalamus (hy-poh-THAL-ah-mus) A small region of the brain that is important in regulating many body functions, including the functioning of the sex hormones.

Hysterectomy Surgical removal of the uterus.

Hysterotomy A method of abortion sometimes used during the second trimester.

Id According to Freud, the part of the personality containing the libido.

Impact What someone else understands the speaker to mean.

"I" language Speaking for yourself, using the word "I"; not mind reading.

Impotence See *erectile disorder*.

In-call service A residence in which prostitutes work regular shifts, selling sexual services on an hourly basis.

Incest taboo A regulation prohibiting sexual interaction between close blood relatives, such as brother and sister or father and daughter.

Incidence The percentage of people giving a particular response.

Indecent exposure Showing one's genitals in a public place to passersby; exhibitionism.

Infertility A woman's inability to conceive and give birth to a living child, or a man's inability to impregnate a woman.

Inhibin A substance secreted by the testes and ovaries which regulates FSH levels.

Inner lips Thin folds of skin lying on either side of the vaginal entrance.

Intent What the speaker means.

Intercoder or interrater reliability In content analysis, the correlation or percentage of agreement between two coders independently rating the same texts.

Intersex An individual who has a mixture of male and female reproductive structures, so that it is not clear at birth whether the individual is a male or a female. Also called a pseudohermaphrodite.

Interstitial cells Cells in the testes that manufacture testosterone.

Intimacy A quality of relationships characterized by commitment, feelings of closeness and trust, and self-disclosure.

Intrafamilial sexual abuse Sexual contact between a child and an adult who is the child's relative or caregiver, such as a stepfather.

Intrauterine device (IUD) A plastic device sometimes containing metal or a hormone that is inserted into the uterus for contraceptive purposes.

Intrauterine insemination   A procedure in which sperm are washed, concentrated, and injected into a woman's uterus.

Introitus   Another word for the vaginal entrance.

In vitro fertilization (IVF)   A procedure in which an egg is fertilized by sperm in a laboratory dish.

Kegel (KAY-gul) exercises   A part of sex therapy for women with orgasmic disorder, in which the woman exercises the muscles surrounding the vagina; also called *pubococcygeal* or *PC muscle exercises.*

Labia majora   See *outer lips.*

Labia minora   See *inner lips.*

Lamaze method   A method of "prepared" childbirth involving relaxation and controlled breathing.

Latent (LAY-tent) syphilis   The third stage of syphilis, which may last for years, during which symptoms disappear although the person is still infected.

Late syphilis   The fourth and final stage of syphilis, during which the disease does damage to major organs of the body, such as the lungs, heart, or brain.

Lea's Shield   A soft, pliable barrier contraceptive device that prevents sperm from entering the cervix.

Legalism   Ethics based on the assumption that there are rules for human conduct and that morality consists of knowing the rules and obeying them.

Leptin   A protein produced in the body that is related to the onset of puberty.

Lesbian   A woman whose sexual orientation is toward other women.

Levelling   Telling your partner what you are feeling by stating your thoughts clearly, simply, and honestly.

Lifelong sexual disorder   A sexual disorder that has been present since the person began sexual functioning.

Lifespan development   Development from birth through old age.

Limbic system   A set of structures in the interior of the brain, including the amygdala, hippocampus, and fornix; believed to be important for sexual behaviour in both animals and humans.

Love story   A story about what love should be like, including characters, a plot, and a theme.

Low sexual desire   See *hypoactive sexual desire.*

Lumpectomy   A surgical treatment for breast cancer in which only the lump and a small bit of surrounding tissue are removed.

Luteinizing hormone (LH)   A hormone secreted by the pituitary; it regulates estrogen secretion and ovum development in the female and testosterone production in the male.

Madam   A woman who manages a brothel, in-call, out-call, or escort service.

Maintaining factors   Various ongoing life circumstances, personal characteristics, and lovemaking patterns that inhibit sexual response.

Male condom   A contraceptive sheath that is placed over the penis.

Male orgasmic disorder   A sexual disorder in which the male cannot have an orgasm, even though he is highly aroused and has had a great deal of sexual stimulation.

Male-to-female transsexual (MtF)   A person who is born with a male body but who has a female identity and wishes to undergo gender reassignment.

Massage parlour   A place where massages, as well as sexual services, can generally be purchased.

Masturbation   Self-stimulation of the genitals to produce sexual arousal.

Matching phenomenon   The tendency for men and women to choose as partners people who match them, i.e., who are similar in attitudes, intelligence, and attractiveness.

Mean   The average of respondents' scores calculated by adding the scores and dividing by the number of people.

Media fetish   A fetish whose object is anything made of a particular substance, such as leather.

Median   The middle score.

Medicalization of sexuality   The process by which certain sexual behaviours or conditions are defined in terms of health and illness, and problematic experiences or practices are given medical treatment.

Medical model   A theoretical model in psychology and psychiatry in which mental problems are thought of as sickness or mental illness; the problems in turn are often thought to be due to biological factors.

Menarche   First menstruation.

Menopause   The cessation of menstruation in middle age.

Menstrual synchrony   The convergence, over several months, of the dates of onset of menstrual periods among women who are in close contact with each other.

Menstruation   The fourth phase of the menstrual cycle, during which the endometrium of the uterus is sloughed off in the menstrual discharge.

Mere-exposure effect   The tendency to like a person more if we have been exposed to him or her repeatedly.

Mind reading   Making assumptions about what your partner thinks or feels.

Minilaparotomy   A method of female sterilization.

Misattribution of arousal   When one is in a stage of physiological arousal (e.g., from exercising or being in a frightening situation), attributing these feelings to love or attraction to the person present.

Miscarriage   The termination of a pregnancy before the fetus is viable, as a result of natural causes (not medical intervention).

Mode   The most frequent score.

Monilia (Moh-NILL-ee-uh)   A form of vaginitis causing a thick, white discharge; also called candida or yeast infection.

Mons pubis   The fatty pad of tissue under the pubic hair.

Moralism   A religious or philosophical attitude that emphasizes moral behaviour, usually according to strict standards, as the highest goal of human life. Moralists tend to favour strict regulation of human conduct to help make people good.

Müllerian ducts   Ducts found in both male and female fetuses; in males they degenerate and in females they develop into the fallopian tubes, the uterus, and the upper part of the vagina.

Multiple orgasm   A series of orgasms occurring within a short period of time.

Myotonia   Muscle contraction.

Natural selection   A process in nature resulting in greater rates of survival of those plants and animals that are adapted to their environment.

Necrophilia   Deriving sexual satisfaction from contact with a dead person.

Non-verbal communication   Communication not through words, but through the body, e.g., eye contact, tone of voice, touching.

Nymphomania   An excessive, insatiable sex drive in a woman.

Obscenity   Something that is offensive according to accepted standards of decency; the legal term of pornography.

Oedipus complex   According to Freud, the sexual attraction of a little boy for his mother.

Onanism   Withdrawal of the penis from the vagina before ejaculation; sometimes also used to refer to masturbation.

Oophorectomy   Surgical removal of the ovaries.

Operant conditioning   The process of changing the frequency of a behaviour (the operant) by following it with positive reinforcement (which will make the behaviour more frequent in the future) or punishment (which should make the behaviour less frequent in the future).

Operational definition   Defining some concept or term by how it is measured, for example, defining intelligence as those abilities that are measured by IQ tests.

Organic factors of sexual disorders   Physical factors, such as disease or injury, that cause sexual disorders.

Organizing effects of hormones   Effects of sex hormones early in development, resulting in a permanent change in the brain or reproductive system.

Orgasm   The third stage of sexual response; an intense sensation that occurs at the peak of sexual arousal and is followed by release of sexual tensions.

Orgasmic platform   A tightening of the entrance to the vagina caused by contractions of the bulbospongiosus muscle (which covers the vestibular bulbs) that occur during the plateau stage of sexual response.

Out-call service   A service that sends a prostitute to a location specified by the client to provide sexual services.

Outer lips   Rounded pads of fatty tissue lying on either side of the vaginal entrance.

Ovaries   Two organs in the female that produce eggs and sex hormones.

Overt homosexual   A homosexual who is "out of the closet," who is open about his or her sexual orientation.

Paraphilia (par-uh-FILL-ee-uh)   Recurring, unconventional sexual behaviour that is obsessive and compulsive.

Paraphrasing   Saying in your own words what you think your partner meant.

Participant-observer technique   A research method in which the scientist becomes part of the community to be studied and makes observations from inside the community.

Passionate love   A state of intense longing for union with the other person and of intense physiological arousal.

Pederasty   Sex between an older man and a younger man, or a boy; sometimes called "boy love."

Pedophilia   Child molesting; an adult having sexual activity with a prepubescent child.

Pelvic inflammatory disease (PID)   Infection and inflammation of the pelvic organs such as the fallopian tubes and the uterus, in the female.

Penile prosthesis (prahs-THEE-sis)   A surgical treatment for erectile dysfunction, in which inflatable tubes are inserted into the penis.

Penile strain gauge   A device used to measure physiological sexual arousal in the male; it is a flexible loop that fits around the base of the penis.

Penis   The male external sexual organ, which functions both in sexual activity and in urination.

Perineum   The skin between the vaginal entrance and the anus.

Permissiveness with affection   A standard in which premarital intercourse is considered acceptable if it occurs in the context of a loving, committed relationship.

Permissiveness without affection   A standard in which premarital intercourse is acceptable without emotional commitment.

Person-centred sex   Sexual expression in which the emphasis is on the relationship and emotions between the two people.

Pheromones   Biochemicals secreted outside the body that are important in communication between animals and that may serve as sex attractants.

Photoplethysmograph   An acrylic cylinder that is placed inside the vagina in order to measure physiological sexual arousal in the female. Also called a photometer.

Pimp   A prostitute's companion, protector, and master.

Pituitary gland   A small endocrine gland located on the lower side of the brain below the hypothalamus; the pituitary is important in regulating levels of sex hormones.

Placenta   An organ formed on the wall of the uterus through which the fetus receives oxygen and nutrients and gets rid of waste products.

Plateau   The second stage of sexual response, just before orgasm.

Pluralism   A philosophical or political attitude that affirms the value of many competing opinions and believes that the truth is discovered in the clash of diverse perspectives. Pluralists, therefore, believe in the maximum human freedom possible.

Polymorphous perverse   Freud's term for the infant's indiscriminate, undifferentiated sexuality.

Polyamory   The "non-possessive, honest, responsible and ethical philosophy and practice of loving multiple people simultaneously."

Population   A group of people a researcher wants to study and make inferences about.

Pornography   Sexually arousing art, literature, or films.

Postpartum depression   Mild to moderate depression in women following the birth of a baby.

Post-traumatic growth   Positive life changes and psychological development following exposure to trauma.

Post-traumatic stress disorder (PTSD)   Long-term psychological distress suffered by someone who has experienced a terrifying event.

Predisposing factors   Experiences that people have had in the past —for example, in childhood—that now affect their sexual response.

Pre-eclampsia   A serious disease of pregnancy, marked by high blood pressure, severe edema, and proteinuria.

Premature (rapid) ejaculation   A sexual disorder in which the male ejaculates too soon and he feels he cannot control when he ejaculates.

Premenstrual dysphoric disorder (PMDD)   A tentative diagnostic category in the DSM-IV, characterized by symptoms such as sadness, anxiety, and irritability in the week before menstruation.

Premenstrual syndrome (PMS)   A combination of severe physical and psychological symptoms, such as depression and irritability, occurring just before menstruation.

Prenatal period (pree-NAY-tul)   The time from conception to birth.

Primary-stage syphilis   The first few weeks of a syphilis infection, during which the chancre is present.

Primipara   A woman having her first baby.

Probability sampling   An excellent method of sampling in research, in which each member of the population has a known probability of being included in the sample.

Problem of refusal or non-response   The problem that some people will refuse to participate in a sex survey, thus making it difficult to have a random sample.

Progesterone   A "female" sex hormone secreted by the ovaries.

Prostaglandins   Chemicals secreted by the uterus that cause the uterine muscles to contract; they are a likely cause of painful menstruation.

Prostate   The gland in the male, located below the bladder, that secretes some of the fluid in semen.

Prostatectomy (pros-tuh-TEK-tuh-mee)   Surgical removal of the prostate.

Prostatitis   An infection, inflammation, or swelling of the prostate gland.

Prostitute/commercial sex worker   A person who engages in sexual acts in return for money or drugs and does so in a promiscuous, fairly non-discriminating fashion.

Pseudocyesis   False pregnancy, in which the woman displays the signs of pregnancy but is not actually pregnant.

Psychoanalytic theory   A psychological theory originated by Sigmund Freud; it contains a basic assumption that part of human personality is unconscious.

Puberty   The time during which there is sudden enlargement and maturation of the gonads, other genitalia, and secondary sex characteristics, so that the individual becomes capable of reproduction.

Pubic lice   Tiny lice that attach themselves to the base of pubic hairs and cause itching; also called crabs or pediculosis pubis.

Pubococcygeus muscle   A muscle around the vaginal entrance.

Purposeful distortion   Purposely giving false information in a survey.

Qualitative research   Research, usually involving interviews, in which the researchers try to make sense of the meanings that people give to their experiences.

Radical mastectomy   A surgical treatment for breast cancer in which the entire breast, as well as underlying muscle and lymph nodes, is removed.

Random sampling   An excellent method of sampling in research, in which each member of the population has an equal chance of being included in the sample.

Refractory period   The period following orgasm during which the male cannot be sexually aroused.

Resolution   The fourth stage of sexual response, in which the body returns to the unaroused state.

Retrograde ejaculation   A condition in which orgasm in the male is not accompanied by an external ejaculation; instead, the ejaculate goes into the urinary bladder.

RU-486   The "abortion pill."

Saliromania   A desire to damage or soil a woman or her clothes.

Sample   A part of a population.

Satyriasis   An excessive, insatiable sex drive in a male.

Schema   A general knowledge framework that a person has about a particular topic.

Scoptophilia   A sexual variation in which the person becomes sexually aroused by observing others' sexual acts and genitals.

Scrotum   The pouch of skin that contains the testes in the male.

Secondary-stage syphilis   The second stage of syphilis, occurring several months after infection, during which the chancre has disappeared and a generalized body rash appears.

Second-stage labour   The stage during which the baby moves out through the vagina and is delivered.

Self-disclosure   Telling personal information to another person.

Self-efficacy   A sense of competence at performing an activity.

Seminal vesicles   Sac-like structures that lie above the prostate which produce about 70 percent of the seminal fluid.

Seminiferous tubules   Tubes in the testes that manufacture sperm.

Sensate focus exercises   A part of the sex therapy developed by Masters and Johnson in which one partner caresses the other, the other communicates what is pleasurable, and there are no performance demands.

Serial monogamy   A premarital sexual pattern in which there is an intention of being faithful to the partner, but the relationship may end and the person will then move on to another partner.

Sex-determining Region, Y chromosome (SRY)   A region on the Y chromosome that causes testes to differentiate prenatally.

Sex tourism   Leisure travel with the purpose of purchasing sexual services.

Sex trafficking   The recruitment and control of persons for sexual exploitation.

Sexual assault   Any non-consensual sexual activity ranging from unwanted touching, to forced oral, anal, or vaginal intercourse, to sexual violence in which the victim is wounded or maimed or his or her life is endangered.

Sexual behaviour   Behaviour that produces arousal and increases the chance of orgasm.

Sexual disorder   A problem with sexual response that causes a person mental distress.

Sexual fantasy   Sexual thoughts or images that alter the person's emotions or physiological state.

Sexual identity   One's self-identity as homosexual, heterosexual, or bisexual.

Sexual health   A state of physical, emotional, mental, and social well-being related to sexuality.

Sexual masochist   A person who derives sexual satisfaction from experiencing pain.

Sexual orientation   A person's erotic and emotional orientation toward members of his or her own gender or members of the other gender.

Sexual sadist   A person who derives sexual satisfaction from inflicting pain, suffering, or humiliation on another person.

Sexual selection   Selection that results from differences in traits affecting access to mates.

Sexuality education   The lifelong process of acquiring information about sexual behaviour and forming attitudes, beliefs, and values about identity, relationships, and intimacy.

SIECCAN   The Sex Information and Education Council of Canada, a national resource for up-to-date information, research, and publication on human sexuality, including sexual health.

Situational sexual disorder   A sexual disorder that a person has in some situations but not in others.

Situationism   Ethics based on the assumption that there are no absolute rules, or at least very few, and that each situation must be judged individually.

Sixty-nining   Simultaneous mouth-genital stimulation; also called "soixante-neuf."

Skene's gland   The female prostate. Also called the paraurethral gland.

Social desirability   The tendency to distort answers to a survey in the direction perceived to be more acceptable.

Social exchange theory   A theory that assumes people will choose actions that maximize rewards and minimize costs.

Socialization   The ways in which society conveys to the individual its norms or expectations for his or her behaviour.

Social learning   In communications theory, the idea that the media provide role models whom we imitate.

Sociobiology   The application of evolutionary biology to understanding the social behaviour of animals, including humans.

Somatic cell nuclear transfer   A cloning technique that involves substituting genetic material from an adult's cell for the nucleus of an egg.

Spectatoring   Masters and Johnson's term for acting as an observer or judge of one's own sexual performance; hypothesized to contribute to sexual disorders.

Sperm   The mature male reproductive cell, capable of fertilizing an egg.

Spermicide   A substance that kills sperm.

Spousal sexual assault   The sexual assault of a person by his or her current or former marital or common-law spouse

Stereotype   A generalization about a group of people (e.g., men) that distinguishes them from others (e.g., women).

Sterilization   A surgical procedure by which an individual is made sterile, that is, incapable of reproducing.

Straight   Heterosexual.

Streetwalker   A lower-status prostitute who walks the streets selling sexual services.

Subincision   A form of male genital cutting in which a slit is made on the lower side of the penis along its entire length.

Supercision (superincision)   A form of male genital cutting in which a slit is made the length of the foreskin on top.

Superego   According to Freud, the part of the personality containing the conscience.

Swinging   A form of extramarital sex in which married couples exchange partners with each other.

Symbolic interaction theory   A theory that proposes human nature and the social order are products of communication among people.

Sympto-thermal method   A type of fertility awareness method of birth control combining both the basal body temperature method and the cervical mucus method.

Syphilis   A sexually transmitted infection that causes a chancre to appear in the primary stage.

Teratogen   A substance that produces defects in a fetus.

Test-retest reliability   A method for testing whether self-reports are reliable or accurate; participants are interviewed (or given a questionnaire) and then interviewed a second time sometime later to determine whether their answers are the same both times.

Testes   The pair of glands in the scrotum that manufacture sperm and sex hormones.

Testosterone   A hormone secreted by the testes in the male (and present at lower levels in the female).

Therapeutic cloning   Creating tissues or cells that are genetically identical to those of a patient to treat disease.

Third-stage labour   The stage during which the afterbirth is expelled.

Toxic shock syndrome   A sometimes fatal bacterial infection associated with tampon use during menstruation.

Transgender   A category including transsexuals (those who think of themselves as a third gender), transvestites, gender blenders, and others.

Transgenderists   People who live part or full time as a member of the other sex.

Transition   The difficult part of labour at the end of the first stage, during which the cervix dilates from 8 to 10 centimetres (3 to 4 inches).

Transsexual   A person whose physical sex does not match their gender identity.

Transvestism   The practice of deriving sexual gratification from dressing as a member of the other gender; transvestic fetishism.

Trichomoniasis (trick-oh-moh-NY-us-is)   A form of vaginitis causing a frothy white or yellow discharge with an unpleasant odour.

Triphasic model   Kaplan's model of sexual response, in which there are three phases: sexual desire, vasocongestion, and muscular contractions.

Triphasic pill   A birth control pill containing a steady level of estrogen and three phases of progesterone, intended to mimic more closely women's natural hormonal cycles.

Two-component theory of love   Berscheid and Walster's theory that two conditions must exist simultaneously for passionate love to occur: physiological arousal and attaching a cognitive label ("love") to the feeling.

Umbilical cord   The tube that connects the fetus to the placenta.

Urophilia (or urolagnia)   Deriving sexual satisfaction from contact with urine.

Uterus   The organ in the female in which the fetus develops.

Vacuum aspiration   A method of abortion that is performed during the first trimester and involves suctioning out the contents of the uterus.

Vagina   The tube-shaped organ in the female into which the penis is inserted during coitus and through which a baby passes during birth.

Vaginal orgasm   Freud's term for orgasm in the female resulting from stimulation of the vagina in heterosexual intercourse; Freud considered vaginal orgasm to be more mature than clitoral orgasm.

Vaginismus (Vaj-in-IS-mus)   A sexual disorder in which there is a spastic contraction of the muscles surrounding the entrance to the vagina, in some cases so severe that penetration is impossible.

Vaginitis   An irritation or inflammation of the vagina, usually causing a discharge.

Validation   Telling your partner that, given his or her point of view, you can see why he or she thinks a certain way.

Vas deferens   The tube through which sperm pass on their way from the testes and epididymis, out of the scrotum, and to the urethra.

Vasectomy   A surgical procedure for male sterilization involving severing of the vas deferens.

Vasocongestion   An accumulation of blood in the blood vessels of a region of the body, especially the genitals; a swelling or erection results.

Vestibule   Area of the vulva enclosed by the inner lips.

Vestibular bulbs   Erectile tissue running under the inner lips and Skene's gland.

Viagra   A drug used in the treatment of erectile disorder; sildenafil.

Volunteer bias   A bias in the results of sex surveys that arises when some people refuse to participate, so that those who are in the sample are volunteers who may in some ways differ from those who refuse to participate.

Voyeur   A person who becomes sexually aroused from secretly viewing nudes.

Voyeurism   Secretly watching people who are nude or engaging in sexual activity.

Vulva   The collective term for the external genitals of the female.

Warts   See *genital warts*.

Withdrawal   A method of birth control in which the man withdraws his penis from his partner's vagina before he has an orgasm.

Wolffian ducts   Ducts found in both male and female fetuses; in females they degenerate and in males they develop into the epididymis, the vas deferens, and the ejaculatory duct.

Zoophilia   Sexual contact with an animal; also called bestiality or sodomy.

Zygote   A fertilized egg.

Acknowledgements

■ Photographs

Chapter 1

p. 5 (left): © AP/Wide World Photos; (right) Culver; p. 6 (left): (a) Reprinted by permission of the Kinsey Institute for Research in Sex, Gender, and Reproduction, Inc., photo by Bill Dellenback; (right) Courtesy A. L. Enterprises; p. 7: © CP Picture Archive/Reed Saxon; p. 9: © AP/Wide World Photos; p. 13: "Beautiful" from *The Clios 2000.* Used with the permission of Films Media Group ® Princeton, NJ. All rights reserved; p.14 (left): © Art Wolfe/Getty; (right): © CP Picture Archive, AP/Apichart Weerawong; p. 18 (left): © Courtesy Prof. Robert Gemme, Département de sexologie, Université du Québec à Montréal; (right): © Lawrence Migdale/Stock, Boston; p. 20 (left): © Meredith F. Small; (right): © Thomas Michael Corcoran/PhotoEdit.

Chapter 2

p. 27 (left): © J.H. Robinson/Photo Researchers; (right): © SuperStock, Inc.; p. 28: "Evolutionary Psychology" from *Sex in Our Century: Love and Science* © The Discovery Channel, used by permission; p. 31: © Lester Lefkowitz/Taxi/Getty; p. 34: © Joel Gordon; p. 38: © Queerstock/Davis Freeman; p. 39: "The Medicalization of Sex" from *The Surprising History of Sex and Love* © The Discovery Channel, used by permission; p. 41: © CP Picture Archive/Chuck Mitchell; p. 45: © EyeWire Collection/Getty Images; p. 46: © Suzanne Arm/The Image Works.

Chapter 3

p. 53: © S. Young-Wolff/PhotoEdit; p. 59: "Alfred Kinsey" from *Sex in Our Century: Love and Science* © The Discovery Channel, used by permission; p. 61 (left): Reprinted by permission of The Kinsey Institute for Research in Sex, Gender and Reproduction, Inc., photo by Bill Dellenback; (right): © Matthew Peyton/Getty Images; p. 64: © Thinkstock/Getty; p. 69: © Bob Daemmrich; p. 70: "Masters and Johnson" from *Sex in Our Century: Love and Science* © The Discovery Channel, used by permission; p. 73: © David Young-Wolff/PhotoEdit.

Chapter 4

p. 81: "Genital Self-Examination" from *Becoming Orgasmic,* Sinclair Intimacy Institute, Mark Schoen, Ph.D., Producer. This program is available in its entirety at www.BetterSex.com; p. 83: © Lori Grinker/Contact Press Images; p. 86: © Hazel Hankin Photography; p. 90 (top): ©Jessica Abad de Gail/AGE Fotostock; (middle): © Joel Gordon; (bottom): © Joel Gordon; p. 91: "Breasts" from *BREASTS: A Documentary,* Directed by Meema Spadola, Produced by Thom Powers & Meema Spadola. © 1996 Meema Spadola. Distributed by: First Run/Icarus Films. For purchase information, visit: www.frif.com; p. 93 (left): © Joel Gordon; (right): © Joel Gordon; p. 98 (top left): © Royalty Free/Corbis; (top right): © DavidParker/SPL/Photo Researchers; (bottom left): Reproduced with permission of the Canadian Cancer Society. © 2003; (bottom right): Reproduced with permission of the Canadian Cancer Society. © 2003; p. 99: © Susan Lerner/Joel Gordon Photography; p. 104: © Joel Gordon.

Chapter 5

p. 109: "Hormones and Sexual Differentiation" from *Understanding Sex* © The Discovery Channel, used by permission; p. 112: Dr. Landrum B. Shettles; p. 123: © CP PictureArchive/Winnipeg Free Press; p. 126 (left): © Joe Sohm/The Image Works; (right): © Elizabeth Crews/The Image Works; p. 127 (left): © Jason Laure/Woodfin Camp; (right): © Blair Seitz/Photo Researchers, Inc.; p. 133: © Amy Etra/PhotoEdit.

Chapter 6

p. 141: Dr. Landrum B. Shettles; p. 143 (top left): © Petit Format/Nestle/Science Source/Photo Researchers; (top right): Lennart Nilsson, from *A Child is Born,* Dell Publishing Company; (bottom left): Lennart Nilsson, from *A Child is Born,* Dell Publishing Company; (bottom right): Lennart Nilsson, from *A Child is Born,* Dell Publishing Company; p. 149: © Spencer Grant/Monkmeyer; p. 151 (left): Streissguth, A.P., Landesman-Dwyer, S., Martin, J.C., & Smith, D.W. (1980). "Teratogenic effects of alcohol in humans and laboratory animals," *Science*, 209, 353-361; (right): © John Chiasson/Gamma Liaison; p. 154 (left): © D. Van Rossum/Petit Format/Photo Researchers, Inc.; (right): © O.V.N./Petit Format/Photo Researchers, Inc.; p. 157: Lawrence Migdale/Photo Researchers, Inc.; p. 159: © Monkmeyer/Byron; p. 163: © Digital Vision/Getty; p. 171 (left): © ISM/Phototake; (right): © Paltera Stefano/Gamma.

Chapter 7

p. 181: Special Collections Department, Hamilton Public Library; p. 184 (top): © Tony Freeman/PhotoEdit; (bottom): © Joel Gordon; p. 186: © Mauritius, GMBH/Phototake; p. 190: © Joel Gordon; p. 191 (both): © Joel Gordon; p. 192: © Tony Freeman/PhotoEdit; p. 193: p. 195: Used with permission from The Children's Defense Fund; p. 199: "Vasectomy" from *Surgical Procedures: Vasectomy/Tubal Ligation.* Used with the permission of Film Media Group ® Princeton, NJ. All rights reserved; p. 200: "Tubal Ligation" from *Surgical Procedures: Vasectomy/Tubal Ligation.* Used with the permission of Film Media Group ® Princeton, NJ. All rights reserved; p. 202: © The McGraw-Hill Companies, Inc./Bob Coyle, photographer; p. 204 (top): Research conducted by Council of Ministers of Education, Canada, with funding provided by Health Canada; (bottom): Research conducted by Council of Ministers of Education, Canada, with funding provided by Health Canada; p. 207: © CP Picture Archive/Paul Chiasson.

Chapter 8

p. 220 (left): © Science VU/Visuals Unlimited; (right): © Bart's Medical Library/Phototake; p. 221: "Herpes" from Sexually Transmitted Diseases: The Silent Epidemic. Used with the permission of Film Media Group ® Princeton, NJ. All rights reserved; p. 222 (left): © Biophoto Associates/Photo Researchers, Inc.; (right): © Biophoto Associates/Photo Researchers, Inc.; p. 225 (top): Courtesy Canadian AIDS Society; (bottom): © CP Picture Archive/Fred Chartrand; p. 229 (left): © Thomas Bowmnan/PhotoEdit; (right): © Claude Poulet/Gamma Liaison; p. 233: © CP Picture Archive; p. 234: © Wilson Chu/Reuters/Corbis; 236: [U.S.] Centers for Disease Control; p. 239 (left): [U.S.] Centers for Disease Control; (right): [U.S.] Centers for Disease Control; p. 241: © E. Gray/ Science Photo Library/Photo Researchers, Inc.

Chapter 9

p. 257: © 2001 from "Human Sex-Response Cycles," by Rosemary Basson in *Journal of Sex and Marital Therapy,* 27(1). Reproduced by permission of Taylor & Francis Group, LLC., http://www.taylorandfrancis.com; p. 258: © Owen Franken/Corbis; p. 262: Courtesy Ellen Stohl; p. 265: © Dr. Scott T. Grafton/Visuals Unlimited; p. 267: © Bob Daemmrich/Stock Boston; p. 269 (left): © Betts Loman/ PhotoEdit; (right): © Luis Fernandez/SuperStock.

Chapter 10

p. 273 (left): © Joel Gordon; (right): © Joel Gordon; p. 276: © Mark Antman/The ImageWorks; p. 278 (top): "Men Talk about Sex" from *Men Talk Sex* by Donald Bull and James

Mulryan. Available from Fanlight Productions, Boston, Massachusetts, 800-937-4113, www.fanlight.com; (bottom): "What Women Want" from *More of What Women Want,* courtesy of the Alexander Institute © 1998 Alexander Institute, www.lovingsex.com; p. 279: © Luiz C. Marico/Peter Arnold, Inc.; p. 299 (left): © Digital Vision/Getty Images; (right): © Bruce Ayres/Tony Stone/Getty; p. 302: © Jack Star/PhotoLink/Getty Images.

Chapter 11

p. 307: © Amy C. Etra/PhotoEdit; p. 308: © Maya Barnes/The Image Works; p. 309: © Cassy Cohen/PhotoEdit; p. 313: © SW Productions; p. 318: © CP Picture Archive/ Aaron Harris; p. 319: © SW Productions/PhotoDisc/Getty Images; p. 321: "Learning to Be Straight" from *Learning to Be Straight: The (De)Construction of Heterosexuality,* produced and directed by Colby Berger and Jim Vetter. © 2001 by Colby Berger and Jim Vetter. For video purchase, supplementary materials, and workshop information, visit www.learningtobestraight.com or email info@learningtobe-straight.com; p. 321: © 2000, The Haworth Press, Inc., Binghamton: NY. "Exotic Dancing and health," *Women & Health,* 31, pp. 87–108; p. 323: © Francesco Venturi/Corbis; p. 327: © CP Picture Archive/John Moore.

Chapter 12

p. 337: © Doug Menuez/PhotoDisc/Getty Images; p. 340 (left): © CP Picture Archive/Kevin Frayer; p. 342: © CP Picture Archive/Edmonton Sun—Dale MacMillan; (right): © PhotoDisc Collection/Getty Images; p. 346 (left): © Ryan McVay/Getty Images; (right): © Paul Vozdic/The Image Bank; p. 347: "Keeping Your Mate" from *The Science of Love: Staying in Love.* Used with permission of Films Media Group® Princeton, NJ. All rights reserved; p. 351: © CP Picture Archive/Ryan Remiorz; p. 353: © Ryan McVay/Getty Images; p. 357: "Menopause" from *When Women Go Through Menopause, Where Do Men Go?* By Elizabeth Sher. Available from Fanlight Productions, Boston, MA, 800-937-4113, www.fanlight.com; p. 362: © Mike Siluk/The Image Works; p. 363: © Photodisc/Getty Images.

Chapter 13

p. 373: © Wayne Levin/Getty; p. 375: © Barbara Penoyar/ PhotoDisc/Getty Images; p. 379: © Kim Bartholomew and L.M. Horowitz, "Attachment Styles Among Young Adults: A Test of a Four Category Model," *Journal of Personality and Social Psychology,* 61, Figure 1, p. 227, © American Psychological Association. Reprinted by permission of the American Psychological Association; p. 381: © Michael Krasowitz/Taxi/Getty; p. 383: "The Dance of Life" from *Understanding Sex* © The Discovery Channel, used by permission; p. 386: © David Young-Wolff/PhotoEdit; p. 387: © Jerry Cooke/Photo Researchers.

Chapter 14

p. 393 (left): © George Simian/Corbis; (right): © Getty Images/Laurence Monneret; p. 396: © CP Picture Archive/John Kenney; © CP Picture Archive/Logan

Wallace; p. 398: © F.A. Rinehart for B.A.E./Smithsonian Institute; p. 401: Photo courtesy of Julia R. Heiman; p. 402: "The Plethysmograph" from *A Man's Guide to Stronger Erections*, Sinclair Intimacy Institute, Mark Schoen, Ph.D., Producer. This program is available in its entirety at www.BetterSex.com; p. 407: © Pascal Le Segretain/Getty Images; p. 412 (left): © AP Wide World Photos; (right): © AP Wide World Photos; p. 413: All photos Courtesy of Dr. Daniel Greenwald; p. 415 (left): © Hulton Archive/Getty Images; (right): © AP/Wide World Photos; p. 416: © Philip Blenksop/Agence VU.

Chapter 15

p. 425: © CP Picture Archive/Fred Chartrand; p. 427: © CP Picture Archive/Frank Gunn; p. 429: "Corey Johnson" from *Corey's Secret*, courtesy of ABC News (*20/20*) and by permission of Corey Johnson. Some footage in the segment is courtesy of Jeff Perrotti; p. 430: © CP Picture Archive/Tannis Toohey; p. 434: © Firooz Zahedi/Showtime; p. 435: © Plush Studios/Brand X Pictures/Getty; p. 437: "Growing up in a Gay Family" from *That's a Family!* Directed by Debra Chasnoff; Executive Producer Helen S. Cohen; Producers Debra Chasnoff, Ariella J. Ben-Dov, and Fawn Yacker; Editor Kate Stilley. To order your own copy of *That's a Family!* visit our Web site: www.womedia.org. © 2000 Women's Educational Media; p. 438 (left): © Geoff Manasse/IPN/Aurora; (right): © Colin McPherson/Corbis Sygma; p. 447: © Jeff Greenberg/PhotoEdit.

Chapter 16

p. 454: © CP Picture Archive/Mike Conley; p. 457: © Joel Gordon; p. 460 (left): © Photofest; (right): © Kevin Winter/Getty Images; p. 462: "Whipsmart" clip from the video *Whipsmart: A Good Vibrations Guide to Beginning S/M for Couples*, produced by Good Vibrations. Available at www.sexpositiveproductions.com, produced by Sarah Kennedy, directed by Laura Plotkin, written by Mistress Morgana, Thomas Roche, and Kathryn Cunningham. © Sexpositive Productions, 2002; p. 463: © Jacques Prayer/Gamma; p. 466: © Jutta Klee/Corbis; p. 467: © Christie's Images/SuperStock; p. 475: © David Harry Stewart/Tony Stone/Getty.

Chapter 17

p. 481: "Behind Closed Doors" from *Date Rape: Behind Closed Doors*. Used with the permission of Films Media Group® Princeton, NJ. All rights reserved; p. 483: © Rhonda Sidney/PhotoEdit; p. 493: © CP Picture Archive/J. T. Lewis; p. 494: © McPherson Colin/Corbis Sygma; p. 496: © Yvonne Hemsey/Gamma Liaison; p. 498 (left): © CP Picture Archive/Darren Makowichuk; (right): © CP Picture Archive/Jonathan Hayward; p. 505: © Richard Townshen/Corbis.

Chapter 18

p. 513: © CP/Toronto Sun/J. T. Lewis; p. 521: © Joel Gordon; p. 524: © 8425/Gamma; p. 525: © Joel Gordon; p. 527: © PhotoFest; p. 529: © Francis Dean/The Image Works;

p. 531: © Candida Royalle, creator of female-centric movies and author of *How to Tell a Naked Man What to Do*; p. 533 (left): © CP Picture Archive/Remi Lemee; (right): © CP Picture Archive/Fred Thornhill.

Chapter 19

p. 547 (left): © Jeff Greenberg/PhotoEdit; (right): © David Young-Wolff/PhotoEdit; p. 558: © Larry Mulvehill/The Image Works.

Chapter 20

p. 570: The Metropolitan Museum of Art, Rogers Fund, 1941 (41.162.101) Neg. #177754; p. 572 (left): "St. Paul's View on Sex" from *The Surprising History of Sex and Love* © The Discovery Channel, used by permission; (right): Hermitage Museum, St. Petersburg, Russia/SuperStock; p. 573: Ognissanti Church, Florence, Italy/Bridgeman Art Library, London/SuperStock; p. 577: © Frances M. Roberts; p. 579: © Lauren Goodsmith/The Image Works; p. 580: © Sujoy Das/Stock, Boston; p. 583: © CP Picture Archive/Tom Hanson; p. 587: National Gallery of Art, Washington, D.C./SuperStock; p. 589: © CP Picture Archive/John Mahoney; p. 593: © Najlah Feanny/Stock, Boston.

Chapter 21

p. 608: © © CP Photo Archive/John Mahler; p. 609: © CP Photo Archive/Chuck Stoody; p. 617: © Robert Nickelsberg/Gamma Liaison/Getty; p. 618: © Jeff Greenberg/PhotoEdit; p. 619: © Mark Richards/PhotoEdit.

■ Line Art and Text

Chapter 1

p. 2:   Edward O. Laumann et al. (1994). The social organization of sexuality: Sexual practices in the United States. Reprinted by permission of the University of Chicago Press and Edward O. Laumann.

Table 1.1:   "Social-Class Variations in Sexual Behaviour in Canada," adapted from Statistics Canada *National Population Health Survey*, 1996–1997.

Table 1.2:   Reprinted with permission of *Maclean's*. www.macleans.ca.

Table 1.3:   Data is adapted in part from Statistics Canada, *National Longitudinal Survey of Children and Youth (NLSCY)*, 2000–20001.

Chapter 3

Table 3.1:   From "The Janus Report," Andrew M. Greeley, *Contemporary Sociology*, vol. 23, pp. 221–23. Reprinted by permission of the American Sociological Society and Andrew M. Greeley.

Chapter 5

p. 108:   "This Way" by Sherri Groveman from *Hermaphrodites with Attitude*, 1995, p. 2. Reprinted by permission of author.

Table 5.2: Bernard Goldstein (1976). *Introduction to Human Sexuality.* New York: McGraw-Hill, pp. 80–81. Reprinted with permission of Bernard Goldstein.

p. 133:   From the *Revised Standard Version of the Bible,* © 1952 (2nd edition 1971) by the Division of Christian Education of the National Council of the Churches of Christ in the United States of America. Used by permission. All rights reserved.

Chapter 6

Table 6.1: Reprinted from the Journal of Psychosomatic Research, vol. 25, R. Kumar, H. A. Brant, and K. M. Robson, "Childbearing and Maternal Sexuality: A Prospective Study of 119 Primiparas," pp. 373–83, © 1981, with permission of Elsevier.

Table 6.2: Adapted from E. Hetherington and R. Parke, Child Psychology, Table 4.2. © McGraw-Hill Companies, Inc.

Table 6.3: From "Sexuality during Pregnancy and the Year Postpartum," by J. S. Hyde, J. D. DeLamater, E. A. Plant, and J. M. Byrd, the Journal of Sex Research, 33 (1996). © 1996 by the Society for the Scientific Study of Sexuality via Copyright Clearance Center. Reprinted with permission.

Chapter 7

In Focus 7.2: Robert Hatcher et al. (1976). Contraceptive Technology, 1976–1977, 8/e. Reprinted with permission of Irvington Publishers, Inc.

Table 7.4: Reproduced with the permission of The Alan Guttmacher Institute, from Henshaw, S. K., "Induced abortion: a world review," *Family Planning Perspectives*, 1990, 22(2): 59–65, 76.; "Abortion Rates around the World," Canadian data only, is adapted in part from the Statistics Canada publication "The Daily," Catalogue 11-001, Induced Abortions, 2001, Wednesday, March 31, 2004.

Chapter 8

In Focus 8.1: Canadian AIDS Society, www.adnaids.ca.

Table 8.1: From *Barrier Contraceptives: Current Status and Future Prospects* by Christine K. Mauck, 1994, John Wiley & Sons, Inc., pp. 203–12. © 1994 Wiley-Liss. This material is used by permission of Wiley-Liss, Inc., a subsidiary of John Wiley & Sons, Inc.

In Focus 8.5: Script for negotiating sex from www.teenwire.com, June 22, 2004. Reprinted with permission from Planned Parenthood ® Federation of America.

Chapter 10

p. 279–80: From *Drive Him Wild* by Graham Masterton. Used by permission of Dutton Signet, a division of Penguin Group (USA) Inc.

p. 280:   From *Sex: An Oral History* by Harry Maurer. Used by permission of Viking Penguin, a division of Penguin Group (USA) Inc.

In Focus 10.5: Reprinted with the permission of Simon & Schuster Adult Publishing Group, from *Why Marriages Succeed or Fail: What You Can Learn from the Breakthrough Research to Make Your Marriage Last,* by John Gottman, Ph.D. © 1997 by John Gottman. All rights reserved.

p. 307, 309: Floyd M. Martinson, The Sexual Life of Children, 1994, Greenwood Publishing Group, Inc. pp. 37, 59, 62. © 1994 by Floyd M. Martinson. Reproduced with the permission of Greenwood Publishing Group, Inc., Westport, CT.

p. 310:   From Starts, Kay J. and Morrison, Eleanor S., Growing Up Sexual, 2nd Edition, HarperCollins, 1996. © 1996 HarperCollins Publishers. Reproduced with permission.

p. 311, 325: Reproduced with permission from Playboy Enterprises, Inc. from *Sexual Behavior in the 1970s* by Morton Hunt. © 1974, 2005 by Morton Hunt.

p. 330:   From Sex in America by Robert T. Michael et al. © 1994 by CSG Enterprises, Inc., Edward O. Laumann, Robert T. Michael, and Gina Kolatta. By permission of Little, Brown and Company, Inc.

Chapter 11

Table 11.1: Research conducted by Council of Ministers of Education, Canada, with funding provided by Health Canada.

Table 11.2: Canadian data is adapted from Statistics Canada, Canadian Community Health Survey (CCHS), 2000–01.

Table 11.3: Reginald W. Bibby (1995). *Social trends Canadian style.* Toronto: Stoddart, pp. 69 & 76.

Table 11.4: Reginald W. Bibby (2001). *Canada's teens: Yesterday, today, and tomorrow.* Toronto: Stoddart.

Chapter 12

p. 343: From the Janus Report on Sexual Behaviour by Samuel S. Janus and Cynthia L. Janus, 1993, John Wiley & Sons, Inc., p. 383. © 1993 by Samuel S. Janus and Cynthia L. Janus. This material is used by permission of John Wiley & Sons, Inc.

Table 12.2: This information was reprinted with permission of the Henry J. Kaiser Family Foundation. The Kaiser Family Foundation, based in Menlo Park, California, is a non-profit, independent national health care philanthropy and is not associated with Kaiser Permanente or Kaiser Industries.

Chapter 13

Table 13.1: Edward O. Laumann et al. (1994). The Social Organization of Sexuality: Sexual Practices in the United States. Reprinted by permission of the University of Chicago Press and Edward O. Laumann.

Table 13.2: Data from Robert Levine et al. (1995). "Love and Marriage in Eleven Cultures," *Journal of Cross-Cultural Psychology,* 26, pp. 554–571. Used by permission of Robert Levine. Reprinted in E. Hatfield amd R. L. Rapson, Love and Sex: Cross-Cultural Perspectives, 1996, Needham Heights, MA: Allyn & Bacon.

Chapter 14

p. 406: Reproduced with permission from Playboy Enterprises, Inc. from *Sexual Behaviour in the 1970s* by Morton Hunt. © 1974, 2005 by Morton Hunt.

Chapter 15

In Focus 15.1: Condensed from Lisa Yost, "Bisexual Tendencies," in L. Hutchins and L. Kaahumanu (eds.), *Bi Any Other Name: Bisexual People Speak Out,* 1991, Alyson Publications. Reprinted with permission of Alyson Publications.

Table 15.2: Edward O. Laumann et al. (1994), *The Social Organization of Sexuality: Sexual Practices in the United States.* Reprinted by permission of the University of Chicago Press and Edward O. Laumann. Canadian data adapted from Statistics Canada, Census of Populations, 2001, available on the Statistics Canada website <http://www40.statcan.ca/101/cst01/demo30a.htm>.

Chapter 16

p. 453: Reprinted with permission from the Diagnostic and Statistical Manual of Mental Disorders, Fourth Edition, Text Revision, © 2000. American Psychiatric Association.

Chapter 17

p. 481-82: From Jean O. Hughes and Bernice R. SAndler, "'Friends' Raping Friends: Could It Happen to You?" 1987, Washington, D.C.: Association of American Colleges.

In Focus 17.2: Jean O. Hughes and Bernice R. SAndler, "'Friends' Raping Friends: Could It Happen to You?" 1987, Washington, D.C.: Association of American Colleges.

Chapter 18

p. 524-25: From *Sex: An Oral History* by Harry Maurer, © 1994 by Harry Maurer. Used by permission of Viking Penguin, a division of Penguin Group (USA) Inc.

Table 18.1: Martin Rimm, "Marketing Pornography on the Information Superhighway," *Georgetown Law Journal,* Vol 83, 1995, p. 1891. Reprinted with the permission of the publisher, Gerogetown Law Journal © 1995.

In Focus 18.2: "Ernie: A Pedophile and Child Pornographer," from *Child Pornography and Sex Rings,* by Ann W. Burgess, 1984, Lexington Books, pp. 26–27. Reprinted by permission of author.

Chapter 19

John P. Wincze & Michael P. Cary, Sexual Disfunction: The Role of Cognitive Interference," *Journal of Consulting and Clinical Psychology,* 1986, 54, pp. 140–148. © 1986 by the American Psychological Association.

In Focus 19.3: © 2001, The Haworth Press, Inc., Binghamton, NY. "A New View of Women's Sexual Problems" by the Working Group for a New View of Women's Sexual Problems from *A New View of Women's Sexual Problems* (eds. Ellyn Kaschak and Leonore Tiefer), pp. 1–8.

Chapter 20

Table 20.1: Adapted from Statistics Canada, Census of the Population, 2001, available on the Statistics Canada website www40.statcan.ca/101/cst01/demo30a.htm.

Chapter 21

p. 600: Anne C. Bernstein and Philip A. Cowan, "Children's Concepts of How People Get Babies," *Child Development,* 46, 1975, pp. 77–92. Reprinted with permission of the Society for Research in Child Development.

Table 21.1: Research conducted by Council of Ministers of Education, Canada, with funding provided by Health Canada.

p. 602-03: Rosemary Zumwalt, "Plain and Fancy: A Content Analysis of Children's Jokes Dealing with Adult Sexuality," *Western Folklore,* 35, 1976, pp. 261, 267. Reprinted by permission of the California Folklore Society.

p. 604-05: Douglas Kirby, "School-Based Programs to Reduce Sexual Risktaking Behaviour," *Journal of School Health,* vol. 62, no. 7, September 1992, p. 281.

In Focus 21.3: From "Sex Education." Reproduced with permission of the Sexuality Information and Education Council of the United States, Inc. (SIECUS). © SIECUS, 130 West 42nd Street, Suite 350, New York, NY, 10036.

Index